ngs gardens o for charit

CW00829516

The Yellow Book 2005

A county by county guide to thousands of gardens in England and Wales, many not normally open to the public

The National Gardens Scheme Charitable Trust
Hatchlands Park, East Clandon,
Guildford, Surrey GU4 7RT

T 01483 211535 **F** 01483 211537 **W** www.ngs.org.uk
© The National Gardens Scheme 2005
Registered Charity No. 279284

Front cover photograph: Great Dixter, East Sussex; Jerry Harpur
Photograph this page: Lower Crawshaw, Yorkshire; Ann Curtis

JACKSONS
OF PICCADILLY

Jacksons of Piccadilly is pleased to support the National Garden Scheme by supplying teas for garden openings nationwide.

As purveyors of speciality teas since the 18th century and a brand of both heritage and quality, it follows that Jacksons of Piccadilly offers the finest teas from around the world. Why not relax and enjoy your favourite blend in the beautiful surroundings of a participating NGS garden?

The full range of Jacksons of Piccadilly teas is available at independent grocers, delicatessens and fine food stores nationwide.

For your nearest Jacksons stockist call 0800 328 5971 or visit the website at www.jacksons-of-piccadilly.com

ngs gardens open for charity

Contents

Full colour sections include over thirty garden photographs
with editorial contributions from Monty Don, Caroline Donald,
Sarah Raven, Joe Swift and Kim Wilde

Photograph: Canonteign, Essex; Michael Howes

ngs gardens open for charity

About the NGS

In 1927 The National Gardens Scheme was founded to raise money for the nurses of the Queen's Institute of District Nursing, now known as The Queen's Nursing Institute, by opening 600 gardens of quality and interest to the public. Today the QNI still receives funding from the NGS along with a whole range of other national nursing, caring and gardening charities, (see page 7).

Now, as a charitable trust, around 3,500 gardens (mostly private) open every year in England and Wales through the hard work and dedication of garden owners and volunteers of the NGS. More than £20 million has been raised for our beneficiary charities with some £1.8 million being donated in 2004.

Please help us to continue the good work by visiting as many gardens this year as you can. We are waiting to welcome you in the true spirit of The National Gardens Scheme.

For more information about us and details of the gardens we open to the public visit our website and our search and mapping facility 'Garden Finder'.

www.ngs.org.uk

Nurse 1912

Carr Sheppards Crosthwaite

Sponsors of the National Gardens Scheme Yellow Book

It is now twelve years since the National Gardens Scheme agreed to our request to sponsor the Yellow Book, and a very happy twelve years it has been - untroubled by the commercial wrangling that sometimes spoils this sort of relationship.

We love the Scheme, partly because a comparison with gardening is often the best way to explain to our clients that investment management also requires patience, vision and long-term commitment.

The principal reason though is the pleasure it gives to so many. It does us no harm, in today's turbulent financial world, to be seen to be standing (or possibly kneeling) alongside people whose preference is for the slower things in life!

We wish the Scheme and all your gardeners much success and enjoyment.

Fred Carr

CARR SHEPPARDS CROSTHWAITE

A member of the Investec Group

2 Gresham Street, London EC2V 7QN

Carr Sheppards Crosthwaite Limited is a member of the London Stock Exchange. Authorised and regulated by the Financial Services Authority.

Charities supported in 2004

Macmillan Cancer Relief
'provides expert care and support for people living with cancer'
NGS income donated contributes to the ongoing training of Macmillan Nurses, funding the equivalent of 123 nurses to date.

Marie Curie Cancer Care
'provides home nursing to terminally ill people'
The donation from The National Gardens Scheme has funded a Marie Curie Nurse to work in each of the NGS counties, providing high quality nursing care and emotional support to terminally ill people and their families in their own homes.

Help the Hospices
'gives grants, advice and training to hospices'
The contribution from the NGS plays a vital part in ensuring we can continue to support the key role played by hospice nurses in caring for patients and their friends and families.

Crossroads - Caring for Carers
'gives care and support to carers'
The contribution from the NGS enables Crossroads to support local schemes to deliver and develop practical services to enable carers to have a break from their caring responsibilities.

The Queen's Nursing Institute
'supports innovation in community nursing and looks after elderly district nurses'
NGS funding has supported over 100 major community nursing projects to date, which provide loving and expert care for a wide range of patients. It also provides a financial lifeline for many district and Queen's nurses who, through age, illness or disability, are no longer able to work.

The Nurses Welfare Service
'assists nurses in personal difficulty'
NGS funds skilled intervention to prevent a problem becoming a crisis which threatens the career of a nurse or midwife.

The Royal Gardeners' Orphan Fund
'helps children in need'
NGS funding enables ongoing support to orphaned and needy horticulturalists' children, including regular allowances, bedding, clothing and the opportunity of a family holiday.

NGS gardeners' bursaries (The National Trust)
'sponsors 15 trainee gardeners'
15 trainee gardeners are sponsored each year through the NT Careership Training Scheme ensuring long term provision of professional gardening skills and techniques.

Perennial–Gardeners' Royal Benevolent Society
'helping horticulturalists in need'
The NGS donation is vital and central to the work of this charity, going directly to horticulturalists in need.

County Nursing Associations
'supports retired and needy nurses'

8

The Finishing Touch to Your Garden

Your Trees Deserve The Best of Care...

For Your Nearest Branch Call Our Head Office - (01342) 717171

BARTLETT TREE EXPERTS

SCIENTIFIC TREE CARE SINCE 1907

Bedfordshire and Cambridgeshire	(01234) 354673
Buckinghamshire and Berkshire	(01494) 677889
Cheshire and Lancashire	(01625) 890150
Gloucestershire and Oxfordshire	(01285) 654370
Kent	(01892) 548955
London and Hertfordshire	(01923) 850322
Somerset and Wales	(01275) 371000
Surrey and Sussex	(01342) 712215
Wiltshire and Hampshire	(01722) 414001
Worcestershire and Warwickshire	(01905) 727412
Yorkshire	(01423) 359090

Gardens of England/Wales 9/17/04 144mmw x 210mm h

Chairman's message 2005

The Yellow Book has come of age! Our new cover design emphasizes the core purpose of The National Gardens Scheme, which is to raise money for national nursing, caring and gardening charities across the country.

This book unlocks the secrets of 3500 gardens, many of them private, which open each year to reveal exceptional examples of planting, design and colour. Garden owners enjoy sharing their gardens with our visitors and we rely on their tireless energy and enthusiasm to provide new experiences for our visitors each season.

The generosity of our visitors, over 750,000 of them, provides donations worth almost £2 million to our beneficiary charities each year. Throughout this book you will find examples of the services funded by this money. Please take some time, if you can, to read about the way in which your garden visit can provide pleasure and help to other people.

I think that visitors would like to share with us our sadness in the recent loss of our President, HRH Princess Alice, Duchess of Gloucester, who died late last year. She was a great and much loved supporter of our charity.

Thank you for buying this book and for visiting our gardens. I look forward to a record season for 2005.

Nicholas Payne.
Chairman.

Photograph: Mike Pritchard

Quality Garden Tours 2005

Brightwater Holidays is the UK's leading specialist Garden Tour Operator. Our fully inclusive itineraries combine the famous and grand gardens with the small and private gardens - most tours also visit specialist nurseries where possible.

Travel by coach, air, ferry and rail from a variety of local pick up points throughout the UK.

Tours include: Tresco in the Scilly Isles, Private Gardens of Cornwall, Arts and Gardens of Cornwall, The Alnwick Garden, Gardens of Jekyll and Lutyens, Shakespeare's Gardens, many regional garden tours throughout England, Scotland, Ireland and Wales, Scottish Island holidays, Botanical and Cultural Explorations of the Mediterranean, Holland at bulbtime, an autumn Rhine Cruise and Long Haul garden destinations such as Japan, California, New Zealand, Uruguay and Mauritius, to name but a few.

If you have your own group and are looking for a tailor made itinerary we are happy to work to suit your interest and budget.

Please contact us for full details and a copy of our comprehensive brochure for 2005.

quality garden & special interest tours

2005

Brightwater Holidays Ltd, Eden Park House, Cupar, Fife KY15 4HS.

Tel: 01334 657155 Fax: 01334 657144
Email: info@brightwaterholidays.com
Website: www.brightwaterholidays.com

Sponsors supporting
The National Gardens Scheme

A member of the Investec Group

Carr Sheppards Crosthwaite

As leading private client stockbrokers and financial advisers, we have enormous interest in people, rather than just the mere science of investment management. So, when we are asked why we are so pleased to support The National Gardens Scheme, the answer is very simple - gardening is by far and away our clients' favourite pastime. We are very proud to be associated with you and long may you flourish!

Jacksons of Piccadilly

Jacksons of Piccadilly has a long-standing relationship with The National Gardens Scheme, supplying quality teas for private garden openings nationwide in support of their commitment to raise money for charity. Established since the 1800s the heritage and quality of Jacksons premium tea blends allows garden owners the opportunity to add value to their garden openings and visitors the opportunity to enhance their visit by enjoying a complementary cup of the finest flavoured Green or Black Speciality Tea.

Jackson-Stops & Staff

Jackson-Stops & Staff are delighted to support The National Gardens Scheme in what we hope will continue to be a long-term association. Jackson-Stops & Staff was founded in 1910 by Herbert Jackson-Stops who developed a name for selling historically and architecturally important country houses. Gardens and gardening have enjoyed a great resurgence in recent years and the synergy between house and garden is possibly more important now than ever before. Many of our clients participate in The National Gardens Scheme and we are pleased to be associated with an organisation through which so many people derive so much pleasure.

Woodmansterne

Woodmansterne Publications Limited

As publishers of fine art and culturally inspired greeting cards, Woodmansterne is delighted to be associated with The National Gardens Scheme. As it is with art, the pursuit of gardening inspires in us a high level of passion and commitment and a desire to express ourselves through the fruits of our labour. A beautiful garden has the power to transform both the creator and the observer. The NGS gently harnesses this quintessentially English love for our gardens and, at the same time, generates funds for such wonderful causes.

For more information on our sponsors visit

www.ngs.org.uk

A unique opportunity for plant hunters and garden enthusiasts to source rare and unusual plants at reasonable prices.

Fairs are attended by specialist nurseries who, as well as growing plants, can give expert advice on their care and planting.

The fairs take place in great locations, most are not normally open to the public... worth a day out in themselves!

Plants will include new introductions to this country, many of them brought back here after plant hunting trips to other countries by the nurserymen and women selling them. There are also plants available that are difficult to propagate and so are in very short supply.

Venue name	Date
The Winter Gardens, Weston-Super-Mare	27/03/2005
Bath Pavilion, Bath	02/04/2005
South West London	10/04/2005
Cheltenham Spa (Town Hall)	16/04/2005
Quenington Old Rectory, Cirencester	24/04/2005
Maxstoke Castle, Birmingham	01/05/2005
Caldicot Castle, South Wales	08/05/2005
Liscombe Park, Wing, Leighton Buzzard	15/05/2005
Oxford Arboretum, Oxford	29/05/2005
Lackham College, Wiltshire	05/06/2005
Lullingstone Castle, Kent	12/06/2005
Westonbirt Arboretum, Gloucestershire	19/06/2005
Fonmon Castle, Nr Cardiff	26/06/2005
Englefield House, Reading	02/07/2005
Lady Farm, Chelmwood, South Bath	10/07/2005
Sulgrave Manor, Banbury	16/07/2005
Harvington Hall, Kidderminster	21/08/2005
Abergavenny Castle, South Wales	27/08/2005

Web:
www.rareplantsfair.com
Tel:
0800 2985479
Email:
info@rareplantsfair.com

Passiflora Mollissima, South Africa. Found flowering outdoors at Lullingstone Castle, Kent

Abbey House Gardens
In the heart of Malmesbury, Wiltshire

"The WOW! factor is here in abundance."
ALAN TITCHMARSH
BBC GARDENER'S WORLD

www.abbeyhousegardens.co.uk
Information: 01666 822212

FREE
Two
adults for
the price of
one*

*Offer applies throughout season on presentation
of this Yellow Book. One person free per book.

Killing slugs the easy way

Gordon Darby loves growing potatoes on his allotment in Kent, but voracious slugs had stopped him growing his favourite variety – Cara, until he used Nemaslug to protect his crop. Slugs also used to help themselves to his pea seedlings.

"I used Nemaslug last year and didn't see a slug on my allotment," said Gordon. "As well as growing Cara potatoes successfully, I had 100% germination with my peas. Allotments are usually so vulnerable to slug damage but using Nemaslug made my allotment slug free."

Explaining the success of Nemaslug Becker Underwood's general manager, nematode division, Dr. Graeme Gowling says, "Slugs usually spend most of their time underground, emerging at night to feed on plants. Nemaslug is the only product that can kill slugs beneath the surface before they can do the damage."

"Wet autumns (like 2004) create good conditions for slugs, which lay eggs ready to emerge the following spring," adds Dr Gowling. "So an early dose of Nemaslug, when the soil temperature reaches 5°C, will be a good preventative measure."

Now with new lower prices, Nemaslug is even better value. Remember, just one simple application gives six weeks control, especially in wet weather which slugs love. **Nemaslug is now £9.99 for a standard pack –** that's less than **24p a day** to protect your valuable plants from voracious slugs.

Also in the best selling Nemasys range
Nemasys Vine Weevil Killer - **£9.99**
Nemasys Chafer Grub Killer - **£9.99**
Nemasys Leather Jacket Killer - **£14.99**
Available from:
Green Gardener – FREEPHONE 0800 085 3105
Just Green Ltd - FREEPHONE 0800 389 6002
Also available from selected garden centres.

Nemasys®

The Simple Solution

www.nemasysinfo.com

Everything in the garden's **threatened**

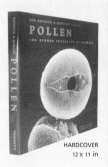

KESSELER & HARLEY

POLLEN

THE HIDDEN SEXUALITY OF FLOWERS

PAPADAKIS PUBLISHER

16 GROSVENOR PLACE LONDON SW1X 7HH TEL. 020 78 23 23 23

18

SongBird Survival

A CHARITY FOR ALL GARDEN-LOVERS AND THOSE WHO CARE FOR THE SONGBIRDS WHOSE FUTURE IS THREATENED BY PREDATION

- A charity that draws attention to the plight of songbirds.
- A charity that lobbies for a change in the law concerning raptors.
- A charity that funds research into the decline of songbirds.
- A charity that can advise on the best ways to frustrate the predation by grey squirrels, cats and corvids.

CALL US TODAY ON 0845 6342468

Email: dawn-chorus@songbird-survival.org.uk
Web: www.songbird-survival.org.uk

SongBird Survival. A company limited by guarantee, and not having a share capital. Registered in England No 4078747 Charity no. 1085281

Jackson-Stops
& Staff

www.jackson-stops.co

For Great
Gardens &
Houses

37 offices nationwid
specialising in the fines
London and Country propertie

primelocatic
.com

How to use this book

Most of the gardens listed are privately owned and open to the public just a few times in the year. They are grouped alphabetically by county. Welsh gardens have their own section starting on page 439. Each entry gives: general location and directions (in italics); a brief description by the owner with the advice of the county team; details of opening times and arrangements. At the start of each county is a diary giving a summary of openings, a map and contact details for the county team. There is a general map overleaf and an index of all gardens from page 496.

Visiting Gardens:

Please remember that most gardens are private property. They are open through the generosity and enthusiasm of their owners and have not been designed for the visiting public. When requested, please stay on the marked paths, avoid hazards and take care to avoid damaging plants. Thank you for your cooperation and enjoy your visit.

Symbols, labels and notes:

The information below is given, as relevant, in each garden entry.

♿	Wheelchair access to at least the main features of the garden. Often disabled parking is available close to, or in the owner's driveway.
🐕	No dogs except assistance dogs. Where dogs are allowed they must be on leads.
🌱	Plants/produce usually for sale. Many garden owners propagate the unusual plants growing in their garden and offer them for sale. If proceeds go elsewhere this is shown at the garden opening.
NCCPG	Garden that holds a NCCPG National Plant Collection®
◆	This symbol denotes a garden which is open to the public on a regular basis. Gardens which carry this symbol contribute to The National Gardens Scheme either by opening on a specific day or days, or by giving a guaranteed contribution to the Scheme. For opening information not given in the garden entry, please refer to the garden directly. Telephone numbers/website details, where available, for all gardens with this symbol are given at the end of the garden text.
Maps	The number shown by each garden entry refers to that garden's position on the county map. The position is approximate; distance and direction from the nearest main town is generally shown in the garden text.
NEW	Garden opening this year for the first time.
Open by Appointment	All gardens open by appointment will be pleased to see visitors by prior arrangement. Some gardens can accommodate clubs and societies, some only small parties and some also have limited parking. All welcome visitors. Telephone direct to make an appointment.
Photographs	Where taken at a garden opening, photographs must not be used for sale or reproduction without prior permission of the owner.
Share to	If 'share to' is shown in a garden text it indicates that a proportion of the money collected will be given to the nominated charity.
TEAS	Tea with biscuits and cake, normally available at a charge. If cream teas, home-made teas or light refreshments are available, this is stated in the garden text.

All distances and sizes are approximate. **Coach parties** – only by appointment, please contact the garden direct to make arrangements. **Children** – must be accompanied by an adult. **Lavatories** – not usually available at private gardens. **Updates** – while every effort is made to ensure that entries are accurate, with so many gardens there will inevitably be last minute changes. These will be publicised locally, and shown on the website. **Website** – details of many NGS gardens and information about special events are on the NGS website.

www.ngs.org.uk

The counties of England and Wales

Note: The areas shown on this map are not necessarily precise geographic counties. Some are areas specific to the administration of The National Gardens Scheme

Help us by giving a donation

Is your passion gardening or just visiting them? Do you care about the welfare of cancer patients or the terminally ill, the well-being of nurses and carers?

If so, please consider donating to The National Gardens Scheme. We exist to support national nursing, caring and gardening charities by opening over 3,500 gardens in England & Wales to the public every year. If you would like to donate we would be delighted to receive your completed form below.

In giving to the NGS you are helping not just one charity, but many.
(See page 7 for details of our beneficiaries)

The National Gardens Scheme donation form

I would like to give a donation to help the NGS in their fundraising activities.

Title: ....Initial: ....Surname: ....

Address: ....

....

Post code: ....Country: ....

Tel: ....

Email: ....

I enclose a cheque/donation in the amount of: ....
(payable to The National Gardens Scheme Charitable Trust)

or please debit my Switch/Master Card/Visa/Delta ....

Expiry Date:.. Issue No (switch only) ....

Signature:..Date: ....

Please return this form to:
NGS (Marketing), Hatchlands Park, East Clandon, Guildford, Surrey GU4 7RT

Please tick this box if you would like an acknowledgement ☐

Please send me details to arrange standing order payments through my bank ☐

So the NGS can claim Gift Aid from the Government on your donation please tick this box ☐
(Please note that for your donation to qualify for Gift Aid you must be a UK taxpayer and the amount of income and/or capital gains tax you pay must at least equal the amount of tax the NGS will reclaim from your donation in the tax year).

To further our charitable aims, we may want to pass on your address details to other organisations who are supportive of our aims and objectives. Please tick the box if you would prefer us not to pass on your details ☐

Thank you for supporting The National Gardens Scheme

Book highlights

What to look for in the Yellow Book 2005

Everyone at the NGS hopes that you will find this year's edition of the famous Yellow Book as enjoyable as ever. With over 3,500 gardens featured, including over 450 new ones, there's sure to be something to please everyone – either close to home or far away. Opportunities exist for a short stroll through a smaller garden packed with surprises followed by a slice of glorious home-made cake, or a longer ramble through woodlands and alongside streams. Listed below are some of the special features to help you get even more enjoyment from the Yellow Book 2005.

The NGS website

The popularity of our website, www.ngs.org.uk continues to grow. On it you will find current news about the NGS and its beneficiary charities. There are features about award-winning gardens, special events and heart-warming stories about how the money raised through garden visiting is used to benefit those in need.

The area where most website visitors end up is the Garden Finder section. Here you can search for gardens by name, county, opening date or description. If you're planning a visit to the Cotswolds in October in search of autumn colour, Garden Finder can help you make your selection. Similarly, it can help you find an alpine garden in Cumbria in May. A large number of our garden owners have photographs of their gardens in Garden Finder, and some have their own web pages, to which we link. Many also take advantage of the opportunity to write an extended description of their garden. If you want to visit by appointment, why not e-mail the garden owner directly to make arrangements. Lastly, you can use the location map to get accurate directions to the garden of your choice. Using the Yellow Book and the website together can really help you to get the most out of your garden visiting.

Accommodation – new for 2005

We are very excited about a brand new listing that you will find at the end of the county sections. For the first time we are featuring a list of garden owners who offer accommodation as well as opening their wonderful gardens for the NGS. We have listed them by county and indicated whether they offer bed and breakfast, self-catering or hotel accommodation. You will also find a reference to accommodation in the main directory with their garden entry. We are sure that many garden visitors will find this an absolute treat – imagine breakfasting with a view of one of these splendid gardens! Go to page 485 for more information.

Evening openings

Many of our garden owners have evening openings – a perfect opportunity to enjoy a summer's evening in a garden, perhaps sipping a glass of wine. The change of light as evening approaches gives the garden a different feel, often romantic, sometimes calming, always an opportunity to leave the stress of the day behind you. Some of the gardens also feature unusual lighting effects, from candles and floating pond lights to up-lighters and tree lights. You will find details of evening openings listed at the end of each county section.

National Plant Collections in the NGS

A new symbol appears in the Yellow Book this year to draw your attention to those gardens which are home to National Plant Collections. Over 120 of these important collections can be seen on NGS open days in 2005. The section also gives more information on the work of the National Council for the Conservation of Plants (NCCPG). A listing by county is given at the back of the book, starting on Page 482. Alternatively, use a refined search in Garden Finder on the website.

Early openings 2006

Don't forget early planning for 2006. Gardens across the country open in February – before the new Yellow Book is published – with glorious displays of spring colour including hellebores, aconites, snowdrops and carpets of spring bulbs.

NGS garden owners and gardeners will be waiting for you as the new garden visiting season begins.

ngs

gardens open
for charity

Every time you visit a garden which opens for the NGS you are helping to raise money for

- **Macmillan Cancer Relief**
- **Marie Curie Cancer Care**
- **Help the Hospices**
- **Crossroads – Caring for Carers**
- **The Queen's Nursing Institute**
- **The Nurses Welfare Service**
- **The Royal Gardeners' Orphan Fund**
- **NGS Gardeners' Bursaries – The National Trust Careership Scheme**
- **Perennial – Gardeners' Royal Benevolent Society**
- **County Nursing Associations**
- **Additional charities nominated by owners**

ENGLAND

Bedfordshire

County Organiser: ·	Mike & Pat Sutcliffe, Valley Forge, 213 Castle Hill Road, Totternhoe, Dunstable LU6 2DA Tel 01525 221676
Press & Publicity Officer:	Mr & Mrs Geoff Barrett, Flaxbourne Farm, Aspley Guise, Milton Keynes MK17 8HZ Tel 01908 585329
County Treasurer:	Mr David Johnston, Seal Point, 7 Wendover Way, Luton LU2 7LS Tel 01582 611567

Maps: Numbers shown next to each garden entry refer to that garden's entry on the county map. This position is approximate; distance and directions from the nearest main town are generally shown in the garden text.
A precise location is available for those gardens featured on the NGS website by visiting www.ngs.org.uk.
Symbols: Information relating to symbols is given on page 21

DATES OF OPENING

Evening openings
See end of county listing

Gardens open to the public
For details see garden description
King's Arms Path Garden, Ampthill *(4)*
The Manor House, Stevington *(5)*

By appointment only
For telephone number and other details see garden description. Private visits welcomed
The Old Stables, Hockliffe *(8)*
Seal Point, Luton *(10)*
Treize, Wootton Green *(14)*
Valley Forge, Totternhoe *(15)*

"You can come down now Henry, they've all gone!"

March 19 Saturday
Swiss Garden, Old Warden Park *(12)*

March 27 Sunday (Easter)
King's Arms Path Garden, Ampthill *(4)*

April 3 Sunday
Tofte Manor, Sharnbrook *(13)*

May 8 Sunday
59 Grange Lane, Bromham *(3)*

May 25 Wednesday
Dawnedge Lodge, Aspley Guise *(1)*

May 29 Sunday
Milton House, Milton, Ernest, nr Bedford *(6)*

June 5 Sunday
The Old Rectory, Pertenhall *(7)*
Southill Park, nr Biggleswade *(11)*

June 12 Sunday
Perch Heights, Felmersham *(9)*

June 15 Wednesday
The Manor House, Stevington **(Evening)** *(5)*

June 19 Sunday
59 Grange Lane, Bromham *(3)*

June 26 Sunday
Flaxbourne Farm, Aspley Guise *(2)*
Tofte Manor, Sharnbrook *(13)*

July 16 Saturday
Flaxbourne Farm, Aspley Guise **(Evening)** *(2)*

July 31 Sunday
Flaxbourne Farm, Aspley Guise *(2)*

September 24 Saturday
Swiss Garden, Old Warden Park *(12)*

DESCRIPTIONS OF GARDENS

Cheddington Gardens
See Buckinghamshire.

Cublington Gardens
See Buckinghamshire.

❶ Dawnedge Lodge, Woburn Lane, Aspley Guise ⊗
(Phil & Lynne Wallace) *5m W of Ampthill. 3m from junction 13 M1. In Aspley Guise, turn L in centre of village at Moore Place Hotel.* Walled garden on top of hill with views to Woburn. Rescued 5yrs ago, with colour themed island beds, pergolas, pots. Cutting garden, Alitex greenhouse and new (2003) woodland garden. Alliums good. *Adm £2.50. Wed 25 May (2-6). Private visits welcome by appt May, June & July, also groups. Tel 01908 582233*

❷ Flaxbourne Farm, Aspley Guise 🅖🅖
(Geoff & Davina Barrett) *5m W of Ampthill. 1m S of junction 13 of M1. Turn R in village centre, 1m over railway line.* A beautiful and entertaining garden of 2 acres, lovingly developed with numerous water features, windmill, modern arches and bridges and small moated castle. Formal front garden, lily pond, herbaceous borders, shrubs and trees recently established. Newly constructed grotto plus large wooden crocodiles and other exciting features to discover. Woburn Sands Band playing throughout openings. Featured in 'Garden News' 2003. Home-made TEAS in aid of St Botolph's Church Fund. *Adm £3.50, chd free. Suns 26 June; 31 July (2-6). Evening Opening £6, wine, Sat 16 July, Garden Concert (7-11). Private visits welcome by appt July & Aug, coaches permitted. Tel 01908 585329*

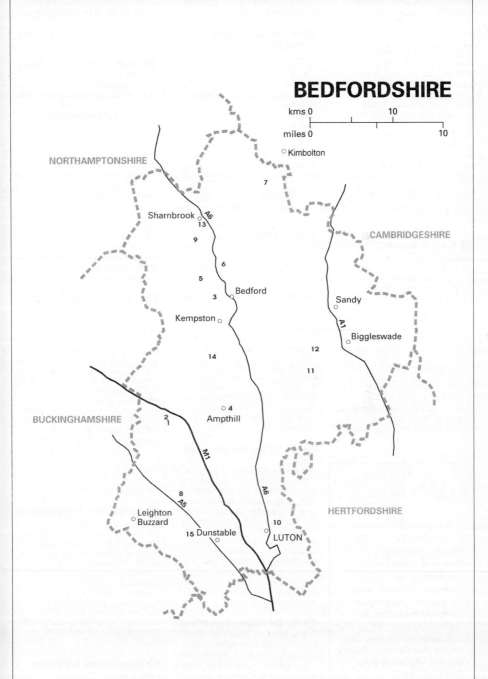

BEDFORDSHIRE

kms 0   10

miles 0   10

NORTHAMPTONSHIRE

Kimbolton

7

Sharnbrook
13
A6

9

CAMBRIDGESHIRE

6

5

3 Bedford

Kempston

Sandy

A1

Biggleswade

12

11

14

4
Ampthill

BUCKINGHAMSHIRE

2
1

M1

8
A5
A6

Leighton
Buzzard

10

15 Dunstable

LUTON

HERTFORDSHIRE

❸ 59 Grange Lane, Bromham &🗇🌐
(Mrs Mary Morris) *3m W of Bedford. A428 to Bromham, sign Oakley, into Village Rd. 3rd turning on L (Grange Lane), 59 is opp Springfield Drive on L.* An informal 150ft organic garden developed over 21yrs. Herbaceous border with colour groupings; mixed border; small woodland garden with camellias and many spring flowers and bulbs. Gravel areas. Some unusual plants and trees; hardy geraniums; pulmonarias. Formal pond and white border. Vegetable garden using raised beds and companion planting. Home-made TEAS. *Adm £2, chd under 16 free. Suns 8 May; 19 June (11-6). Private visits welcome by appt Apr to July (Suns 2-6). Tel 01234 822215*

❹ ◆ King's Arms Path Garden, Ampthill &🗇🌐
(Ampthill Town Council) *8m S of Bedford. Free parking in town centre. Entrance opp old Market Place, down King's Arms Yard.* Small woodland garden of about 1½ acres created by plantsman the late William Nourish. Trees, shrubs, bulbs and many interesting collections. Maintained since 1987 by 'The Friends of the Garden' on behalf of Ampthill Town Council. TEAS 27 March only. *Adm £2, chd free. Suns 13 Feb (2-4); 24 Apr; 29 May; 19 June; 31 July; 28 Aug; 25 Sept (2.30-5), 30 Oct (2-4). For NGS: Sun 27 Mar (2.30-5). Tel 01525 755648 Bryden Keenan bryden.k@ntlworld. com*

ngs gardens open for charity

Every time you visit a garden which opens for the NGS you are helping to raise money for:

• Macmillan Cancer Relief
• Marie Curie Cancer Care
• Help the Hospices
• Crossroads – Caring for Carers
• The Queen's Nursing Institute
• The Nurses Welfare Service
• The Royal Gardeners' Orphan Fund
• NGS Gardeners' Bursaries – The National Trust Careership Scheme
• Perennial – Gardeners' Royal Benevolent Society
• County Nursing Associations
Additional charities nominated by owners

[NEW] Loughton Village Gardens
See Buckinghamshire.

❺ ◆ The Manor House, Stevington &🗇🌐
(Kathy Brown) *5m NW of Bedford. Off A428 through Bromham.* This is a 4-acre garden designed by owner and landscape gardener Kathy Brown featuring meadow perennials, herbaceous borders, cottage garden, ornamental grass parterres, wild flower meadow and formal French-style garden plus unusual containers with summer succulents and other exotics. Roses and viticella clematis festoon the trees, pergolas and old stone walls. Spring and summer bulbs a speciality. Partially suitable for wheelchairs. Featured in 'The Daily Telegraph' 2003. Light refreshments and TEAS. *Adm £3.50, chd free. Suns 29 May; 31 July (2-6).* **For NGS: Evening Opening** *£3.50, wine, Wed 15 June (6-9). Tel 01234 822064 Kathy Brown www.kathybrownsgarden.homestead. com*

❻ Milton House, Milton, Ernest, nr Bedford &🗇🌐
(Mr & Mrs Clifton Ibbett) *4m N of Bedford. On A6, S of village of Milton Ernest. Drive to house is on R.* Formal, terrace and sunken gardens set in large grounds; rose garden; lakes and waterfall with new stone bridge. Guide dogs only. Excellent facilities. Home-made TEAS in aid of All Saints Church, Milton Ernest. *Adm £3, chd free, wheelchair users free. Sun 29 May (1.30-5.30)*

❼ The Old Rectory, Pertenhall &🗇🌐
(Mr & Mrs F R Finston) *1½m SW of Kimbolton. On B660. Approx 10m from Bedford.* 4 acres of mature gardens approached through lime avenue. Walled garden with lily pond and architectural border. Ancient mulberry, medlar, and quince said to be largest recorded in British Isles. Secluded water garden; developing knot garden; shrubberies and herbaceous border; scented and kitchen gardens. Light refreshments and TEAS. *Adm £3, chd free. Sun 5 June (2.30-6)*

❽ The Old Stables, Hockliffe 🗇
(Mr & Mrs D X Victor) *3m N of Dunstable. From A5 in Hockliffe, proceed W on A4012. Turn R after ¼m (signposted Church End), then L at church. Follow lane for ½m & take field track on R.* 2 acres, incl walled garden, with panoramic views of countryside. Large collection of

plants incl peonies, hardy geraniums, clematis and tender bulbs, in formal and informal plantings. *Adm £3. Private visits welcome by appt, also groups. Tel 01525 210633*

❾ Perch Heights, Carlton Road, Felmersham 🗇🌐
(Dr & Mrs Zaki) *7m NW of Bedford. Village between A6 & A509. Entrance Felmersham end of Carlton Rd at national speed limit sign.* 1¾-acre landscaped garden adjoining a meadow and 4-acre woodland; mature trees, sweeping lawns, herbaceous borders, rose garden, bamboos, lily pond. Majority of plants chosen for scent; collections of philadelphus, viburnum, magnolia, peony, geranium and others. Teas in village in aid of WI. *Adm £2, chd free. Sun 12 June (2-6). Private visits welcome by appt May to July.*

Ragged Hall, Gaddesden Row, nr Hemel Hempstead &🗇🌐
See Hertfordshire.

❿ Seal Point, 7 Wendover Way, Luton 🗇🌐
(Mrs Danae Johnston) *2m from Luton town centre. In NE Luton, turning N off Stockingstone Rd A505 into Felstead Way then 2nd L Wendover Way.* A garden of delight, incls wildlife spinney, lovely grasses, unusual trees and shrubs; 3 water features and tree top balcony on which to enjoy refreshments. Danae won Gardener of the year E and SE 1999. We love visitors. Featured in BBC Gardener's World & British Inspirational Gardens book 2004. TEAS. *Adm £3 incl cup of tea, chd free. Private visits welcome by appt May to Sept, large and small groups and coaches also welcome. Tel 01582 611567*

⓫ Southill Park, nr Biggleswade &🗇🌐
(Mr & Mrs Charles Whitbread) *3m W of Biggleswade.* Large garden, with mature trees and flowering shrubs, herbaceous borders, rose garden and wild garden. Rhododendron walks are especially beautiful in the spring. Large conservatory with tropical plants. The parkland was designed by Lancelot 'Capability' Brown in 1777. TEAS. *Adm £3.50, chd £1. Sun 5 June (2-5)*

⓬ Swiss Garden, Old Warden Park &🗇🌐
(Bedfordshire County Council) *2m W of Biggleswade. Signposted from A1 & A600. Designed in 1820s. 9-acre*

miniature landscape garden with winding paths, intertwining ponds, wrought iron bridges, fernery grotto and tiny buildings. Peacocks wander around splendid trees and shrubs, with daffodils, rhododendrons and roses in season. Adjacent to further acres of native woodland. *Adm £3, chd free, concessions £2. Sats 19 Mar (10-4); 24 Sept (10-5)*

⑬ Tofte Manor, Sharnbrook 🌸
(Mrs Suzy Castleman) *8m N of Bedford. Off A6, through Sharnbrook, ¼m N on rd to Souldrop.* 5 acres of mature and beautifully laid out garden restored and modernised to blend with C17 manor house (not open). Mature trees, wonderful spring bulbs, peonies, colour themed herbaceous borders. Sunken area with central arbour and unusual crystal ball like water feature. Beautiful modern statued parterre garden, grass labyrinth in the design of labyrinth at Chartres Cathedral, overhung by pieces of sacred geometry, making this an unusual spiritual garden. Water that has travelled the path of the labyrinth can be drunk. Walks

and wild areas abound. Featured in 'The English Garden' 2003. TEAS. *Adm £2.50, chd free. Suns 3 Apr; 26 June (2-6). Private visits welcome by appt Weds & Fris in June (9-3). Tel 01234 781425*

⑭ Treize, Cranfield Road, Wootton Green 🔶🌀🌸
(Roger & Anna Skipper) *5m SW of Bedford. 10m NE of Milton Keynes. C70 Kempston to Cranfield rd, ½m SW of Wootton. Private Lane on R opp Wootton Green Hamlet sign. Bungalow 100yds along lane on R. Limited parking facilities.* 1-acre plantsman's garden set out for yr-round interest on heavy clay. Hidden gardens and established herbaceous borders; formal pond; rockery, gravel beds and winter walk crowded with spring bulbs. Many varieties of established and younger trees, shrubs and vast collection of perennials, incl over 180 varieties and species of penstemon. Light refreshments and TEAS in aid of Kempston East Methodist Church Vision Fund. *Adm £2, chd free. Private visits welcome by appt mid May to mid July - groups*

max 25. Tel 01234 768640 roger.skipper@btinternet.com

⑮ Valley Forge, 213 Castle Hill Road, Totternhoe 🔶🌀🌸
(Pat & Mike Sutcliffe) *2m W of Dunstable. Turn R off B489 Aston Clinton rd, ½m from Dunstable centre, signposted Totternhoe. Fronting main rd, corner of Chapel Lane, 1m through village.* Garden to rear of C17 grade II listed thatched cottage (not open). ½-acre sloping site, terraced on chalk, planted from scratch by owners. Interestingly landscaped featuring pergolas and archways, shrubs, perennials and trees, incl rare Aylesbury Prune. Site also houses Mike Sutcliffe's famous collection of early Leyland buses (1908-1934). TEAS by arrangement. *Adm £2.50, chd 50p. Private visits welcome by appt May & June, also groups. Tel 01525 221676*

Evening Opening (See also garden description)	
The Manor House	15 June
Flaxbourne Farm	16 July

Berkshire

County Organiser:	Mr Jeremy Bayliss, Sheepbridge Court, Swallowfield, Nr Reading RG7 1PT
	Tel 0118 988 3218
Assistant County Organisers:	
(Press & Publicity Officer)	Mrs Fenja Anderson, Mariners, Mariners Lane, Bradfield, Berkshire RG7 6HU
	Tel 0118 974 5226
South East	Mrs Nina Preston, Timberlea, 17 Oaklands Drive, Wokingham, Berkshire RG41 2SA
	Tel 0118 978 4629
(North West)	Mr Anthony Jones, Meadow House, Ashford Hill, Thatcham, Berkshire RG19 8BN
	Tel 0118 981 6005
(South West)	Mr Christopher Verity, Boundary House, Brimpton Common, Reading RG7 4RT
	Tel 0118 981 4849
(North East)	Ms Trisha Walmsley, 2 Marlow Mill, Mill Road, Marlow, Buckinghamshire SL7 1QD
	Tel 01628 481492
County Treasurer:	Mr Patrick Drew, Handpost, Swallowfield, Nr Reading RG7 1PU Tel: 0118 988 4050

Maps: Numbers shown next to each garden entry refer to that garden's entry on the county map. This position is approximate; distance and directions from the nearest main town are generally shown in the garden text.
A precise location is available for those gardens featured on the NGS website by visiting www.ngs.org.uk.

Symbols: Information relating to symbols is given on page 21

DATES OF OPENING

Evening openings
See end of county listing

Gardens open to the public
For details see garden description
Englefield House, Englefield (6)
Waltham Place Gardens, White Waltham (38)

By appointment only
For telephone number and other details see garden description. Private visits welcomed
Devonia, Broad Lane, Bracknell (4)
Ivydene, Woodley (13)
Potash, Southend Bradfield (23)
Scotlands, nr Wargrave (30)
10 Shaftesbury Close, Harmanswater, Bracknell (31)
Simms Farm House, Mortimer (33)
Two Littlewick Green Gardens, Littlewick Green (37)

February 15 Tuesday
Welford Park, nr Newbury (39)

April 17 Sunday
The Old Rectory Farnborough, Nr Wantage (20)

April 24 Sunday
Odney Club, Cookham (18)
Reynolds Farm, Hurst (26)

April 27 Wednesday
Rooksnest, Lambourn Woodlands (28)

May 8 Sunday
Bradfield Farm, Stanford Dingley (2)
The Harris Garden, Whiteknights, Reading (11)
Whiteknights, Finchampstead (41)

May 15 Sunday
Bearwood College, Winnersh (1)
The Old Rectory Farnborough, Nr Wantage (20)

May 17 Tuesday
Frogmore House Garden, Windsor (10)

May 22 Sunday
Sunningdale Park, Ascot (35)

May 28 Saturday
The RISC Roof Garden, Reading (27)

May 29 Sunday
The RISC Roof Garden, Reading (27)

May 30 Monday (Bank Hol)
Moor Close Gardens, Binfield (17)

June 1 Wednesday
Waltham Place Gardens, White Waltham (38)

June 2 Thursday
Meadow House, Ashford Hill (16)

June 5 Sunday
Farley Hill Place Gardens, Farley Hill (8)
Stockcross House, Stockcross, Newbury (34)
West Wokingham Gardens (40)

June 8 Wednesday
Waltham Place Gardens, White Waltham (38)

June 11 Saturday
Eton College Gardens, Eton (7)

June 12 Sunday
Folly Farm, Sulhamstead (9)
The Old Rectory Burghfield (19)
Prior's Court School, nr Newbury (24)
Shefford Woodlands House, Shefford Woodlands (32)
Woolley Park, nr Wantage (42)

June 15 Wednesday
Waltham Place Gardens, White Waltham (38)

June 16 Thursday
Meadow House, Ashford Hill (16)

June 19 Sunday
Mariners, Bradfield (15)
Moor Close Gardens, Binfield (17)
The Old Rectory Farnborough, Nr Wantage (20)
The Old Rectory Peasemore (21)
Sandleford Place, Newtown, Newbury (29)

June 22 Wednesday
Rooksnest, Lambourn Woodlands (28)
Waltham Place Gardens, White Waltham (38)

June 25 Saturday
The RISC Roof Garden, Reading (27)

June 26 Sunday
Chieveley Manor, Chieveley (3)
The Priory, Beech Hill (25)
The RISC Roof Garden, Reading (27)
Timberlea, Wokingham (36)

June 29 Wednesday
Waltham Place Gardens, White Waltham (38)

July 3 Sunday
Kirby House, Inkpen (14)

July 6 Wednesday
Waltham Place Gardens, White Waltham (38)

July 10 Sunday
Inkpen House, Inkpen (12)

July 13 Wednesday
Waltham Place Gardens, White Waltham (38)

July 14 Thursday
Donnington Castle House, Donnington (5)

July 20 Wednesday
Waltham Place Gardens, White Waltham (38)

July 27 Wednesday
Waltham Place Gardens, White Waltham (38)

BERKSHIRE

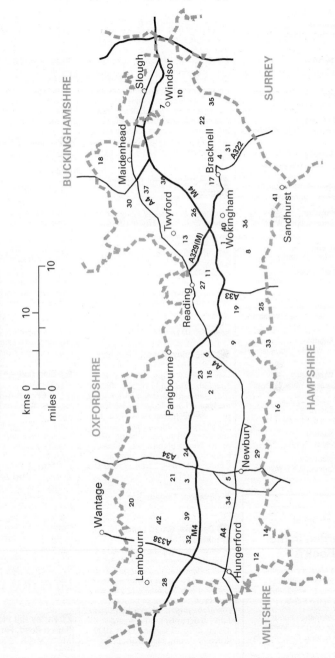

July 30 Saturday
The RISC Roof Garden, Reading *(27)*

July 31 Sunday
The RISC Roof Garden, Reading *(27)*

August 3 Wednesday
Waltham Place Gardens, White Waltham *(38)*

August 10 Wednesday
Waltham Place Gardens, White Waltham *(38)*

August 14 Sunday
Whiteknights, Finchampstead *(41)*

August 17 Wednesday
Waltham Place Gardens, White Waltham *(38)*

August 24 Wednesday
Waltham Place Gardens, White Waltham *(38)*

August 28 Sunday
Old Waterfield, Ascot *(22)*

August 31 Wednesday
Waltham Place Gardens, White Waltham *(38)*

September 4 Sunday
West Wokingham Gardens *(40)*

September 7 Wednesday
Waltham Place Gardens, White Waltham *(38)*

September 14 Wednesday
Waltham Place Gardens, White Waltham *(38)*

September 18 Sunday
The Harris Garden, Whiteknights, Reading *(11)*

September 21 Wednesday
Waltham Place Gardens, White Waltham *(38)*

September 24 Saturday
The RISC Roof Garden, Reading *(27)*

September 25 Sunday
The RISC Roof Garden, Reading *(27)*

September 28 Wednesday
Waltham Place Gardens, White Waltham *(38)*

---

ngs gardens open for charity

Your garden in the Yellow Book?

The NGS is always interested to hear of gardens with potential, large or small, that might open in the future.

For more information about opening your garden, please contact the County Organiser in your area, preferably at the time of year that you would like your garden to open.

DESCRIPTIONS OF GARDENS

❶ Bearwood College, Winnersh &⌾

5m SE of Reading. Off B3030, 1m S of A329/ B3030 intersection at Winnersh, midway between Reading and Wokingham. Look for Bearwood Rd & Bearwood College sign. Late C19 mansion and parkland now used as an independent school. Walks through mature woodland, pinetum, rhododendrons and grassland. Lake and natural margins. Pulham water garden under restoration. Some mansion rooms open. Cream TEAS in aid of Pulham Garden Restoration Fund. *Adm £3, chd free. Sun 15 May (2-5)*

❷ Bradfield Farm, Stanford Dingley &⌾
(Mrs Anna Newton) *8m E of Newbury. In centre of village to S of church & R Pang. House painted pink.* ½-acre plantsman's garden with wide variety of plants. Driveway behind with rare and interesting trees leading (across fields) to 6-acre wild garden beside R Pang with long undisturbed ground and mown walks to enjoy native flora and fauna. Home of Brian Davis Garden School. Teas at Old Boot PH. *Adm £3. Sun 8 May (2-6). Private visits welcome by appt. Tel 0118 974 4113*

❸ Chieveley Manor, Chieveley &⌾⌾
(Mr & Mrs C J Spence) *5m N of Newbury. Take A34 N, pass under M4, then L to Chieveley. After ½m L up Manor Lane.* Large garden with fine views over stud farm. Walled garden containing borders, shrubs and rose garden. Listed house (not open). Newly planted bed. Home-made TEAS in aid of St Mary's Church, Chieveley. *Adm £3, chd free. Sun 26 June (2-5.30)*

◆ Cliveden, Taplow &⌾
See Buckinghamshire.

❹ Devonia, Broad Lane, Bracknell &⌾
(Andrew Radgick) *From M4 take A329(M) towards Bracknell. At 3rd roundabout take 2nd exit into Broad Lane. 3rd house on L after railway bridge. From M3 take A322 towards Bracknell. At Horse & Groom roundabout take 4th exit into Broad Lane.* ⅓-acre plantaholic's garden designed for all seasons. Over 1000 different shrubs, perennials, bulbs and alpines incl many rare and unusual. Wisteria. *Adm £2. Private visits welcome by appt. Tel 01344 450914 aradgick@aol.com*

❺ NEW Donnington Castle House, Castle Lane, Donnington &⌾
(Mr & Mrs B Stewart-Brown) *1m N of Newbury. Follow signs to Donnington Castle. Entrance on R towards top of main castle entrance.* Car-park through wooden gates. Large mature garden with many parts planted during last 3yrs. Herbaceous borders, roses, mixed borders, fine mature trees, lawns. Newly planted woodland and garden walks. Home-made TEAS. *Adm £3, chd free. Thur 14 July (10.30-5). Tel 01635 44705*

❻ ◆ Englefield House, Englefield &⌾⌾
(Sir William & Lady Benyon) *6m W of Reading. 1½m from exit 12 M4. 1m from Theale. Entrance on A340 3m S of Pangbourne.* 9-acre woodland garden with interesting variety of trees and shrubs, stream, water garden descending to formal terraces with stone balustrades. Staircases making background for deep borders. Small enclosed gardens of differing character incl children's garden with joke fountains. All enclosed by deer park with lake. Light refreshments and TEAS at Village shop. *House and Garden Adm £9, Garden only Adm £3, chd free. Open every Mon all yr. Tues to Thurs incl from 1 Apr to 31 Oct (10-6). Tel 01189 302221 benyon@englefield.co.uk*

❼ Eton College Gardens, Eton &⌾⌾
(J N B Cook Esq) *½m N of Windsor. Stations: Windsor Central 1m. Riverside ½m. Parking either off B3022 Slough to Eton rd, signed to R S of junction with Datchet Rd (Pocock's Lane); walk across playing fields to entry. Alternatively continue S on B3022 through T-lights in Eton, then signposted 50yds on L (called Barnes Pool and suitable for those with a wheelchair). 100yds walk to entry.* The Gardens incl Provost's Garden, Fellows' Garden, Headmaster's Garden and Luxmoore's garden (an island in the Thames, created by a housemaster about 1880 and reached across an attractive bridge). Gardens adjoin ancient buildings. Cream TEAS in aid of Datchet PCC. *Adm £2, chd 50p. Sat 11 June (2-6)*

❽ Farley Hill Place Gardens, Church Road, Farley Hill &⌾
(Mr & Mrs R May) *5m S of Reading. 1½m E of Swallowfield.* 5-acre garden, incl 2-acre walled garden. Late C18 with herbaceous borders of mixed planting, 120ft pergola and ½-

acre vegetable garden. 2-acre orchard with wild area. Spring daffodils and primroses a feature. Nut coppice and mature trees. TEAS. *Adm £2.50. Sun 5 June (2-6). Private visits welcome by appt until end of Jun, for groups. Tel 0118 976 1351*

9 Folly Farm, Sulhamstead 🐕🖐️
7m SW of Reading. A4 between Reading and Newbury (2m W of M4 exit 12) take rd marked Sulhamstead at Spring Inn. One of the few remaining gardens where Lutyens architecture remains intact. Garden, laid out by Gertrude Jekyll, has been planted to owners' taste, bearing in mind Jekyll and Lutyens original design. Raised white garden, sunken rose garden; spring bulbs; herbaceous borders; ilex walk; avenues of limes, yew hedges, formal pools. Tropical greenhouses and organic vegetable garden. House (not open). TEAS. *Adm £2.50. Sun 12 June (2-6). Private visits welcome by appt for groups of 15+, coaches permitted. Tel 01635 841541*

10 Frogmore House Garden, Windsor 🖐️🐕
(Her Majesty The Queen) 1m SE of Windsor. Windsor Castle: Entrance via Park St gate into Long Walk (follow AA signs). Visitors are requested kindly to keep on the route to the garden & not stray into the Home Park. Station & bus stop: Windsor (20 mins walk from gardens); Green Line bus no 701, from London. Limited parking for cars only (free). 30 acres of landscaped gardens rich in history and beauty. Large lake, fine trees, lawns, flowers and flowering shrubs. The Royal Mausoleum, within the grounds, will also be open to those visiting the gardens. Refreshment tent adjoining Frogmore House. Coaches by appointment only. For tickets apply to NGS, Hatchlands Park, East Clandon, Guildford, Surrey GU4 7RT enc s.a.e or Tel 01483 211535 stating am or pm. Light refreshments and TEAS. *Adm £3.50 to garden, chd free. Tue 17 May (10-5.30 (last adm 4)). Tel 02077 667305 www.royal.gov.uk*

11 The Harris Garden, Whiteknights, Reading 🖐️🐕
(The University of Reading, School of Plant Sciences) 1½m S of Reading town centre. Off A327, Shinfield Rd. Turn R just inside Pepper Lane entrance to University campus. 12-acre research and teaching garden. Rose gardens, herbaceous borders, winter garden, herb garden, jungle

garden. New water garden. Extensive glasshouses. Many plants labelled. TEAS in aid of Friends of the Harris Garden. *Adm £2.50, chd free. Suns 8 May; 18 Sept (2-6)*

12 Inkpen House, Inkpen 🐕
(Mr & Mrs David Male) 3m SE of Hungerford. Lower Green. Turn off A4 at sign marked Kintbury & Inkpen. Drive into Kintbury. Turn L by shop onto Inkpen Rd. After approx 1m turn R at Xrds. After red telephone kiosk on R take 2nd turn on L marked C13 Church. 4-acre garden laid out at beginning of C18 in the Versailles style with formal planting of avenues and bosquets. Pleached lime walk and walled kitchen garden, water garden. TEAS. *Adm £2.50, chd free. Sun 10 July (2-6)*

13 Ivydene, 283 Loddon Bridge Road, Woodley 🐕
(Janet & Bill Bonney) 3½m W of Reading. A4 out of Reading towards Maidenhead. Woodley lies midway between the two. Loddon Bridge Rd is the main rd through the small town. Garden is about 100yds S of the 'Just Tiles' roundabout. Parking is in adjacent rd. Small urban gardener's garden approx 120ft x 30ft, specialising in ornamental grasses with over 50 varieties integrated into both front and back gardens. Autumn viewing shows grasses to best advantage. 'Garden News' Gardener of the Year, 2003. Ideal Home 2004. TEAS. *Adm £2. Private visits welcome by appt for groups. Tel 0118 969 7591*

14 Kirby House, Inkpen 🐕
(Mr & Mrs R Astor) 3½m SE of Hungerford. A4 to Kintbury. L at Xrds in Kintbury (by Corner Stores) towards Coombe. 2m out of Kintbury turn L immed beyond Crown & Garter PH, turn L at junction, house & garden at bottom of hill on R. 6 acres in beautiful setting with views of South Berkshire Downs across lawn and parkland. Formal rose garden, double herbaceous border in kitchen garden, colour theme border between yew buttress hedges. Lily pond garden, reflecting pond with fountain, lake. C18 Queen Ann house (not open). *Adm £3.50, chd £1. Sun 3 July (2-5)*

Little Coopers, Coopers Hill, Eversley 🖐️
See Hampshire.

15 Mariners, Mariners Lane, Bradfield 🖐️🐕
(Anthony & Fenja Anderson) 10m W of Reading. M4 J12 take A4 direction Newbury 1m. At roundabout exit A340 direction Pangbourne. 400yds turn L direction Bradfield. After 1m, turn L direction Southend Bradfield. After 1m opp signpost direction Tutts Clump turn R into Mariners Lane. Follow yellow signs. 1½-acre sloping site with creative feature made of slopes. Rich mixture of herbaceous planting incl unusual plants and grasses arranged in colour themes with emphasis on plant form and texture. Garden of old varieties of shrub roses, species and climbing roses. Streamside walk, orchard, sundial garden and 1-acre wildflower meadow. Wheelchair access is limited by slopes. *Adm £3, chd under 16 free. Sun 19 June (2-6). Private visits welcome by appt Mon 20th June-Sat 16th July. Tel 0118 974 5226*

16 Meadow House, Ashford Hill 🖐️🐕
(Mr & Mrs G A Jones) 8m SE of Newbury. On B3051. Take turning at SW end of village signposted Wolverton Common & Wheathold. House on R approx 350yds down unmade track. Approx 1¾-acre plantsman's garden in beautiful rural surroundings. Designed by owners to create a feeling of tranquillity and space. Pond with waterside planting; mixed shrub, rose and herbaceous borders. Trellis with wisteria, roses and clematis. *Adm £2.50. Thurs 2, 16 June (11-4). Private visits welcome by appt, coaches permitted. Tel 0118 981 6005*

⑰ Moor Close Gardens, Popeswood Road, Binfield 🚶♿⊕
(Newbold College) *2m W of Bracknell. Off B3408. From Bracknell turn R at Binfield T-lights; from A329(M) take B3408, turn L at Binfield T-lights; then follow signs.* Grade II listed garden designed 1911-13 by Oliver Hill, following Lutyens and Jekyll. The famous architect's first commission and a rare example of his early work. Series of linked courts and gardens incl herb garden, water parterre, Italianate Garden with partitions, pergola and pools. Now in the course of restoration. Cream Teas 19 Jun, TEAS 30 May, in aid of Garden Restoration Fund. *Adm £2, chd free. Mon, 30 May; Sun 19 June (2-5.15). Private visits welcome by appt. Tel 01344 452427 harryleonard@beeb.net*

⑱ Odney Club, Odney Lane, Cookham ♿
(John Lewis Partnership) *3m N of Maidenhead. Off A4094 S of Cookham Bridge. Car park in grounds.* This 120-acre site beside the Thames is continuously developing and takes a full afternoon to visit. A favourite with Stanley Spencer who featured our magnolia in his work. Magnificent wisteria, specimen trees, herbaceous borders, side gardens, spring bedding and ornamental lake. Cream TEAS. *Adm £2.50, chd free (share to Thames Valley Adventure Playground). Sun 24 Apr (2-6)*

The Old House, Bramley Road, Silchester ♿⊕
See Hampshire.

Old Meadows, Bramley Road, Silchester ♿🚶⊕
See Hampshire.

The Old Mill, Ramsbury 🚶⊕
See Wiltshire.

The Old Rectory, Ham ♿🚶⊕
See Wiltshire.

ng's gardens open for charity

The Yellow Book is the UK's most popular garden visiting guide with a circulation of over 60,0000 copies

⑲ The Old Rectory Burghfield ♿🚶⊕
(Mr A R Merton) *5m SW of Reading. Turn S off A4 to Burghfield village; R after Hatch Gate Inn; entrance on R.* 4½-acre plantsman's garden. Snowdrops, hellebores, old rose, shrub borders, woodland area, ponds, orchard, kitchen garden, terrace pots and late summer flowering double herbaceous borders. Georgian house (not open). Home-made TEAS in aid of Beagle Welfare. *Adm £2.50, chd free. Sun 12 June (2-6)*

⑳ The Old Rectory Farnborough, Nr Wantage 🚶⊕
(Mr & Mrs Michael Todhunter) *4m SE of Wantage. From B4494 Wantage-Newbury Rd, 4m from Wantage turn E at sign for Farnborough.* In a series of immaculately tended garden rooms, incl herbaceous borders, arboretum, boules, rose, pool and vegetable gardens, there is an explosion of rare and interesting plants, beautifully combined for colour and texture. With stunning views across the countryside, it is the perfect setting for the C1749 rectory (not open), once home of John Betjeman, in memory of whom John Piper created a window in the local church. TEAS. *Adm £2.50. Suns 17 Apr; 15 May; 19 June (2-5.30). Private visits welcome by appt. Tel 01488 638298*

㉑ The Old Rectory Peasemore 🚶⊕
(Mr & Mrs I D Cameron) *7m N of Newbury. On A34 to M4 J13. N towards Oxford then immed L signed Chieveley. Through Chieveley & onto Peasemore approx 3½m or B4494 from Newbury 6m N signposted Peasemore.* Georgian house (not open) with fine trees in lovely setting. Shrub roses, peonies, rose garden, herbaceous border and double mixed borders, 3-acre wild flower meadow. Home-made TEAS. *Adm £2.50, chd free. Sun 19 June (2-6)*

◆ Old Thatch, Coldmoorholme Lane, Well End ♿🚶⊕
See Buckinghamshire.

㉒ NEW Old Waterfield, Winkfield Road, Ascot ♿🚶⊕
(Hugh & Catherine Stevenson) *6m S of Windsor. On E of A330 (Winkfield Rd) midway between A329 and A332 to SE of Ascot Racecourse. Parking on Practice Ground (by kind permission of Royal Ascot Golf Club) adjacent to house.* 4-acres. The original cottage

garden, incl kitchen garden, was recently extended by 3-acres of specimen trees and orchard planted in 2000. Home-made TEAS in aid of Ascot Day Centre. *Adm £2.50, chd free, concessions £2. Sun 28 Aug (2-5.30)*

㉓ Potash, Mariners Lane, Southend Bradfield ♿
(Mr & Mrs J W C Mooney) *10m W of Reading. From M4 J12 take A4 W 1m. At roundabout exit A340 direction Pangbourne turn L after 400yds direction Bradfield. After 1m turn L direction Southend Bradfield. 1m opposite Southend Bradfield sign turn R. Potash is 400yds on L by Beech Hedge.* 5-acre garden. Wide range of plants, many unusual specimens and interest throughout the yr from snowdrops to autumn colour. Daffodils a feature, shrubs, tea roses, herbaceous borders, bog garden feeding a clay-lined pond, young woodland and space to contemplate. Dog friendly and children under supervision. *Adm £3, chd free. Private visits welcome by appt, incl groups. Tel 0118 9744264 john@mooney9.freeserve.co.uk*

㉔ Prior's Court School, Hermitage, nr Newbury ♿⊕
(Prior's Court Foundation) *5m N of Newbury. From M4 J12 take A34 N to Oxford. 1st slip rd signposted Chieveley & Hermitage. At top of slip rd turn R onto Prior's Court Rd, the entrance to Prior's Court is 100yds on L.* Independent school for children with autism. Grade II listed C18 house (not open) set in 54 acres of parkland. 10-acre wood with a profusion of springtime daffodils and bluebells. Fine beech ave and many mature specimen trees, two formal gardens, walled garden with restored C19 greenhouse, woodland sculpture trail. Grounds are home to a wide and varied collection of contemporary works of art by many major artists. TEAS in aid of The Prior's Court Foundation. *Adm £2.50, chd under 16 free. Sun 12 June (11-3)*

㉕ The Priory, Beech Hill ♿🚶⊕
(Mr & Mrs C Carter) *5m S of Reading. M4 J11. Follow signs to A33, then Beech Hill. When in village turn opp church into Wood Lane, then R down Priory Dr - house at end of drive.* Extensive gardens in grounds of former C12 Benedictine Priory (not open), rebuilt 1648 and renovated 1996 by present owners. Situated in the beautiful surroundings of the R Loddon, the mature gardens are now being restored and re-

developed. Large formal walled garden with espalier fruit trees, lawns, extensive mixed and herbaceous borders, vegetables and roses. Walk across river leads to woodland and lake. Many fine trees. 4 large herbaceous borders being completely replanted. Featured in 'English Garden' magazine, 2004. Home-made TEAS in aid of Beech Hill Horticultural Society. *Adm £2.50, chd free. Sun 26 June (2-6). Private visits welcome by appt. Tel 01189 883146*

㉖ Reynolds Farm, Hurst 🔽🏵
(Mr & Mrs Christopher Wells) *1m S of Twyford. From Twyford turn L off A321 at Hurst into Broad Common Road. After ⅔m L into Broad Common Lane.* Wild woodland garden planted from scratch by present owners over past 40yrs, objective being to maximise pleasure and minimise maintenance. Planting policy has been driven by greed, followed by indigestion - can't resist it, but oh where to put it. Densely planted woodland walks leave little space for weeds whilst providing fun for ourselves, the dog and we hope you as well. *Adm £2, chd free. Sun 24 Apr (2-5.30)*

㉗ The RISC Roof Garden, Reading, 35-39 London Street 🏵
(Reading International Solidarity Centre) *5 mins walk from Oracle shopping centre.* Small town centre roof garden developed to demonstrate sustainability and our dependance on plants. All plants in the garden have an economic use for food, clothing, medicine etc. The garden can accommodate a maximum of 20 people at a time so book a tour if you are not prepared to wait. Roof garden accessible by external staircase. Featured in 'Britain in Bloom' Most innovative Garden. Reading Heritage Award 2003. 'Reading Evening Post', Meridian Regional News T.V. 2004. Home-made TEAS. *Adm £2.50, chd free, concessions £1.50. Sat, Sun 28, 29 May; 25, 26 June; 30, 31 July; 24, 25 Sept, (12-4). Tel 0118 958 6692 www.risc.org.uk/garden*

㉘ Rooksnest, Lambourn Woodlands 🔽🏵🏵
(Dr & Mrs M D Sackler) *2m S of Lambourn. From A338 (Wantage) rd, along B4000. Nearest village, Lambourn. Rooksnest signposted on B4000 in both directions, ie whether approaching from Lambourn or from the A338.* Approx 10-acre exceptionally fine traditional English garden. Recently restored with help

from Arabella Lennox-Boyd. Incl terraces; rose garden, lilies, herbaceous border, herb garden, many specimen trees and fine shrubs. Home-made TEAS. *Adm £2.50. Weds 27 Apr; 22 June (1-5). Private visits welcome by appt. Tel 01488 72991 theresa.sackler@mdsackler. co.uk*

㉙ Sandleford Place, Newtown, Newbury 🔽🏵🏵
(Mr & Mrs Alan Gatward) *1½m S of Newbury. On A339. House is at W side of Swan roundabout.* 4-acre grounds around a former old mill and granary. Some fine large trees. Many varied shrub and herbaceous borders and walled garden all redesigned over past 20yrs. Wide range of plants arranged for yr-round interest of flowers, foliage and scent. Kitchen garden and herb bed. Wild flowers along river. Unusual plants for sale, some seen in the garden. Home-made TEAS in aid of Newtown Church & NGS. *Adm £2.50, chd free. Sun 19 June (2-6). Private visits welcome by appt. Tel 01635 40726 melgatward@bigfoot.com*

㉚ Scotlands, nr Wargrave 🔽
(Mr Michael Payne) *6m W of Maidenhead, 4m E of Henley. In centre of triangle formed by A4130, A321 to Wargrave & A4 at Knowl Hill - midway between Warren Row Village & Cockpole Green.* 4 acres. Clipped yews; shrub borders, grass paths through trees to woodland and pond-gardens with Repton design rustic summer house. Rocks with waterfall and gazebo. Surrounding C17 farmhouse (not open). *Adm £3, chd free. Private visits welcome by appt. Tel 01628 822648*

㉛ 10 Shaftesbury Close, Harmanswater, Bracknell
(Gill Cheetham) *1m S of Bracknell Town Centre. From M4 follow directions to Bracknell and M3. At sports centre roundabout take exit to Harmanswater. Turn L on 2 mini roundabouts into Nightingale Crescent. Shaftesbury Close is 2nd turning on R.* Woodland garden, at its best during winter and spring. Many different ericaceous shrubs and plants. Walled garden, scree and alpine beds. Colour-coordinated herbaceous beds in summer. Home-made TEAS in aid of Motor Neurone Disease Association. *Adm £2.50, chd free. Private visits welcome by appt. Tel 01344 423440 gillcheetham@btopenworld.com*

㉜ Shefford Woodlands House, Shefford Woodlands 🔽🏵
(Mrs Gary Black) *3m N of Hungerford. ½m N of junction 14 of M4 off B4000 (follow sign to Shefford Woodlands).* 4-acre garden. Formal entrance with pond and topiary. Herbaceous borders, incl many old-fashioned roses, delphiniums, clematis, white garden and clipped yews all designed by Arabella Lennox-Boyd. Informal gardens with trees, shrubs and vegetable and cutting garden. Home-made TEAS. *Adm £2.50, chd free. Sun 12 June (2-5.30)*

㉝ Simms Farm House, Mortimer 🔽🏵🏵
(The Rev His Hon Christopher & Mrs Lea) *6m SW of Reading. At mini roundabout on edge of village, from Grazeley, turn R uphill approx 1m; L by church into West End Rd; at next mini roundabout L down Drury Lane; R at T-junction.* 1-acre garden with mixed shrub borders, small rockery; bog garden; formal pond; kitchen garden and unusual plants. Lovely view. *Adm £2.50, chd free. Private visits welcome by appt Apr to Sept. Tel 01189 332360*

㉞ Stockcross House, Church Road, Stockcross, Newbury 🔽🏵🏵
(Susan & Edward Vandyk) *3m W of Newbury. 1m W of A4/A34 (Newbury bypass) junction on B4000. From M4, J14, take B4000 to Stockcross.* 1½-acre garden developed over past 10yrs with an emphasis on plant partnerships and colour combinations. Herbaceous borders, shrubs, roses, perogola and pond, vegetable and cutting gardens, all maintained to a high standard. Home-made TEAS in aid of Stockcross Village Hall. *Adm £2, chd free. Sun 5 June (2-5.30). Private visits welcome by appt. Tel 01635 298016*

㉟ Sunningdale Park, Larch Avenue, Ascot
(Initial Style/CMPS) *6m S of Windsor. On A30 at Sunningdale take Broomhall Lane. After ½m turn R into Larch Ave. Or from A329 turn into Silwood Rd towards Sunningdale.* Over 20 acres of beautifully landscaped gardens reputedly designed after 'Capability' Brown. Terrace garden and Victorian rockery designed by Pulham incl cave and water features. Lake area with paved walks; extensive lawns with specimen trees and flower beds, impressive massed rhododendrons. Beautiful 1m woodland walk. Grade

ll listed building (not open). Free garden history tour 3.30pm. Home-made TEAS. *Adm £4, chd free. Sun 22 May (2-5)*

36 **Timberlea, 17 Oaklands Drive, Wokingham** &⌀⊕
(Mr & Mrs F Preston) *1m SW of Wokingham. From M4 (J10) or M3 (J3). Wokingham town centre take the Camberley Rd A321 under two railway bridges; Tesco store is between both. Immed turn R at mini roundabout after second bridge Molly Millars Lane. Third rd on L is Oaklands Drive; after 100yds turn R into cul-de-sac.* A garden of variety re-designed by the owners over the last 13yrs. The triangular plot (⅓ acre) contains raised vegetable plots, fruit cage, gazebo, pergola, patios and hidden corners through arches which display well-established planting of herbaceous perennial plants. Shrubs, climbers, containers (some colour coded areas) and a shaded woodland spot are viewed from terraces. Secluded decking overlooks a waterfall, stream, pond and circular rose bed in the front garden. 'Real Makeovers' 2003. Prize winner Wokingham Town Garden Awards & Wokingham District 2003 & 2004. 'Amateur Gardening' 2004. Light refreshments and TEAS. *Adm £1.50, chd free. Sun 26 June (2-6). Private visits welcome by appt fo*

groups up to 30. Tel 0118 978 4629 nina.fred@tinyonline.co.uk

37 **Two Littlewick Green Gardens, Littlewick Green**
On A4, 2m W of Maidenhead, turn S into Jubilee Rd. Park on Village Green. The Thatch is next to cricket pitch. Pass Thatch for Rosemary Cottage, 200yds further on, off Coronation Rd. Small village of houses round village green with The Thatch in middle. Home-made TEAS at The Thatch in aid of St John's Church. *Combined adm £3.50 for The Thatch and Rosemary Cottage, £2.50 for The Thatch, chd £1. Private visits welcome by appt, incl coaches. Tel 01628 825718*

Rosemary Cottage (Lynne Emmerson) Small garden limited access, around old gothic-style cottage (not open) with over 50 different clematis. Patio with seasonal colour. Secret gravel garden featuring spring bulbs and cottage favourites incl geraniums, campanulas, pinks and aquilegias, late summer phlox. Rustic seating and water feature.

The Thatch &⌀⊕ (Lynn & David Penfold) ¾-acre exuberant cottage garden complements thatched cottage (not open) on village green. Waterfall, pool, bog garden and terraced beds in old chalkpit. Plants, mostly scented, planted for dry, chalky soil.

Herbaceous beds, shrubs, mature trees, tiny woodland garden. June is high-point of yr, for old roses especially, but garden is fresh and colourful in spring. Featured in 'Amateur Gardening' 2003.

38 ◆ **Waltham Place Gardens, Church Hill, White Waltham** &⊕
(Mr & Mrs N Oppenheimer) *3½m S of Maidenhead. From M4 J8/9 take A404. Follow signs for White Waltham. Pass airfield on RH-side. Take L turn signposted Windsor/Paley St. Pass the church, follow signs for parking. From Bracknell/Wokingham A3095 to A330 direction Maidenhead. Turn L at Paley St B3024 to White Waltham. Follow parking signs.* New style naturalistic gardens (Henk Gerritsen) where weeds meet garden plants in an ancient framework of wonderful specimen trees. With organic kitchen garden and farm, several walled gardens, grasspath maze, lake and woodland with bluebells, camellias and rhododendrons. Explore the boundaries between nature and garden in our 170-acre nature inspired paradise. 'Gardens Illustrated' & 'Sunday Telegraph Magazine' 2003, 'Country Life', 'Organic Gardens' & 'Financial Times' 2004. Home-made TEAS. *Adm £3.50, chd £1. Jun-Sept, Fris for other groups.* **For NGS:** *Weds, 1 June to 28 Sept (10-4). Tel 01628 825517 estateoffice@walthamplace.com*

Marie Curie Cancer Care

Marie Curie Cancer Care is devoted to ensuring that terminally ill people are cared for in a dignified way that enhances their quality of life.

Our nurses, working in the community and in our ten hospices nation-wide, provide expert hands-on care, as well as comfort and emotional support to the family.

Thanks to supporters such as The National Gardens Scheme, our care is always free of charge.

Find out more at **www.mariecurie.org.uk**

㊴ Welford Park, nr Newbury
&⊛
(Mrs J H Puxley) *6m NW of Newbury. On Lambourn Valley Rd. Entrance on Newbury-Lambourn rd. Please use clearly marked car park.* Spacious grounds. Wonderful trees and recently restored gardens in spacious grounds and park. Woodland walk by R Lambourn with aconites, galanthus nivalis followed by crocus. *Adm £3, concessions £2. Tue 15 Feb (2-5)*

West Silchester Hall, Silchester
&⊛
See Hampshire.

㊵ West Wokingham Gardens
1m W of Wokingham. Follow A329 through Wokingham towards Reading. 1m after town centre turn L at Woosehill roundabout. At end of dual carriageway turn R into Northway 1st L into Culloden Way. Crecy Close is 5th on L. For Simons Lane continue over Woosehill roundabout on A329 towards Reading and take 2nd L. Three very different styles of gardens offering variety and ideas for visitors. Home-made TEAS at Simons Lane in aid of Wokingham Centre for Parents, 5 Jun only. *Combined adm £2.50 , chd free. Suns 5 June; 4 Sept (2-5)*
  5 Crecy Close ✄ (Dorothy Harfleet) Small front garden

redesigned in 2001 by Anne Massey to solve parking problem. Features private seating area surrounded by aromatic planting and raised beds planted primarily in perennials for low maintenance gardening.
  6 Crecy Close &✄⊛ (John & Anne Massey) Professional garden designers; the garden offers many design ideas for the small garden, together with interesting and unusual plants. Portfolio on view and raffle for free garden design. Featured as 'English Garden' in Japanese publication 2003 and '25 Beautiful Gardens' Spring 2004. *Private visits welcome by appt. Tel 0118 901 9099*

Dore Cottage, 21 Simons Lane
&⊛ (Jill Wheatley) Organically-run ¼-acre garden, developed since 1996, intensively planted with wide variety of shrubs, herbaceous perennials, climbers and fruit. Rear garden is designed around large pond with water lilies and marginal planting. Paved area features herbs and, in courtyard garden, hosta collection. Summerhouse has display of stitched textiles. HDRA information available on organic methods. *Not open 4 Sept. Private visits welcome by appt June only, no coaches. Tel 0118 377 4040*

White Gables, Breach Lane, Sherfield-on-Loddon &✄⊛
See Hampshire.

㊶ Whiteknights, The Ridges, Finchampstead &✄⊛
(Mrs Heather Bradly) *3m S of Wokingham. B3348 Finchampstead Ridges. Midway between Finchampstead War Memorial & Crowthorne station.* Large garden incl Japanese, Chinese and Mediterranean gardens. Two greenhouses with cacti, lean-to and conservatory, herbaceous border, gravel garden, dwarf conifers and organic vegetable garden all add to the interest. ½th scale model Tudor Village. New Fairy Grotto. *Adm £3, chd 50p. Suns 8 May; 14 Aug (2-5). Private visits welcome by appt. Tel 0118 973 3274*

Whitewalls, Quarry Wood Road, Marlow &✄
See Buckinghamshire.

㊷ Woolley Park, nr Wantage
&✄⊛
(Mrs P Wroughton) *5m S of Wantage. A338. Turn L at sign to Woolley.* Large park, fine trees and views. Two linked walled gardens beautifuly planted. *Adm £2.50. Sun 12 June (2-6)*

Bristol & South Gloucestershire

County Organiser: Mrs Eileen Mantell, Rook Farm, Oldbury-on-Severn, South Gloucestershire BS35 1PL
Tel 01454 412281 email eileen.richard@btopenworld.com

Assistant County Organisers:
(County Leaflet)   Mrs Jean Damey, 2 Hawburn Close, Brislington, Bristol BS4 2PB
Tel 0117 9775587 email jddamey@hotmail.com
Mrs Jane Perkins, Woodland Cottage, Oldbury-on-Severn, South Gloucestershire
BS35 1PL Tel 01454 414570
Mrs Sally Wilton, Manor Side House, Washingpool Hill Road, Tockington, Bristol BS32 4NX
Tel 01454 618760

County Treasurer: Mr R S Bennett, Rook Farm, Oldbury-on-Severn, South Gloucestershire BS35 1PL
Tel 01454 412281

Maps: Numbers shown next to each garden entry refer to that garden's entry on the county map. This position is approximate; distance and directions from the nearest main town are generally shown in the garden text.
A precise location is available for those gardens featured on the NGS website by visiting www.ngs.org.uk.

Symbols: Information relating to symbols is given on page 21

DATES OF OPENING

Evening openings
See end of county listing

Gardens open to the public
For details see garden description
Dyrham Park, Bath *(10)*
Emmaus House, Bristol *(12)*
Lady Farm, Chelwood *(15)*
Sherborne Garden, Litton *(23)*
Special Plants, Nr Cold Ashton *(24)*

By appointment only
*For telephone number and other details see garden description.
Private visits welcomed*
Algars Manor, Iron Acton *(1)*
Algars Mill, Iron Acton *(2)*
The Urn Cottage, Charfield *(28)*

January 30 Sunday
Rock House, Elberton *(20)*

April 3 Sunday
Rock House, Elberton *(20)*

April 24 Sunday
Emmaus House, Bristol *(12)*
25 Hillcrest Road, Redcliffe Bay *(14)*

May 8 Sunday
Windmill Cottage, Backwell *(30)*

May 11 Wednesday
4 Haytor Park, Bristol *(13)*

May 22 Sunday
25 Hillcrest Road, Redcliffe Bay *(14)*

May 29 Sunday
Lady Farm, Chelwood *(15)*

June 3 Friday
Dyrham Park, Bath *(10)*

June 4 Saturday
Dyrham Park, Bath *(10)*

June 5 Sunday
19 Derricke Road, Stockwood, Bristol *(9)*
Teesdale, Thornbury *(26)*

June 9 Thursday
1 Bromley Villas, Stanton Drew **(Evening)**
(5)

June 11 Saturday
Clifton Gardens *(8)*
26 Northumberland Road, Redland *(17)*

June 12 Sunday
The Lintels, Littleton-on-Severn *(16)*
26 Northumberland Road, Redland *(17)*
Rodney Cottage, Backwell **(Day &**
Evening) *(21)*
Sunnyside Cottage, Littleton-on-Severn *(25)*
Walnut Tree Cottage, Littleton-on-Severn *(29)*

June 16 Thursday
Special Plants, Nr Cold Ashton *(24)*

June 18 Saturday
Cedar House, Wrington *(7)*

June 19 Sunday
Cedar House, Wrington *(7)*
Emmaus House, Bristol *(12)*
Windmill Cottage, Backwell *(30)*

June 28 Tuesday
2 Old Tarnwell, Stanton Drew **(By**
appointment only) *(18)*

July 5 Tuesday
2 Old Tarnwell, Stanton Drew **(By**
appointment only) *(18)*

July 6 Wednesday
4 Haytor Park, Bristol *(13)*

July 10 Sunday
19 Derricke Road, Stockwood, Bristol *(9)*
Tranby House, Whitchurch *(27)*

July 13 Wednesday
2 Old Tarnwell, Stanton Drew **(By**
appointment only) *(18)*

July 17 Sunday
25 Hillcrest Road, Redcliffe Bay *(14)*

July 19 Tuesday
Easton-in-Gordano Gardens *(11)*

July 21 Thursday
Special Plants, Nr Cold Ashton *(24)*

July 22 Friday
Saltford Farm Barn, Saltford **(Evening)** *(22)*

July 23 Saturday
Camers, Old Sodbury *(6)*
Saltford Farm Barn, Saltford *(22)*

July 24 Sunday
1 Bromley Villas, Stanton Drew *(5)*
Camers, Old Sodbury *(6)*
Saltford Farm Barn, Saltford *(22)*

July 26 Tuesday
Easton-in-Gordano Gardens *(11)*

July 31 Sunday
Apple Acre, Star, Winscombe *(3)*

August 2 Tuesday
Easton-in-Gordano Gardens *(11)*

August 7 Sunday
19 Derricke Road, Stockwood, Bristol *(9)*
Windmill Cottage, Backwell *(30)*

August 14 Sunday
Teesdale, Thornbury *(26)*
Tranby House, Whitchurch *(27)*

August 18 Thursday
Special Plants, Nr Cold Ashton *(24)*

September 4 Sunday
Beechwell House, Yate *(4)*
Park Farm, Alderley *(19)*

September 11 Sunday
Emmaus House, Bristol *(12)*
Sherborne Garden, Litton *(23)*

September 15 Thursday
Special Plants, Nr Cold Ashton *(24)*

September 25 Sunday
Lady Farm, Chelwood *(15)*
Windmill Cottage, Backwell *(30)*

ngs gardens open for charity

Busy at work?
Try our evening
openings

BRISTOL & SOUTH GLOUCESTERSHIRE

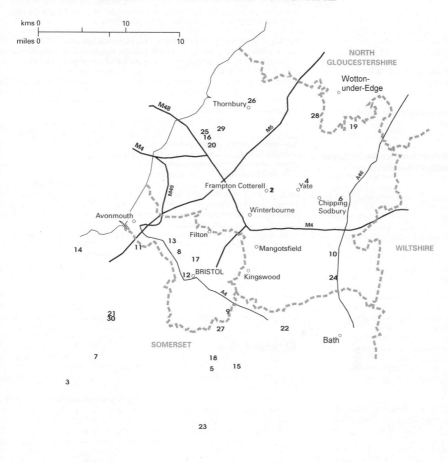

DESCRIPTIONS OF GARDENS

❶ Algars Manor, Station Road, Iron Acton
(Dr & Mrs J M Naish) *9m N of Bristol. 3m W of Yate/Chipping Sodbury. Turn S off Iron Acton bypass B4059, past village green, 200yds, then over level Xing (Station Rd).* 2 acres of woodland garden beside R Frome, mill stream, native plants mixed with collections of 60 magnolias and 70 camellias, eucalyptus and other unusual trees and shrubs. Mar/Apr: camellias, magnolias; Apr/May/June;

rhododendrons, azaleas. Featured in 'Gardens Monthly' and 'The English Garden', 2004. *Private visits welcome by appt for entrance to both Algars Manor & Algars Mill gardens, groups & garden clubs particularly welcome. Combined adm £2, chd free. Tel 01454 228372*

❷ Algars Mill, Station Road, Iron Acton
(Mr & Mrs John Wright) *9m N of Bristol. 3m W of Yate/Chipping Sodbury. (for directions see Algars Manor).* 2-acre woodland garden bisected by R Frome; spring bulbs,

shrubs; very early spring feature (Feb-Mar) of wild Newent daffodils. 300-400yr-old mill house (not open) through which millrace still runs. *Private visits welcome by appt for entrance to both Algars Manor & Algars Mill gardens. Combined adm £2, chd free. Tel 01454 228373 algarsmill@mac.com*

❸ Apple Acre, Star, Winscombe
&⌀⊕
(John & Mary Popham) *15m SW of Bristol. 7m E of Weston-super-Mare. On A38 S of Bristol between Churchill & Sidcot. Down lane next*

to Star Inn. 1-acre plantsman's garden with many mature trees, shrubs and colourful herbaceous borders. Working organic fruit and vegetable garden. Featured in 'Amateur Gardening' magazine 2004. Home-made TEAS in aid of St James' Church. *Adm £2, chd free. Sun 31 July (2-5.30). Private visits welcome by appt. Tel 01934 843789*

Barum, 50 Edward Road, Clevedon ✗❀
See Somerset.

Bath Priory Hotel, Weston Road, Bath ♿✗❀
See Somerset.

❹ Beechwell House, 51 Goose Green, Yate ♿✗❀
(Tim Wilmot) *10m NE of Bristol. From centre of Yate (Shopping & Leisure Centre) or Station Rd B4060, turn N onto Church Rd. After ½m turn L onto Greenways Rd then immed R onto continuation of Church Rd. Goose Green starts after 200yds. After 100yds take R-fork, garden 100yds on L.* Enclosed, level, subtropical garden created over last 15yrs and filled with exotic planting, incl palms (over 12 varieties), tree ferns, yuccas, agaves and succulent bed, phormiums, bamboos, cannas, bananas, gunnera and other 'architectural planting'. Wildlife pond and koi pond. C16 40ft deep well. Yate Large Garden Winner 2003/4, BBC Real Gardens Winner 2004. Home-made TEAS. *Adm £2, chd £1. Sun 4 Sept (1-6) www.beechwell. com*

❺ [NEW] 1 Bromley Villas, 1 Bromley Road, Stanton Drew ✗
(Judith Chubb-Whittle) *7m S of Bristol. From A37 Chelwood roundabout take A368 to Chew Valley Lake. Take 2nd turning on R. Follow car park signs. Park only in designated car park. Strictly no parking on Bromley Rd.* 1 acre of large informal themed plant-packed borders. Architectural and cottage plants, fire pit and bed, circular raised fruit garden, grassed mounds, water features and dramatic new rose tunnel. Still evolving. Home-made TEAS Sun only. *Adm £2.50, chd 50p. Sun 24 July (2-6).* **Evening Opening** *£3.50, wine, Thur 9 June (6-8.30) gardenvisit@qgardening.co.uk*

❻ Camers, Old Sodbury ♿❀
(Mr & Mrs A G Denman) *2m E of Chipping Sodbury. Entrance in Chapel Lane off A432 at Dog Inn.* Plantsman's garden over 2½ acres surrounding Elizabethan farmhouse

(not open) with spectacular views over Severn Vale. Divided into a range of formal and informal areas, incl parterre, Japanese garden, waterfalls, shade garden, white and hot gardens. Range of perennials and shrubs has been selected to give yr-round interest. Walk through wood planted in millennium yr. Dogs must be on leads. Home-made TEAS in aid of Gangama Orphanage - Uganda. *Adm £3, chd free. Sat, Sun 23, 24 July (2-5.30). Private visits welcome by appt for groups of 10 or more. Tel 01454 322430 arnold.denman@camers.org*

❼ Cedar House, High Street, Wrington ♿✗
(Jenny Denny) *12m S of Bristol. On A38. Follow sign for Wrington after airport & on reaching village, garage on L. T-junction turn R up hill. House on L. Parking in village (or at house by special arrangement).* Mature formal garden with specimen trees; lawns; walled herbaceous borders, rose beds, mixed borders, hostas and hydrangea bed, leading to orchard, sculpture park and pond fed by warm springs. *Adm £3, chd free. Sat, Sun 18, 19 June (11-4). Private visits welcome by appt late June - early July. Tel 01934 863375 hamish.denny@which.net*

❽ Clifton Gardens
Close to Clifton Suspension Bridge between the Mansion House & Christ Church. Combined adm £2.50, chd under 16 free. Sat 11 June (2-5.30)

Bell Cottage, 2 Camp Road ♿✗❀ (Jeff & Margaret Palmer) Yr-round town garden of exotic character; rockeries, pond, pergolas.

43 Canynge Road ♿✗ (Martin & Angela Appleby) Happy garden for children and birds: organic vegetables; lovely summerhouse. Each separate lawn area has a different mood.

11 Percival Road ✗❀ (Mr & Mrs R L Bland) Small, enclosed urban garden, most plants in containers. Large variety of individual, interesting plants. 70 tree species.

Congresbury Gardens
See Somerset.

❖ Crowe Hall, Widcombe ♿
See Somerset.

❾ 19 Derricke Road, Stockwood, Bristol ❀
(Myra & David Tucker) *5m S of Bristol city centre. A37 Wells Rd from Bristol, at Whitchurch T-lights (Maes-Knoll PH on corner) L into Staunton Lane, this runs into Stockwood Lane. Continue over 2 white roundabouts, 2nd L, 1st R.* Trees, shrubs and the colour green are backbone of this small yr-round garden created over 12 yrs, with textures, colours and shapes in abundance. Climbers, containers and flowers, plus many features and ideas for small gardens. Not suitable for young children. *Adm £1.50. Suns 5 June; 10 July; 7 Aug (2-6). Private visits welcome by appt. Tel 01275 542727*

❿ ❖ Dyrham Park, Bath ♿✗❀
(The National Trust) *12m E of Bristol. 8m N of Bath. Approached from Bath to Stroud rd (A46), 2m S of Tormarton interchange with M4 exit 18.* Situated on W side of late C17 house. Herbaceous borders, yews clipped as buttresses, ponds and cascade, parish church set on terrace. Niches and carved urns. Long lawn to old West entrance. Restored orangery. Deer park with designated walks giving magnificent views. Light refreshments and TEAS. *House and Garden Adm £8.80, chd £4.35, family £21.75, adm park & garden £3.40, chd £1.70. Fri-Tues, 18 Mar to 30 Oct (11-5).* **For NGS:** *Fri, Sat 3, 4 June (11-5). Tel 01179 372501*

⓫ Easton-in-Gordano Gardens
5m W of Bristol. M5 J19 Gordano Services, exit Bristol. Turn L for Easton-in-Gordano, past King's Arms PH. Park in church hall car park by football field & follow directions in car park. Home-made TEAS at 36 Church Road in aid of St George's Church. *Combined adm £3, chd 50p. Tues 19 , 26 July; 2 Aug (2-5)*

36 Church Road ✗❀ (Mr & Mrs I Crichton) ¼-acre garden developed around ancient dewpond. Unusual secret garden incl large pond with fish, waterfall, and bridge built by local school. Herbaceous borders contain many flower arrangers' plants.

16 Gordano Gardens ♿✗❀ (Mr & Mrs Milsom) Cottage-style garden 80ft long with many pretty and unusual features incl decked area, natural pond with waterfall, grasses and herbaceous plants.

⑫ ◆ Emmaus House, Clifton Hill, Bristol 🔄⊕
(Sisters of La Retraite) *From Clifton Downs down to Clifton Village to bottom of Regent St on R. Opp Saville Place.* 1½ acres with Victorian walled kitchen garden, also fruit, formal herb and Zen gardens. Rose and herbaceous borders, lawns, secret garden with summerhouse. Courtyard garden with original stone watercourse. Ponds with fountains and fine views towards Dundry. Newly excavated remains of old coach house in wild garden. Bristol in Bloom participating garden for 2004 Britain in Bloom. Light refreshments and TEAS on rose lawn (weather permitting) NGS days only. *Adm £2.50, chd free. Groups welcome by prior arrangement.* **For NGS:** *Suns 24 Apr; 19 June; 11 Sept (11-4.30). Tel 0117 907 9950 www.emmaushouse.org.uk*

Guyers House, Pickwick, Corsham 🔄⊠⊕
See Wiltshire.

Harptree Court, East Harptree 🔄⊕
See Somerset.

⑬ 4 Haytor Park, Bristol ⊠⊕
(Mr & Mrs C J Prior) *3m NW of Bristol city centre. Edge of Coombe Dingle. From A4162 Inner Ring Rd between A4 Portway & A4108 Falcondale Rd, take turning into Coombe Bridge Ave, Haytor Park is 1st turning L. No parking in Haytor Park.* Ever-changing urban idyll, full of arches and secret spaces where sculptures lurk and unusual plants abound. Densely planted borders, wildlife pond, water feature and large patio with myriad of pots, all add up to yr-round interest. Wildlife and plantaholics all catered for. Featured in 'Amateur Gardening' & finalist BBC Points West Real Gardens, 2003. Home-made TEAS in aid of The Willow Trust (11 May), Fibromyalgia Association UK (6 July). *Adm £2, chd free. Weds 11 May; 6 July (1.30-5). Private visits welcome by appt. Tel 0117 985 6582*

Hazelbury Manor Gardens, Wadswick, nr Box 🔄⊠⊕
See Wiltshire.

⑭ NEW 25 Hillcrest Road, Redcliffe Bay ⊠
(Colin & Molly Lewis) *2½m from Portishead. Take Nore Rd S out of Portishead centre for 2½m. Past Feddon Village (old Nautical School). Hillcrest Rd is 1st L.* Garden was

originally altered from a slope to terraces. There are now 3 terraces; bottom - a lawn, middle - a formal garden with central fountain and extensively planted, top - a large patio with wisteria-covered pergola and spectacular water feature. Front garden is a riot of colour. Home-made TEAS. *Adm £1.50, chd free. Suns 24 Apr; 22 May; 17 July (10-5). Private visits welcome by appt small groups max 6 persons Apr to Aug. Tel 01275 842331*

Hillesley House, Hillesley, nr Wotton-under-Edge 🔄⊕
See Gloucestershire North & Central.

◆ Iford Manor, nr Bradford-on-Avon
See Wiltshire.

Inwoods, Farleigh Wick 🔄⊕
See Wiltshire.

Jasmine Cottage, 26 Channel Road, Clevedon ⊠⊕
See Somerset.

⑮ ◆ Lady Farm, Chelwood
(Mr & Mrs M Pearce) *8m S of Bristol. 8m W of Bath. On A368 ½m E of Chelwood roundabout (A37 & A368).* Commenced in 1992 after removal of 3 acres of farm buildings. Now approx 12 acres. Spring-fed watercourse. Formal cottage garden. 2004 created 'ravine' with rocks and high waterfall. 'Prairie' planted esp for late summer. 'Steppe' from May onwards. Landscape garden with vistas. Wild flower meadow. Hosta and allium walk. Winning photo at Kew exhibition & numerous magazine features, 2004. Home-made TEAS in summerhouse overlooking lake. *Adm £4, chd under 14 free. Suns Jun, July, Sept & 30 Oct (2-6).*

For NGS: *Suns 29 May; 25 Sept (2-6). Tel 01761 490770, Judy Pearce*

⑯ NEW The Lintels, Littleton-on-Severn 🔄⊠
(Mr & Mrs Ernest Baker) *10m N of Bristol, 3½m SE of Thornbury. From old Severn Bridge on M48 take B4461 to Alveston. In Elberton, take 1st L to Littleton-on-Severn. 4th house 100yds past Field Lane.* Small cottage-type garden in front of house with good variety of herbaceous plants. Main attraction Japanese garden at rear with waterfall, koi carp, stream, tea house. Gravel drive and footpaths make it awkward for wheelchairs but not impossible. *Adm £2, chd free. Sun 12 June (1-5). Also open Sunnyside Cottage & Walnut Tree Cottage, Stock Hill. Private visits welcome by appt. Tel 01454 412765*

Littleton Drew Gardens
See Wiltshire.

Manor Farm, West Kington 🔄⊠
See Wiltshire.

⑰ NEW 26 Northumberland Road, Redland ⊠
(Gwendoline Todd) *Bristol. 5 mins walk from Redland station, close to & parallel with Cranbrook Rd.* Country cottage garden in middle of city with emphasis on scent and yr-round interest. This delightful small garden is packed with a wide range of plants and climbers. Patio is taken over by unusual plants and herbs in pots to provide constantly changing display. Front garden is fernery and home to shade-lovers. TEAS opp at 31 Northumberland Rd. *Adm £1.50. Sat, Sun 11, 12 June (11-6)*

⑱ 2 Old Tarnwell, Stanton Drew ⊗
(Mrs Mary Payne) *6m S of Bristol. Between B3130 & A368 just W of Pensford. Detailed directions will be given when appt is made.* A quart of good plants poured into a quarter-pint sized plot. Mini "steppe"-style planting in front garden. Back garden has colour-themed borders, misty 'puddle' and many ideas for small gardeners! Plant list available. Regret not suitable for children. Featured in 'Gardens Monthly', 'Garden Style' & 'Somerset Life', 2004. **By appointment only** *from 10am on Tues 28 June; 5 July; Wed 13 July. Tel 01275 333146*

⑲ Park Farm, Alderley ♿⊗☺
(Mr & Mrs A J V Shepherd) *1½m S of Wotton-under-Edge. Just before village.* The lake with its waterside plants and large koi carp is the pivotal attraction in a scenically designed 2½-acre garden. Maturing herbaceous borders, young trees and rose garden. New sunken garden. Home-made TEAS. *Adm £3, chd free. Sun 4 Sept (2-6). Private visits welcome by appt. Tel 01453 842123*

♦ Pound Hill House, West Kington ♿⊗☺
See Wiltshire.

Ridleys Cheer, Mountain Bower ♿⊗☺
See Wiltshire.

⑳ Rock House, Elberton ⊗☺
(Mr & Mrs John Gunnery) *10m N of Bristol. 3½m SE Thornbury. From Old Severn Bridge on M48 take B4461 to Alveston. In Elberton, take 1st turning L to Littleton-on-Severn & turn immed R.* 1-acre walled garden undergoing improvement. Pond and old yew tree, mixed borders, cottage garden plants and developing woodland. *Adm £2, chd free (share to St John's Church). Suns 30 Jan for snowdrops (11-4); 3 Apr (2-6). Private visits welcome by appt. Tel 01454 413225*

㉑ NEW Rodney Cottage, 108 Church Lane, Backwell ♿⊗
(Ann & John Belcher) *8m SW of Bristol. Take A370 Backwell. Turn up Dark Lane at T-lights, R into Church Lane, Rodney Cottage ¼m on R. Parking on road.* Medium-sized level garden with immaculate lawns, colourful herbaceous and shrub borders backed by masses of climbers for yr-round interest. Water features, statues and archways into smaller gardens of organically grown fruit and vegetables, white garden and

fernery. Home-made TEAS at St Andrew's Church. **Day & Evening Opening** *Sun 12 June (2-5.30) £2, chd free; (6-9) £3, wine*

㉒ Saltford Farm Barn, 565a Bath Road, Saltford ♿⊗☺
(Eve Hessey) *6m W of Bath. On A4 between Bath & Bristol, Saltford Farm Barn is 1st house on R as you enter village from Bath or last house on L as you leave village from Bristol. Parking arrangements will be signed - busy A4 not suitable for parking.* 1-acre garden with 5 main separate gardens. Large ornamental vegetable garden with trained fruit trees contained in within scented hedges of lavender, rosemary and box. Woodland garden with seasonal shrubs and trees underplanted with spring bulbs, hellebores, ferns, foxgloves and alpine strawberries. Garden of reflection depicting owner's life in New Zealand and England, labyrinth, meadow and orchard. Guide dogs allowed. Winner of Bath Horticultural Show Fruit & Vegetable Cup 2003/2004 & Flower Cup 2004. Cream TEAS. *Adm £2, chd free. Sat, Sun 23, 24 July (2-5.30).* **Evening Opening** *£3, wine, Fri 22 July (6-8.30). Private visits welcome by appt. Tel 01225 873380 eve.hessey@blueyonder.co.uk*

㉓ ♦ Sherborne Garden, Litton ♿
(Mr & Mrs John Southwell) *15m S of Bristol. 15m W of Bath, 7m N of Wells. On B3114 Litton to Harptree rd, ½m past The Kings Arms. Car park in field.* 4½-acre gently sloping garden of considerable horticultural interest. Small pinetum, giant grasses area, woodland garden and 3 linked ponds with bridges. Collections of hollies (100), ferns (250), Asian wild roses with hybrids and climbing species, all well labelled, hemerocallis, water lilies and unusual trees and shrubs. Picnic area. TEAS. *Adm £3, chd free. Mons 30 May to 3 Oct.* **For NGS:** *Sun 11 Sept (11-5). Tel 01761 241220*

㉔ ♦ Special Plants, Nr Cold Ashton ⊗☺
(Derry Watkins) *6m N of Bath. On A46. Turn L into Greenways Lane just before roundabout with A420.* Architect-designed ¾-acre hillside garden with stunning views. Started autumn 1996. Exotic plants, many collected in S Africa. Gravel gardens for borderline hardy plants. Black and white (purple and silver) garden. Vegetable garden and orchard. Hot border. Lemon and lime bank. Annual, biennial and tender plants

for late summer colour. Spring-fed ponds. Bog garden. Woodland walk. Adjoining nursery, open Mar through Sept. Featured in 'Country Living' & 'The Telegraph', 2003. Home-made TEAS in aid of Cancer Research. *Adm £2.50 incl plant list. Every Wed in July & Aug (11-5).* **For NGS:** *Thurs 16 June; 21 July; 18 Aug; 15 Sept (11-5). Tel 01225 891686 www.specialplants.net*

㉕ NEW Sunnyside Cottage, Littleton-on-Severn ♿⊗
(Harold & Hesta Knapp) *11m N of Bristol, 3½m SE of Thornbury. From old Severn Bridge on M48 take B4461 to Alveston. In Elberton, take 1st L to Littleton-on-Severn. Carry on into The Village past the Old School. Sunnyside Cottage opp Evangelical Church.* Approx ½ acre of mixed perennial borders, water feature, shrubs, vegetables, also far-reaching views. *Adm £2, chd free. Sun 12 June (1-5). Open with The Lintels & Walnut Tree Cottage, Stock Hill*

㉖ NEW Teesdale, 60 Park Rd, Thornbury ♿☺
(Shirley & Robert Gorham) *From A38 N of Bristol signed Thornbury: L at T-lights, follow rd through High St, L at town pump, continue down Castle St past church. 60 is opp far end of Castle School. Small car park few yds further on L or park in rd.* ¼-acre plantsman's garden developed over last 20 yrs by present owners. Front garden features topiary and rockeries. Rear garden densely planted with many unusual plants incl exotics (bamboos, bananas, cannas, agaves etc), herbaceous borders, pond, rockeries and many tender plants in containers. Winner Thornbury-in-Bloom Ornamental Front Garden 2003. TEAS in aid of local Scout group. *Adm £2, chd free. Suns 5 June; 14 Aug (2-6)*

㉗ Tranby House, Norton Lane, Whitchurch ⊗☺
(Jan Barkworth) *5m S of Bristol. ½m S of Whitchurch. Leave Bristol on A37 Wells Rd, through Whitchurch village, 1st turning on R signposted Norton Malreward.* 1¼-acre informal garden, designed and planted to encourage wildlife. Wide variety of trees, shrubs and flowers; ponds and wild flower meadow. Plant sales in aid of The Wildlife Trust. TEAS. *Adm £2, chd free. Suns 10 July; 14 Aug (2-5)*

28 The Urn Cottage, Charfield
&⌀⊕
(Mr A C & Dr L A Rosser) 7½m N
of Chipping Sodbury. 7m E of
Thornbury. 3m E of M5 exit 14. In
Charfield at village hall take Little
Bristol Lane, then 400yds, park nr
railway subway; walk under railway
to garden entrance opp or follow
parking signs. Rural, family garden
with Cotswold views. Richly planted
with schemes differing in character
from sun-baked flagstones to
streamside shade. Designer-owner
loves colour, foliage, grasses,
groundcover, well-behaved plants,
continuity of interest and wildlife.
TEAS. Adm £3. Private visits
welcome by appt all yr for groups.
Tel 01453 843156
www.lesleyrossergardens.co.uk

**29 NEW Walnut Tree Cottage,
Stock Hill, Littleton-on-Severn**
⌀⊕
(Mr & Mrs B Price) 11m N of
Bristol, 4½m SE of Thornbury. From
old Severn Bridge on M48 take
B4461 to Alveston. In Elberton, take
1st L to Littleton-on-Severn. Take
Field Lane turning to Lodge Farm.
Walnut Tree Cottage is on R on
Stock Hill rd to Thornbury. Situated
adjacent to farmland, this is a
country garden with unusual and
interesting garden plants and mature
trees. There are wildlife and water
features including a koi pond with a
variety of fish. Domestic ducks and
fantail doves can be seen alongside
native and migratory birds which are
actively encouraged to nest and
breed. Adm £2, chd free. Sun 12 June
(1-5). Open with The Lintels &
Sunnyside Cottage

Warners Court, Charfield &⌀⊕
See Gloucestershire North & Central.

30 Windmill Cottage, Backwell
⌀⊕
(Pam & Alan Harwood) 8m SW of
Bristol. Take A370 Backwell.
Parking available in Backwell & New
Inn (15 min walk). Hillside Rd is
single track lane with no parking
(unless for special reasons). You can
scramble up scree, walk on the wild
side, parade through a pergola,
wander by water. There is scent;
there is colour; and clematis that
clings; these are few of our favourite
things. N-facing garden set in 2 acres
on rocky hillside with outstanding
views. TEAS. Adm £2.50. Suns 8
May; 19 June; 7 Aug; 25 Sept
(2-5.30). Private visits welcome by
appt for groups of 10+. Tel 01275
463492

Evening Opening (See also garden
description)

1 Bromley Villas	9 June
Rodney Cottage	12 June
Saltford Farm Barn	22 July

THE QUEEN'S NURSING INSTITUTE

After 50 years of district nursing, Annie
was looking forward to an active retirement,
shopping, visiting friends and retaining her
independence. Rheumatoid arthritis put paid
to that – until someone told her that the
Queen's Nursing Institute might be able to
help. After learning of her plight, the QNI
arranged for the purchase of a motorised
tricycle. It has become, she says, her lifeline.
There are many Queen's and district nurses
like Annie. Their numbers are growing and
today many of them are in their thirties and
forties. Thankfully they have the comfort of
knowing that the QNI is on hand to help
allay financial fears and provide a sympathetic
ear, through its welfare and beneficence arm.

Since 1927 The National Garden Scheme has
given annual financial assistance to support
the welfare work of the QNI

**For more information contact the QNI
Tel: 020 7490 4227 Website: www.qni.org.uk**

---

ngs gardens open
for charity

The National Trust Careership Scheme

In 2004, five more gardeners commenced a three-
year National Trust vocational training programme in
historic gardening with a bursary from The National
Gardens Scheme. Fifteen trainees at different Trust
gardens throughout England and Wales receive
support from the NGS. The trainees range from
school leavers to those looking to change their
careers. The National Trust's scheme, known as
Careership, combines day-to-day practical experience
under the guidance of a head gardener with periods
of residential training and study at Reaseheath
College, Cheshire.

Applications for places are available from March
2005, and the three year course commences in early
September 2005.

For more information on Careerships, contact:

HR Service Centre – Careership Scheme,
The National Trust, Rowan, Kembrey Park,
Swindon, Wiltshire SN2 8YL
or visit the National Trust Website
www.nationaltrust.org.uk

Buckinghamshire

County Organiser:	Mrs Maggie Bateson, Fressingwood, Hare Lane, Little Kingshill HP16 0EF
	Tel & Fax 01494 866265 email jmbateson@btopenworld.com
Assistant County Organisers:	
(Supplies)	Mrs Rosemary Brown, 2 Spencer Road, Aylesbury HP21 7LR Tel 01296 429605
	Mrs Judy Hart, Kingswood House, The Lee, Great Missenden HP16 9NU
	Tel 01494 837328
	Mrs Mhairi Sharpley, The Old Sun House, Pednor, Chesham HP5 2SZ Tel 01494 782870
County Treasurer:	Mrs Trish Swain, 2 Kingswood Cottages, Swan Lane, The Lee, Nr Great Missenden,
	Buckinghamshire HP16 9NU Tel 01494 837752
Press & Publicity Officer:	Mrs Sandra Wetherall, Holydyke House, Little Missenden, Amersham, Buckinghamshire
	HP7 0RD 01494 862264 email sandra@robertjamespartnership.com

Maps: Numbers shown next to each garden entry refer to that garden's entry on the county map. This position is approximate; distance and directions from the nearest main town are generally shown in the garden text.
A precise location is available for those gardens featured on the NGS website by visiting www.ngs.org.uk.

Symbols: Information relating to symbols is given on page 21

DATES OF OPENING

Evening openings
See end of county listing

Gardens open to the public
For details see garden description
Ascott, Wing, Leighton Buzzard *(2)*
Cliveden, Taplow *(9)*
Cowper & Newton Museum Gardens, Olney *(11)*
Hughenden Manor, Nr High Wycombe *(25)*
Nether Winchendon House, Nether Winchendon *(31)*
Old Thatch, Well End *(35)*
The Plant Specialist, Great Missenden *(40)*
Waddesdon Manor Gardens, Waddesdon *(44)*

By appointment only
For telephone number and other details see garden description.
Private visits welcomed
Abbotts House, Winslow *(1)*
Blossoms, Cobblers Hill *(4)*
100 Church Green Road, Bletchley *(8)*
Court Farm, Worminghall *(10)*
Hall Barn, Beaconsfield *(18)*
19 Highfield Road, Winslow *(20)*
19 Marroway *(30)*
North Down, Chalfont St Giles *(32)*
Turn End, Townside, Haddenham *(42)*
Watercroft, Penn *(45)*

ngs gardens open for charity

More than £20 million has been donated to charity since the NGS began in 1927

March 13 Sunday
Whitchurch Gardens *(47)*

March 27 Sunday (Easter)
Overstroud Cottage, Gt Missenden *(38)*

March 30 Wednesday
Waddesdon Manor Gardens, Waddesdon *(44)*

April 3 Sunday
Chesham Bois House, Chesham Bois, Amersham *(7)*

April 10 Sunday
Long Crendon Gardens, Long Crendon *(27)*
6 Oldfield Close, Little Chalfont *(37)*
Whitchurch Gardens *(47)*

April 14 Thursday
Gipsy House, Gt Missenden *(16)*
The Plant Specialist, Great Missenden *(40)*

April 17 Sunday
Overstroud Cottage, Gt Missenden *(38)*

April 23 Saturday
The Old Vicarage, Padbury *(36)*

April 24 Sunday
Cliveden, Taplow *(9)*
Nether Winchendon House, Nether Winchendon *(31)*
The Old Vicarage, Padbury *(36)*
Whitewalls, Marlow *(49)*

May 1 Sunday
The Manor House, Bledlow *(29)*
Overstroud Cottage, Gt Missenden *(38)*

May 2 Monday (Bank Hol)
Ascott, Wing, Leighton Buzzard *(2)*

May 12 Thursday
Gipsy House, Gt Missenden *(16)*
The Plant Specialist, Great Missenden *(40)*

May 15 Sunday
Fressingwood, Little Kingshill *(15)*
The White House, Denham Village *(48)*

May 18 Wednesday
Dorneywood Garden, Burnham *(13)*

May 22 Sunday
The Old Sun House, Pednor *(34)*

May 29 Sunday
The Lee Gardens, Gt Missenden *(26)*
Quainton Gardens *(41)*

May 30 Monday (Bank Hol)
East Claydon Gardens *(14)*

June 1 Wednesday
Dorneywood Garden, Burnham *(13)*

June 2 Thursday
Homelands, Ellesborough *(24)*

June 5 Sunday
Wichert, Ford *(50)*

June 9 Thursday
Gipsy House, Gt Missenden *(16)*
The Plant Specialist, Great Missenden *(40)*

June 11 Saturday
Cowper & Newton Museum Gardens, Olney *(11)*

June 12 Sunday
Aylesbury Gardens *(3)*
Cowper & Newton Museum Gardens, Olney *(11)*
Hambleden Gardens *(19)*
Hillesden House, Hillesden *(23)*
Long Crendon Gardens, Long Crendon *(27)*
The Manor House, Bledlow *(29)*

June 14 Tuesday
Hillcrest, Marlow *(22)*

June 15 Wednesday
Cowper & Newton Museum Gardens, Olney **(Evening)** *(11)*

June 18 Saturday
Bucksbridge House, Wendover *(5)*
11 The Paddocks, Wendover *(39)*

June 19 Sunday
Bucksbridge House, Wendover *(5)*
Hughenden Manor, Nr High Wycombe *(25)*
11 The Paddocks, Wendover *(39)*
Tythrop Park, Kingsey *(43)*

June 24 Friday
11 The Paddocks, Wendover **(Evening)** *(39)*

BUCKINGHAMSHIRE

kms 0   10

miles 0   10

11

Newport
Pagnell

M1

Wolverton

Milton
Keynes

A5   28

33
Buckingham

A421   8
Bletchley

BEDFORDSHIRE

21

36
23   1
20

Winslow

Leighton
Buzzard

14   12

47

17   A413   2

41   A41   6

A41

44   3

Aylesbury

31   30

Haddenham   39

10   27   42   50

Thame   43   24   5

Princes Risborough   Wendover   26

Oxford

OXFORDSHIRE   29   Great   38   Chesham
Missenden   34   46
16   A413

HERTFORDSHIRE

M40   A40

15   A404   Amersham   37
25   High   45   7
Wycombe   Beaconsfield

18   32   M25

M40   48

Marlow   35   Uxbridge
19   22   49   M40   GREATER
Taplow   9   13   LONDON
Henley on   M25
Thames   M4

BERKSHIRE

June 26 Sunday
Cheddington Gardens *(6)*
Cublington Gardens *(12)*
Loughton Village Gardens *(28)*

July 1 Friday
Old Thatch, Well End *(35)*

July 3 Sunday
Chesham Bois House, Chesham Bois, Amersham *(7)*

July 10 Sunday
Nether Winchendon House, Nether Winchendon *(31)*
Weir Lodge, Chesham *(46)*

July 12 Tuesday
Hillcrest, Marlow *(22)*

July 13 Wednesday
Dorneywood Garden, Burnham *(13)*

July 14 Thursday
Gipsy House, Gt Missenden *(16)*
The Plant Specialist, Great Missenden *(40)*

July 17 Sunday
The White House, Denham Village *(48)*

July 23 Saturday
Odin House, Nr Buckingham *(33)*

July 24 Sunday
Odin House, Nr Buckingham *(33)*
Whitewalls, Marlow *(49)*

July 30 Saturday
Dorneywood Garden, Burnham *(13)*

August 4 Thursday
Homelands, Ellesborough *(24)*

August 6 Saturday
Hill House, Buckingham *(21)*

August 7 Sunday
Grendon Hall - Springhill Prison, Grendon Underwood *(17)*
Hill House, Buckingham *(21)*

August 29 Monday (Bank Hol)
Ascott, Wing, Leighton Buzzard *(2)*

September 7 Wednesday
Cliveden, Taplow *(9)*

September 18 Sunday
Whitewalls, Marlow *(49)*

October 5 Wednesday
Waddesdon Manor Gardens, Waddesdon *(44)*

DESCRIPTIONS OF GARDENS

❶ Abbotts House, 10 Church Street, Winslow 🅶🅰🅸
(Mrs Jane Rennie) *9m N of Aylesbury. On A413 into Winslow. Town centre or street parking. Entrance to garden is off Church Walk, opp the W door to St Laurence Church. ¾-acre garden on different levels. Incl ¼-acre walled kitchen garden renovated and replanted in 1989. Herbaceous borders, herbs, vegetables, recently planted woodland beds, fruit pergola, wall shrubs and climbers; greenhouses, small pond and numerous containers; white wisteria arbour. Limited wheelchair access. Featured in 'Amateur Gardening' Dec 2003. Adm £2. Private visits welcome by appt May-Sept, groups less than 25. Tel 01296 712326*

❷ ◆ Ascott, Wing, Leighton Buzzard 🅶🅰
(Sir Evelyn de Rothschild, The National Trust) *2m SW of Leighton Buzzard, 8m NE of Aylesbury. Via A418. Bus: 141 Aylesbury-Leighton Buzzard. Combining Victorian formality with early C20 natural style and recent plantings to lead it into the C21. Terraced lawns with specimen and ornamental trees; panoramic views to Chilterns. Naturalised bulbs, mirror-image herbaceous borders. Impressive topiary incl box and yew sundial. Adm £4, chd £2. For NGS: Mons 2 May; 29 Aug (2-6 last adm 5). Tel 01296 688242 info@ascottestate.co.uk*

❸ Aylesbury Gardens
¾m SE of Aylesbury Centre. 4 town gardens off A413. TEAS at 7 Westminster Drive. Combined adm £4, chd free. Sun 12 June (2-6)

63 Highbridge Road 🅰 (Jackie & Haydn Goodair) 12 yr-old award-winning and televised town garden with a fine collection of unusual plants, many variegated. Over 150 clematis. Patio, raised pond, many new features including a terracotta seating area using recycled materials.

2 Spenser Road 🅰🅸 (Mr & Mrs G A Brown) Tranquil cottage style garden with many ornamental trees raised from seed. Victorian greenhouse with original features containing a collection of pelargoniums and tender plants.

90 Walton Way 🅶🅰🅸 (Mr & Mrs R Lewis-Smith) Established

garden with wide variety of unusual hardy and tender perennials. Wildlife pond and larger pond with koi carp. Also features utilising an old air raid shelter. Allotment area containing large collection of perennials. *Private visits welcome by appt Jun & Jul only. Tel 01296 481530 lewissmith@btinternet.com*

7 Westminster Drive 🅰🅸 (Mr & Mrs B J Ferguson) Formal town garden with interesting features incl mixed borders, shrubs and annuals. Pergola with hanging baskets, also vegetable parterre and pond.

54a Banbury Road, Brackley 🅰🅸
See Northamptonshire.

❹ Blossoms, Cobblers Hill 🅶🅰
(Dr & Mrs F Hytten) *2½m NW of Great Missenden. By Rignall Rd, signed Butler's Cross, to Kings Lane 1½m on R, then to top of Cobblers Hill. Turn R at yellow stone marker & after 50yds turn R again at stone, marked Blossoms. 4 acres begun as hill-top fields, plus 1-acre beechwood. Lawns, old apple orchard, small lake, water, troughs, scree and patio gardens. Large areas of bluebells, wild daffodils and other spring bulbs. Large climbing roses, flowering cherries and many other interesting trees incl acers, eucalyptus and willows; foliage effects throughout yr. Home-made TEAS. Adm £2. Private visits welcome by appt. Tel 01494 863140*

❺ Bucksbridge House, Heron Path, Wendover 🅶🅰🅸
(Mr & Mrs Jeremy Nicholson) *From Wendover bypass (A413) return into town from Amersham direction. Chapel Lane is 2nd turn on R. House is on L at bottom of lane. Georgian house with established 2-acre garden; large herbaceous border, unusual shrubs and plants, roses, laburnum arches, ornamental vegetable garden and 2 well-stocked greenhouses, new statue. Round rose bed. Home-made TEAS in aid of St Mary's Church. Adm £3. Sat, Sun 18, 19 June (2-6)*

❻ Cheddington Gardens
11m E of Aylesbury, 7m S of Leighton Buzzard. Turn off B489 at Pitstone. Turn off B488 at Cheddington station. Home-made TEAS at Methodist Chapel on the green - 15% in aid of Chapel & St Giles. Combined adm £3. Sun 26 June (2-6)

15 Barkham Close 🅰 (Mr Horace E Fiddler) Small bungalow (not open) around which is a wonderful display of annuals in beds and pots.

Bridge Cottage, Station Road 🌿⌘ (Mr & Mrs J Maddocks-Born) Informal garden of about 1 acre, newly planted, with herbaceous and shrub borders, wildlife and ornamental pond on the site of a 'ridge & furrow' field/fruit orchard.

Rose Cottage, 68 High Street 🌿 (Mrs Margery R Jones) ½-acre cottage garden filled with small rooms with max use of space. A balance of evergreens and deciduous resulting in a garden for all seasons; incl a late border with herbs, vegetable parterre and wildlife pond.

21 Station Road 🌿⌘ (Mr & Mrs P Jay) ½-acre informal garden with wild flower/wildlife conservation area; herbaceous and shrub borders; trees; herbs and kitchen garden.

Woodstock Cottage, 42 High Street 🌿 (Mr & Mrs D Bradford) Front garden laid to gravel with assorted shrubs. Back courtyard and patio with small fountain at base of ancient elder tree.

❼ Chesham Bois House, 85 Bois Lane, Chesham Bois, Amersham 🌿🌿⌘
(Julia Plaistowe) *1m N of Amersham-on-the-Hill. From Amersham-on-the-Hill go along Sycamore Rd, over double mini roundabouts, which turns into Bois Lane. Past village shops, house is then ½m on L. Parking in road or on R at school & at Scout Hut.* Up a drive of mostly old lime trees, a late Georgian house (not open) surrounded by 3 acres of garden of yr-round interest. Walled garden, small canal and rill with gazebo, various flower beds with tender and many unusual plants, clipped trees and lawns. In spring, primroses & daffodils. Mature trees and a walk through old orchard add to the ambiance. TV for Wimbledon fans available. Home-made TEAS. *Adm £2.50, chd under 12 free. Suns 3 Apr (2-5); 3 July (2-6). Private visits welcome by appt. Tel 01494 726476 julia@oeathai.org*

❽ [NEW] 100 Church Green Road, Bletchley 🌿⌘
(Mr & Mrs Gordon Farr) 13m E of Buckingham. 11m N of Leighton Buzzard. Off A421. Turn into Church Green Rd, take L fork half way down adjacent to brick pillar box. Within walking distance of historic Bletchley Park. Long narrow

garden divided into rooms containing herbaceous border, fernery, seating areas. Once described as a Russian Doll - full of surprises. Home-made TEAS in aid of Willen Hospice. *Adm £2. Private visits welcome by appt Mid-May - August. Tel 01908 379289 rosieandgordon@tiscali. co.uk*

❾ ◆ Cliveden, Taplow 🌿🌿
(The National Trust) 2m N of Taplow. Leave M4 at J7 or M40 at J4 & follow brown tourism signs. Separate gardens within extensive grounds, 1st laid out in C18, incl water garden, secret garden; topiary; herbaceous borders; woodland walks and views of R Thames. Timber steps lead down yew tree walk to river. Light refreshments and TEAS. *Adm £7, chd £3.50. 16 Mar - 31 Oct 11-6.* **For NGS:** *Sun 24 Apr; Wed 7 Sept (2-6). Tel 01628 605069*

❿ Court Farm, The Avenue, Worminghall 🌿🌿
(Mr & Mrs H Sants) 8m NE of Oxford. Approx 2m from M40 J8, proceed via Wheatley, follow signs to Waterperry Gardens, then Worminghall. Entrance beyond church at end of The Avenue. Approx 2-acre organic garden. Walled, decorative and productive vegetable garden; wild flower meadow; mixed borders; formal and wildlife ponds. *Adm £2. Private visits welcome by appt. Tel 01844 336248*

⓫ ◆ Cowper & Newton Museum Gardens, Orchardside, Market Place, Olney 🌿🌿⌘
(Mrs E Knight) 5m N of Newport Pagnell. 12m S of Wellingborough. On A509. Please park on Market Place, Cattle Market Car Park or in High Street. Restored walled flower garden with plants pre 1800, many mentioned by C18 poet, William Cowper, who said of himself 'Gardening was, of all employments that in which I succeeded best'. Summerhouse garden in Victorian kitchen style with organic, new and old vegetables. Herb and medicinal plant borders in memory of the garden's original use by an apothecary. Plants in aid of Museum Funds. TEAS at St Peter & St Paul Parish Church NGS days. *Adm £1.50 (Museum extra), chd free. Tues-Sats, Mar-Dec (10-5).* **For NGS:** *Sat, Sun 11, 12 June (10-5).* **Evening Opening** *wine, Wed 15 June (7-9). Tel 01234 713719 liz@elizabethknight.go-plus.net*

⓬ Cublington Gardens
5m SE of Winslow, 5m NE of Aylesbury. From Aylesbury take A413 Buckingham Rd. After 4m, at Whitchurch, turn R to Cublington. Home-made TEAS at The Old Rectory & The Old Stables. *Combined adm £4, chd free. Sun 26 June (2-6)*

Old Manor Cottage, Wing Road 🌿 (Dr J Higgins) Timber-framed cottage with a heavily planted cottage garden giving colour throughout the year. Shade areas, water features, borders and island beds.

The Old Rectory, High Street 🌿⌘ (Mr & Mrs J Naylor) 2-acre country garden with herbaceous border, rose beds, shrubs and mature trees; vegetables; ponds; climbing plants.

The Old Stables, Reads Lane 🌿⌘ (Mr & Mrs S George) Varied established gardens surround C18 house (not open). Borders, trees, water features, lawns, pots, vegetables; restored walls enclose unusual walled garden; maze; putting green, small orchard, tree house, rose garden and revolving summerhouse.

⓭ Dorneywood Garden, Burnham 🌿🌿⌘
(The National Trust) 1m E of Taplow, 5m S of Beaconsfield. From Burnham village take Dropmore Rd, at end of 30mph limit take R fork into Dorneywood Rd. Entrance is 1m on R. From M40 J2, take A355 to Slough then 1st R to Burnham, 2m then 2nd L after Jolly Woodman, signed Dorneywood Rd. Dorneywood is about 1m on L. 6 acres. Country house garden on several levels with herbaceous borders; greenhouses; rose, cottage and kitchen gardens; lily pond and conservatory. TEAS. *Adm £4, chd £4, NT members £2.* **Adm subject to written application only, at least two weeks in advance.** *Weds 18 May; 1 June; 13 July; Sat 30 July (2-5) Apply to: The Secretary, Dorneywood Trust, Dorneywood, Burnham, Bucks SL1 8PY. Private visits welcome by appt Mar- Aug for groups 15-25 on written application. Tel 01628 665361 secretary.dorneywood@btopenworld. com*

⓮ East Claydon Gardens
2½m SW Winslow. Attractive village with beautiful C13 church. TEAS at Village Hall (share to WI). *Combined adm £4, chd free. Mon 30 May (2-6)*

The Emerald, 6 St Mary's Road
♿✂ (Mr & Mrs D Scott) ¾-acre
garden with mature trees, shrubs,
perennial beds and rockery banks
using sleepers and brickwork.
Gravelled and paved area in front
of house with pond and planting.
Vegetable garden with beds
bounded by sleepers.
1 Emerald Close ♿ (Mr & Mrs L
Woodhouse) Small garden with
collection of deciduous and
coniferous bonsai.
Inglenooks, St Mary's Road ♿
(Mr & Mrs D Polhill) *St Mary's
Rd.* Cottage garden surrounding
C17 thatched cottage (not open).
Littleworth Farm, Verney Junction
(Mrs Elspeth O'Halloran) *From
E Claydon, take Sandhill Rd, 1m,
1st R.* ½ acre with walled
herbaceous and formal kitchen
gardens.
The Old Vicarage, Church Way
♿✂☺ (Mr & Mrs Nigel
Turnbull) 1½-acre on clay, started
in 1991 and aiming at yr-round
interest. Shrub roses, herbaceous
and secret dell garden. Natural
clay-lined pond. Planting to
encourage wildlife. *Private visits
welcome by appt except Aug,
adm £2. Tel 01296 712127
turnbullesther@hotmail.com*
The Pump House, St Mary's Road
♿ (Mr & Mrs P M Piddington)
¾-acre garden with mature trees,
shrubs, borders and fishponds.

Evenley Wood Garden, Brackley
♿
See Northamptonshire.

**⑮ Fressingwood, Hare Lane,
Little Kingshill** ♿✂☺
(Mr & Mrs J & M Bateson) *1m S of
Gt Missenden, 4m W of Amersham.
From A413 Amersham to Aylesbury
rd, turn L at Chiltern Hospital,
signed Gt & Little Kingshill. Take 1st
L into Nags Head Lane. Turn R
under railway bridge & 1st L into
New Rd. Continue to top, turn into
Hare Lane, 1st house on R.* ½-acre
garden with yr-round colour.
Shrubbery, small formal garden, herb
garden, pergolas with wisteria, roses
and clematis, topiary. Landscaped
terrace. Formal lily pond and bonsai
collection. Many interesting features.
Home-made TEAS. *Adm £2, chd
free. Sun 15 May (2-6)*

**⑯ Gipsy House, Whitefield Lane,
Gt Missenden** ✂☺
(Mrs Felicity Dahl) *5m NW
Amersham. Take A413 to Gt
Missenden. From High St turn into
Whitefield Lane, continue under*
*railway bridge. Small Georgian house
on R. Parking in field opp house.*
Home of the late Roald Dahl. York
stone terrace, pleached lime walk to
writing hut; shrubs, roses, herbs,
small walled vegetable garden,
wildflower meadow, sunken garden,
gipsy caravan and maze for children.
Home-made TEAS in aid of Roald
Dahl Foundation. *Combined adm
with* **The Plant Specialist** *£4, chd £2.
Thurs 14 Apr; 12 May; 9 June; 14
July (2-5). Private visits welcome by
appt Groups of 10+. Tel 01494
864912
josmith@roalddahlfoundation.org*

**⑰ Grendon Hall - Springhill
Prison, Grendon Underwood** ✂
(Farm Manager - Paul Cooper) *9m N
of Aylesbury. Off A41 between
Bicestor & Aylesbury. Follow signs
to Grendon Underwood, past church
towards Edgecott. The entrance to
the prison is on R.* Seasonal bedding
planted within the grounds of
Grendon Hall. 50,000 plants.
Woodland walk leading to unusual
Buddha Grove. Shrubs, perennials
and gravel garden planted spring
2002. Displays in the boardroom of
the hall. Border in front of hall
replanted Autumn 2004. No cameras
or mobile phones. Light refreshments
and TEAS. *Adm £2.50, chd under 12
free. Sun 7 Aug (11-4)*

**⑱ Hall Barn, Windsor End,
Beaconsfield**
(The Hon Mrs Farncombe) *Lodge
gate 300yds S of St Mary and All
Saint's Church in Old Town centre.*
One of the original gardens opening
in 1927, still owned by member of
Burnham family. Unique landscaped
garden of great historical interest,
laid out in the 1680s. Vast 300-yr-old
curving yew hedge. Formal lake.
Long avenues through the Grove to
temple, classical ornament or statue.
Obelisk with fine carvings in memory
of Edmund Waller's grandson who
completed the garden about 1730.
*Adm £2. Private visits welcome by
appt, apply in writing to the owner at
Hall Barn, Windsor End,
Beaconsfield, HP9 2SG*

⑲ Hambleden Gardens
*3½m NE Henley-on-Thames, 8m
SW High Wycombe. 1m N of A4155.*
TEAS at Hambleden Church Hall in
aid of the Church. *Combined adm
£3.50. Sun 12 June (2-6)*
**The Manor House Gardens,
Hambledon Village** ✂☺ (Maria
Carmela, Viscountess
Hambleden) Conservatory;
shrubs and rose garden with

more than 100 scented
specimens.
Woolleys ♿✂☺ (Mrs Allan
Guthrie) *Garden is ¼m N of
village.* 6½ acres. Elegant garden
with views across valley. Pleached
lime avenue, peony and
delphinium beds and herbaceous
border. Conifer bed and
assortment of specimen trees.
Rose borders, climbing roses and
shrubs. Orchard.

⑳ 19 Highfield Road, Winslow
✂☺
(Mrs Gwladys Tonge) *On A413
Winslow to Buckingham, take last
turning L, 200yds after garage, 50yds
before turning to Great Horwood.*
Very small garden with extensive
range of attractive hardy plants
providing beauty and excitement for
each season. Shrubs, rose pergola,
clematis and other climbers; bulbs,
incl interesting snowdrop collection,
ferns, grasses, evergreen and
herbaceous perennials demonstrate
ingenious use of space and grow
happily together. Home-made TEAS.
*Adm £2, chd free. Private visits
welcome by appt incl groups of up to
20 from Feb (snowdrops). Tel 18002
01296 713489 (text direct - dial all
16 digits) mail@gwladystonge.co.uk*

**㉑ Hill House, Castle Street,
Buckingham** ☺
(Mr & Mrs P Thorogood) *Hill House
is on L of vehicle entrance to Parish
Church (spire very visible) in heart of
Buckingham. Castle St clearly
marked as you face Old Town Hall
at central town roundabout.* Peaceful
⅓-acre town garden on old castle
walls, whose aim is ease of
maintenance and yr-round interest
and colour in relatively small space.
Difficult for wheelchairs. TEAS in aid
of Buckingham Area Citizens Advice
Bureau. *Adm £2, chd free. Sat 6
(2-6), Sun 7 Aug (12-6). Private visits
welcome by appt May to Sept.
Tel 07860 714758 llt@pjt.powernet.
co.uk*

**㉒ NEW Hillcrest, 6 Frieth Road,
Marlow** ✂☺
(Mr & Mrs Ivan Pierce) *2m W of
Marlow. At Marlow turn off A4155
into Oxford rd (by Platts of Marlow).
Continue and rd becomes Chalkpit
Lane. Approx 2m up past Valley
View Stables, Hillcrest is 3rd house
on R.* Garden of just under ¾ acre
developed over the last 4 yrs. Topiary
garden with water feature, circular
gravel bed with variety of grasses.
Several well stocked island beds with
perennials and shrubs. Many pots of
hostas, ferns and summer annuals.

Vegetable garden and large fruit cage. Pleasant countryside view. Light refreshments and TEAS in aid of British Red Cross. *Adm £2, chd free. Tues 14 June; 12 July (11-5). Private visits welcome by appt Groups up to 20, June to mid-July. Tel 01628 483063 marian@hillcrest6.fsnet. co.uk*

㉓ Hillesden House, Church End, Hillesden &⊗⊕
(Mr & Mrs R M Faccenda) *3m S of Buckingham. Next to church in Hillesden.* By superb perpendicular church Cathedral in the Fields; lawns, shrubberies; rose, alpine and foliage gardens; interesting clipped hedges; conservatory; surrounded by park with red deer. Large lakes with ornamental duck and carp. Large wild flower areas. Views over countryside. Home-made TEAS in aid of Hillesden Church. *Adm £2.50, chd free. Sun 12 June (2-5)*

㉔ NEW Homelands, Springs Lane, Ellesborough
(Jean & Tony Young) *6m SE of Aylesbury. On B4010, 1½m W of Wendover, 4m NE of Princes Risborough. Springs Lane is between the Village Hall at Butlers Cross and St. Peter and St. Paul's Church.* ¾-acre garden on chalk with adjoining wild flower meadow. Wildlife pond, rockery, bog garden, water features. Gazebo and pergola walk, wide range of mixed shrub and herbaceous borders. Hidden corners, sitting out areas, gravel bed and vegetable plot. Access by narrow lane with uneven surface. Home-made TEAS in aid of Ellesborough Church. *Adm £2, chd free. Thurs 2 June; 4 Aug (2-5). Private visits welcome by appt No coaches. Tel 01296 622306*

㉕ ◆ Hughenden Manor, Nr High Wycombe &⊗⊕
(The National Trust) *1½m N of High Wycombe. On W side of Great Missenden Rd A4128.* Mary Anne Disraeli's colour schemes inspire spring and summer bedding in formal parterre. Unusual conifers, planted from photographs taken at time of Disraeli's death. Old English apple orchard with picnic area. Beech woodland walks. Mediterranean border. Light refreshments and TEAS. *House and Garden Adm £5, chd £2.50, family £12.50, Garden only Adm £1.90, chd 95p. Mar - Sat & Sun, Apr-Oct, Wed-Sun 11-5. For NGS: Sun 19 June (11-5). Tel 01494 755573 hughendenestate@nationaltrust.org.uk*

㉖ The Lee Gardens, Gt Missenden
3m N of Great Missenden, 3m SE of Wendover. Follow A413 Gt Missenden to Wendover. Turn 3rd R up Rocky Lane. After 2m turn L at 1st Xrds. 200yds turn R down drive. Cream TEAS at Kingswood House in aid of The Lee Church. *Combined adm £4, chd free. Sun 29 May (2-6)*

2 Kingswood Cottages &⊗⊕
(Mr & Mrs J Swain & Master J Swain) Peaceful and relaxing 2-acre garden enclosed by natural meadows. Mixed beds, slate herb garden, terracotta garden, secluded sundial table, wildlife pond, sculptures, natural woodland, specimen trees. Popular with children. Featured in BBC 'Good Homes' magazine 2004.

Kingswood House &⊗⊕ (Mr & Mrs T Hart) 4-acre mature family garden in an 'Area of Outstanding Natural Beauty'. Features incl a white garden surrounding a formal pond with fountain, wildlife pond, hot colour borders, sundial garden, fruit and vegetable areas. Bee-keeping display. *Private visits welcome by appt for groups 20+, May & Jun only. Tel 01494 837328 judy.hart@virgin.net*

㉗ Long Crendon Gardens, Long Crendon
2m N of Thame. On Thame/Bicester rd B4011. Attractive large village with many old/listed buildings. Village maps available for all visitors. TEAS at Church House, High St (both openings), at Croft House (June opening). *Combined adm £3 Apr; £4 June, chd free. Suns 10 Apr; 12 June (2-6)*

Baker's Close (Mr & Mrs Peter Vaines) 2 acres on SW slope. Partly walled with courtyard, terraced lawns, rockery with pond, roses, shrubs, herbaceous plantings and wild area.

Barry's Close & (Mr & Mrs Richard Salmon) *On LH-side just entering village from Bicester direction.* 2-acre, sloping garden with interesting collection of trees and shrubs. Herbaceous border, spring-fed pools and water garden.

Braddens Yard, 18 High Street ⊕ (Mr & Mrs P Simpson) *Opp Churchill PH.* ½-acre walled garden, largely created over past 15yrs. Collection of roses, herbaceous and climbing plants. Arched walk with clematis, honeysuckle and roses; pond;

small bothy garden. *Not open 10 Apr*

Croft House, 1 Thame Road &⊗⊕ (Cdr & Mrs Peter Everett) *On corner of Square & High St.* ½-acre walled garden with a variety of plants and shrubs, some unusual and of interest to flower arrangers. Water feature, greenhouse and conservatory. *Not open 10 Apr. Private visits welcome by appt. Tel 01844 208451 peverett@nihdram.co.uk*

NEW Lavender Cottage ⊗ (Robyn & Simon Stevens) Walled cottage garden based on inter-connecting circles with terraced patio leading down onto lawn, an eclectic mix of mature and young planting. *Not open 10 Apr*

Manor House, 114 High Street (Mr & Mrs N West) *Turn R by church, entrance through wrought iron gates.* 6-acre garden, lawns sweep down to 2 ornamental lakes, each with small island; walk along lower lake with many varieties of willow. New herbaceous borders, fine views towards Chilterns.

Mulberry House ⊗ (Mr & Mrs C Weston) *Opposite the 'Eight Bells'.* 1-acre, old vicarage garden, recently restored. Set amongst mature trees, now incl formal knot garden, woodland walk, pond, extensive sloping lawns and a notable monkey puzzle tree. *Not open 10 Apr*

The Old Crown, 97 Bicester Road ⊕ (Mr & Mrs R H Bradbury) *100yds past Chandos PH.* 1¼ acre on SW slope. More than 250 assorted roses, colourful annual and perennial plants in numerous beds, incl 50-60 clematis; flowering shrubs; assorted colourful pots and containers; statues; 2 sizeable vegetable plots. Great variety and very many spring bulbs.

Thornton Cottage ⊗⊕ (Charlotte Duncan) *Frogmore Lane is turning off village square. Car park 250 yds.* Typical country cottage garden with a beautiful outlook. Feature of flowering shrubs in unspoilt setting with herbaceous beds and borders. Many roses - bushes, ramblers and climbers. *Not open 10 April*

Todbury, 17 High Street (Mr & Mrs D Bevan) *House situated halfway along High St, nearly opp surgery. Please walk up driveway.* ½ acre of cottage garden, hidden from High St. Knot garden and vegetable beds;

extensive lawn with 2-tier pond and water feature. Large established shrubs and vast variety of perennials throughout. *Not open 10 April*

28 NEW Loughton Village Gardens
(Mr R Blackburn) *1m W of Central Milton Keynes. Between Watling Street (V4) and Portway roundabout (A5). Off Portway (H5) then follow signs. Car park in paddock - signed.* A village at the heart of the new town of Milton Keynes. Maps for all visitors. Flower Festival in church with plants for sale. TEAS in aid of All Saints Parish Church. *Combined adm £4, chd free. Sun 26 June (11.30-5.30)*

NEW Beech Cottage, 3 School Lane (Mr & Mrs A Rose) This listed cottage and barn are situated in the picturesque setting of Loughton's Conservation Area. Colourful garden contains an ancient Copper Beech and Walnut tree with patios, containers and hanging baskets. 2003 - Winner, Milton Keynes Garden Competition.

NEW Gardeners Cottage, 5 School Lane (Sally Hart-Ives & Don Reid) Georgian Cottage adjacent to All Saints Church. Following several years under cover, the garden was newly created in 2001. York stone patio steps down to mixed beds. Informal cottage style planting with herb and vegetable beds.

NEW 2 Lucy Lane (Mr & Mrs P Wason) Started from scratch 6-yrs ago, this landscaped garden is wrapped around a modern bungalow. The natural slope has been used to create rockery, patio, pond and mixed borders. Runner up - Milton Keynes Garden Competiton 2004.

NEW Manor Cottage (Gillian O'Reilly) Large garden on the edge of Loughton Brook. Created from a wilderness 20-yrs ago. Now a beautiful cottage garden. Mixed herbaceous borders, orchard, many mature fruit trees, water feature and ancient poplar tree. *Private visits welcome by appt. Tel 01908 666442*

NEW Nordberie, 110 Linceslade Grove (John & Rozi Rowcroft James) Surprisingly mature garden, 33x45ft, constructed by the present owners in 2001-02. Combines traditional and modern ideas including herb garden,

walled patio, fish pond, grasses, climbers and shrubs surrounding a central lawn.

29 The Manor House, Bledlow
(The Lord & Lady Carrington) *9m NW of High Wycombe, 3m SW of Princes Risborough. ½m off B4009 in middle of Bledlow village. Station: Princes Risborough, 2½m.* Paved garden, parterres, shrub borders, old roses and walled kitchen garden. Water garden with paths, bridges and walkways, fed by 14 chalk springs. Also 2 acres with sculptures and landscaped planting. TEAS May; Home-made TEAS June. *Adm £4.50, chd free. Suns 1 May; 12 June (2-6)*

30 NEW 19 Marroway
(Mr & Mrs P Pateman) *3m S of Aylesbury. On B4544 which runs between A41 and A413. Situated approx 150m from A413 end.* ⅓-acre relaxed organic garden, wildlife friendly. Large number of roses, perennials and shrubs in mixed borders. Many trellises and poles supporting clematis and other climbers. 2 ponds, raised beds, several fruit trees and willow tunnel. Vegetable garden. TEAS in aid of Wluest Horse & Pony Trust. *Adm £2. Private visits welcome by appt inc groups. Tel 01296 613271*

31 ◆ Nether Winchendon House, Nether Winchendon
(Mr Robert Spencer Bernard) *6m SW of Aylesbury, 6m from Thame.* 5 acres; fine and rare trees and shrubs, variety of hedges, herbaceous borders and naturalised spring bulbs. Recent changes. Medieval and Tudor manor house (not open) in picturesque village with beautiful church. TEAS, weather permitting. *Adm £2, chd free.* **For NGS:** *Suns 24 Apr; 10 July (2-5.30)*

32 North Down, Dodds Lane, Chalfont St Giles
(John & Merida Saunders) *4m SE of Amersham, 4m NE of Beaconsfield. Opp the green in centre of village, at Crown Inn, turn into UpCorner, on to Silver Hill. At top of hill fork R into Dodds Lane. N Down is 6th opening on L. Limited parking in Dodds Lane.* ¾-acre sloping N-facing compartmentalised site with mature trees. Difficult stony soil. Designed with scenic effect in mind and interest throughout the yr. Large grassed areas with island beds of mixed perennials, shrubs and some unusual plants. Variety of rhododendrons, azaleas, acers, 70+ clematis and other climbers. Displays of sempervivum

varieties, alpines, grasses and ferns. Small patio/water feature. Greenhouse. Italianate front patio to owners' design. Autumn colour. *Adm £2, chd under 16 free. Private visits welcome by appt incl groups of 10 or more. Tel 01494 872928*

33 Odin House, Foscote, Nr Buckingham
(Chris & Jenni Burton) *2m N of Buckingham. From Buckingham centre A413 towards Towcester. 200yds after Maids Moreton sign turn R into Village. At T-junction turn L towards Leckhamstead. After 300yds turn R to Foscote. Odin House 1st on L. Park in lane.* Sloping site previously part of a field extending to about 1 acre. Created by owners since 1990 to support wildlife with native trees and shrubs. Features herbaceous borders, new woodland area, formal vegetable garden, Japanese garden with koi pond (with very friendly fish!), wildlife pond with bog garden. Bantams, doves, dogs. Crafts for sale. Cream TEAS in aid of W I (Church Funds). *Adm £2.50, chd accompanied, free. Sat, Sun 23, 24 July (1-6). Private visits welcome by appt inc groups, weekday afternoons or evenings. Tel 01280 823291 chris-jen@odinhouse.freeserve.co.uk*

Odney Club, Odney Lane, Cookham
See Berkshire.

34 The Old Sun House, Pednor
(Mr & Mrs M Sharpley) *3m E of Gt Missenden, 2m W of Chesham. From Gt Missenden take B485 to Chesham, 1st L & follow signs approx 2m. From Chesham Church St (B485) follow signs approx 1½m.* 5-acre garden, abundant with wildlife, set on a Chiltern ridge giving superb views. The garden is surrounded by mature trees with inner plantings of unusual trees and shrubs. Features incl large ornamental pond with walkway; vegetable and herb garden; interesting woodland walk; white peafowl, guinea fowl, pheasantry and chickens. Home-made TEAS. *Adm £2.50, chd free. Sun 22 May (2-6)*

35 ◆ Old Thatch, Coldmoorholme Lane, Well End
(Jacky Hawthorne) *3m E Marlow, 1m NW Bourne End. Off A4155. Thatched house on L, just before the Spade Oak public house. Public car park 100yds further on towards the R Thames.* Listed thatched cottage (not open), famous home of Enid

Blyton and source of many of her stories. 2 acres, derelict in 1990, now contain beautiful palettes of colour, stunning ornamental grasses and wonderful design features. Cottage garden, lavender terrace, rose arbour, formal garden, water circle. Teas in room claimed by EB to be Dick Turpin's stable, containing secret treasures! Home-made TEAS. *Adm £2.50, chd £1. Fris, Sats 13 May to 13 Aug (11-5).* **For NGS:** *Fri 1 July (11-5). Tel 01628 527518*

36 The Old Vicarage, Padbury &⬚⬚
(Mr & Mrs H Morley-Fletcher) 2m S of Buckingham, 4m NW of Winslow. On A413 follow signs in village. 2½ acres on 3 levels, flowering shrubs and trees. Vegetable garden, pond and sunken garden, parterre and millennium arch. Magnolias and trilliums. Home-made TEAS in aid of League of Friends of Buckingham Hospital. Adm £2, chd free. Sat, Sun 23, 24 Apr (2-6). Private visits welcome by appt. Tel 01280 813045 hmorley-fletcher@btclick.co.uk

37 6 Oldfield Close, Little Chalfont ⬚⬚
(Jolyon & Phyllis Lea) 3m E of Amersham. Take A404 E through Little Chalfont, turn 1st R after railway bridge, then R again into Oakington Ave. Mature ⅜-acre garden of shrub borders, peat beds, rock plants, troughs and alpine house. Over 2,000 species and varieties of rare and interesting plants, incl spring bulbs, cyclamen and dwarf rhododendrons. Wide range of plants in aid of Bethany Village Leprosy Soc, India. TEAS in aid of Bethany Village. Adm £1.50, chd free. Sun 10 Apr (2-5). Private visits welcome by appt. Tel 01494 762384

38 Overstroud Cottage, The Dell, Frith Hill, Gt Missenden ⬚⬚
(Mr & Mrs Jonathan Brooke) Turn E off A413 at Gt Missenden onto B485 Frith Hill to Chesham rd. White Gothic cottage set back in lay-by 100yds up hill on L. Parking on R at church. Artistic chalk garden on 2 levels. Collection of C17/C18 plants. Potager. Snowdrops, narcissi, hellebores, primulas, pulmonarias, geraniums, species roses and lily pond. Cream TEAS at Parish Church. Adm £2, chd 50p. Suns 27 Mar; 17 Apr; 1 May (2-6). Private visits welcome by appt for groups, Apr-Jun. Tel 01494 862701

39 11 The Paddocks, Wendover &⬚⬚
(Mr & Mrs E Rye) 5m from Aylesbury. On A413. At Wendover after approx ½m, turn L at mini-roundabout into Wharf Rd. Entrance is 2nd on L. From Gt Missenden, turn L at Clock Tower, then R at next mini-roundabout. Parking at Bucksbridge Hse, Sat & Sun only. Small peaceful garden with mixed borders of colourful herbaceous perennials and a special show of David Austin roses and delphiniums. Cool hosta walk and tremendous variety of plants in a small area.. Winner of Aylesbury Vale Small Gardens 2003. Adm £2, chd free. Sat, Sun 18, 19 June (2-6). **Evening Opening** *£2, wine, Fri 24 June (6-8.30). Tel 01296 623870*

Patchwork, 22 Hall Park Gate, Berkhamsted ⬚
See Hertfordshire.

40 NEW ◆ The Plant Specialist, Whitefield Lane, Great Missenden &⬚⬚
(Sean Walter) 5m NW Amersham. A413 to Gt Missenden. Whitefield Lane opp Missenden Abbey. Under railway bridge on the L. Large display borders illustrating herbaceous perennials and grasses for sale in nursery. Thur-Sat, Apr to Oct, 10-6. **For NGS:** *Combined adm with Gipsy House £4, chd £2, Thurs 14 Apr; 12 May; 9 June; 14 July (2-5). Tel 01494 866681*

41 Quainton Gardens
7m NW of Aylesbury, 7m SW of Winslow. Nr Waddesdon turn off A41. TEAS at Brudenell House in aid of New Memorial Hall Fund. Combined adm £4. Sun 29 May (2-6)

Brudenell House, Church Street ⬚
(Dr & Mrs H Beric Wright) 2½ acres with contrasting areas; dell with 160yr-old specimen trees, soft fruit and vegetables. Large pond for reflections. Substantial changes will have taken place since last year.

Capricorner, Church Street *(Mrs G Davis) Small garden planted for yr-round interest with many scented plants, semi-wild area with interesting trees.*

31 The Green &⬚ *(Mr & Mrs D Hanson) Old well-worked organic garden. Clematis, shrubs and small pond; small vegetable patch.*

Thorngumbald, 13 Station Road ⬚
(Jane Lydall) Small heavily planted cottage garden designed for year round interest and to

please all the senses. Prize winner 'Country Living' Organic Gardener 2003, 'Ideal Home' & ITV Britain's Best Back Gardens 2004. *Private visits welcome by appt. Tel 01296 655356*

Ragged Hall, Gaddesden Row, nr Hemel Hempstead &⬚⬚
See Hertfordshire.

Scotlands, nr Wargrave &
See Berkshire.

42 Turn End, Townside, Haddenham &⬚
(Peter Aldington) 3m NE of Thame, 5m SW of Aylesbury. Turn off A418 to Haddenham. Turn at Rising Sun to Townside. Please park at a distance with consideration for neighbours. Architect's own post-war listed house (not open). Garden less than 1 acre, space used to create illusion of size. Series of enclosed gardens, sunken or raised, sunny or shady, each different yet harmonious, contrast with lawns, borders and glades. Spring bulbs, irises, old roses and climbers. Courtyard with fish pool. Please telephone for adm prices (share to Turn End Charitable Trust). Private visits welcome by appt for groups of 10+. Tel 01844 291383/291817 turnend.peter@macunlimited.net

43 Tythrop Park, Kingsey &⬚
(Jonathan & Medina Marks) 2m E of Thame, 4m NW of Princes Risborough. Via A4129; lodge gates just outside Kingsey. 7 acres. Formal gardens with many fine trees and shrubs. Intricate dwarf box parterre with fountains. Large walled garden with wide variety of fruit trees, soft fruits and vegetables, divided by rows of roses and flowers. Magnificent greenhouse containing 'Black Hamburgh' and 'Muscat Hamburgh' vines propagated from vine at Hampton Court 150yrs ago. Secluded water garden with attractive walks and old roses. Nut grove; wilderness area; arboretum. Home-made TEAS. Adm £3, chd free (share to NCH Action for Children). Sun 19 June (2-6)

44 ◆ Waddesdon Manor Gardens, Waddesdon ⬚⬚
(The National Trust) 4m NW of Aylesbury, 6m NE of Thame. Off A41 between Aylesbury & Bicester on Waddesdon Estate. Manor Gardens, designed for Baron Ferdinand de Rothschild, feature a magnificent parterre and three-dimensional carpet bedding displays, rose garden and rococo-style aviary. The Water Garden is a private garden

restored by Lord Rothschild with naturalistic outcrops of Pulham rock, cascading water, still ponds and intricate planting. Water garden only accessible as part of guided tour, departing from stables courtyard, 11-3 (last tour). Cream TEAS. *Adm £6, chd £3. Wed to Sun, 23 March to 23 Dec & weekends in Jan & Feb.* **For NGS:** *Weds 30 Mar; 5 Oct (11-3). Tel 01296 653226*

45 Watercroft, Church Road, Penn 🚫♿
(Mr & Mrs Paul Hunnings) *3m NW of Beaconsfield, 3m W of Amersham. On B474, 600yds on L past Holy Trinity Church.* Mature 3-acre chalk and clay garden. Unusual spring bulbs and hellebores. Large weeping ash. Rose walk with 250 roses. Courtyard with summer pots incl fuchsias and box topiary. Large natural old pond with diving ducks. Italianate garden with 11-yr-old yew hedges and fine view. Wild flower meadow with wild roses. Formal herb garden with culinary herbs, small vegetable garden with hele hedge. New glasshouse with unusual pelargoniums. Home-made TEAS. *Adm £3, chd free. Private visits welcome by appt for groups, mid-June to mid-July. Evening visits, wine. Tel 01494 816535*

46 Weir Lodge, Latimer Road, Chesham ♿
(Mr & Mrs Mungo Aldridge) *1m SE of Chesham. On unclassified rd. From Chesham turn off A416 at mini-roundabout signposted Chenies & Latimer. From Rickmansworth turn R from A404 at signpost for Chenies, proceed 4m. ¾ acre on bank of R Chess.* Natural stream with bridges, ponds and planted banks. Gravelled terrace with sun-loving plants. Assorted containers; mixed beds, moisture-loving plants, wood carvings and sculptures. Mature trees, incl fine beeches in adjoining paddock, with two pet sheep. TEAS in aid of Friends of St Mary's Church. *Adm £2, chd free. Sun 10 July (2-5.30). Private visits welcome by appt June & July only. Tel 01494 793504 mungo.aldridge@btinternet.com*

47 Whitchurch Gardens
4m N of Aylesbury, 4m S of Winslow. On A413. Large village with many thatched cottages in the quieter older parts, down small lanes. Village maps provided. Home-made TEAS, at and in aid of, the Church Hall 10 Apr, at Priory Court on 13 Mar in aid of Alzeheimers Society. *Combined adm £2.50 March, £4 Apr, chd free. Suns 13 Mar (2-5) ; 10 Apr (2-6)*

Fielding House ♿🚫⊕ (Mrs A Fraser) Designed and planted by the present owner over the last 9½yrs this is a free draining, windswept, partly sloping, SW-facing garden. The large walnut tree dominating the garden has recently had a drastic haircut, reducing its bulk by a third. Patio, gravel areas, raised beds, mixed shrub and herbaceous border. Hellebores, erythronium and tulip species in Mar.

Park House Barn (John & Mary Amos) Very small walled garden, gravel area, raised beds with herbaceous plants, roses and clematis. Many pots and containers. *Not open 13 Mar*

Priory Court, 52 High Street ♿🚫⊕ (Mr & Mrs Ian Durrell) Approx ⅔-acre, split-level, all-season walled garden with bulbs, rose beds, shrubbery, herb bed, fruit cage and herbaceous borders. Water feature, decking and summer house.

Thatchings (Mr & Mrs S Cole) Traditional cottage garden with informal flower beds, vegetable garden, bog garden and orchard. *Not open 13 Mar*

Yew Tree Cottage ♿🚫 (Mr & Mrs B S Foulger) 3-tier garden incl water features and wooded area. Panoramic views of the Vale of Aylesbury and the castle mound. A haven for birds. *Not open 13 Mar*

48 The White House, Village Road, Denham Village ♿⊕
(Mr & Mrs P G Courtenay-Luck) *3m NW of Uxbridge, 7m E of Beaconsfield. Signed from A40 or A412; nearest station Denham*

Green. Underground Uxbridge. Parking in village rd. The White House is in centre of village. Well established 6-acre, formal garden in picturesque setting. Mature trees and hedges, with R Misbourne meandering through lawns. Shrubberies, flower beds, rockery, rose garden and orchard. Large walled garden with Italian garden and developing laburnum walk; herb garden, vegetable plot and Victorian greenhouses. Home-made TEAS in aid of Red Cross. *Adm £3, chd under 13 free. Suns 15 May; 17 July (2-5)*

49 Whitewalls, Quarry Wood Road, Marlow ♿🚫
(Mr W H Williams) *½m S Marlow. From Marlow cross over bridge. 1st L, 3rd house on L, white garden wall.* Thames-side garden approx ½ acre with spectacular view of weir. Large lily pond, interesting planting of trees, shrubs, herbaceous perennials and bedding, large conservatory. *Adm £2, chd free. Suns 24 Apr; 24 July; 18 Sept (2-5). Private visits welcome by appt. Tel 01628 482573*

50 Wichert, Ford ♿🚫
(Mr & Mrs C Siggers) *5m SW of Aylesbury, 5m NE of Thame. From Aylesbury take A418 towards Thame. Turn L at Bugle Horn into Portway. After 3m turn L into Ford. Park in village. Entrance for pedestrians & parking for disabled drivers in drive immediately beyond The Old Bakehouse.* Approx 1½ acres developed into separate gardens: silver and pearl, shade, fern, kitchen and pavement. Two mazes, orchard, willow arbour, ponds and wild garden with copse. A garden which blends into rural surroundings. Home-made TEAS in aid of Ford Village Society. *Adm £2, chd free. Sun 5 June (2-6)*

Evening Opening (See also garden description)	
Cowper & Newton Museum Gardens	15 June
11 The Paddocks	24 June

Nurses Welfare Service

"Somebody gave me the number of the Nurses Welfare Service who turned out to be my lifeline. They listened, offered advice and support, and suddenly I felt I could see a twinkle of light at the end of a very long tunnel."

"Mary", paediatric nurse, back to work thanks to the NWS - and The National Gardens Scheme!

Helping Nurses and Midwives in crisis
020 7233 5500
www.nurseswelfareservice.co.uk

Cambridgeshire

County Organisers:
(South)   Lady Nourse, Dullingham House, Dullingham, Newmarket, Suffolk CB8 9UP
                                           Tel 01638 508186
(North)   Mr George Stevenson, 1a The Village, Orton Longueville, Peterborough, Cambridgeshire
                                           PE2 7DN Tel 01733 391506
Assistant County Organiser: Mrs Pam Bullivant, Rosewell House, 60 Prickwillow Road, Ely, Cambridgeshire CB7 4TX
                                           Tel 01353 667355
(South)   Mrs Alison Gould, The Grange, Church Road, Easton, Nr Huntingdon, Cambridgeshire
                                           PE18 0TU Tel 01480 891043
County Treasurers: Mr John Drake, Hardwicke House, High Ditch Road, Fen Ditton, Cambridgeshire CB5 8TF
                                           Tel 01223 292246
(North)   Mrs Christine Stevenson, 1a The Village, Orton Longueville, Peterborough, Cambridgeshire
                                           PE2 7DN Tel 01733 391506

Maps: Numbers shown next to each garden entry refer to that garden's entry on the county map. This position is approximate; distance and directions from the nearest main town are generally shown in the garden text. A precise location is available for those gardens featured on the NGS website by visiting www.ngs.org.uk.

Symbols: Information relating to symbols is given on page 21

DATES OF OPENING

Evening openings
See end of county listing

Private gardens open regularly for NGS
The Crossing House, Shepreth *(11)*

Gardens open to the public
For details see garden description
Anglesey Abbey, Gardens & Lode Mill, Cambridge *(2)*
Docwra's Manor, Shepreth *(12)*
Elgood's Brewery Gardens, Wisbech *(14)*
The Manor, Hemingford Grey *(27)*
Peckover House, North Brink *(32)*
Wimpole Hall, Arrington *(43)*

By appointment only
For telephone number and other details see garden description. Private visits welcomed
Childerley Hall, Dry Drayton *(8)*
The Crossing House, Shepreth *(11)*

Greystones, Comberton *(19)*
Mill House, Bassingbourn *(28)*
Mosspaul, March *(29)*

March 13 Sunday
Florence House, Wisbech *(18)*

March 20 Sunday
Balsham Manor and Maze, Balsham *(4)*

March 27 Sunday (Easter)
Bainton House & Maxey *(3)*
Kirtling Tower, Kirtling *(23)*
Netherhall Manor, Soham *(30)*

March 28 Monday (Easter)
Weaver's Cottage, West Wickham *(39)*

April 3 Sunday
Chippenham Park, Chippenham, nr Newmarket *(9)*
Kirtling Tower, Kirtling *(23)*
Trinity College, Fellows' Garden, Cambridge *(37)*

April 10 Sunday
Barton Gardens, Cambridge *(5)*

April 20 Wednesday
Florence House, Wisbech *(18)*

April 24 Sunday
Leckhampton, Cambridge *(24)*

May 1 Sunday
Netherhall Manor, Soham *(30)*

May 2 Monday (Bank Hol)
Ely Gardens I *(15)*

May 8 Sunday
Barton Gardens, Cambridge *(5)*
Docwra's Manor, Shepreth *(12)*
Tetworth Hall, nr Sandy, Beds *(36)*

May 15 Sunday
Nuns Manor, Shepreth *(31)*

May 22 Sunday
Abbots Ripton Hall, Abbots Ripton *(1)*

May 29 Sunday
Florence House, Wisbech *(18)*
Island Hall, Godmanchester *(21)*

June 4 Saturday
Cherryoaks, Burrough Green *(7)*

June 5 Sunday
Cherryoaks, Burrough Green *(7)*
Ely Gardens II *(16)*

June 12 Sunday
Catworth, Molesworth & Brington Gardens, nr Huntingdon *(6)*
Chippenham Park, Chippenham, nr Newmarket *(9)*
Madingley Hall, nr Cambridge *(26)*
Upton Gardens *(38)*
Wilburton Gardens *(42)*

June 18 Saturday
21 Lode Road, Lode *(25)*

June 19 Sunday
Elgood's Brewery Gardens, Wisbech *(14)*
21 Lode Road, Lode *(25)*
Nuns Manor, Shepreth *(31)*
Sawston Gardens *(34)*
Sutton Gardens, nr Ely *(35)*
Whittlesford Gardens *(41)*

"Kenneth is a bit of a perfectionist when it comes to lawncare!"

CAMBRIDGESHIRE

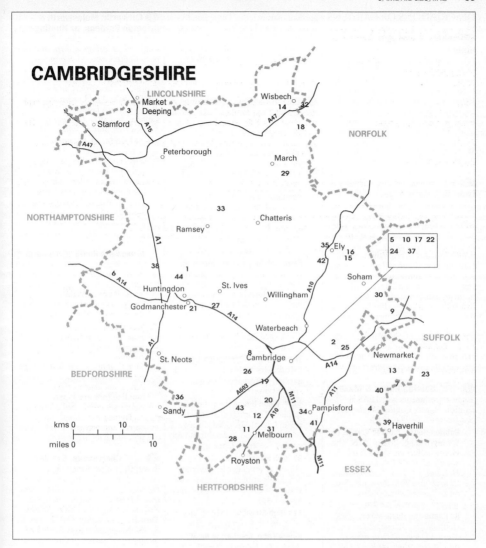

June 21 Tuesday
Peckover House, North Brink **(Evening)** *(32)*

June 22 Wednesday
Florence House, Wisbech *(18)*

June 25 Saturday
21 Lode Road, Lode *(25)*

June 26 Sunday
Anglesey Abbey, Gardens & Lode Mill, Cambridge *(2)*
21 Lode Road, Lode *(25)*
Wytchwood, 7 Owl End, Great Stukeley *(44)*

July 3 Sunday
Clare College, Fellows' Garden, Cambridge *(10)*

Dullingham House, nr Newmarket *(13)*
Emmanuel College Garden & Fellows' Garden, Cambridge *(17)*

July 10 Sunday
King's College Fellows' Garden, Cambridge *(22)*
Ramsey Forty Foot, nr Ramsey *(33)*

July 17 Sunday
83 High Street, Harlton *(20)*

July 20 Wednesday
Florence House, Wisbech *(18)*

July 21 Thursday
Wimpole Hall, Arrington *(43)*

August 7 Sunday
Netherhall Manor, Soham *(30)*

August 14 Sunday
Netherhall Manor, Soham *(30)*

August 24 Wednesday
Florence House, Wisbech *(18)*

August 29 Monday (Bank Hol)
West Wratting Park, West Wratting *(40)*

September 4 Sunday
Anglesey Abbey, Gardens & Lode Mill, Cambridge *(2)*

September 11 Sunday
Florence House, Wisbech *(18)*

October 23 Sunday
Chippenham Park, Chippenham, nr Newmarket *(9)*

DESCRIPTIONS OF GARDENS

❶ Abbots Ripton Hall, Abbots Ripton
(The Lord & Lady De Ramsey) *2m N of Huntingdon. On B1090.* Laning Roper, Humphrey Waterfield and Jim Russell helped design the garden. Extensive herbaceous borders; rose circle with both old and modern roses. Many follies and lake. Home-made TEAS. *Adm £3.50, chd under 12 free (share to Ramsey Abbey Walled Kitchen Garden Trust). Sun 22 May (2-5)*

❷ ◆ Anglesey Abbey, Gardens & Lode Mill, Cambridge ⬤⬤⬤
(The National Trust) *6m NE of Cambridge. From A14 turn N on to B1102 through Stow-cum-Quy.* 100 acres surrounding an Elizabethan manor created from the remains of a priory founded in reign of Henry I. Garden created during last 70 years; avenues of beautiful trees; groups of statuary; hedges enclosing small intimate gardens; daffodils and hyacinths; herbaceous border (June); dahlia beds (July-October); winter garden. TEAS. *House and Garden adm £7, Garden only adm £4.30, chd £2.15.* **For NGS:** *Suns 26 June; 4 Sept (10.30-5.30). Tel 01223 810080 angleseyabbey@nationaltrust.org.uk*

❸ NEW Bainton House & Maxey
Light refreshments and TEAS at Bainton House. *Combined adm £3, chd free. Sun 27 Mar (2-5)*

  Bainton House, Bainton Village, nr Stamford ⬤⬤ (Major W & The Hon Mrs Birkbeck) *3m E of Stamford. B1443 Stamford-Helpston rd. Turn N at Bainton Church into Tallington Rd. ¼m on L.* 2 acres with borders, spinney and wild garden.

  8a Castle End Road, Maxey ⬤⬤
(John & Sue Dinenage) *1m N of Market Deeping. Turn off A15 into Maxey, then 1st R.* ½-acre plant lover's garden on heavy clay. Herbaceous perennials, mixed shrubs, climbers especially clematis, and interesting trees; planted since 1978. *Adm £1.50, chd free. Private visits welcome by appt, adm £2. Tel 01778 345177 jdinenage@iee.org.uk*

❹ Balsham Manor and Maze, 42 High St, Balsham ⬤⬤⬤
(Mr & Mrs J Potter) *10m SE of Cambridge. 10m S of Newmarket. 3m E of A11. Opp village green.* 3 acres of formal and wild garden. Spring bulbs, herbaceous and mixed borders, shrubbery and vegetable

garden; mature trees. Large pond, hedge maze and modern sculptures. Home-made TEAS in aid of MAGPAS First Responder Scheme. *Adm £2.50, chd £1. Sun 20 Mar (1-5)*

❺ Barton Gardens, Cambridge
3½m SW at Cambridge. Take A603, in village turn R for Comberton Rd. Delightful group of gardens of wide appeal and expertise. Light refreshments and TEAS at Village Hall in aid of Church (Apr), Tennis Club (May). *Combined adm £3, chd free. Suns 10 Apr; 8 May (2-5)*

  13 Allens Close (Mrs R Wright) *Approached from High Street.* Small award winning, domestic garden. Beautifully tendered flowers. Be amazed at what can be done in a restricted space.

  Farm Cottage, 18 High Street ⬤
(Dr R M Belbin) Courtyard and walled herbaceous garden with water features. Garden opens out into a woodland bank with spring flowers. Gate at rear of gardens leads into The Vatches TV Award Best Back Garden in Cambridgeshire 2004.

  The Gables, 11 Comberton Road
(Mr & Mrs M Noble) 2-acre old garden, mature trees, ha-ha, spring flowers.

  NEW Glebe House (David & Sue Rapley) *Top of High St.* 1-acre mature, partly wooded garden with large pond, formal fruit/herb garden - recently landscaped.

  37 High Street ⬤⬤ (Mrs Frances Hayes) A small garden designed at 2 levels at the rear with a wide variety of choice plants. *Not open Sun 10 Apr*

  114 High Street ⬤ (Mr & Mrs Greenfield) A cottage garden.

  King's Tithe, Comberton Road
(Major C H Thorne) Small domestic garden. Good throughway to larger garden of The Gables.

  31 New Road (Dr D Macdonald) Cottage garden with some unusual plants.

  The Seven Houses, Comberton Road ⬤ (Perennial (GRBS)) Small bungalow estate. 1½-acre spring garden; bulbs naturalised in orchard. Colourful summer borders.

  The Vatches *Opp village pond, entrance via Farm Cottage.* Landscaped paddock with mature trees, shrubs and attractive views.

❻ Catworth, Molesworth & Brington Gardens, nr Huntingdon
10m W of Huntingdon. For Catworth & Brington turn off A14 onto B660 (Catworth S bound) approx 7m W of A14 junction with A1. Village is on the N side of A14 flyover. Molesworth is on the A14, 8m W of the A1. Home-made TEAS at Molesworth House & Yew Tree Cottage, Brington. *Combined adm £2, chd free. Sun 12 June (2-6)*

  32 High Street, Catworth ⬤
(Colin Small) Long narrow garden approx ¼-acre. Large informal patio; pergola with herbaceous borders and containers of unusual foliage plants; lawn with herbaceous borders either side, native woodland area. Many rare plants, collection of salvias and ferns.

  Molesworth House, Molesworth ⬤
(John Prentis) *Next to the church in Molesworth.* Classic Victorian rectory garden of approx 2½ acres. Bit of everything; old-fashioned and proud of it. Also rather groovy new tropical house.

  Yew Tree Cottage, Brington ⬤⬤⬤ (Mr & Mrs D G Eggleston) *After village sign continue past school, up hill, Yew Tree Cottage is thatched cottage on L.* Informal garden, approx 1-acre, complements the C17 building (not open) and comprises flower beds, lawns, vegetable patch, boggy area, copses and orchard. Plants in pots and hanging baskets.

❼ NEW Cherryoaks, Bradley Road, Burrough Green ⬤⬤⬤
(Sylvia & Ron Allworthy) *6m S of Newmarket. From A11 Northbound take A1304 Newmarket, turn R at Xrds in Six Mile Bottom to Brinkley. Turn L at T-junction B1052, then R B1061 Newmarket to Haverhill rd. As you enter Burrough Green house 1st on L next to 40 limit sign. Parking both sides of rd on verges.* Approx 2-acre garden, established and maintained by ourselves over 7yrs. Planted for foliage effect, flower and plant interest all yr-round. Large pond and waterfall with bog garden. Patio with water feature, overflowing with containers of acid lovers as soil is clay. Posts, ropes and structure full of clematis, roses, wisteria etc. Aboretum, soft fruit, vegetables and compost area. Our haven. Home-made TEAS in aid of BG Reading Room (Sun only). *Adm £2, chd 50p. Sat, Sun 4, 5 June (11-5). Private visits welcome by appt Apr to Sept. Tel 01638 507479*

8 Childerley Hall, Dry Drayton ⌖

(Mr & Mrs John Jenkins) *6m W of Cambridge. On A428 opp Caldecote turn.* 4 acres of mixed planting with special emphasis on shrub roses. *Adm £2.50. Private visits welcome by appt. Tel 01954 210271*

9 Chippenham Park, Chippenham, nr Newmarket ⌖

(Mr & Mrs Eustace Crawley) *5m NE of Newmarket. 1m off A11.* The house (not open), gardens, lake, canals and 350-acre park enclosed by wall 3½m long, built after Admiral Lord Russell petitioned William III in 1696 for permission to make a park. Gardens have been extended and restocked by Anne Crawley, a descendant of John Tharp who bought the estate in 1791. Superb display of daffodils and early flowering shrubs followed by extensive summer borders and dramatic autumn colours. Specialist plants for sale. Dogs welcome on leads only. Featured in 'Country Life' 2003. Light Refreshments and TEAS. *Adm £3, chd free. Suns 3 Apr; 12 June; 23 Oct (11-5)*

10 Clare College, Trinity Lane, Fellows' Garden, Cambridge ⌖⌖

(The Master & Fellows) *Central to city. From Queens Rd or city centre via Senate House Passage, Old Court & Clare Bridge.* 2 acres. One of the most famous gardens on the Cambridge Backs. Herbaceous borders; sunken pond garden and fine specimen trees. *Adm £2.50, chd under 16 free. Sun 3 July (2-6) www.clare.cam.ac.uk*

11 The Crossing House, Shepreth ⌖

(Mr & Mrs Douglas Fuller & John Marlar) *8m SW of Cambridge. ½m W of A10.* Internationally famous as King's Cross-Cambridge railway runs alongside garden. Small cottage garden with many old-fashioned plants grown in mixed beds in company with modern varieties. Shrubs, bulbs and many alpines in rock beds. *Adm collection box. Private visits welcome by appt. Open daily dawn till dusk, no coaches Tel 01763 261071*

12 ◆ Docwra's Manor, Shepreth ⌖⌖

(Mrs John Raven) *½m W of A10. Cambridge-Royston bus stops at gate opp the War Memorial in Shepreth. King's Cross-Cambridge train stop 5 min walk.* 2½ acres of choice plants in series of enclosed gardens. TEAS in aid of local church (NGS day). *Adm £3, chd under 16 free. All yr Weds, Fris (10-4), 1st Sun in month Mar to Oct (2-4).* **For NGS:** *Sun 8 May (2-5). Tel 01763 260235*

13 Dullingham House, nr Newmarket ⌖⌖

(Sir Martin & Lady Nourse) *4m S of Newmarket. Off A1034.* Repton garden. Historic bowling green. Magnificent large herbaceous borders enclosed by substantial walls. Water garden; and lovely views across parkland. Home-made TEAS in aid of WI. *Adm £3.50, chd free. Sun 3 July (2-6). Private visits welcome by appt, June & July. Tel 01638 508186 nourse@dircon.co.uk*

14 ◆ Elgood's Brewery Gardens, Wisbech ⌖⌖

(Elgood & Sons Ltd) *On the N Brink of the R Nene approx 1m W of the town centre.* Approx 4-acres. Established in the Georgian era and restored around many of the original 200yr-old specimen trees. Lawns, lake, rockery, herb gardens and maze. Light refreshments and TEAS. *Adm £2.50, chd 6-16yrs /concessions £2. Tue to Thur 26 Apr to 29 Sept.* **For NGS:** *Sun 19 June (11.30-4.30). Tel 01945 583160 Kate Pateman info@elgoods-brewery.co.uk*

15 Ely Gardens I
14m N of Cambridge. Approaching Ely from A10 follow signs to the cathedral. 2 gardens, nr to Cathedral. TEAS at The Old Fire Engine House in aid of Sue Ryder Care. *Combined adm £2, chd 50p. Mon 2 May (2-5)*

The Old Fire Engine House, St Mary's Street ⌖ (Mr & Mrs M R Jarman) Delightful walled country garden with mixed herbaceous borders and wild flowers.

The Old Palace ⌖⌖⌖ (Sue Ryder Care) 1½ acres with duck pond in fine setting next to cathedral. Interesting mixed borders, superb trees, oldest and largest London plane tree in the country. Re-creation of Chelsea Flower Show 2003 Courtyard Bronze Medal Garden.

16 Ely Gardens II
Approaching Ely from A10 follow signs to the cathedral. . Maps given at first garden visited. TEAS at The Old Palace. *Adm Combined £3, chd 50p (share to Sue Ryder Care). Sun 5 June (2-6)*

Belmont House ⌖⌖ (Mr & Mrs P J Stanning) Designed ½-acre garden with interesting and unusual plants. 'Garden Answers' feature 2003.

The Bishop's House, The Gallery ⌖ (The Rt Reverend the Bishop of Ely & Mrs Russell) Walled garden, former cloisters of monastery. Mixed herbaceous, box hedge, rose and kitchen garden.

NEW **Hazeldene, 36 Barton Road** ⌖⌖ (Mike & Juliette Tuplin) Organic garden reflecting an interest in wildlife. Interesting planting and structures incl kitchen garden with raised beds.

The Old Palace ⌖⌖⌖ (Sue Ryder Care) (See separate entry).

50A Prickwillow Road ⌖ (Mr & Mrs J Hunter) Enthusiast's small walled garden, densely planted with variety of interesting plants.

Queen's Hall ⌖⌖⌖ (R & S Freestone) 90% medieval garden - with a twist.

Rosewell House, 60 Prickwillow Road ⌖⌖ (Mr & Mrs A Bullivant) Well-stocked garden with emphasis on perennial planting. Splendid views of cathedral and surrounding fenland. Recently acquired meadow being developed to encourage wild flowers and wildlife.

NEW **5 Springhead Lane** ⌖ (Lynmaree Barron) Small, low maintenance garden with a few containers and a mix of ornamental and edible produce.

17 Emmanuel College Garden & Fellows' Garden, Cambridge ⌖⌖
Car parks at Parker's Piece & Lion Yard, within 5 mins walk. One of the most beautiful gardens in Cambridge. Buildings of C17 to C20 surrounding 3 large gardens with pools, herb garden, herbaceous borders, fine trees incl Dawn Redwood. On this date access allowed to Fellows' Garden with magnificent oriental Plane and more herbaceous borders. *Adm £2, chd free. Sun 3 July (2.30-5)*

18 Florence House, Back Road, Fridaybridge, Wisbech ⌖⌖⌖
(Mr & Mrs A Stevenson) *3½m S of Wisbech. On B1101. In Fridaybridge centre turn R in front of Chequers PH on to Back Rd.* Large sweeping borders in this 25yr-old 1½-acre garden, growing a modern mix of trees, shrubs, perennials and grasses in C21 style. The new paddock borders start bold and exotic leading to greens and creams, mauves, red and blues finishing with a woodland area underplanted with bulbs, ferns, hellebores. WC. Picnic area for Wed

openings. TEAS (Suns). *Adm £2, chd 50p. Suns 13 Mar; 29 May; 11 Sept (12-4); Weds 20 Apr; 22 June; 20 July; 24 Aug; (10-4). Private visits welcome by appt. Tel 01945 860268 roddy@lasmotors.freeserve.co.uk*

⑲ Greystones, 19 Swaynes Lane, Comberton 🅑🅧🅗
(Dr & Mrs L Davies) *5m SW of Cambridge. From M11, junction 12, take A603 away from Cambridge then 1st R onto B1046 to Comberton. 1½m. Plantswoman's garden of approx ½-acre planted with a wide range of flowering plants. Colour-themed borders framed by foliage and shrubs with gravel beds, troughs, water feature and potager. Adm £2. Private visits welcome by appt June, July, Sept & Oct, also groups. Tel 01223 264159 alison@ldassoc.demon.co.uk*

⑳ 83 High Street, Harlton 🅑🅧🅗
(Dr Ruth Chippindale) *7m SW of Cambridge. From Cambridge - A603 (toward Sandy). After 6m turn L (S) for Harlton. ½-acre interesting design which incl many different features, colours and a wide diversity of plants. Home-made TEAS in aid of Harlton Church Restoration Fund. Adm £2, chd free. Sun 17 July (2-5). Private visits welcome by appt. Tel 01223 262170*

㉑ Island Hall, Godmanchester 🅧🅗
(Mr Christopher & Lady Linda Vane Percy) *1m S of Huntingdon (A1). In centre of Godmanchester next to free car park. 15m NW of Cambridge (A14).* 3-acre grounds. Mid C18 mansion (not open). Tranquil riverside setting with mature trees. Chinese bridge over Saxon mill race to an embowered island with wild flowers. Garden restored in 1983 to mid C18 formal design, with box hedging, clipped hornbeams, parterres, topiary and good vistas over borrowed landscape, punctuated with C18 wrought iron and stone urns. Home-made TEAS. *Adm £3, chd free. Sun 29 May (12-5). Private visits welcome by appt May to Sept. Tel 01480 459676 cvp@cvpdesigns. com*

㉒ King's College Fellows' Garden, Queens Road, Cambridge 🅑🅧
(Provost & Scholars of King's College) *Entry by gate at junction of Queens Rd & West Rd. Parking at Lion's Yard 10mins walk.* Fine example of a Victorian garden with rare specimen trees. Cream TEAS. *Adm £2, chd free. Sun 10 July (2-6) domus.bursar@kings.cam.ac.uk*

㉓ Kirtling Tower, Newmarket Road, Kirtling 🅧🅗
(Lord & Lady Fairhaven) *6m SE of Newmarket. From Newmarket head towards the Saxon Street village, through village to Kirtling, turn L at war memorial, entrance is signed on L.* Kirtling Tower is surrounded on 3 sides by a moat. The garden of 5-acres was started by the present owners 4yrs ago. Main features are the spring garden, secret garden and walled garden. The spring garden is planted with 50,000 bulbs - daffodils, narcissus and camassias in memory of The Hon Rupert Broughton (1970-2000). Light refreshments and TEAS in aid of All Saints Church, Kirtling. *Adm £3.50, chd free. Suns 27 Mar; 3 Apr (11-4)*

㉔ Leckhampton, 37 Grange Road, Cambridge 🅑🅧
(Corpus Christi College) *Runs N to S between Madingley Rd (A1303) & A603. Drive entrance opp Selwyn College.* 10 acres. Originally laid out by William Robinson as garden of Leckhampton. Formal lawns, rose garden, small herbaceous beds, extensive wild garden with bulbs, cowslips, prunus and fine specimen trees. Home-made TEAS. *Adm £3, chd free. Sun 24 Apr (2-6)*

㉕ 21 Lode Road, Lode 🅑🅧
(Mr Richard P Ayres) *10m NE of Cambridge. Take B1102 from Stow-cum-Quy roundabout NE of Cambridge at junction with A14. Lode is 2m from roundabout.* Small garden adjoining C15 thatched cottage (not open) designed by the owner (retired head gardener at Anglesey Abbey NT). Planted with bold groups of herbaceous plants complementing a fine lawn and creating an element of mystery and delight. TEAS in aid of St James

Church, Lode. *Adm £2, chd £1. Sats, Suns 18, 19, 25, 26 June (11-5)*

㉖ Madingley Hall, nr Cambridge 🅧
(University of Cambridge) *4m W of Cambridge. 1m from M11 Exit 13.* C16 Hall (not open) set in 8 acres of attractive grounds. Features incl landscaped walled garden with hazel walk, alpine bed, medicinal border and rose pergola. Meadow, topiary and mature trees. Cream TEAS. *Adm £2, chd free (share to Madingley Church Restoration Fund). Sun 12 June (2.30-5.30) www.cont-ed.cam.ac.uk*

㉗ ♦ The Manor, Hemingford Grey 🅑🅗
(Mrs D S Boston) *4m E of Huntingdon. Off A14. Entrance to garden by small gate off river towpath. No parking at house except for disabled by arrangement with owner. Park in village.* Garden designed and planted by author Lucy Boston, surrounds C12 manor house on which her Green Knowe Books were based (house open only by prior appt). 4 acres with topiary; over 200 old roses and large herbaceous borders with mainly scented plants. Enclosed by river, moat and wilderness. *Adm £2, chd free. Open Daily (11-5) (dusk in winter). Tel 01480 463134 www.greenknowe.co.uk*

㉘ Mill House, North End, Bassingbourn 🅑🅧🅗
(Mr & Mrs A Jackson) *2m N of Royston. On the NW outskirts of Bassingbourn. 1m from Church, on the rd to Shingay. Take North End at the war memorial in the centre of Bassingbourn which is just W of the A1198 (do not take Mill Lane).* Garden created out of open countryside by garden designer owners. Clever use of walls, pergolas, water and varying land levels provide a backdrop for many very fascinating plants notably clematis, giving interest and colour throughout the yr. Topiary. *Adm £3. Private visits welcome by appt May to Sept, groups welcome. Tel 01763 243491 millhouseval@btinternet.com*

㉙ Mosspaul, 6 Orchard Road, March 🅑
(Dinah Lilley) *Nr Town Centre. Take 3rd turning on L off Elwyn Rd, straight down, 4th house on R.* Well-established garden developed over 40yrs with a variety of mature shrubs, fine conifers and ornamental trees . Mixed and herbaceous borders framing a circular lawn. Pergola with

ngs
gardens open for charity

£1.84 million donated to national nursing, caring and gardening charities in 2004

roses and clematis; fruit garden with Cordon apples and pears, soft fruit cages. *Adm £2, chd free. Private visits welcome by appt May to Aug. Tel 01354 653396*

30 Netherhall Manor, Soham ♿✂
(Timothy Clark) *Enter Soham from Newmarket, Tanners Lane is 2nd R 100yds after cemetery. Enter Soham from Ely, Tanners Lane is 2nd L after War Memorial.* 1-acre walled garden incl courtyard. April - Crown Imperials, Victorian hyacinths and old primroses. May - florist's ranunculus (picotee and bizarre), and tulips (rose, bizarre, bybloemen). Aug - formal beds of Victorian pelargoniums, calceolarias, fuchsia, lobelias and heliotropes, an organic seasonal kitchen garden. Author of Margery Fish's *Country Gardening*. Featured in 'Cambridgeshire Life' 2004. Home-made TEAS in aid of Fordham Society. *Adm £2, chd free. Suns 27 Mar; 1 May; 7, 14 Aug (2-5)*

31 Nuns Manor, 65 Frog End, Shepreth ♿✂☺
(Mr & Mrs J R L Brashaw) *8m SW of Cambridge. 300yds from A10 Melbourn-Shepreth Xrds.* Delightful 2-acre garden surrounding C16 farmhouse, designed, created and maintained by owners. Plantsman's garden with interesting plants in mixed and herbaceous borders with large pond and kitchen garden. Light alkaline soil favours many self seeding eremurus and alliums, at their best in May and June. Home-made TEAS in aid of Shepreth Church. *Adm £2.50, chd free. Suns 15 May; 19 June (2-5.30). Private visits welcome by appt for groups May & June. Tel 01763 260313*

32 ◆ Peckover House, North Brink
(National Trust) *In Wisbech on banks of R Nene. Park at Chapel Rd car park by rugby club, walk up alongside Wisbech Arms PH, turn R at river, Peckover 50yds on R.* Beautiful 2-acre late Victorian walled garden. Pool gardens, summerhouses and herbaceous borders make this a delightfully tranquil oasis in the middle of this market town. Victorian orangery with 300yr-old orange trees. Croquet played on back lawn. Light refreshments and TEAS in C17 Reedbarn. *House and Garden adm £4.50 , chd £2.25. Sats, Suns Tues, Weds & Bank Hols 19 Mar to 6 Nov (12-5).* **For NGS: Evening Opening** *£3, wine, Tue 21 June (6.30-9.30). Tel 01945 583463 peckover@nationaltrust.org.uk*

33 Ramsey Forty Foot, nr Ramsey
3m N of Ramsey. (B1096). From Ramsey travel through Ramsey Forty Foot, just before bridge over drain, turn R, First Cottage 300yds on R, next door to The Elms. Home-made TEAS at First Cottage & The Willows in aid of Ramsey Abbey Walled Kitchen Garden Restoration. *Combined adm £2, chd free. Sun 10 July (2-6)*

The Elms (Mrs J Shotbolt & Mr R Shotbolt) Large water garden beautifully landscaped with shrubs, water lilies, ferns and large tank koi carp. Mirror carp in lakes; 2 acres full of unusual plants; spring flowers.

First Cottage ♿☺ (Mr & Mrs R Fort) 150ft x 40ft garden with herbaceous borders, shrub beds; ornamental pond and rockery. Minature steam railway.

Riverside (Mr & Mrs J Parker) Riverside garden with tropical theme, incl tree ferns, bananas, gingers, gunneras, bamboo. (next to The Willows).

The Willows ☺ (Jane & Andrew Sills) *Turn L down private rd opp George PH. Park in Hollow Rd.* ½-acre cottage garden with riverside location. Old roses, herbaceous beds; shrubs, ferns; pond; vegetable and herb garden.

34 Sawston Gardens
5m SE of Cambridge. 3m from J10 M11. A505 follow signs to Sawston. A large village with several Grade II listed buildings. Home-made TEAS at & in aid of St Mary's Church. *Combined adm £3, chd 50p. Sun 19 June (2-6)*

30 Churchfield Avenue (Mr & Mrs I Butler) An ex council property with medium-sized garden. Circular lawns surrounded by shrubs, annual and perennial plants. Decking area covered by a grapevined pergola. Small pond with waterfall.

Goslings Farmhouse, 149 High Street ♿✂ (Dr & Mrs Kierstan) Georgian farmhouse (not open). A garden featuring sweeping herbaceous borders, yew hedges and a small vegetable garden.

[NEW] **54 High Street** (Dr & Mrs Maunder) Traditional garden with lawns, flowers, fruit and vegetables.

Tudor House, 1 Catley's Walk (Mr & Mrs Butler) 1½ acres of mature trees and lawns with artificially

constructed stream and large pond. Courtyard garden on-going project.

Vine Cottage ♿ (Dr & Mrs T Wreghitt) C17 house (not open) surrounded by mature garden. Contemporary garden featuring Japanese courtyard adjacent to recent extension.

35 Sutton Gardens, nr Ely
6m W of Ely. On A142 turn L at roundabout to Sutton. Home-made TEAS at 37 Mepal Rd & The Burystead. *Combined adm £3, chd free. Sun 19 June (2-6)*

Bury Lane Cottage, Bury Lane ♿✂☺ (Rod Read & Nicky Berry-Read) Informal family country garden of 1¼ acres with yellow border, pond, pergolas, shade beds and bog garden. A young wood, rose arches and children's Iceni roundhouse.

The Burystead, Bury Lane ♿✂☺ (Sarah Cleverdon & Stephen Tebboth) ½-acre walled courtyard garden of formal design, set against a backdrop of a recently restored C16 thatched barn. Semi mature planting and trained fruit in former farmyard. Newly planted orchard and wildlife pond.

7 Lawn Lane ♿✂☺ (Mrs T Kybird & Mr D Smith) Interesting garden with many features on two levels. Planted with perennials, shrubs, climbers; hanging baskets. Featured in Britains Inspirational Gardens, 'Garden Answers' & 'Cambridge Evening News' 2004.

9 Lawn Lane ✂ (Mrs M W Evans) Garden with clear views across fenland and church, variety of shrubs, pond and seating areas. Low maintenance.

37 Mepal Road ✂☺ (Pat & Tim Smith) Combination of old roses, perennials and shrubs. Pond, bog garden and wild flowers. Fruit trees and vegetable garden. ½-acre.

41 Mepal Road ✂☺ (Jean & Douglas Kiddy) Small cottage garden with interesting variety of perennials and shrubs.

19 The Row ✂☺ (Alistair & Jane Huck) Approx ½-acre family garden, started 11yrs ago. Decking, water feature, some unusual trees, shrubs, perennials, fruit and vegetables. Wildlife area with long grass. Ongoing projects, new pond.

Sutton St Edmund Village Gardens
See Lincolnshire.

㊱ Tetworth Hall, nr Sandy, Beds ⚁⊕
(Lady Crossman) *4m NE of Sandy. ½m N of Gamlingay. 6m SE of St Neots. Off Everton-Waresley Rd.* Large woodland and bog garden on acid soil; rhododendrons; azaleas, unusual shrubs and plants; fine trees. Queen Anne house (not open). TEAS in aid of Waresley Church. *Adm £3, chd free. Sun 8 May (2-5). Private visits welcome by appt 15 Apr to 15 June. Tel 01767 650212*

㊲ Trinity College, Fellows' Garden, Queen's Road, Cambridge ⚁⊗
City centre. Garden of 8 acres, originally laid out in the 1870s by W B Thomas. Lawns with mixed borders, shrubs and specimen trees. Drifts of spring bulbs. Recent extension of landscaped area among new college buildings to W of main garden. *Adm £2, chd free. Sun 3 Apr (2-5). Tel 01223 338400*

㊳ Upton Gardens
8m NW of Huntingdon. From A1(M) from N, & A14 from Cambridge, take B1043 (The Alconburys) & follow signs to Upton. From A1 from S take B1043 (The Alconburys) & follow signs to Upton. Village maps given to all visitors. TEAS at village hall, Plants at village church. *Combined adm £3, chd free. Sun 12 June (1-5)*

 NEW Granary Cottage (Mr David Oakley) Family garden; mixture of lawn, trees and vegetables.

 Meadow Heights ⚁ (Nora & Tony Wood) Well-stocked large garden overlooking paddock and stables. Emphasis on perennial planting, mature conifers and shrubs. Fruit cage.

 Rivendell ⚁⊗ (David & Beryl Stewart) Mixed garden with flower borders, fruit trees, vegetable plot, herb bed and small greenhouse.

 School House ⊗ (Lynn & Bill Gibson) *½-acre country garden* with arbours, retreats and glasshouses. Specialising in tender, scented and climbing plants. Collections of datura, hibiscus, gingers, jasmine, lonicera, oleander, hosta and magnolia grandiflora.

 Stangate House (Lyn & Malcolm Alder) Overlooking village pond and church. Rear garden has views over open farmland, being laid mainly to lawn with borders

of mixed shrubs and flowers with patio areas.

 1 Upton Park (Mr & Mrs Dove) Medium-sized family garden with rockeries, conifers, herbaceous borders and water features.

 NEW The Warren (David & Melanie Holt) English country garden with water features and Mediterranean aspects.

 NEW Woodend (Roger & Dorothy Holt) Small rural garden established over 4yrs into different rooms divided by tunnel arbour and raised bed. Herbaceous plants, shrubs and climbers introduced for colour throughout the yr.

㊴ Weaver's Cottage, 35 Streetly End, West Wickham ⚁⊕ NCCPG
(Miss Sylvia Norton) *8m NW of Haverhill. On A1307 between Linton & Haverhill turn N at Horseheath towards W Wickham. Weaver's Cottage is 9th on R after 40 sign.* ½-acre garden exuberantly planted for fragrance with spring bulbs; shrubs; herbaceous; climbers; old roses. Scree garden. NCCPG National Collection of *Lathyrus*. Silver Gilt Medal Hampton Court 2004. TEAS. *Adm £2, chd 50p. Mon 28 Mar (2-6). Private visits welcome by appt. Tel 01223 892399*

㊵ West Wratting Park, West Wratting ⚁⊗⊕
(Mr & Mrs Henry D'Abo) *8m S of Newmarket. From A11, between Worsted Lodge & Six Mile Bottom, turn E to Balsham; then N along B1052 to West Wratting; Park is at E end of village.* Georgian house (only orangery open), beautifully situated in rolling country, with fine trees. Rose and herbaceous gardens. *Adm £2. Mon 29 Aug (2-5)*

㊶ Whittlesford Gardens
7m S of Cambridge. 1m NE of J10 M11 & A505. Flowers in Parish Church C11. Tractor train rides, maps. Parking nr church. Home-made TEAS at Rayners Farm & Church in aid of Parish Church. *Combined adm £3, chd free. Sun 19 June (2-6)*

 NEW 43 The Lawn ⚁⊗ (Mr & Mrs R Redman) Mediterranean-themed garden with a geometric design, sculptures and water features.

 23 Newton Road ⊕ (Mr F Winter) Cottage garden, herbaceous plants, shrubs, fish pond. Allotment consisting of vegetables, fruit, flowers and bird aviary.

NEW No 1 Wren Park (Mr Ashley Arbon) Restful area with pond and water feature, trees, shrub borders and chickens.

 14 North Road ⊗ (Mr & Mrs R Adderley) Shady secluded garden with rockery and pond.

 5 Parsonage Court ⚁⊗ (Mrs L Button) *Please park on rd.* Trees, shrubs and large pond.

 Rayners Farm ⚁ (Mr & Mrs C Morton) Medieval-style raised herb beds in walled garden of C15 timber-framed farmhouse (not open). Restored barns, large pond and free-range poultry.

 Ryecroft, 1 Middlemoor Road (Mr & Mrs P A Goodman) Paddock; shrubs and compost making.

 11 Scotts Gardens ⚁⊕ (Mr & Mrs M Walker) Shady walled garden with shrub borders; pond and waterfall.

 The Shrubberies (Mr & Mrs D Eastwood) Well-established garden with box hedging; roses and bantams.

 21 West End ⚁ (Mr & Mrs George Jezierski) Cottage garden, herbaceous beds, shrubs, pond and vegetable area.

 Woodlands ⚁ (Mr & Mrs P Smail) Formal garden and woodland with wildlife pond.

㊷ Wilburton Gardens
4m SW of Ely. Wilburton stands on the A1123 & B1049 (The Twenty Pence Rd). TEAS at Long Balland in aid of St Peter's Church, Wilburton. *Combined adm £2.50, chd free. Sun 12 June (2-5.30)*

 Long Balland, Twenty Pence Road ⚁⊗ (Mrs Susan Everitt) *Opp Twentypence Garden Centre. Parking at garden centre.* 1-acre garden with herbaceous borders, shrubs, old-fashioned roses and pergola covered in clematis, honeysuckle and climbing roses. Many varities of fruit trees in orchard.

 3 Millfield Lane ⚁⊗ (Brian & Ruth Everitt) *On A1123 to village take 2nd L Millfield Lane, bungalow 2nd on L. ¾-acre* garden with herbaceous borders, shrubs and roses. 96ft pergola with clematis, roses, honeysuckle and wisteria. Island beds, two small ponds, gazebo and summerhouse with patio. Small coppice of silver birch underplanted with bulbs.

 Redlands, Twenty Pence Road ⚁⊗⊕ (Wendy Francis-Wood & Derek Wood) 2-acre garden designed informally where plants are encouraged to 'do their own thing'. Winding paths lead to different vistas and roses clamber everywhere. Perennials and shrubs follow spring bulbs for continuous scent and colour. *Private visits welcome by appt for coaches & large groups Apr to June. Tel 01353 740073*

43 ◆ Wimpole Hall, Arrington
&⃝⃝NCCPG
(The National Trust) *5m N of Royston. Signed off A603 to Sandy 7m from Cambridge or off A1198.* Part of 350-acre park. Restored Dutch garden and Victorian parterres

on N lawns. Fine trees, marked walks in park. National Collection of walnuts. Walled vegetable garden. Chance to see the recreated Sir John Soane glasshouse financed with the help of the National Gardens Scheme. Light refreshments and TEAS. *Adm £3, chd free.* **For NGS:** *Thur 21 July (10.30-5). Tel 01223 206000 www.wimpole.org*

44 Wytchwood, 7 Owl End, Great Stukeley ⃝⃝
(Mr David Cox) 2m N of Huntingdon. On B1043. Parking at village hall, Owl End. 2-acre garden. Brightly planted borders of

perennials, annuals and shrubs, lawns and ponds. Dry garden planted 2001. 1 acre of wild plants, grasses set among rowan, maple and birch trees leading to spinney. Planted with native trees, ferns, hostas and foxgloves. Plenty of seats and shade. Haven for wildlife. Home-made TEAS. *Adm £2, chd 50p. Sun 26 June (1.30-5.30). Private visits welcome by appt. Tel 01480 454835*

Evening Opening (See also garden description)

Peckover House   21 June

Carmarthenshire & Pembrokeshire
See separate Welsh section on page 439

Ceredigion/Cardiganshire
See separate Welsh section on page 444

Cheshire & Wirral

County Organiser:	Nicholas Payne, The Mount, Whirley, Macclesfield SK11 9PB Tel 01625 422920
Assistant County Organisers:	Juliet Hill, Salterswell House, Tarporley CW6 0ED Tel 01829 732804
	John Hinde, Maylands, Latchford Road, Gayton, Wirral CH60 3RN Tel 0151 342 8557
	Romy Holmes, Bowmere Cottage, Bowmere Road, Tarporley CW6 0BS Tel 01829 732053
Press & Publicity Officer:	Peter Johnson, Church Cottage, Birtles Lane, Over Alderley, Macclesfield SK10 4RX Tel 01625 860206
	Ros Mahon, Rectory Cottage, Eaton, Congleton CW12 2ND Tel 01260 274777
	Pat McMillan, Ridgehill, Sutton, Macclesfield SK11 0LU Tel 01260 252353
	Sally Sutcliffe, Little Somerley, Woodland Court, Utkinton, Tarporley CW6 0LJ Tel 01829 730149
	Alex Willcocks, Crowley Lodge, Arley, Northwich CW9 6NR Tel 01565 777381

Maps: Numbers shown next to each garden entry refer to that garden's entry on the county map. This position is approximate; distance and directions from the nearest main town are generally shown in the garden text.
A precise location is available for those gardens featured on the NGS website by visiting www.ngs.org.uk.

Symbols: Information relating to symbols is given on page 21

DATES OF OPENING

Evening openings
See end of county listing

Gardens open to the public
For details see garden description
Adlington Hall, Macclesfield *(1)*
Arley Hall & Gardens, Northwich *(2)*
Cholmondeley Castle Garden, Malpas *(11)*
Dunham Massey, Altrincham *(16)*
Hare Hill Gardens, Over Alderley *(24)*
Lyme Park, Disley *(33)*
Norton Priory Museum & Gardens, Runcorn *(42)*
Peover Hall Gardens, Knutsford *(48)*
The Quinta Arboretum, Swettenham *(51)*
Rode Hall, Scholar Green *(53)*
Tatton Park, Knutsford *(61)*

By appointment only
For telephone number and other details see garden description. Private visits welcomed
Laneside Cottage, Pott Shrigley *(30)*
Lynwood, Burton *(34)*
Rosewood, Puddington *(55)*

February 20 Sunday
Tulip Tree Cottage, Coppenhall, Crewe *(63)*

April 3 Sunday
Parm Place, Great Budworth *(47)*

April 10 Sunday
Poulton Hall, Poulton Lancelyn, Bebington *(50)*
The Quinta Arboretum, Swettenham *(51)*
The Well House, Tilston *(67)*

April 17 Sunday
Briarfield, Burton, S Wirral *(7)*
Lyme Park, Disley *(33)*

April 20 Wednesday
Tirley Garth, Utkinton *(62)*

April 24 Sunday
Dunham Massey, Altrincham *(16)*
Greenhills Farm, Lower Whitley *(22)*
Orchard House, Alsager *(46)*
Tirley Garth, Utkinton *(62)*

May 1 Sunday
Greyfriars, Wistaston, Crewe *(23)*
35 Heyes Lane, Timperley, Altrincham *(27)*
Long Acre, Bunbury *(31)*
Mount Pleasant, Kelsall *(41)*
St Davids House, Noctorum *(56)*
Tushingham Hall, Whitchurch *(64)*

May 2 Monday (Bank Hol)
Gayton Gardens, Gayton *(20)*
Greyfriars, Wistaston, Crewe *(23)*
Mount Pleasant, Kelsall *(41)*

May 4 Wednesday
Tatton Park, Knutsford *(61)*

May 8 Sunday
Hare Hill Gardens, Over Alderley *(24)*
Haughton Hall, Bunbury *(25)*
The Manor House & Honeysuckle Cottage, Chelford *(36)*

May 14 Saturday
Bank House, Bickerton *(4)*
Peover Hall Gardens, Knutsford *(48)*

May 15 Sunday
Bank House, Bickerton *(4)*
Bolesworth Castle, Tattenhall *(5)*
Peover Hall Gardens, Knutsford *(48)*
Willaston Village Gardens, Willaston *(69)*

May 18 Wednesday
50 Mostyn Road, Hazel Grove *(39)*
Reaseheath College, Nantwich *(52)*

Your garden in the Yellow Book?

ngs

gardens open
for charity

The NGS is always interested to hear of gardens with potential, large or small, that might open in the future.

For more information about opening your garden, please contact the County Organiser in your area, preferably at the time of year that you would like your garden to open.

CHESHIRE & WIRRAL

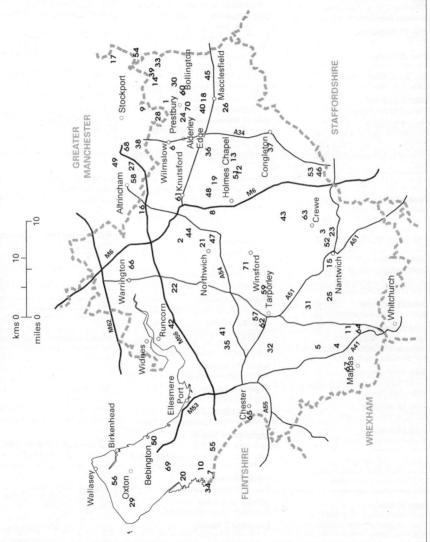

kms 0   10   10

miles 0   10

May 21 Saturday
9 Bourne Street, Wilmslow *(6)*
Tulip Tree Cottage, Coppenhall, Crewe *(63)*

May 22 Sunday
9 Bourne Street, Wilmslow *(6)*
Dorfold Hall, Nantwich *(15)*
Henbury Hall, nr Macclesfield *(26)*
Manley Knoll, Manley *(35)*
Tulip Tree Cottage, Coppenhall, Crewe *(63)*
Withinlee Road Gardens, Prestbury *(70)*

May 25 Wednesday
Reaseheath College, Nantwich *(52)*

May 29 Sunday
Far Hills, Henbury *(18)*
The Mount, Whirley, Henbury, nr
   Macclesfield *(40)*

June 1 Wednesday
Orchard House, Alsager *(46)*

June 4 Saturday
Bank House, Bickerton *(4)*
Moor House, Brereton Heath *(37)*
Norton Priory Museum & Gardens, Runcorn *(42)*
The Old Parsonage, Arley Green, via Arley
   Hall & Gardens *(44)*

June 5 Sunday
Bank House, Bickerton *(4)*
12 Burnham Close, Cheadle Hulme *(9)*
Free Green Farm, Lower Peover *(19)*
Moor House, Brereton Heath *(37)*
The Old Parsonage, Arley Green, via Arley
   Hall & Gardens *(44)*
Orchard House, Alsager *(46)*
Sandymere, Cotebrook *(57)*
West Drive Gardens, Gatley *(68)*

June 11 Sunday
Bucklow Farm, Plumley *(8)*

June 12 Sunday
Adlington Hall, Macclesfield *(1)*
Badgerswood Gardens, Wistaston *(3)*
199 Stockport Road, Timperley *(58)*

June 15 Wednesday
50 Mostyn Road, Hazel Grove *(39)*
Tatton Park, Knutsford *(61)*

June 18 Saturday
17 Poplar Grove, Sale *(49)*

June 19 Sunday
Gayton Gardens, Gayton *(20)*
Great Budworth Gardens *(21)*
Long Acre, Bunbury *(31)*
Lower Huxley Hall, nr Hargrave *(32)*
The Old Hough, Warmingham *(43)*
17 Poplar Grove, Sale *(49)*

June 26 Sunday
Burton Village Gardens, S Wirral *(10)*
Deans Rough Farm, Lower Withington *(13)*
Swingate Cottage, Whiteley Green *(60)*

July 2 Saturday
One House Nursery, Rainow *(45)*

July 3 Sunday
One House Nursery, Rainow *(45)*

July 6 Wednesday
Cholmondeley Castle Garden, Malpas *(11)*

July 9 Saturday
The Covey, Goostrey *(12)*

July 10 Sunday
The Covey, Goostrey *(12)*
Edith Terrace Gardens, Compstall, nr
   Marple *(17)*
73 Hill Top Avenue, Cheadle Hulme *(28)*
The Manor House & Honeysuckle Cottage,
   Chelford *(36)*
Poulton Hall, Poulton Lancelyn, Bebington
   (50)
Warrington Gardens *(66)*

July 13 Wednesday
Wood End Cottage, Whitegate *(71)*

July 14 Thursday
Wood End Cottage, Whitegate **(Evening)**
   (71)

July 17 Sunday
Hunstanton Close Gardens, Upton,
   Birkenhead *(29)*
Sunnyside Farm, Little Budworth *(59)*
Two Upton Park Gardens, Upton by Chester
   (65)

July 30 Saturday
19 Dorchester Road, Hazel Grove *(14)*

July 31 Sunday
19 Dorchester Road, Hazel Grove *(14)*
31 Moss Lane, Styal *(38)*

August 6 Saturday
Arley Hall & Gardens, Northwich *(2)*

August 7 Sunday
Dunham Massey, Altrincham *(16)*
73 Hill Top Avenue, Cheadle Hulme *(28)*
199 Stockport Road, Timperley *(58)*

August 13 Saturday
Rose Hill Gardens, Marple *(54)*

August 14 Sunday
Rose Hill Gardens, Marple *(54)*

August 21 Sunday
Sunnyside Farm, Little Budworth *(59)*

September 4 Sunday
Lyme Park, Disley *(33)*
The Manor House & Honeysuckle Cottage,
   Chelford *(36)*

October 9 Sunday
Dunham Massey, Altrincham *(16)*

October 16 Sunday
Bolesworth Castle, Tattenhall *(5)*

November 6 Sunday
The Quinta Arboretum, Swettenham *(51)*

DESCRIPTIONS OF GARDENS

❶ ◆ Adlington Hall, Macclesfield
⊗⊞
(Mrs Camilla Legh) *4m N of
Macclesfield. Well signed off A523 at
Adlington.* 6 acres of formal gardens
with herbaceous borders, rose
garden; rockeries; yew maze; water
garden created in 2002. Lawns with
open views across ha-ha. 32-acre
wilderness with mature plantings,
various follies incl a 'Temple to
Diana'; woodland walk. Yew and
ancient lime walks. Birch grove and
flower meadow; penstemon parterre.
Limited wheelchair access. Light
refreshments and TEAS. *House &
garden £5, chd £1.50, Weds June to
Aug (2-5).* **For NGS:** *Sun 12 June
(1.30-5), garden £3.50, chd 50p.
House £2.50, chd £1. Tel 01625
829206 enquiries@adlingtonhall.com*

**Arbour Cottage, Napley,
Muckleston** ⓰⊗⊞
See Staffordshire & part of West
Midlands.

**❷ ◆ Arley Hall & Gardens,
Northwich** ⓰⊞
(The Viscount Ashbrook) *5m N of
Northwich. Well signed from M6 J19
& 20, & M56 J9 & 10.* 8-acre main
garden, incl the environs and the
Grove approx 20 acres. Twin
herbaceous borders, avenue of
evergreen oak, walled gardens,
azaleas, shrub roses, rhododendrons;
vinery; woodland garden. Specialist
nursery adjacent. Light refreshments
and TEAS. *House & garden adm
£7.20. Garden only £4.70, chd £2,
concessions £4.20. Tues to Suns &
Bank Hols 27 Mar to 2 Oct (11-5).
Hall open Tues & Suns only.* **For NGS:**
*Sat 6 Aug (11-5). Tel 01565 777353
enquiries@arleyhallandgardens.com*

**❸ Badgerswood Gardens, 100
Church Lane, Wistaston** ⓰⊗⊞
(Karen White & Mary Sadler) *2m
SW of Crewe. Midway between
Crewe & Nantwich off A534, take
Church Lane approx ½m to No. 100.
Car park 3 mins walk from garden.* 2
individual gardens set in approx ⅔
acre. Diverse planting with mature
trees incl a wide range of shade and
sun-loving plants. Several colourful
herbaceous borders and interesting
island beds featuring varied shrubs
and perennials. Also a productive
kitchen garden, fruit trees, wildlife
pond and restful seating areas.
Home-made TEAS. *Adm £3, chd free
(share to St Luke's Hospice). Sun 12
June (12-5)*

---

❹ Bank House, Goldford Lane, Bickerton 🅖🅗
(Dr & Mrs M A Voisey) *4m NE of Malpas. 11m S of Chester on A41 turn L at Broxton roundabout to Nantwich on A534. Take 5th R (1¾m) to Bickerton. Take 2nd R into Goldford Lane. Bank House is nearly 1m on L.* 1¾-acre garden situated at the foot of Bickerton Hill, in an area of outstanding beauty, with extensive views to Derbyshire and the Marches. Sheltered, terraced borders stocked with a wide range of shrubs, trees and herbaceous plants; established wild garden, Millennium garden with water features and productive vegetable garden. Field parking. Home-made TEAS in aid of Age Concern, Malpas & Bickerton Church. *Adm £2.50, chd 50p. Sats, Suns 14, 15 May; 4, 5 June (2-6)*

◆ Biddulph Grange Garden, Biddulph 🅗🅖
See Staffordshire & part of West Midlands.

❺ Bolesworth Castle, Tattenhall 🅖🅗
(Mr & Mrs A G Barbour) *8m S of Chester. Enter by lodge on A41.* Landscape with rhododendrons, shrubs and borders. Woodland walk replanted 1993-2004. Home-made TEAS. *Adm £3.50, chd free (share to Burwardsley Church). Suns 15 May; 16 Oct (2-5)*

❻ 9 Bourne Street, Wilmslow 🅗
(Lucille Sumner & Melanie & Keith Harris) *¼m W of central Wilmslow. Take A538 from Wilmslow towards Manchester Airport. Bourne St 2nd st on L after fire station. Or from M56 (J6), take A538 to Wilmslow. Bourne St on R.* ¼-acre organic garden, evolved over three generations of one family. Mature trees incl *ginkgo biloba*, azaleas, rhododendrons and exotic foliage. Fish pond; greenhouse; water features and hens. A peaceful and secret garden with a surprise around every corner. TEAS. *Adm £2.50, chd free. Sat 21, Sun 22 May (11-5)*

❼ Briarfield, The Rake, Burton, S Wirral 🅗🅖
(Liz Carter) *9m NW of Chester. Turn off A540 at Willaston-Burton Xrds T-lights & follow rd for 1m to Burton village centre.* Designed for yr-round interest, the S-facing slope provides a sheltered environment for many specialist plants. The main garden, with maturing trees and shrubs interspersed with seasonal bulbs, alpines and herbaceous plants, includes a modern blue garden. Both

this, and the more intimate home garden, have a variety of interesting water features, some deep. TEAS in aid of Claire House Children's Hospice. *Adm £3, chd free. Sun 17 Apr (2-5). Also opening with* **Burton Village Gardens** *Sun 26 June. Private visits welcome by appt. Tel 0151 336 2304 carter.burton@virgin.net*

❽ NEW Bucklow Farm, Pinfold Lane, Plumley 🅗
(Dawn & Peter Freeman) *2m S of Knutsford. M6 J19, head to Chester A556. L at 2nd set of T-lights by Smoker PH. In 1¼m L at concealed Xrds, 1st R. From Knutsford A5033, L at Sudlow Lane. Follow rd, becomes Pinfold Lane.* Country garden with shrubs, perennial borders, rambling roses, herb garden, vegetable patch, wildlife pond/water feature and alpines. Landscaped and planted over the last 18yrs with recorded changes. Free range hens. Home-made TEAS. *Adm £3, chd 50p (share to Knutsford Methodist Church). Sat 11 June (2-6)*

❾ 12 Burnham Close, Cheadle Hulme 🅗 NCCPG
(Mr & Mrs Tim Saville) *4m S of Stockport. Leave A34 at Cheadle on B5358 towards Heald Green. Turn L at 1st T-lights to Cheadle Hulme & L at Ryecroft Arms PH down Conway Rd. Park opp school on Henley Ave. Burnham Close is 3rd R off Henley Ave.* Plantsperson's suburban garden of two halves. Colour combinations on one side from 90 David Austin and old roses, violas and clematis etc; on the other from the variegated foliage of perennials and shrubs. The borders, gravel scree and patios feature over 400 hostas, incl many new American introductions. National Collection of brunnera on display. Featured in 'Garden Answers' 2004. Home-made TEAS. *Adm £2.50, chd 50p. Sun 5 June (2-5.30)*

❿ Burton Village Gardens, S Wirral
9m NW of Chester. Turn off A540 at Willaston-Burton Xrds T-lights & follow rd for 1m to Burton. All gardens in centre of village, maps given to all visitors. TEAS at Village Hall in aid of Claire House Children's Hospice. *Combined adm £4, chd free. Sun 26 June (2-6)*

Bank Cottage, Burton 🅗 (J R & Bunny Beecroft) A cottage garden tucked in between high hedges of privet and thorn. It is made up of several little rooms thickly planted with flowers, herbs and

roses, wonderful colours and scents. Topiary is a speciality.
Briarfield, The Rake, Burton 🅗🅖 (Liz Carter) (See separate entry).
Burton Manor, Burton 🅗🅖 (College Principal, Keith Chandler) Three geometric gardens on E, S and N sides of house, essentially as designed by Thomas Mawson in 1906, with mature trees; sunken parterre; yew hedges; formal flower beds and deep lily ponds.

⓫ ◆ Cholmondeley Castle Garden, Malpas 🅖🅗
(The Marchioness of Cholmondeley) *4m NE of Malpas. Off A41 Chester-Whitchurch rd & A49 Whitchurch-Tarporley rd.* Romantically landscaped gardens. Azaleas, rhododendrons, flowering shrubs, rare trees, herbaceous borders and water gardens. Lakeside picnic area; rare breeds of farm animals, incl llamas. Private chapel in the park. Weekend 'Telegraph' feature 2003. Light refreshments and TEAS. *Garden adm £3.50, chd £1.50. Weds, Thurs, Suns & Bank Hols Apr to Sept .* **For NGS:** *Wed 6 July (11.30-5). Tel 01829 720383*

⓬ The Covey, Mill Lane, Goostrey 🅗
(Zena & Andrew Lloyd) *8m S of Knutsford. A50 towards Holmes Chapel. Turn L into New Platt Lane. 2m to village centre, turn L into Mill Lane. The Covey is approx 50yds from the main rd on the LH-side. Please park carefully on Mill Lane.* Small garden redesigned and planted in 2002, incorporating a SW-facing patio area linked to 2 formal fish ponds, with interesting pathways leading to a shady area and Japanese-style garden. Home-made TEAS. *Adm £2.50, chd free. Sat, Sun 9, 10 July (2-5)*

⓭ Deans Rough Farm, Lower Withington 🅖🅗🅖
(Mr & Mrs Brian Chesworth) *3m S of Chelford. 5m N of Holmes Chapel. A535 nr Jodrell Bank turn into Catchpenny Lane. 1½m turn R into no through rd (opp bungalow), 400yds turn L into Deans Rough Farm.* Area of 1½ acres; informal cottage garden around house. Herbaceous and mixed borders and old roses. Potager; large natural pond with wild flowers. Woodland area with bog garden. Home-made TEAS in aid of Boys & Girls Welfare Society. *Adm £3, chd free. Sun 26 June (2-6)*

⑭ NEW 19 Dorchester Road, Hazel Grove &⌖&
(John & Sandra Shatwell) *4m S of Stockport. On A5143 at junction of Dorchester Rd and Jacksons Lane. From Stockport take A6 S for approx 1m, R on A5102 for 2m, L at roundabout on A5143, past swimming pool and shops to Dorchester Rd. Garden on L after mini-roundabout. Parking at shops or school (further up Jacksons Lane).* Suburban garden redesigned and planted in 2003. 150sq yd front garden with David Austin and hybrid tea roses around a central gazebo. 400sq yd back garden with pond and waterfall, pergola, lawn. Colour-themed borders with perennials, annuals and small trees set against a background of beech trees. TEAS. *Adm £2.50, chd free. Sat, Sun 30, 31 July (1-5)*

⑮ Dorfold Hall, Nantwich ⌖⌖
(Mr & Mrs Richard Roundell) *1m W of Nantwich. On A534 between Nantwich & Acton.* 18-acre garden surrounding C17 house (not open) with formal approach; lawns and herbaceous borders; spectacular spring woodland garden with rhododendrons, azaleas, magnolias and bulbs. TEAS in aid of Acton Parish Church. *Adm £4, chd £2. Sun 22 May (2-5.30)*

⑯ ♦ Dunham Massey, Altrincham &⌖⌖
(The National Trust) *3m SW of Altrincham. Off A56. Well signed.* Great plantsman's garden. Magnificent trees reflected in moat; richly planted borders vibrant with colour and subtle textures. The Orangery, Mount and Bark House give a sense of the garden's long history. Sweeping lawns, lush borders, shady woodland, a formal parterre set the stage while collections of shade-, moisture- and acid-loving plants such as blue poppies, Chinese lilies and hydrangeas contribute to an ever-changing scene. Light refreshments and TEAS. *House & garden adm £6.50. Garden only £4.50, chd £2.25. Daily 19 Mar to 30 Oct. For NGS: Suns 18 Apr; 7 Aug; 9 Oct (11-5.30). Tel 0161 941 1025 dunhammassey@nationaltrust.org.uk*

⑰ Edith Terrace Gardens, Compstall, nr Marple ⌖
(The Edith Terrace Group) *6m E of Stockport. Take Bredbury junction off M60. Follow Romiley-Marple Bridge sign on B6104. Turn into Compstall at Etherow Country Park sign. Take 1st R, situated at end of Montagu St. Parking in village public* car parks - short walk to Edith Terrace. Series of gardens in mixed style from cottage to formal, situated to front and rear of Victorian terrace; described by BBC 'Gardeners' World' magazine as 'a colourful and beautiful living space'. Mixed herbaceous perennials, ornamental backyards and back alleyway. In lakeside setting in the conserved mill village of Compstall, adjacent to Etherow Country Park. BBC 'Gardeners' World' TV and magazine features, competition winner Japanese TV 2004. Home-made TEAS. *Adm £3, chd free. Sun 10 July (1-5)*

⑱ Far Hills, Andertons Lane, Henbury ⌖⌖
(Mr & Mrs Ian Warburton) *2m W of Macclesfield. Along A537 opp Blacksmiths Arms. At Henbury go up Pepper St. Turn L into Church Lane then Andertons Lane in 100yds.* Mixed ½-acre garden; planted for yr-round interest with regard to wildlife. Trees; shrubs; herbaceous perennials; small pond; fruit and vegetable area; native copse. Home-made TEAS at The Mount in aid of East Cheshire Hospice. *Combined adm with* **The Mount** *£4, chd free. Sun 29 May (2-5.30). Private visits welcome by appt. Tel 01625 431800*

Field House Farm, Pipe Gate &
See Staffordshire & part of West Midlands.

⑲ Free Green Farm, Free Green Lane, Lower Peover &⌖⌖
(Sir Philip & Lady Haworth) *3m S of Knutsford. Free Green Lane connects A50 with B5081. From Holmes Chapel on A50 turn L after Drovers Arms. From Knutsford on B5081 turn L into Broom Lane, then L into Free Green Lane.* 2-acre garden with pleached limes, herbaceous borders, ponds, parterre; collection of hebes, garden of the senses and British woodland. Home-made TEAS in aid of Just Drop-in Youth Info & Advice, Macclesfield. *Adm £3.50, chd free. Sun 5 June (2-6)*

⑳ Gayton Gardens, Gayton &
7m S of Birkenhead, SE of Heswall. From the Devon Doorway/Glegg Arms roundabout at Heswall, travel SE in the Chester direction for about ¼m. Turn R into Gayton Lane. For Maylands, take 3rd L into Latchford Road. Garden is on L with parking on rd. For 29 Dee Park Rd, continue on Gayton Lane, take 5th turn to L, garden on L. For 69 Well Lane, continue on Gayton Lane until junction with Well Lane and turn L. Garden on L in approx 100yds. All gardens are about ¼m apart, but take care walking down Gayton Lane as no pavement exists. Maps available at each garden. TEAS at 69 Well Lane in aid of St John's Hospice, Clatterbridge. *Combined adm £3.50, chd free. Mon 2 May; Sun 19 June (2-5.30)*

NEW 29 Dee Park Road &⌖ (E Lewis) Mature trees, climbing roses, clematis, mixed shrub and herbaceous borders and island beds provide yr-round interest. A hidden garden and lovely patio with beautiful colourful shrubs. Gravel areas with thymes and many alpines. Limited wheelchair access. *Not open 2 May*

Maylands, Latchford Road &⌖⌖
(John & Ann Hinde) Approx ½ acre, contains developing plantings in established setting. Mature trees provide backdrop for range of growing conditions and long season. Incl rhododendrons, wisteria, magnolias and other spring-flowering shrubs; shaded areas; wildlife pond; large rockery; herbaceous borders; small vegetable and fruit area. *Private visits welcome by appt. Tel 0151 342 1636 john.hinde@maylands.com*

69 Well Lane &⌖⌖ (Angus & Sally Clark) This undulating and established ¾-acre garden, surrounded by a woodland backdrop, has sandy acid soil and contains interesting shrubs, many spring flowering (rhododendrons, azaleas, magnolias etc). Herbaceous, soft fruit and vegetable areas. Small wild flower meadow with old restored farm outbuildings. Limited wheelchair access. *Private visits welcome by appt. Tel 0151 342 3321 aandsclark@aol.com*

㉑ Great Budworth Gardens
3m N of Northwich. Great Budworth is on E side of A559 between Northwich & Warrington, 4m from J10 M56, also 4m from J19 M6. Parm Place is W of village High St whilst Westage Farm is 400yds E of village. Parking available for both gardens. Home-made TEAS at both gardens (in aid of St Rocco's Hospice, Warrington at Westage Farm only). *Combined adm £4, £2.50 one garden, chd free (share to Great Ormond Street Hospital at Parm Place only). Sun 19 June (1-5)*

Parm Place, High Street &⌖⌖
(Peter & Jane Fairclough) (See separate entry).

Westage Farm ♿🐕🏡 (Jean & Peter Davies) Family garden incl herbaceous and mixed borders, vegetable plot, 2 greenhouses, orchard planted in 1994 and flower arranger's cutting garden. Small vineyard (1996) from which wine has been produced. Decking and pebble garden, children's play area, patio with chimneys. Woodland garden and wild garden to complement duck pond. Paddock with friendly sheep, donkey, goat and free range hens. *Private visits welcome by appt. Tel 01606 892383 pj@budworth94.fsnet.co.uk*

㉒ Greenhills Farm, Greenhill Lane, Lower Whitley ♿🐕🏡 (Mr & Mrs Peter Johnson) *7m S of Warrington. From J10 M56 take A49 S. In 1m turn R signed Grimsditch Lane, 1st L, Greenhill Lane take L fork to end. From S go up A49 towards Warrington, turn L 1m before M56 signed Grimsditch Lane.* Approx 1½ acres of yr-round interest. A colourful spring garden with shrubs, herbaceous borders, bulbs, specimen trees and a small lake have made a beautifully landscaped garden. Featured in 'Cheshire Life' 2003. Home-made TEAS in aid of St Luke's Church, Whitley. *Adm £3, chd free. Sun 24 Apr (2-5)*

㉓ Greyfriars, 11 Sandylands Park, Wistaston, Crewe 🐕🏡 (Mick & Helen Pierce) *2m SW of Crewe. Midway between Nantwich & Crewe, on A534 towards Crewe, take Church Lane opp Huntsbank Business Centre then 1st L into Sandylands Park.* Small plant lover's garden which is packed full of interest, with ponds and streams, grasses, herbaceous borders, small trees and shrubs, camellias, rhododendrons, azaleas, lovely spring bulbs, ferns and a peat border. Greenhouse featuring American woodlanders, insectivorous plants and a small bonsai collection. A true plantaholic's garden. Featured in 'Sunday Sentinel' 2004. Home-made TEAS. *Adm £2, chd free (share to Brighton & Hove and West Sussex branches of Deaf Children's Society). Sun, Mon 1, 2 May (1.30-5). Private visits welcome by appt, parties welcome, coaches permitted. Tel 01270 567820 mick@pierce2504.fsnet.co.uk*

㉔ ◆ Hare Hill Gardens, Over Alderley ♿🐕 (The National Trust) *2m E of Alderley Edge. Between Alderley*

Edge & Prestbury. Turn off N at B5087 at Greyhound Rd. Attractive spring garden featuring a fine display of rhododendrons and azaleas; good collection of hollies and other specimen trees and shrubs. 10-acre garden incl a walled garden which hosts many wall shrubs incl clematis and vines; borders are planted with agapanthus and geraniums. Partially suitable for wheelchairs. *Adm £2.70, chd £1.25.* **For NGS:** *Sun 8 May (10-5). Tel 01625 828836 mike.scott@nationaltrust.org.uk*

㉕ Haughton Hall, Bunbury 🏡 (Mr & Mrs R J Posnett) *5m NW of Nantwich. Off A534 Nantwich to Wrexham rd, 6m SE of Tarporley via A49.* Medium-sized garden; species rhododendrons, azaleas, shrubs, rock garden; lake with temple; waterfall. Collection of ornamental trees. Home-made TEAS. *Adm £3, chd £1. Sun 8 May (2-6)*

㉖ Henbury Hall, nr Macclesfield ♿🐕🏡 (Sebastian de Ferranti Esq) *2m W of Macclesfield. On A537. Turn down School Lane Henbury at Blacksmiths Arms. East Lodge on R.* Large garden with lake, beautifully landscaped and full of variety. Azaleas, rhododendrons, flowering shrubs; rare trees; herbaceous borders. TEAS in aid of East Cheshire Hospice. *Adm £5, chd £1. Sun 22 May (2-5)*

㉗ 35 Heyes Lane, Timperley, Altrincham 🐕🏡 (Mr & Mrs David Eastwood) *1½m NE of Altrincham. Heyes Lane, a turning off Park Rd (B5165) 1m from junction with A56 Altrincham-Manchester rd. Or from A560 turn W in Timperley Village for ¼m. Newsagents shop on corner.* Small suburban garden 30ft x 90ft on sandy soil, maintained by a keen plantswoman member of the Organic Movement (HDRA). Several changes to this yr-round garden; trees; small pond; greenhouses; 16 kinds of fruit with a good collection of interesting and unusual plants. Featured in RHS 'The Garden' 2004; on itinerary for Trafford in Bloom. *Adm £2.50 incl TEA, chd free. Sun 1 May (2-5)*

㉘ 73 Hill Top Avenue, Cheadle Hulme 🐕🏡 (Mr & Mrs Martin Land) *4m S of Stockport. Turn off A34 (new by-pass) at roundabout signed Cheadle Hulme (B5094). Take 2nd turn L into Gillbent Rd, signed Cheadle Hulme Sports Centre. Go to end, small roundabout, turn R into Church Rd. 2nd rd on L is Hill Top*

Ave. From Stockport or Bramhall turn R or L into Church Rd by The Church Inn. Hill Top Ave is 1st rd on R. ⅓-acre plantswoman's garden. Plantings of herbaceous, shrub and climbing roses, clematis, pond, damp area, shrubs and small trees. Home-made TEAS. *Adm £2.50, chd free. Suns 10 July; 7 Aug (2-6). Private visits welcome by appt, for groups of 4+. Tel 0161 486 0055*

㉙ Hunstanton Close Gardens, Upton, Birkenhead *2m W of Birkenhead. Leave M53 at J2, then J2A signed Upton. Turn L at pillar box, Doncaster Drive. T-junction turn L then 2nd R into Norwich Drive 200yds on R. Park by small woods, walk through woods to Hunstanton Close (50yds) R.* Cream TEAS at 7 Hunstanton Close. *Combined adm £3, chd over 10 50p (share to Royal School for the Blind, Liverpool). Sun 17 July (1-5.30)*

Annag, 7 Hunstanton Close 🐕🏡 (John & Maureen Beard) Superb design and structure, exciting, fascinating, peaceful, quirky, impressionable, mind-blowing, imaginative, fantastic, surprising, cheeky and full of fun, a beautiful jungle, so much to see, inspiring to all who visit - comments from visitors in 2004. Intense planting and garden features, English, Oriental, Mediterranean Terrace and Fun Garden blend into one. With cream teas to die for, make this plantswoman's garden the one to visit in 2005. 'Garden News' winner 2004. *Private visits welcome by appt. Tel 0151 604 1375 whiskers@annag.fsnet.co.uk*

9 Hunstanton Close 🐕🏡 (Brian & Jennifer Sorrie) Well-stocked medium sized garden. Large fish pond incorporating rockery, waterfall and fountain, amply planted with lilies etc. Slatted pathways with summerhouse, pergola, arbour, greenhouse and raised beds via stepping stones. Decked area with seating to relax.

㉚ Laneside Cottage, Long Lane, Pott Shrigley 🐕🏡 (Dr & Mrs David Parker) *4m N of Macclesfield. Turn E off A523, Macclesfield - Stockport rd, at Adlington T-lights, signed to Pott Shrigley, for approx 2m. Turn R onto Long Lane. Laneside Cottage 2nd house on R, approx ½m.* 2-acre exuberant garden overlooking Cheshire Plain. Formal shrub garden, woodland path with deciduous hollies, calycanthus and ptelia. Fern walk with bulbs and hellebores. Experimental prairie planting. Natural lake and birch wood. Potager of vegetables and fruit. New cutting garden. Always colourful. A warm welcome. Featured in 'Cheshire Life' 2003. *Adm £3, chd £1.50. Private visits welcome by appt. Tel 01625 560234*

㉛ Long Acre, Wyche Lane, Bunbury 🌳😊
(Mr & Mrs M Bourne) *3½m SE of Tarporley. On A49. Turn 2nd L after Wild Boar Hotel to Bunbury. L at 1st rd junction then 1st R by Nags Head PH 400yds on L. From A51 turn to Bunbury until Nags Head. Turn into Wyche Lane before PH car park. 400yds to garden.* Plantswoman's garden of approx 1 acre with unusual plants. Roses, pool gardens, small vineyard with fruit and vegetables. Exotic conservatory; herbaceous; specialise in proteas, S African bulbs, begonia, clivia and streptocarpus. Spring garden with camellias, magnolias, bulbs. Paddock with ponies, poultry, goat. Featured in RHS 'The Garden', 'Visit Britain', 'Signature', 'Travel Journal' 2004. Home-made TEAS. *Adm £3, chd free (share to St Boniface Church, Horses & Ponies Protection Association). Suns 1 May; 19 June (2-5). Private visits welcome by appt for groups of 10+ only. Tel 01829 260944*

㉜ Lower Huxley Hall, nr Hargrave 🚻🌳
(Neville & Juliet Whitbread) *6½m W of Chester. Between Huxley and Hargrave which is approx 10 mins from Tarporley, Tarvin and Waverton.* 5½-acre garden with pergolas, arches, roses and herbaceous borders in a picturesque and romantic setting. Home-made TEAS in aid of Tarporley Cottage Hospital. *Adm £3, chd £1. Sun 19 June (2.30-5.30)*

㉝ ◆ Lyme Park, Disley 🚻🌳
(The National Trust) *6m SE of Stockport. Just W of Disley on A6.* 17-acre garden retaining many original features from Tudor and Jacobean times. High Victorian style bedding, Dutch garden, Gertrude Jekyll style herbaceous border, Edwardian rose garden, Wyatt orangery and many other features. Also rare trees, lake, ravine garden, lawns, mixed borders and rare Wyatt garden. Light refreshments and TEAS. *House & garden adm £6.20, chd £3.10, family £15. Garden only £3, chd £1.50. Park £4 per car.* **For NGS:** *Suns 17 Apr; 4 Sept (11-5). Tel 01663 762023*

㉞ Lynwood, Burton 😊
(Philip & Pauline Wright) *9m NW of Chester. Turn off A540 at Willaston-Burton Xrds (T-lights) & follow rd for 1m to Burton & on towards Neston. Lynwood immed past 30mph limit sign.* Plantswoman Pauline Wright has spent 35yrs designing this spectacular ½-acre garden overlooking the Dee estuary. From the sunken sandstone pond to the woodland area separated by clematis-clad trellis, this garden of differing herbaceous borders will delight with its colour and variety of planting. Uneven sufaces. Home-made TEAS. *Adm £2, chd free. Private visits welcome by appt. Tel 0151 336 2311*

㉟ Manley Knoll, Manley 🚻
(Mr & Mrs R Fildes) *3m N of Tarvin. On B5393, via Ashton & Mouldsworth. 3m S of Frodsham, via Alvanley.* Terraced garden with rhododendrons, azaleas etc. Quarry garden. TEAS in aid of Manley Church. *Adm £3.50, chd free. Sun 22 May (2-5)*

㊱ The Manor House & Honeysuckle Cottage, Chelford 🚻🌳😊
(Lynne Murphy, The Manor House; Mike Jehan & David Kent, Honeysuckle Cottage) *6m W of Macclesfield. 5m E of Knutsford, on A537 Knutsford to Macclesfield rd. At roundabout in Chelford (Shell Garage) follow signs for car parking.* The Manor House: garden of 12 acres, undergoing redevelopment. Variety and many interesting features. Formal pond, lake, stream and water features. Walled garden, conservatory, herbaceous and elegant planting. Bold and unusual sculptures. New for summer 2005, prairie garden leading down to lake. Honeysuckle cottage: plantsperson's courtyard garden crammed with colour and interest. Always something new. Home-made TEAS in aid of East Cheshire Hospice. *Combined adm £3.50, chd free. Suns 8 May; 10 July: 4 September (2.30-5). Private visits welcome by appt, May to Sept, for groups of 12+. Tel 01625 861038*

㊲ NEW Moor House, Brereton Heath Lane, Brereton Heath 🚻🌳 NCCPG
(Mr & Mrs Alan Simpson) *3m W of Congleton. Off A54, 3m from either Congleton or Holmes Chapel, turn into Brereton Heath Lane. Moor House approx 300yds on L.* ⅔ dry sandy garden which incl extensive herbaceous borders, pergola, pond

with bog garden and cool wooded area. Wide variety of planting ranges throught herbaceous plants, shrubs and climbers. National Collection of Osteospermum. TEAS. *Adm £2.50, chd free. Sat, Sun 4, 5 June (11-4). Private visits welcome by appt. Tel 01477 533377 simpson2001@onetel.com*

㊳ 31 Moss Lane, Styal 🚻🌳😊
(Anne & Stephen Beswick) *2m N of Wilmslow. From M56 J5 towards Airport Terminal 1 then Cheadle, continue to T-junction. Turn R at T-lights then next R to Moss Lane. No 31 is 200yds on L.* Designer's evolving garden balancing enthusiasm with the need for low maintenance. Ground cover, mixed borders, wild flower area, wildlife pond, secret garden and fruit arch. N-facing front garden specialising in shady planting and ferns. TEAS. *Adm £2.50, chd 50p. Sun 31 July (2-6)*

㊴ NEW 50 Mostyn Road, Hazel Grove 🌳
(Steve & Norma Wright) *3m SE of Stockport. From Poynton A523 to Hazel Grove. L at 1st T-lights to Dean Lane. R at next T-lights to Chester Rd. L at 1st Lyndhurst Ave, R into Mostyn Rd at T-junction. From Stockport A6 to Hazel Grove. Just past Stepping Hill, R at Sainsbury's to New Moor Lane. Over 2 railway bridges, immed L into Aldwyn Cres. Go to bottom, R into Mostyn Rd.* Approx 9yds x 40yds rear garden. Ornamental trees, shrubs and perennials with high degree of control. Half the garden laid out in Japanese style; serene and secluded haven. Small pond with unfenced bridge. Acers, cornus, bamboos etc. Established over 30yrs, ongoing. Light refreshments and TEAS. *Adm £2, chd £1 (share to Stockport Alzheimer's Society). Weds 18 May; 15 June (3-8). Private visits welcome by appt May to July. Tel 0161 483 5695*

㊵ The Mount, Andertons Lane, Whirley, Henbury, nr Macclesfield 🚻🌳😊
(Mr & Mrs Nicholas Payne) *2m due W of Macclesfield. Along A537 opp Blacksmiths Arms. At Henbury go up Pepper St. Turn L into Church Lane then Andertons Lane in 100yds.* Approx 2 acres with interesting trees incl *Eucryphia x nymansensis*, fern leaved beech and *Sciadopitys*. Shrubberies; herbaceous border and short vista of Irish yews. Home-made TEAS in aid of East Cheshire Hospice. *Combined adm with* **Far Hills** *£4, chd free. Sun 29 May*

(2-5.30). *Private visits welcome by appt. Tel 01625 422920*

41 Mount Pleasant, Yeld Lane, Kelsall ⚑⚙✦

(Dave Darlington & Louise Worthington) *8m E of Chester. Off A54 at T-lights into Kelsall. Turn into Yeld Lane opp Th'ouse at Top PH, 200yds on L.* 6 acres of landscaped garden and woodland started in 1994 with impressive views over the Cheshire countryside. Steeply terraced in places. Specimen trees, rhododendrons, azaleas, conifers, mixed and herbaceous borders; 3 ponds, formal and wildlife. Vegetable garden and new stumpery in 2004. Cream TEAS in aid of Tarporley Hospital. *Adm £3, chd 50p. Sun, Mon 1, 2 May (12-5). Private visits welcome by appt May to Sept, groups of 15 or more, coaches permitted. Tel 01829 751592*

42 ◆ Norton Priory Museum & Gardens, Runcorn ⚑⚙✦

(Norton Priory Museum Trust) *2m SW of Runcorn. From M56 J11 turn for Warrington & follow signs. From Warrington take A56 for Runcorn & follow signs.* 16 acres of gardens. Georgian summerhouses, rock garden and stream glade, 3-acre walled garden of similar date (1760s) recently restored. Rosewalk, colour borders, herb and cottage gardens. Priory ruins also open with medieval herb garden and sensory planters. Featured on Channel 4 Hidden Gardens. Light refreshments and TEAS. *Adm £4.25, chd £2.95, concessions £2.95. Museum open all yr 12-5, weekends & Bank Hols 12-6. Walled garden open Apr to Oct 1.30-4.30.* **For NGS:** *Sat 4 June (1.30-4.30). Tel 01928 569895 Steve Miller www.nortonpriory.org*

43 The Old Hough, Warmingham ⚑⚙

(Mr & Mrs D S Varey) *3m from Middlewich. On A530 to Nantwich, turn L to Warmingham & L again T-junction or L on A533 from Sandbach to Middlewich & R at T-junction.* 12yr-old, 2½-acre garden, appropriate for the period house it surrounds. Peaceful privacy assured by farm range and mature oak wood. Hard landscaping uses harmonious, old materials. Design incorporates 2 water features. Lawns, trees with fabulous bark; many borders, exuberantly planted, where choice plants mingle with old favourites. Ample parking. WC. Home-made TEAS in aid of Warmingham Church.

Adm £3.50, chd under 12 50p. Sun 19 June (2-5)

44 The Old Parsonage, Arley Green, via Arley Hall & Gardens ⚑✦

(The Viscount & Viscountess Ashbrook) *5m NNE of Northwich. 3m Great Budworth. M6 J19 & 20 & M56 J10. Follow signs to Arley Hall & Gardens. From Arley Hall notices to Old Parsonage which lies across park at Arley Green.* 2-acre garden in attractive and secretive rural setting in secluded part of Arley Estate, with ancient yew hedges, herbaceous and mixed borders, shrub roses, climbers, leading to woodland garden and pond with gunnera and water plants. Rhododendrons, azaleas, meconopsis, cardiocrinums. Home-made TEAS. *Adm £3.50, chd £1.75 (share to Save The Children Fund). Sat, Sun 4, 5 June (2-6)*

45 One House Nursery, Rainow ⚙✦

(Louise Baylis) *2½m NE of Macclesfield. 2½ m from Macclesfield station on A537 Macclesfield to Buxton rd.* ½-acre plantswoman's garden featuring hostas, rare and unusual woodland and sun-loving perennials, rockery, gravel garden, sculptures and hornbeam arbour. Stunning views over Cheshire Plain. A short walk away is an atmospheric ½-acre historic early C18 walled kitchen garden, hidden for 60yrs and partially restored. Heritage vegetables, gardening bygones, orchard with rare-breed pigs. Home-made TEAS in aid of East Cheshire

Hospice. *Adm £2.50, chd free. Sat, Sun 2, 3 July (10-5)*

46 Orchard House, 72 Audley Road, Alsager ⚑✦

(Mr & Mrs J Trinder) *6m S of Congleton. At T-lights in Alsager town centre turn S towards Audley, house is 300yds on R beyond level Xing.* This ½-acre garden has been planted by enthusiastic plant collectors and features snowdrops, spring bulbs, hellebores, alpines, irises, grasses, geraniums and later herbaceous perennials. Home-made TEAS. *Adm £2, chd free. Sun 24 Apr; Wed 1, Sun 5 June (1-5.30). Private visits welcome by appt. Tel 01270 874833 john@jtrinder.fsnet.co.uk*

47 Parm Place, High Street, Great Budworth ⚑⚙✦

(Peter & Jane Fairclough) *3m N of Northwich. Great Budworth on E side of A559 between Northwich & Warrington, 4m from J10 M56, also 4m from J19 M6. Parm Place is W of village on S side of High Street.* Well-stocked ½-acre garden with stunning views towards S Cheshire. Shrubs, camellias, herbaceous borders, stream and ponds. Bog, scree bed, grasses, rockery, large collection of spring bulbs, hellebores, spring blossom. Home-made TEAS. *Adm £2.50, chd free (share to Great Ormond Street Hospital). Sun 3 Apr (1-5). Also opening with* **Great Budworth Gardens** *Sun 19 June. Private visits welcome by appt. Tel 01606 891131 pfair@btinternet.com*

DANGER
GIANT VENUS
FLY-TRAP

48 ◆ Peover Hall Gardens, Knutsford 🔊🐕
(Randle Brooks Esq) *4m S of Knutsford. Turn off A50 at Whipping Stocks Inn, down Stocks Lane. Follow signs to Peover Hall & Church. Entrance off Goostrey Lane clearly signed.* 15 acres. 5 walled gardens; C19 dell, rhododendrons, pleached limes, topiary. Grade II Carolean Stables and C18 park. TEAS. *Adm £3, chd £2. Mons, Thurs except Bank Hols Apr to Oct.* **For NGS:** *Sat, Sun 14, 15 May (2-6) . Tel 01565 830395 Richard Massey*

49 17 Poplar Grove, Sale 🐕🗺
(Mr Gordon Cooke) *3m N of Altrincham. From the A6144 at Brooklands station turn down Hope Rd. Poplar Grove 3rd on R.* This garden is 'deceptively spacious', being two gardens joined together. The potter/landscape designer owner has added an exhibition space this season and the garden features a living roof, scented area and pebble mosaic 'cave'. Many tender plants thrive in this city microclimate. Featured in 'Gardeners' World' Magazine 2003, 'The Independent' 2004. Winner Manchester heat of Britain's Best Back Garden, ITV 2005. Home-made TEAS in aid of The Stroke Association. *Adm £2.50, chd 50p. Sat, Sun 18, 19 June (2-5)*

50 Poulton Hall, Poulton Lancelyn, Bebington 🔊🐕🗺
(The Lancelyn Green Family) *2m S of Bebington. From M53, J4 towards Bebington; at T-lights R along Poulton Rd; house 1m on R.* 3 acres; front lawns with view of the house, wild flower meadow, shrubbery and walled gardens. Features incl Alice in Wonderland Walk and wood sculptures by Jim Heath - the Jabberwock, the Storyteller's Chair and Robin Hood (these relate to the books of Roger Lancelyn Green). Sundial garden for the visually impaired, sponsored by Bebington Rotary Club. Herb garden parterre and witch's garden. New Viking head bronze sculpture. Home-made TEAS. *Adm £3, chd free. Suns 10 Apr; 10 July (2-6). Private visits welcome by appt. Tel 0151 334 2057*

51 ◆ The Quinta Arboretum, Swettenham 🔊
(Tatton Garden Society) *5m NW of Congleton. Turn off A54 N 2m W of Congleton or turn E off A535 at Twemlow Green, NE of Holmes Chapel. Follow signs to Swettenham. Parking at Swettenham Arms PH. Entrance at side of PH.* Arboretum on a 28-acre site established since 1948 with over 4,000 species of trees incl collections of birch, pine, oak and flowering shrubs. Bluebell bank and snowdrops. 40 camellias planted 2004. TEAS NGS days only, in aid of St Peter's Church, Swettenham. *Adm £3 incl guided tour, chd free. Daily (not Christmas Day) 9 to dusk.* **NGS:** *Suns 10 Apr; 6 Nov (11-4). Tel 01477 537698 (answerphone) www.tattongardensociety.co.uk*

52 Reaseheath College, Reaseheath, Nantwich 🔊🐕🗺
(Reaseheath College) *1½m N of Nantwich. On A51. 1½m from Nantwich on A51 Chester rd.* Gardens of 12 acres, used as a teaching resource, based on a Victorian Garden containing many mature trees of horticultural interest. Glasshouses; model fruit, herb, woodland lakeside and herbaceous border; extensive shrub borders and lawns. Gravel garden. Adjacent nursery and garden centre. TEAS. *Adm £2.50, chd free. Weds 18, 25 May (2-4). Tel 01270 613214 www.reaseheath.ac.uk*

45 Rockside, off Church Street, Mow Cop 🐕🗺
See Staffordshire & part of West Midlands.

53 ◆ Rode Hall, Scholar Green (Sir Richard & Lady Baker Wilbraham) *5m SW of Congleton. Between Scholar Green (A34) & Rode Heath (A50).* Nesfield's terrace and rose garden with view over Humphry Repton's landscape is a feature of Rode gardens, as is the woodland garden with terraced rock garden and grotto. Other attractions incl the walk to the lake, restored ice house and working walled kitchen garden. Fine display of snowdrops in February. Home-made TEAS. *House & Garden adm £5, concessions £3.50. Garden only £3, concessions/chd over 12 £2. Snowdrops 8 Feb to 27 Feb (12-4) daily. Tues, Weds, Thurs & Bank Hols 1 April to 30 Sept (2-5). Tel 01270 882961 www.rodehall.co.uk*

54 Rose Hill Gardens, Marple *4m SE of Stockport. Turn L off Stockport Road, Marple, at Marple Hall Drive. Westbrook is approx 500 yds on L opp The Turnpike. Claremont Avenue 1st on L.* Marple is a very small town linking suburbia with the countryside. Combined *adm £3, chd £1. Sat, Sun 13, 14 Aug (2-6)*

2 Claremont Avenue, Marple 🐕🗺
(Eric & Maggie Britten) Artist and plantswoman's small garden, densely planted with a huge variety of plants, many unusual. With hand-built pottery and other imaginitive features, there is a surprise round every corner. Small wildlife pond and waterfall, bog garden, secret woodland garden, raised beds, living willow 'den'. This is a relaxed, fun garden, where plants take precedence. Exhibition and sale of silk paintings. *Private visits welcome by appt. Tel 0161 427 5182 marple.brittenfamily@cwctv.net*

Westbrook, 35 Marple Hall Drive, Marple 🐕🗺
(Banny & Ingrid Banerjee) A small suburban garden of unusual shape and interesting layout. The front garden has a formal look with borders of roses, fuchsias and lilies. There are archways, urns and pots. The back garden has a small lawn, seating area and herbs, fruit and flowers growing in a profusion of colour and perfume.

55 Rosewood, Puddington 🔊🗺
(Mr & Mrs C E J Brabin) *6m N of Chester. Turn L (W) off Chester to Hoylake A540 to Puddington. Telephone for precise directions.* 1-acre garden incl small wood, pond with bogside species, rhododendron, magnolia and azalea species and hybrids; many unusual trees. Most of the new plantings are grown from seed by owner and include many George Forrest introductions. TEAS. *Adm £2.50, chd free. Private visits welcome by appt at any time of yr, no minimum group size. Tel 0151 353 1193*

56 St Davids House, St Davids Lane, Noctorum 🗺
(Ian Mitchell) *3½m SW of Birkenhead Town Hall. Take A553 then A502 through Claughton Village. After 2 sets of T-lights, 1st L (Noctorum Lane). After Xrds, St Davids Lane is 1st on R.* Victorian garden of 1½ acres recently restored to original 1864 probable planting. Azaleas, camellias, rhododendrons, herbaceous and mixed borders, rockeries, pond, pine and silver birch copse with winding steep paths. Excellent views of Clwyd Hills, Snowdonia and Irish Sea. Featured in 'Liverpool Daily Post' 2004. Home-made TEAS. *Adm £2.50, chd free. Sun 1 May (1-6). Private visits welcome by appt. Tel 0151 652 5236*

57 Sandymere, Cotebrook
&⌀⊕
(John & Alex Timpson) *5m N of Tarporley. On A54 about 300yds W of T-lights at Xrds of A49/A54.* 16 landscaped acres of beautiful Cheshire countryside with terraces and walled garden. Wide variety of hostas and damp lovers at the little pond; the long views, native wildlife and tranquillity of 3 lakes. Elegant planting schemes, shady seats and sun-splashed borders, mature pine woods and rolling lawns accented by graceful wooden structures. Different every year: witness the evolution. TEAS. *Adm £3.50, chd free. Sun 5 June (2-5.30)*

Smithy Cottage, Mucklestone
⌀⊕
See Staffordshire & part of West Midlands.

58 199 Stockport Road, Timperley ⌀
(Eric & Shirley Robinson) *1½m NE of Altrincham. Take A560 out of Altrincham, in 1m take B5165 towards Timperley. B5165 is Stockport rd.* Overstuffed, cottage-style garden owned by 2 plantaholics, one an enthusiastic gardener, the other a very keen flower arranger. The garden is full of colourful herbaceous perennials, shrubs and hostas, and has a small brick-built pond complete with small koi and goldfish. You will not believe how many plants there are in such a small garden. Home-made TEAS in aid of Girl Guiding Greater Manchester West. *Adm £2, chd free. Suns 12 June; 7 Aug (1-5)*

59 Sunnyside Farm, Shop Lane, Little Budworth &⌀⊕
(Mike & Joan Smeethe) *3m NE of Tarporley. Off A54 approx 1m E of T-lights at Xrds of A49/A54. Signed field parking reached by taking track opp Longstone Lane 250yds W of Shrewsbury Arms.* 1½-acre plantsperson's country garden leads to lovely ¾-acre wild flower meadow and 3-acre wood. Designed as a series of interconnecting gardens with contrasting moods incl exuberant cottage-style garden, tranquil pond garden, orchard with beehives and ornamental kitchen garden approached through newly-planted Chanticleer pear tunnel. Features incl rose- and wisteria-clad pergola, arches, lime arbour, Piet Oudolf-inspired border with dramatic perennials and grasses. A wealth of unusual plants and interesting colour schemes. Home-made TEAS in aid of St Peter's Church, Little Budworth.

Adm £3, chd free. Suns 17 July; 21 Aug (1-5). Private visits welcome by appt. Tel 01829 760618

60 Swingate Cottage, Holehouse Lane, Whiteley Green ⌀⊕
(James & Emma Gleave) *3m N of Macclesfield. Holehouse Lane is E off A523 ¼m S of Legh Arms & 2m N of Macclesfield after Prestbury Nurseries. Garden is 1m on R.* 2-acre country garden. Lawns with open views across ha-ha to the Peak District. Native woodlands with stream. 4 water features, incl lily pond, koi carp pond, pond with duck island and a well. Walled garden contains vegetables and fruit trees, the main garden comprises extensive herbaceous planting. Formal knot garden. Books, plants and crafts for sale. Home-made TEAS in aid of East Cheshire Hospice. *Adm £4, chd 50p. Sun 26 June (1-5)*

61 ◆ Tatton Park, Knutsford
&⌀⊕
(The National Trust, leased to Cheshire County Council) *2½m N of Knutsford. Well signed on M56 J7 & from M6 J19.* Features include orangery by Wyatt, fernery by Paxton, restored Japanese garden, Italian and rose gardens. Greek monument and African hut. Hybrid azaleas and rhododendrons; swamp cypresses, tree ferns, tall redwoods, bamboos and pines. New this year, fully restored productive walled gardens. 'The Independent' No 1 Stately Home and Gardens 2004. Light refreshments and TEAS. *House & garden adm £4.60, adult Discovery Saver ticket. Garden only £3, chd £2. 19 Mar to 2 Oct Tues to Suns (10-6 last entry 5); 4 Oct to 31 Mar Tues to Suns (11 to 4, last entry 3).* **For NGS:** *Weds 4 May; 15 June www.tattonpark.org.uk*

62 NEW Tirley Garth, Utkinton
&⌀⊕
2m N of Tarporley. 2m S of Kelsall. Entrance 500yds from village of Utkinton. At N of Tarporley take Utkinton rd. 40-acre garden, terraced and landscaped. Designed by Thomas Mawson, it is the only Grade II* Arts & Crafts garden in Cheshire and is considered an exceptionally important example of an early C20 garden laid out in both formal and informal styles, which remain complete and in excellent condition. Light refreshments and TEAS in aid of local charities. *Adm £4, chd free. Wed 20, Sun 24 Apr (1-5)*

63 Tulip Tree Cottage, 85 Warmingham Road, Coppenhall, Crewe ⌀⊕
(Mr & Mrs A Mann) *3m N of Crewe town centre. On the rd between Leighton Hospital & Warmingham Village. Close by White Lion Inn, Coppenhall, Crewe.* ⅔-acre plantsman's garden, with shrubs, new perennial borders, raised beds, troughs, rock garden, peat garden, pond and greenhouse with cacti and succulents. Speciality alpines. Home-made TEAS. *Adm £2.50, chd free. Sun 20 Feb (11-3); Sat, Sun 21, 22 May (1-5) mannallen@tiscali.co.uk*

64 Tushingham Hall, Whitchurch
&
(Mr & Mrs P Moore Dutton) *3m N of Whitchurch. Signed off A41 Chester to Whitchurch rd.* Medium-sized garden in beautiful surroundings; bluebell wood alongside pool; ancient oak, girth 26ft. TEAS. *Adm £3, chd free (share to St Chad's Church, Tushingham). Sun 1 May (2-5.30)*

65 Two Upton Park Gardens, Upton by Chester
1½m NE of Chester. From A41 ring rd NE of Chester turn towards Chester at Shell garage T-lights at Upton Heath. Proceed ½m down Heath Rd (traffic calming) to mini roundabout, turn L. After ¼m car park is on R beside library. Follow signs to walk 200yds across playing field. Disabled parking available, directions from marshall in car park. Home-made TEAS at 80 Upton Park in aid of The Hospice of the Good Shepherd. *Combined adm £3, chd free. Sun 17 July (11-5)*

44 Upton Park, Upton by Chester
&⌀⊕ (John & Christine Browne) A ⅓-acre informal cottage garden with a well-stocked vegetable patch, soft and stone fruit, greenhouse with peaches, shrubbery and herbaceous borders. Interesting plants for sale. *Private visits welcome by appt, incl spring visits. Tel 01244 382008*

80 Upton Park, Upton by Chester
&⌀⊕ (Lynne & Phil Pearn) Plantswoman's garden of ¼ acre designed for yr-round interest and constantly changing. Featuring mixed beds where interesting iron and willow work features mingle with the flowers, colourful banked herbaceous bed, small vegetable plot, greenhouses, fernery and pond. Courtyard area with ancient espalier pear tree, numerous pots, a well and Victorian conservatory with vine

and bougainvillea. *Private visits welcome by appt. Tel 01244 390326 lynnepearn@hotmail. com*

66 Warrington Gardens
Approx 1m from Warrington town centre. From Stockton Heath N on A49 over swing bridge. L at 2nd set of T-lights into Gainsborough Rd. Gardens 5 mins walk from each other. TEAS at 62 Irwell Rd. *Combined adm £3, chd free. Sun 10 July (11-6)*

  68 Cranborne Avenue 🖉⊕ *(Mr & Mrs J Carter) From Gainsborough Rd, 4th L into Cranborne Ave.* Small garden of elegant design. Bold architectural planting is enhanced by water, glass and statuary bringing a peaceful atmosphere, much needed in today's world. Creative use of angles will deceive your eye!

  62 Irwell Road, Warrington 🖉 *(Mr & Mrs D Griffiths) From Gainsborough Rd, 2nd R into Irwell Rd. No 62 approx halfway down on R.* Award-winning secret garden with a magical atmosphere. Prepare to be 'spellbound' when you visit this tiny, but inspirational, garden. Evening openings enhanced by candlelight and fragrance. Winner of Best Patio, 'Garden News' competition 2003. *Private visits welcome by appt July only, evenings a speciality. Tel 01925 244267 digriffiths62@hotmail. com*

Weeping Ash, Bents Garden Centre, Warrington Road, Glazebury 🖑🖉
See Lancashire, Merseyside & Greater Manchester.

67 The Well House, Tilston 🖉
(Mrs S H French-Greenslade) 3m NW of Malpas. Nr Malpas. On A41, 1st turn R after Broxton roundabout, L on Malpas Rd through Tilston. House & antique shop on L. 1-acre cottage garden, bridge over natural stream, spring bulbs, perennials, herbs and shrubs. New triple pond and waterfall feature. Adjoining field being made into wild flower meadow; first seeding late 2003. Large bog area of kingcups and ragged robin. Prizewinner Chester in Bloom 2004. Home-made TEAS. *Adm £3, chd free (share to Cystic Fibrosis Trust). Sun 10 Apr (1.30-4.30). Private visits*

welcome by appt, Feb to Sept. Early Feb snowdrops, Mar & Apr bulbs. Groups and coaches permitted. *Tel 01829 250332*

68 West Drive Gardens, 4, 6, 9 West Drive, Gatley 🖉⊕
(Mr & Mrs K Marsden, Mr & Mrs D J Gane, Mr & Mrs T Bishop) 4m N of Wilmslow. On B5166. From J5 (M56) drive past airport to B5166 (Styal Rd). L towards Gatley. Pass over T-lights at Heald Green. West Drive is last turn on R before Gatley Village. Cul-de-sac, please do not park beyond the notice. Within these 3 secluded gardens, you will find herbaceous and mixed borders; wildlife pond; vegetable plots and gravel gardens. Hostas, grasses, ferns and sempervivums mingle with stone and terracotta pieces. Woodland walk continues to be developed. Victorian rope garden, stone and slate circles added in 2004. Home-made TEAS. *Combined adm £4, chd free (share to Sight Savers International). Sun 5 June (11-4)*

69 Willaston Village Gardens, Willaston
8m N of Chester. Take A540 Chester to West Kirby rd; turn R on B5151 to Willaston; at village centre turn R into Hooton Rd. Overdale Rd is ¼m L. Change Lane is a further 400yds on R opp garage. All 3 gardens are entered from Change Hey garden. Home-made TEAS at Change Hey in aid of RNLI. *Combined adm £3.50, chd £1. Sun 15 May (2-5)*

  Change Hey, Change Lane 🖑🖉 *(Mr & Mrs Keith Butcher)* 2-acre garden with mature trees, developing woodland area underplanted with rhododendrons and azaleas.

  NEW **The Dutch House, Park Road** 🖑🖉 *(Joan & Michael Ring)* ⅓-acre cottage-style garden with some formality. The rear garden vista, terminating with a 1920 Boulton & Paul revolving summerhouse, is surrounded on 2 sides by mature beech, oak and pine trees.

  Silverburn, Park Road 🖑🖉 *(Prof M P & Dr A M Escudier)* Just under ½-acre garden designed by garden owners. A plantsman's garden with interesting herbaceous beds and mixed borders, species and old-fashioned roses, rhododendrons, azaleas, attractive trees, vegetable garden and small orchard.

70 NEW Withinlee Road Gardens, Prestbury
3m NW of Macclesfield. Take A538 from Wilmslow to Prestbury; pass Bull's Head on R then after 1m turn R into Withinlee Rd. From Prestbury follow A538 towards Wilmslow, turn L after top of Castle Hill into Withinlee Rd. TEAS at Withinlee Ridge in aid of John Muir Trust. *Combined adm £4, chd free. Sun 22 May (2-5)*

  NEW **Glynleigh** 🖉 *(Mr & Mrs C Hamilton)* Unique garden designed to create views through the use of a wide variety of unusual planting combinations. Hundreds of mature and recent plantings of rhododendrons and spring-flowering shrubs, trees and groundcovers make this garden strikingly colourful and inspiring. A deep water pond, rockery, rhododendron cone and pergola give added interest.

  NEW **Withinlee Ridge** 🖉⊕ *(Mr & Mrs M G Rusbridge)* Approx 1 acre with mature trees, rhododendrons, unusual shrubs incl Embothrium *lanceolatum*, Cornus *kousa*, Eucryphia *nymansensis*, Berberis *temolaica*, cistus: rockery with 'silver' saxifrages, dwarf rhododendrons, ericaceous shrubs, small alpine house; mixed borders and a small pond.

71 Wood End Cottage, Grange Lane, Whitegate 🖉⊕
(Mr & Mrs M R Everett) 4m SW of Northwich. Turn S off A556 (Northwich bypass) at Sandiway PO T-lights; after 1¾m, turn L to Whitegate village; opp school follow Grange Lane for 300yds. Traditional plantsman's country garden of ½ acre in attractive setting, gently sloping to a natural stream. Shade and moisture-loving plants. Well-stocked herbaceous borders with many unusual plants. Red border, roses and clematis. Background of mature trees. Home-made TEAS. *Adm £2.50, chd free (share to RNIB). Wed 13 July (2-5).* **Evening Opening**, *£3.50, wine, Thur 14 July (6-8). Private visits welcome by appt. Tel 01606 888236*

Evening Opening (See also garden description)

Wood End Cottage   14 July

Cornwall

County Organiser: Mr William Croggon, Creed House , Creed, Grampound, Truro TR2 4SL Tel 01872 530372
Assistant County Organisers:
(Leaflet/Yellow Books)　Mr & Mrs Michael Cole, Nansawsan House, Ladock, Truro, Cornwall TR2 4PW
Tel 01726 882 392
Mrs Lally Croggon, Creed House, Creed, Grampound, Nr Truro, Cornwall TR2 4SL
Tel 01872 530372
Miss Caroline Latham, Stonaford Manor, North Hill, Launceston, Cornwall PL15 7PE
Tel 01566 782970
Mrs Jill Morison, Boskenna, St Martin, Manaccan, Helston, Cornwall TR12 6BS
Tel 01326 231 210
Mrs Alison O'Connor, Tregoose, Grampound, Truro, Cornwall TR2 4DB Tel 01726 882460
Mrs Ginny Vyvyan-Robinson, Mellingey Mill House, St Issey, Wadebridge, Cornwall
PL27 7QU Tel 01841 540 511
Mrs Marion Stanley, Mazey Cottage, Tangies, Gunwallowe, Helston, Cornwall TR12 7PU
(Press & Publicity Officer)　Mrs Elizabeth Waldron Yeo, Penbre, Trelill, Bodmin PL30 3HZ Tel 01208 850 793
County Treasurer:　Mr Nigel Rimmer, 11 Melvill Road, Falmouth, Cornwall TR11 4AS Tel 01326 313 429

Maps:　Numbers shown next to each garden entry refer to that garden's entry on the county map. This position is approximate; distance and directions from the nearest main town are generally shown in the garden text.
A precise location is available for those gardens featured on the NGS website by visiting www.ngs.org.uk.
Symbols: Information relating to symbols is given on page 21

DATES OF OPENING

Evening openings
See end of county listing

Gardens open to the public
For details see garden description
Boconnoc, Lostwithiel (1)
Bonython Manor, Cury Cross Lanes (3)
Carwinion, Mawnan Smith (7)
Cotehele, Saltash (10)
Creed House, Creed (11)
Eden Project, Bodelva (12)
Flambards Victorian Village Garden, Helston (13)
Glendurgan, Mawnan Smith (14)
Headland, Polruan (17)
The Lost Gardens of Heligan, Pentewan (18)
Hidden Valley Gardens, Treesmill (19)
The Japanese Garden & Bonsai Nursery, St Mawgan (23)
Ken Caro, Bicton, nr Liskeard (24)
Lanhydrock, Bodmin (27)
Marsh Villa Gardens, Par (29)
The Old Mill Herbary, Helland Bridge (32)
Paradise Park, Hayle (33)
Pencarrow, Bodmin (34)
Penjerrick Garden, Budock, nr Falmouth (35)
Pine Lodge Gardens & Nursery, Holmbush, St Austell (36)

Pinsla Garden & Nursery, Cardinham (37)
Potager Garden, High Cross, Constantine (40)
Prideaux Place, Padstow (42)
Roseland House, Chacewater (46)
St Michael's Mount, Marazion (47)
Scawn Mill Garden, nr Dobwalls (48)
Trebah, Mawnan Smith (50)
Tregenna Castle Hotel, St Ives (52)
Tregrehan, Par (53)
Trelissick, Feock (54)
Trengwainton, Madron, nr Penzance (57)
Trerice, nr Newquay (58)
Tresco Abbey Gardens, Isles of Scilly (59)
Trevarno Estate Gardens and National Museum of Gardening, Helston (60)
Trewithen, Truro (62)

February 20 Sunday
Trengwainton, Madron, nr Penzance (57)

March 13 Sunday
Ince Castle, Saltash (22)

March 20 Sunday
Poundstock Gardens, Poundstock (41)

April 10 Sunday
Ince Castle, Saltash (22)
Pencarrow, Bodmin (34)

April 16 Saturday
Trelissick, Feock (54)

April 17 Sunday
Penjerrick Garden, Budock, nr Falmouth (35)

April 23 Saturday
Chygurno, Lamorna (9)
Glendurgan, Mawnan Smith (14)

April 24 Sunday
Bodwannick, Nanstallon (2)
Chygurno, Lamorna (9)
Ladock House, Ladock (26)
Pinsla Garden & Nursery, Cardinham (37)
Polgwynne, Feock (38)
Porthpean House Garden, Lower Porthpean (39)

April 29 Friday
St Michael's Mount, Marazion (47)

May 1 Sunday
Goenrounsen, Summercourt (15)
Hallowarren, Carne, Manaccan (16)
Tregrehan, Par (53)
Veryan Gardens, Truro (63)

May 5 Thursday
Headland, Polruan (17)

May 8 Sunday
Boconnoc, Lostwithiel (1)
Creed House, Creed (11)
Nansawsan House, Ladock, Truro (31)
The Old Mill Herbary, Helland Bridge (32)
Poundstock Gardens, Poundstock (41)

May 14 Saturday
Trenance, Launceston (55)

May 15 Sunday
Ince Castle, Saltash (22)
Lanhydrock, Bodmin (27)
Trenance, Launceston (55)
Trewan Hall, St Columb (61)
Wheal Darlington, Longrock (64)

May 16 Monday
Cotehele, Saltash (10)

ngs
gardens open
for charity

More than £20 million has been donated
to charity since the NGS began in 1927

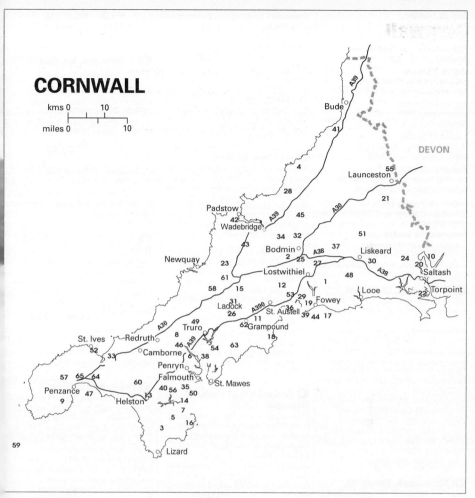

CORNWALL

kms 0   10

miles 0   10

Bude

DEVON

Launceston

Padstow
Wadebridge

Newquay

Bodmin
Lostwithiel
Liskeard
Saltash
Torpoint
Looe
Fowey
St. Austell
Grampound
Truro
St. Ives Redruth
Camborne
Penryn
Falmouth
St. Mawes
Penzance
Helston

Lizard

May 19 Thursday
Headland, Polruan *(17)*

May 22 Sunday
Hallowarren, Carne, Manaccan *(16)*
Long Hay, Treligga, Delabole *(28)*
Readymoney Cove, Fowey *(44)*

May 26 Thursday
Headland, Polruan *(17)*

May 27 Friday
Marsh Villa Gardens, Par **(Evening)** *(29)*

May 29 Sunday
Bonython Manor, Cury Cross Lanes *(3)*
Carclew Gardens, Perran-ar-Worthal *(6)*
Kingberry, Bodmin *(25)*
Roseland House, Chacewater *(46)*
Trenarth, Constantine **(Evening)** *(56)*

May 30 Monday (Bank Hol)
The Japanese Garden & Bonsai Nursery, St
Mawgan *(23)*

June 4 Saturday
Chygurno, Lamorna *(9)*
Higher Truscott, Launceston *(21)*

June 5 Sunday
Chygurno, Lamorna *(9)*
Higher Truscott, Launceston *(21)*
The Ranch House, St Issey *(43)*
Rose Cottage, St Breward *(45)*

June 12 Sunday
Long Hay, Treligga, Delabole *(28)*
The Ranch House, St Issey *(43)*

June 16 Thursday
Paradise Park, Hayle *(33)*

June 18 Saturday
Chacewater Garden Safari, Truro *(8)*
Meheniot Gardens, Meheniot Village *(30)*

June 19 Sunday
Caervallack, St Martin in Meneague *(5)*
Chacewater Garden Safari, Truro *(8)*
Meheniot Gardens, Meheniot Village *(30)*

The Ranch House, St Issey *(43)*
Scawn Mill Garden, nr Dobwalls *(48)*

June 26 Sunday
The Ranch House, St Issey *(43)*

July 9 Saturday
Boscastle Gardens *(4)*

July 10 Sunday
Bodwannick, Nanstallon *(2)*
Boscastle Gardens *(4)*
Potager Garden, High Cross, Constantine *(40)*
Rose Cottage, St Breward *(45)*
Springfield Farm Garden, Allet nr Truro *(49)*

July 17 Sunday
Kingberry, Bodmin *(25)*
Scawn Mill Garden, nr Dobwalls *(48)*

July 24 Sunday
Tregenna Castle Hotel, St Ives *(52)*

July 26 Tuesday
Trerice, nr Newquay *(58)*

July 31 Sunday
Roseland House, Chacewater *(46)*
Windman Cottage, Gulval *(65)*

August 7 Sunday
Highcroft Gardens, Cargreen *(20)*
Poundstock Gardens, Poundstock *(41)*

August 14 Sunday
Goenrounsen, Summercourt *(15)*
Trenarth, Constantine *(56)*

August 21 Sunday
Highcroft Gardens, Cargreen *(20)*
Marsh Villa Gardens, Par *(29)*

August 28 Sunday
Bonython Manor, Cury Cross Lanes *(3)*
Roseland House, Chacewater *(46)*

August 29 Monday (Bank Hol)
The Japanese Garden & Bonsai Nursery, St Mawgan *(23)*

September 25 Sunday
Trebartha, nr Launceston *(51)*

DESCRIPTIONS OF GARDENS

❶ ◆ Boconnoc, Lostwithiel 🔊📷
(Mr Anthony Fortescue) *4m E of Lostwithiel. 2m E of A390. Turn off A390 at Middle Taphouse.* Gardens covering some 20 acres, surrounded by parkland and woods. Magnificent trees, flowering shrubs and views. Set in C18 picturesque landscape which surrounds the church and Boconnoc House (both open). Teas in the stable yard designed by Sir John Soane. 'Country Life' 2004. Simon Jenkins - '1000 Best Houses' 2004. Cream TEAS. *Adm £3 , chd £1.* Suns 17 Apr-29 May and Wed, Thur in May, 2-5.30. **For NGS:** *Sun 8 May (2-5.30). Tel 01208 872507 www.boconnocenterprises.co.uk*

❷ Bodwannick, Nanstallon
(Mr P M & Mrs W M Appleton) *2½m W of Bodmin. A389 turn at Pottery signposted Nanstallon, L at Xrds signposted Hoopers Bridge then sharp R.* Approx 1-acre compact garden incl water garden, herbaceous, granite Cornish cross, roses, shade garden and shrubs. Over 50 varieties of daffodils and narcissi. Large stone circle. Plantsman's garden. Runner-up Granada TV Secret Garden Competition 2003. TEAS in aid of Fleet. *Adm £2.50. Suns 24 Apr; 10 July (2-5.30). Private visits welcome by appt. Tel 01208 831427*

❸ ◆ Bonython Manor, Cury Cross Lanes 🔊📷
(Mr & Mrs Richard Nathan) *5m S of Helston. On main A3083 Helston to Lizard Rd. Turn L at Cury Cross Lanes (Wheel Inn). Entrance 300yds on R.* Magnificent 20-acre colour

garden incl sweeping hydrangea drive to Georgian manor (not open). Herbaceous walled garden, potager with vegetables and picking flowers; 3 lakes in valley planted with ornamental grasses, perennials and South African flowers. A 'must see' for all seasons colour. Accommodation. Home-made TEAS. *Adm £5, chd £1.50. Tues to Fri 1 Apr to 30 Sept.* **For NGS:** *Suns 29 May; 28 Aug (10-4.30). Tel 01326 240550 www.bonythonmanor.co.uk*

❹ Boscastle Gardens
6m N of Camelford. Park in doctor's surgery car park at top of village (clearly signposted). Limited parking for disabled at both gardens. Maps provided. Home-made TEAS at Half Acre in aid of British Red Cross. *Combined adm £2.50, chd 50p. Sat, Sun, 9, 10 July (1.30-6)*

Half Acre 🔊📷 (Carole Vincent) Sculpture in an acre of 3 gardens: cottage; small wood; the blue circle garden, constructed in colour concrete with Mediterranean planting. Studio open.

Wildwood 📷 (Alex & Ian Stewart) Garden of magic deception. Front traditional, rear - lawns leading to wood with pond, tree ferns and shade-loving shrubs.

❺ ◆ Caervallack, St Martin in Meneague 🔊📷📷
(Mrs L Robinson) *5m SE of Helston. Go through Mawgan village, over 2 bridges, past Gear Farm shop; Caervallack is next farmhouse on LH-side.* Plantsman's garden arranged in rooms. Cob walls, water features and many varieties of old fashioned roses. Thatched courtyard garden; semi-walled orchard and vegetable plot; pergola leading to circular meditation room. Wild 2-acre field. New for 2005: 40ft timber suspension bridge. Cream TEAS. *Adm £2.50, chd free. Sun 19 June (2-5). Private visits welcome by appt. Tel 01326 221339*

❻ Carclew Gardens, Perran-ar-Worthal 📷
(The Chope Family) *5m SW of Truro. From A39 turn E at Perran-ar-Worthal. Bus: alight Perran-ar-Worthal 1m.* One of the original NGS gardens first opened in 1927 and home to the 'Sir Charles Lemon' rhododendron. 200 years of history are reflected in this large private garden with rare and mature specimen trees and shrubs, 'listed' walls, fine terraces and ornamental water. Home-made TEAS. *Adm*

£3.50, chd free. Sun 29 May (12-6). Private visits welcome by appt. Tel 01872 864070

❼ ◆ Carwinion, Mawnan Smith 🔊📷
(Mr H A E & Mrs J E Rogers) *3m S of Falmouth. Via Carwinion Rd.* Luxuriant, traditional, 14-acre Cornish Valley garden with delightful walks running down to the Helford River. Home of the UK's premier collection of bamboos. Hardy fern nursery. Ferns and wild flowers abound. A garden of yesterday, today and tomorrow. Accommodation. Cream TEAS 1 Apr to mid Sept. *Adm £3, chd free. Open all year (10-5.30). Tel 01326 250258 www.carwinion. co.uk*

❽ Chacewater Garden Safari, Truro
(Mr & Mrs C Pridham) *4m W of Truro. On the old Redruth Rd accessed from A390. Parking in free village car park .* Small cottage gardens, riverside retreats, 1-acre gardens, all full of surprises. Maps and tickets from Sunny Corner adjacent to car park. Home-made TEAS Roseland House. *Adm £4, chd free (share to 1st Redruth Guides). Sat,Sun 18, 19 June (1-6)*

❾ Chygurno, Lamorna
(Dr & Mrs Robert Moule) *4m S of Penzance. Off B3315. Follow signs for Lamorna Cove Hotel. Garden is at top of hill, past Hotel on LH side.* 3-acre garden on W side of Lamorna Valley with wonderful views of Lamorna Cove. Planting started in 1998, mainly S hemisphere shrubs and exotics with hydrangeas, camellias and rhododendrons. Woodland area with tree ferns set against large granite outcrops. Garden is terraced with very steep steps and paths. Well worth the effort. *Adm £2.50, chd free. Sat, Sun 23, 24 Apr; 4, 5 June (11-5)*

❿ ◆ Cotehele, Saltash 🔊📷📷
(The National Trust) *2m E of St Dominick. 4m from Gunnislake. (Turn at St Ann's Chapel); 8m SW of Tavistock; 14m from Plymouth via Tamar Bridge.* Formal garden, orchard and meadow. Terrace garden falling to sheltered valley with ponds, stream and unusual shrubs. Fine medieval house (one of the least altered in the country); armour, tapestries, furniture. Light refreshments and TEAS. *House and Garden Adm £7.40, Garden only Adm £4.40, chd £2.20. Daily 10.30-*

dusk. **For NGS:** *Mon 16 May (10.30-dusk). Tel 01579 351346 www.nationaltrust.org.uk*

⓫ ◆ Creed House, Creed ⊛
(Mr & Mrs W R Croggon) *6m SW of St Austell. From the centre of Grampound on A390, take rd signposted to Creed. After 1m turn L opp Creed Church & garden is on L.* 5-acre landscaped Georgian rectory garden; tranquil rural setting; spacious lawns. Tree collection; rhododendrons; sunken cobbled yard and formal walled herbaceous garden. Trickle stream to ponds and bog. Natural woodland walk. Restoration began 1974 - continues and incl recent planting. Accommodation. Cream TEAS on NGS day only. *Adm £3, chd free. Open daily Mar to Oct 10-5.* **For NGS:** *Sun 8 May (10-5). Tel 01872 530372*

⓬ ◆ Eden Project, Bodelva 🚶♿⊛
4m E of St Austell. Signposted with brown signs from A30 & A390. The world's largest greenhouses nestle in a giant 50-metre deep crater the size of 30 football pitches, the centrepiece of a spectacular global garden. Eden is a gateway into the fascinating world of plants and people and a vibrant reminder of how we need each other for our mutual survival. Light refreshments and TEAS. *Adm £12.50, chd £5, concessions £9.50, Family £30. April-Oct 10-6, last adm 4.30. Nov-Mar 10-4.30, last adm 3. See website for full details www.edenproject.com*

⓭ ◆ Flambards Victorian Village Garden, Helston 🚶♿⊛
(Mr & Mrs Douglas Kingsford Hale) *½m E of Helston. From A394 follow official brown & white signs to Flambards, located on A3083.* Well designed and maintained 20-acre site with interesting sections of very colourful award-winning bedding displays and hanging baskets. Mature trees, named shrubs of varied and striking foliage. Re-creation of a Victorian village and several exhibitions illustrating wartime Britain, Cornwall at war and the history of aviation. An excellent family day out. Wheelchairs available. Winner 2004 all categories Kerrier D.C. Commercial Gardens. Light Refreshments and TEAS. *Adm £9.95 (Adults15-54) £5.75 (Concessions 55+), chd £8.95 (5-14). Most days Easter - Oct. Phone for details. Tel 01326 573404 www.flambards.co.uk*

⓮ ◆ Glendurgan, Mawnan Smith ♿⊛
(The National Trust) *5m SW of Falmouth. Take rd to Helford Passage. Follow NT sign-posts.* Walled garden; laurel maze; giant's stride, valley with specimen trees, bluebells and primulas running down to Durgan fishing village on R Helford. Featured on BBC Gardeners World, June 2004. Light Refreshments and TEAS. *Adm £4.50, chd £2.20. Tues - Sat 12 Feb to 29 Oct incl Bank Hols. Closed Good Friday.* **For NGS:** *Sat 23 Apr (10.30-5.30. Last adm 4.30). Tel 01872 862090 chris.curtis@nationaltrust.org.uk*

⓯ Goenrounsen, Carnego Lane, Summercourt 🚶♿⊛
(Andrew & Angela Bailey) *10 m NE of Truro. Exit A30 for Summercourt. At centre of village T-lights with 'corner shop'. Take the lane down beside shop (Carnego Lane). Goenrounsen is 1/2 m on LH-side.* Formal garden with mature acid-loving shrubs and specimen trees surrounded by wildflower meadow, young arboretum, orchard and large wildlife pond. An old cornish lane leads to copse of ancient oaks underplanted with young treeferns. Also a hydrangea garden with 750 shrubs. A beautiful and tranquil setting of 13-acres. Cream TEAS in aid of Summercourt Memorial Hall. *Adm £3, chd free. Suns 1 May; 14 Aug (2-5). Private visits welcome by appt Groups of 6-24. No access for coaches. Tel 01872 510604 goenrounsen@yahoo.co.uk*

⓰ Hallowarren, Carne, Manaccan ♿⊛
(Mr & Mrs Mark Osman) *10m E of Helston. 1m out of the centre of Manaccan village. Down hill past inn on R, follow signpost to Carne.* House on R. 2-acre garden and orchard leading to a beautiful wooded valley and bordering stream. Mixture of the natural and cultivated, bog and cottage garden with primulas, lilies and kitchen herbs, unusual shrubs and trees. Newly opened woodland walk along valley. The ethos of this garden is harmony with nature and it is run on organic lines. Ducks, geese and chickens. Featured in 'Country Homes & Interiors' 2004. Winner Kerrier D.C. Woodland & Shrub Garden 2004. Light refreshments and TEAS in aid of St Anthony Church. *Adm £2.50, chd free. Suns 1, 22 May (12-5). Private visits welcome by appt. Tel 01326 231224*

⓱ ◆ Headland, Polruan ⊛
(Jean Hill) *½m SE of Fowey. Passenger ferry from Fowey, 10 min walk along West St & up Battery Lane. Or follow signs to Polruan (on E of Fowey Estuary). Ignore first car park, turn L for second car park (overlooking harbour) turn L (on foot) down St Saviour's Hill.* 1¼-acre cliff garden with magnificent sea, coastal and estuary views on 3 sides. Planted to withstand salty gales yet incl subtropical plants with intimate places to sit and savour the views. Paths wind through the garden past rocky outcrops down to a secluded swimming cove. Featured in 'The Garden' RHS 2003. Cream TEAS. *Adm £2.50, chd £1. Thurs only 5 May to 1 Sept (2-6).* **For NGS:** *Thu 5, 19, 26 May (2-6). Tel 01726 870243 www.headlandgarden.co.uk*

⓲ ◆ The Lost Gardens of Heligan, Pentewan 🚶♿⊛
(Heligan Gardens Ltd) *5m S of St Austell. From St Austell take B3273 signposted Mevagissey, follow signs.* 'The Nation's Favourite Garden' offers 200-acres for exploration, which include productive gardens, pleasure grounds, a lush 22-acre subtropical jungle, and walks through sustainably managed ancient woodlands, wetlands and farmland. Light refreshments and TEAS. *Adm £7.50, chd £4, concessions £7. Daily all year except 24, 25 Dec from 10am. Tel 01726 845100 www.heligan.com*

⓳ ◆ Hidden Valley Gardens, Treesmill ⊛
(Mr & Mrs P Howard) *2m SW of Lostwithiel. From St Austell, take A390 towards Lostwithiel. After 6m turn R on to B3269 signposted Fowey, after 210yds turn R signposted Treesmill. After 1m turn L, signposted to the gardens (½m).* 3-acre developing garden in secluded valley with small nursery, mostly stocked with plants from the garden. Mediterranean area with gazebo and country views. Courtyard garden with raised beds, wildlife pond and bog. Many other herbaceous beds with cottage-style planting incl a hot colour border and iris bed. Many plants labelled. Accommodation. TEAS. *Adm Donations. Daily Mon 1 Mar to Sun 31 Oct (10-6). Tel 01208 873225 www.hiddenvalleygardens.co.uk*

⓴ Highcroft Gardens, Cargreen ♿⊛
(Mr & Mrs B J Richards) *5m NW of Saltash. 5m from Callington on A388 take Landulph Cargreen turning. 2m*

on turn L at Landulph Xrds. Parking by Methodist Church. 3-acre garden developed over 21yrs in beautiful Tamar Valley. Herbaceous borders, patio garden, lawn borders, arboretum and buddleia bank. New ⅓ acre of grass and herbaceous prairie planting now complete. Cream TEAS in aid of Landulph Methodist Church. *Adm £2.50, chd free. Suns 7, 21 Aug (1.30-5.30). Private visits welcome by appt Aug only for groups of 10+. Tel 01752 842219*

㉑ Higher Truscott, St Stephens, Launceston 🌸❀
(Mr & Mrs J C Maun) 3m NW of Launceston. From Launceston B3254 turn W at St Stephens toward Egloskerry. Signposted. 1-acre plantsman's garden. Elevated position with fine views. Trees and shrubs with interesting underplanting. Year round interest with climbers, herbaceous, alpines and troughs. Partial wheelchair access. Home-made TEAS in aid of St Stephen's Church. *Adm £2.50, chd free. Sat, Sun 4, 5 June (2-5)*

㉒ Ince Castle, Saltash ♿
(Lord and Lady Boyd) 3m SW of Saltash. From A38 at Stoketon Cross take turn signed Trematon, then Elmgate. 5-acre garden, woodlands, borders, orchard, bulbs, shell house and lovely views of R Lynher. TEAS. *Adm £3.00, chd free (share to RHS). Suns 13 Mar; 10 Apr; 15 May (2-5)*

"Is that a helter-skelter tree, Mum?"

㉓ ◆ The Japanese Garden & Bonsai Nursery, St Mawgan ♿🌸❀
(Mr & Mrs Hore) 6m E of Newquay. 1½m from North coast. Signs from A3059 & B3276. Authentic Japanese garden set in 1½ acres, water garden with Koi pond, stroll and Zen gardens, bamboo grove. Japanese maples, azaleas and ornamental grasses in abundance. Specialist Bonsai and Japanese garden nurseries adjacent. *Adm £3.50, chd £1.50, Groups 10+ £3. Open all yr, closed Xmas day to New Year's day (10-6) (5.30 winter).* **For NGS:** *Mons 30 May; 29 Aug (10-6). Tel 01637 860116 www.thebonsainursery.com*

㉔ ◆ Ken Caro, Bicton, nr Liskeard 🌸❀
(Mr K R Willcock & Mrs Willcock) 5m NE of Liskeard. From A390 to Callington turn off N at St Ive. Take Pensilva Rd, follow brown tourist signs, approx 1m off main rd. 4-acre connoisseur's garden. Panoramic views, full of unusual plants and shrubs with year round colour. Lily ponds. New for 2005 - garden sculptures. TEAS. *Adm £3.50, Groups £3.25. Sun to Fri 27 Feb-30 Sept (10-6). Tel 01579 362446*

㉕ Kingberry, Rhind Street, Bodmin 🌸❀
(Dr & Mrs M S Stead) N-side of town, 100yds uphill from Westberry Hotel. Limited parking on hill, otherwise car parks in town centre. Surprising haven in centre of this county town. Formal town garden with abundantly planted herbaceous borders, original stone walls covered in climbers, ornamental pond, gravel terrace, conservatory filled with tender specimens and more informal orchard. ⅔ acre. Home-made TEAS in aid of FLEET. *Adm £2.50. Suns 29 May; 17 July (2-6)*

㉖ Ladock House, Ladock ♿❀
(G J & Lady Mary Holborow) 7m E of Truro. On B3275. Car park & entrance by church. Georgian Old Rectory with 4-acres of lawns, rhododendrons, camellias and azaleas with many woodland glades all planted during the last 30yrs. Bluebell walk. Cream TEAS in aid of Ladock Church. *Adm £2.50, chd free. Sun 24 Apr (2-5). Private visits welcome by appt Mar - Jun, groups of 10+. Tel 01726 882274*

㉗ ◆ Lanhydrock, Bodmin ♿🌸❀
(The National Trust) 2½m SE of Bodmin. 2½m on B3268. Station: Bodmin Parkway 1¾m. Large

garden. Formal garden laid out 1857; shrub garden with good specimens of rhododendrons and magnolias and fine views. Cream TEAS in Servants Hall. *House and Garden Adm £7.90, Garden only Adm £4.40, chd £2.20.* **For NGS:** *Sun 15 May (10.30-6)*

㉘ Long Hay, Treligga, Delabole ❀❀
(Bett & Mick Hartley) 10m N of Wadebridge. Take B3314 Pendoggett to Delabole Rd. Turn L at Westdowns from Pendoggett, R fom Delabole. Signposted Treligga (N). Turn L after entering hamlet. Long Hay on L, after 30yds white gate. Parking past gate, turn L into farmyard. Abundant cottage garden with beautiful vistas of the N coast and sea. Herbaceous beds, shrubs, pond, greenhouse and lawns. ⅔ acre. Meadow overlooking sea with paths leading to copse, vegetable plots, orchard and greenhouse. Cream TEAS 22 May in aid of Wateraid and, 12 Jun, Merlin Project. *Adm £2.50, chd free. Suns 22 May; 12 June (2-5)*

㉙ ◆ Marsh Villa Gardens, Par ♿❀
(Judith Stephens) 5m E of St Austell. Leave A390 at St Blazey T-lights, by the church. Take 1st L, garden 600yds on L. Approx 3-acre garden featuring large pond, streams, bog garden. Extensive herbaceous beds, mixed borders, woodland and marshland walks in former estuary. Home-made TEAS. *Adm £3, chd free. Suns to Weds Apr to Oct (11-6).* **For NGS:** *Sun 21 Aug (11-6).* **Evening Opening** *£4, wine, Fri 27 May (6-9). Tel 01726 815920*

㉚ NEW Meheniot Gardens, Meheniot Village ❀❀
(Mrs V.J. Sturdy) 4m SE of Liskeard. Take the A38 from Liskeard to Plymouth. Take the Menheniot turning NE 1m to centre of the village. An attractive village with many interesting and varied gardens. Maps and tickets from Lamorna, East Road. Home-made TEAS at Bodway Farm in aid of Methodist Church. *Adm £3.50, chd free. Sat, Sun 18, 19 June (2-6)*

㉛ Nansawsan House, Ladock, Truro ♿❀❀
(Michael & Maureen Cole) 7m E of Truro. On B3275, follow yellow signs. Use Falmouth Arms and Community Hall car parks. 1½-acre garden, once part of large Victorian garden. Rhododendrons, camellias, azaleas, some unusual trees and shrubs; terrace overlooking lawn,

gazebo, greenhouse and pond. Cream TEAS in aid of Ladock Parish Church. *Adm £2.50, chd free. Sun 8 May (2-5). Private visits welcome by appt March - June. Tel 01726 882392*

32 ◆ **The Old Mill Herbary, Helland Bridge** 🚻🌳
(Mr & Mrs R D Whurr) *2½m N of Bodmin. Access from A30 1m N of Bodmin or from B3266 Bodmin/Camelford rd. Parking for coaches in Camel Trail car park.* Unique 5-acre semi-wild herb and water gardens, set in an oasis of tranquillity by R Camel and C14 Helland Bridge. 400 yr-old woodland, secret island walks. 1¾-acre lawned arboretum with named unusual trees, terraced gardens, mill leat, chamomile lawn, set around unabashed greek/roman fertility theme, collection of medicinal plants. Coaches must access only from A30 & parking is strictly by appointment. Home-made TEAS NGS day only. *Adm £3.50, chd £1.50. Daily 25 Mar- 30 Sept except Weds (10-5).* **For NGS:** *Sun 8 May (2-6). Tel 01208 841206 www.oldmillherbary.co.uk*

33 ◆ **Paradise Park, Hayle** 🚻🌳🌿
(Mr Michael Reynolds) *2m SE of St Ives. Follow the A30 to Hayle, go to St Ives-St Erth roundabout then follow official brown & white signs to Paradise Park.* Flamingos on the lawns of the sheltered Victorian walled garden, at the centre of this 14-acre tropical bird garden, set the scene. Pergola walks with clematis and roses, plus many Australasian plants and Parrot Jungle with waterfall, streams, tree ferns, bamboo and lilies. Newly created Gazebo Garden is drift planted with sun-loving plants. Home of the World Parrot Trust. Light refreshments and TEAS. Adm Phone for prices. *Daily all yr from 10 .* **For NGS:** *Thu 16 June (10-5). Tel 01736 751020 www.paradisepark.org*

34 ◆ **Pencarrow, Bodmin** 🚻🌳
Molesworth-St Aubyn family) *4m NW of Bodmin. Signed off A389 & B3266.* Family owned and lived in Georgian House with 50 acres formal and woodland gardens listed Grade II laid out in 1840s. Marked walks past Victorian rockery; Italian and American gardens; lake and ice house. Over 650 different varieties of rhododendrons, internationally known conifer collection. Independent Newspaper 'Top Fifty Stately Homes' listed at 21 and in its Top Ten Gardens. The Dog's Trust

UK Top Attraction Award 2004. Cream TEAS. *House and Garden Adm £7.50, Garden only Adm £4, chd £1. Daily 1 Mar to 31 Oct, house Suns to Thurs (11-5) 27 Mar to 27 Oct.* **For NGS:** *Sun 10 Apr (9.30-5 last entry 5.30). Tel 01208 841369 www.pencarrow.co.uk*

35 ◆ **Penjerrick Garden, Budock, nr Falmouth** 🌳
(Mrs Rachel Morin) *3m SW of Falmouth. Between Budock-Mawnan Smith, opp. Penmorvah Manor Hotel. Room for one coach outside gate.* 15-acre subtropical garden, home to important rhododendron hybrids and the C19 Quaker Fox family. The upper garden with sea view contains rhododendrons, camellias, magnolias, bamboos, tree ferns and magnificent trees. Across a bridge a luxuriant valley features ponds in a wild primeval setting. Suitable for adventurous fit people wearing gumboots. *Adm £2.50, chd £1. Weds, Fris, Suns; Mar to Sept (1.30-4.30).* **For NGS:** *Sun 17 Apr (12-4 last adm). Tel 01872 870105*

36 ◆ **Pine Lodge Gardens & Nursery, Holmbush, St Austell** 🚻🌳📷 NCCPG
(Mr & Mrs R H J Clemo) *1m SE of St Austell centre. On A390 E of St Austell between Holmbush & St Blazey.* 30-acre estate comprises gardens within a garden. Some 6,000 plants, all labelled, have been thoughtfully laid out using original designs and colour combinations to provide maximum interest. Rhododendrons, magnolias, camellias, herbaceous borders with many rare and tender plants, marsh gardens, tranquil fish ponds, lake with black swans within the park, pinetum. Japanese garden and arboretum. Holder of National Collection of Grevilleas. 'Western Morning News' 2004. Light refreshments and TEAS. *Adm £5, chd £3. Open daily 1 Mar to 31 Oct (10-6). Tel 01726 73500 www.pine-lodge.co.uk*

37 ◆ **Pinsla Garden & Nursery, Cardinham** 🚻🌳
(Mark & Claire Woodbine) *3½m E of Bodmin. From A30 roundabout take A38 towards Plymouth, 1st L to Cardinham & Fletchers Bridge, 2m on R.* Romantic 1½ acres of inspirational planting and design surrounded by woodland. Herbaceous and shrub borders, jungle, ponds, cottage garden, orchard, alpines on scree; stone circle in meadow; tree tunnel. Paths lined with granite boulders and set with

slate, stone and incised abstract patterns. Home-made TEAS in courtyard. *Adm £2, chd free. Daily 1 Mar to 31 Oct 10-6.* **For NGS:** *Sun 24 Apr (10-6). Tel 01208 821339 www.pinslagarden.co.uk*

38 ◆ **Polgwynne, Feock** 🚻🌳
(Mrs P Davey) *5m S of Truro. Via A39 (Truro-Falmouth rd) & then B3289 to 1st Xrds: straight on ½m short of Feock village.* 4½-acre garden and grounds. Fruit and vegetable garden, woodlands extending to shore of Carrick Roads; magnificent maidenhair tree (female, 12ft girth), probably the largest in Britain; other beautiful trees; many rare and unusual shrubs. Lovely setting and view of Carrick Roads. Cream TEAS in aid of Feock Church on 24th April. *Adm £3, chd free. Sun 24 Apr (2-5). Private visits welcome by appt. Tel 01872 862612*

39 ◆ **Porthpean House Garden, Lower Porthpean**
(Mrs C Petherick) *1½m SE of St Austell. Off A390 take turning to Porthpean, straight for ½m past Mount Edgecombe Hospice. Turn L down Porthpean Beach Rd. Large White House at bottom of hill on L. Car park 50yds on R.* Specialist camellia garden with many rare cultivars. Beautiful view over St Austell Bay. Garden just above beach. Primrose and bluebell bank a prominent feature in spring. Cream TEAS. *Adm £2.50, chd free. Sun 24 Apr (2-5)*

40 ◆ **Potager Garden, High Cross, Constantine** 🚻🌳
(Peter Skerrett & Dan Thomas) *7m W of Falmouth. Towards Constantine. In High Cross turn L at grass triangle with white sign-post towards Port Navas. Potager is 100yds on R.* 5-acre derelict nursery reinvented in Jan 2000. Potager aims to demonstrate ideas of sustainability through gardening philosophy, craft working, art and design. Restored glasshouses and workshops are devoted to permaculture, propagation, wood and metal craft. Visitors can relax in the evolving organic garden. Light refreshments and TEAS. *Adm £1.50, chd free. 25-28 Mar & Suns & Bank Hols Apr-Sept.* **For NGS:** *Sun 10 July (11-4). Tel 01326 341258 www.potagergardennursery.co.uk*

41 NEW **Poundstock Gardens, Poundstock**
5m S of Bude, off A39. Direction maps given to visitors. Cream TEAS at The Barn in aid of Poundstock

Church. Homemade Lunches & TEAS at Southfield. *Combined adm £2.50, chd free. Suns 20 Mar; 8 May; 7 Aug (11-5)*

NEW The Barn House Garden 🅶🅰🅰 (Tim & Sandy Dingle) *From A39 take Widemouth, Bude (coastal route). L at Widemouth Manor Hotel towards Millook for ½m.* 9-yr-old garden in exposed coastal situation. Herbaceous and shrub borders, kitchen garden, pond. Beautiful views. Wildlife walk through 10-acre field, not suitable for less able.

Southfield, Vicarage Lane 🅰 (Mr PR & Mrs JA Marfleet) *Off A39 at Bangor Xrds (chapel on corner). Turn into Vicarage Lane, signed Poundstock Church. Approx 200yds on L.* 3-acres of wildlife woodland and garden. Woodland walks with daffodils, rhododendrons and hydrangeas. Mainly broadleaf trees planted 1994. Garden with borders of mixed shrubs, trees and perennial plants giving yr-round interest. Kitchen garden, chickens and ducks. Beautiful views. *Private visits welcome by appt. Tel 01288 361233*

42 ◆ Prideaux Place, Padstow (Mr & Mrs Peter Prideaux-Brune) *½m W of Padstow centre. On the edge of Padstow from ring rd (A389), follow brown signs for Prideaux Place.* Surrounding Elizabethan house the present main grounds were laid out in the early C18 by Edmund Prideaux. Ancient deer park with stunning views over Camel estuary; newly planted lime avenue; Victorian woodland walks. Restored sunken formal garden. A garden of vistas. Light refreshments and TEAS. *House and Garden Adm £6.50 Groups 20+ £5, Garden only Adm £2, chd £1. 27-31 Mar and 8 May-6 Oct, Sun-Thurs 12.30-5 garden open. House open 1.30. Tel 01841 532411 office@prideauxplace.fsnet.co.uk*

43 The Ranch House, St Issey 🅶🅰 (Mr & Mrs W E Corley) *4m SW of Wadebridge. In St Issey on A389 to Padstow, turn L opp Ring of Bells PH . After 15yds, drive on RH-side. Some parking at PH also church car-park.* 1½ acres of sheltered gardens, full of interesting shrubs and features, professionally designed and further developed over 30yrs to incl the kitchen garden; chickens, hedges and rooms, rainwater collection system. *Adm £2, chd free. Suns, 5 June to 26 June (2-6)*

44 Readymoney Cove, Fowey 🅰 (Mr & Mrs A S M Read) *½m SW of Fowey centre. At entrance of R Fowey near St Catherine's Castle. Park in Readymoney Beach car park & follow signs from lower end of car park to garden.* 1¼-acre tranquil valley garden with stream. Bog garden and waterside planting incl primula, astilbe, gunnera, arum lilies, hostas and wild orchids. Hillside walk through bamboo planting with views over garden to estuary. Hydrangeas, roses and climbers around house. Open during Daphne du Maurier Festival 7 to 15 May (1-5). Featured in 'Country Life' 2004. Home-made TEAS in aid of El Chaco Forest Regeneration Project. *Adm £2.50, chd free.* **For NGS:** *Sun 22 May (1-5)*

45 Rose Cottage, St Breward 🅶🅰 (Mrs Paddy Powell) *8m NE of Bodmin. From centre of St Breward village go down hill 1m towards Wenford Bridge. At 1st Xrds turn L opp farm lane. Garden is 800yds on R after dangerous bend.* 1-acre cottage garden on several levels surrounding 3 cottages. Strong emphasis on firm structure in open rural setting using the local granite and slate. Wide range of planting in mixed herbaceous borders with lilies, foxgloves, alliums and oriental poppies in abundance. Many hardy shrubs and wind-tolerant trees. Lawns, paved areas and stream. Home-made TEAS in aid of Arthritis Research Campaign. *Adm £2.50, chd free. Suns 5 June; 10 July (2-5.30)*

46 ◆ Roseland House, Chacewater 🅶🅰 NCCPG (Mr & Mrs Pridham) *4m W of Truro. At Truro end of main st. Parking in village car park (100yds) or surrounding rds.* 1-acre garden subdivided by walls and trellises hosting a wide range of climbers. Mixed borders of unusual plants, Victorian conservatory and greenhouse extend the gardening yr. Holders of National Collection of Clematis *viticella cvs.* Home-made TEAS. *Adm £2.50, chd free. Tues, Weds pm Apr to Sept.* **For NGS:** *Suns 29 May; 31 July; 28 Aug (2-5). Tel 01872 560451 www.roselandhouse.co.uk*

47 ◆ St Michael's Mount, Marazion (James & Mary St Aubyn) *2½m E of Penzance. ½m from shore at Marazion by Causeway; otherwise by ferry.* Flowering shrubs; rock plants, spectacular castle; fine sea views.

Light refreshments and TEAS. *Adm Castle & Garden £8.50, chd £2.75, Castle only £5.50, chd £2.75, Garden only Adm £3, chd free. Gardens, 1 May-30 Jun Mon- Fri, 1 Jul-31 Oct Thur -Fri. Castle, 1 Apr-31 Oct Sun-Fri.* **For NGS:** *Fri 29 Apr (10.30-5.30, last adm 4.45, on island). Tel 01736 710507*

48 ◆ Scawn Mill Garden, nr Dobwalls 🅶🅰🅰 (Annie & Julian Ball) *2½m SW of Liskeard. From A38 at the E end of Dobwalls take sign post to Duloe, Herodsfoot & Looe for 1½ m. Turn R at sign for Scawn & continue for 1m down to river.* East meets west in Cornish valley beside C17 corn mill on West Looe River. Take an afternoon to relax by the tranquil water-lily lake and enjoy terraces of azaleas, Japanese maples, primulas and hostas. Discover bamboo groves through Penpaly beech wood planted in 1992. Public footpath follows the river to Herodsfoot. Home-made TEAS. *Adm £2.50, chd free. 17 Apr, 15 May, 14 Aug, 18 Sept.* **For NGS:** *Suns 19 June; 17 July (2-5). Tel 01579 320497*

49 ◆ Springfield Farm Garden, Allet nr Truro 🅶🅰 (Mrs J M Cook) *3m NW of Truro. From Truro take B3284 to Allet. Turn R at Cornwall Wildlife Trust. Springfield is 4th on R.* Informal 2½-acre plantsman's garden, started 1980. Many mature trees and unusual shrubs. Ponds and water garden with bog plants and herbaceous plantings. Featured in 'Women's Weekly 2004 Summer Special'. Home-made TEAS. *Adm £2.50, chd free. Sun 10 July (2-5). Private visits welcome by appt. Tel 01872 540492*

50 ◆ Trebah, Mawnan Smith 🅶🅰 (Trebah Garden Trust) *4m from Falmouth. Follow tourism signs from Hillhead Roundabout on A39 approach to Falmouth or Treliever Cross Roundabout on junction of A39-A394. Parking (free) access for coaches.* 26-acre S-facing ravine garden, planted in 1830s. Extensive collection rare/mature trees/shrubs incl glades; huge tree ferns 100yrs old, subtropical exotics. Hydrangea collection covers 2½ acres. Water garden, waterfalls, rock pool stocked with mature koi carp. Enchanted garden for plantsman/artist/family. Play area/trails for children. Use of private beach. New reception building houses café, shop and art gallery. Light Refreshments and

TEAS. Adm £5.50, chd £3,
concessions £5. Daily all yr
(10.30-5). Tel 01326 250448
www.trebah-garden.co.uk

51 Trebartha, nr Launceston
(The Latham Family) 6m SW of
Launceston. North Hill, SW of
Launceston. Nr junction of B3254 &
B3257. Wooded area with lake
surrounded by walks of flowering
shrubs; woodland trail through fine
woods with cascades and waterfalls;
American glade with fine trees. No
coaches. Home-made TEAS. Adm £3,
chd free. Sun 25 Sept (2-5)

**52 ◆ Tregenna Castle Hotel, St
Ives** 🚻♿
½m from St Ives centre. Leave A30
West Hayle, A3074 to St Ives. After
Carbis Bay signs to Tregenna Castle
LH-side. Magnificent setting
overlooking St Ives Bay. A garden
mix within 72-acre estate incl
rediscovered woodland garden and
newly-created water garden and
subtropical walled garden, designed
by Chelsea Gold medallist John
Moreland. Adm £2, chd free. Open
all yr dawn to dusk. For NGS: Sun 24
July (10.30-4.30). Tel 01736 367525
johnmoreland@supanet.com

53 ◆ Tregrehan, Par 🚻♿
(Mr T Hudson) 1m W of St Blazey.
Entrance on A390 opp Britannia Inn.
Garden largely created since early
C19. Woodland of 20 acres
containing fine trees, award winning
camellias raised by late owner and
many interesting plants forming a
temperate rainforest. Show
greenhouses built 1846, a feature
containing softer species. TEAS. Adm
£4, chd free. Mid Mar - mid Jun,
Weds to Suns, Bank Hol Mons,

closed Easter Sun (10.30-5); Mid
June to end Aug, Weds (2-5). For
NGS: Sun 1 May (10.30 - 5).
Tel 01726 814389

54 ◆ Trelissick, Feock 🚻♿ NCCPG
(The National Trust) 4m S of Truro.
Nr King Harry Ferry. On B3289.
Planted with tender shrubs;
magnolias, camellias and
rhododendrons with many named
species characteristic of Cornish
gardens. Fine woodlands encircle the
gardens through which a varied
circular walk can be enjoyed. Superb
view over Falmouth harbour.
Georgian house (not open). Now
accessible by foot ferry from Truro,
Falmouth and St Mawes, Apr-Sept.
National Collection of Photinias and
Azaras. Light Refreshments and
TEAS in Barn Restaurant &
Courtyard Room. Adm £5, chd
£2.50. Daily mid Feb to end Oct
10.30-5.30, plus winter opening, ring
for details. Tel 01872 862090 . For
NGS: Sat 16 Apr (10.30-5.30)

**55 Trenance, Windmill Hill,
Launceston** 🚻♿
(Mr & Mrs John Dingle) ½m S of
Launceston centre. Follow signs for
Leisure Centre along Dunheved Rd.
At College end of rd take sharp L
bend & immed after this take another
L turning into Windmill Hill.
Trenance is approx 200yds on L. 2-
acre garden for all seasons. Wide
variety of trees and shrubs incl
rhododendrons, camellias, azaleas,
acers, cornus, magnolias, heathers
and conifers, Ballard hellebores, 100
varieties hardy geraniums,
delphiniums, herbaceous borders,
hostas and clematis. Several smaller
gardens within the main garden.
Cream TEAS in aid of Parkinson's
Disease Society. Adm £2.50, chd free.
Sat, Sun 14, 15 May (2-5.30). Private

visits welcome by appt 16 May-30
Jun groups of 10+. Tel 01566
772067

**56 Trenarth, High Cross,
Constantine** 🚻
(Mrs L M Nottingham) 6m SW of
Falmouth. Nearest main rds A39-
A394 Truro to Helston-Falmouth:
follow signs for Constantine. At High
Cross garage, 1½m before
Constantine, turn L signed Mawnan,
then R after 30yds down dead end
lane: Trenarth is ½m at end of this
lane. Diverse 3-acre garden round old
farmhouse with C18 listed garden
walls, yew 'rooms', Elizabethan
courtyard and lovely woodland walk
through woods to the Helford.
Modern planting in a mature setting,
with an emphasis on structures,
variety and unusual plants. Home-
made TEAS in aid of Save the
Children. Adm £2.50, chd free. Sun
14 Aug (2-5). Evening Opening £3.50
wine, Sun 29 May (6-8). Private visits
welcome by appt. Tel 01326 340444
lmnott@lineone.net

**57 ◆ Trengwainton, Madron, nr
Penzance** 🚻♿
(The National Trust) 2m NW of
Penzance. ½m W of Heamoor. On
Penzance-Morvah rd (B3312), ½m
off St Just rd (A3071). Sheltered
garden with an abundance of exotic
trees and shrubs. Picturesque stream
running through valley and stunning
views of Mounts Bay from terrace.
No dogs in tearoom garden. Light
refreshments and TEAS. Adm £4.50,
chd £2.20, family £11.20. Suns to
Thurs, 13 Feb to 31 Mar (10-5), 1
Apr to 30 Sept (10-5.30) 3-30 Oct
(10-5). For NGS: Sun 20 Feb (10-5).
Tel 01736 363148
www@nationaltrust.org.uk

help the hospices

58 ◆ Trerice, nr Newquay

&⊛⊜

(The National Trust) *3m SE of Newquay. From Newquay via A392 & A3058; turn R at Kestle Mill (NT sign posts).* Summer/autumn-flowering garden unusual in content and layout and for neutral alkaline soil varieties. Orchard planted with old varieties of fruit trees. Small museum traces history of lawn mower. Light refreshments and TEAS. *House and Garden Adm £5.50, chd £2.75. Daily except Tues & Sats 20 Mar to 30 Oct plus Tues 26 July-30 Aug (11-5.30, last adm 5).* For NGS: *Tue 26 July (11-5.30). Tel 01637 875404 www.nationaltrust.org.uk*

59 ◆ Tresco Abbey Gardens, Isles of Scilly &⊜

(Mr R A Dorrien-Smith) *28m SW Lands End. Direct helicopter flight from Penzance or ferry to St Mary's and inter-island launch.* Unique collection of subtropical plants including exotic species from more than 80 countries from Brazil to South Africa and Burma to New Zealand. Also Valhalla Museum of shipwrecked figureheads. Light refreshments and TEAS. *Adm £8.50, chd free. Daily 10-4. Tel 01720 424105 mikenelhams@tresco.co.uk*

60 ◆ Trevarno Estate Gardens and National Museum of Gardening, Helston &⊜

(Messrs M Sagin & N Helsby) *3m NW of Helston. Signed from Crowntown on the B3303.* Unforgettable gardening experience combining Victorian and Georgian gardens with fountain garden conservatory, unique range of craft workshops and National Museum of Gardening. Britain's largest and most comprehensive collection of antique tools, implements, memorabilia and ephemera creatively displayed to illustrate how gardens and gardening influence most people's lives. Ongoing restoration projects. Museum 'Gardening Which' feature 2004. Garden 'Cornwall Today' 2004. Light refreshments and TEAS. *Adm £4.95, chd £1.95, concessions £4.25. Open daily all yr 10.30-5. Tel 01326 574274 enquiry@trevarnoestate.fsnet.co.uk*

61 Trewan Hall, St Columb &⊜

(Mrs P M Hill) *6m E of Newquay. N of St Columb Major, off A39 to Wadebridge. 1st turning on L signposted to St Eval & Talskiddy.*

Entrance ¾m on L in woodland. Set in 36 acres of fields and bluebell woodland, with gardens round the house. Mixed beds, roses and specimen trees. Driveway bordered by rhododendrons and hydrangeas. Lovely views over the Lanherne Valley. Trewan Hall (not open) built in 1633 is a fine centrepiece for garden. Home-made TEAS in aid of Cornwall Deaf Children's Society. *Adm £2.50, chd free. Sun 15 May (2-5.30)*

62 ◆ Trewithen, Truro &⊜

(Mr & Mrs Michael Galsworthy) *½m E of Probus. Entrance on A390 Truro-St Austell rd. Signposted.* Internationally renowned and historic garden of 30 acres laid out between 1912 and 1960 with much of original seed and plant material collected by Ward and Forrest. Famed for towering magnolias and rhododendrons and a very large collection of camellias. Flattish ground amidst original woodland park and magnificent landscaped lawn vistas. Light refreshments and TEAS. *House and Garden Adm £9, Garden only Adm £4.75 Mar-Jun, £4.25 July-Sept, chd free, Groups 20+ £4.25 Mar-Jun, £4 Jul-Sept. Mons to Sats 1 Mar to 30 Sept also Suns Mar Apr, May (10-4.30). Tel 01726 883647 www.trewithen-estategardens.co.uk*

63 Veryan Gardens, Truro

6m SE of Truro. 4m S of Tregony. Veryan is signposted from A3078 (Tregony-St Mawes). Small village off main rd famous for its 5 round houses. Home-made TEAS at Trist House in aid of Veryan Church. *Combined adm £4, chd 50p. Sun 1 May (2-5.30)*

Tregarthen, Veryan (Dr & Mrs A G Cowen) *Nr centre of village with entrance immed beside village stores/PO.* Plantperson's garden of 1 acre with semi-formal gardens near house giving way to less formal plantings along stream, across which is a section of woodland. Camellias, magnolias, hellebores and daffodils predominate. Access through garden to Trist House. Open 1 May 2005 only.

Trist House &⊜ (Mr & Mrs Graham Salmon) *Centre of Veryan on the Portloe rd just past the PO stores.* 5-acre garden initially laid out in 1830s when house was built, with Italian terraces, specimen trees and 12

rockeries - the largest 30ft high and set beside small lake. Since 1994 the much overgrown rockeries have been cleared and replanted and delightful rose terraces, lawns and borders laid out around the house. *Private visits welcome by appt. Tel 01872 501422 www.tristhouse.co.uk*

64 Wheal Darlington, Longrock &⊛⊜

(Mr & Mrs Gerald Sandy) *2m E of Penzance. From roundabout at junction of A30 & A394, take rd to Marazion then almost immed 1st L, before St Theresa's Cheshire Home. Private approach lane is not suitable for full size coaches.* 3-acre garden on edge of Marazion Marsh RSPB Reserve. Views of St. Michael's Mount beyond the marsh. Approx 1-acre of lawns, mixed borders, shrubberies, woodland, wildflowers, ponds and bog garden. Remainder being uncultivated meadow surrounded by an interesting variety of trees. Ducks. Cream TEAS in aid of St Julia's Hospice. *Adm £2.50, chd free. Sun 15 May (1-5). Private visits welcome by appt June & July only. Tel 01736 710911*

65 NEW Windman Cottage, Trezelah, Gulval

(Bryon & Barbara Cook) *2m NE of Penzance. Take B3311 sign-posted St Ives through Gulval to Badgers Xrds, turn L sign-posted Trezelah/Chysaucster. After ½m 1st turning L signed Trezelah. Entrance 200metres at bottom of the lane.* Started in 1997 from a derelict field full of rubbish and brambles. Now ¾-acre of landscaped coastal gardens for the plantsman, containing many unusual and southern hemisphere plants, stream and ponds. 2-acre meadow with superb views across Mounts Bay. Featured in 'Garden News' 2003. Winner 3 consecutive years Ludguan H. S. Home-made TEAS in aid of Médecins Sans Frontières. *Adm £2.50, chd free. Sun 31 July (1-5). Private visits welcome by appt Jun,Jul,Aug Groups of 10+. Tel 01736 330688 barbaracook@cooptel.net*

Evening Opening (See also garden description)

Marsh Villa Gardens 27 May
Trenarth 29 May

Cumbria

County Organiser: Mrs Linda Orchant, High Cross Lodge, Bridge Lane, Troutbeck, Windermere, Cumbria
                                          LA23 1LA Tel 015394 88521
Assistant County Organisers:
Press & Publicity Officer   Mr Brian Adams, Low Mill House, Underbarrow, Kendal, Cumbria LA8 8BL
                                          Tel 015395 68635
(North East)   Mrs Sue Jones, Birkby Lodge, Crosby, Maryport, Cumbria CA15 6RN
                                          Tel 01900 813192 Fax 01900 817737
(South West)   Mr John Maddison, Buckbarrow House, Denton Park Court, Gosforth, Seascale, Cumbria
                                          CA20 1BN Tel 019467 25431
(North East)   Mrs Alannah Rylands, Crookdake Farm, Aspatria, Wigton, Cumbria CA7 3SH
                                          Tel 016973 20413
County Treasurer: Mr Derek Farman, Mill House, Winster, Windermere, Cumbria LA23 3NW
                                          Tel 015394 44893

Maps: Numbers shown next to each garden entry refer to that garden's entry on the county map. This position is approximate;
             distance and directions from the nearest main town are generally shown in the garden text.
             A precise location is available for those gardens featured on the NGS website by visiting www.ngs.org.uk.
Symbols: Information relating to symbols is given on page 21

DATES OF OPENING

Evening openings
See end of county listing

Gardens open to the public
For details see garden description
Acorn Bank, Temple Sowerby (1)
Brockhole, Windermere (6)
Conishead Priory (12)
Copt Howe, Chapel Stile, Great Langdale
(13)
Dalemain, Penrith (16)
Holehird Gardens, Windermere (26)
Holker Hall Gardens, Cark-in-Cartmel (27)
Hutton-in-the-Forest, Penrith (30)
Sizergh Castle, nr Kendal (47)
Stagshaw, nr Ambleside (48)

By appointment only
For telephone number and other
details see garden description.
Private visits welcomed
Buckbarrow House, Gosforth (7)
The Old Rectory, Dean (39)

March 25 Friday (Easter)
Copt Howe, Chapel Stile, Great Langdale
(13)

March 26 Saturday (Easter)
Copt Howe, Chapel Stile, Great Langdale
(13)

March 27 Sunday (Easter)
Copt Howe, Chapel Stile, Great Langdale
(13)

March 28 Monday (Easter)
Copt Howe, Chapel Stile, Great Langdale
(13)

April 15 Friday
Copt Howe, Chapel Stile, Great Langdale
(13)

April 16 Saturday
Copt Howe, Chapel Stile, Great Langdale
(13)

April 17 Sunday
Copt Howe, Chapel Stile, Great Langdale
(13)

April 24 Sunday
Stagshaw, nr Ambleside (48)

April 29 Friday
Copt Howe, Chapel Stile, Great Langdale
(13)

April 30 Saturday
Copt Howe, Chapel Stile, Great Langdale
(13)

May 1 Sunday
Dalemain, Penrith (16)
Dallam Tower, Milnthorpe (17)
The Nook, Helton (38)

May 2 Monday (Bank Hol)
Copt Howe, Chapel Stile, Great Langdale
(13)
Hollace, Torver (28)

May 4 Wednesday
Chapelside, Mungrisdale, Penrith (10)

May 7 Saturday
Acorn Bank, Temple Sowerby (1)

May 8 Sunday
Summerdale House, Nook, nr Lupton (50)
Windy Hall, Windermere (54)

May 11 Wednesday
Chapelside, Mungrisdale, Penrith (10)
Lakeside Hotel, Newby Bridge (31)

May 14 Saturday
The Miller Howe Hotel, Windermere (35)
Underwood House, Bootle, Millom (52)

May 15 Sunday
Matson Ground, Windermere (34)
Warth Sutton Cottage, Crooklands,
Milnthorpe (53)

May 17 Tuesday
High Rigg, Grange-in-Borrowdale (25)
Scarthwaite, Grange-in-Borrowdale (45)

May 18 Wednesday
Chapelside, Mungrisdale, Penrith (10)

May 21 Saturday
Lindeth Fell Country House Hotel, Bowness
on-Windermere (33)

May 24 Tuesday
Scarthwaite, Grange-in-Borrowdale (45)

May 25 Wednesday
Chapelside, Mungrisdale, Penrith (10)

May 27 Friday
Copt Howe, Chapel Stile, Great Langdale
(13)

May 28 Saturday
Copt Howe, Chapel Stile, Great Langdale
(13)

May 29 Sunday
Copt Howe, Chapel Stile, Great Langdale
(13)
Halecat, Witherslack (20)

May 30 Monday (Bank Hol)
Copt Howe, Chapel Stile, Great Langdale
(13)
Haverbrack, Milnthorpe (21)

May 31 Tuesday
Scarthwaite, Grange-in-Borrowdale (45)

June 1 Wednesday
Chapelside, Mungrisdale, Penrith (10)

June 4 Saturday
Sizergh Castle, nr Kendal (47)

June 5 Sunday
High Beckside Farm, Cartmel (22)
Hutton-in-the-Forest, Penrith (30)
1 Queens Place, Kendal (43)
Stagshaw, nr Ambleside (48)

June 7 Tuesday
Scarthwaite, Grange-in-Borrowdale (45)

June 8 Wednesday
Chapelside, Mungrisdale, Penrith (10)

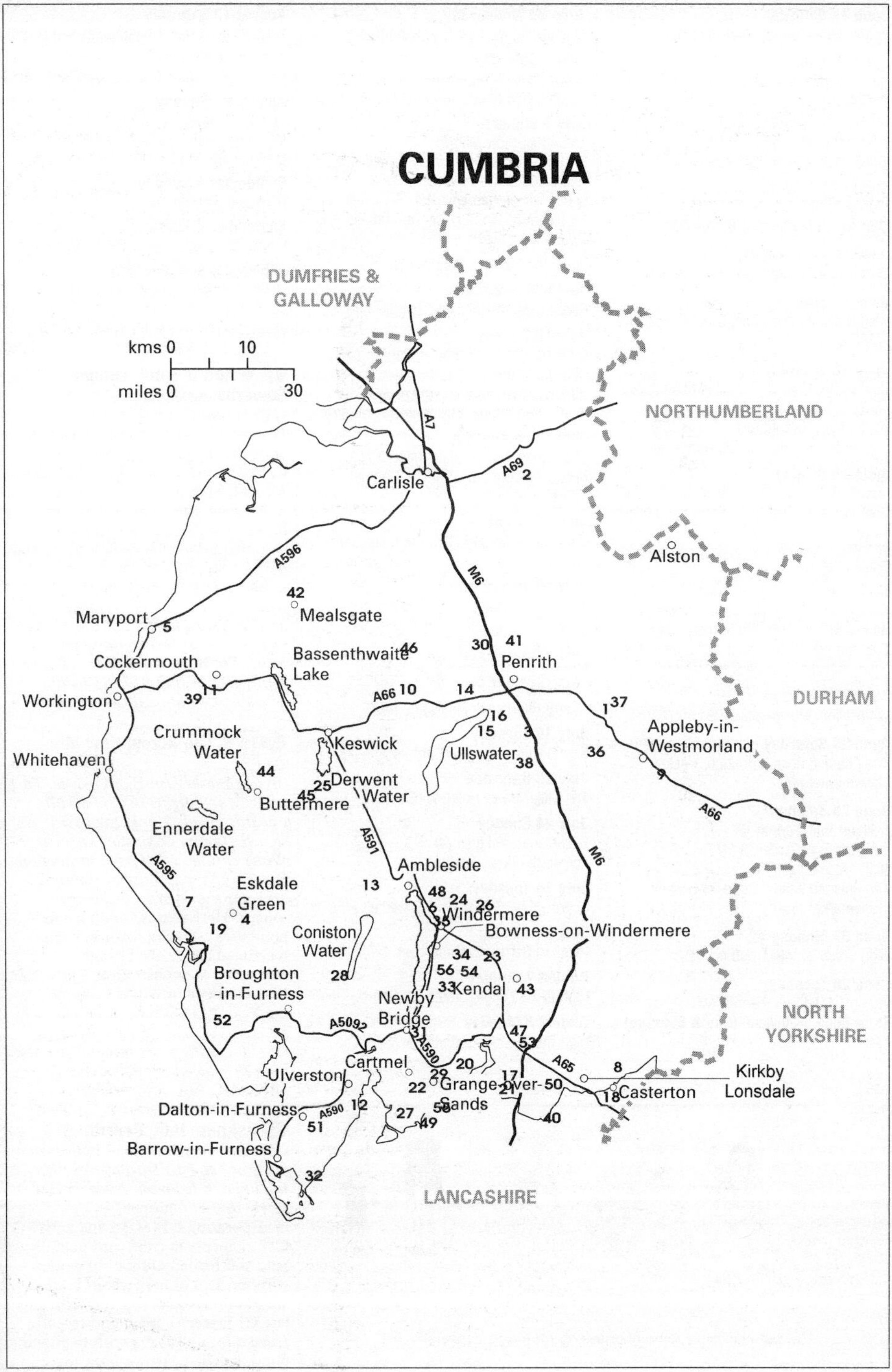

CUMBRIA

DUMFRIES &
GALLOWAY

NORTHUMBERLAND

kms 0   10
miles 0   30

A7

A69 2
Carlisle

Alston

A596

42
Maryport 5   Mealsgate
Cockermouth   Bassenthwaite 46   30   41
                   Lake   Penrith
Workington   39 11   A66 10   14
                                              1 37
Crummock   Appleby-in-
  Water   Keswick   16   Westmorland
Whitehaven   15   3
                   44   25 Derwent Ullswater 38   36
                   45 Buttermere Water
                                                       9
Ennerdale   A66
  Water
                                   M6
           A595
                   Eskdale   13   Ambleside
           7   Green   48 24 26
              19   4   6 Windermere
                   Coniston   Bowness-on-Windermere
                    Water   34 23
Broughton   56 54
 -in-Furness   28   33 Kendal 43
                   Newby
           52   Bridge
                   A5092 31
                              A590   47
           Ulverston Cartmel   29 20 53   A65   8
Dalton-in-Furness   22 Grange-over- 50   Kirkby
                   A590 12   Sands 17 21   Lonsdale
                        51   27   49 58 40   18 Casterton
Barrow-in-Furness
                        32

LANCASHIRE

DURHAM

NORTH
YORKSHIRE

June 11 Saturday
Acorn Bank, Temple Sowerby *(1)*

June 12 Sunday
Birkby Lodge, Crosby *(5)*
Conishead Priory *(12)*
Quarry Hill House, Mealsgate *(42)*
1 Queens Place, Kendal *(43)*
Windy Hall, Windermere *(54)*

June 14 Tuesday
Plumpton Old Hall, Penrith *(41)*
Scarthwaite, Grange-in-Borrowdale *(45)*

June 15 Wednesday
Chapelside, Mungrisdale, Penrith *(10)*

June 17 Friday
Copt Howe, Chapel Stile, Great Langdale *(13)*

June 18 Saturday
Copt Howe, Chapel Stile, Great Langdale *(13)*
Holme Crag, Grange-over-Sands *(29)*
Rannerdale Cottage, Buttermere *(44)*

June 19 Sunday
Castle Bank, Appleby-in-Westmorland *(9)*
Copt Howe, Chapel Stile, Great Langdale *(13)*
Fell Yeat, Casterton, nr Kirkby Lonsdale *(18)*
Halecat, Witherslack *(20)*
Holme Crag, Grange-over-Sands *(29)*
Pear Tree Cottage, Burton-in-Kendal *(40)*
Rannerdale Cottage, Buttermere *(44)*
Summerdale House, Nook, nr Lupton *(50)*
Yews, Bowness-on-Windermere *(56)*

June 22 Wednesday
Chapelside, Mungrisdale, Penrith *(10)*

June 25 Saturday
The Scented Rose Garden, nr Hesket Newmarket *(46)*

June 26 Sunday
Askham Hall, Penrith *(3)*
Cockermouth Gardens *(11)*
High Cross Lodge, Troutbeck *(24)*
The Scented Rose Garden, nr Hesket Newmarket *(46)*

June 27 Monday
High Cross Lodge, Troutbeck *(24)*

June 28 Tuesday
Plumpton Old Hall, Penrith *(41)*
Stone Edge, Allithwaite **(Day & Evening)** *(49)*

June 29 Wednesday
Chapelside, Mungrisdale, Penrith *(10)*

July 2 Saturday
Acorn Bank, Temple Sowerby *(1)*
21 Ulverston Road, Dalton-in-Furness *(51)*

July 3 Sunday
The Acres, How Mill *(2)*
Casterton School, nr Kirkby Lonsdale *(8)*
Dacre Lodge, Dacre *(15)*
Leece Village Gardens *(32)*
21 Ulverston Road, Dalton-in-Furness *(51)*

July 5 Tuesday
Plumpton Old Hall, Penrith *(41)*

July 6 Wednesday
Chapelside, Mungrisdale, Penrith *(10)*

July 10 Sunday
Cumbria Campus Gardens, Penrith *(14)*
Halecat, Witherslack *(20)*
High Cleabarrow, Windermere *(23)*
Pear Tree Cottage, Burton-in-Kendal *(40)*

July 13 Wednesday
Chapelside, Mungrisdale, Penrith *(10)*
Holker Hall Gardens, Cark-in-Cartmel **(Evening)** *(27)*

July 15 Friday
Copt Howe, Chapel Stile, Great Langdale *(13)*

July 16 Saturday
Copt Howe, Chapel Stile, Great Langdale *(13)*

July 17 Sunday
Newbiggin Hall, Newbiggin, Temple Sowerby *(37)*
Quarry Hill House, Mealsgate *(42)*

July 19 Tuesday
Scarthwaite, Grange-in-Borrowdale *(45)*

July 23 Saturday
The Miller Howe Hotel, Windermere *(35)*

July 24 Sunday
Beckstones, Eskdale *(4)*
Foresters House, Eskdale *(19)*

July 26 Tuesday
Scarthwaite, Grange-in-Borrowdale *(45)*

July 31 Sunday
Holehird Gardens, Windermere *(26)*

August 7 Sunday
High Cross Lodge, Troutbeck *(24)*

August 8 Monday
High Cross Lodge, Troutbeck *(24)*

August 13 Saturday
Yewbarrow House, Grange-over-Sands *(55)*

August 14 Sunday
Yewbarrow House, Grange-over-Sands *(55)*

August 21 Sunday
Hutton-in-the-Forest, Penrith *(30)*
Morland House, Morland, nr Penrith *(36)*
Summerdale House, Nook, nr Lupton *(50)*

September 4 Sunday
Dalemain, Penrith *(16)*

September 6 Tuesday
Castle Bank, Appleby-in-Westmorland *(9)*

September 7 Wednesday
Lakeside Hotel, Newby Bridge *(31)*

DESCRIPTIONS OF GARDENS

❶ ◆ Acorn Bank, Temple Sowerby 🅱♿️🌳
(The National Trust) 6m E of Penrith. On A66; ½m N of Temple Sowerby. Bus: Penrith-Appleby or Carlisle-Darlington; alight Culgaith Rd end. Medium-sized walled garden; fine herb garden; orchard and mixed borders; wild garden with woodland/riverside walk leading to a partly restored watermill open to the public. Dogs on leads only in woodland walk. Light refreshments and TEAS. Adm £3, chd £1.50. Wed to Sun Mar to Oct & Bank Hol Mons. **For NGS:** *Sats 7 May; 11 June; 2 July (10-5). Tel 017683 61893 acornbank@nationaltrust.org.uk*

❷ NEW The Acres, How Mill 🅱♿️
(Lynda Fraser) 7m E of Carlisle. Turn off A69 at T-lights in Corby Hill towards Heads Nook, take 1st R signed Hayton & Castle Carrock. White cottage 2¾m from turning on R at fork. ⅓-acre organic flower arranger's garden specialising in foliage. Herbaceous, wildlife and pond areas. Design features using reclaimed materials. Flower Arranging Demonstration 3 July. 5th BBC Gardener's World Gardener of the Year 2003. TEAS. Adm £2, chd 50p, concessions £1. Sun 3 July (11-5). Private visits welcome by appt May to Sept, max 50, coaches permitted

❸ Askham Hall, Penrith ♿️🌳
(The Earl & Countess of Lonsdale) 5m S of Penrith. Turn off A6 for Lowther & Askham. Askham Hall is a pele tower (not open), incorporating C14, C16 and early C18 elements in courtyard plan. Splendid formal outlines of garden with terraces of herbaceous borders and original topiary, probably from late C17. Herb garden and recently created meadow area with trees and pond. Kitchen garden, basically

"... but I distinctly remember asking for Morris dancers!"

organic. Home-made TEAS in aid of Askham & Lowther Church. *Adm £2.50, chd free. Sun 26 June (2-5)*

❹ Beckstones, Eskdale Green, Eskdale 🚻🐕♿
(Ron & Audrey Postlethwaite) *17m S of Whitehaven. Leave A595 at Gosforth, after centre of village R fork continue along rd through Santon Bridge. Pass Bower House Inn, after 250yds turn R immed before Fell View Garage.* Grassy areas with various specimen trees and shrubs, herbaceous plantings and pond with carp. Beautiful views of Eskdale. Home-made TEAS. *Adm £2, chd free. Sun 24 July (1-5). Also open* **Foresters House**

❺ NEW Birkby Lodge, Crosby 🚻🐕
(Mrs Sue Jones) *2½m NE of Maryport. On A596 after village of Birkby & before village of Crosby. Gates on L before speed limit.* Interesting 1½ acres of mature garden surrounded by woodland shelter belt on edge of Solway. Herbaceous, shrubs, bamboo's and interesting trees. Home-made TEAS. *Adm £3, chd under 16 free. Sun 12 June (12-5)*

❻ ◆ Brockhole, Windermere 🚻♿
(Lake District National Park Authority) *2m NW of Windermere. On A591 between Windermere & Ambleside.* 10 acres, formal gardens, designed by Thomas Mawson. Acid soils and mild aspect, many unusual or slightly tender plants, shrub roses, herbaceous borders, scented garden. 20 acres informal grounds, wide variety of trees and shrubs. Wild flower meadow, adventure playground. Access to shores of Windermere. Light refreshments and TEAS. *Adm free (pay and display parking). Open dawn to dusk all-yr-round. Tel 015394 46601 www.lake-district.gov.uk*

❼ Buckbarrow House, Denton Park Court, Gosforth 🐕♿
(John Maddison) *13m S of Whitehaven. Turn off A595. Through centre of Gosforth Village. At 'Y' junction take L fork towards Wasdale. After 150yds turn L (before church) into Denton Park. Keep bearing R. House is last on R in Denton Park Court.* Small densely planted garden approx 23yds x 49yds. Numerous compartments incl wildlife pond, Japanese gravel garden, shrub area, cottage garden borders and natural stream. Decking area. *Adm £2.50, chd free. Private visits welcome by appt, groups up to*

15. Tel 019467 25431 JohnMaddGosf@aol.com

❽ Casterton School, nr Kirkby Lonsdale 🐕♿
1¼m NE of Kirkby Lonsdale. From A65 at Devil's Bridge take A683 N. Casterton is 1¼m from this junction. In Casterton Village, R turning in front of church leads directly to school. Set in the beautiful Lune Valley the school gardens are a plantsman's delight consisting of several compartments; exotic border with large collection of rare and tender perennials, peaceful white garden full of butterflies, rose garden, woodland walk, children's garden and wildlife pond. C17 and Memorial gardens. Large collection of salvia. Featured in 'Cumbria Life' 2004. Home-made TEAS in aid of Holy Trinity Church, Casterton. *Adm £2, chd free. Sun 3 July (2-6)*

❾ NEW Castle Bank, Appleby-in-Westmorland 🚻🐕♿
(Mrs R R Holmes) *¾m SW of Appleby. On B6260 Appleby to Orton: 12m from J38 M6. On A66 Appleby is approx 38m NW of Scotch Corner. Parking very limited at garden, please park in Appleby.* The 3-acre garden lay derelict for 30yrs. The R Eden's weir sounds throughout the long walk under yews and across the lawns now set with beds of perennials and grasses. The walled garden with climbing roses, borders and shrubbery home to many small birds. Featured in 'Cumbria Life' 2004. *Adm £2.50, chd free. Sun 19 June; Tue 6 Sept (2-5)*

❿ Chapelside, Mungrisdale, Penrith 🐕♿
(Tricia & Robin Acland) *8m W of Penrith. On A66 take unclassified rd N, signed Mungrisdale Village. House is far end of scattered village on L immed after tiny church on R. Use parish church room parking at foot of our short drive.* 1-acre garden run on organic lines, using local stone creatively. Wide range of plants for yr-round interest in relaxed style, incl hostas, ferns and eryngiums. Tree, meadow, tiny stream and large pond in informally at foot of fell for wildlife. Fine views, so unkind winds. Art constructions in and out. *Adm £2, chd free (share to Mungrisdale Parish Church). Weds, 4 May to 13 July (1.30-5.30). Private visits welcome by appt, most other times, eg Apr for fritillaries. Tel 01768 779672 racland@enterprise.net*

⓫ NEW Cockermouth Gardens
15m W of Keswick. Off A66. Attractive old market town on NW edge of Lake District. Wordsworth's birth place. Maps given to all visitors. *Combined adm £3, chd under 12 free. Sun 26 June (12-5)*

NEW 16 Brigham Road 🐕 (I M & D Walker) *Off A5086 Lamplugh Rd towards town centre, turn L into Brigham Rd, garden on R.* Town house, secluded garden relatively long and thin, densely planted with tall herbaceous plants and herbs. Featured in 'Cumbria Life' 2004.

NEW 8 Holmewood Avenue 🐕 (Anne & Roger Asquith) *Off Brigham Rd on R.* Constantly evolving ¼-acre garden, owing more to a love of plants than to a formal garden design. Greenhouse, raised vegetable beds, soft fruit, wilflife ponds and well-stocked mixed borders.

NEW 52 The Parklands 🚻🐕 (Mr & Mrs Browning) *A5086 Lamplugh Rd turn L into Fitz Rd, at end of Fitz Rd continue through Gravel Lane. Turn L into Parklands Estate. up hill turn L into cul-de-sac after group of bungalows, garden 2nd on R.* Limited disabled parking available. Modern garden incorporating wood, canvas, galvanised steel, pebbles and water to create an industrial beach.

NEW Rubby Banks Cottage, Rubby Banks Road, off New Road 🚻🐕 (Mrs Margaret Thurm) *Approach via New Rd off Station Rd (beside West Cumberland Farmers) turn R on riverbank. House last on lane. Park in Sainsburys car park. No vehicle access is possible.* Approx 1-acre along western bank of R Cocker below Harris Park. Surrounded by mature trees, mainly oak. Herbaceous, shrub and rose borders. Interesting trees, secluded walled area on site of old mill.

⓬ ◆ Conishead Priory 🚻♿
(Manjushri Buddhist Centre) *2m S of Ulverston. Junction 36 M6 onto A590 to Ulverston, then A5087 Coast Rd to Barrow. The Priory is approx 2m outside Ulverston on the L after the long limestone wall.* 50 acres of mature woodland with paths down to the beach and unusual specimen trees. Ornamental beds, some of which are not normally open to the public. Temple garden incl newly restored greenhouse. 5-acre lake and wildlife garden; cottage

garden and arboretum. House tours & Temple 2.30 & 3.45 pm approx 1hr . Featured in 'Lancashire & Lake District Life' & Winner Cumbria in Bloom, South Lakeland 2004. Cream TEAS. *House tour £1 (with garden ticket), Garden only adm £2.50, chd £1.50. Open all yr (except festival times 21 May to 5 June & 16 July to 15 August).* **For NGS:** *Sun 12 June (2-6). Tel 01229 584029 www.manjushri.org.uk*

⓭ ◆ Copt Howe, Chapel Stile, Great Langdale ⊕
(Professor R N Haszeldine) *5m W of Ambleside.* 2-acre plantsman's mountain paradise garden. Superb views Langdale Pikes. Extensive collections of acers, camellias, azaleas, rhododendrons, oaks, beeches, rare shrubs, trees, unusual perennials; herbaceous and bulbous species; alpines, trough gardens; rare conifers; expedition plants from worldwide mountainous regions. Outstanding spring colour. Wildlife sanctuary, red squirrels, badgers, slow-worms, hotel for wild birds. Major new garden extensions. Featured in 'Gardening Which', 'Country Life' ,' Westmorland Gazette' and various TV programmes 2004. *Adm £3, chd free. Open additional days Apr to Aug.* **For NGS:** *Fri to Mon 25 to 28 Mar; Fri to Sun 15 to 17 Apr; Fri, Sat 29, 30 Apr; Mon 2 May; Fri to Mon 27 to 30 May; Fri to Sun 17 to 19 June ; Fri, Sat 15, 16 July (12-5) . Tel 015394 37685 for recorded message*

⓮ Cumbria Campus Gardens, Newton Rigg, Penrith ⓑ⊗⊕
1m W of Penrith. 3m W from junctions 40 & 41 off M6. ½m off the B5288 W of Penrith. The Campus gardens have much of horticultural interest incl extensive herbaceous borders, wide range of ornamental trees and shrubs, pond and organic gardens; woodland walk, scented garden, arboretum and tropical display house. Recently created annual meadows and exciting willow structures. Cumbria Organic Gardeners Society stand. Medal Winner Borders Spring Flower Show & Holker Hall Garden Festival 2004. Light refreshments and TEAS. *Adm £2.50, chd free. Sun 10 July (11-4). Tel 01768 863791*

⓯ Dacre Lodge, Dacre ⊕
(Mrs T Washington) *5m W of Penrith. About 4½m from exit 40 off the M6. Turn W onto A66 to Keswick & then L onto A592 signed Ullswater & Dalemain R to Dacre.*

After ½m entrance gate on L. Approx 1-acre with herbaceous border and beds of perennial plants, roses and shrubs. Interesting trees and delightful riverside walk. Dogs on leads. Cream TEAS in aid of Dacre Church. *Adm £2, chd free. Sun 3 July (10.30-4.30)*

⓰ ◆ Dalemain, Penrith ⓑ⊗⊕
(Mr & Mrs R B Hasell-McCosh) *3m SW of Penrith. On A592 Penrith to Ullswater - 3m from M6 junction 40.* Delightful 5-acre plantsman's gardens, set against the grandeur of the Lakeland Fells and parkland. Herbaceous borders; rose walk with old-fashioned roses and named ancient apple trees; *Abies Cephalonica* fir; tulip tree and Tudor knot garden. Wild garden with blue Himalayan poppies. Woodland walks. Light refreshments and TEAS. *House and garden adm £6, garden only adm £4, chd free. Suns to Thurs 20 Mar to 30 Oct (house 11-4) (gdns 10.30-5), Mons to Thurs 31 Oct to 12 Dec, 2 Feb to mid Mar (gdns only 10-4).* **For NGS:** *Suns 1 May; 4 Sept (10.30-5). Tel 017684 86450 www.dalemain.com*

⓱ Dallam Tower, Milnthorpe
(Mr & Mrs R T Villiers-Smith) *7m S of Kendal. 7m N of Carnforth. Nr junction of A6 & B5282. Station: Arnside, 4m; Lancaster, 15m.* Large garden; natural rock garden, water garden; wood walks, lawns, shrubs. C19 cast iron orangery. Cream TEAS in aid of Beetham C of E School. *Adm £2.50, chd free. Sun 1 May (2-5)*

⓲ Fell Yeat, Casterton, nr Kirkby Lonsdale ⓑ⊗⊕ [NCCPG]
(Mr & Mrs O S Benson) *1m E of Casterton Village. On the rd to Bull Pot. Leave A65 at Devils Bridge, follow A683 for 1m, take the R fork to High Casterton at golf course, straight across at two sets of Xrds, the house is immed on the L, ¼m from no-through-rd sign.* 1-acre informal country garden with many unusual plants. Divided into garden 'rooms'. 2 small ponds, herbaceous borders, old roses, ferns and small developing woodland garden. National Collection of *Ligularia.* Cream TEAS in aid of Holy Trinity Church, Casterton. *Adm £2.50, chd 50p. Sun 19 June (1.30-5)*

⓳ [NEW] Foresters House, Eskdale Green, Eskdale ⓑ⊗
(Mike & Marion Clarke) *17m S of Whithaven. Leave A595 at Gosforth after centre of village R fork, continue along through Stanton*

Bridge, pass Bower House Inn. After 250yds turn L before Fell View Cottage. Large grass lawn with interesting borders, some raised specimen trees and shrubs. Fantasic view of local fells. *Adm £2, chd free. Sun 24 July (1-5). Also open* **Beckstones**

⓴ Halecat, Witherslack ⓑ⊕
(Mrs Michael Stanley) *10m SW of Kendal. From A590 turn into Witherslack following the Halecat brown signs. L in township at another brown sign & L again, signpost 'Cartmel Fell'; gates on L & Halecat Nursery. Map on Halecat website.* Medium-sized garden; mixed shrub and herbaceous borders, terrace, sunken garden; gazebo; daffodils and cherries in spring; wild flower meadow; beautiful view over Kent estuary to Arnside. Adjacent nursery. Light refreshments and TEAS. *Adm £2, chd free. Suns 29 May; 19 June; 10 July (12.30-4.30) www.halecat.co.uk*

㉑ [NEW] Haverbrack, Milnthorpe
(Mr & Mrs B Reckitt) *7m S of Kendal, 7m N of Carnforth. 1m from Milnthorpe. From A6 Milnthorpe T-lights take B5282 to Arnside: after ¼m over stone bridge L through Dallam Park to T-junction, turn R, approx 150yds turn L into driveway.* Varied garden of 1½ acres, mature shubs and trees. Deep well-stocked herbaceous borders, lawns, limestone rockery and secret garden. Cream TEAS in aid of Marie Curie Cancer Care. *Adm £3, chd £1. Mon 30 May (2-5)*

㉒ High Beckside Farm, Beckside, Cartmel ⊗
(Mr & Mrs P J McCabe) *1¼m N of Cartmel. Take Haverthwaite rd, R at the village shop in square.* Semi-wild garden, conservation area with ponds, waterfowl. Large variety of plants and shrubs. Approx 3 acres of mixed woodland, 11 acres of wild flowers on hillside with views over valley and bay. Small house garden. 5 mins walk to ponds. Stout shoes. TEAS. *Adm £2.50, chd free. Sun 5 June (1-5). Private visits welcome by appt June to Aug, no coaches. Tel 015395 36528*

㉓ High Cleabarrow, Windermere ⓑ⊗⊕
(Mr & Mrs R T Brown) *3m SE of Windermere. Off B5284 Crook to Kendal rd opp Windermere Golf Club.* 2-acre plantswoman's garden. Owner designed. A garden for all seasons comprising mixed borders, traditional rose garden, rocky

outcrop cleared and planted with azaleas, rhododendrons and ferns, alpines, pond and waterside planting, cobble bed. Many unusual plants with a keen eye for plant association. Favoured plant groups, hydrangeas, hardy geraniums, hostas, hellebores and roses. Exciting new plantings and features always in progress. A garden for the connoisseur. Featured in 'Homes & Antiques', 'Gardens North West' & 'Gardening Which' 2003. Home-made TEAS. *Adm £3, chd under 10 free. Sun 10 July (11-5.30). Private visits welcome by appt for groups of 10+. Tel 01539 42808 www.highcleabarrow.com*

㉔ High Cross Lodge, Bridge Lane, Troutbeck ⚙⚙
(Mr & Mrs Sydney Orchant) *2½m N of Windermere. From Windermere, after Lakes School turn R into Bridge Lane off A591 next to YHA.* A tropical-style garden designed by owner for all-yr interest. 1-acre gently sloping garden in a woodland setting with local slate terracing and cascading serpentine stream. Spectacular display of tree ferns, trachycarpus, cordylines and phormiums, many other non-hardy exotics. Collection of acers, ferns and pristine slug free hostas. New perfumed white garden surrounds a delightful summerhouse, new bog garden, other projects underway. Featured in 'Lancashire Life', 25 Beautiful Gardens. Winner Cumbria in Bloom Special Category 2003. 'Amateur Gardening's Georgeous Gardens' magazine 2004. Home-made TEAS. *Adm £3, chd under 12 free. Suns, Mons 26, 27 June; 7, 8 Aug (11-4). Private visits welcome by appt May, June, July & Aug only. Groups of 15+. Tel 01539 88521 Linda@highcrosslodge.fsnet.co.uk*

㉕ High Rigg, Grange-in-Borrowdale
(Miss Barbara Newton) *6m S of Keswick. From Keswick take B5289 to Grange; cross rd bridge, suitable for minibuses. House ½m on L.* ¾-acre fellside garden with mixed shrub/herbaceous border, rock and bog gardens. Rhododendrons, azaleas and many other shrubs and trees. *Adm £2, chd free. Tue 17 May (11-5). Also open* **Scarthwaite**

㉖ ◆ Holehird Gardens, Windermere ⚙⚙⚙ NCCPG
(Lakeland Horticultural Society) *2m N of Windermere. Off A592 Patterdale Rd. Garden signed on R.* Garden of 10 acres run by volunteers of the Lakeland Horticultural Society,

dedicated to promoting knowledge of the cultivation of alpine and herbaceous plants, shrubs and trees, especially those suited to Lakeland conditions. Walled garden with mixed borders. Alpine and tufa houses. One of the best labelled gardens in the UK. National Collections of *Astilbe, Hydrangea* and *Polystichum* (ferns). BBC Gardeners' World Top 50 Gardens, Voted 49th Best Garden in Europe by The 'Independent' and Cumbria in Bloom Award 2004. *Adm £2, by donation, chd free. Open daily dawn to dusk.* **For NGS:** *Sun 31 July (10-5). Tel 01539 46008 Mar to Oct only*

㉗ ◆ Holker Hall Gardens, Cark-in-Cartmel ⚙⚙⚙ NCCPG
(Lord & Lady Cavendish) *4m W of Grange-over-Sands. 12m W of M6 (junction 36).* A garden for all seasons within the Gulf Stream, benefiting plants from throughout the world incl exotic planting. Woodland garden with extensive collection of rhododendrons flowering Jan to late summer. National Collection of *Styracaceae.* Ancient oaks, magnolias, camellias and largest common lime in UK. Garden festival 4 to 6 June. Light refreshments and TEAS. *House and garden adm £7.50, chd £4.75, garden only £4.50, chd £2.75. Sun to Fri 20 Mar to 30 Oct (10-5.30).* **For NGS: Evening Opening** *£3, wine, Wed 13 July (6-9). Tel 01539 58328 www.holker-hall.co.uk*

㉘ Hollace, Torver ⚙⚙
(Mr & Mrs R Prickett) *9½m SW of Ambleside. 2½m SW from Coniston on A593, N from Greenodd on A5092-A5084 8m, NE from Broughton-in-Furness on A593 6m. Follow signs in Torver Village. Limited parking.* Approx 1-acre garden. Lawns, herbaceous, heather borders and fruit and vegetables. Emphasis will be on the sale of plants (no bedding plants) for NGS. Then open for 4 weeks when signs are displayed. *Adm by donations (share to M.C.R.). Mon 2 May (1-5). Private visits welcome by appt. Tel 01539 41416*

㉙ Holme Crag, Witherslack, Grange-over-Sands ⚙
(Mr Jack Watson) *3m N of Grange-over-Sands. Off A590 Barrow Rd through Witherslack. Turn L signed Halecat. Turn L at next rd on junction. Just past tel kiosk in Newton Rd. Signpost approx 1m.* 4 acres designed to encourage wildlife. Bird garden with large pond and

rockeries; 22 different species nest. Scree beds. Azaleas, rhododendrons, mature shrubs and trees, spring garden, primulas, bulbs. *Adm £2.50, chd free. Sat, Sun 18, 19 June (12-4)*

㉚ ◆ Hutton-in-the-Forest, Penrith ⚙
(Lord Inglewood) *6m NW of Penrith. On B5305, 3m from exit 41 of M6.* Magnificent grounds with C18 walled flower garden, terraces and lake. C19 low garden, specimen trees and topiary; woodland walk and dovecote. Medieval house with C17, C18 and C19 additions. Light refreshments and TEAS. *House and garden adm £5, chd £2.50, students £3.50, family £13.50, garden only adm £3, chd free, students £1.50. House Thurs, Fris, Suns, Bank Hol Mons 25 Mar to 3 Apr & 1 May to 2 Oct. Gardens open daily (except Sats) 25 Mar to 31 Oct.* **For NGS:** *Suns 5 June; 21 Aug (11-5). Tel 017684 84449 www.hutton-in-the-forest. co.uk*

㉛ NEW Lakeside Hotel, Lake Windermere, Newby Bridge ⚙⚙
(Mr N R Talbot) *1m N of Newby Bridge. On S shore of Lake Windermere. From A590 at Newby Bridge, cross the bridge which leads onto the Hawkshead rd. Follow this rd for 1m, hotel on the R.* Magnificent lake shore setting overlooking Gummers How. Gardens planted with a spectacular range of interesting trees, shrubs and perennials. Aromatherapy, scented and subtropical themed gardens. Winter border. Huge rooftop garden with espalier apples. A wealth of seasonal bedding utilising uncommon and rare varieties. Lakeview conservatory filled with scented pelargoniums. Accommodation. Light refreshments and TEAS in aid of Boarbank Hall Nursing Home. *Adm £2.50, chd free. Weds 11 May; 7 Sept (11-5). Private visits welcome by appt. Tel 01539 30001 www.lakesidehotel.co.uk/gardens*

32 Leece Village Gardens
2m E of Barrow-in-Furness. 6m SW of Ulverston. Junction 36 M6 onto A590 to Ulverston. A5087 coast rd to Barrow. Approx 8m turn R for Leece Village (signed, look for concrete sea wall on L). Village parking for gardens. Small village clustered around tarn. Maps given to all visitors. Home-made TEAS at & in aid of Village Hall. *Combined adm £2.50, chd free. Sun 3 July (11-5)*

Briar Cottage 👤🐕🏠 (Zoe Norman) Small cottage garden in the countryside featuring wildlife pond and many herbaceous perennials.

Downfield House 👤🐕🏠 (Mrs Alison Bolt) Approx ½ acre of mature garden containing an interesting collection of hardy geraniums and several varieties of buddleia. Trees, shrubs and vegetables.

Raising House 🐕🏠 (Vivien & Neil Hudson) Plant lovers garden on SW slope. Developed (with still more to do) over last 3yrs with emphasis on flowering plants, incl many unusual shrubs, grasses, herbaceous perennials and climbers. Alpine scree and troughs. Access by steps. *Private visits welcome by appt, small parties only. Tel 01229 431539 mikehuddy@aol.com*

Winander 🐕🏠 (Mrs Enid Cockshott) 1-acre, eco-friendly garden amid mature trees on an E-facing slope. Patio area with wildlife pond; large organic vegetable and fruit area. Alpines, mixed borders, quiet seating areas with views across Leece Tarn and out to Morecambe Bay.

[NEW] **Woodgarth** 🐕🏠 (Harry & Rita Butcher) Medium-sized garden with herbaceous border, tradtionally planted containers and grenhouse. Small lawned area backing onto trees with under storey, leading to wild area for butterflies, moths and other insects.

33 Lindeth Fell Country House Hotel, Bowness-on-Windermere 👤
(Air Cdr & Mrs P A Kennedy) *1m S of Bowness, on A5074.* 6 acres of lawns and landscaped grounds on the hills above Lake Windermere, designed by Mawson around 1907; conifers and specimen trees best in spring and early summer with a colourful display of rhododendrons, azaleas and Japanese maples; grounds offer splendid views to Coniston mountains. Top terrace suitable for wheelchairs. Accommodation. Cream TEAS. *Adm £3, chd free. Sat 21 May (1-5). Private visits welcome by appt. Tel 015394 43286 www.lindethfell.co.uk*

34 Matson Ground, Windermere 👤🐕🏠
(Matson Ground Estate Co Ltd) *⅔m E of Bowness. From Kendal turn R off B5284 signposted Heathwaite, 100yds after Windermere Golf Club. Garden on L after 1/3m. From Bowness turn L onto B5284 from A5074. After ½m turn L at Xrds. Garden on L ½m along lane.* Stream flows through ornamental garden to large pond in the wild garden of spring bulbs, later wild flowers. Azaleas, rhododendrons, large mixed shrub/herbaceous borders, topiary work, white garden, spring/summer border, camomile lawn on terrace. ½-acre walled kitchen garden and greenhouses. 2-acre woodland. TEAS. *Adm £2.50, chd free. Sun 15 May (1-5)*

35 The Miller Howe Hotel, Windermere
(Charles Garside) *From Windermere take A591 towards Ambleside, turn L on A592 (Rayrigg Rd). Miller Howe approx 310yds on R.* 5½ acres of grounds with spectacular views of Lake Windermere, the fells and mountains. Many specimen plants and trees. Front entrance guarded by a magnificent monkey puzzle tree. Working herb garden, pond and lawn banks dotted with statues. This is a woodland garden with azaleas, rhododendrons, variety of heathers and a bluebell wood. Accommodation. TEAS. *Adm £2.50. Sats 14 May; 23 July (11-5) www.millerhowe.com*

36 [NEW] Morland House, Morland, nr Penrith
(Mrs Suzie Markham) *7m SE of Penrith. From S: through Shap on A6, approx 1½m turn R to Morland. In Morland down hill bearing R. At bottom of hill 'the square' Crown Inn on R, Morland House on L. From E: 1m after Appleby turn L to Bolton & Morland. Through Bolton, continue 2m turn L then R to Morland, entering square opp side to above. From N: A6 S from Penrith 1m turn L to Cliburn. In Cliburn R to Morland. In Morland bear L down hill to square, then as above.* Victorian garden undergoing long term restoration. Quarry garden separated from main garden by beck walk. Herbaceous borders, rose border with ramblers. Collection of tender plants. The head office of

Travelling Light. *Adm £2.50, chd free. Sun 21 Aug (2-5)*

37 Newbiggin Hall, Newbiggin, Temple Sowerby 👤
(Major & Mrs J H C Sawrey-Cookson) *8m E of Penrith. In village of Newbiggin, 2½m from A66 at Temple Sowerby or Kirkby Thore. Entrance to garden signed from Xrds in village.* Approx 7 acres of mature garden under gradual restoration. Formal garden; yews, lawns, old roses, herbaceous borders, avenues of trees incl sycamore and pleached lime. Informal garden; specimen and ancient trees, shrubs (especially rhododendrons). Woodland and beckside walk. Exhibition of history of garden. Dogs on leads. Home-made TEAS. *Adm £2.50, chd free. Sun 17 July (2-5)*

38 The Nook, Helton 👤🐕🏠
(Brenda & Philip Freedman) *6m S of Penrith. A6 S from Penrith. After Eamont Bridge turn R to Pooley Bridge. Fork L to Askham. Through Askham 1m to Helton. Follow signs.* ⅓-acre with outstanding views of Lowther valley and fells beyond. Plantsmans' garden, with many unusual plants. Garden divided into 3 areas: front cottage flower garden, side fruit and vegetable garden, main garden with species rhododendrums, rockeries, new scree garden, stone troughs, herbs, conifers, pond and water garden. Home-made TEAS. *Adm £2.50, chd free. Sun 1 May (11-4). Private visits welcome by appt May only, groups up to 20. No coaches. Tel 01931 712496 pfreedman@helton.demon.co.uk*

39 [NEW] The Old Rectory, Dean 🐕
(Mr F H & Mrs J S Wheeler) *5m SW of Cockermouth. Last house in Dean on rd to Workington, on L beyond church.* 1 acre with interest throughout the year, series of informal rooms with wide range of trees, shrubs and plants, many relatively tender. *Adm £2, chd free. Private visits welcome by appt throughout the year, groups also welcome. Tel 01946 861840*

40 [NEW] Pear Tree Cottage, Dalton, Burton-in-Kendal 🐕🏠
(Mr & Mrs A Greening) *4m W of Kirkby Lonsdale. 10m S of Kendal. From village of Burton-in-Kendal (A6070), follow Vicarage Lane for 1m. Parking at farm, 50yds before garden (signed).* ⅓-acre cottage garden in country setting. Garden and planting designed by present owners to encourage wildlife and harmonise with the natural

landscape, whilst providing yr-round interest. Well-stocked herbaceous borders, rockeries and mature shrubs. Informal pond, bog garden and fernery. Small organic vegetable plot. TEAS. *Adm £2.50, chd free (share to Myasthenia Gravis Assoc). Suns 19 June; 10 July (11-5). Private visits welcome by appt, for small groups, June to Aug only. Tel 01524 781624 www.peartreecottagecumbria.co.uk*

41 Plumpton Old Hall, Plumpton, Penrith 🅱🗙🏠
(Mr & Mrs Peter Thompson) *4m N of Penrith. Farm on A6. ¼m S of village Xrds. Farmhouse garden, courtyard, mixed borders, pond with wildlife area, gravel garden and organic vegetable plot. Adm £2.50, chd free. Tues 14, 28 June; 5 July (1-5)*

42 Quarry Hill House, Mealsgate 🅱🗙🏠
(Mr & Mrs Charles Woodhouse) *1m E of Mealsgate. (8m SSW of Wigton). At Mealsgate, on A595 Cockermouth to Carlisle rd, turn E onto B5299 for Boltongate, Ireby & Caldbeck. Approx 1m along rd, entrance gates to Quarry Hill House on L. Parkland setting with views of Skiddaw, northern fells and Solway Firth.* 3-acre traditional gardens, created over many years by the late Rosemary Shaw and her gardener Terry Hodgson. Herbaceous borders, shrubs, trees and large vegetable garden. Also wild flowers and many specimen trees in 25-acre park. Dyke kest created in 2001 by Peter Whiles. Re-creation for wildlife of ponds and wetlands in former shooting woods. Featured in 'Cumbria Life' 2003 & 'Cumberland News' 2004. Home-made TEAS. *Adm £3, chd free (share to Hospice at Home, Carlisle & North Lakeland). Suns 12 June; 17 July (1.30-5). Tel 016973 71225 charles.woodhouse@ukgateway.net*

43 1 Queens Place, Queens Road, Kendal 🗙
(Mr & Mrs T Hunte) *From Windermere A591 to Plumgarth's roundabout. A5284 Kendal for 1m, turn R into Queens Rd, 500yds on L.* High on a hillside overlooking Kendal and the fells beyond, a spectacular town garden with a touch of the tropics, gently sloping with cleverly designed limestone terraces and pathways. Packed with very interesting plantings incl tree ferns, trachycarpus, phormiums, grasses, herbaceous perennials, and small alpine garden. Winner Kendal in Bloom 2003/04, Featured in 'Garden News' & 'Cumbria Life' 2004. *Adm*

£2, chd free. Suns 5, 12 June (11-4) . Private visits welcome by appt. Tel 01539 730786

44 Rannerdale Cottage, Buttermere 🏠
(The McElney Family) *8m S of Cockermouth. 10m W of Keswick. B5289 on Crummock Water, in the Buttermere Valley. ½-acre cottage garden with beck and woodland walk overlooking Crummock Water, splendid mountain views.* Herbaceous, shrubs, roses, perennial geraniums, tree peonies, pond with fish. Home-made TEAS. *Adm £2, chd free (share to The Museum of East Asian Art, Bath). Sat, Sun 18, 19 June (11-5)*

45 Scarthwaite, Grange-in-Borrowdale 🗙
(Mr & Mrs E C Hicks) *5m S of Keswick. From Keswick take B5289 to Grange. Cross rd bridge, into village, house ¼m on L. Bridge NOT suitable for coaches but mini buses may cross. (¼m walk from far side of bridge for coach parties). The Keswick/Seatoller bus & Stagecoach Honister Rambler bus stop at Grange Bridge. This ½-acre garden gives the impression of woodland; focusing on naturalistic planting of ferns, hostas and bulbs, many varieties of hardy geraniums, clematis and other plants growing in the profusion of a cottage garden. Adm £2, chd free. Tues 17 May to 14 June; 19, 26 July (11-5). Also open* **High Rigg** *Tues 17 May. Private visits welcome by appt, no access for coaches. Tel 017687 77233*

46 [NEW] The Scented Rose Garden, Stewart Hill Barn, nr Hesket Newmarket 🅱🗙🏠
(Mr I Billot & Mrs J Flower) *7m W of Penrith. On A66 take unclassified re signed Hutton Roof. Follow rd for 5m to Haltcliff Bridge. Turn R at 2nd Newsham signpost. Garden at top of*

hill. New ½-acre rose garden created 800ft up, marvellous views to Carrock Fell. Garden run oranically by ex-head gardener Sudley Castle. Small ornamental vegetable garden, rambling and climbing rose arches. Herbaceous beds with mixture of David Austen English roses, old fashioned and shrub roses. Adjacent Rose Nursery. Share of plants sales to Air Ambulance. Presenter Stately Gardens Border TV 2004. *Adm £2, chd free, concessions £1.50. Sat, Sun 25, 26 June (11-6)*

47 ◆ Sizergh Castle, nr Kendal 🅱🗙🏠 NCCPG
(The National Trust) *3m S of Kendal. Approach rd leaves A590 close to & S of A590/A591 interchange.* ⅞-acre limestone rock garden, largest owned by The National Trust; collection of Japanese maples, dwarf conifers, hardy ferns, primulas, gentians, perennials and bulbs; water garden, aquatic plants; on castle walls shrubs and climbers, many half-hardy; south garden with specimen roses, lilies, shrubs and ground cover. Wild flower areas, herbaceous borders, crab apple orchard with spring bulbs, 'Dutch' garden. Terraced garden and lake; kitchen garden, vegetables, herbs, flowers; fruit orchard with spring bulbs. *House and Garden adm £5.80, Garden only adm £3.50, chd £1.70. Open Suns to Thurs 23 Mar to 30 Oct.* **For NGS:** *Sat 4 June (12.30-5.30) www.nationaltrust.org.uk*

48 ◆ Stagshaw, nr Ambleside
(The National Trust) *½m S of Ambleside. Turn E off A591, Windermere-Ambleside rd. Bus 555 Kendal-Keswick alight Waterhead.* Woodland garden incl fine collection of rhododendrons and azaleas. Ericaceous trees and shrubs incl magnolias, camellias, embothriums. Views over Windermere. *Adm £2, chd £1.* **For NGS:** *Suns 24 Apr; 5 June (10-6.30) windermere@nationaltrust.org.uk*

49 NEW Stone Edge, Jack Hill, Allithwaite 🚹🚫
(Ian & Julie Chambers) *2m W of Grange-over-Sands. On B5277. Jack Hill is on L just before Allithwaite Village. Parking available in The Pheasant Inn car park at bottom of Jack Hill.* A garden in harmony with nature; incl formal lavender garden; border with shrubs, climbers and perennials; herbs grown for use in the kitchen. Spectacular specimens form a Mediterranean garden; woodland garden meanders down to a pond. Pots abound. Fantasic views over Morecambe Bay. A plantsman's paradise. TEAS in aid of St Mary's Hospice, Ulverston. *Adm £2.50, chd free.* Tue 28 June **Day & Evening Opening** *£2.50, wine, (10-5 6-8). Private visits welcome by appt. Tel 015395 33895*

50 Summerdale House, Nook, nr Lupton 🚫🅑
(David & Gail Sheals) *7m S of Kendal. 6m W of Kirkby Lonsdale. From junction 36 M6 take A65 to Kirkby Lonsdale at Nook take R turn Farleton.* 1½-acre part-walled garden in process of restoration and development by owners. Varied and interesting range of herbaceous perennials. Herbaceous border, pond garden, small gravel garden, woodland planting and old orchard, soft fruit and vegetable garden. Home-made TEAS. *Adm £3, chd free.* Suns 8 May; 19 June; 21 Aug *(11-5). Private visits welcome by appt. Tel 015395 67210 sheals@btinternet.com*

51 21 Ulverston Road, Dalton-in-Furness
(Mr Barney Somers) *3m NE of Barrow-in-Furness. From Ulverston, approach on main rd to Dalton A590 off bypass roundabout, house on RH-side just before Horse & Jockey PH. Park in public car park Tudor Square.* Garden is behind house down narrow lane. Small terraced garden, subsequently enlarged, created initially by present owner's deceased wife. Modernist Japanese influenced garden with interesting use

of stone and metal, designed to be labour-saving. Fruit trees, shrub roses, wild area. TEAS in aid of Marie Curie Cancer Care. *Adm £2, chd free.* Sat, Sun 2, 3 July *(11-4)*

52 NEW Underwood House, Bootle, Millom 🚹🚫
(Val & Jim Jones) *26m S of Whitehaven. From Whitehaven: S on A595 through centre of Bootle. Turn L onto unmarked rd just past the PO leading upto fell. Underwood ½m on L. From Millom: 8m N on A595. Turn R before entering centre of Bootle then as above.* Numerous areas of garden surrounding the house. Spring display of rhododendrons, azaleas, camellias and other flowering shrubs and bulbs. Walled vegetable garden. Views of Black Combe. Home-made TEAS in aid of Abbeyfield Black Combe Society. *Adm £2.50, chd free.* Sat 14 May *(2-5). Private visits welcome by appt. Tel 01229 718202 jim-jones@btinternet.com*

53 Warth Sutton Cottage, Crooklands, Milnthorpe 🚹🚫🅑
(Simon Robinson) *6m S of Kendal. 7m W of Kirkby Lonsdale. 1m from junction 36 M6. Take A6070 to Burton/Holme, after ¼m take 1st R at farm. Follow lane back over M6. House can be seen from bridge.* 1-acre cottage garden with both formal and informal planting. Wide herbaceous borders with fruit trees, containing both usual and unusual plants especially hardy geraniums, campanulas, alliums and salvias etc. Featured in 'Cumbria Life' 2004. Home-made TEAS. *Adm £2.50, chd free.* Sun 15 May *(12-5)*

54 Windy Hall, Crook Road, Windermere 🚫 NCCPG
(Diane & David Kinsman) *8m NW of Kendal. On B5284 up Linthwaite Country House Hotel driveway.* 4-acre owner designed and maintained garden. Woodland underplanted with species rhododendrons, magnolias and hydrangeas; Japanese influenced quarry garden; alpine area with gunnera; wild flower meadow;

kitchen, 'privy' and 'Best' gardens. Waterfowl garden with many stewartias. Redesigned pond garden with plants raised from seed collected by David in China. NCCPG Collections of *Aruncus* and *Filipendula*; rare sheep and pheasants. Home-made TEAS. *Adm £2.50, chd free.* Suns 8 May; 12 June *(10-5). Private visits welcome by appt. Tel 015394 46238 dph@ceh.ac.uk*

55 Yewbarrow House, Hampsfell Road, Grange-over-Sands 🅑
(Jonathan & Margaret Denby) *Follow signs in centre of Grange. Turn R at HSBC Bank into Pig Lane, 1st L into Hampsfell Rd. Garden 200yds on L.* New Mediterranean style garden on 4½-acre elevated site with magnificent views over Morecambe Bay. The garden features a restored walled Victorian kitchen garden; Italianate terrace garden; exotic gravel garden; fern garden and Japanese Hot Spring pool. Gold Award 2003. 'The Independent', 'House Beautiful', 'Traditional Homes & Gardens' features 2003, 'Daily Telegraph' & 'Cumbria Life' 2004. Cream TEAS. *Adm £3, chd free.* Sat, Sun 13, 14 Aug *(11-4). Private visits welcome by appt. Tel 015395 32469 www.yewbarrowhouse.co.uk*

56 Yews, Bowness-on-Windermere 🚹🚫🅑
(Sir Oliver & Lady Scott) *1m S of Bowness-on-Windermere. A5074. Middle Entrance Drive, 50yds.* Medium-sized formal Edwardian garden; fine trees, ha-ha, herbaceous borders; greenhouse. Bog area being developed, bamboo, primula, hosta. Young yew maze. Partially suitable for wheelchairs. Home-made TEAS. *Adm £2.50, chd free.* Sun 19 June *(2-5)*

Evening Opening (See also garden description)	
Stone Edge	28 June
Holker Hall Gardens	13 July

Denbighshire & Colwyn
See separate Welsh section on page 448

Derbyshire

County Organisers: Mr & Mrs Graham Dougan, Field Farm, Field Lane, Kirk Ireton, Ashbourne, Derbyshire DE6 3JU Tel 01335 370958

County Treasurers: Mr & Mrs Peter Spencer, The Riddings Farm, Kirk Ireton, Ashbourne, Derbyshire DE6 3LB Tel 01335 370331

Maps: Numbers shown next to each garden entry refer to that garden's entry on the county map. This position is approximate; distance and directions from the nearest main town are generally shown in the garden text. A precise location is available for those gardens featured on the NGS website by visiting www.ngs.org.uk.

Symbols: Information relating to symbols is given on page 21

DATES OF OPENING

Evening openings
See end of county listing

Gardens open to the public
For details see garden description
Bluebell Arboretum, Smisby *(3)*
Calke Abbey, Ticknall *(5)*
Cascades, Bonsall *(6)*
Hardwick Hall, Doe Lea *(20)*
Hopton Hall Gardens, Hopton Village *(23)*
Kedleston Hall, Kedleston *(25)*
Lea Gardens, Lea, Nr Matlock *(26)*
Renishaw Hall, Renishaw *(38)*
Tissington Hall, nr Ashbourne *(47)*
Yew Tree Farm, Tansley *(54)*

By appointment only
For telephone number and other details see garden description. Private visits welcomed
Birchfield, Ashford in the Water *(2)*
The Gardens at Dobholme Fishery, Troway, nr Coal Aston *(19)*
Hillside, New Whittington *(22)*
Horsleygate Hall, Holmesfield *(24)*
Spindlewood, Darley Dale *(42)*
Spring Tops Cottage, Jericho, Earl Sterndale *(44)*
Thatched Farm, Radbourne *(46)*
26 Wheeldon Avenue, Derby *(50)*
Yew Tree Bungalow, Tansley *(53)*

February 20 Sunday
Cherry Tree Cottage, Hilton *(8)*

April 3 Sunday
Dove Cottage, Clifton, Ashbourne *(14)*

April 13 Wednesday
Cascades, Bonsall *(6)*

April 17 Sunday
Cherry Tree Cottage, Hilton *(8)*
The Riddings Farm, Kirk Ireton *(39)*

April 20 Wednesday
Bluebell Arboretum, Smisby *(3)*

April 24 Sunday
Bluebell Arboretum, Smisby *(3)*
Fir Croft, Calver *(17)*
35 Wyver Lane, Belper *(52)*

May 1 Sunday
Gamesley Fold Cottage, Glossop *(18)*
The Riddings Farm, Kirk Ireton *(39)*

May 2 Monday (Bank Hol)
Oaks Lane Farm, Kelstedge *(33)*

May 8 Sunday
Broomfield Hall, Morley *(4)*
Cloud Cottage, Simmondley *(10)*
Dove Cottage, Clifton, Ashbourne *(14)*
Fir Croft, Calver *(17)*

May 15 Sunday
Cherry Tree Cottage, Hilton *(8)*
Cloud Cottage, Simmondley *(10)*
Field Farm, Kirk Ireton *(16)*
Locko Park, Spondon *(27)*

May 18 Wednesday
Bluebell Arboretum, Smisby *(3)*

May 22 Sunday
Bluebell Arboretum, Smisby *(3)*
Cashel, Kirk Ireton *(7)*
Cloud Cottage, Simmondley *(10)*
Dam Farm House, Ednaston *(12)*
Fir Croft, Calver *(17)*
Postern House, Turnditch *(37)*
Windward, Wirksworth *(51)*

May 25 Wednesday
Cascades, Bonsall *(6)*
Kedleston Hall, Kedleston *(25)*

May 29 Sunday
10 Chestnut Way, Repton *(9)*
Dove Cottage, Clifton, Ashbourne *(14)*
Gamesley Fold Cottage, Glossop *(18)*

May 30 Monday (Bank Hol)
10 Chestnut Way, Repton *(9)*
Shatton Hall Farm, Bamford *(40)*

June 1 Wednesday
Field Farm, Kirk Ireton *(16)*

June 2 Thursday
Field Farm, Kirk Ireton *(16)*
Gamesley Fold Cottage, Glossop *(18)*

June 4 Saturday
334 Belper Road, Stanley Common *(1)*

June 5 Sunday
334 Belper Road, Stanley Common *(1)*
35 Wyver Lane, Belper *(52)*

June 12 Sunday
Cherry Tree Cottage, Hilton *(8)*
Clovermead, Findern, Derby *(11)*
Fir Croft, Calver *(17)*
Gamesley Fold Cottage, Glossop *(18)*
Otterbrook, Chinley *(34)*
Park Hall, Walton, Chesterfield *(35)*
Yew Tree Farm, Tansley *(54)*

June 15 Wednesday
Bluebell Arboretum, Smisby *(3)*

June 16 Thursday
Gamesley Fold Cottage, Glossop **(Evening)** *(18)*

June 19 Sunday
Bluebell Arboretum, Smisby *(3)*
Field Farm, Kirk Ireton *(16)*

June 22 Wednesday
Cascades, Bonsall *(6)*

June 26 Sunday
Dove Cottage, Clifton, Ashbourne *(14)*
Fanshawe Gate Hall, Holmesfield *(15)*
Gamesley Fold Cottage, Glossop *(18)*
Otterbrook, Chinley *(34)*
Park Hall, Walton, Chesterfield *(35)*
Postern House, Turnditch *(37)*

July 3 Sunday
Fanshawe Gate Hall, Holmesfield *(15)*
Longarth Piece, Ilkeston *(28)*

July 6 Wednesday
Postern House, Turnditch **(Evening)** *(37)*

July 10 Sunday
Cherry Tree Cottage, Hilton *(8)*
Fanshawe Gate Hall, Holmesfield *(15)*
The Spinney, Combs *(43)*

July 13 Wednesday
Cascades, Bonsall *(6)*
10 Chestnut Way, Repton **(Evening)** *(9)*

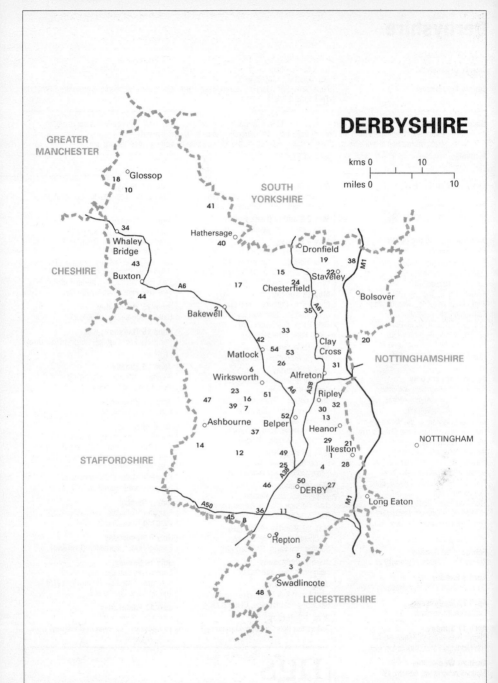

DERBYSHIRE

GREATER
MANCHESTER

SOUTH
YORKSHIRE

kms 0   10
miles 0   10

Glossop
18
10

41

34
Hathersage
40
Whaley
Bridge
43
Dronfield
19
38
M1

CHESHIRE
Buxton
44
A6
15
17
Chesterfield
24
Staveley
22
Bolsover

Bakewell
2
35
A61

33
Clay
Cross
20

42
54 53
Matlock
26
31
NOTTINGHAMSHIRE

6
Wirksworth
Alfreton
A38

23
16
51
A6
Ripley
47
39 7
30 32
13
Ashbourne
Belper
52
Heanor

37
14
12
49
29 21
Ilkeston
1
NOTTINGHAM

STAFFORDSHIRE
25
4
28

46
50
DERBY
27

A50
36
11
M1
Long Eaton

45 8

9
Repton

5

3

48
Swadlincote

LEICESTERSHIRE

July 17 Sunday
Cascades, Bonsall *(6)*
Hardwick Hall, Doe Lea *(20)*

July 20 Wednesday
Bluebell Arboretum, Smisby *(3)*
Calke Abbey, Ticknall *(5)*

July 24 Sunday
Bluebell Arboretum, Smisby *(3)*
Clovermead, Findern, Derby *(11)*
Dam Farm House, Ednaston *(12)*
274 Heanor Road, Ilkeston *(21)*
2 Manvers Street, Ripley *(30)*
Markham Villa, Newton *(31)*
The Riddings Farm, Kirk Ireton *(39)*

July 31 Sunday
Dove Cottage, Clifton, Ashbourne *(14)*
Shatton Hall Farm, Bamford *(40)*

August 3 Wednesday
Cascades, Bonsall *(6)*

August 7 Sunday
62A Denby Lane, Loscoe *(13)*
9 Main Street, Horsley Woodhouse *(29)*
7 Warren Drive, Linton *(48)*

August 14 Sunday
23 Mill Lane, Codnor *(32)*
The Shooting Lodge, Bamford *(41)*
Sycamore Farm, Foston *(45)*
Wharfedale, Duffield *(49)*

August 20 Saturday
19 Portland Street, Etwall *(36)*

August 21 Sunday
19 Portland Street, Etwall *(36)*

August 24 Wednesday
Bluebell Arboretum, Smisby *(3)*

August 28 Sunday
Bluebell Arboretum, Smisby *(3)*

August 29 Monday (Bank Hol)
Tissington Hall, nr Ashbourne *(47)*

August 30 Tuesday
Tissington Hall, nr Ashbourne *(47)*

September 4 Sunday
The Riddings Farm, Kirk Ireton *(39)*
Sycamore Farm, Foston *(45)*
7 Warren Drive, Linton *(48)*

September 21 Wednesday
Bluebell Arboretum, Smisby *(3)*

September 25 Sunday
Bluebell Arboretum, Smisby *(3)*

October 26 Wednesday
Bluebell Arboretum, Smisby *(3)*

October 30 Sunday
Bluebell Arboretum, Smisby *(3)*

2006

February 19 Sunday
Cherry Tree Cottage, Hilton *(8)*

DESCRIPTIONS OF GARDENS

The Beeches, Mill Street, Rocester 🚻🐕❀
See Staffordshire & part of West Midlands.

❶ 334 Belper Road, Stanley Common 🚻🐕❀
(Gill & Colin Hancock) *7m N of Derby. 3m W of Ilkeston. On A609, ¾m from Rose & Crown Xrds (A608). Please park in field up farm drive or Working Men's Club rear car park if wet.* ¾-acre garden. Large herbaceous island bed, shrub borders, pergolas and new kitchen garden. Small water features, natural wildlife pond and conservatory with streptocarpus; ½m walk through recently planted wood and around ½-acre lake. Home-made TEAS. *Adm £2, chd free. Sat, Sun 4, 5 June (2.30-5.30). Private visits welcome by appt. Tel 0115 9301 061*

❷ Birchfield, Dukes Drive, Ashford in the Water ❀
(Brian Parker) *2m NW of Bakewell. On A6 to Buxton.* Beautifully situated terraced garden of approx ¾ acre. Designed for yr-round colour, it contains wide variety of shrubs and perennials, bulbs, water and scree gardens. Arboretum with wild flowers has been developed on a further 1¼ acres. TEAS. *Adm £2, chd free (share to Thornhill Memorial Trust). Private visits welcome by appt, individuals & groups Apr to Sept. Tel 01629 813800 www.birchfieldgarden.com*

❸ ◆ Bluebell Arboretum, Smisby 🚻❀
(Robert & Suzette Vernon) *1m N of Ashby-de-la-Zouch. Arboretum is clearly signposted in Annwell Lane, ¼m S, through village of Smisby. Smisby is off B5006, between Ticknall & Ashby-de-la-Zouch.* 5-acre arboretum planted in last 14yrs incl many specimens of rare trees and shrubs. Bring wellingtons in wet weather. Please be aware this is not a wood full of bluebells, despite the name. Adjacent specialist nursery. TEAS. *Adm £2.50, chd free.* **For NGS:** *Weds, Suns 20, 24 Apr; 15, 19 June; 20, 24 July; 24, 28 Aug; 21, 25 Sept; 26, 30 Oct. Weds (9-5); Suns (10.30-4.30). Tel 07801 688963 sales@bluebellnursery.com*

Brook House Farm, Dagdale, Bramshall, Uttoxeter 🚻🐕❀
See Staffordshire & part of West Midlands.

❹ Broomfield Hall, Morley 🚻🐕❀
(Derby College) *4m N of Derby. 6m S of Heanor On A608.* Landscaped garden of 25 acres. Shrubs, trees, rose collection, herbaceous borders; glasshouses; walled garden; garden tour guides. Themed gardens, plant centre. Silver Medal Winners Chelsea Flower Show, Large Gold Medal Winners Derbyshire County Show & Bakewell Show, 2004. Light refreshments and TEAS. *Adm £2, chd free, concessions £1. Sun 8 May (10-4). Private visits welcome by appt. Tel 01332 836600 www.derby-college.ac.uk*

❺ ◆ Calke Abbey, Ticknall 🚻🐕❀
(The National Trust) *10m S of Derby. On A514 at Ticknall between Swadlincote & Melbourne.* Extensive late C18 walled gardens. Flower garden with summer bedding and famous auricula theatre. Impressive collection of glasshouses and garden buildings. Vegetable garden growing heirloom varieties of fruit and vegetables, on sale to visitors. Light refreshments and TEAS. *House and Garden adm £6.30, chd £3.10, family £15.70, Garden only £3.80, chd £1.90, family £9.50. Wed - Sun Apr to Oct (11-5.30, last adm 5).* **For NGS:** *Wed 20 July. Tel 01332 863822*

❻ ◆ Cascades, Clatterway, Bonsall 🚻❀
(Alan & Elizabeth Clements) *5m SW of Matlock. From Cromford A6 T-lights turn towards Wirksworth. Turn R along Via Gellia, signed Buxton & Bonsall. After 1m turn R up hill towards Bonsall village.* Cascades on R at top of hill. Historic 4-acre garden set on many levels and surrounded by mature trees, high cliffs and banks, divided into garden rooms with stream, canal and pond. Each has its own character and a wide variety of plants shrubs and trees. Featured in 'Derbyshire Life' 2003 & 'Reflections' 2004. TEAS. *Adm £2, chd free. Every Sun, April to end Sept. Weekdays & Sats by appt.* **For NGS:** *Weds 13 Apr; 25 May; 22 June; 13 July; 3 Aug. Sun 17 July (10-5). Tel 01629 822813 www.cascadesgardens.com*

❼ Cashel, Kirk Ireton ❀
(Anita & Jeremy Butt) *2m S of Wirksworth. Turn off B5023 (Duffield-Wirksworth rd). Follow rd to Kirk Ireton, take sharp R turn at church corner. Follow lane for 219yds. Garden on R, car parking 54yds beyond the house.* 3 acres situated on sloping site featuring

terraced ravine and views of Ecclesbourne Valley. Many interesting trees, plants and shrubs. TEAS in aid of Kirk Ireton Church. *Adm £2, chd free. Sun 22 May (2-5). Private visits welcome by appt. Tel 01335 370495*

❽ Cherry Tree Cottage, Sutton Lane, Hilton 🚻🐕🏡
(Mrs A Hamblin) *7m W of Derby. Turn off A516 opp the Old Talbot Inn in village centre.* Plant lover's C18 cottage garden. Approx ⅓ acre with herbaceous borders, herb and scree garden, gravel garden with small water feature. Many unusual and interesting plants. Species aquilegias, geraniums, iris, campanula, pulmonaria etc. *Adm £2, chd free. Suns 20 Feb (Snowdrop & Hellebore day); 17 Apr; 15 May; 12 June; 10 July (2-5); 19 Feb 2006. Private visits welcome by appt. Tel 01283 733778*

❾ 10 Chestnut Way, Repton 🚻🏡
(Robert & Pauline Little) *6m S of Derby. From A38, S of Derby, follow signs to Willington, then Repton. In Repton turn R at roundabout. Chestnut Way is ¼m up hill, on L.* An unusual-shaped ⅓-acre organic garden developed over last 16yrs for yr-round interest. Clematis, hardy perennials and shade loving plants artistically arranged in an informal style with grass paths, mature trees, ponds and vegetable garden. Peaceful, with plenty of seats to relax on, much more than just a collection of plants. Prize-winner in Repton Front Garden Competition 2004. Home-made TEAS. *Adm £2, chd free. Sun, Mon 29, 30 May (1-5).* **Evening Opening** *£3, wine, Wed 13 July (6-9). Private visits welcome by appt, groups of 10+. Tel 01283 702267 www.dunelm.org.uk/homepages/ ?john.little*

❿ Cloud Cottage, Simmondley 🚻
(Mr & Mrs R G Lomas) *1m SW of Glossop. On High Lane between Simmondley & Charlesworth. From M67 take A57, turn R at Mottram (1st T-lights) through Broadbottom & Charlesworth. In Charlesworth Town Lane by the side of Grey Mare. Cloud Cottage is ½m on R. From Glossop, A57 towards Manchester, turn L at 2nd of two mini roundabouts up Simmondley Lane, Cloud Cottage is on L after passing Hare & Hounds.* 1¼-acre arboretum/rhododendron garden. Altitude 750ft on side of hill in Peak District National Park. Collections of

conifers, most over 40yrs old. Species and hybrid rhododendron; wide variety of shrubs; Japanese-inspired garden with 3 ponds. *Adm £2, chd free. Suns 8, 15, 22 May (2-5). Private visits welcome by appt May only. Tel 01457 862033*

⓫ NEW Clovermead, Commonpiece Lane, Findern, Derby 🐕🏡
(David & Rosemary Noblet) *4m S of Derby. From Findern village green, turn R at church into Lower Green, R turn into Commonpiece Lane, approx 500yds on R.* Cottage garden set in approx ¾ acre. Garden rooms full of perennial flowers. Honeysuckle, roses, jasmine and sweet peas scent the air. Pergolas and archways with clematis, fishponds and bandstand with seating. Greenhouses, vegetable plot and wildlife orchard. Home-made TEAS in aid of NSPCC. *Adm £2, chd free. Suns 12 June; 24 July (2-6)*

NEW 7 Collygate, Swingate, Kimberley 🚻🐕🏡
See Nottinghamshire.

⓬ Dam Farm House, Yeldersley Lane, Ednaston 🚻🐕🏡
(Mrs J M Player) *5m SE of Ashbourne. On A52, opp Ednaston village turn, gate on R 500yds.* 3 acres incl a young arboretum, beautifully situated. Contains mixed borders, scree. Unusual plants have been collected. Home-made TEAS. *Adm £3, chd free. Suns 22 May; 24 July (2-4.30). Private visits welcome by appt. Tel 01335 360291*

⓭ 62A Denby Lane, Loscoe
(Mrs J Charlesworth) *12m NW of Nottingham. Between Codnor & Heanor, on A6007. Follow Denby sign.* Interesting garden with heathers, ferns, grasses, conifers and shrubs; 2 small water features; Japanese features. Chrysanthemums and dahlias, bedding plants. Light refreshments and TEAS. *Adm £1.50, chd free. Sun 7 Aug (2-5)*

⓮ Dove Cottage, Clifton, Ashbourne 🐕🏡
(Stephen & Anne Liverman) *1½m SW of Ashbourne. Enter Clifton village. Turn R at Xrds by church. Travel 100yds turn L, Dove Cottage 1st house on L. Always well signed on open days.* ¾-acre garden by R Dove, extensively replanted winter 2003 - 2004. Emphasis on establishing collections of hardy plants and shrubs incl alchemillas, alliums, berberis, geraniums, euphorbias, hostas, lilies, variegated

and silver foliage plants inc astrantias. Plantsman's garden. Area growing new heucheras and other purple flowering plants and foliage. Woodland area extensively planted with daffodils for early visitors. TEAS. *Adm £2.50, chd free (share to British Heart Foundation). Suns 3 Apr; 8, 29 May; 26 June; 31 July (1-5). Private visits welcome by appt. Tel 01335 343545 stephenliverman@hotmail.com*

⓯ Fanshawe Gate Hall, Holmesfield 🚻🐕🏡
(Mr & Mrs John Ramsden) *2m W of Dronfield. Situated on the edge of the Peak National Park. Follow B6054 towards Owler Bar. 1st R turn after Robin Hood Inn signposted Fanshawe Gate Lane.* C13 seat of the Fanshawe family. Old-fashioned cottage-style garden. Many stone features, fine C16 dovecote. Upper walled garden with herbaceous, variegated and fern plantings, water features, terracing and lawns. Lower courtyard with knot garden and herb border. Restored terraced orchard representing a medieval tilt yard; wildlife pond; potager. Garden continues to develop. Light refreshments and TEAS. *Adm £2, chd free (share to Oesophageal Patients Association). Suns 26 June; 3, 10 July (11-5). Private visits welcome by appt June & July only, groups of 10+. Tel 0114 289 0391 www.fgh.org.uk*

⓰ Field Farm, Kirk Ireton 🚻🏡
(Graham & Irene Dougan) *2m S of Wirksworth. At top of Main St, Kirk Ireton turn L signed Blackwall, on sharp RH-bend find Field Lane (unmade rd), Field Farm 400yds.* Garden for plant lovers in beautiful setting with glorious views. 2 acres overflowing with rare trees and shrubs, mixed herbaceous beds, borders; arches; pergolas; water features; alpines; fuchsias and herbs. Shrub and climbing roses planted imaginatively throughout the garden. Gravelled courtyard with raised beds, troughs, planters, summer baskets and pots. Spring bulbs and new foliage, summer fragrance and autumn colour. An idyllic garden planted for all seasons. Featured in 'The English Garden' & on BBC E Midlands Today Down The Garden Path, 2004. Home-made TEAS. *Adm £2.50, chd free. Suns 15 May; 19 Jun (2-5); Wed, Thur 1, 2 June (11-5). Private visits welcome by appt. Tel 01335 370958 www.fieldfarmgarden.info*

⏴17⏵ Fir Croft, Froggatt Road, Calver 🔣🚫🈁

(Dr S B Furness) *4m N of Bakewell. At junction of B6001 with A625 (formerly B6054), adjacent to Power Garage.* Massive scree with many rarities. Plantsman's garden; rockeries; water garden and nursery; extensive collection (over 3000 varieties) of alpines; conifers; over 800 sempervivums, 500 saxifrages and 350 primulas. Tufa and scree beds. *Adm by donation. Suns 24 Apr; 8, 22 May; 12 June (2-5). Private visits welcome by appt for groups of 10+, in writing to Fir Croft, Froggatt Rd, Calver, Hope Valley S32 3ZD www.alpineplantcentre.co.uk*

⏴18⏵ Gamesley Fold Cottage, Glossop 🚫🈁

(Mrs G Carr) *2m W of Glossop. Off A626 Glossop to Marple rd, nr Charlesworth. Turn down lane directly opp St Margaret's School. White cottage at bottom.* Old-fashioned cottage garden. Spring garden with herbaceous borders, wild flowers and herbs in profusion to attract butterflies and wildlife. Adjacent wild flower plant nursery. Home-made TEAS. *Adm £2, chd free. Suns 1, 29 May; 12, 26 June (1-5); Thur 2 June (12-4).* **Evening Opening** *£2, Thur 16 June (6-9). Private visits welcome by appt for groups of 10+. Tel 01457 867856 www.gamesleyfold.co.uk*

⏴19⏵ The Gardens at Dobholme Fishery, Troway, nr Coal Aston 🈁

(Paul & Pauline Calvert) *3m NE of Dronfield. Halfway along B6056, Dronfield to Eckington rd, 2½m from each. Coming from Dronfield turn L at Blackamoor Head Inn for Troway. Follow signs in village.* Situated in beautiful conservation area of Moss Valley. Developed on sloping site of approx 3 acres around fishing ponds. Designed to encourage wildlife; planted in a wild, natural look. Heavy clay with many springs; stone quarried from the site is widely used to pave the pond sides. Sloping uneven terrain. Potager vegetable garden and herb garden. *Adm £2, chd free. Private visits welcome by appt for groups of 6+. Tel 01246 451337*

Grafton Cottage, Barton-under-Needwood 🚫🈁

See Staffordshire & part of West Midlands.

⏴20⏵ ◆ Hardwick Hall, Doe Lea 🔣🚫

(The National Trust) *8m SE of Chesterfield. S of A617. Signed from J29 M1.* Grass walks between yew and hornbeam hedges; cedar trees; herb garden; herbaceous and rose borders. Finest example of Elizabethan house in the country. Light refreshments and TEAS. *House and Garden adm £7.20, chd £3.60, family £18. Garden only £3.90, chd £1.95, family £9.25. Wed to Sun, 23 Mar to 30 Oct (11-5.30).* **For NGS:** *Sun 17 July. Tel 01246 858405 rachel.coulton@nationaltrust.org.uk*

⏴21⏵ 274 Heanor Road, Ilkeston 🈁

(Mr & Mrs G Seagrave) *1m N of Ilkeston. On A6007, 2m from Heanor towards Ilkeston, opp Ilkeston Hospital.* Large yr-round garden, with over 50 slow and medium varieties of conifer, 150 different shrubs, ornamental trees, herbaceous plants; cut flower beds; small wooded area; vegetables; varieties of soft, top and stone fruit; greenhouses; pergolas, gazebo; topiary. The garden is planted for maximum colour effects. Erewash Borough Council 1st prize Grand Award 2003, 2nd Mixed Gardens 2004. TEAS. *Adm £1.50, chd free. Sun 24 July (2-5.30)*

⏴22⏵ Hillside, 286 Handley Road, New Whittington 🈁

(E J Lee) *3m N of Chesterfield. From A6135, take B6052 through Eckington & Marsh Lane 3m. Turn L at Xrds signed Whittington, then 1m. From Coal Aston (Sheffield), take B6056 towards Chesterfield to give way sign, then 1m. From Chesterfield, take B6052.* ½-acre sloping site. Herbaceous borders, rock garden, alpines, streams, pools, bog gardens, alpine house. Acers, bamboos, collection of approx 150 varieties of ferns, eucalypts, euphorbias, grasses, conifers, Himalayan bed. 1500 plants permanently labelled. TEAS. *Adm £2, chd free. Private visits welcome by appt, groups of 10+. Tel 01246 454960*

◆ Hodsock Priory Gardens, Blyth 🔣🚫🈁

See Nottinghamshire.

⏴23⏵ ◆ Hopton Hall Gardens, Hopton Village 🔣🚫🈁

(Mr & Mrs W Brogden) *6m NE of Ashbourne. From B5035 (Ashbourne to Matlock rd) turn into villages of Carsington & Hopton. Continue through village, Hall & gardens clearly signposted. Follow signs to car park.* Beautiful snowdrops set in 5 acres of natural woodland plus 4 acres of formal gardens incl an historic walled garden, rose walk and formal lawns. 8 acres of informal garden incl 2 ponds, small wildlife lake and 2 small arboretums. Mainly firm paths. Light refreshments and TEAS. *Adm £2.50, chd under 16 free. Sat 29 Jan to Sun 27 Feb 2005 incl (10.30-4). Sat 28 Jan to Sun 26 Feb 2006. Tel 01629 540458 www.snowdropsathoptonhall.com*

"We don't get much trouble from the neighbours now!"

㉔ Horsleygate Hall, Horsleygate Lane, Holmesfield 🗝️⊕
(Robert & Margaret Ford) *6m NE of Chesterfield. Follow B6051 from Owler Bar (A621) towards Chesterfield; after 1m take 1st L onto Horsleygate Lane. Park in field on R.* 2-acre plantsman's garden. Sloping site incl woodland garden; hot sun terrace; rockeries; pools; fern area; jungle garden; mixed borders and ornamental kitchen garden. An overall theme of informality with walls, terraces, paths and statuary. *Private visits welcome by appt. Tel 0114 289 0333*

㉕ ◆ Kedleston Hall, Kedleston 🗝️🗝️
(The National Trust) *5m NW of Derby. Signed from junction of A38-A52.* 12 acres. A broad open lawn, bounded by a ha-ha, marks the C18 informal garden. Formal layout to the W was introduced early this century when summerhouse and orangery, both designed by George Richardson in late C18, were moved to their present position. Gardens at their best during May and June when the azaleas and rhododendrons are one mass of colour. The Long Walk, a woodland walk of some 3m, is bright with spring flowers. Light refreshments and TEAS. *House and Garden adm £6.30, chd £3. Park and garden only £2.80, chd £1.40. Daily 19 Mar to 31 Oct (10-6).* **For NGS:** *Wed 25 May (10-6). Tel 01332 842393 colin.chappell@nationaltrust.org.uk*

㉖ ◆ Lea Gardens, Lea, Nr Matlock 🗝️⊕
(Mr & Mrs J Tye) *5m SE of Matlock. Lea. Off A6. Also off A615.* Rare collection of rhododendrons, azaleas, kalmias, alpines and conifers in delightful woodland setting. Gardens are sited on remains of medieval quarry and cover about 4 acres. Specialised plant nursery of rhododendrons and azaleas on site. Light refreshments and TEAS. *Adm £3.50, chd 50p. Daily 20 Mar to 30 June (10-5). Tel 01629 534380/534260*

㉗ Locko Park, Spondon ⊕
(Mrs Lucy Palmer) *6m NE of Derby. From A52 Borrowash bypass, 2m N via B6001, turn to Spondon.* Large garden; pleasure gardens; rose gardens. House (not open) by Smith of Warwick with Victorian additions. Chapel (open) Charles II, with original ceiling. TEAS. *Adm £2, chd free. Sun 15 May (2-5)*

㉘ Longarth Piece, 159 Longfield Lane, Ilkeston 🗝️⊕
(Diane & David Bennett) *1m S of Ilkeston. (Stanton side) off Quarry Hill, opp Hallam Fields Junior School.* Described by visitors as an artist's garden; large, informal garden, overflowing with fruit, shrubs, flowers; 2 small fish ponds and conservatory. Strong emphasis on texture, colour and lots of unexpected corners. Home-made TEAS. *Adm £1.50, chd free. Sun 3 July (2-5.30). Private visits welcome by appt, evening garden visits and supper May & June. Tel 0115 849 3559*

㉙ 9 Main Street, Horsley Woodhouse 🗝️
(Alison Napier) *3m SW of Heanor. 6m N of Derby. Turn off A608 Derby to Heanor rd at Smalley, towards Belper, (A609). Garden on A609, 1m from Smalley turning.* ½-acre hilltop garden overlooking lovely farmland view. Terracing, borders, lawns and pergola create space for an informal layout with planting for colour effect. Features incl large wildlife pond with water lilies, bog garden and small formal pool. Emphasis on carefully selected herbaceous perennials mixed with shrubs and old-fashioned roses. Wheelchair-adapted WC. Home-made TEAS. *Adm £2, chd free, wheelchair users free. Sun 7 Aug (1-5)*

㉚ 2 Manvers Street, Ripley 🗝️🗝️⊕
(Mrs D Wood & Mr D Hawkins) *Ripley Town centre to Derby rd turn L opp Leisure Centre onto Heath Rd. 1st turn R onto Meadow Rd, 1st L onto Manvers St.* S-facing secluded colourful garden with patio, lawn, mixed borders, incl perennials, annuals and shrubs. Fish pond, water features; pergola supporting Virginia creeper and clematis. Arbour with seating and several summer hanging baskets and planters. Home-made TEAS. *Adm £2, chd free. Sun 24 July (2-6). Private visits welcome by appt, July & Aug only. Tel 01773 743962*

㉛ Markham Villa, 60 Alfreton Road, Newton 🗝️⊕
(Ann & Kevin Briggs) *2m NE of Alfreton. A38 N from Derby. Take Alfreton/Matlock junction along A61. Turn R following Blackwell signs. 1½m to Newton. Approx ⅔ acre.* Small front garden, house garden with rejuvenated and extended beds; pond; walkways and features. Paddock garden with series of gardens for different purposes and

moods. Greenhouses; vegetable plot; orchard; summerhouse and fragrant garden with camomile lawn. Extensively planted for all-round interest of flower, foliage, colour and texture. TEAS. *Adm £2, chd free. Sun 24 July (1-5). Private visits welcome by appt for groups of 10+ Aug only. Tel 01773 778982 markhamvilla1@hotmail.com*

㉜ 23 Mill Lane, Codnor 🗝️⊕
(Mrs S Jackson) *12m NW of Nottingham. 10m N of Derby. Mill Lane situated opp Codnor Market Place (Clock Tower) on A610. 2 car parks nearby.* Lawn, herbaceous borders, pond, waterfall; clematis and Mediterranean garden. Light refreshments and TEAS. *Adm £1.50, chd free. Sun 14 Aug (1-6). Private visits welcome by appt, July & Aug only. Tel 01773 745707*

㉝ Oaks Lane Farm, Kelstedge 🗝️⊕
(Mr & Mrs J R Hunter) *5m W of Chesterfield. Ashover nr Chesterfield. At Kelstedge on A632 from Chesterfield, just before Kelstedge Inn, turn R up Kelstedge Lane, in ½m take 1st R into Oaks Lane, garden & car park 100yds on R.* Large informal garden with rhododendrons, mixed borders, spring bulbs and hellebores, old fashioned roses, euphorbias, hostas and many rare plants, shrubs and trees. Woodland area. Natural streams and small bog garden. Featured in 'Derbyshire Life' 2004. TEAS. *Adm £2, chd free. Mon 2 May (1-5). Private visits welcome by appt, May to Aug. Tel 01246 590324*

The Old Rectory, Clifton Campville 🗝️🗝️⊕
See Staffordshire & part of West Midlands.

㉞ Otterbrook, Alders Lane, Chinley 🗝️⊕
(Mary & Dennis Sharp) *3m W of Whaley Bridge. Otterbrook is reached by 300yd walk up Alders Lane on outskirts of village off Buxton Rd (B6062) between Chinley & Chapel-en-le-Frith. Parking is very limited at house so please park on Buxton Rd.* Plantperson's garden of approx 1 acre created by owners over 30yrs. The use of trees, shrubs and perennials in a variety of associations and in conjunction with various structures provides a colour-themed garden full of interest and surprises. 2 ponds, bridge, folly, bog garden, grass border, kitchen garden, small fernery. Home-made TEAS. *Adm £2, chd free. Suns 12, 26 June (2-5).*

Private visits welcome by appt.
Tel 01663 750335

35 NEW **Park Hall, Walton Back Lane, Walton, Chesterfield** ⌖⊕
(Kim & Margaret Staniforth) *2m SW of Chesterfield. From Chesterfield take A632 for Matlock. After derestriction sign, turn R into Acorn Ridge and then L into Walton Back Lane. 300yds on R, at end of high stone wall. Park on field side of Walton Back Lane only.* 2 acres surrounding C17 house (not open). Restored formal garden originally laid out in 1933 with terraces, herbaceous borders, rhododendrons, camellias and hardy shrubs; new garden started in 2000 with small ponds, pergolas, arbour, roses and circle of pleached hornbeams; lawns and small area of parkland with forest trees. Home-made TEAS St Luke's Hospice. *Adm £3, chd 50p. Suns 12, 26 June (2-5.30). Private visits welcome by appt for parties of 20+. Tel 01246 567412 kim.staniforth@virgin.net*

36 **19 Portland Street, Etwall** ⌖⌖
(Paul & Fran Harvey) *6m W of Derby. In centre of Etwall Village, at Spread Eagle PH turn into Willington Rd then immed R into Portland St (behind PH car park).* Our tranquil garden is packed with plants for yr-round interest. This ⅓ acre has been developed over the past 11 yrs. Many rare and unusual shrubs and perennials, fabulous colour and tremendous scent; pond, small stream; oriental garden; pergola; exhibition dahlias and gladioli; collections incl picea, agapanthus and crocosmia, but no lawn. Home-made TEAS. *Adm £2, chd free. Sat, Sun 20, 21 Aug (11-5). Private visits welcome by appt. Tel 01283 734360*

37 **Postern House, Turnditch** ⌖⌖⊕
(Liz & Nick Ruby) *3m W of Belper. Off A517 Belper to Ashbourne rd, entering Turnditch from Belper direction 50yds past bridge over river; turn L into unmarked lane (just before 30mph sign). 3rd house on R.* ⅓-acre garden with 1-acre paddock set in beautiful rolling countryside. Large borders and island beds bursting with many different herbaceous plants and shrubs incl large collection of hostas and hardy geraniums. Climbers ramble over walls, trees and large gazebo. Pots, troughs and baskets add colourful seasonal interest. Small water features, seating areas, courtyard, greenhouse, fruit and vegetables.

Adjacent small nursery. Light refreshments and TEAS. *Adm £2, chd free. Suns 22 May; 26 June (2-5).*
Evening Opening *£4, wine, Wed 6 July (6-9). Tel 01773 550732 www.postern.co.uk*

38 ◆ **Renishaw Hall, Renishaw** ⌖⌖ NCCPG
(Sir Reresby & Lady Sitwell) *6m NE of Chesterfield. Situated equidistant 6m from both Sheffield & Old Chesterfield on A6135, 3m from its junction with M1 J30.* Italian-style garden with terraces, old ponds, yew hedges and pyramids. National Collection of yuccas. Nature reserve, woodland garden, herbaceous plants and shrubs; museum; lakeside walk. Sculpture park. New for this yr, laburnum tunnel and bluebell fortnight. Light refreshments and TEAS Apr to Sept. *Adm £3.80, chd £3, concessions £3. Thurs to Suns, Bank Hol Mons 24 Mar to 2 Oct (10.30-4.30). Tel 01246 432310 www.sitwell.co.uk*

39 **The Riddings Farm, Kirk Ireton** ⌖⊕
(The Spencer Family) *7m NE of Ashbourne. Between Ashbourne & Wirksworth. Leave Kirk Ireton via Gorsey Lane (close to Barley Mow). Turn L at T-junction onto Broom Lane. 1st R into Hays Lane.* Informal hillside garden about ¾ acre, with lovely views. A garden for romantics and children of all ages, with winding woodland paths, bridges, pergolas and surprises. Fragrant carpets of primulas in spring. A peaceful paradise. Picnic/parking field looking over Carsington Water. New Oriental garden. Unusual plants propagated for adjacent nursery. Accommodation. TEAS in aid of Ashbourne Animal Welfare. *Adm £2, chd free. Suns 17 Apr; 1 May; 24 July; 4 Sept (2-5). Private visits welcome by appt. Tel 01335 370331*

Rose Cottage, 82 Main Road, Underwood ⌖⌖⊕
See Nottinghamshire.

40 **Shatton Hall Farm, Bamford** ⊕
(Mr & Mrs J Kellie) *3m W of Hathersage. Take A6187 from Hathersage, turn L to Shatton, after 2m (opp High Peak Garden Centre). After ½m turn R through ford, drive ½m & house is on L over cattle grids.* Original walled garden of C16. Farmhouse now spills out to water gardens and sheltered slopes, planted informally and merging into the picturesque landscape. Among the great variety of unusual plants and

shrubs, sculpture and willow features add interest to this maturing and still expanding garden. Ancient woodland and streamside walks can also be enjoyed. Home-made TEAS. *Adm £2.50, chd 50p. Mon 30 May; Sun 31 July (1.30-5). Private visits welcome by appt. Tel 01433 620635 jk@shatton.co.uk*

41 NEW **The Shooting Lodge, Derwent, Bamford** ⌖⊕
(Jane & Jon Bond) *8m W of Sheffield. Travelling from Sheffield towards Manchester on A57, turn R ½m after the junction with A6013. Continue for 2m to mini-roundabout then follow signs.* Set in a valley of exceptional beauty, this is a garden which wraps around its house. It is an attempt to create a 'controlled' environment within the boundary walls which is as beautiful as the natural environment without. A reflection of the Bond family's love of colour and their desire to experiment with different colour combinations, it evokes a variety of moods throughout the seasons. Home-made TEAS in aid of The Belles of St Henry's Women's Group. *Adm £2.50, chd free. Sun 14 Aug (12-6). Private visits welcome by appt Aug & Sept only. Tel 01433 659767*

42 **Spindlewood, Strathallan Close, Darley Dale** ⌖⊕
(Mr & Mrs J G Ball) *3m N of Matlock. After The Grouse Inn, turn R up Whitworth Rd. Park on L by railings, on Whitworth Rd. Elderly/disabled may continue to private parking areas down the Close and within entrance to garden.* ¾-acre setting, bordering wild area. S-facing garden with patio plantings and containers. Herbs. Mixed and herbaceous borders with stream, cascades, wildlife pond and bog garden. Garden compartments and features being added regularly. *Adm £2, chd free (share to Dale Road Church, Darley Dale). Private visits welcome by appt June & July, afternoons preferred. Tel 01629 735701*

43 **The Spinney, Combs** ⊕
(Mrs C Lawton) *3m SE of Whaley Bridge. From Chapel-en-le-Frith take B5470 towards Whaley Bridge. Through Chapel-en-le-Frith turn L for Combs at Hanging Gate PH. Pass reservoir to Combs village. Limited parking at house. Park in village nr Beehive where transport is available if required, or ½m walk, turning L at Beehive & continuing uphill to The Spinney.* Steep, sloping ½-acre garden with panoramic views. Mixed

planting incl alpines, shrubs, herbaceous, roses and hostas. Large fish pond with marginal plantings; wild flower bank; greenhouse and patios. New koi pool and stream. Recent addition of raised beds vegetable garden. Not suitable for disabled or wheelchairs. Cream TEAS. *Adm £2, chd free. Sun 10 July (2-5). Private visits welcome by appt, no parking for coaches. Tel 01298 812221*

㊹ Spring Tops Cottage, Jericho, Earl Sterndale
(Margaret & David Lampard) *5m S of Buxton. Take A515 Ashbourne to Buxton rd. 5m from Buxton turn L at Book Store Xrds. Take B5053 Longnor rd under railway bridge. Past Quarry, ½m on take L fork in rd, 3rd house on L.* Approx ¼ acre. Designed round large natural rocky limestone outcrop, with many paths; 3 pools; waterfall and fish. Cottage garden border, extensive views over peak district, over 1,000ft above sea level. Featured in 'Amateur Gardening' 2004. Home-made TEAS. *Adm £1.50, chd free. Private visits welcome by appt, May to Sept. Tel 01298 83277*

Station Road Gardens, Rolleston on Dove
See Staffordshire & part of West Midlands.

Stonehill Quarry Garden, Great Gate, Croxden
See Staffordshire & part of West Midlands.

㊺ Sycamore Farm, Church Broughton Road, Foston NCCPG
(A J Robinson) *10m SW of Derby. From Derby take A516 Hilton. Continue through to Hatton. Straight on through T-lights & take 1st R then 2nd L.* ⅓-acre garden planted for late summer colour. Large collection (300+ varieties) of tender perennials including National Collection of argyranthemums (100+ varieties), salvias, dahlias and penstemons. Traditional herbaceous border, old roses and vegetable garden. Featured in 'Amateur Gardening' 2003. TEAS. *Adm £2, chd free. Suns 14 Aug; 4 Sept (2-5.30). Private visits welcome by appt Aug & Sept only. Tel 01283 815635*

㊻ Thatched Farm, Radbourne
(Mr & Mrs R A Pegram) *2m N of Derby ring rd. Exit A52 Derby-Ashbourne rd.* The original garden has been reduced in size to ease maintenance. The same range of trees, shrubs, bulbs, alpines, bog garden plants, hardy and tender perennials are now colour-themed. A rill has been introduced and the garden fenced to provide more shelter. A wild flower area is now established. Featured in 'Gardeners' World', 2003. TEAS. *Adm £2.50, chd free. Private visits welcome by appt May, June & July. Coaches permitted. Groups of 10+. Tel 01332 824507 pegramra@aol.com*

㊼ ◆ Tissington Hall, nr Ashbourne
(Sir Richard & Lady FitzHerbert) *4m N of Ashbourne. E of A515 on Ashbourne to Buxton rd.* Large garden; roses, herbaceous borders. *Adm £2, chd £1. Daily 28 Mar to 1 Apr; 30 May to 3 June. Tues to Fri incl, 19 July to 26 Aug (1.30 - 4.30).* **For NGS:** *Mon, Tues 29, 30 Aug (1.30-4.30). Tel 01335 352200 tisshall@dircon.co.uk*

㊽ NEW 7 Warren Drive, Linton
(Keith & Phyl Hutchinson) *6m SE of Burton-on-Trent. Take A444 out of Burton for 5m. After Toons Warehouse on R, take 3rd exit at roundabout. Take 1st R & continue for 1m uphill past The Square & Compass PH on R. After 200yds turn L into Warren Drive.* Yr-round cottage-style wildlife garden on 2 levels, overlooking peaceful countryside. Small stream to wildlife pond and bog area, pergolas, gazebo, decking with many pots, vegetable plot, mixed borders; all extensively planted incl grasses, plants attractive to butterflies, bees and birds - many providing nesting sites (7 nests 2004). Seating to view. Light refreshments and TEAS. *Adm £2, chd free. Suns 7 Aug; 4 Sept (2-6). Private visits welcome by appt. Tel 01283 761088 keith-phyl@hutch7warren.freeserve.co.uk*

㊾ Wharfedale, 34 Broadway, Duffield
(Roger & Sue Roberts) *4m N of Derby. Turn onto B5023 Wirksworth rd (Broadway) off A6 midway between Belper & Derby.* Plant enthusiasts' garden with over 800 varieties of choice and unusual shrubs, trees, perennials and bulbs. Themed borders incl Mediterranean, late summer tropical and single colour schemes. Cottage garden to front. 10yrs old with Italianate walled scented garden and woodland pond with raised walkway. Eclectic and unusual garden providing lots of ideas. Phase 1 of Japanese-style garden being developed. Home-made TEAS. *Adm £2, chd free. Sun 14 Aug (10.30-5). Private visits welcome by appt, for groups of 15+ from 4 Apr to 14 Oct, evenings and weekends only. Tel 01332 841905*

◆ Whatton Gardens, nr Loughborough
See Leicestershire & Rutland.

㊿ 26 Wheeldon Avenue, Derby
(Ian Griffiths) *1m N of Derby. 1m from city centre & approached directly off the Kedleston Rd or from A6 Duffield Rd via West Bank Ave.* Tiny Victorian walled garden near to city centre. Lawn and herbaceous borders with old roses, lupins, delphiniums and foxgloves. Small terrace with topiary and herb garden. Limited on-street parking. Featured on BBC TV and in numerous publications, 2004. TEAS. *Adm £2, chd £1. Private visits welcome by appt, June to Aug incl, groups of 4+. Tel 01332 342204*

(51) NEW Windward, 62 Summer Lane, Wirksworth
(Audrey Winkler) *5m S of Matlock. ½m from Wirksworth town centre off B5023 Wirksworth to Duffield rd. After approx 300yds, turn R at mini island onto Summer Lane. Windward is approx 500yds on R, rockery at roadside.* Lush, green garden of about 1 acre, wildlife-friendly and almost organic. Romantic ambiance with mature trees and shrubs and interesting nooks and crannies. Ponds, hostas, gravel garden, rockery, grasses, rhododendrons, Leylandii, crinkle-crankle hedge, mixed borders and small meadow area. A garden for relaxation with several seating areas. Featured in 'Derbyshire Life' 2004. Home-made TEAS. *Adm £2, chd free (share to Victim Support). Sun 22 May (11-5). Private visits welcome by appt Apr to Oct, groups of 10+. Tel 01629 822681 audrey.winkler@w3z.co.uk*

(52) 35 Wyver Lane, Belper
(Jim & Brenda Stannering) *8m N of Derby. Take A6 from Derby through Belper to T-lights at triangle. Turn L for A517 to Ashbourne, over river bridge, 1st R onto Wyver Lane. Parking in River Gardens, entrance on A6.* Cottage garden of approx 500sq yds on side of R Derwent opp Belper River Gardens. Full of hardy perennial plants with pergola, troughs, greenhouse, small pond. Featured in 'Amateur Gardening', 'Gorgeous Gardens', 2004. Home-made TEAS in aid of Shottlegate &

District WI. *Adm £1.50, chd free. Suns 24 Apr; 5 June (1-5). Private visits welcome by appt, Apr to July. Tel 01773 824280*

53 ◆ **Yew Tree Bungalow, Thatchers Lane, Tansley** 🌿🅷
(Jayne Conquest) *2m E of Matlock.* On A615, 2nd R after Tavern at Tansley. ½-acre informal plantswoman's garden. Wide range of herbaceous plants and shrubs, many rare and unusual incl hardy geraniums, penstemons, campanulas and variegated foliage plants. Vegetable and herb gardens. *Adm*

£1.50, chd free. Private visits welcome by appt July only. Tel 01629 57377

54 ◆ **Yew Tree Farm, Thatchers Lane, Tansley** 🌿🅷
(Mrs Avril Buckley) *2m E of Matlock.* On A615, 2nd R after The Tavern at Tansley. If approaching from Alfreton, 1st L on entering Tansley. 1-acre country garden with stream-fed pond and terrace area. Ornamental and productive kitchen garden. Garden rooms of herbaceous perennials; woodland garden with choice shade-loving plants; gold and

purple-themed shrubbery. Adjacent specialist plant nursery. Home-made TEAS. *Adm £1.50, chd free. Open 13 June to 3 July for groups of 12+ by prior arrangement.* **For NGS:** *Sun 12 June (12-5). Tel 01629 57493 or 07787 963966 avril@yewtreefarm1.fslife.co.uk*

Evening Opening (See also garden description)

Gamesley Fold Cottage
            16 June
Postern House   6 July
10 Chestnut Way   13 July

THE QUEEN'S NURSING INSTITUTE

Mandy is a young mother living in a remote part of Yorkshire. After the birth of her baby she felt isolated and friendless. Thanks to a local project organised by her health visitor she now meets other mums and their babies at weekly 'toddler and baby walks' club, funded by the Queen's Nursing Institute through its Developing Practice Award scheme. She is getting fit and her baby is getting used to fresh air and exercise.

Each year throughout England, Wales and Northern Ireland, similar projects, developed and led by community nurses, are transforming the lives of thousands of people like Mandy. Many of them focus on the needs of elderly people. Others are helping young people with learning difficulties and teenagers coping with the pressures of modern life. The award scheme, which is open to school nurses, district nurses, practice nurses, midwives, health visitors and community psychiatric nurses is made possible through the generous financial support of The National Garden Scheme.

For more information contact the QNI
Tel: 020 7490 4227 Website: www.qni.org.uk

---

ngs
gardens open
for charity

£1.84 million donated to national nursing, caring and gardening charities in 2004

Devon

County Organisers: Mr & Mrs Michael Stone, The Cider House, Buckland Abbey, Yelverton, Devon PL20 6EZ
Tel 01822 853285

Assistant County Organisers:

(Central Devon)   Mrs Miranda Allhusen, Sutton Mead, Moretonhampstead, Newton Abbot, Devon TQ13 8PW
Tel 01647 440296

(South Devon)   Mrs Sheila Blake, Higher Homefield, Sherford, Kingsbridge, Devon TQ7 2AT
Tel 01548 531229

(East Devon)   Mrs Ruth Charter, Ravenhill, Long Dogs Lane, Ottery St Mary, Devon EX11 1HX
Tel 01404 814798

(Press & Publicity Officer)   Mr Alan Davis, Paddocks, Stafford Lane, Colyford, Devon EX24 6HQ Tel 01297 552472

(Torbay)   Mrs Jo Gibson, Arcadia, Ashcombe Road, Dawlish, Devon EX7 0QW Tel 01626 862102

(North Devon)   Mrs Jo Hynes, Higher Cherubeer, Dolton, Winkleigh, Devon EX19 8PP Tel 01805 804265

(Exeter)   Dr & Mrs John Lloyd, Little Cumbre, 145 Pennsylvania Road, Exeter, Devon EX4 6OZ
Tel 01392 258315

(Northeast Devon)   Mrs Diane Rowe, Little Southey, Northcott, Cullompton, Devon EX15 3LT
Tel 01884 840545

(Southwest Devon)   Mrs Marjorie Travis, Wrangaton House, Wrangaton, Devon TQ10 9HH Tel 01364 72104

County Treasurer: Mrs Julia Tremlett, Bickham House, Kenn, Nr Exeter, Devon EX6 7XL Tel 01392 832671

Maps: Numbers shown next to each garden entry refer to that garden's entry on the county map. This position is approximate;
distance and directions from the nearest main town are generally shown in the garden text.
A precise location is available for those gardens featured on the NGS website by visiting www.ngs.org.uk.

Symbols: Information relating to symbols is given on page 21

DATES OF OPENING

Evening openings
See end of county listing

Private gardens open regularly for NGS
Fast Rabbit Farm, Ash Cross, Dartmouth
(36)
The Gate House, Lee, Coastal Village *(39)*
Newton Farm, Hemyock *(67)*
Sherwood, Newton St Cyres *(86)*
Yonder Hill, Colaton Raleigh *(107)*

Gardens open to the public
For details see garden description
Arlington Court, Arlington, Barnstaple *(4)*
Barleycott, Blakewell *(7)*
Bicton College, East Budleigh *(10)*
Burrow Farm Gardens, Dalwood *(15)*
Castle Drogo, Drewsteignton *(17)*
Castle Hill, Filleigh *(18)*
Cliffe, Lee, Ilfracombe *(23)*
Coleton Fishacre, nr Kingswear *(24)*
Dartington Hall Gardens, Dartington *(29)*
Docton Mill Gardens, Lymebridge *(32)*
The Garden House, Buckland Monachorum
(38)
Hartland Abbey, Hartland, nr Bideford *(43)*
Heddon Hall, Parracombe *(45)*
Killerton Garden, Broadclyst *(53)*
Knightshayes Court Garden, Tiverton *(55)*
Lukesland, Ivybridge *(60)*
Marwood Hill, Marwood *(61)*
Overbeck's, Sharpitor, Salcombe *(69)*
Plant World, Newton Abbot *(73)*
Pleasant View, Newton Abbot *(74)*
RHS Garden Rosemoor, Great Torrington
(78)
Rock House Garden, Chudleigh *(79)*

Saltram House, Plympton *(81)*
Sampford Shrubs, Holbrook, Sampford
Peverell *(82)*
Winsford Walled Garden, Halwill Junction
(103)

By appointment only
*For telephone number and other
details see garden description.
Private visits welcomed*
The Gate House, Lee, Coastal Village *(39)*
Hamblyn's Coombe, Dittisham *(42)*
Lee Ford, Budleigh Salterton *(56)*
Rowden Gardens, Brentor *(80)*
Webbery Gardens *(98)*

February 6 Sunday
Little Cumbre, Exeter *(58)*

February 13 Sunday
Little Cumbre, Exeter *(58)*

February 20 Sunday
Little Cumbre, Exeter *(58)*

February 26 Saturday
Bertie's Cottage Garden, Yeoford, Crediton
(8)

February 27 Sunday
Little Cumbre, Exeter *(58)*

March 4 Friday
Dippers, Shaugh Prior *(31)*

March 5 Saturday
Dippers, Shaugh Prior *(31)*

March 6 Sunday
Fast Rabbit Farm, Ash Cross, Dartmouth
(36)

Sowton Mill, Dunsford *(92)*
Yonder Hill, Colaton Raleigh *(107)*

March 11 Friday
Dippers, Shaugh Prior *(31)*

March 12 Saturday
Newton Farm, Hemyock *(67)*

March 13 Sunday
Fast Rabbit Farm, Ash Cross, Dartmouth
(36)
Newton Farm, Hemyock *(67)*
Yonder Hill, Colaton Raleigh *(107)*

March 16 Wednesday
Bicton College, East Budleigh *(10)*

March 18 Friday
Dippers, Shaugh Prior *(31)*

March 20 Sunday
Fast Rabbit Farm, Ash Cross, Dartmouth
(36)
Higher Knowle, Lustleigh *(47)*
Yonder Hill, Colaton Raleigh *(107)*

March 25 Friday (Easter)
The Downes, Monkleigh *(33)*
Fast Rabbit Farm, Ash Cross, Dartmouth
(36)
Yonder Hill, Colaton Raleigh *(107)*

March 26 Saturday (Easter)
Dippers, Shaugh Prior *(31)*

March 27 Sunday (Easter)
Fast Rabbit Farm, Ash Cross, Dartmouth
(36)
Higher Knowle, Lustleigh *(47)*
The Moorings, Rocombe *(64)*
Yonder Hill, Colaton Raleigh *(107)*

March 28 Monday (Easter)
Fast Rabbit Farm, Ash Cross, Dartmouth
(36)
Higher Knowle, Lustleigh *(47)*

The Moorings, Rocombe *(64)*
Yonder Hill, Colaton Raleigh *(107)*
March 30 Wednesday
Bicton College, East Budleigh *(10)*
38 Phillipps Avenue, Exmouth *(70)*
April 3 Sunday
Fast Rabbit Farm, Ash Cross, Dartmouth *(36)*
Heathercombe, Manaton *(44)*
Higher Knowle, Lustleigh *(47)*
Saltram House, Plympton *(81)*
Yonder Hill, Colaton Raleigh *(107)*
April 6 Wednesday
38 Phillipps Avenue, Exmouth *(70)*
April 7 Thursday
Sampford Shrubs, Holbrook, Sampford Peverell *(82)*
April 8 Friday
Sampford Shrubs, Holbrook, Sampford Peverell *(82)*
April 10 Sunday
Bickham House, Kenn *(9)*
Fast Rabbit Farm, Ash Cross, Dartmouth *(36)*
Higher Knowle, Lustleigh *(47)*
Wrangaton House, Wrangaton *(106)*
Yonder Hill, Colaton Raleigh *(107)*
April 12 Tuesday
Bickham House, Kenn *(9)*
April 13 Wednesday
Bickham House, Kenn *(9)*
April 16 Saturday
Bertie's Cottage Garden, Yeoford, Crediton *(8)*
Shobrooke Park Gardens, Crediton *(88)*
April 17 Sunday
Coleton Fishacre, nr Kingswear *(24)*
Fast Rabbit Farm, Ash Cross, Dartmouth *(36)*
Higher Knowle, Lustleigh *(47)*
Kia-Ora Farm & Gardens, Cullompton *(52)*
Killerton Garden, Broadclyst *(53)*
Knightshayes Court Garden, Tiverton *(55)*
Milland Farm, nr Northlew *(63)*
Whitstone Farm, Bovey Tracey *(102)*
Yonder Hill, Colaton Raleigh *(107)*
April 20 Wednesday
38 Phillipps Avenue, Exmouth *(70)*
April 23 Saturday
Cleave House, Sticklepath *(22)*
Haldon Grange, Dunchideock *(41)*
April 24 Sunday
Andrew's Corner, Belstone *(3)*
Ashley Gardens, Tiverton *(5)*
Castle Drogo, Drewsteignton *(17)*
Castle Hill, Filleigh *(18)*
Chapel Farm House, Halwill Junction *(19)*
Cleave House, Sticklepath *(22)*
Dartington Hall Gardens, Dartington *(29)*
Fast Rabbit Farm, Ash Cross, Dartmouth *(36)*
Gorwell House, Barnstaple *(40)*
Haldon Grange, Dunchideock *(41)*
Higher Knowle, Lustleigh *(47)*
Rock House Garden, Chudleigh *(79)*
St Merryn, Braunton *(94)*
Yonder Hill, Colaton Raleigh *(107)*

April 27 Wednesday
Metcombe Brake, Higher Metcombe *(62)*
April 28 Thursday
Shilhay, Stoodleigh *(87)*
Spillifords Wildlife Garden, Lower Washfield, Tiverton *(93)*
April 29 Friday
Sampford Shrubs, Holbrook, Sampford Peverell *(82)*
April 30 Saturday
Dicot, Chardstock *(30)*
Haldon Grange, Dunchideock *(41)*
Mothecombe Gardens, nr Holbeton *(66)*
Sampford Shrubs, Holbrook, Sampford Peverell *(82)*
May 1 Sunday
Andrew's Corner, Belstone *(3)*
Dicot, Chardstock *(30)*
Fast Rabbit Farm, Ash Cross, Dartmouth *(36)*
Haldon Grange, Dunchideock *(41)*
Heddon Hall, Parracombe *(45)*
Higher Knowle, Lustleigh *(47)*
Kia-Ora Farm & Gardens, Cullompton *(52)*
Metcombe Brake, Higher Metcombe *(62)*
Milland Farm, nr Northlew *(63)*
Mothecombe Gardens, nr Holbeton *(66)*
Sowton Mill, Dunsford *(92)*
Taikoo, Belstone *(95)*
Wood Barton, Kentisbeare *(105)*
Wrangaton House, Wrangaton *(106)*
Yonder Hill, Colaton Raleigh *(107)*
May 2 Monday (Bank Hol)
Fast Rabbit Farm, Ash Cross, Dartmouth *(36)*
Haldon Grange, Dunchideock *(41)*
Higher Knowle, Lustleigh *(47)*
Kia-Ora Farm & Gardens, Cullompton *(52)*
Metcombe Brake, Higher Metcombe *(62)*
Milland Farm, nr Northlew *(63)*
38 Phillipps Avenue, Exmouth *(70)*
Wood Barton, Kentisbeare *(105)*
Wrangaton House, Wrangaton *(106)*
Yonder Hill, Colaton Raleigh *(107)*
May 4 Wednesday
38 Phillipps Avenue, Exmouth *(70)*
May 5 Thursday
Spillifords Wildlife Garden, Lower Washfield, Tiverton *(93)*
May 7 Saturday
Bertie's Cottage Garden, Yeoford, Crediton *(8)*
May 8 Sunday
Bickham House, Kenn *(9)*
Fast Rabbit Farm, Ash Cross, Dartmouth *(36)*
Higher Knowle, Lustleigh *(47)*
The Lodge, Mannamead, Plymouth *(59)*
Metcombe Brake, Higher Metcombe *(62)*
Whitstone Farm, Bovey Tracey *(102)*
Yonder Hill, Colaton Raleigh *(107)*
May 10 Tuesday
Bickham House, Kenn *(9)*
May 11 Wednesday
Bickham House, Kenn *(9)*
Newton Farm, Hemyock *(67)*
38 Phillipps Avenue, Exmouth *(70)*

May 14 Saturday
Shobrooke Park Gardens, Crediton *(88)*
Withleigh Farm, Withleigh Village *(104)*
May 15 Sunday
Andrew's Corner, Belstone *(3)*
Arlington Court, Arlington, Barnstaple *(4)*
The Cider House, Buckland Abbey *(21)*
Coleton Fishacre, nr Kingswear *(24)*
Dartington Hall Gardens, Dartington *(29)*
Fast Rabbit Farm, Ash Cross, Dartmouth *(36)*
Higher Knowle, Lustleigh *(47)*
Kia-Ora Farm & Gardens, Cullompton *(52)*
Saltram House, Plympton *(81)*
Southcombe House, Widecombe-in-the-Moor *(90)*
Withleigh Farm, Withleigh Village *(104)*
Yonder Hill, Colaton Raleigh *(107)*
May 19 Thursday
Little Ash Farm, Fenny Bridges, Honiton *(57)*
Spillifords Wildlife Garden, Lower Washfield, Tiverton *(93)*
May 21 Saturday
Heathercombe, Manaton *(44)*
The Old Glebe, Eggesford *(68)*
Pikes Cottage, Madford, Hemyock *(71)*
May 22 Sunday
Barleycott, Blakewell *(7)*
Castle Hill, Filleigh *(18)*
Fast Rabbit Farm, Ash Cross, Dartmouth *(36)*
Gorwell House, Barnstaple *(40)*
Heathercombe, Manaton *(44)*
Higher Knowle, Lustleigh *(47)*
Inglewood, Newton Ferrers *(50)*
The Old Glebe, Eggesford *(68)*
Pikes Cottage, Madford, Hemyock *(71)*
Pleasant View, Newton Abbot *(74)*
Rock House Garden, Chudleigh *(79)*
St Merryn, Braunton *(94)*
Yonder Hill, Colaton Raleigh *(107)*
May 24 Tuesday
Cliffe, Lee, Ilfracombe *(23)*
May 25 Wednesday
38 Phillipps Avenue, Exmouth *(70)*
May 26 Thursday
Cliffe, Lee, Ilfracombe *(23)*
Shilhay, Stoodleigh *(87)*
May 27 Friday
Sampford Shrubs, Holbrook, Sampford Peverell *(82)*

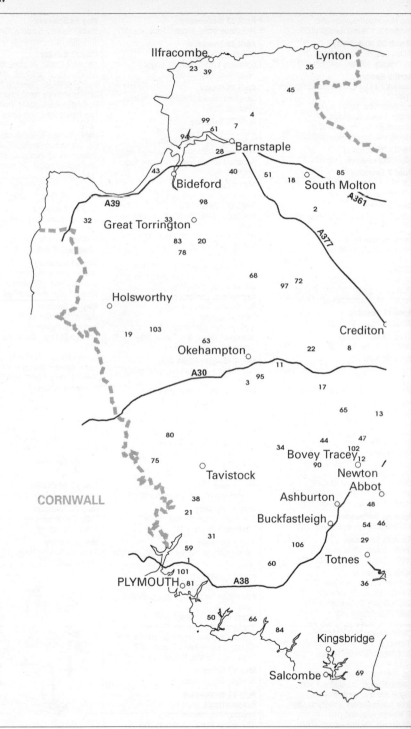

Ilfracombe
23 39

Lynton
35

45

4

99
94 61 7
28 Barnstaple

43
Bideford
40 51 18 South Molton
85

A39
98
2

32 Great Torrington 33
83 20
78

A361

A377

68
97 72

Holsworthy

19 103

Crediton

63
Okehampton
22 8

A30
11
3 95
17

65
13

80

34 44 47
102
Bovey Tracey 12
75
90

Tavistock
Newton
Abbot

CORNWALL
38
Ashburton
48

21

Buckfastleigh
54 46

31
29

59
106

1
60
Totnes

101
36

PLYMOUTH 81
A38

50 66

84

Kingsbridge

Salcombe 69

DEVON

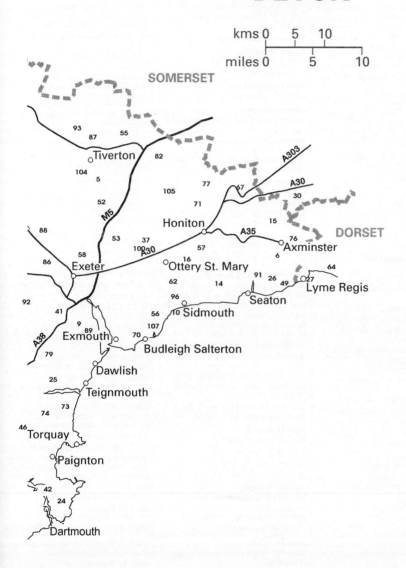

kms 0   5   10

miles 0   5   10

SOMERSET

93
87   55
°Tiverton   82

A303

104
5   77   67   A30
105   71   30

52

M5

Honiton   15

88   DORSET

53   37   A35   76
58   100 30   57   °Axminster
86   Exeter   6

62   16   °Ottery St. Mary   91   26   49   °27   64
14   °Lyme Regis

92   96   Seaton
41   56   10 Sidmouth
9   89   107
Exmouth°   70°
79   Budleigh Salterton

A38

°Dawlish
25
Teignmouth
74   73

46 Torquay
°Paignton

42
24

°Dartmouth

May 28 Saturday
Heathercombe, Manaton *(44)*
Moretonhampstead Gardens *(65)*
Pine Cottage, Eggesford *(72)*
Sampford Shrubs, Holbrook, Sampford
Peverell *(82)*
The Water Garden, Wembworthy *(97)*
Whibble Hill House, Plymouth *(101)*

May 29 Sunday
Alswood, George Nympton *(2)*
Andrew's Corner, Belstone *(3)*
Bridford Gardens *(13)*
Chapel Farm House, Halwill Junction *(19)*
Cherubeer Gardens, Dolton *(20)*
Durcombe Water, Barbrook, Lynton *(35)*
Fast Rabbit Farm, Ash Cross, Dartmouth
(36)
Heathercombe, Manaton *(44)*
Higher Knowle, Lustleigh *(47)*
Kia-Ora Farm & Gardens, Cullompton *(52)*
Kingston House, Staverton *(54)*
Milland Farm, nr Northlew *(63)*
The Moorings, Rocombe *(64)*
Moretonhampstead Gardens *(65)*
The Old Glebe, Eggesford *(68)*
Pine Cottage, Eggesford *(72)*
Southcombe House, Widecombe-in-the-
Moor *(90)*
Taikoo, Belstone *(95)*
The Water Garden, Wembworthy *(97)*
Westcott Barton, Marwood, Barnstaple *(99)*
Whibble Hill House, Plymouth *(101)*
Yonder Hill, Colaton Raleigh *(107)*

May 30 Monday (Bank Hol)
Bridford Gardens *(13)*
Cadhay, Ottery St Mary *(16)*
Fast Rabbit Farm, Ash Cross, Dartmouth
(36)
Higher Knowle, Lustleigh *(47)*
Kia-Ora Farm & Gardens, Cullompton *(52)*
Milland Farm, nr Northlew *(63)*
The Moorings, Rocombe *(64)*
Moretonhampstead Gardens *(65)*
The Old Glebe, Eggesford *(68)*
Pine Cottage, Eggesford *(72)*
Southcombe House, Widecombe-in-the-
Moor *(90)*
The Water Garden, Wembworthy *(97)*
Westcott Barton, Marwood, Barnstaple *(99)*
Yonder Hill, Colaton Raleigh *(107)*

May 31 Tuesday
Cliffe, Lee, Ilfracombe *(23)*

June 1 Wednesday
Cadhay, Ottery St Mary *(16)*
Newton Farm, Hemyock *(67)*
Pleasant View, Newton Abbot *(74)*

June 2 Thursday
Cadhay, Ottery St Mary *(16)*
Cliffe, Lee, Ilfracombe *(23)*

June 4 Saturday
Bovey Tracey Gardens *(12)*
Cleave House, Sticklepath *(22)*
Newton Farm, Hemyock *(67)*
Southleigh Gardens *(91)*
The Water Garden, Wembworthy *(97)*

June 5 Sunday
Andrew's Corner, Belstone *(3)*
Bovey Tracey Gardens *(12)*
Cleave House, Sticklepath *(22)*

Drury Head Cottage, Postbridge *(34)*
Fast Rabbit Farm, Ash Cross, Dartmouth
(36)
Inglewood, Newton Ferrers *(50)*
Newton Farm, Hemyock *(67)*
Southcombe House, Widecombe-in-the-
Moor *(90)*
Southleigh Gardens *(91)*
The Water Garden, Wembworthy *(97)*
Yonder Hill, Colaton Raleigh *(107)*

June 7 Tuesday
Cliffe, Lee, Ilfracombe *(23)*

June 8 Wednesday
Newton Farm, Hemyock *(67)*
38 Phillipps Avenue, Exmouth *(70)*

June 9 Thursday
Cliffe, Lee, Ilfracombe *(23)*

June 11 Saturday
Bertie's Cottage Garden, Yeoford, Crediton
(8)
Blackhall Manor, South Tawton *(11)*
Combpyne Manor *(27)*
Shobrooke Park Gardens, Crediton *(88)*
The Water Garden, Wembworthy *(97)*

June 12 Sunday
Andrew's Corner, Belstone *(3)*
Bickham House, Kenn *(9)*
Blackhall Manor, South Tawton *(11)*
Chapel Farm House, Halwill Junction *(19)*
Combpyne Manor *(27)*
The Downes, Monkleigh *(33)*
Fast Rabbit Farm, Ash Cross, Dartmouth
(36)
Gorwell House, Barnstaple *(40)*
Hortus, Rousdon *(49)*
Kia-Ora Farm & Gardens, Cullompton *(52)*
Kingston House, Staverton **(Evening)** *(54)*
The Lodge, Mannamead, Plymouth *(59)*
Milland Farm, nr Northlew *(63)*
Portington, nr Lamerton *(75)*
Regency House, Hemyock *(77)*
School House, Little Torrington, Torrington
(83)
South Kenwood, Oxton, nr Kenton *(89)*
Southcombe House, Widecombe-in-the-
Moor *(90)*
The Water Garden, Wembworthy *(97)*
Yonder Hill, Colaton Raleigh *(107)*

June 14 Tuesday
Bickham House, Kenn *(9)*

June 15 Wednesday
Bickham House, Kenn *(9)*
Newton Farm, Hemyock *(67)*

June 16 Thursday
Sampford Shrubs, Holbrook, Sampford
Peverell *(82)*
Spillifords Wildlife Garden, Lower
Washfield, Tiverton *(93)*

June 17 Friday
Sampford Shrubs, Holbrook, Sampford
Peverell *(82)*

June 18 Saturday
Axminster & Kilmington Gardens, Axminster
(6)
Dicot, Chardstock *(30)*
Newton Farm, Hemyock *(67)*
Pine Cottage, Eggesford *(72)*

1 Tipton Lodge, Sidmouth *(96)*
The Water Garden, Wembworthy *(97)*

June 19 Sunday
Axminster & Kilmington Gardens, Axminster
(6)
Bridford Gardens **(Evening)** *(13)*
Bundels, Sidbury *(14)*
The Cider House, Buckland Abbey *(21)*
The Croft, Yarnscombe *(28)*
Dicot, Chardstock *(30)*
Drury Head Cottage, Postbridge *(34)*
Fast Rabbit Farm, Ash Cross, Dartmouth
(36)
Newton Farm, Hemyock *(67)*
Overbeck's, Sharpitor, Salcombe *(69)*
Pine Cottage, Eggesford *(72)*
Portington, nr Lamerton *(75)*
Scypen, Ringmore *(84)*
South Kenwood, Oxton, nr Kenton *(89)*
Southcombe House, Widecombe-in-the-
Moor *(90)*
St Merryn, Braunton *(94)*
1 Tipton Lodge, Sidmouth *(96)*
The Water Garden, Wembworthy *(97)*
Yonder Hill, Colaton Raleigh *(107)*

June 22 Wednesday
Newton Farm, Hemyock *(67)*
38 Phillipps Avenue, Exmouth *(70)*
Scypen, Ringmore *(84)*

June 23 Thursday
The Cider House, Buckland Abbey
(Evening) *(21)*

June 25 Saturday
Collepardo, Newton Abbot *(25)*
Newton Farm, Hemyock *(67)*
The Water Garden, Wembworthy *(97)*

June 26 Sunday
Alswood, George Nympton *(2)*
Barleycott, Blakewell *(7)*
Collepardo, Newton Abbot *(25)*
Fast Rabbit Farm, Ash Cross, Dartmouth
(36)
Kerscott House, Swimbridge *(51)*
Kia-Ora Farm & Gardens, Cullompton *(52)*
Kingston House, Staverton *(54)*
Little Ash Farm, Fenny Bridges, Honiton
(57)
Milland Farm, nr Northlew *(63)*
Newton Farm, Hemyock *(67)*
Pleasant View, Newton Abbot *(74)*
Rock House Garden, Chudleigh *(79)*
The Water Garden, Wembworthy *(97)*
Westcott Barton, Marwood, Barnstaple *(99)*
Westwood Gardens, nr Broadclyst *(100)*
Winsford Walled Garden, Halwill Junction
(103)
Yonder Hill, Colaton Raleigh *(107)*

June 27 Monday
Collepardo, Newton Abbot *(25)*
Westcott Barton, Marwood, Barnstaple *(99)*

June 28 Tuesday
Collepardo, Newton Abbot *(25)*

June 29 Wednesday
Collepardo, Newton Abbot *(25)*
Newton Farm, Hemyock *(67)*

June 30 Thursday
Collepardo, Newton Abbot *(25)*
Spillifords Wildlife Garden, Lower
Washfield, Tiverton *(93)*

July 1 Friday
Collepardo, Newton Abbot *(25)*

July 2 Saturday
Arlington Court, Arlington, Barnstaple *(4)*
Collepardo, Newton Abbot *(25)*
Newton Farm, Hemyock *(67)*
The Water Garden, Wembworthy *(97)*

July 3 Sunday
Cherubeer Gardens, Dolton *(20)*
Collepardo, Newton Abbot *(25)*
Durcombe Water, Barbrook, Lynton *(35)*
Newton Farm, Hemyock *(67)*
Regency House, Hemyock *(77)*
The Water Garden, Wembworthy *(97)*
Yonder Hill, Colaton Raleigh *(107)*

July 6 Wednesday
Newton Farm, Hemyock *(67)*

July 7 Thursday
Shapcott Barton Estate, East Knowstone *(85)*
Spillifords Wildlife Garden, Lower Washfield, Tiverton *(93)*

July 8 Friday
Shapcott Barton Estate, East Knowstone *(85)*

July 9 Saturday
Combpyne Manor *(27)*
Pikes Cottage, Madford, Hemyock *(71)*
The Water Garden, Wembworthy *(97)*

July 10 Sunday
Bickham House, Kenn *(9)*
Castle Drogo, Drewsteignton *(17)*
Colyford Gardens *(26)*
Combpyne Manor *(27)*
Kia-Ora Farm & Gardens, Cullompton *(52)*
Kingston House, Staverton *(54)*
Milland Farm, nr Northlew *(63)*
Pikes Cottage, Madford, Hemyock *(71)*
Sowton Mill, Dunsford *(92)*
The Water Garden, Wembworthy *(97)*
Yonder Hill, Colaton Raleigh *(107)*

July 12 Tuesday
Bickham House, Kenn *(9)*

July 13 Wednesday
Bickham House, Kenn *(9)*
Bicton College, East Budleigh *(10)*
Newton Farm, Hemyock *(67)*
Pleasant View, Newton Abbot *(74)*

July 14 Thursday
The Garden House, Buckland Monachorum *(38)*

July 15 Friday
Docton Mill Gardens, Lymebridge *(32)*
Shapcott Barton Estate, East Knowstone *(85)*

July 16 Saturday
Bertie's Cottage Garden, Yeoford, Crediton *(8)*
Newton Farm, Hemyock *(67)*
Pine Cottage, Eggesford *(72)*
Shapcott Barton Estate, East Knowstone *(85)*
The Water Garden, Wembworthy *(97)*

July 17 Sunday
Colyford Gardens *(26)*
The Croft, Yarnscombe *(28)*
Hortus, Rousdon *(49)*

Newton Farm, Hemyock *(67)*
Pine Cottage, Eggesford *(72)*
Shapcott Barton Estate, East Knowstone *(85)*
The Water Garden, Wembworthy *(97)*
Yonder Hill, Colaton Raleigh *(107)*

July 19 Tuesday
Cliffe, Lee, Ilfracombe *(23)*

July 20 Wednesday
Newton Farm, Hemyock *(67)*
Shapcott Barton Estate, East Knowstone *(85)*

July 21 Thursday
Cliffe, Lee, Ilfracombe *(23)*
Shapcott Barton Estate, East Knowstone *(85)*

July 22 Friday
Andrew's Corner, Belstone **(Evening)** *(3)*

July 23 Saturday
The African Garden, Estover, Plymouth *(1)*
Andrew's Corner, Belstone **(Evening)** *(3)*
Dicot, Chardstock *(30)*
Newton Farm, Hemyock *(67)*
Prospect House, Axminster *(76)*
Shapcott Barton Estate, East Knowstone *(85)*
The Water Garden, Wembworthy *(97)*

July 24 Sunday
The African Garden, Estover, Plymouth *(1)*
Barleycott, Blakewell *(7)*
Chapel Farm House, Halwill Junction *(19)*
Dicot, Chardstock *(30)*
Gorwell House, Barnstaple *(40)*
Kia-Ora Farm & Gardens, Cullompton *(52)*
Little Ash Farm, Fenny Bridges, Honiton *(57)*
The Lodge, Mannamead, Plymouth *(59)*
Newton Farm, Hemyock *(67)*
Prospect House, Axminster *(76)*
Rock House Garden, Chudleigh *(79)*
School House, Little Torrington, Torrington *(83)*
Shapcott Barton Estate, East Knowstone *(85)*
The Water Garden, Wembworthy *(97)*
Westwood Gardens, nr Broadclyst *(100)*
Yonder Hill, Colaton Raleigh *(107)*

July 27 Wednesday
Newton Farm, Hemyock *(67)*
Shapcott Barton Estate, East Knowstone *(85)*
Winsford Walled Garden, Halwill Junction *(103)*

July 28 Thursday
Spillifords Wildlife Garden, Lower Washfield, Tiverton *(93)*
Winsford Walled Garden, Halwill Junction *(103)*

July 29 Friday
Sampford Shrubs, Holbrook, Sampford Peverell *(82)*

July 30 Saturday
The African Garden, Estover, Plymouth *(1)*
Cleave House, Sticklepath *(22)*
Sampford Shrubs, Holbrook, Sampford Peverell *(82)*
The Water Garden, Wembworthy *(97)*

July 31 Sunday
The African Garden, Estover, Plymouth *(1)*
Alswood, George Nympton *(2)*
Cleave House, Sticklepath *(22)*
Heddon Hall, Parracombe *(45)*
Hole Farm, nr Bickington *(48)*
Kerscott House, Swimbridge *(51)*
Milland Farm, nr Northlew *(63)*
The Water Garden, Wembworthy *(97)*
Westcott Barton, Marwood, Barnstaple *(99)*
Yonder Hill, Colaton Raleigh *(107)*

August 1 Monday
Westcott Barton, Marwood, Barnstaple *(99)*

August 2 Tuesday
Shapcott Barton Estate, East Knowstone *(85)*

August 3 Wednesday
Newton Farm, Hemyock *(67)*
Pleasant View, Newton Abbot *(74)*

August 6 Saturday
Bertie's Cottage Garden, Yeoford, Crediton *(8)*
Newton Farm, Hemyock *(67)*

August 7 Sunday
Durcombe Water, Barbrook, Lynton *(35)*
Kia-Ora Farm & Gardens, Cullompton *(52)*
Newton Farm, Hemyock *(67)*
Yonder Hill, Colaton Raleigh *(107)*

August 10 Wednesday
Newton Farm, Hemyock *(67)*

August 13 Saturday
Newton Farm, Hemyock *(67)*
Pine Cottage, Eggesford *(72)*

August 14 Sunday
Bickham House, Kenn *(9)*
Chapel Farm House, Halwill Junction *(19)*
Hortus, Rousdon *(49)*
Little Ash Farm, Fenny Bridges, Honiton *(57)*
Newton Farm, Hemyock *(67)*
Pine Cottage, Eggesford *(72)*
Yonder Hill, Colaton Raleigh *(107)*

August 16 Tuesday
Bickham House, Kenn *(9)*

August 17 Wednesday
Bickham House, Kenn *(9)*
Newton Farm, Hemyock *(67)*

August 18 Thursday
The Garden House, Buckland Monachorum *(38)*

August 21 Sunday
The Croft, Yarnscombe *(28)*
Yonder Hill, Colaton Raleigh *(107)*

August 24 Wednesday
Newton Farm, Hemyock *(67)*

August 26 Friday
Sampford Shrubs, Holbrook, Sampford Peverell *(82)*

August 27 Saturday
Sampford Shrubs, Holbrook, Sampford Peverell *(82)*

August 28 Sunday
Alswood, George Nympton *(2)*
Bridford Gardens *(13)*
1 Feebers Cottage, Westwood, nr Broadclyst *(37)*
Kerscott House, Swimbridge *(51)*

Kia-Ora Farm & Gardens, Cullompton *(52)*
Milland Farm, nr Northlew *(63)*
Westcott Barton, Marwood, Barnstaple *(99)*
Winsford Walled Garden, Halwill Junction *(103)*
Yonder Hill, Colaton Raleigh *(107)*
August 29 Monday (Bank Hol)
Bridford Gardens *(13)*
Kia-Ora Farm & Gardens, Cullompton *(52)*
Milland Farm, nr Northlew *(63)*
Westcott Barton, Marwood, Barnstaple *(99)*
Winsford Walled Garden, Halwill Junction *(103)*
Yonder Hill, Colaton Raleigh *(107)*
August 31 Wednesday
Newton Farm, Hemyock *(67)*
September 3 Saturday
Combpyne Manor *(27)*
September 4 Sunday
The Cider House, Buckland Abbey *(21)*
Combpyne Manor *(27)*
Gorwell House, Barnstaple *(40)*
Yonder Hill, Colaton Raleigh *(107)*
September 7 Wednesday
Newton Farm, Hemyock *(67)*
September 10 Saturday
Bertie's Cottage Garden, Yeoford, Crediton *(8)*
Newton Farm, Hemyock *(67)*
Pine Cottage, Eggesford *(72)*
September 11 Sunday
Bickham House, Kenn *(9)*
High Barn, Torbryan *(46)*
Kia-Ora Farm & Gardens, Cullompton *(52)*
Killerton Garden, Broadclyst *(53)*
Milland Farm, nr Northlew *(63)*
Newton Farm, Hemyock *(67)*
Pine Cottage, Eggesford *(72)*
Rock House Garden, Chudleigh *(79)*
Yonder Hill, Colaton Raleigh *(107)*
September 13 Tuesday
Bickham House, Kenn *(9)*
September 14 Wednesday
Bickham House, Kenn *(9)*
September 16 Friday
Sampford Shrubs, Holbrook, Sampford Peverell *(82)*
September 17 Saturday
Pikes Cottage, Madford, Hemyock *(71)*
Sampford Shrubs, Holbrook, Sampford Peverell *(82)*
September 18 Sunday
1 Feebers Cottage, Westwood, nr Broadclyst *(37)*
High Barn, Torbryan *(46)*
Hortus, Rousdon *(49)*
Knightshayes Court Garden, Tiverton *(55)*
Pikes Cottage, Madford, Hemyock *(71)*
Rock House Garden, Chudleigh *(79)*
Winsford Walled Garden, Halwill Junction *(103)*
Yonder Hill, Colaton Raleigh *(107)*
September 25 Sunday
Chapel Farm House, Halwill Junction *(19)*
Rock House Garden, Chudleigh *(79)*
Westcott Barton, Marwood, Barnstaple *(99)*
Yonder Hill, Colaton Raleigh *(107)*

September 26 Monday
Westcott Barton, Marwood, Barnstaple *(99)*
September 29 Thursday
Shilhay, Stoodleigh *(87)*
October 2 Sunday
1 Feebers Cottage, Westwood, nr Broadclyst *(37)*
Gorwell House, Barnstaple *(40)*
Yonder Hill, Colaton Raleigh *(107)*
October 15 Saturday
Pikes Cottage, Madford, Hemyock *(71)*
October 16 Sunday
Pikes Cottage, Madford, Hemyock *(71)*
October 19 Wednesday
Bicton College, East Budleigh *(10)*
October 23 Sunday
Rock House Garden, Chudleigh *(79)*
2006
February 5 Sunday
Cherubeer Gardens, Dolton *(20)*
Little Cumbre, Exeter *(58)*
February 12 Sunday
Little Cumbre, Exeter *(58)*
February 19 Sunday
Little Cumbre, Exeter *(58)*
February 26 Sunday
Little Cumbre, Exeter *(58)*

DESCRIPTIONS OF GARDENS

❶ The African Garden, 96 Wasdale Gardens, Estover, Plymouth ⚙✿ NCCPG
(Mr & Mrs D Fenwick) *From A38 Forder Valley junction, follow signs for Estover, turn R off Forder Valley Rd into Novorossisk Rd, turn L at ASDA sign. Turn L at 2nd mini roundabout past ASDA junction opposite Estover Community College, 1st L into Wasdale Gardens. Car park RH-side of 102. 96 is beyond 95 and 94 at W end of car park.* Small garden totally dedicated to South and Southern African bulbs and other plants. National Collections of Crocosmia with Chasmanthe, Tulbaghia, Amaryllis, Eucomis with Galtonia and Freesia (Anomatheca Group). Featured in 'Garden Life' 2004. *Adm £2, chd £1. Sats, Suns 23, 24, 30, 31 July (10-4). Private visits welcome by appt for groups only. Tel 01752 301402 www.theafricangarden.com*

❷ Alswood, George Nympton ♿✿✉
(Mr R Radford) *2m S of Molton. Halfway between the villages of George Nympton & Alswear.* 2-acre garden, also a newly planted 4-acre arboretum, enthusiastically designed and maintained by owner; a plantsman's paradise, planned to give interest and colour all yr, set in rural area, beautiful views of the Crooked

Oak and Mole valleys. Vast collection of unusual trees and shrubs, spectacular herbaceous, erica and aquatic areas; pond and stream; unique iron and granite architectural features. Home-made TEAS.Teas & plants not for NGS. *Adm £2, chd free. Suns 29 May; 26 June; 31 July; 28 Aug (2-5.30)*

❸ Andrew's Corner, Belstone ♿✿✉
(Robin & Edwina Hill) *3m E of Okehampton. Signed to Belstone. Parking restricted but cars may be left on nearby common.* Plantsman's, wildlife friendly, garden 1,000ft up on Dartmoor, overlooking Taw Valley; wide range of unusual trees, shrubs, herbaceous plants for yr-round effect incl alpines, rhododendrons, bulbs, conifers, ponds; well labelled. Candlelit evening openings. Home-made TEAS. *Adm £2. Suns 24 Apr; 1, 15, 29 May; 5, 12 June (2.30-5.30).* **Evening Opening** *£3.50, wine, Fri 22, Sat 23 July (7-10). Private visits welcome by appt. Tel 01837 840332 edwina-robin.hill@virgin.net*

❹ ◆ Arlington Court, Arlington, Barnstaple ♿✉
(The National Trust) *7m NE of Barnstaple. On A39. Use A399 if coming from S.* Rolling parkland and woods with lake. Rhododendrons and azaleas; fine specimen trees; small terraced Victorian garden with herbaceous borders and conservatory. Walled garden in process of being restored. Regency house containing fascinating collections. Carriage collection in the stables, carriage rides. Light refreshments and TEAS. *House and garden adm £6.50, chd £3.20, family £16.20, garden only adm £4.20, chd £2.10. Suns to Fris 20 Mar to 30 Oct (10.30-5); July & Aug every day.* **For NGS:** *Sun 15 May; Sat 2 July (10.30-5). Tel 01271 851123 Rebecca Aubrey-Fletcher rebecca.aubreyfletch@nationaltrust.org.uk*

❺ NEW Ashley Gardens, Tiverton
On A396 S of Tiverton by town boundary. Home-made TEAS at Ashley Coombe in aid of African Enterprise Trust & at Exe Tor in aid of Anthony Nolan Trust. *Combined adm £2.50, chd free. Sun 24 Apr (2-5.30)*

NEW Ashley Coombe ✿✉ (Dr & Mrs J Anderson) *Turn off A396 signposted Ashley.* The original garden of Ashley Coombe and its adjoining neighbour was designed in the 1960s by a well known local nursery as one large woodland-spring garden. In the last 3 yrs the garden has been replanned to incorporate the best of the original planting and now includes two ponds; wild flower lawn; rose and clematis rope garden; herbaceous section incl plants with foliage effect and colour; rockery/scree; thus providing yr-round interest. Featured in 'Devon Life' 2003. *Private visits welcome by appt, groups of 10 or more. Coaches permitted. Tel 01884 259971 dorothyanderson@uku.co.uk*

NEW **Exe Tor, Ashley, Tiverton** 🌲🏡 (Mr & Mrs B Wynniatt) *On A396 immed S of Tiverton. Nr Howden Court.* Approx ½-acre garden created by the present owners in the last 8 yrs, incl variety and interest with herbaceous borders, water features, bedding, foliage, shrubs and fruit trees. Park in Howden Court. Home-made TEAS. *Private visits welcome by appt. Tel 01884 253197*

6 **NEW** **Axminster & Kilmington Gardens, Axminster** Small market town best known as the home of Axminster carpets. Light refreshments and TEAS at Prospect House. *Combined adm £2.50. Sat 18, Sun 19 June (2-6)*

NEW **Prospect House, Lyme Road, Axminster** 🌲🏡 (Peter Wadeley) *From Axminster town centre (Trinity Square) proceed uphill past the George Hotel into Lyme St & Lyme Rd. Prospect House is approx ½m up the rd on the R just before petrol station.* (See separate entry).

Ways Cottage, Kilmington (Jane Lucas) *1km W of Axminster. From Axminster on A35, turn L before the Old Inn (signposted Whitford). Park in Kilmington village hall car park next to church. Entrance to garden is 200m on R next to village store.* Romantic cottage garden with exuberant planting. Full borders of roses and well chosen perennials. Attractive, unusual frog-friendly pool with small waterfall. Featured in 'Woman & Home' & 'Gardens Monthly', 2003.

7 ◆ **Barleycott, Blakewell** 🌲 (Les & Barbara Shapland) *2m N of Barnstaple. Blakewell, nr Barnstaple. ½m past hospital off B3230 to Ilfracombe at Blakewell Fisheries. Follow signs to Barleycott.* 3-acre, S-sloping garden started in 1989 set in beautiful countryside. Unusual trees,

conifers and shrubs. A lavender walk, vegetable plot, orchard and pond. Lime tree avenue leading to folly and secret Japanese-style garden. Lower garden, rockpool, with large waterfall. Home-made TEAS Suns only. *Adm £2. Every Tues May to Oct (11-5).* **For NGS:** *Suns 22 May; 26 June; 24 July (11-5). Tel 01271 375002*

8 **NEW** **Bertie's Cottage Garden, Yeoford, Crediton** 🌲 (Patti O'Brien) *1½m S of Yeoford, 3m N of Cheriton Bishop. Off A30 to Cheriton Bishop, R to Yeoford, 3m to Woodland X, L to Hittisleigh, 600m on R. OR from Yeoford, R to Hittisleigh, 1st L to Woodland Head, ¾m on L.* Small garden in a sheltered rural setting comprising six 'rooms' of distinct character from exotic mixed borders to grasses, formal planting to a sedum roof. A designer's garden in its sixth year from scratch, it explores the potential of the small space and the balance between art and plantsmanship. *Adm £2, chd £1, concessions £1.50. Sat 26 Feb (11-4); Sats 16 Apr; 7 May; 11 June; 16 July; 6 Aug; 10 Sept (11-5). Private visits welcome by appt. Tel 01647 24704 pattisgarden@aol.com*

9 **Bickham House, Kenn** 🌲🏡 (Mr & Mrs John Tremlett) *6m S of Exeter. 1m off A38. Leave dual carriageway at Kennford Services, follow signs to Kenn. 1st R in village, follow lane for ¾m to end of no-through rd.* 7 acres in secluded wooded valley; lawns, mature trees and shrubs, naturalised bulbs, mixed borders with unusual perennials, wild flower banks for butterflies. Edwardian conservatory, small formal parterre with lily pond; walled kitchen garden with profusion of vegetables, fruit and flowers, palm tree avenue leading to Millennium summerhouse. Lakeside walk. Featured in 'Devon Life' 2003, 'Devon Today' & 'Devon Life' 2004. Cream TEAS. *Adm £2.50, chd 50p. Suns, Tues, Weds 10, 12, 13 Apr; 8, 10, 11 May; 12, 14, 15 June; 10, 12, 13 July; 14, 16, 17 Aug; 11, 13, 14 Sept (2-5). Private visits welcome by appt. Tel 01392 832671 jandjtremlett@hotmail.com*

10 ◆ **Bicton College, East Budleigh** 🌲🏡 NCCPG *3m N of Budleigh Salterton. Use Sidmouth Lodge entrance on B3178.* Renowned monkey puzzle avenue; walled garden. Rich variety of plants in beds and borders, laid out for teaching and effect. National

Collections of agapanthus and pittosporum; arboretum with magnolias, cherries and camellias. Light refreshments and TEAS. *Adm £2, chd under 16 free. Open Mon to Fri, except Bank Hols (10-4.30) Closed Xmas week.* **For NGS:** *Weds 16, 30 Mar; 13 July; 19 Oct (10-4.30). Tel 01395 562353 P Champion pechampion@bicton.ac.uk*

11 **Blackhall Manor, South Tawton** 🌲🏡 (Roger & Jacqueline Yeates) *South Tawton. Park in village square, walk through churchyard.* Small garden around C16 thatched listed house (not open) on northern edge of Dartmoor. Planted with trees, shrubs, and herbaceous perennials to give interest throughout the yr. Cobbled paths and pond. *Adm £3, chd 50p. Sat, Sun 11, 12 June (2-6). Private visits welcome by appt June & July only. Tel 01837 840171 jacqueline.yeates@btinternet.com*

12 **Bovey Tracey Gardens** *6m N of Newton Abbot. Gateway to Dartmoor. Take A382 to Bovey Tracey. Car parking available at Mary St & Station Rd car parks.* Home-made TEAS at Ashwell. *Combined adm £3. Sat, Sun 4, 5 June (2-6)*

NEW **Ashwell, East Street** 🌲 (Bill & Diane Riddell) 1-acre Victorian walled garden presently undergoing restoration. On a steep slope with glorious views. Vineyard, orchard and mature trees incl impressive arbutus.

Brook Lodge, Newton Road 🌲 (Mr & Mrs J Radford) *Opp S J Hales, Newton Rd. Park in Station Rd.* Small garden with brook. Variety of hard and soft planting.

NEW **Cranbrook, Moreton Road** 🌲 (Nigel & Ann Gillingham) *Within 30yds of hospital.* Rescued from a neglected state 2 yrs ago. A developing herbaceous border and well-stocked fruit and vegetable area. S-facing with views of Dartmoor.

Lamorran, Furzeleigh Lane 🌲 (Sally & Andrew Morgan) *30yds up from Bovey Hospital entrance.* Hillside family garden with moorland views, mixed planting incl herbaceous, alpine and vegetables.

NEW **Parke View, Fore Street** 🌲 (Peter & Judy Hall) *Next to The Old Cottage tea shop.* 4-acre mini-estate in the heart of Bovey with 1 acre of garden mostly developed in the last 10 yrs.

⓭ Bridford Gardens
11m from Exeter on Moretonhampstead rd. L at Nogsland Farm then L over bridge into Teign Valley Road. R after Venn Park Garage up Bridford Hill into village, L after Chapel Down Hill, 100yds R at fork signed Hennock. Garden 1m on R. Cluster of gardens in village on N edge of Dartmoor. Cream TEAS at Middle Hole Farm. Combined adm £3.50, chd under 12 free. *Sun 29, Mon 30 May; Sun 28, Mon 29 Aug (2-6).* **Evening Opening** *£5, wine, Sun 19 June (6-9.30). Private visits welcome by appt, only small mini coaches, 10 seaters. Tel 01647 252310 Lower Hole Farm clapton@eurobell.co.uk*

Lower Hole Farm (Ted & Annette Clapton) 6 acres sloping land with views over Bridford and Teign valley. Path through newly planted woodland meandering through ferny glades. Delightful woods with fast-running stream and natural granite outcrops. Mixed shrub and herbaceous borders. Fruit and vegetable garden.

Middle Hole Farm, Bridford (Brian & Anne McMillan) 2½-acre cottage garden with variety of old and new herbaceous plants; many unusual varieties of ornamental grasses; bog garden; stream, small lake; 3 ponds. Laburnum and rose and wisteria walks. Rockery. Orchard with bulbs. Rhododendron, pieris and acer bank. Walled garden. Raised patio. Herb and vegetable gardens. Nursery. Footpath leading to Lower Hole Farm.

⓮ Bundels, Ridgway, Sidbury 🅰🌱
(Alan & Barbara Softly) *4m N of Sidmouth. From Sidmouth A375 turn L at free car park in Sidbury. From Honiton A375, turn R. Garden 100yds up Ridgway on L.* 1½-acre organic garden incl small wood and ponds set round C16 thatched cottage (not open); many varieties of old-fashioned and other shrub roses. Typical cottage garden with accent on preservation of wildlife - owl, bird and bat boxes - badger tracks. Adm £2, chd free if accompanied. *Sun 19 June (10-12.30 & 2-5.30)*

⓯ ◆ Burrow Farm Gardens, Dalwood 🅰🌱
(Mary & John Benger) *3½m W of Axminster. From A35 turn N at Taunton Xrds then follow brown signs.* Secluded 10-acre garden of informal design with many unusual shrubs and herbaceous plants. Pergola walk with shrub roses. Woodland with rhododendrons and azaleas, ponds and large bog garden. Terraced courtyard featuring later flowering plants. Rill garden with water feature; traditional stone summerhouse and informal planting all with wonderful views. Light refreshments and TEAS. Adm £3.50, chd 50p. *1 Apr to 30 Sept, daily (10-7). Tel 01404 831285 Mary Benger www.burrowfarmgardens. co.uk*

⓰ Cadhay, Ottery St Mary 🅰🌱😊
(Rupert Thistlethwayte) *1m NW of Ottery St Mary. On B3176.* Tranquil 2-acre garden in lovely setting between the Elizabethan Manor house (not open) and ancient stew ponds. Carefully planned double herbaceous borders particularly colourful in summer. Small part-walled water garden, roses and clematis. TEAS. Adm £2, chd 50p. *Mon 30 May; Wed, Thur 1, 2 June (2-5.30)*

⓱ ◆ Castle Drogo, Drewsteignton 🅰🌱😊
(The National Trust) *12m W of Exeter. 5m S of A30. Follow brown signs.* Medium-sized Grade II* listed garden with formal structures designed by George Dillistone during the late 1920s. These consist of formal rose beds, herbaceous borders and circular croquet lawn surrounded by mature yew hedges. Outside these areas are woodland and shrubbery overlooking spectacular views of the Teign Valley Gorge and Dartmoor. Light refreshments and TEAS. *House and garden adm £6.50 & chd £3.20, garden only adm £4, chd £2. Daily all year 10.30-5.30. For NGS: Suns 24 Apr; 10 July (10.30-5.30). Tel 01647 433306 Catherine Maddern catherine.maddern@nationaltrust. org.uk*

⓲ ◆ Castle Hill, Filleigh
(The Earl & Countess of Arran) *4m W of South Molton. From A361 Tiverton to Barnstaple leave at Little Chef roundabout on B3226 signed Filleigh.* Palladian house in extensive C18 Grade I landscape park and garden. Arboretum and woodlands with camellias, rhododendrons, magnolias, azaleas and other shrubs and rare trees in abundance. Summer millenium garden designed by Xa Tollemache with topiary water sculpture by Giles Rayner. Many C18 follies and a 1730 castle on the hill with magnificent views to Exmoor, Dartmoor and Lundy Island. Dogs on leads and picnics welcome on NGS days. Limited disabled access. Adm £4, chd free, disabled free. *Suns, Mons, Weds, Fris 25 Mar to 29 Aug (11-5).* **For NGS:** *Suns 24 Apr; 22 May (11-5)*

⓳ Chapel Farm House, Halwill Junction 🅰🌱😊
(Robin & Toshie Hull) *12m NW of Okehampton. On A3079. At W end of village.* Approx ½ acre created 14yrs ago by present owners, landscaped with shrub borders, heathers, rhododendrons and azalea and alpine bed. Kitchen garden. 2 small greenhouses for mixed use; small bonsai collection. Adm £2, chd 50p. *Suns 24 Apr; 29 May; 12 June; 24 July; 14 Aug; 25 Sept (11-5). Private visits welcome by appt. Tel 01409 221594*

⓴ Cherubeer Gardens, Dolton
8m SE of Great Torrington. 2m E of Dolton. From A3124 turn S towards Stafford Moor Fisheries, take 1st R, gardens are 500m on L. Home-made TEAS at Higher Cherubeer. Combined adm £3, chd free. *Suns 29 May; 3 July (2-6); Sun 5 Feb (11-3) 2006*

Cherubeer 🌱 (Janet Brown) Cottage garden set around a C15 thatched house (not open). Garden divided into compartments with ponds, paths, and steps filled with colourful perennials and herbs set off by mature shrubs and trees. *Not open 5 Feb 2006*

Higher Cherubeer 🅰🌱😊 (Jo & Tom Hynes) 1-acre country garden with gravelled courtyard, raised beds and alpine troughs, lawns, large herbaceous border, shady woodland beds, large kitchen garden, greenhouse, colourful collection of basketry willows, nature conservation interest. Winter opening for early bulbs, snowdrop varieties and hellebores. Featured on BBC 1's 2004 Chelsea Flower Show Preview.

Middle Cherubeer 🅰🌱 (Barty & Heather Hynes) A colourful garden developed over the last eight years. Three separate areas with bog garden, pond and massed herbaceous perennials interlinked with paths.

㉑ The Cider House, Buckland Abbey 🚫♿⚘

(Mr & Mrs M J Stone) *8m N of Plymouth. Yelverton. From A386 Plymouth to Tavistock rd, follow NT signs to Buckland Abbey. At Xrds before Abbey entrance turn N signed Buckland Monachorum. Drive 200yds on L, or short walk for visitors to Abbey.* 3 acres in peaceful surroundings looking down to Tavy valley. Terrace gardens complement the medieval house (not open), herb garden, woodland and herbaceous borders, wild garden with rhododendrons, camellias and other shrubs. Former walled kitchen garden productively maintained to give abundance of fruit, vegetables and flowers. Accommodation. Featured in 'The English Garden', 2003 & 'Devon Country Gardener' 2004. Cream TEAS. *Adm £3, chd £1. Suns 15 May; 19 June; 4 Sept (2-6). Evening Opening £5, wine, Thur 23 June (6.30-8). Private visits welcome by appt. Tel 01822 853285 michael.stone@cider-house.co.uk*

㉒ Cleave House, Sticklepath 🚫♿⚘ NCCPG

(Ann & Roger Bowden) *3 ½m E of Okehampton. On old A30 towards Exeter. Cleave House on L in village, on main rd just past R turn for Skaigh.* ½-acre garden with mixed planting for all season interest. National Collection of hostas with 1000 varieties. Cream TEAS. *Adm £2, chd free. Sats, Suns 23, 24 Apr; 4, 5 June; 30, 31 July (10.30-5). Private visits welcome by appt. Tel 01837 840481 bowdens2@eclipse.co.uk*

㉓ ◆ Cliffe, Lee, Ilfracombe ⚘ NCCPG

(Mrs Veronica Gilbert) *3m W of Ilfracombe. Garden is past the sea front at Lee, 150yds up the coast rd, through the wrought iron gates on the L. Lee Bay car park 260yds (no parking on approach rd).* Cliffside garden with spectacular coastal scenery. Mixture of planting incl shade and woodland. Camellias, daffodils and azaleas in spring. National Collection of heucheras and schizostylis. Always something to see. Mixed herbaceous borders. *Adm £2. Daily Mar to Sept (10-5) .* **For NGS:** *Adm £2.50. Tue 24, Thur 26, Tue 31 May; Thur 2, Tue 7, Thur 9 June; Tue 19, Thur 21 July (10-5)*

㉔ ◆ Coleton Fishacre, nr Kingswear 🚫♿⚘

The National Trust) *3m E of Dartmouth. Lower Ferry Road. Follow brown tourist signs. Coach parties must book.* 24-acre garden

created by Rupert and Lady Dorothy D'Oyly Carte between 1925 and 1948. Re-established and developed by NT since 1983. Wide range of tender and uncommon trees and shrubs in spectacular coastal setting. Light refreshments and TEAS. *House and garden adm £5.50 chd £2.75, garden only adm £4.40, chd £2.10. .* **For NGS:** *Suns 17 Apr; 15 May (10.30-5.30). Tel 01803 752466 David Mason coletonfishacre@nationaltrust.org.uk*

㉕ Collepardo, 3 Keyberry Park, Newton Abbot 🚫♿⚘

(Betty & Don Frampton) *Take A380 for Newton Abbot. From Penn Inn roundabout follow sign for town centre. Take 1st L, 1st R, 2nd L.* ¼-acre town garden completely redesigned as a grass-free garden for the plantsperson. Garden is laid out in series of interlinked areas to give emphasis on colour and form. Includes 60ft semi-circular rockery, many unusual herbaceous perennials, pond and walkway. Cream TEAS. *Adm £2. Daily Sat 25 June to Thur 30 June; Fri 1, Sat 2, Sun 3 July (11-5)*

㉖ Colyford Gardens

Midway between Sidmouth & Lyme Regis. Far E of Devon off A3052. An ancient borough renowned for a Michaelmas Goose Fayre that dates from 1208. Home-made TEAS at Paddocks in aid of Cancer Research. *Combined adm £2.50, chd free. Suns 10, 17 July (2-6)*

Paddocks, Stafford Lane 🚫♿⚘

(Alan & Wendy Davis) *W end of Colyford. Park in Colyton Grammar School.* 2 acres to stroll around and enjoy the views of beautiful Axe estuary. Gentle sloping lawn (no steps) and numerous borders which overflow with interesting shrubs. In addition there are herbaceous borders, heather bed, vegetable plot and a Bear. *Private visits welcome by appt. Tel 01297 552472*

The Vinyard, Seaton Road 🚫♿⚘

(Mollie & Michael Pickup) *At Colyford PO turn off A3052 into Seaton Rd, 5th house on L.* Flower arranger's 1¼-acre garden with extensive sea and Axe valley views. Many shrubs and perennials, woodland area, small orchard, soft fruit, vegetables, ponds and scree bed. Delightful, tranquil setting within natural Devon banks.

㉗ Combpyne Manor 🚫♿⚘

(Nicky & Donald Campbell) *4m W of Lyme Regis. From Rousdon (A3052) follow sign to Combpyne.* 3½ acres of mature contrast gardens geared to conservation and wildlife. Unusual planting within medieval walls for yr-round interest. Large organic vegetable plot. 'Wild' garden with contoured paths managed to reduce fertility and create flower-rich slopes. Native woodland area. Wonderful views. Home-made TEAS in aid of Axe Vale District Conservation Society 'Car' St Mary's Church, Combpyne. *Adm £2, chd 50p. Sats, Suns 11, 12 June; 9, 10 July; 3, 4 Sept (11-5)*

㉘ The Croft, Yarnscombe 🚫♿⚘

(Sam & Margaret Jewell) *4m NE of Torrington, 8m S of Barnstaple. From A377, turn W opp Chapelton railway stn. After 3m drive on L at village sign. From B3232, ¼m N of Hunshaw TV mast Xrds, turn E for 2m.* 1-acre plantswoman's garden on edge of village with unspoilt distant views. Creating Japanese garden area. Also wide selection of unusual plants and shrubs. Island beds, much herbaceous material, ponds and bog area. *Adm £2.50, chd free. Suns 19 June; 17 July; 21 Aug (2-6). Private visits welcome by appt. Tel 01769 560535*

㉙ ◆ Dartington Hall Gardens, Dartington 🚫♿⚘

(Dartington Hall Trust) *1 ½m NW of Totnes. From Totnes take A384, turn R at Dartington Parish Church. Proceed up hill for 1m. The hall & gardens are on R. Car parking on L.* 28-acre modern garden, created since 1925 around C14 medieval hall (not open). Courtyard and tournament ground. Recent additions incl dry landscape Japanese garden. Extensive wild flower meadows and new mixed shrub and herbaceous border. Guided tour of Hall & Garden available at 2pm. Light refreshments and TEAS available. *Adm £2. Open yr round.* **For NGS:** *Suns 24 Apr; 15 May (dawn to dusk). Tel 01803 862367 G A Gammin gardens@dartingtonhall.org.uk*

㉚ Dicot, Chardstock ⚘

(Mr & Mrs F Clarkson) *5m N of Axminster. Axminster to Chard A358 at Tytherleigh to Chardstock. R at George Inn, L fork to Hook, R to Burridge, 2nd house on L.* 3-acre enthusiasts' garden; trees, unusual shrubs and conifers, bog orchids in June. Stream, mixed borders, fish pool, Japanese garden, and other surprises. TEAS. *Adm £2.50, chd £1. Sats, Suns 30 Apr; 1 May; 18, 19 June; 23, 24 July (2-5.30). Private visits welcome by appt. Tel 01460 220364 www.dicot.co.uk*

⓷ Dippers, Shaugh Prior

🚻♿NCCPG

(Mr & Mrs R J Hubble) *8m NE of Plymouth. Garden 100yds down lane opp church near top of village. Park in village or at Whitethorn public house. No parking in lane but dropping off point for disabled. ¾-acre plantsman's garden containing around 2500 different plants. Emphasis on foliage contrast and all-yr interest. Large colour range of hellebores, snowdrop collection, dwarf rhododendrons, extensive collection of alpines in raised beds, troughs, tufa and alpine house. National Collection of dianthus (pinks). Unusual trees and shrubs. Wildlife features. Adm £2, chd free. Fris 4, 11, 18, Sats 5, 26 Mar (11-4). Private visits welcome by appt Feb & Mar; April to June Fris only. Tel 01752 839407 hubbles@dippers.fsnet.co.uk*

⓸ ◆ Docton Mill Gardens, Lymebridge ♿

(Mr Borrett) *12m W of Bideford. Nr Hartland. Follow brown flower signs from Hartland or West Country Inn on A39. Less than 1m from the sea, nestling in one of Devon's outstanding beauty spots. A garden for all seasons. Restored mill (open) surrounded by 8 acres of gardens, created around original mill streams, encompassing an exceptional bog garden, orchard and natural woodland. Additions to garden include magnolia collection with greatly extended herbaceous border, planting of woodland walk, summer garden and new stream garden. Light refreshments and TEAS. Adm £4, chd under 16 free, concessions £3.75. 1st Mar to 31st Oct incl (10-6). For NGS: Fri 15 July (10-6). Tel 01237 441369 John Borrett www.doctonmill.co.uk*

⓹ The Downes, Monkleigh ♿♿

(Mr & Mrs R C Stanley-Baker) *3m NW of Great Torrington. On A386 to Bideford turn L (W) up drive, ¼m beyond layby. Do not go to Monkleigh. 15 acres with landscaped*

lawns; fine views overlooking fields and woodlands in Torridge Valley; many unusual trees and shrubs; small arboretum; woodland walks. TEAS *Sats & Suns only. Adm £2, chd 20p. Fri 25 Mar; Sun 12 June (all day). Private visits welcome by appt, no coaches. Tel 01805 622244*

⓺ Drury Head Cottage, Postbridge ♿♿

(Mr & Mrs Doyle) *10m NE of Tavistock. From Moretonhampstead take B3212 to Postbridge or from Tavistock B3357, turning L at Two Bridges. Garden next to Church in village. Park in village hall car park. Over 1000ft up on Dartmoor. 1-acre organic cottage garden. Shrubs, small collection irises, hemerocallis, hardy geraniums, shrub roses, candelabra primulas. Fish and wildlife pond, small waterfall and bog garden. Small knot garden with old-fashioned pinks and mints. Gravelled area with phlox, pinks, thymes. 2-acre wild flower meadow. TEAS. Adm £2, chd 75p. Suns 5, 19 June (2-5.30)*

⓻ Durcombe Water, Furzehill, Barbrook, Lynton

(Pam & David Sydenham) *3m S of Lynton. From Barnstaple take A39 towards Lynton. On entering village of Barbrook go past Total garage (do not turn to Lynton) take the next turn R (about 100yds). Follow this single track rd for 2m, white gates on L. Set in the Exmoor National Park beside open moorland with superb views, a delightfully secluded steeply terraced garden providing a profusion of yr-round colour. Includes conifers, heathers, many old-fashioned annuals and perennials together with trees and shrubs. The garden offers peace and tranquillity enhanced by spring-fed streams and ponds, and waterfalls dropping 40ft via 8 tiered ponds. Fruit and vegetable garden and many unusual features. Large extension in progress (2½ acres total garden) with ponds, waterfalls, landscaping and small woodland. Home-made TEAS. Adm £2.50 (share to Barbrook Village Hall Trust). Suns 29 May; 3 July; 7 Aug (1.30-5.30). Private visits welcome by appt. Tel 01598 753658*

⓭ Fast Rabbit Farm, Ash Cross, Dartmouth

(Mr A S Mort & Ms Stevie Rogers) *1½m W of Dartmouth. Off A3122 Dartmouth to Totnes rd, pass park & ride. Turn L at sign for Hillfield. From Totnes or Kingsbridge, pass Woodland Park on R, at second turn R follow signs. Garden created in sheltered valley with natural stream. Several ponds and lake; partially wooded; rockery; extensively planted; extends to 12 acres plus new woodland planting and walks created through woodland at head of valley. Some level walks. Disabled and less mobile please phone or call at farmhouse prior to visit. Specialist nursery open w/ends. Green Tourism Bronze Award 2003. Adm £2.50, chd 50p. Suns, 6 Mar to 26 June; Fri 25, Mon 28 Mar; Mons 2, 30 May (11-5). Private visits welcome by appt and guided walks. Tel 01803 712437 www.fastrabbitfarm.co.uk*

⓮ 1 Feebers Cottage, Westwood, nr Broadclyst ♿♿♿

(Mr & Mrs M S Squires) *8m NE of Exeter. From B3181 (formerly A38) Exeter to Taunton rd, at Dog Village bear E to Whimple, after 1½m fork L for Westwood. Evolving cottage garden of ¾ acre specialising in unusual plants. Maze of pathways leads to informal areas of specimen trees, bulbs, wild flowers, willows and Amos Perry's Iris sibirica all growing in heavy clay soil. Also raised alpine areas and a 'Heritage' HDRA vegetable garden. Light refreshments and TEAS. Adm £2, chd free. Suns 28 Aug; 18 Sept; 2 Oct (12noon-4). Opening with 3 Feebers Cottage as Westwood Gardens 26 June; 24 July (2-6). Private visits welcome by appt. Tel 01404 822118*

Fernhill, nr Wellington ♿♿
See Somerset.

◆ Forde Abbey Gardens, Chard ♿♿
See Dorset.

⓯ ◆ The Garden House, Buckland Monachorum ♿♿

(The Fortescue Garden Trust) *10m N of Plymouth. Yelverton. W of A386. 8 acres, incl romantic terraced walled garden surrounding ruins of medieval vicarage. Modern areas in pioneering 'new naturalism' style inspired by great natural landscapes (the desert flowering of South Africa, Cretan olive groves, English cottage gardens). More than 6,000 varieties. Light refreshments and TEAS. Adm £4.50, chd £1, concessions £4. Open daily 1 Mar to 31 Oct (10.30-5) Last*

adm 4.30pm. **For NGS:** *Thurs 14 July;*
18 Aug (10.30-5). Tel 01822 854769
Stuart Fraser
www.thegardenhouse.org.uk

③⁹ The Gate House, Lee, Coastal
Village 🔆 NCCPG
(Mr & Mrs D Booker) *3m W of*
Ilfracombe. Park in village car park.
Take lane alongside The Grampus
public house. Garden is approx 30
metres past inn buildings. 2¼ acres,
where no chemicals are used, only
few minutes walk from the sea and
dramatic coastal scenery. Peaceful
streamside garden with range of
habitats; bog garden, National
Collection of Rodgersia, at their best
June/July, woodland, herbaceous
borders, patio gardens with semi-
hardy 'exotics'. *Private visits*
welcome by appt . Open most days
May through August but essential to
phone first. Tel 01271 862409
www.leebay.co.uk/Gardens open

④⁰ Gorwell House, Barnstaple
🔆 ⊕
(Dr J A Marston) *1m E of Barnstaple*
centre. On Bratton Fleming rd, drive
entrance between two lodges on left.
4 acres of trees and shrubs, rare and
tender; walled garden, mostly created
since 1982; grotto; small temple;
summerhouse with views across
estuary to Hartland Point. Cream
TEAS not Apr or Oct. *Adm £3, chd*
free. Suns 24 Apr; 22 May; 12 June;
24 July; 4 Sept; 2 Oct (2-6)

◆ Greencombe, Porlock
🔆 ⊗ ⊕ NCCPG
See Somerset.

④¹ Haldon Grange, Dunchideock
⊗ ⊕
Ted Phythian) *5m SW of Exeter.*
From A30 at Exeter pass through Ide
village to Dunchideock 5m. In centre
of village turn L to Lord Haldon
Hotel, Haldon Grange is just past
drive of hotel. From A38 (S) turn L
on top of Haldon Hill follow
Dunchideock signs, R at village
centre (thatched house). 8-acre well
established garden with camellias,
magnolias, azaleas and
rhododendrons; rare and mature
trees; small lake and ponds with river
and water cascades as a feature. Light
refreshments and TEAS. *Adm £2, chd*
50p. Sat 23, Sun 24, Sat 30 Apr; Sun
1, Mon 2 May (11-5). Private visits
welcome by appt. Tel 01392 832349
phythian@tinyworld.co.uk

④² Hamblyn's Coombe, Dittisham
(Robert & Bridget McCrum) *3m N*
of Dartmouth. From Red Lion Inn
follow The Level until it forks & go
straight up steep private road and
through 'River Farm' gate. Continue
straight on to end of farm track as
signposted. 7-acre garden with
stunning views across the river to
Greenway House and sloping steeply
to R Dart at bottom of garden.
Extensive planting of trees and shrubs
with unusual design features
accompanying Bridget McCrum's
stone carvings and bronzes. Wild
flower meadow and woods. Good
rhododendrons and camellias, ferns
and bamboos, acers and hydrangeas.
Exceptional autumn colour. Dogs on
leads. Featured in 'The Times',
'Telegraph' & 'English Garden' 2004.
Selected for 'Modern Garden' Open
Day 2004. *Adm £3, chd free. Private*
visits welcome by appt all yr except
July & Aug (2-5). Tel 01803 722228

Hangeridge Farm, Wrangway
🔆 ⊗ ⊕
See Somerset.

④³ ◆ Hartland Abbey, Hartland,
nr Bideford ⊕
(Sir Hugh & Lady Stucley) *15m W of*
Bideford, 15m N of Bude. Turn off
A39 W of Clovelly Cross to
Hartland. Abbey between Hartland
& Hartland Quay. Historic family
home since Dissolution in beautiful
valley with walk to remote Atlantic
cove. Winding paths lead to bog
garden and fernery by Jekyll, lost
since 1914 and discovered in 1998.
Woodland gardens of
rhododendrons, azaleas, camellias,
hydrangeas, gunnera etc lead to three
newly restored C18 walled gardens.
Herbaceous and tender perennials,
huge *Echium pininana* and vegetables
thrive here once again. Glasshouses.
Peacocks, Welsh mountain sheep.
Wonderful bluebells in April.
Featured in 'The English Garden',
2003 & 'Night & Day' magazine
2004. Cream TEAS available only
when house is open. *House and*
garden adm £6.50 adult, OAPs £6,
chd £1.50, garden only adm £4.50,
chd 50p, concessions £4. Gardens
only: open daily except Sats 25 Mar
to 2 Oct. House & gardens: 25 Mar
to 2 Oct, Weds, Thurs, Suns, Bank
Hols & Tues in July & Aug (2-5.30).
Tel 01884 860225 Lady Stucley
www.hartlandabbey.com

④⁴ Heathercombe, Manaton
(Claude & Margaret Pike Woodlands
Trust) *7m NW of Bovey Tracey.*
From Bovey Tracey take rd to Becky
Falls and Manaton. Continue on
same rd for 2m beyond village. At
Heatree Cross follow sign straight
ahead to Heathercombe. At top of
hill continue straight ahead to
Heathercombe. (From Widecombe
take rd past Natsworthy). Tranquil
wooded valley 1000ft up on
Dartmoor provides setting for
arboretum of unusual trees, many
varieties of rhododendrons and other
shrubs. Woodland walks beside
streams and ponds amongst
snowdrops, daffodils and bluebells;
summer cottage garden; recently
established wild flower meadow and
orchard. Well-labelled, providing yr-
round interest. *Adm £2.50, chd free.*
Sun 3 Apr; Sats, Suns 21, 22, 28, 29
May (2-5.30). Private visits welcome
by appt. Tel 01647 221222 or 01626
354404 johndpike@aol.com

④⁵ ◆ Heddon Hall, Parracombe
🔆 ⊕
(Mr & Mrs Fred de Falbe) *10m NE*
of Barnstaple. Off A39. 400yds N up
hill from village centre. Entrance to
drive on R. Beautiful mature garden
on edge of Exmoor extending to 4
acres. Walled garden with flowers,
fruit and vegetables within a formal
design by Penelope Hobhouse. Secret
flower garden with many unusual
plants. Shaded shrubbery sloping
down to a water garden. Fernery and
small arboretum. Cream TEAS. *Adm*
£3.50, chd free. Weds, Fris, Suns,
May to July; Bank Hols (2-5.30). **For**
NGS: *Suns 1 May; 31 July (2-5.30).*
Tel 01598 763788

④⁶ High Barn, Torbryan 🔆 ⊕
(John & Ann Holl) *4m S of Newton*
Abbot. From Ipplepen (on A381)
take Broadhempston Rd. Turn L at
Poole Cross signed to Totnes. Garden
400yds on L. Developing garden of 1
acre, started in 1992 from traditional
cider orchard. Herbaceous borders;
gravel garden; apple trees with
climbing roses; species roses; unusual
shrubs and trees. Becoming less
formal and aiming to encourage
wildlife in lower part of garden with
views of pond. New rill garden.
Home-made TEAS. *Adm £2, chd*
free. Suns 11, 18 Sept (2-6). Private
visits welcome by appt. Tel 01803
812339 john-ann@ambrook.fsnet.
co.uk

④⁷ Higher Knowle, Lustleigh
(Mr & Mrs D R A Quicke) *3m NW*
of Bovey Tracey. Take A382 towards
Moretonhampstead. In 2½m turn L
for Lustleigh; in ¼m L then R; in ¼m
steep drive L. 3-acre woodland
garden around 1914 house (not open)
with Lutyens style features.
Spectacular views to Dartmoor,
sheltered hillside garden usually
avoids late frosts. Old oak wood with
primroses and bluebells among giant
boulders, mature Asiatic magnolias in

late March, camellias, new hybrid magnolias, rhododendrons, azaleas and embothriums. Featured in RHS 'The Garden' 2004. *Adm £2.50, chd free. Suns & Bank Hol Mons 20 Mar to 30 May (2-6). Private visits welcome by appt Mar to May incl. Tel 01647 277275*

48 Hole Farm, nr Bickington ⬤
(Rev Ian Graham-Orlebar) 5m NE of Ashburton. From A383 Ashburton to Newton Abbot rd, 3m NE of Ashburton signed Gale, Burne, Woodland. Follow signs to Farlacombe, after 2m, at top of hill, lane on R to Hole Farm. 2½-acre valley garden, with woodland, wild garden, 2 ponds, herbaceous borders, bog areas and wildlife plantation. Old farm and buildings, not open. Home-made TEAS. *Adm £3, chd £1. Sun 31 July (2-5). Private visits welcome by appt. Tel 01626 821298 www.holefarm.co.uk*

Hooper's Holding, 45 High Street, Hinton St George ⬤
See Somerset.

49 Hortus, Shrubbery Bungalow, School Lane, Rousdon ⬤⬤
(Mark & Marie-Elaine Houghton) 3m E of Seaton. On A3052 midway bet Seaton & Lyme Regis, next to Rousdon garage. Look for roadside signs & red phone box. Imaginatively designed garden created from scratch in 2003. Pebble beach with seaside flowers; gravel terrace with over 50 grasses; scented walk; Mediterranean patio with tender plants in pots; experimental border of native flowers and grasses; colour-themed borders with many unusual plants. Adjacent nursery. Home-made TEAS. *Adm £2, chd 50p. Suns 12 June; 17 July; 14 Aug; 18 Sept (11-5) www.hortusnursery.com*

50 Inglewood, 81 Court Road, Newton Ferrers ⬤⬤
(Vivian & Patsy Stevenson) 10m E of Plymouth. Take A374 Plymouth to Kingsbridge rd. At Yealmpton, turn S to Newton Ferrers. At Green Xrds (signed), turn R into Parsonage Rd then along Court Rd for ¾m. Entrance on L. Unusual situation overlooking R Yealm. Steep garden with many terraces with a fair few plants; always trying to improve. Home-made TEAS. *Adm £2.50. Suns 22 May; 5 June (2-5)*

51 Kerscott House, Swimbridge ⬤⬤
(Jessica & Peter Duncan) 6m E of Barnstaple. On Barnstaple-South Molton rd, 1m E of Swimbridge turn R at top of hill, immed fork L, 100yds on L, 1st gate past house. 6 acres surrounding C16 farmhouse (not open) in peaceful rural setting. Ornamental trees, wide selection of shrubs, herbaceous and tender perennials, ponds and bog garden. Mediterranean garden within roofless barn. Living willow constructions and natural sculptures. 2½ acres woodland planted 1995, wildlife meadow with ponds. Cream TEAS. *Adm £2, chd free. Suns 26 June; 31 July; 28 Aug (2-6). Private visits welcome by appt, groups of 10 or more. Tel 01271 830943 www.kerscottgarden.co.uk*

52 Kia-Ora Farm & Gardens, Knowle Lane, Cullompton ⬤⬤⬤
(Mrs M B Disney) 6m SE of Tiverton. Junction 28 of M5. From Cullompton town centre, turn R beside Manor House Hotel. After approx ½m, turn L into Langlands Rd. At T-junction, turn R, after 300yds, turn R again. Garden beside rugby club. 10 acres of extensively planted gardens and lakes. Charming, peaceful garden with lawns, large lakes, ponds, bog garden and various water features incl ducks and wildlife. Many areas with individual character, mature trees and shrubs, rhododendrons, azaleas, heathers, roses, herbaceous borders and rockeries. Several new features incl nursery avenue, wisteria walk and many more!! Surprises everywhere. Featured in 'Express & Echo', 2004; ITV Carlton 2003, 'Mid Devon Gazette', 2004. Home-made TEAS. *Adm £2.50, chd 50p. Suns 17 Apr; 1, 15, 29, May; 12, 26 June; 10, 24 July; 7, 28, Aug; 11 Sept; Mons 2, 30 May; 29 Aug (2-6). Private visits welcome by appt, coach access & parking, afternoon or evening, cream teas or BBQ. Tel 01884 32347 www.kiaorafarm.co.uk*

53 ◆ Killerton Garden, Broadclyst ⬤⬤⬤
(The National Trust) 8m N of Exeter. Take B3181 Exeter to Cullompton rd, after 7m fork left & follow NT signs. 20 acres of spectacular hillside gardens with naturalised bulbs sweeping down to large open lawns. Delightful walks through fine collection of rare trees and shrubs; herbaceous borders. Light refreshments and TEAS. *House and garden adm £6.50, chd £3, groups £5.50, chd £1.75, garden only adm £5, chd £2.50, concessions, group 15+ £4.30, chd £1.60. Daily all year (10.30-dusk). For NGS: Suns 17 Apr; 11 Sept (10.30-dusk)*

54 Kingston House, Staverton ⬤⬤
(Mr & Mrs M R Corfield) 4m NE of Totnes. A384 Totnes to Buckfastleigh, from Staverton, 1m due N of Sea Trout Inn, follow signs to Kingston. George II 1735 house grade II (not open). Gardens being restored in keeping with the period. Walled garden, rose garden, pleached limes and hornbeams, vegetable garden. Unusual formal garden with santolinas, lavender and camomile. Large new formal parterre. Accommodation. Cream TEAS. *Adm £2.50, chd £1 (share to Animals in Distress). Suns 29 May; 26 June; 10 July (2-6).* **Evening Opening** *£3.50, wine, Sun 12 June (6-9). Tel 01803 762235 www.kingston-estate.co.uk*

55 ◆ Knightshayes Court Garden, Tiverton ⬤⬤⬤
(The National Trust) 2m N of Tiverton. Via A396 Tiverton to Bampton rd; turn E in Bolham, signed Knightshayes; entrance ½m on L. Large 'Garden in the Wood', 50 acres of landscaped gardens with pleasant walks and views over Exe valley. Choice collections of unusual plants, incl acers, birches, rhododendrons, azaleas, camellias, magnolias, roses, spring bulbs, alpines and herbaceous borders; formal gardens; walled kitchen garden. Light refreshments and TEAS. *House and garden adm £6.20, chd £3.10, garden only adm £4.80, chd £2.40, NT members free. Open daily 23 Mar to 30 Oct (11-5). For NGS: Suns 17 Apr; 18 Sept (11-5.30). Tel 01884 254665 Penny Woollams*

56 Lee Ford, Budleigh Salterton ⬤⬤
(Mr & Mrs N Lindsay-Fynn) In Knowle village. Extensive, formal and woodland garden, largely developed in the 1950s, but recently much extended with mass displays of camellias, rhododendrons and azaleas, incl many rare varieties. Traditional walled garden filled with fruit and vegetables, herb garden, bog garden, rose garden, hydrangea collection, greenhouses. Ornamental conservatory and Adam pavilion. Light refreshments and TEAS. *Adm £4 & £1 guided tour. Minimum charge per group £64, chd free. Private visits welcome by appt for pre-booked parties of 16 or more, Mon to Thur (10-4) Fri (10-3) Apr to Sept. Tel 01395 445894 crescent@leeford.co.uk*

57 Little Ash Farm, Fenny Bridges, Honiton 🚻✏️🏠
(Sadie & Robert Reid) *3m W of Honiton. Leave A30 at Iron Bridge from Honiton 1m, Patteson's Cross from Exeter ½m, & follow NGS signs. Peaceful garden within 1 acre with adjoining farmland and extensive views. Immaculate lawns, new and established trees and shrubs. Three linked ponds and delightful rill through the garden. Fruit and vegetable garden and new 'grape' house. Golf putting course. Accommodation. Home-made TEAS. Adm £2.50, chd free. Thur 19 May; Suns 26 June; 24 July; 14 Aug (2-6). Private visits welcome by appt. Tel 01404 850271*

58 Little Cumbre, 145 Pennsylvania Road, Exeter ✏️🏠
(Dr & Mrs John Lloyd) *1m due N of city centre. Near top of hill, 50yds below tel kiosk. Extensive views to Dartmoor and Exe Estuary. ½-acre formal garden with shrubs and bulbs plus ½ acre of woodland. Wonderful display of snowdrops, about 30 varieties, and many different coloured hellebores. Scented winter shrubs. Featured in 'Western Morning News' 2003 & 2004; 'Devon Life' 2004. Adm £2, chd free. Suns 6, 13, 20, 27 Feb (1-4); Suns 5, 12, 19, 26 Feb '1-4) 2006. Private visits welcome by appt, groups of 10 or more. Tel 01392 258315*

59 The Lodge, Hartley Avenue, Mannamead, Plymouth 🚻🏠
Mr & Mrs M H Tregaskis) *1½m from centre of Plymouth via Mutley Plain. Turn R at Henders Corner into Eggbuckland Rd, 3rd R at tel kiosk to end of cul de sac. ½-acre, S-sloping aspect with variety of citrus fruits, olives, unusual shrubs, conifers, camellias and ground cover plants. Large vegetable area. Former local authority nursery with range of lean-to glasshouses for fruit and tender subjects. TEAS. Adm £2.50, chd free (share to St Luke's Hospice). Suns 8 May; 12 June; 24 July (2-5). Private visits welcome by appt. Tel 01752 220849*

60 ◆ Lukesland, Ivybridge
(Mrs R Howell) *10m E of Plymouth. Turn off A38 at Ivybridge. 1½m N in Harford rd, E side of Erme valley. 15 acres of flowering shrubs, wild flowers and rare trees with pinetum in Dartmoor National Park. Beautiful setting of small valley around Addicombe Brook with lakes, numerous waterfalls and pools. Extensive and unusual collection of rhododendrons, a champion*

Magnolia campbellii and a huge Davidia involucrata. Home-made TEAS. Adm £3.50, chd free. Suns, Weds & Bank Hol Mons, 27 Mar to 12 June (2-6). Tel 01752 893390 Mrs R Howell Living_Resources@compuserve.com

61 ◆ Marwood Hill, Marwood 🚻🏠 NCCPG
(Dr J A Snowdon) *4m N of Barnstaple. Signed from A361 Barnstaple to Braunton rd & B3230 Barnstaple to Ilfracombe rd. Outside Guineaford village, opp Marwood church. 20 acres with 3 small lakes. Extensive collection of camellias under glass and in open; daffodils; rhododendrons, rare flowering shrubs, rock and alpine scree; waterside planting; bog garden; many clematis; Australian native plants and many eucalyptus. National Collections of astilbe, Iris ensata, tulbaghia. Adm £3, chd free. Open every day except Christmas Day, dawn to dusk. Tel 01271 342528 Malcolm Pharoah www.marwoodhillgarden.co.uk*

Melplash Court, Melplash 🚻🏠
See Dorset.

62 NEW Metcombe Brake, Higher Metcombe 🚻
(Mike & Kate Peirce) *2½m SW of Ottery St Mary. From A30 (E of Exeter) Daisymount turnoff. Take B3180 S, past 2 L turns to West Hill. Turn L at Tipton Cross & travel 0.7m towards Tipton St John; or from A3052 turn N on B3180 at Halfway Inn. Travel 1.6m & turn R at Tipton Cross etc. 6 acres of woodland garden planted in 1930s; being extensively restored. Many interesting trees. Lots of camellias, rhododendrons and azaleas. Acers in stream walk. Cyclamen, snowdrops and daffodils in season and a spectacular 2-acre bluebell wood. Lovely views over Otter valley. Have a wonderful wander! Restricted garden access for wheelchairs. Garden will not open if very windy. Home-made TEAS. Adm £2.50, chd free. Wed 27 Apr; Sun 1, Mon 2, Sun 8 May (2-5.30)*

63 Milland Farm, nr Northlew ✏️🏠
(Julia & John Barton) *5m NW of Okehampton. Leave A30 at Sowton Cross Services (western end of Okehampton bypass). Take A386 towards Bideford & Torrington heading N. After approx 3m (stay on A386) at Hilltown Cross turn L towards Northlew. Proceed for 3m then at bottom of steep hill, turn R*

towards Inwardleigh. Milland Farm is 2nd entrance on L. 1-acre country garden surrounded by fields and bordered by a small river. The garden features a S-facing gravel area. A herb garden, unusual perennials, two small ponds and planting for damp conditions and heavy clay soil. Extended herbaceous borders and woodland plantings for 2005. TEAS. Adm £2, chd free. Sun 17 Apr; Suns, Mons 1, 2, 29, 30 May; Suns 12, 26 June; 10, 31 July; Sun 28, Mon 29 Aug; Sun 11 Sept (11-6). Private visits welcome by appt. Tel 01837 810313 milland.farm@btopenworld. com

64 The Moorings, Rocombe
(Mrs Enid Marriage) *2m NW of Lyme Regis. Uplyme. From Lyme Regis, after 1m on B3165, turn R signposted Rocombe, over Xrds, ignore narrow lane signposted Rocombe, continue ½m , park on verge on L. From Axminster, straight at Hunters Lodge then fork R twice, straight at Xrds. ¾m on R. 3 acres of peaceful woodland garden, developed since 1965, on hillside with terraced paths, overlooking unspoilt countryside. Fine trees incl many species eucalyptus, unusual pines, nothofagus; flowering shrubs; snowdrops, daffodils and other spring flowers, ground cover, many ferns, autumn colour. Adm £2, chd free. Suns, Mons, 27, 28 Mar; 29, 30 May (11-5). Private visits welcome by appt. Tel 01297 443295 www.tapestry.org.uk*

65 Moretonhampstead Gardens
12m W of Exeter & N of Newton Abbot. On eastern slopes of Dartmoor National Park. Parking at both gardens. Winner of 'Devon Village of the Year', 2002, located at the geographical centre of the county. Dogs on leads welcome. Cream TEAS at both gardens. Combined adm £3, chd free. Sat, Sun, Mon 28, 29, 30 May (2-6)

Mardon 🚻 (Graham & Mary Wilson) *From centre of village, head towards church, turn L into Lime St. Bottom of hill on R. 4 acres with lawns and terraces, wild flower meadow, pond with thatched boat house, stream, water meadow, large herbaceous border, vegetable garden. Fine views.*

Sutton Mead 🏠 (Edward & Miranda Allhusen) *½m N of village on A382. R at de-restriction sign. 3½-acres. Magnificent views of Dartmoor hills. Rhododendrons, azaleas and bluebell woodland. Granite* walls and unusual gothic arched concrete greenhouse. Bog garden and spring-fed ponds. Roses, mixed borders, vegetable garden and hornbeam tunnel. *Private visits welcome by appt.* Tel 01647 440296 *Miranda@Allhusen.co.uk*

66 Mothecombe Gardens, nr Holbeton
10m SE of Plymouth. From A379 bet Yealmpton & Modbury turn S for Holbeton. Continue 2m to Mothecombe. Small hamlet of thatched estate cottages leading to Queen Anne house. Home-made TEAS at Mothecombe House courtyard in aid of Holbeton Church. *Combined adm £3. Sat 30 Apr; Sun 1 May (2-5)*

83 Mothecombe ⊕ (Mr B K Newton) Newly planted cottage garden, S-facing, wide range of plants, many unusual and tender varieties, ornamental herb garden, views across Mothecombe Grove and to sea.

Mothecombe House ⓰⊗⊕ (Mr & Mrs A Mildmay-White) Walled gardens, herbaceous borders. Orchard with spring bulbs; camellia walk and flowering shrubs. Bog garden; streams and pond; bluebell woods leading to private beach. Queen Anne house, not open. *Private visits welcome by appt.* Tel 01752 830444

67 Newton Farm, Hemyock NCCPG
(Mr & Mrs J F J M Ward) *½m S of Hemyock. On Old Dunkeswell Abbey Rd, from Wellington take Monument Hemyock Rd in centre of Hemyock turn L by pump, Honiton take Taunton rd top of hill L to Dunkeswell aerodrome turn R at first major xrds follow signs.* 5 acres in Blackdown Hills with views over Culm Valley. S-facing garden: 8 large herbaceous borders, young maze, hornbeam walk, iris and hemerocallis garden. N garden: dwarf rhododendrons, dwarf conifers and pines. Large collection autumn gentians, bog. Woodland garden, many rare and unusual trees. Planting and development continue. New 1½ acres open grown *Iris ensata* and hemerocallis for the visitor to walk through. National Collection of gentianas. Cream TEAS. *Adm £2 (share to Blackdown Support). Sat, Sun 12, 13 Mar; Wed 11 May; Weds June, July & Aug; Sats, Suns 4, 5, 18, 19, 25, 26 June; 2, 3, 16, 17, 23, 24 July; 6, 7, 13, 14 Aug; Wed 7, Sat 10, Sun 11 Sept. Sats, Suns (10-6); Weds*

(2-5). Private visits welcome by appt. Tel 01823 680410

68 The Old Glebe, Eggesford
⓰⊗⊕
(Mr & Mrs Nigel Wright) *20m NW of Exeter. Turn S off A377 at Eggesford station (½-way between Exeter & Barnstaple), cross railway & River Taw, drive straight uphill (signed Brushford) for ¾m; turn R into bridleway.* 7-acre garden of former Georgian rectory (not open) with mature trees and several lawns, courtyard, walled herbaceous borders, bog garden and small lake; emphasis on species and hybrid rhododendrons and azaleas, 750 varieties. Private rhododendron nursery (by appt). Home-made TEAS. *Adm £2.50, chd £1 (share to Chulmleigh & District Abbeyfield). Sat 21, Suns 22, 29, Mon 30 May (2-6)*

The Old Rectory, Netherbury ⊗⊕
See Dorset.

69 ◆ Overbeck's, Sharpitor, Salcombe ⊗⊕
(The National Trust) *1½m SW of Salcombe. From Salcombe or Malborough follow NT signs.* 7-acre exotic coastal garden, Grade II* listed, with rare plants and shrubs; spectacular views over Salcombe estuary. Light refreshments and TEAS. *House and garden adm £5, garden only adm £4.50, chd £2.25. Daily all yr (10-6).* **For NGS:** *Sun 19 June (10-6).* Tel 01548 842893

70 38 Phillipps Avenue, Exmouth ⊗⊕
(Mr & Mrs R G Stuckey) *On A376 from Exeter, turn L into Hulham Rd just before 1st set of T-lights, 1st L into Phillipps Avenue.* Small highly specialised and extensive collection of alpine and rock garden plants in scree beds, raised beds and troughs. Many rare and unusual specimens. Small nursery attached selling mainly alpine plants, 10 per cent donated to NGS. *Adm £1, chd free. Weds 30 Mar; 6, 20 Apr; Mon 2, Weds 4, 11, 25 May; 8, 22 June (2-5). Private visits welcome by appt.* Tel 01395 273636 *stuckeysalpines@aol.com*

71 Pikes Cottage, Madford, Hemyock ⓰⊕
(Christine & Brian Carver) *7m N of Honiton. Off A30 to Wolford Chapel & through Dunkeswell towards Hemyock, then follow signs from Gypsy Cross. Or 7m S of Wellington off M5 at junction 26 to Hemyock, then follow signs. Turn in at gates opp Madford Farm & up farm track.*

Set in 19 acres of bluebell woods (hilly access). 6 acres of cultivated garden incl herb area, scree, shrubs, Antipodean and sensory gardens. 1½-acre lawn slopes to large pond. Steps up to newly planted arboretum. Seating. Wisteria tunnel. Featured in 'The Times' 2004. Cream TEAS. *Adm £2, chd free. Sats, Suns 21, 22 May; 9, 10 July; 17, 18 Sept; 15, 16 Oct (10-6). Private visits welcome by appt . Open anytime but please phone first to check if convenient.* Tel 01823 680345

72 Pine Cottage, No 1 Fourways, Eggesford ⊕ NCCPG
(Dick & Lorna Fulcher) *1m SW of Chulmleigh. Turn S off A377 at Eggesford station (halfway between Exeter & Barnstaple). 1m uphill beside war memorial cross. Parking in field beside Tarka Trail.* Small plantsman's garden with a variety of hardy and tender perennials incl meconopsis, primulas, crocosmia and hedychiums etc. Many different plants propagated on site in nursery. National Collection of agapanthus, at their best in July and August. *Adm £1.50. Sat 28, Sun 29, Mon 30 May; Sats, Suns 18, 19 June; 16, 17 July; 13, 14 Aug; 10, 11 Sept (2-5). Combined with* **The Old Glebe, Eggesford** *29, 30 May. Private visits welcome by appt.* Tel 01769 580076 *www.pcplants.co.uk*

73 ◆ Plant World, St Marychurch Road, Newton Abbot ⊕
(Ray Brown) *1½m from Penn Inn roundabout. Follow brown tourist signs at the end of the A380 dual carriageway from Exeter.* The 4 acres of landscape gardens has been called Devon's "little outdoor Eden". Representing each of the five continents it offers an extensive collection of indigenous plants. Home-made TEAS. *Adm £2, chd free. Open 7 days/week Apr to Oct (9-5).* Tel 01803 872939 *www.plantworld-devon.co.uk*

74 ◆ Pleasant View, Newton Abbot ⓰⊗⊕ NCCPG
(Mr & Mrs B D Yeo) *2m from Newton Abbot. Two Mile Oak, Nr Denbury. On A381 to Totnes. R at Two Mile Oak public house signed Denbury. ¾m on L.* 2-acre plantsman's garden with wide range of choice and uncommon shrubs giving colour all season. Additional 2-acre field planted as an arboretum with individual specimen shrubs. Buddleia avenue and other features to encourage wildlife. National Collections of abelia and salvia. Adjacent nursery. Featured in 'Devon

Life' 2003 & 2004 & 'The English Garden', 2003; 'Daily Telegraph' Nursery of the Week, 2003. *Adm £2.50, chd 50p.* **For NGS:** *Suns 22 May; 26 June; Weds 1 June; 13 July; 3 Aug (2-5). Tel 01803 813388 Mrs C Yeo*

75 Portington, nr Lamerton ⊕
(Mr & Mrs I A Dingle) *3m NW of Tavistock. From Tavistock B3362 to Launceston. ¼m beyond Blacksmiths Arms, Lamerton, fork L (signed Chipshop). Over Xrds (signed Horsebridge) first L then L again (signed Portington). From Launceston turn R at Carrs Garage and R again (signed Horsebridge), then as above.* Garden in peaceful rural setting with fine views over surrounding countryside. Mixed planting with shrubs and borders. Walk through woodland and fields to small lake. Home-made TEAS. *Adm £2 (share to St Luke's Hospice). Suns 12, 19 June (2-5.30)*

NEW Poundstock Gardens, Poundstock
See Cornwall.

Southfield, Vicarage Lane ⊕ See Cornwall.

76 NEW Prospect House, Lyme Road, Axminster ⊛⊕
(Peter Wadeley) *From Axminster town centre (Trinity Square) proceed uphill past the George Hotel into Lyme St & Lyme Rd. Prospect House is approx ½m up the road on R-hand side, just before petrol station. Park on road.* 1-acre plantsman's garden hidden behind high stone walls and with Axe valley views. Well stocked borders with rare shrubs and colourful perennials, many reckoned to be borderline tender. 100 varieties of salvia, some for sale. A gem, not to be missed. Light refreshments and TEAS. *Adm £2, chd free. Sat 23, Sun 24 July (2-6). Open with* **Ways Cottage, Kilmington** *18, 19 June*

77 Regency House, Hemyock
♿⊛⊕
(Mrs Jenny Parsons) *8m N of Honiton. M5 junction 26. From Hemyock take Dunkeswell-Honiton rd. Entrance is ½m on R from Catherine Wheel public house & church.* 5-acre plantsman's garden, approached across a private ford. Walled vegetable and fruit garden, lake, ponds, bog plantings and sweeping lawns. The shelter afforded by southern slope allows many unusual and slightly tender plants. Visitors will be provided with comprehensive plant list and map. Accommodation. Cream TEAS. *Adm*

£2.50, chd £1.25. Suns 12 June; 3 July (11-6). Private visits welcome by appt. Tel 01823 680238

78 ◆ RHS Garden Rosemoor, Great Torrington ♿⊛⊕
(The Royal Horticultural Society) *1m SE of Great Torrington. On A3124 to Exeter (formerly B3220).* 40-acre plantsman's garden plus woodlands; rhododendrons (species and hybrids), ornamental trees and shrubs, woodland garden, species and old-fashioned roses, scree and raised beds with alpine plants, arboretum. 2000 roses in 200 varieties, two colour-theme gardens, herb garden, potager, 220yds of herbaceous border, large stream and bog garden, cottage garden, foliage and plantsman's garden and fruit and vegetable garden. Light refreshments and TEAS. *Adm £5.50, chd £1.50, £4.50 for groups 10+. Apr to Sept (10-6); Oct to Mar (10-5). Tel 01805 624067 www.rhs.org.uk*

79 ◆ Rock House Garden, Station Hill, Chudleigh
(Mrs D B & B Boulton) *8m SW of Exeter. A38 Exeter to Plymouth signed Chudleigh. S edge of town. Entrance at Rock Nursery.* Garden in ancient bishop's palace quarry with massive limestone rock. Delights for all seasons. Rare and unusual trees and shrubs. Massed bulbs in spring. Autumn brings one of the finest displays of cyclamen. Cave and ponds with koi and orfe. Walk with spectacular views of Dartmoor and access to Chudleigh rock, glen and waterfall. Some areas difficult for less able-bodied persons (steps & steep slopes). Light refreshments and TEAS. *Adm £3, chd £1.50. Open all year, except Christmas week & New Year's Day.* **For NGS:** *Suns 24 Apr; 22 May; 26 June; 24 July; 11, 18, 25 Sept; 23 Oct (9-5). Tel 01626 852134 www.therockgardens.co.uk*

80 Rowden Gardens, Brentor
♿⊛⊕ NCCPG
(Mr & Mrs John Carter) *4m N of Tavistock. On Lydford to Tavistock rd (not A386). Take sign to Liddaton. Gardens 300yds on R.* Much televised 1-acre garden with canal-like ponds displaying largest collection of water iris in the country, including new varieties; also huge number of aquatics and water lilies. 3 colour themed ponds/borders. Herbaceous and bog gardens. Large plantings of dierama, ferns, grasses, ligularia, rheum and rodgersia. 4 National Collections (caltha, polygonum, ranunculus ficaria and water iris). Adjacent Nursery.

Featured in 'Gardening Which' 2004. *Adm £2, chd free. Private visits welcome by appt all yr round. Tel 01822 810275*

81 ◆ Saltram House, Plympton
♿⊛⊕
(The National Trust) *3m E of Plymouth. S of A38, 2m W of Plympton.* 20 acres with fine specimen trees; spring garden; rhododendrons and azaleas. C18 orangery and octagonal garden house. (George II mansion with magnificent plasterwork and decorations, incl 2 rooms designed by Robert Adam). Good variety of evergreens, incl many tender and unusual shrubs, esp from the southern hemisphere. Long grass areas with bulbs and wild flowers, new developments. Gallery with arts and crafts for sale. TEAS. *House and garden adm £7, chd £3.50, garden only adm £3.50, chd £1.80. Sats to Thurs Jan to Xmas (11-5).* **For NGS:** *Suns 3 Apr; 15 May (11-5). Tel 01752 333505 Ms P Hammond penny.hammond@nationaltrust.org.uk*

82 ◆ Sampford Shrubs, Holbrook, Sampford Peverell
⊛⊕ NCCPG
(Martin Hughes-Jones & Susan Proud) *1m from M5 junction 27. Follow signs to 'Minnows' camping site then continue 300 metres up Holbrook Hill (on Holcombe Rogus Rd).* 2-acre S-facing garden with innovative plantings inspired by natural plant populations; vibrant Mediterranean colours; the garden continually evolves - many experimental plantings - wet garden, stone garden. Perfumes, songbirds and nests everywhere. Large crocosmia and pulmonaria collections, National Collection of Helenium, organic vegetable garden. Picnicking in garden welcome. Featured in 'Gardeners' World' 2004. *Adm £2, chd free. Thurs to Sats, Apr to Sept (9-5).* **For NGS:** *Thur 7, Fris 8, 29, Sat 30 Apr; Fri 27, Sat 28 May; Thur 16, Fri 17 June; Fri 29, Sat 30 July; Fri 26, Sat 27 Aug; Fri 16, Sat 17 Sept (9-5). Tel 01884 821164 www.samshrub.co.uk*

83 School House, Little Torrington, Torrington ⊛⊕
(Mr & Mrs M Sampson) *2m S Torrington on A386. Village of Little Torrington signposted, follow signs to village green, park here, walk 50yds along bridle path to School House. ⅔-acre* informally planted cottage garden. Wild life pond with adjacent 'natural' planting under old apple tree. 2 ornamental pools. An

arbour and pergola with a variety of climbers. Trees, shrubs, herbaceous and annual planting with some colour-themed areas. Small raised bed for alpines. Home-made TEAS in aid of Little Torrington Village Hall. *Adm £2, chd free. Suns 12 June; 24 July (2-5.30). Private visits welcome by appt. Tel 01805 623445*

84 Scypen, Ringmore 🅰️🅰️
(John & Ann Bracey) *10m W of Kingsbridge. A379 (Plymouth-Kingsbridge rd) 1m E of Modbury R on B3392 (signed Bigbury). After 3½m turn R at Old Chapel Inn, signed Ringmore.* ½-acre garden designed and made by architect owner with views of coast and countryside. Many unusual features incl millenium globe, bottle play house, pools with double helix fountain, sundial and sculptural walls. Plants chosen to give yr-round interest, tolerate salty winds and poor well-drained soil. Chamomile and thyme lawns. Featured in '25 Beautiful Gardens' 2003 & 'Gardens Monthly' 2004. Home-made TEAS. *Adm £2, chd 50p. Sun 19, Wed 22 June (2-5)*

85 Shapcott Barton Estate, (East Knowstone Manor), East Knowstone 🅰️🅰️🅰️ NCCPG
(Anita Allen) *13m NW of Tiverton. Junction 27 M5 take Tiverton exit. 6½m to roundabout, take exit South Molton 10m, on A361. Turn R signed Knowstone (picnic area). Leave A361 at this point, travel 1¼m to Roachhill, through this hamlet, turn L at Wiston Cross, entrance on L ¼m.* Approx 5 acres of 200-acre estate. Development work is ongoing to enhance the beauty of the medieval manor and the mature trees which frame it. Restored old fish ponds and woodland garden around Culm Measures; stream and peat bog areas. The National Collection of Shasta Daisies (*Leucanthemum superbum*) during July (over 70 cultivars). New orchard planted with unusual fruit trees. TEAS available on NGS days. Picnics welcome. *Adm £2, chd 50p. Thur 7, Fris 8, 15, Sat 16, Sun 17, Wed 20, Thur 21, Sat 23, Sun 24, Wed 27 July; Tue 2 Aug (11-5). Private visits welcome by appt 15 June to 10 August. Tel 01398 341664 A Allen*

86 Sherwood, Newton St Cyres 🅰️🅰️ NCCPG
(John & Prue Quicke) *2m SE of Crediton. Off A377 Exeter to Barnstaple rd, ¾m Crediton side of Newton St Cyres, signed Sherwood, entrance to drive in 1¾m.* 14 acres comprising 2 steep valleys. Mature trees, wild daffodils, primroses, bluebells and other wild flowers; extensive collections of magnolias, camellias, rhododendrons, azaleas (mainly deciduous), heathers, acers, cotoneasters, hostas, hydrangeas, buddleias, berberis and other ornamental trees and shrubs. National Collections of magnolias, Knap Hill azaleas and berberis. Access for wheelchairs, but steep in places. Plant sales from Sherwood Cottage, not for NGS. Featured in 'Gardens Illustrated' 2004. *Adm £2.50, chd under 12 free (share to UNICEF). Every Sun throughout the year (2-5). Private visits welcome by appt. Tel 01392 851216*

87 NEW Shilhay, Stoodleigh 🅰️🅰️
(P M Pennington) *4m N of Tiverton. Take A396 Tiverton to Bampton rd. After 3m turn L over iron bridge, signposted Stoodleigh. 1m up Stoodleigh Drive. Shilhay on R.* 3-acre garden with grassy open spaces, mixed herbaceous and shrub borders and numerous native and exotic trees and shrubs. Patio, small pool, gravel bed and tufa wall are habitats for other plants. A winding path leads up the sloping garden to views of the bosky Exe valley. *Adm £2, chd 50p. Thurs 28 Apr; 26 May; 29 Sept (2-5)*

88 Shobrooke Park Gardens, Crediton 🅰️
(Dr & Mrs J R Shelley) *1m NE of Crediton. On A3072.* 15-acre woodland garden laid out in mid-C19 incl extensive Portland Stone terraces with views over 200-acre park with ponds. In process of being restored with extensive new planting amongst old rhododendrons incl reconstructed Victorian rose garden. Cream TEAS in aid of Posbury Chapel. *Adm £3, chd free. Sats 16 Apr; 14 May; 11 June (2-5). Private visits welcome by appt. Tel 01363 775153 clare@shobrookepark.com*

89 South Kenwood, Oxton, nr Kenton 🅰️
(Sir John & Lady Jennings) *6m S of Exeter. From A380 (Exeter to Newton Abbot-Torquay rd) turn L signposted Mamhead & Starcross. After 2m turn L for Oxton. Take next L for Oxton. In 1m turn L to South Kenwood. From coast road turn R at Starcross into New Road. After ¼m turn R for Mamhead. In 2m turn R for Oxton, then as above.* 10-acre garden in wooded valley nestling under the Haldon hills. Streams running through, well-planted ponds, bog gardens and small lake with wildfowl. Colour-themed borders, lawns, terrace, pergola walk, rose garden and conservatory. Masses of interesting planting, shrubs and mature trees. Cream TEAS in aid of Children's Hospice South West. *Adm £2.50. Suns 12, 19 June (2-5)*

90 Southcombe House, Widecombe-in-the-Moor 🅰️
(Dr & Mrs JR Seale) *6m W of Bovey Tracey. After village church take rd SW for 200yds then sharp R, sign posted Southcombe, up steep hill. After 200yds, pass C17 farmhouse & park on L. Alternatively park in public car park in village and walk.* 5 acres, SE-facing garden, arboretum and wild flower meadow with bulbs in spring and four orchid species (Early Purple, Southern Marsh, Common Spotted and Greater Butterfly). On steep slope at 900ft above sea level with fine views to nearby tors. Featured in 'The Garden' 2003, 'Dartmoor Country Magazine' 2004, 'English Nature Magazine' 2004. *Adm £2.50, chd 50p. Suns 15, 29, Mon 30 May; Suns 5, 12, 19 June (2-5). Private visits welcome by appt. Tel 01364 621365*

91 Southleigh Gardens
2m W of Colyton. Signs from Hangmans Cross on A3052 or from Hare & Hounds, Putt's Corner on Honiton-Sidmouth rd, then 2nd turning on L past Farway Wildlife Park, via 2m lane. Parking at village hall or considerably in rd below. Home-made TEAS in village hall in aid of Southleigh Church & Hall. *Combined adm £2.50, chd 50p. Sat 4, Sun 5 June (2-5.30)*

Mulberry House 🅰️ (Thomasina & Bill Tarling) Created on sloping field in 1998. Divided into pond, stream and waterfall with bursting borders, spreading grasses, old rose hedges, ornamental gazebo, vegetable garden, decorative chicken run, lots of seats and lovely rural views. *Private visits welcome by appt. Tel 01404 871566*

Popes Cottage 🅰️🅰️ (Irene & Eric Daniels) ⅔acre country garden blending into spectacular valley view. Mixed borders of shrubs, perennials and alpines, some unusual. Small fruit and vegetable section with bulging greenhouse. Artificial stream through small ponds. Emphasis on wildlife.

92 Sowton Mill, Dunsford 🅰️
(A Cooke & S Newman) *7m W of Exeter. From Dunsford take B3193 S for ½m. Entrance straight ahead off sharp R bend by bridge. From A38 N along Teign Valley for 8m. Sharp R*

after humpback bridge. 4 acres laid out around former mill (not open), leat and river. Part woodland with multitudes of wildflowers in spring, ornamental trees and shrubs, mixed borders and scree. Yr-round interest. Home-made TEAS. *Adm £2.50, chd free (share to Cygnet Training Theatre). Suns 6 Mar; 1 May; 10 July (2-6). Private visits welcome by appt. Tel 01647 252347 or 01647 252263 sonia.n@tesco.net*

93 Spillifords Wildlife Garden, Lower Washfield, Tiverton
(Dr Gavin Haig) 3m N of Tiverton. Tiverton. Take A396 Tiverton to Bampton rd, turn L over iron bridge signposted Stoodleigh.Turn L again after crossing bridge marked Washfield, & L again on hill following Washfield sign. Bridge is approx 2m from link rd roundabout. Spillifords is 1st house on L after Hatswell, just into Lower Washfield. Parking in top field through double five barred gate. Specialist wildlife garden leading down to wide area R Exe. (Unsuitable for disabled). Banks and islands of mixed wild flowers and herbs. Many nesting birds, including flycatchers and warblers. Ponds and marsh areas. Riverside tree house, and 50 nestboxes. About 30 different butterflies - including rare Marsh Fritillary. Picnic areas. About 4 acres. Regular monthly articles 'Devon Life', BBC 'Gardeners' World' 2004. Home-made TEAS. *Adm £3, chd £1. Thurs 28 Apr; 5, 19 May; 16, 30 June; 7, 28 July (3-5.30). Private visits welcome by appt, no coaches. Tel 01884 252422*

94 St Merryn, Higher Park Road, Braunton &⊗⊕
(Dr W & Mrs Ros Bradford) In centre of Braunton turn R at T-lights round Nat West Bank. At top of Heanton St turn L and immed R into Lower Park Rd. Continue until you see Tyspane Nursing Home on L then turn L into unmarked lane & R at top. Pink house 200yds on R. Parking where available in nearby roads. Sheltered ⅔-acre cottage style garden with emphasis on scent and colour and planned for all-yr interest. Small fish ponds, thatched summerhouse, rockery, shrub and herbaceous borders with seating and winding paths set off by lawns and mature trees. Home-made TEAS in aid of St Brannock's Church Restoration Fund. *Adm £2. Suns 24 Apr; 22 May; 19 June (12-5). Private visits welcome by appt. Tel 01271 813805 ros@st-merryn.co.uk*

95 Taikoo, Belstone ⊗
(Richard & Rosamund Bernays) 3m SE of Okehampton. Fork L at stocks in middle of village. 300yds on R. Park in field. A 3-acre hillside moorland garden, restored over past 6yrs. Interesting collections of rhododendrons, fuchsias, hydrangeas, magnolias, camellias, roses and other shrubs and trees. Herb garden and water features. Magnificent views over Dartmoor. Cream TEAS. *Adm £3, chd £1. Suns 1, 29 May (2-5)*

96 1 Tipton Lodge, Tipton St John, Sidmouth &⊗⊕
(Angela Avis & Robin Pickering) 3m N of Sidmouth. From Exeter take A3052 towards Sidmouth. Turn L on B3176 at Bowd Inn toward Ottery St Mary. After 1½m turn into Tipton St John. After the village sign, 1 Tipton Lodge is the second driveway on R about 100yds before Golden Lion PH. Parking for disabled only, other parking in village. ½acre designed to reflect mid-Victorian house. Formal grass walks between double herbaceous borders and avenue of white weeping old roses. Organic vegetables. Developing fernery including tree ferns. Exuberant romantic planting. Home-made TEAS in aid of Tipton St John playing field. *Adm £2. Sat 18, Sun 19 June (11-6)*

Watcombe, 92 Church Road, Winscombe &⊗⊕
See Somerset.

97 The Water Garden, Wembworthy &⊗⊕
(Mr J M Smith) 10m NE of Okehampton. From A377 at Eggesford station follow signs to Wembworthy (2m W). From Winkleigh take Wembworthy to Eggesford rd (2m E). Turn at Xrd sign at Lymington Arms. A naturalistic William Robinson-style 1-acre garden attempted here with 'wilderness' planting, incorporating exotics and native species esp around a clay pond/swamp area with a 60 metre board walk of distressed oak allowing close inspection of plants and wildlife. Many other water features displayed among irises, ferns, trees, shrubs, clematis and unusual plants. Some hot, dry, stony slopes, conservatory. New potager garden of five raised beds with vegetables and flowers. WC. Plant sales proceeds to Multiple Sclerosis Society. Home-made TEAS. *Adm £2, chd 50p. Sat 28, Sun 29, Mon 30 May; every Sat & Sun during June & July (2-6). Private visits welcome by appt. Tel 01837 83566*

98 Webbery Gardens
2½m E of Bideford. Either from Bideford (East the Water) along Alverdiscott Rd, or from Barnstaple to Torrington on the B3232, take rd to Bideford at Alverdiscott and pass through Stoney Cross. Combined adm £2.50, chd 50p. Private visits welcome by appt Apr to Sept incl (2-6)

Little Webbery &⊗⊕ *(Mr & Mrs J A Yewdall)* Approx 3 acres in valley setting with pond, lake, mature trees and 2 ha-has. Walled kitchen garden with box hedging; greenhouse; rose garden; trellises; shrubs and climbing plants. *Private visits welcome by appt. Tel 01271 858206 jayewdall@aol.com*

Little Webbery Cottage &⊗⊕ *(Mr & Mrs J A Yewdall)* Self contained cottage garden with wide selection of flowering plants and shrubs incl pergolas with roses, clematis and jasmine. *Private visits welcome by appt. Tel 01271 858206 jayewdall@aol.com*

99 Westcott Barton, Marwood, Barnstaple &&
(Heidi Amschwand) 4m N of Barnstaple. From Barnstaple 4m N to Guineaford, continue N for 1m. Turn L, signed Middle Marwood, 2nd L at Westcott Barton sign. 2-acre developing valley garden with stream, bridge and several ponds. Wide variety of planting: rhododendrons, camellias, clematis, hydrangeas, gunnera, rose garden. Masses of interest. Garden surrounds C12 farmhouse (not open) with cobbled courtyard and range of outbuildings with water wheel. Accommodation. Cream TEAS. *Adm £2, chd free. Suns, Mons 29, 30 May; 26, 27 June; 31 July; 1, 28, 29 Aug; 25, 26 Sept (2-6)*

100 NEW Westwood Gardens, nr Broadclyst
8m NE of Exeter. From B3187 Exeter to Taunton bear E at Dog Village to Whimple. After 1½m fork L for Westwood. Cottage gardens in a Devon hamlet. Cream TEAS 26 June & 24 July. *Combined adm £2, chd free. Suns 26 June; 24 July (2-6)*

1 Feebers Cottage &&⊗⊕ *(Mr & Mrs Squires) (See separate entry). Private visits welcome by appt. Tel 01404 822118*

NEW 3 Feebers Cottage &&⊗
(Richard & Karen Burrell) ⅓-acre cottage garden with formal borders and vegetables.

101 NEW Whibble Hill House, 9 Priory Road, Plymouth 🚫
(Dr Imogen Montague) *1¼m from centre of Plymouth. Via Mutley Plain & Mannamead Rd. Turn R at Emmanuel Church T-lights into Compton Park Rd. Follow rd downhill until L-hand fork into Priory Rd. House 30yds on L, street parking.* Small Georgian walled garden planted in 2003, crammed with extensive collection of bamboos, acers and other exotic and architectural plants mixed with herbaceous perennials. Central formal beds, others more 'jungly'.Wildlife pond, bog garden, tree fern grove and Edwardian conservatory. Sloping garden with many steps. Home-made TEAS. *Adm £1.50, chd free. Sat 28, Sun 29 May (10-6). Private visits welcome by appt June, July & Aug. Tel 01752 227307 imontague@hotmail.com*

102 Whitstone Farm, Whitstone Lane, Bovey Tracey 🚫⊕
(Katie & Alan Bunn) *½m N of Bovey Tracey. From A382 turn toward hospital (signed hospital opp golf range) after ½m turn L at swinging*

sign 'Private road leading to Whitstone'. Follow lane uphill & bend to L. Whitstone Farm is on R at end of long barn.* Over 3 acres of steep hillside garden with stunning views of Haytor and Dartmoor. An aboretum planted 35yrs ago of over 250 trees from all over the world, including magnolias, camellias, acers, alders, betula and sorbus. Water feature. Limited parking. Accommodation. TEAS in aid of Devon Air Ambulance (Apr) & Macmillan Nurses (May). *Adm £3, chd free. Suns 17 Apr; 8 May (2-5)*

103 ◆ Winsford Walled Garden, Halwill Junction 🚫
(Aileen Birks & Mike Gilmore) *10m NW of Okehampton. On A4079 follow brown tourism signs from centre of Halwill Junction.* Inspirational garden. Started from scratch in 1999. What has been achieved since will undoubtedly amaze. Summer interest packed with features past (1883) and present. Heading towards 4000 varieties in just over an acre. Original teak greenhouses. Well labelled. Covered exhibition. Electric disability vehicles.

Mini buses by appt. Guided tours. Accommodation. TEAS. *Adm £4, chd under 14 free. Daily 1 May to 31 Oct incl (10.30-5.30).* **For NGS:** *Sun 26 June; Wed 27, Thur 28 July; Sun 28, Mon 29 Aug; Sun 18 Sept (10.30-5.30). Tel 01409 221477 Mike or Aileen www.winsfordwalledgarden.co.uk*

104 Withleigh Farm, Withleigh Village ⊕
(T Matheson) *3m W of Tiverton. On B3137, 10yds W of 1st small 30mph sign on L, entrance to drive by white gate.* Peaceful undisturbed rural setting with valley garden, 21yrs in making; stream, pond and waterside plantings; bluebell walk under canopy of mature oak and beech; wild flower meadow, primroses and daffodils in spring: wild orchids in June. TEAS. *Adm £2.50, chd free. Sat, Sun 14, 15 May (2-5). Private visits welcome by appt. Tel 01884 253853*

Wolverhollow, Elsdons Lane, Monkton Wyld 🚫⊕
See Dorset.

ngs
gardens open for charity

Every time you visit a garden which opens for the NGS you are helping to raise money for

- Macmillan Cancer Relief
- Marie Curie Cancer Care
- Help the Hospices
- Crossroads – Caring for Carers
- The Queen's Nursing Institute
- The Nurses Welfare Service
- The Royal Gardeners' Orphan Fund
- NGS Gardeners' Bursaries – The National Trust Careership Scheme
- Perennial – Gardeners' Royal Benevolent Society
- County Nursing Associations
- Additional charities nominated by owners

105 Wood Barton, Kentisbeare

(Mr & Mrs Richard Horton) 8m SE of Tiverton. 3m from M5 junction 28. Take A373 Cullompton to Honiton rd. After 2m turn L signed Bradfield & Willand on Horn Rd for 1m, turn R at Xrds. Farm drive ½m on L. Bull on sign. 2 acre arboretum planted 55yrs ago with species trees on S-facing slope. Magnolias, two davidia, azaleas, camellias, rhododendrons, acers; several ponds and water feature. Autumn colour. Home-made TEAS. Adm £2, chd free. Sun 1, Mon 2 May (2-5). Private visits welcome by appt. Tel 01884 266285

106 Wrangaton House, Wrangaton

(R L & M C Travis) 15m E of Plymouth. Midway between Ivybridge and South Brent. ½m N of A38. From S Exeter leave A38 at Wrangaton Cross. Cross over to N of A38 and proceed W ½m. From Plymouth leave A38 at Ivybridge and take Exeter Road for 3m. Both directions turn N at Blacksmith Lane. Wrangaton House is ¼m on L past thatched cottage. 3 acres mature garden to mellow manor house (not open) on S slopes of Dartmoor. Large pool, water plants, streams; rhododendrons, azaleas, camellias and bulbs. Adjacent bluebell wood of 1½ acres. Beautiful situation. Lovely spring flowering cherries, shrubs and flowers. Home-made TEAS. Adm £2.50, chd under 16 free. Sun 10 Apr; Sun, Mon 1, 2 May (2-5)

107 Yonder Hill, Shepherds Lane, Colaton Raleigh

(Judy McKay & Eddie Stevenson) 3m N of Budleigh Salterton. On B3178 Newton Poppleford to Colaton Raleigh rd, take turning L signed to Dotton, then immed R into small lane. ¼m, 1st house on R. Ample parking. Peaceful 3-acre paradise in magnificent setting. Wide variety of unusual and interesting planting with surprises round every corner. A haven where you can relax and forget your troubles for a while. Tea/coffee and biscuits in rest room, make it yourself just as you like it. Wheelchair available. TEAS. Adm £2, chd £1. Every Sun from 6 Mar to 2 Oct incl; Fri 25 Mar; Bank Hol Mons 28 Mar; 2, 30 May; 29 Aug (1-5). Private visits welcome by appt. Tel 01395 567075

Evening Opening (See also garden description)

Kingston House	12 June
Bridford Gardens	19 June
The Cider House	23 June
Andrew's Corner	22 July
Andrew's Corner	23 July

 gardens open for charity

Your garden in the Yellow Book?

The NGS is always interested to hear of gardens with potential, large or small, that might open in the future.

For more information about opening your garden, please contact the County Organiser in your area, preferably at the time of year that you would like your garden to open.

Dorset

County Organiser:
(West Central Dorset)

Mrs Harriet Boileau, Rampisham Manor, Dorchester DT2 0PT
Tel 01935 83612 email harriet@cubbins.co.uk

Assistant County Organisers:
(North Dorset)

Miss Jane Bennett, The Maples, West Street, Fontmell Magna, Shaftesbury SP7 0PF
Tel 01747 811766

(South Dorset)

Mr & Mrs Anthony Bush, Holworth Farmhouse, Holworth, Dorchester DT2 8NH
Tel 01305 852242 email bushinarcadia@yahoo.co.uk

(Press & Publicity Officer) (East Dorset)

Mrs Diana Guy, Welcome Thatch, Witchampton, Wimborne BH21 5AR
Tel 01258 840894 email diana.welcomethatch@btopenworld.com

(Central Dorset)

Mrs Wendy Jackson, Vine Cottage, Melcombe Bingham, Dorchester, Dorset DT2 7PE
Tel 01258 880720 email wendy@vinecott.fsnet.co.uk

(Leaflet Editor & Advertising) (South West Dorset)

Mrs Carol Lindsay, The Old Rectory, Litton Cheney, Dorchester DT2 9AH
Tel 01308 482383 email hugh_lindsay@talk21.com

(Bournemouth & Poole)

Mrs Penny Slade, 46 Roslin Road South, Bournemouth BH3 7EG Tel 01202 510243

(Leaflet distribution)

Ms Susan Wreford, The Old Rectory, West Compton, Dorchester DT2 0EY
Tel 01300 320007

County Treasurer:

Mr Michael Gallagher, 6 West Street, Chickerell, Weymouth DT3 4DY
Tel 01305 772557 email michael.gallagher1@virgin.net

Maps: Numbers shown next to each garden entry refer to that garden's entry on the county map. This position is approximate; distance and directions from the nearest main town are generally shown in the garden text.
A precise location is available for those gardens featured on the NGS website by visiting www.ngs.org.uk.

Symbols: Information relating to symbols is given on page 21

DATES OF OPENING

Evening openings
See end of county listing

Gardens open to the public
For details see garden description

Abbotsbury Gardens, nr Weymouth (1)
Compton Acres Gardens, Poole (15)
Cranborne Manor Garden, Cranborne (19)
Edmondsham House, nr Cranborne (23)
Forde Abbey Gardens, Chard (27)
Hilltop, Woodville, Stour Provost (35)
Holworth Farmhouse, Holworth, nr
    Owermoigne (36)
Horn Park, Beaminster (37)
Ivy Cottage, Ansty (39)
Kingston Lacy, Wimborne Minster (43)
Kingston Maurward Gardens, Dorchester (44)
Knoll Gardens and Nursery, Hampreston (46)
Larmer Tree Garden, Nr Tollard Royal (50)
Mapperton Gardens, nr Beaminster (54)
Minterne, Minterne Magna (61)
Moreton Gardens, nr Dorchester (63)
Sherborne Castle, Sherborne (81)
Snape Cottage, Chaffeymoor (83)
Stapehill Abbey, Ferndown (85)
Sticky Wicket, Buckland Newton (86)
Toad Hall, The Cross, Shillingstone (90)
Upwey Wishing Well, Upwey (92)

By appointment only
For telephone number and other
details see garden description.
Private visits welcomed
Weston House, Buckhorn Weston (97)

January 1 Saturday
Kingston Maurward Gardens, Dorchester (44)

January 2 Sunday
Kingston Maurward Gardens, Dorchester (44)

January 3 Monday
Kingston Maurward Gardens, Dorchester (44)

January 4 Tuesday
Kingston Maurward Gardens, Dorchester (44)

February 10 Thursday
Langebride House, Long Bredy (49)

February 17 Thursday
Langebride House, Long Bredy (49)

February 19 Saturday
Welcome Thatch, Witchampton (94)

February 20 Sunday
Welcome Thatch, Witchampton (94)

February 24 Thursday
Langebride House, Long Bredy (49)

February 27 Sunday
Mews Cottage, Portland (57)

March 3 Thursday
Langebride House, Long Bredy (49)

March 6 Sunday
Ashley Park Farm, Damerham (3)

Frankham Farm, Ryme Intrinseca (28)
Welcome Thatch, Witchampton (94)

March 10 Thursday
Langebride House, Long Bredy (49)

March 13 Sunday
Mews Cottage, Portland (57)

March 17 Thursday
Langebride House, Long Bredy (49)

March 20 Sunday
Snape Cottage, Chaffeymoor (83)

March 22 Tuesday
Throop Mill Cottage, Throop (88)

March 23 Wednesday
Cranborne Manor Garden, Cranborne (19)

March 24 Thursday
Langebride House, Long Bredy (49)

March 25 Friday (Easter)
44 Daws Avenue, Wallisdown (20)

March 27 Sunday (Easter)
Ashley Park Farm, Damerham (3)
Deans Court, Wimborne Minster (21)
Manor Orchard, Stratton (52)
The Old Rectory, Litton Cheney (68)
The Old Rectory, Netherbury (69)
The Red House, Alderholt (74)

March 28 Monday (Easter)
Ashley Park Farm, Damerham (3)
Deans Court, Wimborne Minster (21)
Edmondsham House, nr Cranborne (23)
Frankham Farm, Ryme Intrinseca (28)

March 30 Wednesday
Manor Orchard, Stratton (52)

April 3 Sunday
Domineys Yard, Buckland Newton *(22)*
Fernhill House, Witchampton *(25)*
The Red House, Alderholt *(74)*
Welcome Thatch, Witchampton *(94)*
April 6 Wednesday
Edmondsham House, nr Cranborne *(23)*
April 10 Sunday
Beech Mead, Ferndown *(5)*
Bexington, Lytchett Matravers *(6)*
Ivy House, Piddletrenthide *(40)*
April 13 Wednesday
Edmondsham House, nr Cranborne *(23)*
April 15 Friday
Knitson Old Farmhouse, nr Swanage *(45)*
April 16 Saturday
Knitson Old Farmhouse, nr Swanage *(45)*
April 17 Sunday
Frankham Farm, Ryme Intrinseca *(28)*
Knitson Old Farmhouse, nr Swanage *(45)*
The Red House, Alderholt *(74)*
April 20 Wednesday
Edmondsham House, nr Cranborne *(23)*
April 24 Sunday
Chideock Manor, Chideock, nr Bridport *(13)*
Corfe Barn, Broadstone *(17)*
Galpin Cottage, Tarrant Keyneston *(29)*
The Old Rectory, Netherbury *(69)*
54 Parkwood Road, Bournemouth *(71)*
46 Roslin Road South, Talbot Woods *(76)*
Wentworth College, Bournemouth *(95)*
April 27 Wednesday
Chideock Manor, Chideock, nr Bridport *(13)*
Edmondsham House, nr Cranborne *(23)*
Horn Park, Beaminster *(37)*
May 1 Sunday
Ashley Park Farm, Damerham *(3)*
15a Cassel Avenue, Westbourne *(11)*
Deans Court, Wimborne Minster *(21)*
Ivy House, Piddletrenthide *(40)*
10 Milner Road, Westbourne, Bournemouth *(60)*
The Old Rectory, Litton Cheney *(68)*
24a Western Avenue, Branksome Park, Poole *(96)*
May 2 Monday (Bank Hol)
Ashley Park Farm, Damerham *(3)*
15a Cassel Avenue, Westbourne *(11)*
Deans Court, Wimborne Minster *(21)*
Frankham Farm, Ryme Intrinseca *(28)*
10 Milner Road, Westbourne, Bournemouth *(60)*
May 3 Tuesday
'Ola', Weymouth *(65)*
May 4 Wednesday
Rampisham Manor, Rampisham *(73)*
May 5 Thursday
Ivy Cottage, Ansty *(39)*
May 7 Saturday
38 Canford Bottom, Wimborne *(10)*
54 Parkwood Road, Bournemouth **(Evening)** *(71)*
May 8 Sunday
Bexington, Lytchett Matravers *(6)*
38 Canford Bottom, Wimborne *(10)*
15a Cassel Avenue, Westbourne *(11)*
Japanese Gardens, Crossways *(41)*

Larmer Tree Garden, Nr Tollard Royal *(50)*
Mews Cottage, Portland *(57)*
Welcome Thatch, Witchampton *(94)*
Wolverhollow, Monkton Wyld *(99)*
May 10 Tuesday
Knowle Farm, Uploders, nr Bridport *(47)*
Pear Tree Farm, Loscombe, Melplash *(72)*
Wolverhollow, Monkton Wyld *(99)*
May 12 Thursday
Hilltop, Woodville, Stour Provost *(35)*
Ivy Cottage, Ansty *(39)*
The Secret Garden, Hilfield *(79)*
May 13 Friday
The Secret Garden, Hilfield *(79)*
May 14 Saturday
The Secret Garden, Hilfield *(79)*
May 15 Sunday
44 Daws Avenue, Wallisdown *(20)*
Domineys Yard, Buckland Newton *(22)*
Holworth Farmhouse, Holworth, nr Owermoigne *(36)*
The Mill House, Netherbury *(58)*
Moigne Combe, nr Crossways, Dorchester *(62)*
The Old Rectory, Netherbury *(69)*
54 Parkwood Road, Bournemouth *(71)*
The Secret Garden, Hilfield *(79)*
May 17 Tuesday
'Ola', Weymouth *(65)*
May 19 Thursday
Hilltop, Woodville, Stour Provost *(35)*
May 22 Sunday
Bracken Cottage and The Ferns, East Burton, Wool *(7)*
Frankham Farm, Ryme Intrinseca *(28)*
Galpin Cottage, Tarrant Keyneston *(29)*
11 Greensome Drive, Ferndown *(31)*
Ham Gate, Sturminster Newton *(32)*
Highwood Garden, Charborough Park *(34)*
Melplash Court, Melplash *(56)*
Mews Cottage, Portland *(57)*
Moigne Combe, nr Crossways, Dorchester *(62)*
Slape Manor, Netherbury *(82)*
Talbot Woods Gardens, Talbot Woods, Bournemouth *(87)*
May 24 Tuesday
Mappercombe Manor, Nettlecombe, Nr Bridport *(53)*
Pear Tree Farm, Loscombe, Melplash *(72)*
May 26 Thursday
Hilltop, Woodville, Stour Provost *(35)*
Langebride House, Long Bredy *(49)*
Mappercombe Manor, Nettlecombe, Nr Bridport **(Evening)** *(53)*
May 29 Sunday
Ashley Park Farm, Damerham *(3)*
Coombe Cottage, Shillingstone *(16)*
Corfe Barn, Broadstone *(17)*
Deans Court, Wimborne Minster *(21)*
6 Farm Road, West Moors *(24)*
Highwood Garden, Charborough Park *(34)*
Mayo Farm, Shaftesbury *(55)*
Snape Cottage, Chaffeymoor *(83)*
Toad Hall, The Cross, Shillingstone *(90)*
May 30 Monday (Bank Hol)
Ashley Park Farm, Damerham *(3)*

Bracken Cottage and The Ferns, East Burton, Wool *(7)*
Corfe Barn, Broadstone *(17)*
Deans Court, Wimborne Minster *(21)*
May 31 Tuesday
'Ola', Weymouth *(65)*
June 1 Wednesday
Broomhill, Rampisham *(9)*
Innsacre, Shipton Gorge *(38)*
Mayo Farm, Shaftesbury *(55)*
Rampisham Manor, Rampisham *(73)*
June 2 Thursday
Hilltop, Woodville, Stour Provost *(35)*
Ivy Cottage, Ansty *(39)*
Vine Cottage, Melcombe Bingham *(93)*
June 4 Saturday
Chesil Gallery, Chiswell, Portland *(12)*
Millmead, Winterborne Stickland *(59)*
Saulfland Lodge, Highcliffe *(77)*
June 5 Sunday
The Avenue Gardens, Wimborne *(4)*
Chesil Gallery, Chiswell, Portland *(12)*
Holworth Farmhouse, Holworth, nr Owermoigne *(36)*
Ivy House, Piddletrenthide *(40)*
Kingston Lacy, Wimborne Minster *(43)*
Mews Cottage, Portland *(57)*
Millmead, Winterborne Stickland *(59)*
The Old Rectory, Fifehead Magdalen *(67)*
Windy Willums, Christchurch *(98)*
June 6 Monday
4 Flower Cottage, Lower Waterston *(26)*
June 7 Tuesday
44 Daws Avenue, Wallisdown *(20)*
The Scented Garden, Littlebredy **(Day & Evening)** *(78)*
Windy Willums, Christchurch *(98)*

"Is that a helter-skelter tree, Mum?"

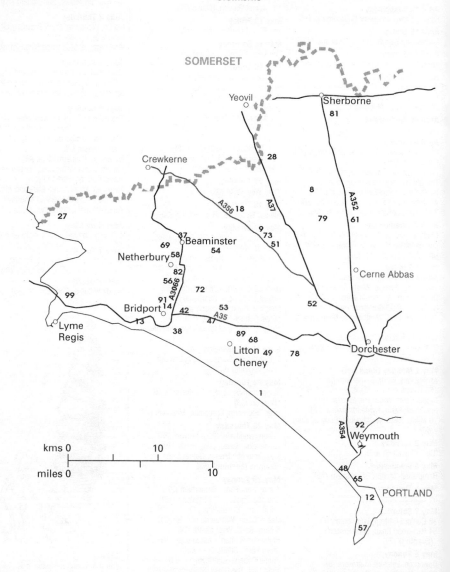

Crewkerne

SOMERSET

Yeovil

Sherborne
81

Crewkerne

28

8

A356 18   A37   79   A352 61

27

37
69 Beaminster
Netherbury 58   9 73
82   54   51

56
A3066   72
99
91   52
Bridport 14 42   53
13   47
38   A35
Lyme   89 68
Regis   Litton 49   78
Cheney

Cerne Abbas

Dorchester

1

kms 0   10
miles 0   10   92
A354 Weymouth

48
65
12   PORTLAND

57

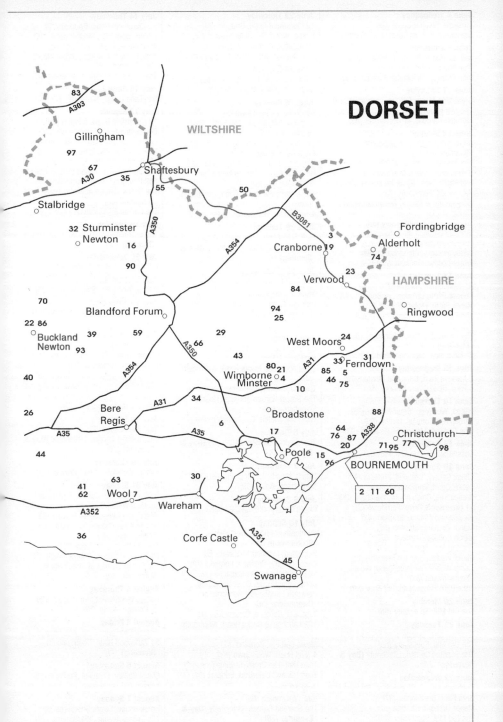

DORSET

WILTSHIRE

83
A303

Gillingham
97

67
A30   35
55

Shaftesbury

50

Stalbridge

32 Sturminster
Newton   16

A350

A354

B3081

3

Cranborne 19

Fordingbridge

Alderholt
74

90

Verwood
84

23

HAMPSHIRE

70

Blandford Forum

94
25

Ringwood

22 86
Buckland   39   59
Newton 93

29

West Moors 24

40

A354

A350   66

43

80 21
Wimborne 4
Minster   10

A31

31
33 Ferndown
85   5
46 75

26

Bere
Regis

A31

34

6

Broadstone

88

A35

A35

17

64
76 87
20

A338

Christchurch

44

71 95 77
Poole 15   98
96

BOURNEMOUTH

41
63
62   Wool 7

A352

30

Wareham

2 11 60

36

Corfe Castle

A351

45

Swanage

June 8 Wednesday
Innsacre, Shipton Gorge *(38)*
Stanbridge Mill, nr Gussage All Saints *(84)*
June 9 Thursday
Hilltop, Woodville, Stour Provost *(35)*
Ivy Cottage, Ansty *(39)*
Vine Cottage, Melcombe Bingham *(93)*
June 11 Saturday
Cranborne Manor Garden, Cranborne *(19)*
The Mill House, Netherbury *(58)*
Moreton Gardens, nr Dorchester *(63)*
June 12 Sunday
89 Alumhurst Road, Westbourne,
Bournemouth *(2)*
The Avenue Gardens, Wimborne *(4)*
Bexington, Lytchett Matravers *(6)*
Frankham Farm, Ryme Intrinseca *(28)*
Hazelwood, Ferndown *(33)*
Mappercombe Manor, Nettlecombe, Nr
Bridport *(53)*
The Mill House, Netherbury *(58)*
Moreton Gardens, nr Dorchester *(63)*
The Old Rectory, Netherbury *(69)*
Windy Willums, Christchurch *(98)*
Wolverhollow, Monkton Wyld *(99)*
June 14 Tuesday
Broomhill, Rampisham *(9)*
Knowle Farm, Uploders, nr Bridport *(47)*
Manor Farm, Higher Wraxall *(51)*
The Old Rectory, Litton Cheney *(68)*
Pear Tree Farm, Loscombe, Melplash *(72)*
The Scented Garden, Littlebredy **(Day &
Evening)** *(78)*
Wolverhollow, Monkton Wyld *(99)*
June 15 Wednesday
Domineys Yard, Buckland Newton *(22)*
6 Farm Road, West Moors *(24)*
June 16 Thursday
Hilltop, Woodville, Stour Provost *(35)*
Throop Mill Cottage, Throop *(88)*
Vine Cottage, Melcombe Bingham *(93)*
June 18 Saturday
Chesil Gallery, Chiswell, Portland *(12)*
June 19 Sunday
Chesil Gallery, Chiswell, Portland *(12)*
Deans Court, Wimborne Minster *(21)*
Greenacres, Coldharbour, Wareham *(30)*
11 Greensome Drive, Ferndown *(31)*
19 Jessopp Avenue, Bridport *(42)*
Manor Orchard, Stratton *(52)*
Mews Cottage, Portland *(57)*
The Old Mill, Spetisbury *(66)*
Sticky Wicket, Buckland Newton *(86)*
Talbot Woods Gardens, Talbot Woods,
Bournemouth *(87)*
Tithe Barn House, Litton Cheney *(89)*
June 20 Monday
The Old Mill, Spetisbury *(66)*
June 21 Tuesday
Knowle Farm, Uploders, nr Bridport *(47)*
The Old Mill, Spetisbury *(66)*
The Scented Garden, Littlebredy **(Day &
Evening)** *(78)*
June 22 Wednesday
Chideock Manor, Chideock, nr Bridport *(13)*
Horn Park, Beaminster *(37)*
Manor Orchard, Stratton *(52)*
The Old Mill, Spetisbury *(66)*

June 23 Thursday
12 Claremont Road, Bridport *(14)*
Hilltop, Woodville, Stour Provost *(35)*
19 Jessopp Avenue, Bridport *(42)*
Vine Cottage, Melcombe Bingham *(93)*
June 25 Saturday
Galpin Cottage, Tarrant Keyneston *(29)*
Saulfland Lodge, Highcliffe *(77)*
June 26 Sunday
Beech Mead, Ferndown *(5)*
Bracken Cottage and The Ferns, East
Burton, Wool *(7)*
Chideock Manor, Chideock, nr Bridport *(13)*
Corfe Barn, Broadstone *(17)*
Galpin Cottage, Tarrant Keyneston *(29)*
Holworth Farmhouse, Holworth, nr
Owermoigne *(36)*
102 Lanehouse Rocks Road, Weymouth
(48)
4 Noel Road, Wallisdown *(64)*
June 28 Tuesday
Pear Tree Farm, Loscombe, Melplash *(72)*
The Scented Garden, Littlebredy **(Day &
Evening)** *(78)*
June 29 Wednesday
Melplash Court, Melplash *(56)*
June 30 Thursday
Bracken Cottage and The Ferns, East
Burton, Wool *(7)*
Hilltop, Woodville, Stour Provost *(35)*
July 3 Sunday
6 Farm Road, West Moors *(24)*
Hazelwood, Ferndown *(33)*
102 Lanehouse Rocks Road, Weymouth
(48)
The Old Rectory, Netherbury *(69)*
The Secret Garden at Serles House,
Wimborne *(80)*
Welcome Thatch, Witchampton *(94)*
July 5 Tuesday
The Scented Garden, Littlebredy **(Day &
Evening)** *(78)*
July 7 Thursday
Hilltop, Woodville, Stour Provost *(35)*
Ivy Cottage, Ansty *(39)*
July 9 Saturday
Chesil Gallery, Chiswell, Portland *(12)*
July 10 Sunday
89 Alumhurst Road, Westbourne,
Bournemouth *(2)*
Bexington, Lytchett Matravers *(6)*
Chesil Gallery, Chiswell, Portland *(12)*
Coombe Cottage, Shillingstone *(16)*
Corscombe House, Corscombe *(18)*
Holworth Farmhouse, Holworth, nr
Owermoigne *(36)*
Japanese Gardens, Crossways *(41)*
102 Lanehouse Rocks Road, Weymouth
(48)
Mews Cottage, Portland *(57)*
4 Noel Road, Wallisdown *(64)*
Toad Hall, The Cross, Shillingstone *(90)*
Toad Hill and L'Horizon, Bridport *(91)*
July 12 Tuesday
'Ola', Weymouth *(65)*
The Scented Garden, Littlebredy **(Day &
Evening)** *(78)*

July 14 Thursday
12 Claremont Road, Bridport *(14)*
Hilltop, Woodville, Stour Provost *(35)*
Ivy Cottage, Ansty *(39)*
Talbot Woods Gardens, Talbot Woods,
Bournemouth *(87)*
Toad Hill and L'Horizon, Bridport *(91)*
July 16 Saturday
Saulfland Lodge, Highcliffe *(77)*
July 17 Sunday
12 Claremont Road, Bridport *(14)*
Corscombe House, Corscombe *(18)*
Greenacres, Coldharbour, Wareham *(30)*
Hilltop, Woodville, Stour Provost *(35)*
19 Jessopp Avenue, Bridport *(42)*
Rampisham Manor, Rampisham *(73)*
357 Ringwood Road, Ferndown *(75)*
The Secret Garden at Serles House,
Wimborne *(80)*
Toad Hill and L'Horizon, Bridport *(91)*
July 19 Tuesday
The Scented Garden, Littlebredy **(Day &
Evening)** *(78)*
July 20 Wednesday
6 Farm Road, West Moors *(24)*
July 21 Thursday
Hilltop, Woodville, Stour Provost *(35)*
July 23 Saturday
Chesil Gallery, Chiswell, Portland *(12)*
July 24 Sunday
Bracken Cottage and The Ferns, East
Burton, Wool *(7)*
Chesil Gallery, Chiswell, Portland *(12)*
Hazelwood, Ferndown *(33)*
Hilltop, Woodville, Stour Provost *(35)*
102 Lanehouse Rocks Road, Weymouth
(48)
Mews Cottage, Portland *(57)*
July 26 Tuesday
'Ola', Weymouth *(65)*
The Scented Garden, Littlebredy **(Day &
Evening)** *(78)*
July 28 Thursday
Hilltop, Woodville, Stour Provost *(35)*
July 31 Sunday
Bracken Cottage and The Ferns, East
Burton, Wool *(7)*
Hilltop, Woodville, Stour Provost *(35)*
Holworth Farmhouse, Holworth, nr
Owermoigne *(36)*
The Old Rectory, Pulham *(70)*
54 Parkwood Road, Bournemouth *(71)*
The Secret Garden at Serles House,
Wimborne *(80)*
August 4 Thursday
Hilltop, Woodville, Stour Provost *(35)*
Ivy Cottage, Ansty *(39)*
August 5 Friday
Knitson Old Farmhouse, nr Swanage *(45)*
54 Parkwood Road, Bournemouth
(Evening) *(71)*
August 6 Saturday
Chesil Gallery, Chiswell, Portland *(12)*
Knitson Old Farmhouse, nr Swanage *(45)*
August 7 Sunday
Brook House, Leigh, Sherborne *(8)*
15a Cassel Avenue, Westbourne *(11)*

Chesil Gallery, Chiswell, Portland *(12)*
Hilltop, Woodville, Stour Provost *(35)*
Knitson Old Farmhouse, nr Swanage *(45)*
102 Lanehouse Rocks Road, Weymouth *(48)*
Mews Cottage, Portland *(57)*

August 8 Monday
Knitson Old Farmhouse, nr Swanage *(45)*

August 9 Tuesday
Knitson Old Farmhouse, nr Swanage *(45)*

August 10 Wednesday
89 Alumhurst Road, Westbourne, Bournemouth *(2)*
Brook House, Leigh, Sherborne *(8)*
Knitson Old Farmhouse, nr Swanage *(45)*

August 11 Thursday
Hilltop, Woodville, Stour Provost *(35)*
Ivy Cottage, Ansty *(39)*
Knitson Old Farmhouse, nr Swanage *(45)*

August 12 Friday
Knitson Old Farmhouse, nr Swanage *(45)*

August 13 Saturday
Knitson Old Farmhouse, nr Swanage *(45)*

August 14 Sunday
Bexington, Lytchett Matravers *(6)*
Broomhill, Rampisham *(9)*
Domineys Yard, Buckland Newton *(22)*
Hazelwood, Ferndown *(33)*
Hilltop, Woodville, Stour Provost *(35)*
Knitson Old Farmhouse, nr Swanage *(45)*
357 Ringwood Road, Ferndown *(75)*
The Secret Garden at Serles House, Wimborne *(80)*

August 16 Tuesday
Knowle Farm, Uploders, nr Bridport *(47)*

August 17 Wednesday
89 Alumhurst Road, Westbourne, Bournemouth *(2)*

August 18 Thursday
Hilltop, Woodville, Stour Provost *(35)*

August 21 Sunday
Brook House, Leigh, Sherborne *(8)*
Greenacres, Coldharbour, Wareham *(30)*
Hilltop, Woodville, Stour Provost *(35)*
Mews Cottage, Portland *(57)*
Sticky Wicket, Buckland Newton *(86)*
24a Western Avenue, Branksome Park, Poole *(96)*

August 24 Wednesday
89 Alumhurst Road, Westbourne, Bournemouth *(2)*
Brook House, Leigh, Sherborne *(8)*

August 28 Sunday
Bracken Cottage and The Ferns, East Burton, Wool **(Day & Evening)** *(7)*
Coombe Cottage, Shillingstone *(16)*
Deans Court, Wimborne Minster *(21)*
Galpin Cottage, Tarrant Keyneston *(29)*
Manor Farm, Higher Wraxall *(51)*
The Secret Garden at Serles House, Wimborne *(80)*
Toad Hall, The Cross, Shillingstone *(90)*

August 29 Monday (Bank Hol)
Bracken Cottage and The Ferns, East Burton, Wool *(7)*
Deans Court, Wimborne Minster *(21)*
Galpin Cottage, Tarrant Keyneston *(29)*

The Secret Garden at Serles House, Wimborne *(80)*

August 31 Wednesday
89 Alumhurst Road, Westbourne, Bournemouth *(2)*

September 1 Thursday
Ivy Cottage, Ansty *(39)*

September 8 Thursday
Ivy Cottage, Ansty *(39)*

September 11 Sunday
Bexington, Lytchett Matravers *(6)*
44 Daws Avenue, Wallisdown *(20)*
Deans Court, Wimborne Minster *(21)*
4 Flower Cottage, Lower Waterston *(26)*

September 18 Sunday
Wentworth College, Bournemouth *(95)*

September 25 Sunday
19 Jessopp Avenue, Bridport *(42)*

October 5 Wednesday
Edmondsham House, nr Cranborne *(23)*

October 9 Sunday
Mews Cottage, Portland *(57)*

October 12 Wednesday
Edmondsham House, nr Cranborne *(23)*

October 19 Wednesday
Edmondsham House, nr Cranborne *(23)*

October 23 Sunday
Mews Cottage, Portland *(57)*

October 26 Wednesday
Edmondsham House, nr Cranborne *(23)*

December 22 Thursday
Kingston Maurward Gardens, Dorchester *(44)*

December 23 Friday
Kingston Maurward Gardens, Dorchester *(44)*

December 24 Saturday
Kingston Maurward Gardens, Dorchester *(44)*

December 25 Sunday
Kingston Maurward Gardens, Dorchester *(44)*

December 26 Monday
Kingston Maurward Gardens, Dorchester *(44)*

December 27 Tuesday
Kingston Maurward Gardens, Dorchester *(44)*

December 28 Wednesday
Kingston Maurward Gardens, Dorchester *(44)*

December 29 Thursday
Kingston Maurward Gardens, Dorchester *(44)*

December 30 Friday
Kingston Maurward Gardens, Dorchester *(44)*

December 31 Saturday
Kingston Maurward Gardens, Dorchester *(44)*

DESCRIPTIONS OF GARDENS

❶ ◆ Abbotsbury Gardens, nr Weymouth ⬚⬚
(Curator/Head Gardener, Ilchester Estates) *8m W of Weymouth. From B3157 Weymouth-Bridport, 200yds W of Abbotsbury village.* 20 acres, started in 1760 and considerably extended in C19. Much recent replanting, very fine collection of rhododendrons, camellias, azaleas. Unique maritime micro-climate enables a flourishing Mediterranean bank and southern hemisphere garden to grow rare and tender plants. In summer there are palm trees, bananas, cannas; ponds and streamside plantings. Children's play area, sculpture trail, plant sales, shop, aviaries and Colonial tea-house. Light refreshments and TEAS. *Adm £6.80, chd £4, OAP £6. Mar to Oct (10-6) Nov to Feb (10-4). Tel 01305 871412 www.abbotsbury-tourism. co.uk*

❷ 89 Alumhurst Road, Westbourne, Bournemouth ⬚⬚
(Mrs S Dennett) *2m W of Bournemouth. Follow Alumchine rd signs. From centre of Westbourne turn S into Alumhurst Rd for 1m. On yellow bus route.* Small town garden, approx 60ft x 60ft, providing yr-round colour. Mainly shrubs, unusual perennials, grasses and ferns. Courtyard with raised beds and containers with many varieties of clematis, trachelospermum and wisteria. Gravel pathways. Home-made TEAS. *Adm £1.50, chd 50p. Suns 12 June; 10 July; Weds 10, 17, 24, 31 Aug (2-5)*

◆ Apple Court, Lymington ⬚⬚⬚
See Hampshire.

❸ Ashley Park Farm, Damerham ⬚
(Mr & Mrs David Dampney) *3m W of Fordingbridge. 4m E of Cranborne. Follow yellow signs off old B3078, immed W of Damerham.* Country garden set within 5 acres, with yew hedges protecting formal areas. Mixed borders and interesting climbers for S-facing walls. Natural stream, when active, incorporates water features. Visitors are invited to walk to bluebell woods via the growing arboretum planted with bamboos, unusual trees and shrubs incl magnolias and viburnum. Wildflowers encouraged. Plants incl bamboos for sale. Featured in 'Dorset Society' and on Prime Time 2003. Home-made TEAS in aid of St George's Church, Damerham. *Adm £2.50, chd free. Sun 6 Mar; Suns,*

Mons 27, 28 Mar; 1, 2, 29, 30 May (2-5.30). Also open **The Red House, Alderholt** *27 Mar*

❹ NEW The Avenue Gardens, Wimborne
Off B3073, E of town, very near Wimborne market. Home-made TEAS at Lanherne in aid of Wimborne First School. *Combined adm £3, chd free. Suns 5, 12 June (2-5)*

> **NEW Lanherne, 16 Avenue Road** ✖ ⊕ (Lynne & Peter Williams) Created around a Victorian villa, the home of author/poet Thomas Hardy from 1881-1883 (not open), the garden has been designed by landscape architect owner Lynne and combines interesting planting combinations and unusual plants with sculptural elements incl dovecote, pergola, water features, sundial. Some of Hardy's writing will be displayed around the garden. Home-made TEAS in aid of Wimborne First School. *Adm £3, chd free*

> **The Lodge, 36a Avenue Road** ✖ ⊕ (Mrs Carol Pytlik) This little gem (approx 84ft x 24ft) of a town garden in the Italian style, has been created by the owner/garden designer around a Victorian house in conservation area. Packs in plants, colour, theatrical summer house, knot garden, water features and lots of ideas.

❺ NEW Beech Mead, 13 St Mary's Road, Ferndown 🅱 ✖ ⊕
(Susan & Peter Clarkson) *From town centre take Church Rd, turn R into St Mary's Rd. 2mins walk from nearby free Tesco car park.* Newly created colourful garden containing a large and varied collection of perennials, flowering climbers, acers, grasses and phormiums. Circular lawn surrounded by gravelled areas, slate beds and bog garden; small pond and stream. A garden that explodes with colour and interest, a must for the plantaholic. Group Winner Ferndown in Bloom 2004. Light refreshments and TEAS in aid of Ferndown Middle School. *Adm £1.50, chd free. Suns 10 Apr; 26 June (10.30-6). Private visits welcome by appt. Tel 01202 874224*

❻ Bexington, Lime Kiln Road, Lytchett Matravers 🅱 ✖ ⊕
(Mr & Mrs Robin Crumpler) *5m SW of Wimborne Minster. Opp old school at W end of village.* Colourful garden of ½ acre maintained by owners, with mixed borders of many interesting and unusual plants, shrubs and trees. Bog garden of primulas,

hostas etc. Four rockeries of alpines, with walkways over bog area connecting two lawns, making a garden of interest from spring bulbs to autumn colour. Cream TEAS in aid of Alzheimers Disease Society. *Adm £1.50, chd free. Suns 10 Apr; 8 May; 12 June; 10 July; 14 Aug; 11 Sept (2-6). Private visits welcome by appt. Tel 01202 622068*

❼ Bracken Cottage and The Ferns, East Burton, Wool
6m W of Wareham on A352 to Dorchester. Approaching Wool from Wareham, turn R just before level crossing into East Burton Rd. Bracken Cottage is on R, next to The Ferns, just under a mile down this rd. A hamlet little changed since Hardy's time with thatched cottages and watermill - map of walks available. Home-made TEAS in aid of RNLI. *Combined adm £2.50 (£3 incl adm to toy museum), chd free. Suns 22 May; 26 June; 24, 31 July (2-5); 28 Aug (4-6); Mons 30 May; 29 Aug; Thur 30 June (2-5)* **Evening Opening** *£3, wine, Sun 28 Aug (6-8)*

> **Bracken Cottage** 🅱 ⊕ (Paul & Maureen Cosway) Many interesting and unusual plants. Colour-themed borders lead down to small river. The design (incl water features and tropical beds) should interest visitors of all ages. New features incl miniature 'hobbit garden'. Scheduled to feature in 'Dorset Life' 2005. *Private visits welcome by appt. Tel 01929 405614*

> **The Ferns** 🅱 ⊕ (John & Jill Redfern) Profusely planted with varied herbaceous borders and shrubs. Interesting use of hard landscaping. Fruit and vegetable garden leads to small woodland garden and stream. New features incl New scene from Dorset clay-mining history. Specialist plant sale on 26 June. Scheduled to feature in 'Dorset Life' 2005. *Private visits welcome by appt throughout May, June and July. Tel 01929 462678*

❽ Brook House, Leigh, Sherborne 🅱 ✖ ⊕
(Philip & Sylvia Bryan) *6m SW of Sherborne. At Bridge Garage, Leigh take turning signposted Batcombe & Hilfield. House is 200yds on R.* ¾-acre garden, designed and maintained by the owners since 1994. Bordered by stream with waterside plantings. Double herbaceous borders with rose ropes, lily pond, daylily garden, fruit and vegetables. Featured in 'Dorset' magazine 2004. Cream TEAS in aid

of Leigh Church. *Adm £2, chd free. Suns, Weds 7, 10, 21, 24 Aug (2-5)*

❾ Broomhill, Rampisham 🅱 ⊕
(Mr & Mrs D Parry) *11m NW of Dorchester. From Yeovil take A37 towards Dorchester, 7m turn R signed Evershot. From Dorchester take A37 to Yeovil, 4m turn L A356 signed Crewkerne; at start of wireless masts R to Rampisham. Follow signs.* Delightful 1-acre family garden, which incorporates a disused farmyard and paddock. Pretty trellised entrance leads to an abundance of exciting plantings in mixed borders and island beds. Lawns slope gently down to large wildlife pond and bog garden. Mown paths take you around the pond to a less formal area of mixed trees and shrubs. Home-made TEAS in aid of Wraxall PCC. *Adm £2.50, chd under 16 free. Wed 1, Tue 14 June; Sun 14 Aug (2-6). Open with* **Rampisham Manor** *1 June,* **Manor Farm, Wraxall** *14 June. Private visits welcome by appt June to Sept. Tel 01935 83266*

❿ 38 Canford Bottom, Wimborne 🅱 ✖ ⊕
(Freda & Tony Holloway) *2m E of Wimborne. From Canford Bottom roundabout exit N marked Colehill, take lane 100yds on R adjacent Ellford Bodyworks. Last house in lane.* Good all-yr-round plantsman's garden specialising in rare and unusual perennials and flowering shrubs with many varieties of aquilegias. Cottage garden with water features, Japanese garden, scree and bog gardens, working 'O' gauge model railway. Lunches, Light refreshments and TEAS. *Adm £1.50, chd free. Sat, Sun 7, 8 May (11-4)*

⓫ 15a Cassel Avenue, Westbourne
(John & Jeannie Blay) *2m W of Bournemouth. From centre of Westbourne turn S into Alumhurst Rd, take 8th turning on R into Mountbatten Rd then 1st L into Cassel Ave.* Unique Chine garden of ½ acre. Wooded coastal site, steeply banked and spanned by a bridge with 330 tonnes of Purbeck stone incorporated in the original construction. 2 ponds, formal lawn surrounded by clipped hedge, Palladian rotunda and sculptural pieces. Planting incl subtropical species, ferns, mature shrubs, azaleas, rhododendrons, pieris and hydrangeas together with numerous perennials. Due to steep steps and uneven paths the garden is unsuitable for the less mobile. *Adm £2, chd 50p.*

Sun, Mon 1, 2 May; Suns 8 May; 7 Aug (2-5)

⓬ Chesil Gallery, Chiswell, Portland
(Mrs Margaret Somerville) *3m N of Portland. S of Weymouth. Follow signs to Portland; from Victoria Square turn R into Chiswell, & immed R into Pebble Lane. Park in car park.* Small and delightful shingle garden in the lee of the Chesil Bank. Two courtyard gardens provide a domestic adjunct to artists' studio. On upper level flowering plants of coastal regions (some rare) have been naturalised. Information on the Chesil Beach and its ecology. Featured in 'Gardenlife' 2003. *Adm £1.50, chd free (share to Chiswell Community Trust). Sats, Suns 4, 5, 18, 19 June; 9, 10, 23, 24 July; 6, 7 Aug (2-5). Open with* **Mews Cottage** *Suns 19 June; 10, 24 July; 7 Aug*

⓭ NEW Chideock Manor, Chideock, nr Bridport ⌖
(Mr & Mrs Howard Coates) *2m W of Bridport. On A35. In centre of village turn N at church. The Manor is ¼m along this rd on R.* Large formal and informal gardens, some in process of development. Bog garden beside stream. Woodland and lakeside walks. Walled vegetable garden and orchard. Yew hedges and many mature trees. Lime walk. Herbaceous borders. Rose and clematis arches. Fine views. Home-made TEAS in aid of Marie Curie Cancer Care. *Adm £3.50. Suns 24 Apr; 26 June; Weds 27 Apr; 22 June (2-6)*

⓮ 12 Claremont Road, Bridport ⌖
(Jean & Glanville Magor) *From Bridport, N on A3066 for ½m, into St Andrews Rd, R into Coneygar Rd, R into St Katherines Ave, L into Claremont Rd. Park with consideration on rd.* Small rear-sloping garden with terraces and rockeries planted informally, cottage garden style, with herbaceous perennials. Beyond a rose-covered trellis, through arches, are more formal beds of annuals, perennials and vegetables. There are a few steps with handrails, but easy walking. Display of owner's carved puppets in conservatory. *Adm £2, chd free. Thurs 23 June; 14 July; Sun 17 July (2-6)*

⓯ ◆ Compton Acres Gardens, Poole ⌖⌖⌖
(Director) *2m E of Poole. Signed from Bournemouth & Poole. Wilts & Dorset Buses 150, 151. Yellow Bus 12 stops at entrance.* Set in 10 acres with spectacular views overlooking Poole Harbour and the Purbeck Hills. Enjoy exploring each garden with its own individual charm, character and beauty. Started in 1920 as a private garden, the ongoing refurbishment and planting programme is well underway and will give interest to visitors all yr round. Light refreshments and TEAS. *Adm £5.95, chd £3.95, concessions £5.45. Open all year (9-5.30 or dusk). Tel 01202 700778 www.comptonacres.co.uk*

⓰ Coombe Cottage, Shillingstone ⌖
(Mike & Jennie Adams) *5m NW of Blandford. On A357 next to PO Stores on main rd. Parking advised in Gunn Lane.* ½-acre plantsman's cottage garden, enclosed by walls and hedges, with a dense, catholic mix of herbaceous and woody perennials, climbers, bulbs and self-seeding annuals (many unusual and subtropical), in broad borders and in a large plant house. *Adm £2, chd free. Suns 29 May; 10 July; 28 Aug (2-6). Private visits welcome by appt. Tel 01258 860220 mja@bryanston. co.uk*

⓱ Corfe Barn, Corfe Lodge Road, Broadstone ⌖⌖
(Mr & Mrs John McDavid) *1m W of Broadstone centre. From main roundabout in Broadstone, W along Clarendon Rd ¾m, N into Roman Rd, after 50yds W into Corfe Lodge Rd.* ⅔ acre on three levels on site of C19 lavender farm. Informal country garden with much to interest both gardeners and flower arrangers. Parts of the original farm have been incorporated in the design. A particular feature of the garden is the use made of old walls. Featured in 'Amateur Gardening' & Top Soil radio programme, 2004. Home-made TEAS. *Adm £1, chd free. Suns 24 Apr; 29 May; 26 June; Mon 30 May (2-5)*

⓲ Corscombe House, Corscombe
(Jim Bartos) *3½m N of Beaminster. From Dorchester A356 to Crewkerne, take 1st turn to Corscombe, R signed Church. Or A37 Yeovil to Dorchester, turn W signed Sutton Bingham/ Halstock/ Corscombe. Straight past Fox Inn, up hill, L signed Church.* Garden established since 1995 in grounds of former rectory with view of Church. Garden rooms with colour-themed cool and hot borders, sunny and shady beds, parterre, reflecting pool, orchard with wild flower meadow, part-walled vegetable garden. Cream TEAS in Rectory 10 July only in aid of Corscombe Church. *Adm £2, chd free. Suns 10, 17 July (2-6). Open with* **Rampisham Manor** *17 July*

⓳ ◆ Cranborne Manor Garden, Cranborne ⌖⌖⌖
(The Marquess & Marchioness of Salisbury) *10m N of Wimborne. On B3078.* Beautiful metallic garden laid out in C17 by John Tradescant and enlarged in C20, featuring several gardens surrounded by walls and yew hedges: white garden, herb and mount gardens, water and wild garden. Many interesting plants, with fine trees and avenues. Light refreshments and TEAS. *Adm £4, chd 50p, concessions £3.50 (share to Dorset & Somerset Air Ambulance Trust). Weds Mar-Sept (9-5). For NGS: Wed 23 Mar; Sat 11 June (9-5). Tel 01725 517248 www.cranborne. co.uk*

⓴ 44 Daws Avenue, Wallisdown ⌖⌖
(Carol & John Farrance) *3m W of Bournemouth. Going N from Wallisdown roundabout take 1st L into Canford Ave then 1st R into Daws Ave.* Small town garden offering yr-round interest with emphasis in spring on camellias and magnolias, underplanted with daphnes, hellebores, erythroniums and trilliums. Roses provide summer colour and in autumn rare hydrangeas, hibiscus and eucryphias are in bloom. Small courtyard leads to main area, where stream can be appreciated from summerhouse. Home-made TEAS (Cream TEAS May & June). *Adm £1.50, chd free. Fri 25 Mar; Sun 15 May; Tue 7 June; Sun 11 Sept (2-5)*

㉑ Deans Court, Deans Court Lane, Wimborne Minster ⌖⌖⌖
(Sir Michael & Lady Hanham) *¼m SE of Minster. Just off B3073 in centre of Wimborne. Entry from Deans Court Lane - continuation of High St at junction with East St & King St over pavement & past bollard. Free parking.* 13 acres on R Allen; partly wild, with historic specimen trees. House originally the Deanery to the Minster. Herb garden, rose garden. Long serpentine wall. The house will be open by prior written appointment. Deans Court, Wimborne BH21 1EE. Produce usually for sale. Home-made TEAS. *Adm £3, chd £1, concessions £2. Suns, BH Mons 27, 28 Mar; 1, 2, 29, 30 May; 19 June; 28, 29 Aug; 11 Sept; Suns (2-6), Mons (10-6)*

㉒ Domineys Yard, Buckland Newton 🚻🐕♿

(Mr & Mrs W Gueterbock) *11m N of Dorchester. 2m E A352 or take B3143. Take 'no through rd' between Church & Gaggle of Geese. Entrance 100yds on L. Park & picnic in 4½-acre arboretum. 2½ acres of garden on greensand soil. Trees, shrubs, herbaceous and bulbs along with fruit and vegetables thrive. This soil adapts for both acid and lime-loving plants in different areas. Both spring and autumn provide much of interest, not just the summer months. A new formal layout on the old grass tennis court contrasts with the general informality. Home-made TEAS. Adm £3, chd free. Suns 3 Apr; 15 May; 14 Aug; Wed 15 June (2-6). Private visits welcome by appt. Tel 01300 345295 www.domineys.com*

㉓ ◆ Edmondsham House, nr Cranborne 🚻🐕♿

(Mrs Julia Smith) *9m NE of Wimborne. 9m W of Ringwood. Between Cranborne & Verwood. Edmondsham off B3081. An historic 6-acre garden of C16 house. Interesting mature specimen trees and shrubs. Spring bulbs and blossom, autumn cyclamen. Early church, Victorian dairy and stable block, medieval grass cock pit. Walled garden with vegetables, fruit and traditional herbaceous borders planted to sustain long period of interest. Managed organically. TEAS NGS days except 28 Mar. House and Garden Adm £3, chd £1, under 5 free, Garden only Adm £1.50, 50p, under 5 free. Weds, Suns, 1 Apr to 31 Oct (2-5), house also open on NGS days. For NGS: Mon 28 Mar; Weds 6, 13, 20, 27 Apr; 5, 12, 19, 26 Oct (2-5). Tel 01725 517207*

㉔ 6 Farm Road, West Moors 🐕♿

(Mrs Jenny Stokes) *8m N of Bournemouth. Off B3072 Bournemouth-Verwood rd. In centre of village turn W opp sign for medical centre into Farm Rd, garden 100yds on R. A colourful garden just 90ft x 40ft but packed with a wide range of unusual plants chosen to give a long period of interest. Designed by the owner to be a tranquil haven in a busy world. Good use of climbers supported by string 'cobwebs'. Small pool and rill with decked seating area. Featured in 'Amateur Gardening' 2004. TEAS. Adm £1.50, chd free. Suns 29 May; 3 July; Weds 15 June; 20 July (2-5). Private visits welcome by appt. Tel 01202 855687*

㉕ Fernhill House, Lower Street, Witchampton 🚻🐕♿

(Mrs Henry Hildyard) *3½m N of Wimborne. B3078 L to Witchampton then L up Lower St. (Blandford rd) house on R 200yds. Please park in adjacent meadow (signed). Spring flowers, blossom and bulbs in a country garden of 3 acres set in an historic village. Woodland walk around pond through orchard with massed planting of daffodils and naturalised fritillaries. Stone terrace with pergola leads to large herbaceous border surrounding formal pool. Home-made TEAS at and in aid of Witchampton Village Hall. Adm £2, chd free. Sun 3 Apr (2-5). Also open Welcome Thatch. Private visits welcome by appt Apr to 30 June. Tel 01258 840105*

㉖ 4 Flower Cottage, Lower Waterston 🚻♿

(Mrs A J Penniston) *5m NE of Dorchester. From Puddletown on B3142 take rd from bypass for Piddlehinton & Piddletrenthide. 2m on R. ⅓-acre cottage garden, with herbaceous borders, scree, fernery and vegetables within a design of several small gardens. Featured in 'Dorset' magazine 2004. Cream TEAS. Adm £1.50, chd free. Mon 6 June; Sun 11 Sept (2-6). Private visits welcome by appt, coaches permitted. Tel 01305 848694*

㉗ ◆ Forde Abbey Gardens, Chard 🚻♿

(Mr Mark Roper) *4m SE of Chard. Signed off A30 Chard-Crewkerne & A358 Chard-Axminster. Also from Broadwindsor. 30 acres, fine shrubs, magnificent specimen trees, ponds, herbaceous borders, rockery, bog garden containing superb collection of Asiatic primulas, Ionic temple, working kitchen garden supplying the restaurant. For adm price please contact the information centre. Light refreshments and TEAS. Gardens open daily throughout the yr (10 - last adm 4.30). Tel 01460 221290, Carolyn Clay www.fordeabbey. co.uk*

㉘ Frankham Farm, Ryme Intrinseca 🚻🐕♿

(Mr & Mrs R G Earle) *3m S of Yeovil. A37 Yeovil-Dorchester; turn E; drive ¼m on L. 3½-acre garden, begun in 1960s by owners for yr-round interest. Perennials and roses round house and stone farm buildings. Extensive wall plantings incl roses and clematis, productive vegetable and fruit garden. Many unusual shrubs and trees, particularly hardwoods, shelter belts of trees*

forming woodland walks, under-planted with camellias, rhododendrons, hydrangeas and spring bulbs. Plenty to see from February onwards. 12 June special day for trees. Home-made TEAS and plants in aid of Cystic Fibrosis Trust & Ryme Church. Adm £2.50, chd free. Suns 6 Mar; 17 Apr; 22 May; 12 June; Mons 28 Mar; 2 May (2-5.30). *Private visits welcome by appt, individuals or groups. Tel 01935 872304*

㉙ NEW Galpin Cottage, 2 Valley Road, Tarrant Keyneston ♿

(Chris & Reg Porter) *3m SE Blandford. On B3082 Blandford to Wimborne rd turn at sign to Tarrant Keyneston, garden approx 700yds on R. Parking available at nearby village hall, otherwise park sympathetically in rd. Colourful garden 30ft x 80ft created over 11 yrs on slight slope. Gravel paths wind round island beds packed full of plants chosen for seasonal interest, bulbs and spring flowers lead into early summer perennials and iris, dahlias feature in August. Raised pond and bog garden; summerhouse; containers with unusual plants. Light refreshments and TEAS in aid of village hall and local church. Adm £1.50, chd 50p, children under 10 free. Suns 24 Apr; 22 May; Sat, Sun 25, 26 June; Sun, Mon 28, 29 Aug (2-6). Also open The Secret Garden at Serles House 28, 29 Aug*

Grange Farm, Kilmington 🚻🐕♿

See Wiltshire.

㉚ Greenacres, Bere Road, Coldharbour, Wareham 🚻🐕♿

(John & Pat Jacobs) *2½m NW of Wareham. From roundabout adjacent to station take Wareham-Bere Regis rd. House ½m past Silent Woman Inn. ⅔-acre plantswoman's garden nestling in Wareham Forest. Lawns punctuated by colourful island beds designed for summer interest. Unusual perennials, shrubs and specimen trees, incl a flowering-size liriodendron. Stone water feature with 2 small ponds connected by tumbling water. Home-made TEAS. Adm £2, chd free. Suns 19 June; 10 July; 21 Aug (2-6). Private visits welcome by appt June, July, Aug, coaches welcome & groups. Tel 01929 553821*

㉛ 11 Greensome Drive, Ferndown 🚻♿

(Ray & Glynis Cook) *¾m from centre of Ferndown. At Trickett's Cross, turn L into Turbary Rd, then 1st R & 2nd L. An interesting cottage* style with good perennials incl hardy geraniums, day lilies, irises and phlox. Delphiniums are our speciality. Rambler roses. Conservatory, small pond with area for moisture-loving plants and island bed featuring dahlias for late summer interest. Front garden has gravel and pebble bed with grasses and a heather bed with spring bulbs and alliums. Winner of Ferndown in Bloom, Gardens That Open for Charity category 2004 & featured in '25 Beautiful Gardens' 2004. Home-made TEAS. *Adm £1.50, chd 50p. Suns 22 May; 19 June (1.30-5). Private visits welcome by appt. Tel 01202 877852*

㉜ Ham Gate, Penny Street, Sturminster Newton 🔿🎗
(Mr & Mrs H E M Barnes) 7½m W of Blandford. 8½m E of Sherborne. Off A357 take turn opp Nat West Bank. Park in car park or down Penny St. Ham Gate at bottom of Penny St. Informal, wildlife-friendly garden, with mature trees, mixed borders and rolling lawns. Tranquil setting beside the R Stour and with distant views over the water meadows. Home-made TEAS in aid of Cancer Research UK. *Adm £2, chd under 17 free. Sun 22 May (2-6)*

㉝ Hazelwood, 19 Hazel Drive, Ferndown 🔿🎗🎗
(Keith & Christine Wilcox) 1m N of Ferndown. Wimborne Rd E, N into Queens Rd at T-lights then L into Beaufoys Ave & immed R into Willow Way. Bottom of hill turn R into Hazel Drive. Plantsman's garden 114ft × 60ft with much to investigate. Varied areas where intense planting of exotics and perennial families grow amongst shrubs and trees, gathered from far and wide. Foliage is important and water is used to create different habitats. Enhanced by the backdrop of a nature reserve, supporting prolific wildlife. A calm and relaxing atmosphere for the visitor. Home-made TEAS in aid of Cat Protection, Bournemouth branch. *Adm £1.50, chd 50p. Suns 12 June; 3, 24 July; 14 Aug (11-5). Private visits welcome by appt. Tel 01202 876497 keithchristine19@fsmail.net*

NEW Heaven's Door, Rimpton 🔿
See Somerset.

㉞ Highwood Garden, Charborough Park 🎗
(H W Drax Esq) 6m E of Bere Regis. Behind long wall. Enter park by any lodge on A31; follow signpost to Estate Office, then Highwood Garden. Large woodland garden with

rhododendrons and azaleas. Unsuitable for wheelchairs. TEAS in aid of local charities. *Adm £3.50, chd £1.50. Suns 22, 29 May (2.30-6)*

㉟ ◆ Hilltop, Woodville, Stour Provost 🎗🎗
(Josse & Brian Emerson) 5m N of Sturminster Newton. On B3092 turn R at Stour Provost Xrds, signed Woodville. After 1¼m thatched cottage on R. Well-established garden overflowing with a wealth of different and interesting perennials. Bold yet complimentary plant combinations in curved and sweeping borders give colourful and truly inspirational display. Relax, take a seat in this peaceful country garden and absorb the tranquility of the Blackmore Vale. Regrettably unsuitable for wheelchairs. Includes small nursery. Featured on ITV Garden Makers 2004. Home-made TEAS (July & Aug). *Adm £1.50, chd free.* **For NGS:** *Thurs 12, 19, 26 May; 2, 9, 16, 23, 30 June; 7, 14, 21, 28 July; Suns 17, 24, 31 July; Thurs 4, 11, 18 Aug; Suns 7, 14, 21 Aug (Thurs 10-6, Suns 2-6). Tel 01747 838512 www.hilltopgarden.co.uk*

㊱ ◆ Holworth Farmhouse, Holworth, nr Owermoigne 🎗🎗
(Anthony & Philippa Bush) 7m E of Dorchester. 1m S of A352. Follow signs to Holworth. Over past 25yrs this unique setting has been transformed into a garden with a range of styles and wide variety of features. Here you have the formal and informal, light and shade, running and still water, places to explore and places for peaceful contemplation. Planted with wide range of mature and unusual trees, shrubs and perennials and surrounded by stunning views. Limited wheelchair access. Featured in 'Dorset' and 'Dorset Life' magazines 2004. Home-made TEAS. *Adm £2.50, chd free. Every Wed 4 May to 7 Sept incl (2-6).* **For NGS:** *Suns 15 May; 5, 26 June; 10, 31 July (2-6). Tel 01305 852242 bushinarcadia@yahoo.co.uk*

㊲ ◆ Horn Park, Beaminster 🔿
(Mr & Mrs David Ashcroft) 1½m N of Beaminster. On A3066, L before tunnel (see signs). Large garden with magnificent view to sea. Partial disabled access. Plantsman's garden, many rare plants and shrubs in terraced, herbaceous, rock and water gardens. Woodland garden and walks in bluebell woods. Good autumn colouring. Wild flower meadow with 164 varieties incl orchids. Home-made TEAS. *Adm £3.50, chd under*

16 free. Tues to Thurs, April to Oct by prior arrangement. **For NGS:** Weds 27 Apr; 22 June (2-5). Tel 01308 862212

Hortus, Shrubbery Bungalow, School Lane, Rousdon 🎗🎗
See Devon.

㊳ Innsacre, Shipton Gorge 🎗
(General Sir Geoffrey & Lady Howlett) 2m E of Bridport, take 1st signed turning to Shipton Gorge & from Dorchester direction take 2nd signed turning. House is 1st on L. Limited parking. A delightful varied garden on a hillside. Formal rose-garden and herbaceous border, slopes to higher level, shrubs and colourful trees. A gateway leads to a spring garden, backdropped by a huge copper beech. Small vegetable garden and orchard. Woodland and deep gorge running whole length of garden. Hilly. Not suitable for wheelchairs. Stout shoes recommended. Home-made TEAS in aid of village church (1 June), Elizabeth Finn Trust (8 June). *Adm £2, chd 50p. Weds 1, 8 June (2-6)*

㊴ ◆ Ivy Cottage, Aller Lane, Ansty 🎗
(Anne & Alan Stevens) 12m N of Dorchester. Ansty is 6m N of Puddletown & 4m W of Milton Abbas. Aller Lane is a turning near the Fox Inn, Ansty. Sparkling little stream runs through this charming cottage garden of 1¾ acres. Plantsman's garden specialising in unusual perennials, moisture-loving plants; specimen trees and shrubs. Many of the plants are grown specially to encourage birds, bees and butterflies to the garden. Well laid out kitchen garden with a mixture of vegetables, fruit and flowers. *Adm £2.75, chd free. Thurs May to Sept incl (10-5).* **For NGS:** *Thurs 5, 12 May; 2, 9 June; 7, 14 July; 4, 11 Aug; 1, 8 Sept (10-5). Open with* **Vine Cottage** *2, 9 June. Tel 01258 880053*

㊵ Ivy House, Piddletrenthide 🎗🎗
(Bridget Bowen) 8m N of Dorchester. On B3143. In middle of Piddletrenthide village, opp PO & near Piddle Inn. Unusual and challenging ½-acre plantsman's garden set on a steep Dorset hillside, with fine views. Mixed borders, wildlife ponds, organic potager and fruit garden. Mediterranean garden planted with grasses and kniphofia and new insect-attractant bank. Featured in 'Dorset Life' magazine 2003. Light refreshments and TEAS (April), Home-made TEAS (May &

June). *Adm £2.50, chd free. Suns 10 Apr (12-4); 1 May; 5 June (2-6)*

㊶ Japanese Gardens, 38 Bingham's Road, Crossways 🅰
(Mr & Mrs Geoffrey Northcote) *6m E of Dorchester. Off Dick O th' Banks Rd, & the B3390. Parking in village.* Two unusual small gardens, designed by owner. Front garden features 'Turtle' island and contrasting yellow/blue borders. 'Sansui' and 'Moon Gate' mural paintings. Rear garden 26ft x 36ft symbolises 'River of Life' with 'Moon Waves' bridge, railed decking, carved red granite features amid contrasting red/green foliage and flower forms. *Adm £2, chd £1. Suns 8 May; 10 July (1-5). Private visits welcome by appt Apr to Sept, max 12 persons. Tel 01305 854538*

㊷ 19 Jessopp Avenue, Bridport
(Mrs M Spurdle) *1m E of Bridport centre. On entering Bridport on A35 from Dorchester turn R into Lee Lane and 2nd L into Jessopp Ave.* Small garden planted informally with wide borders of colour from roses, annuals, herbaceous perennials etc. Cottage garden style. Plant-filled conservatory and patio. Easy walking, good autumn colour. 2nd prize Melplash Small Gardens 2004. Home-made TEAS in aid of Sunnyridge Animal Rescue. *Adm £1.50, chd free. Suns 19 June; 17 July; 25 Sept; Thur 23 June (2-6)*

㊸ ◆ Kingston Lacy, Wimborne Minster 🅰 NCCPG
(The National Trust) *1½m W of Wimborne Minster. On the Wimborne-Blandford rd B3082.* 32-acre garden, 9 acres of lawn, lime avenue, rhododendrons, azaleas and National Collection of convallarias. The parterre in spring is planted with wallflowers and forget-me-nots, in summer with salmon-pink Begonia semperflorens and Heliotropum 'Marine'. Victorian fernery with 25 different types of fern and National Collection of Anemone nemorosa. Roses incl 'Bonica', 'Cardinal Hume', 'Nozomi' and 'Amber Queen'. Light refreshments and TEAS. *House and Garden Adm £8, chd £4, Garden only Adm £4, chd £2. Daily 18 Mar to 30 Oct (10.30-6).* **For NGS:** *Sun 5 June. Tel 01202 883402 kingstonlacy@nationaltrust.org.uk*

㊹ ◆ Kingston Maurward Gardens, Dorchester 🅰 NCCPG
1m E of Dorchester. Off A35. Follow brown Tourist Information signs. National Collections of penstemons and salvias. Classic

Georgian mansion (not open) set in 35 acres of gardens laid out in C18 and C20 with 5-acre lake. Terraces and gardens divided by hedges and stone balustrades. Stone features and interesting plants. Elizabethan walled garden laid out as demonstration. Nature and tree trails. Animal park. Light refreshments and TEAS. *Adm £4, chd £2.50. Open daily 5 Jan to 19 Dec (10-5.30 or dusk if earlier).* **For NGS:** *Sat to Tue, 1 to 4 Jan; Thur to Sat, 22 to 31 Dec (10-dusk). Tel 01305 215003 Ginny Rolls www.kmc.ac.uk/gardens*

㊺ Knitson Old Farmhouse, nr Swanage 🅰
(Rachel & Mark Helfer) *1m W of Swanage. 3m E of Corfe Castle. Signposted L off A351 Knitson. Ample parking in yard or in adjacent field.* Mature cottage garden. Herbaceous borders, rockeries, climbers, shrubs - 40 hostas. Large organic kitchen garden for self-sufficiency in fruit and vegetables incl kiwis! Many Roman and Medieval Purbeck stone artefacts used in garden design, with ancient stone cottage and new moon-arch as backdrops. Cream TEAS in aid of Dorset & Somerset Air Ambulance. *Adm £2, chd 50p, concessions £1.50. Fris to Suns 15 to 17 Apr; 5 to 14 Aug (1-5). Private visits welcome by appt. Tel 01929 422836 mark@knitson.freeserve.co.uk*

㊻ ◆ Knoll Gardens and Nursery, Hampreston 🅰 NCCPG
(Mr Neil Lucas) *2½m W of Ferndown. ETB brown signs from A31. Large car park.* Exciting collection of grasses and perennials thrives within a mature framework of unusual trees, shrubs, waterfalls and pools. Mediterranean-style gravel garden, eye-catching Dragon Garden and exotic Summer Garden. National Collections of Ceanothus (deciduous cultivars), pennisetum and phygelius. Light Refreshments and TEAS. *Adm £4, chd £2.50, concessions £3.50. Weds to Suns 19 Jan to 18 Dec (10-5 or dusk if earlier). Tel 01202 873931 www.knollgardens.co.uk*

㊼ NEW Knowle Farm, Uploders, nr Bridport 🅰
(Alison & John Halliday) *1½m E of Bridport. Leave A35 signposted to Uploders about 2m E of Bridport. Turn back under A35 to reach Uploders. Turn L at T-junction (Crown Inn on L). Knowle Farm is 200yds on R, opp chapel. Careful roadside parking unless using Crown Inn (lunches served).* 1-acre informal valley garden on 3 levels with slopes

and steps bordered by R Asker. Wide variety of interesting plants with extensive new planting around old trees and mature shrubs. Bog garden, rose walk, orchard meadow, riverside walk, kitchen garden, hens. Plantaholics' greenhouse. Limited access for wheelchairs. *Adm £2.50. Tues 10 May; 14, 21 June; 16 Aug (12-6). Private visits welcome by appt. Tel 01308 485492 alison@knowle-farm.fsnet.co.uk*

㊽ 102 Lanehouse Rocks Road, Weymouth 🅰
(Julie Aston & Paul Smith) *Lanehouse Rocks Rd is off Chickerell Rd on W side of Weymouth, N of Wyke Regis. No 102 is on R nr petrol station.* Small town garden with patio area enclosed by specimen palms and agaves. Honeysuckle archway leads to gravelled pond area and waterfall, full of large Koi carp. Borders of geraniums, phormiums and fatsias give an exotic feel, while baskets and containers add a riot of colour. Prize-winner Weymouth in Bloom 2003/4. Home-made TEAS. *Adm £2, chd free. Suns 26 June; 3, 10, 24 July; 7 Aug (11-4). Private visits welcome by appt. Tel 01305 774892 juliepaul@lanehouserocks. freeserve.co.uk*

㊾ Langebride House, Long Bredy 🅰
(Mrs J Greener) *8m W of Dorchester. Between Bridport & Dorchester. S off A35, well signed.* Substantial old rectory garden with many designs for easier management. 200-yr-old beech trees, pleached limes, yew hedges, extensive collections of spring bulbs, herbaceous plants, flowering trees and shrubs. *Adm £3. Thurs 10, 17, 24 Feb; 3, 10, 17, 24 Mar (2-4.30); 26 May (2-5). Private visits welcome by appt. Tel 01308 482257*

㊿ ◆ Larmer Tree Garden, Nr Tollard Royal 🅰
(Rushmore Estate) *10m SE of Shaftesbury. Take B3081 from Shaftesbury up Zig Zag Hill then follow brown flower signs. Or use A354 Salisbury/Blandford rd, follow brown signs.* Victorian pleasure garden built to "enlighten and educate" by philanthropist Augustus Pitt Rivers in 1880. Dell garden contains acid-loving plants, crinodendron, eucryphias, hydrangeas, camellias and rhododendrons. "Quarters" with beautiful shrub beds, many unusual trees and shrubs. Indian buildings, singing theatre, temple and thatched buildings. Featured on Meridian TV Garden Makers 2004. Light

refreshments and TEAS. *Adm £2.50, chd free.* **For NGS:** *Sun 8 May (11-5). Tel 01725 516957 Alan Bird*

51 NEW **Manor Farm, Higher Wraxall** ⊕
(Vianna Dene) *10m NW of Dorchester. From Yeovil take A37 towards Dorchester. 7m turn R signed Evershot. Turn L in Rampisham, 1m turn R - see signs.* ⅔-acre young garden. Exciting colour and plant combinations. Sunken parterre surrounded with old roses and the wildlife pond area sympathetically planted, blending with the stunning W Dorset backdrop. Ongoing projects. Home-made TEAS in aid of Wraxall Church 28 Aug. *Adm £2.50, chd free. Tue 14 June; Sun 28 Aug (2-6). Open with* **Broomhill** *14 June*

Manor Farm, Middle Chinnock ⊗
See Somerset.

The Manor House, Martin, Fordingbridge ⊕⊗⊕
See Hampshire.

52 **Manor Orchard, Stratton** ⊕⊕
(Mr & Mrs G B David) *3m NW of Dorchester. Off A37 to Yeovil, turn into village, gardens signed at church.* 1-acre garden planted for yr-round interest. Spring bulbs, hellebores, herbaceous and shrub borders, lawns, pond, roses, vine. Kitchen garden with pergola, fruit tunnel and topiary. Home-made TEAS in aid of Stratton Church and Village Hall. *Adm £2, chd free. Suns 27 Mar; 19 June; Weds 30 Mar; 22 June (2-5.30)*

53 **Mappercombe Manor, Nettlecombe, Nr Bridport** ⊗⊕
(Lt Cdr William & Mrs Crutchley) *4m NE of Bridport. From A35 at Bridport take A3066 towards Beaminster. Turn R after Gore Cross roundabout, towards Powerstock. Go through West Milton & after bridge bear L. At next junction leave Powerstock on your L and go up hill. Bear R at the Marquis of Lorne PH.* Monks' rest house with stew pond and dovecote. S-facing gardens on 4 levels with ancient monastic route. Approx 4 acres. Apart from stone work and mature trees, garden mostly replanted in last 15 yrs. (Gravel paths). TEAS 12 June only in aid of Powerstock Hut. *Adm £2.50, chd free. Tue 24 May; Sun 12 June (2-5.30).* **Evening Opening** *£2.50, Thur 26 May (5.30-8)*

54 ♦ **Mapperton Gardens, nr Beaminster** ⊕⊗⊕
(The Earl & Countess of Sandwich) *6m N of Bridport. Off A35/A3066. 2m SE of Beaminster off B3163.* Terraced valley gardens surrounding Tudor/Jacobean manor house. On upper levels, walled croquet lawn, orangery and Italianate formal garden with fountains, topiary, grottoes, ponds and herbaceous borders. Below, C17 summerhouse, fishponds, topiary and borders. Lower garden with specimen shrubs and rare trees, leading to woodland and spring gardens. Featured in 'The English Garden', 'Country Life' 2003, 'Gardens Illustrated', 'English Home', 'Country House & Home' 2004. Light refreshments and TEAS at Sawmill Café. *House and Garden Adm £6.50 for groups of 20+, Garden only Adm £4, chd £2, under 5 free. 1 Mar to 31 Oct (2-6). Tel 01308 862645 Anthea Archdale office@mapperton.com*

55 **Mayo Farm, Higher Blandford Road, Shaftesbury** ⊗⊕
(Robin & Trish Porteous) *½m E of Shaftesbury. On B3081 Shaftesbury to Blandford rd on outskirts of Shaftesbury.* 2-acre garden with walled areas, ponds and herbaceous borders which has spectacular views of Melbury Hill and the edge of the Blackmore Vale. Home-made TEAS. *Adm £2, chd free. Sun 29 May; Wed 1 June (2-6)*

56 **Melplash Court, Melplash** ⊕⊕
(Mrs Timothy Lewis) *4m N of Bridport. On A3066, just N of Melplash. Turn W & enter between field gates next to big gates & long ave of chestnut trees.* Gardens, originally designed by Lady Diana Tiarks, continue to evolve and consist of park planting, bog garden, croquet lawn and adjacent borders. Formal kitchen garden and herb garden, ponds, streams and lake; new borders and areas of interest are added and opened up each yr. Cream TEAS in aid of Melplash Church. *Adm £3, chd under 12 free. Sun 22 May; Wed 29 June (2-6)*

57 **Mews Cottage, 34 Easton Street, Portland** ⊗⊕ NCCPG
(Peter & Jill Pitman) *3m S of Weymouth. Situated on top of the Island, 50yds past Punchbowl Inn, small lane on L. Park in main street & follow signs.* Spring sees hellebores, snowdrops and other bulbs. Summer, over 90 named agapanthus grow amongst National Collection of penstemon. New

fernery with fossil collection. Autumn colour is crowned by *Nerine bowdenii*, plus pond with arum lilies with herbaceous planting all in ¼ acre. Limited wheelchair access. Home-made TEAS in aid of St John Ambulance, Portland. *Adm £1.50. Suns 27 Feb; 13 Mar; 8, 22 May; 5, 19 June; 10, 24 July; 7, 21 Aug; 9, 23 Oct (2-5). Open with* **Chesil Gallery** *Suns 19 June; 10, 24 July; 7 Aug. Private visits welcome for groups of 10+, teas if required. Tel 01305 820377 penstemon@waitrose.com*

58 **The Mill House, Crook Hill, Netherbury** ⊕⊕
(Michael & Giustina Ryan) *1m S of Beaminster. Turn R off A3066 Beaminster to Bridport rd at signpost to Netherbury. Car park at Xrds at bottom of hill.* Several small gardens arranged round the Mill, its stream and pond, incl formal walled garden, terraced flower garden and mill stream garden. Emphasis on scented flowers, hardy geraniums, lilies and water irises. The remaining 4 acres of grounds are being developed with a wide variety of recently planted trees: magnolias, acers, oaks, eucalyptus, birches and conifers. Cream TEAS in aid of Netherbury Parish Church. *Adm £2.50, chd free. Sun 15 May; Sat, Sun 11, 12 June (2-6). Private visits welcome by appt for groups. Tel 01308 488267 themillhouse@dial.pipex.com*

59 **Millmead, West Street, Winterborne Stickland** ⊗⊕
(Michele Barker) *4m SW of Blandford Forum. After Crown PH turn R down West St, signed Winterborne Houghton. 1st L after 30mph sign.* This ⅓-acre garden is a showcase for its owner, a talented garden designer. Divided into rooms which belie its sloping nature, the emphasis is on architectural structure, topiary and imaginative planting. Recently extended by a Mediterranean courtyard, it is full of ideas for any gardeners wishing to renovate their own gardens. *Adm £2.50, chd 50p. Sat, Sun 4, 5 June (2-5.30)*

ngs gardens open for charity

Busy at work?
Try our evening openings

60 10 Milner Road, Westbourne, Bournemouth &🌢
(Mr & Mrs Colin Harding) 1½m W of Bournemouth. E of Westbourne on Poole Rd. S at T-lights into Clarendon Rd. Cross over Westcliff Rd into Westovercliff Dr. 1st R, then 1st L and 1st R into Milner Rd. This modern clifftop garden was designed and constructed by Colin Harding in 1986 in a natural style with key formal accents. Variety of spring bulbs amongst a wide range of mature camellias, magnolias and rhododendrons. Natural driftwood sculptures incl driftwood conservatory. Light refreshments and TEAS in aid of SPRING (Support for Parents and Relatives in Neonatal Grief). Adm £2.50, chd 50p. Sun, Mon 1, 2 May (11-5)

61 ◆ Minterne, Minterne Magna
(The Lord Digby) 2m N of Cerne Abbas. On A352 Dorchester-Sherborne rd. Minterne valley, landscaped in C18, home of the Churchill and Digby families for 350yrs. Wild woodland gardens are laid out in a horseshoe below Minterne House, with over 1m of walks, providing a new vista at each turn. Rhododendrons and magnolias tower over small lakes, streams, and cascades. Maples and many rare trees provide spectacular autumn colouring. Adm £4, chd free. Open daily 1 Mar to 10 Nov (10-7). Tel 01300 341370

62 Moigne Combe, nr Crossways, Dorchester &
(Major General H M G Bond) 6m E of Dorchester. 1½m N of Owermoigne. Turn off A352 Dorchester-Wareham rd. Signed from B3390 at Crossways. Medium-sized garden; wild garden and shrubbery, heathers, azaleas, rhododendrons etc. Woodland paths and lake walk. Limited access for wheelchairs. Dogs on leads. Adm £2, chd free. Suns 15, 22 May (2-5). Tel 01305 852265

63 ◆ Moreton Gardens, nr Dorchester &🌢🏠
(Mrs Philippa Hobbs) 7m E of Dorchester. 3m W of Wool. Signed from B3390 & 1m E of Moreton station. Next to Lawrence of Arabia's grave in village of Moreton. A garden recreated in an old setting in the picturesque village of Moreton. 3 acres of lawns, mixed borders, woodland, stream and ponds, bog garden, pergola; summerhouse and fountain. Tearooms in village. Adm £3, chd under 16 free. Daily Mar to Sept (10-5), Oct to Feb (10-4). **For NGS:** Sat, Sun 11, 12 June (10-5).

Tel 01929 405084
www.moretondorset.co.uk

64 4 Noel Road, Wallisdown 🌢
(Lesley & Ivor Pond) 4m NE of Poole. From Wallisdown Xrds enter Kinson Rd. Take 5th rd on R, Kingsbere Ave. Noel Rd is first on R. Small garden, 100ft × 30ft, with big ideas. On sloping ground there are many Roman features incl water features and a temple. Most planting is in containers. "I also like a big element of surprise and you do not get more surprising than a Roman Temple at the end of a suburban garden." 'Amateur Gardening' 2003. Home-made TEAS in aid of Bournemouth Heart Club. Adm £1.50, chd 75p. Suns 26 June; 10 July (2-5)

Oakdene, Sandleheath, Fordingbridge &🌢🏠
See Hampshire.

65 NEW 'Ola', 47 Old Castle Road, Weymouth 🌢🏠
(Jane Uff & Elaine Smith) Rodwell, Weymouth. 1m from Weymouth centre. Follow signs to Portland. Off Buxton Rd, proceed to lower end of Old Castle Rd. Bungalow just past Sandsfoot Castle ruins/gardens. Easy access by foot off Rodwell Trail at Sandsfoot Castle. Seaside garden with stunning views overlooking Portland Harbour. 1930s-designed garden, once part of Sandfoot Castle estate. Mixed herbaceous borders, shrubs and roses. Rockeries, fish pond, vegetables, orchard and "7 dwarfs" bank. Circular sunken stone walled area with box bushes and statuary. Lovingly restored from neglected overgrown "jungle". Home-made TEAS. Adm £1.50, chd 50p. Tues 3, 17, 31 May; 12, 26 July (2-5)

66 The Old Mill, Spetisbury &🌢
(The Rev & Mrs J Hamilton-Brown) 3m SE of Blandford. Spetisbury village opp school on A350. 2 acres water gardens and natural ponds by R Stour; choice trees and plants. Caltha collection. Summer borders, roses, clematis and grasses, potager vegetable garden. Adm £3, chd free. Sun to Wed, 19 to 22 June (2-5)

67 The Old Rectory, Fifehead Magdalen &🏠
(Mrs Patricia Lidsey) 5m S of Gillingham. Just S of A30. Medium-sized garden with interesting shrubs and perennials; pond; grandchildren's garden. Cream TEAS in aid of Fifehead Magdalen Church. Adm £2, chd free. Sun 5 June (2-6). Private

visits welcome by appt. Tel 01258 820293

68 The Old Rectory, Litton Cheney 🏠
(Mr & Mrs Hugh Lindsay) 9m W of Dorchester. 1m S of A35, 6m E of Bridport. Small village in the beautiful Bride Valley. Park in village and follow signs. Steep paths lead to 4 acres of natural woodland with many springs, streams and 2 small lakes; mostly native plants and many primulas (stout shoes recommended). Small walled garden, partly paved, formal layout with informal planting and a prolific quince tree. Wild flower lawn. Some wheelchair access. Home-made TEAS in aid of Red Cross (Easter Sun), St Marys Church, Litton Cheney (May & June). Adm £3, chd free. Suns 27 Mar (2-5); 1 May; Tue 14 June (2-6)

69 The Old Rectory, Netherbury 🌢🏠
(Amanda & Simon Mehigan) 2m SW of Beaminster. Turn off A3066 Beaminster/Bridport rd & go over river Brit, into centre of village & up hill. The Old Rectory is on L opp church. Parking available in Millhouse field. Garden of approx 5 acres incl formal courtyard, bog garden with stream and pond, vegetable garden, wild flower areas and orchards featuring spring bulbs, hellebores, bog primulas and irises. Many mature broadleaved trees incl massive ginkgo. TEAS. Adm £3, chd free. Suns 27 Mar; 24 Apr; 15 May; 12 June; 3 July (2-6)

70 The Old Rectory, Pulham &🏠
(Mr & Mrs N Elliott) 13m N of Dorchester. 8m SE of Sherborne. On B3143 turn E at Xrds in Pulham. 3 acres of formal and informal gardens around fine C18 rectory with superb views to Bulbarrow. Yew hedges enclose circular herbaceous borders. Mature trees and shrubs. Restored pond with waterfall. Exuberantly planted terrace and terrace beds. Formal box parterres. Pots, roses, clematis, lawns, ha-ha. Two 5-acre woods and shrubbery with mown rides. Home-made TEAS in aid of Pulham Church. Adm £2.50, chd free. Sun 31 July (2-6). Private visits welcome by appt weekends only. Tel 01258 817595

71 NEW 54 Parkwood Road, Bournemouth &🌢🏠
(Mr & Mrs Andrew Rickett) 3m E of Bournemouth. Turn S off Christchurch Rd between Boscombe and Pokesdown Station. Small town garden, approx 30ft x 120 ft, planted

out 3yrs ago by enthusiastic first time gardeners. Herbaceous perennials and shrubs with mature trees, small pond and lawn give the garden a natural, relaxed atmosphere. Contrasting areas of moisture, shade and dryness. Illuminated garden with live piano music for evening openings. Home-made TEAS. *Adm £1.50, chd free. Suns 24 Apr; 15 May; 31 July (2-5).* **Evening Openings** *£2, wine, Sat 7 May; Fri 5 Aug (7.30-9.30)*

72 Pear Tree Farm, Loscombe, Melplash
(Major & Mrs J L Poë) *3½m N of Bridport. 3m S of Beaminster, turn off A3066 in Melplash opp The Half Moon PH. After approx ½m take R fork signed Loscombe, approx 1m turn L at T-junction up cul-de-sac for 250yds, turn L into yard (avoid 2 entrances to 1st house on L). ½-acre garden designed to harmonise with the beauty of the surrounding landscape. Developed over the last 14yrs, features a number of small rooms all differing in style and composition, packed with many unusual plants and climbers on tripods and archways. Conservatory with many tender plants. 2 small ponds with running water and wildflower area. Plant sale 24 May. Adm £2, chd under 14 free. Tues 10, 24 May; 14, 28 June (2-6). Private visits welcome by appt. Tel 01308 488223 poe@loscombe. freeserve.co.uk*

73 Rampisham Manor, Rampisham 🅱️😊
(Mr & Mrs Boileau) *11m NW of Dorchester. From Yeovil take A37 towards Dorchester, 7m turn R signed Evershot. From Dorchester take A37 to Yeovil, 4m turn L A356 signed Crewkerne; at start of wireless masts R to Rampisham. Follow signs. 3-acre garden. Mixture of formal and flowing planting with emphasis on colour combinations and plant families; water and young woodland garden in a peaceful and lovely rural setting. Many spring bulbs incl species tulips. Home-made TEAS 4 May & 1 June. Cream Teas 10 July in aid of St Michael & All Angels Church. Adm £2.50, chd free. Wed 4 May (2-5); Wed 1 June (2-6); Sun 17 July (2-5). Open with* **Broomhill** *1 June,* **Corscombe House** *17 July. Private visits welcome by appt. Tel 01935 83612 harriet@cubbins. co.uk*

74 The Red House, Daggons Road, Alderholt 🅱️😊
(Mr David Peck) *½m W of Alderholt. Cranborne-Fordingbridge rd*

(B3078). ¼m W of Churchill Arms. Limited parking in drive for disabled only, otherwise at the Churchill Arms. 1¾-acre garden devoted to mature collections of magnolias, camellias and rhododendrons mainly planted over the last 20yrs. Camellia reticulata hybrids not widely grown in the UK are of particular interest. Many wild daffodils in wide grassed areas. TEAS in aid of Alderholt Youth Assoc. Adm £2.50, chd 0.50, concessions £1. Suns 27 Mar; 3, 17 Apr (2-5). Also open **Ashley Park Farm** *27 Mar*

75 357 Ringwood Road, Ferndown 🅱️😊
(Lyn & Malcolm Ovens) *¾m S of Ferndown. On A348 towards Longham. Parking in nearby side roads. Compact 100ft × 30ft colourful garden which has evolved over the past 9yrs. Front planted with selection of perennials, lillies and 95 different clematis in a cottage style to give colour until late summer. Arched doorway leads to an enclosed, part Mediterranean, area containing cannas, gazania, brugmansia, oleander etc. Water features and numerous pots and containers. Conservatory with bougainvillea, small aviary. 'A garden that is loved, and it shows'. Overall winner Ferndown in Bloom 2003, 'Gorgeous Gardens' feature 2004. Home-made TEAS. Adm £1.50, chd 50p. Suns 17 July; 14 Aug (2-5). Private visits welcome by appt late June to early Sept only. Tel 01202 896071 www.mgovens.freeserve.co.uk*

76 46 Roslin Road South, Talbot Woods 🅱️😊
(Dr & Mrs Malcolm Slade) *1m NW of Bournemouth. W of N and of Glenferness Ave in Talbot Woods area of Bournemouth. Plantswoman's ⅔-acre walled town garden planted with many unusual and rare plants. Sunken gravel garden with collection of grasses, surrounded by colourful mixed borders. Features incl many well planted containers, raised octagonal alpine bed, rose pergola leading to enclosed patio, cutting beds and fruit cage, greenhouses and frames. Partially accessible for wheelchairs. Home-made TEAS. Adm £2, chd free. Sun 24 Apr (2-5). Also open with* **Talbot Woods Gardens** *22 May; 19 June; 14 July. Private visits welcome by appt. Tel 01202 510243*

Sandle Cottage, Sandleheath 🅱️😊
See Hampshire.

77 Saulfland Lodge, 254 Smugglers Lane North, Highcliffe 🅱️😊
(Miss Pauline Chard) *2m E of Christchurch. Drive SE from Somerford roundabout on Highcliffe Rd then L at 1st roundabout into Hoburne Lane. Garden is on corner of Saulfland Dr, Smugglers Lane North and Hoburne Lane. A town garden containing plant-packed borders surrounding lawns, pond and small wooded walk. Summerhouse and quiet area. Created over several years as a haven for owner and abundant wildlife, with the vision of Isaiah in mind. "For behold I create new heavens and a new earth. They shall not hurt nor destroy". A garden of peace and tranquility for all. Cream TEAS. Adm £2. Sats 4, 25 June; 16 July (11-4). Private visits welcome by appt May, June & July, coaches permitted. Tel 01425 275760 pmcatsaulfland@aol.com*

78 The Scented Garden, Littlebredy 🅱️😊
(Chris & Judy Yates) *8m W of Dorchester. 10m E of Bridport. 1½m S of A35. Park on Littlebredy village green by round bus shelter. 400yd walk to garden (not ideal for the disabled or small children). Steeply-sloping S-facing 1-acre Victorian walled garden, in tranquil setting, being lovingly restored. Abundance of old roses and stately delphiniums. Colour-themed beds and borders, which contain many unusual plants. Collections of lavender (over 100), hardy geraniums, shade border with many hostas, 'hot' garden and grassery. Adm £2, chd 50p (share to Littlebredy Church).* **Day & Evening openings** *Tues 7, 14, 21, 28 June; 5, 12, 19, 26 July (2.30-8)*

79 The Secret Garden, The Friary, Hilfield 🅱️
(The Society of St Francis) *10m N of Dorchester. On A352. 1st L after village, 1st turning on R signed The Friary. From Yeovil turn off A37 signed Batcombe, 3rd turning on L. Small woodland garden begun in 1950s then neglected. Reclamation began in 1984. New plantings added in 1998-1999, bamboo in 2004. Mature trees, rhododendrons, azaleas, magnolias, camellias (some camellias grown from seed collected in China), other choice shrubs with a stream on all sides crossed by bridges. Stout shoes recommended. Home-made TEAS. Adm £2.50, chd free. Thur to Sun, 12 to 15 May (2-5). Private visits welcome by appt. Tel 01300 341345*

⑧⓪ The Secret Garden at Serles House, 47 Victoria Road, Wimborne
(Ian Willis) *On B3802 W of town, very near hospital, Westfield car park is about 300yds away. Off-road parking close by.* Regarded locally and by visiting media as 'A masterpiece of an eccentric' this unconventional garden offers delight and surprise. A mystical Anglo-Indian conservatory leads into a riot of fantasy, meticulous in detail, with water features; rill, folly, shell grotto and jubilee obelisk all complemented by original planting designed for summer interest. Featured in 'Dorset' magazine 2003, 'Garden Answers' & Meridian TV's The Garden Makers, 2004. 1st prize Wimborne in Bloom 'Best Garden Open to the Public' 2004. *Adm £1.50, chd free (share to The Wimborne Civic Society). Suns 3, 17, 31 July; 14 Aug; Sun, Mon 28, 29 Aug (2.30-5.30). Also open* **Galpin Cottage, Tarrant Keyneston** *28, 29 Aug. Private visits welcome by appt. Tel 01202 880430*

⑧① ◆ Sherborne Castle, Sherborne &
(Mr J K Wingfield Digby) *½m E of Sherborne. Follow brown signs to 'Sherborne Castles' from A30 & A352.* 20+ acres. A Capability Brown garden with magnificent vistas across the surrounding landscape, incl lake and fine ruined castle. Herbaceous planting, notable trees, a mixture of ornamental planting and managed wilderness are all linked together with lawn and pathways providing colour and interest throughout the seasons. New 'Dry Grounds Walk' for spring 2005. Light refreshments and TEAS. *Castle and Garden Adm £7.50, OAPs £7, chd free, Garden only Adm £3.50, chd free. Open daily except Mons (open BH Mons) and Fris, 22 Mar to 30 Oct (11-4.30 (last entry)). Sats only, Castle opens 2.30. Tel 01935 813182 www.sherbornecastle.com*

⑧② Slape Manor, Netherbury &⊛
(Mr & Mrs Antony Hichens) *1m S of Beaminster. Turn W off A3066 to village of Netherbury. House ½m S of Netherbury on back rd to Bridport.* River valley garden, extensive lawns, streams and lake. Azaleas, rhododendrons, large clump *Phyllostachys nigra* 'Boryana' and specimen trees. Home-made TEAS. *Adm £3, chd under 12 free. Sun 22 May (2-6)*

⑧③ ◆ Snape Cottage, Chaffeymoor ⊛⊛
(Ian & Angela Whinfield) *5m NW of Gillingham. At W end of Bourton. Opp Chiffchaffs.* Plantsman's country garden full of old-fashioned and uncommon perennials, clearly labelled. Organically managed and planted for yr-round interest with large collections of snowdrops, hellebores, 'old' daffodils, pulmonarias, auriculas, geraniums, dianthus, irises and asters. Special emphasis on plant history and nature conservation. Beautiful views, wildlife pond. Redesigned borders for 2005. TEAS. *Adm £2.50. Last 2 Suns in each month Feb to Sept incl; every Thur May to Aug incl (10.30-5). For* **NGS:** *Sun 20 Mar; 29 May (10.30-5). Tel 01747 840330 (evenings) www.snapestakes.com*

⑧④ Stanbridge Mill, nr Gussage All Saints &⊛⊛
(Mr James Fairfax) *7m N of Wimborne. On B3078 to Cranborne 150yds from Horton Inn on Shaftesbury rd.* Hidden garden created in 1990s around C18 water mill (not open) on R Allen. Series of linked formal gardens featuring herbaceous and iris borders, pleached limes, white walk, wisteria-clad pergola, prairie planting and grass maze. 20-acre nature reserve with reed beds and established shelter belts. Grazing meadows with wild flowers and flock of Dorset Horn sheep. NGS and NCCPG plant stalls and local nursery. TEAS in aid of local School of Chaos charity. *Adm £4, chd 50p. Wed 8 June (10.30-6)*

⑧⑤ ◆ Stapehill Abbey, Ferndown &⊛⊛
(Mr & Mrs John Pickard, Garden Managers) *2½m W of Ferndown. On the old A31, towards Wimborne, ½m E of Canford Bottom roundabout.* Early C19 abbey set amidst a walled garden. Herbaceous borders, rose garden and arbours, wisteria and laburnum walk, cottage garden, water features, rockery and lake, hot house and stunning Japanese garden. Lots of rare and unusual plants, a true gardener's paradise. Light refreshments and TEAS. *Adm £7.50, chd £4.50, concessions £7. Daily Apr to Sept (10-5), Weds to Suns Oct to Mar (10-4), closed 22 Dec to 31 Jan. Tel 01202 861686*

⑧⑥ ◆ Sticky Wicket, Buckland Newton &⊛⊛
(Mrs P Lewis) *11m N of Dorchester. 9m S of Sherborne. 3m E of A352 or take B3143 from Sturminster Newton. T-junction midway church,*

school & 300yds from Gaggle of Geese PH. Created since 1986, the garden is designed and planted as a haven for wildlife. Wandering through the 3 acres of gardens and meadows is a delightful experience and opportunity for both naturalist and plantsman to enjoy the colour-blended mingling of ornamental and edible plants with wild flowers and grasses. Featured in many national magazines and books 2003/2004. Home-made TEAS on NGS days. *Adm £3.50, chd £1.50. Thurs/Fris 1 June to 30 Sept incl (10.30-8). For* **NGS:** *Suns 19 June; 21 Aug (2-8). Tel 01300 345476 www.stickywicketgarden.co.uk*

◆ Stourhead Garden, Stourton &⊛
See Wiltshire.

⑧⑦ NEW Talbot Woods Gardens, Talbot Woods, Bournemouth
1m NW of centre of Bournemouth. W of N end of Glenferness Ave. Well treed 'Garden Suburb' laid out among pines and heathland species suited to the light sandy soil. Home-made TEAS at 80 Keith Road Suns, 46 Roslin Road South Thur. *Combined adm £5, chd free. Suns 22 May; 19 June; Thur 14 July (2-5)*
74 Keith Road ⊛ (Mr J Dustan) Suburban cottage-style garden of ¼ acre, consisting of mixed borders of annuals, perennials, shrubs and fruit. Features incl pond, arches, lawn, summerhouse, and productive greenhouse. Many climbing plants and new features incl gazebo.
80 Keith Road ⊛ (Mr Howard Ffitch) Enclosed ¼-acre town garden. Lower garden laid out around two vistas in yellow, pink, mauve and white. Main vista leads to Italian-inspired formal upper garden which in turn leads to summerhouse garden.
NEW 46 Roslin Road South &⊛⊛ (Dr & Mrs Malcolm Slade) (see separate entry).

⑧⑧ Throop Mill Cottage, Throop Road, Throop &
(Dr & Mrs James Fisher) *3m N of Bournemouth town centre. Turn N at the Broadway roundabout on the A3060 Wimborne to Christchurch rd (Castle Lane). At a mini roundabout in ½m turn R into Taylor Dr. The car park is at the point Taylor Dr joins Throop Rd.* Though only an acre of riverside garden, the use of devices usually associated with C18

landscape gardens makes it look far larger. A ha-ha keeps horses out and extends the view. An obelisk stands on a mound. Riverside walk and valley with collection of ferns. Home-made TEAS. *Adm £2, chd 50p. Tue 22 Mar (2-4); Thur 16 June (2-5.30). Private visits welcome by appt. Tel 01202 515781 james.f.fisher@talk21.com*

89 Tithe Barn House, Chalk Pit Lane, Litton Cheney 🌣🚻♿
(Letizia & Antony Longland) *10m W of Dorchester. 1m S of A35. Small village in beautiful Bride Valley. Follow signs in centre of village. Park on verge.* Just over an acre plus paddock. Wonderful views of almost the entire Bride Valley. Garden being restored and enhanced since 2000. Trees, shrubs, incl good roses, climbers and herbaceous plants, many pots, reflecting pool. TEAS in aid of Marie Curie Cancer Care. *Adm £2.50, chd free. Sun 19 June (2-6). Private visits welcome by appt for groups of 10+. Tel 01308 482219*

90 ◆ Toad Hall, The Cross, Shillingstone ♿🚻
(Elizabeth Arden & Norman Rogerson) *5m NW of Blandford. On A357. Drive is opp Old Village Cross on highest point of village. Parking in village.* Plantsman's country garden still developing. 1-acre on S-facing slope with wonderful views. Several different styled areas and growing habitats. Gardens incl Italian, decking, water, rockery, vegetable and wild. New area experimenting with different types of annual meadow and grass beds. Home-made TEAS NGS days & groups by appt. *Adm £2.50, chd 50p, under 5 free. Thurs May - Aug (2-5).* **For NGS:** *Suns 29 May; 10 July; 28 Aug (2-6). Tel 01258 861941 www.toadhalluk.co.uk*

91 Toad Hill and L'Horizon, Bridport
From Bridport, go N on A3066 for ½m, L into St Andrews Rd, R into Coneygar Rd, R into St Katherines Ave. Considerate parking in the ave. On edge of Bridport, two adjacent and quite contrasting gardens. Home-made TEAS in aid of Bridport League of Hospital Friends. *Combined adm £2.50, chd free.* Suns 10, 17 July; Thur 14 July (2-6)

L'Horizon, 43 St Katherines Avenue 🌣 (Jenny & Patrick Pleasance) A tranquil oasis of upward rolling grass with delightful, informal, well-established mixed borders, central rockery and large pond.

Peaceful, a place for comtemplation and relaxation. Lovingly worked and cared for over 16 yrs.

Toad Hill, 45 St Katherines Avenue, Bridport 🌣🚻 (Peter & Brenda Rushen) ⅓- acre lush paradise with a taste for the exotic, created entirely by the owners. The front is cottage whilst the rear terraced on 7 levels has Japanese, herbaceous, wildlife with ponds, herbs and subtropical. Finalist BBC Gardeners' World Gardener of the Year Competition, 2003. Featured in 'Gardeners' World' magazine 2004. *Private visits welcome by appt July only. Tel 01308 421726 peter-rushen@beeb.net*

92 ◆ Upwey Wishing Well, 161 Church Street, Upwey ♿🌣🚻
(Mr & Mrs Gordon Miners) *3m N of Weymouth. On B3159 & just off Dorchester to Weymouth rd (A354).* A tranquil, well-stocked water garden. Large natural spring, which is the source of the R Wey, is known as the Wishing Well and is an ancient monument. A fine show of bog primulas in May/June. Huge gunneras and unusual foliage plants provide a unique and exotic setting. Light refreshments and TEAS. *Entrance through café, adm free, but donations welcomed for National Gardens Scheme charities. Open daily (10-5) 1 Apr to 30 Sept, closed Mons Oct to Mar. Tel 01305 814470*

93 Vine Cottage, Melcombe Bingham
(Wendy & Robert Jackson) *11m NE of Dorchester. Melcombe Bingham is 5m N of Puddletown and 5m W of Milton Abbas. Vine Cottage is in centre of village and just ¼m past Fox Inn.* Compact, well-stocked cottage garden with a wealth of interesting and unusual perennials and numerous containers. Specific areas incl patios, pergola, arch trelliswork that host many roses and clematis, plus alpine-planted sink gardens. Emphasis on imaginative use of colour. Partially accessible for wheelchairs. Featured in '25 Beautiful Gardens' 2004. Light refreshments and TEAS. *Adm £2.50, chd free. Thurs 2, 9, 16, 23 June (11-5). Open with Ivy Cottage 2, 9 June*

Waterdale House, East Knoyle 🚻
See Wiltshire.

Wayford Manor, Crewkerne 🚻
See Somerset.

94 Welcome Thatch, Witchampton 🌣🚻
(Mrs Diana Guy) *3½m N of Wimborne. B3078 L to Witchampton, thence through village past church & shop to last but one on R. Parking available in club car park, otherwise on road beyond the cottage.* Created around a listed thatched cottage (not open) as a cottage garden for the C21 combining traditional with modern planting. Dry river bed border, decking with pots of exotics, stream and pool, potager, oriential-style area, wildlife pond and prairie garden. Unusual plants, hellebores. BBC Gardener of The Year Winner 2004. Featured on Meridian TV's Garden Makers, 2004 & How to be a Gardener Part 2, 2003. Featured in 'Gardens Monthly' & 'Dorset Country Gardener' 2004 & 'Gardeners' World' magazine 2005. TEAS in aid of PALS Pre School, 19 Feb, at and in aid of Village Hall 3 Apr. TEAS in aid of NGS on other days. *Adm £2, chd free. Sat, Sun 19, 20 Feb (1-4), Hellebore w/e; Suns 6 Mar; 3 Apr; 8 May; 3 July (2-5.30). Also open Fernhill House Sun 3 Apr. Private visits welcome by appt March - July. Tel 01258 840894 diana.welcomethatch@btopenworld.com*

95 Wentworth College, College Road, Bournemouth
(The Bursar) *3m E of Bournemouth. Turn N from Boscombe Overcliff Drive into Woodland Ave. Then 1st R into College Rd.* Originally the seaside estate of Lord Portman, Wentworth Lodge was built in 1872. The main Victorian house has gradually been extended to accommodate the needs of Wentworth College. Formal gardens have been restored to reflect their origins. The grounds also incl woodland with mature specimen trees and rhododendrons in approx 3 acres. Home-made TEAS. *Adm £2.50, chd free. Suns 24 Apr; 18 Sept (2-5)*

96 24a Western Avenue, Branksome Park, Poole 🌣
(Mr & Mrs Peter Jackson) *3m W of Bournemouth. Central in Branksome Park, ½m from Compton Acres.* Perhaps best summarized in National and Regional media comments: "A gold mine of a garden - you'll be inspired", "The world changes from leafy suburb to pure Mediterranean". Award-winning 1-acre garden offering the widest variety of design and planting. The woodland (camellias, cherries, hostas) is at its

best in May. The Italian courtyard, wall garden and subtropical planting peak in Aug. Rose garden, topiary, wood sculpture. *Adm £2.50, chd free. Suns 1 May; 21 Aug (2-6). Private visits welcome by appt May & Aug only. Tel 01202 708388*

97 Weston House, Buckhorn Weston 🔲🐕⊕
(Mr & Mrs E A W Bullock) *4m W of Gillingham. 4m SE of Wincanton. From A30 turn N to Kington Magna, continue towards Buckhorn Weston & after railway bridge take L turn towards Wincanton. 2nd on L is Weston House.* 1-acre partly walled garden with mixed borders, clematis, climbing roses and about 850 old and new varieties. Unusual trees. Shade-loving plants and ferns beyond plus wildlife and flower meadow with natural pond. Small orchard with roses and ornamental grasses. Lawns frame views of the Blackmore Vale. Featured in 'The Times', 2004. Light refreshments and TEAS by arrangement. *Adm £2.50, chd free. Private visits welcome by appt May, June, July, Sept incl groups and coaches. Tel 01963 371005*

White Barn, Woodend Road, Crow Hill, Ringwood 🔲🐕⊕
See Hampshire.

98 Windy Willums, 38 Island View Avenue, Christchurch 🐕⊕
(Mrs J King) *6m E of Bournemouth. From A35 Somerford roundabout, take A337 for Highcliffe. At next roundabout take last exit (Runway). 2nd L after Sandpiper PH. Car park 100yds past garden.* A peaceful haven close to the sea. ½-acre garden divided into 3 rooms, each with its own colour theme and naturalistic planting. Large collection of roses and clematis, unusual and scented perennials and shrubs within formal boundaries of yew hedging. Gravel garden where plants are left to self-seed. Wild but tamed. Places to sit and ponder. Finalist BBC Gardener of the Year 2003. Featured in 'Gardeners' World' 2004. TEAS. *Adm £2, chd 50p. Suns 5, 12 June, Tue 7 June (2-5)*

99 Wolverhollow, Elsdons Lane, Monkton Wyld 🐕⊕
(Mr & Mrs D Wiscombe) *4m N of Lyme Regis. 4m NW of Charmouth. Monkton Wyld is signposted from A35 approx 4m NW of Charmouth*

off dual carriageway. Wolverhollow is next to the church. ¾-acre of informal garden on different levels (some uneven surfaces). Borders, rockeries, bog gardens and shrubs. Woodland area leads to steep-sided stream. Wide range of plants. TEAS in aid of RSPCA. *Adm £2, chd 50p. Suns, Tues 8, 10 May; 12, 14 June (11-5). Private visits welcome by appt. Tel 01297 560610*

Woodside, East Stoke, Stoke-sub-Hamdon 🔲⊕
See Somerset.

Evening Opening (See also garden description)	
54 Parkwood Road	7 May
Mappercombe Manor	
	26 May
The Scented Garden	7 June
The Scented Garden	14 June
The Scented Garden	21 June
The Scented Garden	28 June
The Scented Garden	5 July
The Scented Garden	12 July
The Scented Garden	19 July
The Scented Garden	26 July
54 Parkwood Road	5 August
Bracken Cottage and The Ferns	28 August

THE ROYAL GARDENERS' ORPHAN FUND

The RGOF has been helping the orphaned children of professional horticulturists since 1887. In 1985, the scope of the Fund was broadened. Now all the children in need, whose parents are employed in horticulture, may qualify for assistance. The RGOF gives quarterly allowances to orphaned children, and grants to those in need for school expenses, winter clothing, bedding and holidays.

The donation our Fund receives each year from The National Gardens Scheme is invaluable in enabling the continuation of our work.

For more information about the RGOF, please contact the Secretary,
Mrs Kate Wallis
14 Scholars Mews, Welwyn Garden City,
Hertfordshire AL8 7JQ
Tel/Fax: 01707 333663
email: rgof@btopenworld.com
web: www.rgof.org.uk

County Durham

County Organiser:	Mrs Elizabeth Carrick, Green House, Stone Man Lane, Gayles, nr Richmond, North Yorkshire DL11 7JB Tel 01833 621199
Assistant County Organiser:	Mrs Shanah Smailes, The Stables, Chapman's Court, Catterick Village, North Yorkshire DL10 7UE Tel 01748 812887

Maps: Numbers shown next to each garden entry refer to that garden's entry on the county map. This position is approximate; distance and directions from the nearest main town are generally shown in the garden text.
A precise location is available for those gardens featured on the NGS website by visiting www.ngs.org.uk.

Symbols: Information relating to symbols is given on page 21

DATES OF OPENING

Evening openings
See end of county listing

Gardens open to the public
For details see garden description
Raby Castle, Staindrop *(13)*

April 24 Sunday
The Old Vicarage, Hutton Magna *(11)*

May 15 Sunday
Croft Hall, Croft-on-Tees *(7)*

May 29 Sunday
Polemonium Plantery, Trimdon Grange *(12)*

May 30 Monday (Bank Hol)
Polemonium Plantery, Trimdon Grange *(12)*

June 12 Sunday
Thorpe Gardens, Thorpe *(16)*

June 19 Sunday
Bleach Green Farm, Durham *(4)*

June 26 Sunday
Thornton Hall, Darlington *(15)*
Westholme Hall, Winston *(17)*

July 3 Sunday
Ashes House, Stanhope *(1)*

July 10 Sunday
Barningham Village Gardens *(2)*
12 & 13 Durham Road, Middle Herrington, Sunderland *(8)*
Low Walworth Hall, Darlington *(9)*
The Old Vicarage, Bolam, Darlington *(10)*

July 17 Sunday
Bedburn Hall, Hamsterley *(3)*
Cotherstone Village Gardens *(6)*

July 24 Sunday
Ravensford Farm, Hamsterley, Bishop Auckland *(14)*

August 7 Sunday
Browside, Boldron, Barnard Castle *(5)*

August 28 Sunday
Polemonium Plantery, Trimdon Grange *(12)*

August 29 Monday (Bank Hol)
Polemonium Plantery, Trimdon Grange *(12)*

DESCRIPTIONS OF GARDENS

❶ Ashes House, Stanhope ♿✂
(Mr & Mrs R Bibby) ½m N of Stanhope on B6278. 20m W of Durham. At W end of Stanhope turn R at Grey Bull PH onto B6278 towards Edmundbyers. Entrance to garden ½m up hill on R. S-facing 1-acre country garden featuring long herbaceous border backed by high stone walls, sloping lawns and outstanding views. Rose bed recently restocked with old English roses; shrubberies; wide variety of espalier and standard fruit trees. Traditional vegetable garden; greenhouse and conservatory with orchids and collection of semi-tropical plants. Home-made TEAS. *Adm £2.50, chd free (share to Weardale branch of MS Society & S Durham Healthcare NHS Trust Children's Diabetes Trust Fund). Sun 3 July (2-6)*

❷ NEW Barningham Village Gardens ♿✂
6m SE of Barnard Castle. 9m W of Scotch Corner turn S off A66 at Greta Bridge, or from A66 motel via Newsham. Quaint moorland village in conservation area. Approx 6-8 gardens open incl rarely-opened plantsman's garden. Partial wheelchair access. Home-made TEAS in Village Hall. *Adm £3, chd free. Sun 10 July (2-5.30)*

❸ Bedburn Hall, Hamsterley ♿✂
(I G Bonas) 9m NW of Bishop Auckland. From A68 at Witton-le-Wear, turn off W to Hamsterley; turn N from Hamsterley to Bedburn, 1m. From Wolsingham on B6293 turn off SE for 3m. Medium-sized S-facing terraced garden with large conservatory and greenhouse, lake, streams, woodland, lawns. Fuchsia collection and lavender bed, herbaceous border, fruit cage and rose garden. Home-made TEAS. *Adm £3, chd free (share to St James*

Church, Hamsterley). Sun 17 July (2-6). Private visits welcome by appt June, July & Aug. Tel 01388 488231

❹ Bleach Green Farm, Durham ✂
(John & Helen Charlton) 3m SW of Durham. Take A690 towards Crook & turn at Lord Boyne PH. Approx 1m pass large white farmhouse on R. 100yds drive on R through fields. Young 1-acre garden set around restored C18 farmhouse (not open). Series of themed interlocking gardens: seaside border, ornamental pond, orchard, summerhouse, yellow and white garden, herb and vegetable gardens. Poultry, unusual sculptures and structures. Additional woodland area. Featured in 'Exclusive' magazine 2004. Home-made TEAS in aid of Breakthrough Breast Cancer. *Adm £2.50, chd free. Sun 19 June (2-5.30)*

❺ Browside, Boldron, Barnard Castle ♿✂
(Mr & Mrs R D Kearton) 3m S of Barnard Castle. On A66 3m W of Greta Bridge, turn R to Boldron, then proceed ½m, entrance opp junction. From Barnard Castle take A67 to Bowes, after 2m turn L to Boldron. 1¼ acres with unusual water features and large collection of conifers, wide range of plants and imaginative stone objects. Home-made TEAS. *Adm £2.50, chd free. Sun 7 Aug (1-5.30)*

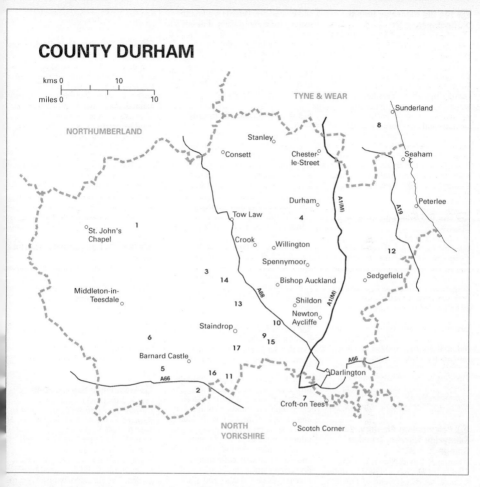

COUNTY DURHAM

kms 0   10

miles 0   10

NORTHUMBERLAND

TYNE & WEAR

Sunderland

Stanley

Consett

Chester-le-Street

Seaham

Durham

Peterlee

Tow Law

St. John's Chapel

Crook

Willington

Spennymoor

Bishop Auckland

Sedgefield

Middleton-in-Teesdale

Shildon

Newton Aycliffe

Staindrop

Barnard Castle

A66

Darlington

Croft-on Tees

NORTH YORKSHIRE

Scotch Corner

---

6 **NEW** **Cotherstone Village Gardens** ♿✿
4m NW of Barnard Castle. On B6277 Middleton-in-Teesdale rd. Picturesque Teesdale village at the confluence of rivers Tees and Balder. 13+ gardens incl allotments. Partial wheelchair access. Home-made TEAS in Village Hall. *Adm £3, chd free. Sun 17 July (2-5.30)*

7 **Croft Hall, Croft-on-Tees** ♿✿
(Mr & Mrs Trevor Chaytor Norris) *3m S of Darlington. On A167 to Northallerton, 6m from Scotch Corner. Croft Hall is 1st house on R as you enter village from Scotch Corner.* Mature garden of 5 acres comprising specimen trees (tulip trees, oak species, acers), cut and topiary yew hedging, box parterre, rose borders, herbaceous borders,

pond and bog garden. Soft, top fruit and vegetables. Home-made TEAS. *Adm £3, chd 50p. Sun 15 May (2-6)*

8 **12 & 13 Durham Road, Middle Herrington, Sunderland** ♿✿✿
(Mr R F Heron & Mr & Mrs A C Winfield) *3½m SW of Sunderland city centre on A690. From A19/A690 junction take rd towards city centre. After 1st roundabout gardens 150yds on L on main rd. From city centre take A690. 150yds before Board Inn roundabout turn R into St Chad's Rd. Entrance to gardens on St Chad's Rd, please park with consideration for residents' access.* Two extensive mature gardens with a fine display of roses and perennials in borders. Interesting specimen trees incl eucalyptus and abutilon; Elizabethan knot garden and unusual plants. Greenhouse display of fuchsia,

pelargonium and streptocarpus. Home-made TEAS in aid of St Benedict's Hospice. *Adm £2.50, chd free. Sun 10 July (2-5.30)*

9 **Low Walworth Hall, Darlington** ♿✿
(Mr & Mrs Worrall) *3½m NW of Darlington. On B6279 Staindrop rd (½m drive).* Old walled garden; herbaceous borders, shrubs, roses; formal and wildlife ponds. Japanese and Zen gardens. Millennium fantasy garden and secret garden. Fruit and vegetable gardens. Tree walk. New for 2005 - African theme garden. Home-made TEAS. *Adm £3, chd free. Sun 10 July (2-5). Private visits welcome by appt. Tel 01325 468004 vanessaworrall@hotmail.com*

⓿ The Old Vicarage, Bolam, Darlington ⟨&⟩⟨⌀⟩⟨☺⟩
(Dr & Mrs Geoffrey Marsh) *12m W of Darlington. B6275 (Deere Street) Piercebridge/Royal Oak rd. Turn W at Leggs Cross Xrds, ½m to village.* The garden at the home of Jean and Geoffrey Marsh is on an open S-facing slope above Teesdale with views. A large collection of plants, particularly a fine collection of clematis and two borders of old roses. There are delphiniums and peonies, lilies and lavender, and some unusual plants. The village of Bolam is very small and totally unspoilt. Light refreshments and TEAS at the Countryman Inn. *Adm £2, chd free. Sun 10 July (2-5)*

⓫ The Old Vicarage, Hutton Magna ⟨⌀⟩⟨☺⟩
(Mr & Mrs D M Raw) *8m SE of Barnard Castle. 6m W of Scotch Corner on A66, Penrith direction. Signed Hutton Magna R. Continue to, and through, village. Garden 200yds past village on L, on corner of T-junction.* S-facing garden, elevation 450ft. Plantings, since 1978, now maturing within original design contemporary to 1887 house (not open). Cut and topiary hedging, old orchard; rose and herbaceous borders featuring hellebores in profusion, with tulips and primulas. Opening to incl nearby Penny Bit House with large and interesting plant sale. TEAS. *Adm £2.50, chd (up to 12) 50p. Sun 24 Apr (2-5.30)*

⓬ Polemonium Plantery, 28 Sunnyside Terrace, Trimdon Grange ⟨⌀⟩⟨☺⟩⟨NCCPG⟩
(Dianne & David Nichol-Brown) *10m SE of Durham. Signed Trimdon Grange, off A181. S end of Trimdon Grange village behind infants school. Turn L at St Aidan's Church, then R at tel box.* National Collection of polemoniums and related genera among a wide variety of other plants. Cottage garden with pond, alpines

and containers. Pergola leading to secret garden, with scented plants and a selection of unusual containers and features, including a children's treasure hunt. Home-made TEAS. *Adm £2, chd free. Suns, Mons 29, 30 May; 28, 29 Aug (11-5). Private visits welcome by appt. Tel 01429 881529 www.polemonium.co.uk*

⓭ ◆ Raby Castle, Staindrop ⟨&⟩⟨⌀⟩⟨☺⟩
(Lord Barnard) *12m NW of Darlington, 1m N of Staindrop. On A688.* C18 walled gardens set within the grounds of Raby Castle. The gardens, which now extend to 5 acres, display herbaceous borders, old yew hedges, formal rose gardens and informal heather and conifer gardens. RHS Membership Garden. Light refreshments and TEAS. *Castle, park & gardens adm £9, chd £4, concessions £8. Park & gardens only £4, chd £2.50, concessions £3.50. Bank Hol weekends Sats to Weds; May & Sept Weds & Suns: June to Aug daily except Sats 11-5.30 . Tel 01833 660202 www.rabycastle.com*

⓮ Ravensford Farm, Hamsterley, Bishop Auckland ⟨&⟩⟨⌀⟩⟨☺⟩
(Mr & Mrs J Peacock) *7m W of Bishop Auckland. From A68 at Witton-le-Wear turn off W to Hamsterley. Go through village & turn L just before tennis courts.* 2½-acre garden created since 1986 to blend with surrounding countryside and provide yr-round colour. Small wood being progressively underplanted, orchard, 2 ponds, sunken garden, rhododendron walk and mixed borders containing flowering shrubs, many roses and herbaceous borders - and a few surprises. Wheelchair access only with assistance. Featured on Yorkshire TV and in 'Northern Echo' 2003. TEAS. *Adm £3, chd £1. Sun 24 July (2-5). Private visits welcome by appt, no coaches please. Tel 01388*

488305 peacock@members.V21.co.uk

⓯ ⟨NEW⟩ Thornton Hall, Darlington ⟨&⟩⟨⌀⟩⟨☺⟩
(Mr & Mrs M P Manners) *2½m NW of Darlington. On B6279 Staindrop Rd.* C16 Grade I listed hall (not open). 2-acre walled gardens, recently planted. Plantsman's garden with an emphasis on colour-themed borders, plant associations, form and foliage. Unusual perennials, interspersed with interesting trees and shrubs in mixed herbaceous borders, incl large collection of hostas and interesting roses. 2 ponds, one with designer waterfall. Home-made TEAS in aid of Church funds. *Adm £2.50, chd 50p. Sun 26 June (1-5). Private visits welcome by appt June & July, coaches welcome. Tel 01325 374260*

⓰ ⟨NEW⟩ Thorpe Gardens, Thorpe ⟨&⟩⟨☺⟩
5m SE of Barnard Castle. 9m from Scotch Corner W on A66. Turn R at Peel House Farm Shop signed Wycliffe and Whorlton, 1m from A66. Charming hamlet, 3-4 cottage gardens, one approx ¼-acre with some unusual plants. Small varied gardens in peaceful country setting. Cream TEAS at Orchard House. *Combined adm £2, chd free. Sun 12 June (2-5)*

⓱ Westholme Hall, Winston ⟨&⟩⟨☺⟩
(Mr & Mrs J H McBain) *11m W of Darlington. From A67 Darlington to Barnard Castle rd, nr Winston turn N onto B6274.* 5 acres of gardens and grounds laid out in 1892 surround Jacobean house (not open). Rhododendrons, flowering shrubs, mixed borders, old-fashioned rose garden. The croquet lawn leads on to orchard, stream and woodland. Woodland walk to lake. Home-made TEAS in aid of St Andrew's Church. *Adm £2.50, chd 50p. Sun 26 June (2-6). Private visits welcome by appt. Tel 01325 730442*

St. Crispin's Belly Dancing Display Team

"... but I distinctly remember asking for Morris dancers!"

Essex

County Organiser:	Mrs Jill Cowley, Park Farm, Chatham Hall Lane, Great Waltham, Essex CM3 1BZ
	Tel 01245 360 871
Assistant County Organisers:	Cecilia Lady Grey, Elmbridge Mill, Mill End, Little Easton, Dunmow CM6 2HZ
	Tel 01371 872586
	Mrs Rosie Welchman, The Old Rectory, Little Sampford, Essex CB10 2QD
	Tel 01799 586230
County Treasurer:	Mr Eric Brown, 107 Castle Street, Saffron Walden, Essex CB10 1BQ

Maps: Numbers shown next to each garden entry refer to that garden's entry on the county map. This position is approximate; distance and directions from the nearest main town are generally shown in the garden text.
A precise location is available for those gardens featured on the NGS website by visiting www.ngs.org.uk.
Symbols: Information relating to symbols is given on page 21

DATES OF OPENING

Evening openings
See end of county listing

Private gardens open regularly for NGS
Feeringbury Manor, Feering *(8)*

Gardens open to the public
For details see garden description
Beth Chatto Gardens, Elmstead Market *(2)*
The Gardens of Easton Lodge, Great
 Dunmow *(9)*
The Gibberd Garden, Harlow *(10)*
Glen Chantry, Wickham Bishops *(11)*
Green Island, Ardleigh *(12)*
RHS Garden Hyde Hall, Rettendon *(16)*
Spains Hall, Finchingfield *(28)*
Westlands, Rettendon *(32)*

March 13 Sunday
Writtle College, Writtle *(36)*

March 27 Sunday (Easter)
Green Island, Ardleigh *(12)*

April 1 Friday
Feeringbury Manor, Feering *(8)*
Glen Chantry, Wickham Bishops *(11)*

April 7 Thursday
Barnards Farm, West Horndon *(1)*
Feeringbury Manor, Feering *(8)*

April 8 Friday
Dragons, Boyton Cross *(6)*
Feeringbury Manor, Feering *(8)*

April 12 Tuesday
Dragons, Boyton Cross *(6)*

April 14 Thursday
Barnards Farm, West Horndon *(1)*
Feeringbury Manor, Feering *(8)*

April 15 Friday
Feeringbury Manor, Feering *(8)*

April 17 Sunday
Tudor Roost, Fingringhoe *(30)*

April 21 Thursday
Barnards Farm, West Horndon *(1)*
Feeringbury Manor, Feering *(8)*

April 22 Friday
Feeringbury Manor, Feering *(8)*

April 24 Sunday
Hobbans Farm, Bobbingworth *(14)*
Horkesley Hall, Colchester *(15)*

April 28 Thursday
Barnards Farm, West Horndon *(1)*
Feeringbury Manor, Feering *(8)*
Olivers, Colchester *(22)*

April 29 Friday
Feeringbury Manor, Feering *(8)*
Wickham Place Farm, Wickham Bishops
 (34)

May 1 Sunday
Olivers, Colchester *(22)*

May 2 Monday (Bank Hol)
Olivers, Colchester *(22)*

May 4 Wednesday
Saling Hall, Great Saling *(25)*
Westlands, Rettendon *(32)*

May 5 Thursday
Barnards Farm, West Horndon **(Evening)**
 (1)
Feeringbury Manor, Feering *(8)*
Olivers, Colchester *(22)*

May 6 Friday
Feeringbury Manor, Feering *(8)*
Glen Chantry, Wickham Bishops *(11)*
Wickham Place Farm, Wickham Bishops
 (34)

May 8 Sunday
Hobbans Farm, Bobbingworth *(14)*

May 10 Tuesday
Dragons, Boyton Cross *(6)*

May 11 Wednesday
Saling Hall, Great Saling *(25)*
Westlands, Rettendon *(32)*

May 12 Thursday
Feeringbury Manor, Feering *(8)*
Olivers, Colchester *(22)*

May 13 Friday
Dragons, Boyton Cross *(6)*
Feeringbury Manor, Feering *(8)*
Wickham Place Farm, Wickham Bishops
 (34)

May 15 Sunday
Broomfield Primary School, Broomfield, nr
 Chelmsford *(3)*

May 18 Wednesday
Saling Hall, Great Saling *(25)*
Westlands, Rettendon *(32)*

May 19 Thursday
Feeringbury Manor, Feering *(8)*
Olivers, Colchester *(22)*

May 20 Friday
Feeringbury Manor, Feering *(8)*
Wickham Place Farm, Wickham Bishops
 (34)

May 22 Sunday
Canonteign, Hawkwell *(4)*
Green Island, Ardleigh *(12)*
Hobbans Farm, Bobbingworth *(14)*

Moverons, Brightlingsea *(20)*
Shrubs Farm, Lamarsh *(26)*
Ulting Wick, Ulting *(31)*

May 25 Wednesday
Saling Hall, Great Saling *(25)*
Westlands, Rettendon *(32)*

May 26 Thursday
Feeringbury Manor, Feering *(8)*

May 27 Friday
Feeringbury Manor, Feering *(8)*
Wickham Place Farm, Wickham Bishops
 (34)

May 29 Sunday
Tudor Roost, Fingringhoe *(30)*
Wickets, Langley Upper Green *(33)*

May 30 Monday (Bank Hol)
Little Easton Gardens *(17)*
Tudor Roost, Fingringhoe *(30)*
Wickets, Langley Upper Green *(33)*
Woolards Ash & Little Hallingbury Gardens
 (35)

June 1 Wednesday
Saling Hall, Great Saling *(25)*
Westlands, Rettendon *(32)*

June 2 Thursday
Barnards Farm, West Horndon *(1)*
Feeringbury Manor, Feering *(8)*

June 3 Friday
Feeringbury Manor, Feering *(8)*
Glen Chantry, Wickham Bishops *(11)*
Wickham Place Farm, Wickham Bishops
 (34)

ESSEX

kms 0   10

miles 0   10

CAMBRIDGESHIRE

SUFFOLK

24

o Saffron Walden

Bures o
26   Harwich

33   Thaxted   15
5   Halstead   A604   12
        28   25
Bishop's   9   Braintree   Colchester oElmstead   13
Stortford 17   A120   8   22 Market
        Great   27
        Dunmow   Clacton-
35   Witham   11   oTiptree   30   on-Sea
                              34   20   29
Harlow o 70   14   3   21   West
              Chelmsford o   Maldon   Mersea
Waitham Epping   Chipping 6 36   31
Abbey   o   Ongar o
              19   32 16   Burnham-on-
                                          Crouch o
o Chigwell   o Billericay
              o Brentwood   A127   23
7   o Rayleigh
        1 o Basildon   4
GREATER   o Southend-on-Sea
LONDON   18

o Grays

M11
A120
A12
A12
M25
A13
A127

HERTFORDSHIRE

June 4 Saturday
Hannams Hall, Tendring *(13)*

June 5 Sunday
Hannams Hall, Tendring *(13)*
The Old Rectory, Boreham *(21)*
South Green Farmhouse, Fingringhoe *(27)*
Wickets, Langley Upper Green *(33)*

June 8 Wednesday
Moverons, Brightlingsea *(20)*
Saling Hall, Great Saling *(25)*
Tudor Roost, Fingringhoe *(30)*
Westlands, Rettendon *(32)*

June 9 Thursday
Barnards Farm, West Horndon *(1)*
Feeringbury Manor, Feering *(8)*

June 10 Friday
Dragons, Boyton Cross *(6)*
Feeringbury Manor, Feering *(8)*
Wickham Place Farm, Wickham Bishops
(34)

June 12 Sunday
Clavering Gardens *(5)*

Edelweiss, Hornchurch *(7)*
Hobbans Farm, Bobbingworth *(14)*
Moverons, Brightlingsea *(20)*
Orchard Cottage, Rayleigh *(23)*
Shrubs Farm, Lamarsh *(26)*
Westlands, Rettendon *(32)*
Wickets, Langley Upper Green *(33)*
Writtle College, Writtle *(36)*

June 14 Tuesday
Dragons, Boyton Cross *(6)*

June 15 Wednesday
Saling Hall, Great Saling *(25)*
Tudor Roost, Fingringhoe *(30)*
Westlands, Rettendon *(32)*

June 16 Thursday
Barnards Farm, West Horndon *(1)*
Feeringbury Manor, Feering *(8)*

June 17 Friday
Feeringbury Manor, Feering *(8)*
Wickham Place Farm, Wickham Bishops
(34)

June 19 Sunday
Wickets, Langley Upper Green *(33)*

June 22 Wednesday
Saling Hall, Great Saling *(25)*
Tudor Roost, Fingringhoe *(30)*
Westlands, Rettendon *(32)*

June 23 Thursday
Barnards Farm, West Horndon *(1)*
Feeringbury Manor, Feering *(8)*

June 24 Friday
Feeringbury Manor, Feering *(8)*
Wickham Place Farm, Wickham Bishops
(34)

June 26 Sunday
Barnards Farm, West Horndon *(1)*
Hobbans Farm, Bobbingworth *(14)*
Parsonage House, Helions Bumpstead *(24)*

June 29 Wednesday
Saling Hall, Great Saling *(25)*
Tudor Roost, Fingringhoe *(30)*
Westlands, Rettendon *(32)*

June 30 Thursday
Barnards Farm, West Horndon *(1)*
Feeringbury Manor, Feering *(8)*

July 1 Friday
Feeringbury Manor, Feering *(8)*
Glen Chantry, Wickham Bishops *(11)*
Wickham Place Farm, Wickham Bishops *(34)*

July 3 Sunday
Little Myles, Stondon Massey *(19)*

July 6 Wednesday
Saling Hall, Great Saling *(25)*
Spains Hall, Finchingfield *(28)*
Westlands, Rettendon *(32)*

July 7 Thursday
Barnards Farm, West Horndon *(1)*
Feeringbury Manor, Feering *(8)*

July 8 Friday
Dragons, Boyton Cross *(6)*
Feeringbury Manor, Feering *(8)*
Wickham Place Farm, Wickham Bishops *(34)*

July 10 Sunday
Hobbans Farm, Bobbingworth *(14)*

July 12 Tuesday
Dragons, Boyton Cross *(6)*

July 13 Wednesday
Saling Hall, Great Saling *(25)*
Westlands, Rettendon *(32)*

July 14 Thursday
Barnards Farm, West Horndon *(1)*
Feeringbury Manor, Feering *(8)*

July 15 Friday
Feeringbury Manor, Feering *(8)*
Wickham Place Farm, Wickham Bishops *(34)*

July 16 Saturday
Springvale, St Osyth *(29)*

July 17 Sunday
Edelweiss, Hornchurch *(7)*
Springvale, St Osyth *(29)*

July 20 Wednesday
Saling Hall, Great Saling *(25)*
Westlands, Rettendon *(32)*

July 21 Thursday
Barnards Farm, West Horndon *(1)*
Feeringbury Manor, Feering *(8)*

July 22 Friday
Feeringbury Manor, Feering *(8)*
Wickham Place Farm, Wickham Bishops *(34)*

July 24 Sunday
Canonteign, Hawkwell *(4)*
Green Island, Ardleigh *(12)*
Hobbans Farm, Bobbingworth *(14)*
Orchard Cottage, Rayleigh *(23)*
Tudor Roost, Fingringhoe *(30)*

July 27 Wednesday
Saling Hall, Great Saling *(25)*
Westlands, Rettendon *(32)*

July 28 Thursday
Barnards Farm, West Horndon *(1)*
Feeringbury Manor, Feering *(8)*

July 29 Friday
Feeringbury Manor, Feering *(8)*

Wickham Place Farm, Wickham Bishops *(34)*

July 31 Sunday
Edelweiss, Hornchurch *(7)*

August 3 Wednesday
Westlands, Rettendon *(32)*

August 5 Friday
Glen Chantry, Wickham Bishops *(11)*

August 9 Tuesday
Dragons, Boyton Cross *(6)*

August 10 Wednesday
Westlands, Rettendon *(32)*

August 12 Friday
Dragons, Boyton Cross *(6)*

August 14 Sunday
Edelweiss, Hornchurch *(7)*
Tudor Roost, Fingringhoe *(30)*

August 17 Wednesday
Westlands, Rettendon *(32)*

August 24 Wednesday
Westlands, Rettendon *(32)*

August 28 Sunday
Edelweiss, Hornchurch *(7)*
Little Foxes, Thorpe Bay *(18)*

August 29 Monday (Bank Hol)
Edelweiss, Hornchurch *(7)*

August 31 Wednesday
Little Foxes, Thorpe Bay *(18)*
Westlands, Rettendon *(32)*

September 1 Thursday
Feeringbury Manor, Feering *(8)*

September 2 Friday
Feeringbury Manor, Feering *(8)*
Glen Chantry, Wickham Bishops *(11)*
Wickham Place Farm, Wickham Bishops *(34)*

September 4 Sunday
Barnards Farm, West Horndon *(1)*
Hobbans Farm, Bobbingworth *(14)*

September 7 Wednesday
Westlands, Rettendon *(32)*

September 8 Thursday
Feeringbury Manor, Feering *(8)*

September 9 Friday
Dragons, Boyton Cross *(6)*

Feeringbury Manor, Feering *(8)*
Wickham Place Farm, Wickham Bishops *(34)*

September 10 Saturday
Moverons, Brightlingsea *(20)*

September 11 Sunday
Moverons, Brightlingsea *(20)*

September 13 Tuesday
Dragons, Boyton Cross *(6)*

September 14 Wednesday
Westlands, Rettendon *(32)*

September 15 Thursday
Feeringbury Manor, Feering *(8)*

September 16 Friday
Feeringbury Manor, Feering *(8)*
Wickham Place Farm, Wickham Bishops *(34)*

September 18 Sunday
Hobbans Farm, Bobbingworth *(14)*

September 21 Wednesday
Westlands, Rettendon *(32)*

September 22 Thursday
Feeringbury Manor, Feering *(8)*

September 23 Friday
Feeringbury Manor, Feering *(8)*
Wickham Place Farm, Wickham Bishops *(34)*

September 25 Sunday
Horkesley Hall, Colchester *(15)*
Writtle College, Writtle *(36)*

September 28 Wednesday
Westlands, Rettendon *(32)*

September 29 Thursday
Feeringbury Manor, Feering *(8)*

September 30 Friday
Feeringbury Manor, Feering *(8)*
Wickham Place Farm, Wickham Bishops *(34)*

October 2 Sunday
Green Island, Ardleigh *(12)*

DESCRIPTIONS OF GARDENS

Balsham Manor and Maze, 42 High St, Balsham ♿⊘📷
See Cambridgeshire.

❶ Barnards Farm, Brentwood Road, West Horndon ♿⊘📷 NCCPG
(Bernard & Sylvia Holmes & The Christabella Charitable Trust) 5m S of Brentwood. On A128, 1½m S of A127. Created from farmland around a Georgian farmhouse (not open). Partially designed from the air. Aviators welcome. Modern sculptures, brick and willow mazes, herbaceous borders, 17 hectares of grounds, ponds, woodland, arboretum, living wall, National Collection of malus, Japanese garden, long avenue, bog garden, €uro wood, belvedere, museum (Suns only), parterre and ornamental vegetable garden and 'The Sitooterie'. Finalist Shed of the Year competition, TV - Richard & Judy, Garden Makers London Tonight, Chelsea Show, Essex Radio and 'Daily Express 2004. TEAS (Suns), Light lunches (Thurs). Adm £3.50, chd free (share to St Francis Church, West Horndon). Thus 7 Apr to 28 Apr; 2 June to 28 July (11-4); Suns 26 June; 4 Sept (2-5.30). **Evening Opening** £3.50, Teas, Thur 5 May (6-9). Private visits welcome by appt, for groups of 30+, special needs 10+. Tel 01277 811262
www.barnardsfarm.org

❷ ◆ Beth Chatto Gardens, Elmstead Market ♿⊘📷
(Mrs Beth Chatto) ¼m E of Elmstead Market. On A133. 5 acres of attractively landscaped garden with many unusual plants, shown in wide range of conditions from hot and dry to water garden. Famous gravel garden and woodland garden. Light refreshments and TEAS (Apr to Oct). Adm £4, chd under 14 free. Mons to Sats, Mar to Oct (9-5); Mons to Fris Nov to Feb (9-4). Tel 01206 822007
www.bethchatto.co.uk

❸ NEW **Broomfield Primary School, Broomfield, nr Chelmsford** ♿📷
(BBC Neighbourhood Garden for Broomfield Primary School) From Chelmsford town centre follow signs towards Broomfield Hospital , turn L into Mill Lane, school on R. This small 'Secret' garden constructed by BBC Neighbourhood Garden for volunteers, parents, children and friends, provides quiet corners, woven willow tunnel and refuge for wildlife and the children, as well as being a teaching resource. BBC

Gardeners World & BBC Radio Essex 2004. TEAS & Garden Advice stand. Adm £1.50, chd free. Sun 15 May (2-5)

❹ Canonteign, 47 Hill Lane, Hawkwell ⊘
(Margaret Taylor) 4m NE of Rayleigh. Leave A127 at Rayleigh Weir, take A129 to Rayleigh through town. Then B1013 to Hockley-Hawkwell 4m. Train: 10 min walk from Hockley station. Bus: no 8 Rayleigh-Southend White Hart Garage stop, 2 min walk. Exciting colourful garden, approx 76ft x 70ft, many different scenes. Tender plants and varied perennials, unusual plants in containers, water features, aviary, fish, arches and pergolas. Topiarised conifers. Conservatory with bougainvillea and other varieties of plants. Light refreshments and TEAS. Adm £1.50, chd free. Suns 22 May; 24 July (12.30-5). Private visits welcome by appt May to Sept. Tel 01702 206387

❺ Clavering Gardens
7m N of Bishops Stortford. On B1038. Turn W off B1383 at Newport. Home-made TEAS. Combined adm £3.50, chd under 14 free (share to Clavering Jubilee Field). Sun 12 June (2-5)

Brooklands (Mr & Mrs John Noble) 1½ acres walled garden, dramatic herbaceous and shrub borders, rustic rose trellis, arboretum. Extended garden planting in old orchard.

Clavering Court (Mr & Mrs S R Elvidge) Approx 1½ acres, fine trees, shrubs and borders. Walled garden, Edwardian greenhouse.

Deers ♿ (Mr & Mrs S H Cooke) 9 acres. Shrub and herbaceous borders; ponds with water lilies; old roses in formal garden; pool garden; walled vegetable garden; field and woodland walks.

Piercewebbs (Mr & Mrs B R William-Powlett) Old walled garden, shrubs, lawns, ha-ha, yew with topiary and stilt hedges, pond and trellised rose garden. Mown walks through newly planted trees. Extensive views.

Shovellers, Stickling Green (Miss J & Miss E Ludgate) 3-acre cottage garden with orchard and meadows.

❻ Dragons, Boyton Cross ⊘📷
(Mrs Margot Grice) 5m W of Chelmsford. On A1060. Between The Hare PH & The Keys Hotel. Plantsman's garden of ⅔ acre. Front garden, mature dwarf conifers and

grasses, 2 ponds, patios, scree garden and colour-themed borders. Summerhouse overlooking stream and farmland. TEAS. Adm £2, chd 50p. Fris, Tues 8, 12 Apr; 10, 13 May; 10, 14 June; 8, 12 July; 9, 12 Aug; 9, 13 Sept (10-5). Private visits welcome by appt. Tel 01245 248651

❼ Edelweiss, 20 Hartland Road, Hornchurch 📷
(Joan H Hogg /Pat F Lowery) 6m SW of Brentwood. From Romford E along the A124 past Tesco on L, turn R into Albany Rd opp church on corner of Park Lane on the L. Go to the bottom of Albany Rd, humps all the way, turn L at the end into Hartland Rd. Small town garden 200ft x 25ft. Laid out to maximise small narrow plot and featuring many containers, baskets, seasonal bedding and mixed borders. Narrow access and steps not suitable for push-chairs. Cream TEAS in aid of Little Acorns Church Pre-school. Adm £1.50. Suns 12 June; 17, 31 July; 14, 28, Aug, Mon 29 Aug (3-6). Private visits welcome by appt June to Aug. Tel 01708 454610

❽ Feeringbury Manor, Coggeshall Road, Feering ♿⊘📷
(Mr & Mrs Giles Coode-Adams) 12m SW of Colchester. Between Coggeshall & Feering. Well-established and designed 7-acre garden, mixing formal and informal. Overflowing with plants both common and rare. Former rose bed now new mixed pink, white and mauve bed. Very detailed planting throughout with many annuals and perennials grown from seed by gardener, Ellen Fairbanks-Weston. Wild flower beds designed by Diane Howse. Sculptures by Ben Coode-Adams. Adm £2.50, chd free. Thus, Fris, 1 Apr to 29 July; 1 Sept to 30 Sept (8-4). Private visits welcome by appt. Tel 01376 561946

❾ ◆ The Gardens of Easton Lodge, Great Dunmow ♿📷
(Mr & Mrs B Creasey) 1½m N of Dunmow. Brown heritage signs from A120, W of Dunmow. Home of 'Darling Daisy', Countess of Warwick, who in 1903 commissioned Harold Peto to lay out Italian and Japanese gardens. Abandoned 1950; major restoration since 1993 incl brick and cobble courtyard, ponds, C17 dovecote, conservatory and pavilion. Work started on sunken Italian garden. Living millennium sundial and Shakespeare border. History Exhibition. Light refreshments and TEAS. Adm £3.80, chd £1.50, concessions £3.50. Fris,

Sats, Suns 25 Mar to 30 Oct (12-6).
Tel 01371 876979
enquiries@eastonlodge.co.uk

10 ◆ **The Gibberd Garden, Marsh Lane, Harlow** 🅑
(The Gibberd Garden Trust) *3m E of Harlow. Marsh Lane is a narrow turning off B183 Rd (to Hatfield Heath), approx 1m E of the junction with A414. Look for 'Gibberd Garden' brown signs on A414 & on R opp garden entrance on B183.* 7-acre C20 garden designed by Sir Frederick Gibberd, on side of small valley. Terraces, wild garden, landscaped vistas, pools and streams, 'Roman Temple', moated log 'castle', gazebo, tree house and large collection of modern sculpture. Home-made TEAS. *Adm £4, chd free, concessions £2.50. Weds, Sats, Suns, Bank Hols Apr to Sept (2-6).*
Tel 01279 442112
www.thegibberdgarden.co.uk

11 ◆ **Glen Chantry, Wickham Bishops** 🅑
(Mr & Mrs W G Staines) *1½m SE of Witham. Take Maldon Rd from Witham & 1st L to Wickham Bishops. Cross narrow bridge over R Blackwater. Turn immed L up Ishams Chase by side of Blue Mills.* 3-acre garden, emphasis on mixed borders, unusual perennials and shrub roses. Limestone rock gardens, ponds, formal specialist white garden, foliage beds with grasses and hostas. Adjacent Specialist Perennial Nursery. Featured in 'Country Living', 'Garden Which', 2003, 'Gardens Monthly' & TV Garden Makers 2004. DIY TEAS. *Adm £2.50, chd 50p. Fris, Sats 1 Apr to 24 Sept. For NGS: Fris 1 Apr; 6 May; 3 June; 1 July; 5 Aug; 2 Sept (10-4).*
Tel 01621 891342

12 ◆ **Green Island, Ardleigh** 🅑
(Fiona Edmond) *3m NE of Colchester. From Ardleigh village centre, take B1029 towards Great Bromley. Park Rd is 2nd on R after level Xing. Garden is last on L.* 'A garden in the making', professionally designed by Fiona Edmond, beautifully situated in 19 acres of woodland. Huge variety of unusual plants with lots of interest all yr with emphasis on scent and autumn colour. Mixed borders, Japanese garden, water garden, woodland walks, seaside garden, bamboo dell, tree house and gravel garden. Garden design exhibition, contemporary sculptures. Large area of woodland redevelopment open 2005. Featured in 'Essex Life' 2004. Home-made

TEAS (Suns, Bank Hols & by prior arrangement). *Adm £2.50, chd 50p. Weds, Thurs & 1st 3 Suns 1 March to 3 Oct. For NGS: Suns 27 Mar; 22 May; 24 July; 2 Oct (1-5). Tel 01206 230455 www.greenislandgardens. co.uk*

13 [NEW] **Hannams Hall, Thorpe Road, Tendring** 🅑
(Mr & Mrs W Gibbon) *10m E of Colchester. From A120 take B1035 at Horsley Cross, through Tendring Village (approx 3m) pass Cherry Tree PH on R, after ½m over small bridge 1st house L.* C17 house (not open) set in 6 acres of formal and informal gardens and grounds with extensive views over open countryside. Herbaceous, mixed borders and shrubberies many interesting trees. Lawns and mown walks through wild grass and flower meadows, woodland walks, ponds and stream. Walled vegetable pottager and orchard. Home-made TEAS in aid of St Edmunds Church, Tendring. *Adm £2.50, chd free. Sat, Sun 4, 5 June (2-6)*

24 Hills Road, Buckhurst Hill 🅑
See London.

14 **Hobbans Farm, Bobbingworth** 🅑
(John & Ann Webster) *10m W of Chelmsford. N of A414 between Ongar 'Four Wantz' roundabout & N Weald 'Talbot' roundabout just past Blake Hall Gardens. 1st farm entrance on R after St Germain's Church.* Mature, romantic informal gardens, set in 2 acres surrounding C15 farmhouse (not open). Unusual plants; clematis, old roses, small herb garden with gazebo, courtyard, pot yard, vegetable garden, orchard, wild garden with ponds, bulbs, trees and shrubs. Set in pastures with fine views. New malus walk, fledgling ditch garden and bridge. Home-made TEAS. *Adm £2.50, chd free. Suns 24 Apr; 8, 22 May; 12, 26 June; 10, 24 July; 4, 18 Sept (2-5.30). Private visits welcome by appt. Tel 01277 890245*

15 **Horkesley Hall, Little Horkesley, Colchester** 🅑
(Mr & Mrs Johnny Eddis) *3m N of Colchester. W of A134. Access is via church car park.* 7-8 acres of varied garden surrounding classical house (not open). Appeal for children and adults. 2 lakes, large walled garden, pear avenue, Victorian glasshouse, blossom, bulbs, rhododendrons and herbaceous. Ever-increasing cutflower and vegetable garden. Wonderful bird life. Further grassland and wood.

Several new changes this yr. TEAS in aid of Little Horkesley Church. *Adm £2, chd free. Suns 24 Apr; 25 Sept (11-5). Private visits welcome by appt, coaches permitted. Teas.*
Tel 01206 271371
pollyeddis@hotmail.com

16 ◆ **RHS Garden Hyde Hall, Rettendon** 🅑 NCCPG
(Royal Horticultural Society) *7m SE of Chelmsford, 6m NE of Wickford. Signed from A130, at Rettendon.* 28-acre mixed garden. Many flowering trees, shrubs, perennials and colour themed borders, spring and summer bulbs. Large ponds with water lilies and marginal plants, woodland and alpine plantings. Extensive rose gardens. National Collection of viburnum. Highly acclaimed 'Dry Garden' of drought tolerant plants. Eastern Region Small Visitor Attraction of the Year 2003. Light refreshments and TEAS. *Adm £4.50, chd £1 (6-16), carer of disabled visitor free. Open all yr except Christmas Day; Apr to Sept (10-6); Oct to Mar (10-5) or dusk.*
Tel 01245 400256 www.rhs.org.uk

17 **Little Easton Gardens**
½m N of Great Dunmow. 1st turning L, on the B184 to Thaxted. Small village with lovely church and lakes. Home-made TEAS. *Combined adm £3, chd free. Mon 30 May (2-5)*

Church Lodge 🅑 (Vivienne Crossland) A fun garden. Infused with vibrance and peace which will both surprise and delight! Many quirky corners and interesting features - look for the surprising stag.

Elmbridge Mill, Mill End 🅑 (Cecilia Lady Gray) Mill house (not open) with mill stream one side flowing under the house, the R Chelmer on the other side. Approx 1 acre of trees, flowers and shrubs; roses climbing through orchard trees; walk up to mill pool with the addition of a new bridge across the mill race. Romantic garden full of interesting plants.

⑱ Little Foxes, Marcus Gardens, Thorpe Bay 🅰🎨⊞

(Mrs Dorothy Goode) 2½m E of Southend. From Thorpe Bay station (S-side) proceed E, take 4th on R into Marcus Ave then 2nd L into Marcus Gdns. Garden close to seaside, but totally secluded with a boundary of ornamental trees and conifers. The ⅓-acre within comprises several island beds and long borders set in lawns and planted with an interesting variety of colourful perennials, grasses, dwarf conifers, shrubs and beautiful foliage. Many planted containers. Colour themed areas and pretty water feature. Collection of special hostas. A tranquil garden for plant-lovers. Featured in 'Amateur Gardening' 2003. TEAS. Adm £1.50, chd 50p. Sun, Wed 28, 31 Aug (2-5). Private visits welcome by appt. Tel 01702 587972

⑲ Little Myles, Ongar Road, Stondon Massey 🅰🎨⊞

(Judy & Adrian Cowan) 1½m SE of Chipping Ongar. Turn off A128 at Stag PH, Marden Ash, (Ongar) towards Stondon Massey. Over bridge, 1st house on R after S bend. (400yds the Ongar side of Stondon Massey Church). Romantic garden surrounded by wild flowers and grasses, set in 3 acres. Full borders, hidden features, meandering paths, pond, hornbeam pergola and stream. Herb garden, full of nectar-rich and scented herbs, used for handmade herbal cosmetics. Herbal cosmetics for sale. Home-made TEAS. Adm £3, chd £1. Sun 3 July (11-4)

⑳ Moverons, Brightlingsea 🎨⊞

(Lesley Orrock) 7m SE of Colchester. Via B1027. Turn R in Thorrington onto B1029 signed Brightlingsea. At old church turn R signed Moverons Farm, follow lane & garden signs for approx 1m. 4½-acre garden under development and designed by owner. Stunning views across Colne Estuary. Planting begun in Nov 1997 incls walled garden, poolside planting and mixed borders in full sun and shade planted with a good variety of shrubs and perennials. 2 large ponds with landscaped vistas and mature trees. New projects constantly underway. Home-made TEAS. Adm £2.50, chd free. Suns 22 May; 12 June; 11 Sept; Wed 8 June; Sat 10 Sept (11-5). Private visits welcome by appt. Tel 01206 305498 lesley@moverons.com

㉑ The Old Rectory, Boreham 🅰🎨⊞

(Sir Jeffery & Lady Bowman) 4m NE of Chelmsford. Take B1137 Boreham Village, turn into Church Rd at Red Lion PH. ½m along on R opp church. 2½-acre garden with ponds, stream, interesting trees and shrubs, herbaceous borders and kitchen garden. Cream TEAS. Adm £2.50. Sun 5 June (2-5). Private visits welcome by appt May & June. Tel 01245 467233

㉒ Olivers, Olivers Lane, Colchester 🅰🎨⊞

(Mr & Mrs D Edwards) 3m SW of Colchester. Between B1022 & B1026. From zoo continue 1m towards Colchester. Turn R at roundabout (Cunobelin Way) & R into Olivers Lane. From Colchester via Maldon Rd turn L at roundabout, R into Olivers Lane. Peaceful wooded garden overlooking Roman river valley. Dramatic bedding, yew backed borders closely planted with wide variety of plants. Teas on terrace of C18 redbrick house (not open) overlooking lakes, lawns and meadow. Woodland with fine trees, underplanted with shrubs and carpeted with a mass of spring bulbs and bluebells. Home-made TEAS Sun & Mon only. Adm £2.50, chd free. Sun, Mon 1, 2 May; Thurs 28 Apr; , 5 12, 19 May (2-6). Private visits welcome by appt. Tel 01206 330575 gay.edwards@virgin.net

㉓ NEW Orchard Cottage, 219 Hockley Road, Rayleigh 🅰🎨

(Heather & Harry Brickwood) 1m from town centre. On NE edge of Rayleigh. Leave A127 at Rayleigh and take B1013 to Hockley. Garden opp the white & blue sign for Hockley. Park opp on grass. The ¾-acre garden surrounds the house (not open), laid out to lawn with long borders and island beds; these contain trees, unusual shrubs, herbaceous perennials and many lilies. The rear garden has 2 ponds connected by a stream. Look out for Betula utilis Jacquemontii, aquilegias, agapanthus and several varieties of hoheria. Represented Rayleigh in Britain in Bloom 2003. TEAS. Adm £2.50, chd free. Suns 12 June; 24 July (11-5). Private visits welcome by appt. Tel 01268 743838 harrybrickwood@btinternet.com

㉔ Parsonage House, Helions Bumpstead 🅰🎨⊞

(The Hon & Mrs Nigel Turner) 3m S of Haverhill. 8m NE of Saffron Walden. From Xrds in village centre turn up Church Hill, follow rd for

1m. Park in field opp. C15 house (not open) surrounded by 3 acres of formal gardens with mixed borders, topiary, pond, potager and greenhouse. Further 3-acre wild flower meadow with rare trees and further 3 acres of newly-planted orchard of old East Anglian apple varieties. Home-made TEAS. Adm £3. Sun 26 June (2-5)

㉕ Saling Hall, Great Saling 🅰🎨

(Mr & Mrs Hugh Johnson) 6m NW of Braintree. Turn N off B1256 (old A120) between Gt Dunmow & Braintree signed Great Saling & the Bardfields. Saling Hall is at end of village on L. 12-acre garden of many moods created since 1960s. Old walled flower gardens; landscape with many rare trees and shrubs; moat, ponds, groves and glades. Temple of Pisces. Hugh Johnson is 'Tradescant' of the RHS. Adm £3, chd free. Weds 4 May to 27 July (2-5). Private visits welcome by appt weekdays only, by written application to: Saling Hall, Great Saling, Braintree, Essex CM7 5DT

㉖ Shrubs Farm, Lamarsh 🅰

(Mr & Mrs Robert Erith) 1¼m from Bures. On rd to Lamarsh, the drive is signed to Shrubs Farm. 2 acres of mature and developing gardens with shrub borders, lawns, roses and trees. For walkers there are 50 acres of parkland and meadow with wild flower paths and woodland trails. Dogs on lead in this area. Much new hedgerow and tree planting incl over 50 species of Oak has taken place over the past 25yrs. Superb 10m views to N and E over the Stour valley. Ancient coppice and pollard trees in the woods incl the largest goat willow (Salix caprea) in England. Light refreshments and TEAS in aid of Holy Innocents Church, Lamarsh. Adm £3, chd free. Suns 22 May; 12 June (2-5). Private visits welcome by appt. Tel 01787 227520 www.shrubsfarm.co.uk

㉗ South Green Farmhouse, Fingringhoe 🅰

(Z E Jopling) 6m S of Colchester. Straight across in centre of village leaving Whalebone public house on R. South Green Farmhouse is 1m from Xrds. N.B. ignore turning to nature reserve. An oasis in the midst of Essex farmland looking across the Colne estuary, organic 1-acre garden of herbs, vegetables, borders, maze, shrubs, peace and tranquillity. TEAS. Adm £2.50, chd free. Sun 5 June (2-5)

Kim Wilde

Horticulturist and popstar

Photograph: Colin Bell

My garden (and its organic engine)

My garden really came to life in '96 when I married and became pregnant with my first child Harry in '97. I decided to create a garden where there had never been one before. I was so sure that the time for making gardens would run out once a baby (or two) were on the scene so armed

only with 'Rosemary Verey's Garden Plans', coupled with minimal horticultural knowledge, my husband Hal and I marked out an area for growing vegetables, a formal avenue and herb garden.

Our hawthorn avenue of crataegus laevigata 'Paul's Scarlet', under planted with clipped box balls, ground cover geraniums, nepeta and allium aflatunense was pure imitation of the famous laburnum avenue at the late Rosemary Verey's home at Barnsley House (minus the poisonous, though beautiful laburnum!).

We grow vegetables and fruit in 8 raised beds, some of which we give over to the children to encourage them into the garden. Last year they planted a rainbow of annuals, and some very tall sunflowers.

My introduction to Capel Manor Horticultural College was the single biggest influence upon the gradual change in my being 'interested' in all things horticultural to being completely hooked! After a few short summer courses in planting and design I felt like a born-again individual who had discovered a new and enlightening path.

Photographs: Ian Gowland

Subsequently I spent two years attending an evening class in plants and planting design, and the knowledge I have gained from my time there has had a large impact on our own garden as well as others with which I have been involved. Miscanthus (giant grass), stipa (feather grass), eryngium (sea holly), echinacea (cone flower), sedums, knautia and the long flowering, scented verbena bonariensis crowd a space once covered in grass, while musa basjoo (banana), canna and hedychium (ginger-wort) add a touch of the exotic to what was once a tired, shrubby border.

Beyond the garden is a two acre field which is gradually being planted up with woodland, and where we have reinstated the hedgerows with native species. Organic garden and kitchen waste is recycled to produce an indispensable compost heap...the engine of the garden, and pesticides are obsolete as the diverse planting encourages plenty of insect life which pollinates flowers, devours pests as well as provides food for wildlife.

Uniting a nation of garden lovers as well as giving invaluable assistance to the charities it supports, The National Gardens Scheme is a treasure trove of information. You never know, perhaps my garden will some day be in its pages!

Photograph: Colin Bell

BBC Neighbourhood Gardener

By Jessica Palmer, BBC Neighbourhood Gardener Project Manager

BBC Neighbourhood Gardener was inspired by the highly successful US Master Gardener initiative, launched in the UK by Monty Don on Gardeners' World in spring 2004 and featured again in the programme in September. It's also the talking point on dozens of local radio gardening shows so you may already be familiar with the idea. In case it's new to you, BBC Neighbourhood Gardener is a nationwide gardening mentor scheme which aims to create a nation of better gardeners. Volunteers with a love of gardening, and time to spare, get involved with their local community in a variety of ways to pass on their knowledge, skills and, most importantly,

their enthusiasm. But it's a two way learning process. At the same time as they are passing on knowledge to others, they can enrol on one of several horticultural courses and a volunteer skills training at colleges around the country. They develop their own skills and become a fully qualified BBC Neighbourhood Gardener.

Now two of the gardens that have flourished under the care of some of the pioneer BBC Neighbourhood Gardeners: the Sensory Garden at Belstead Special School in Ipswich and the Secret Garden at Broomfield Primary School in Chelmsford, are to join the NGS and will open for the first time in 2005.

The Pinewood & Chantry WI working on the Belstead Special School project

The Sensory Garden at Belstead Special School in Ipswich was built in 1991, but despite the sterling efforts of the local Pinewood and Chantry Women's Institute, who had taken on the task of maintaining the garden as part of a Local Community Challenge, the thugs of the plant world had taken over. Mary Dixon, the WI leader, contacted her local college for advice and was offered a team of pioneer Neighbourhood Gardeners; college students who were piloting the scheme locally. The team found themselves sharing their garden design and planting expertise with the WI volunteers, as well as offering sessions on recognising weeds or pruning and training plants. Gary Hardman, one of the Neighbourhood Gardener Pioneers involved says:

"It gives me a great buzz when I hear someone pass on to someone else something that I have taught to them - the seeds of knowledge are being sown."

At Broomfield Primary School in Chelmsford, Essex, a team of pioneer BBC Neighbourhood Gardeners were brought in to help parents create a Secret Garden. Together the Neighbourhood Gardener pioneers and parents transformed a neglected patch of land into a Secret Garden with a willow arch and totem pole. Building the sensory garden has improved the school environment and, in turn, has enriched the lives of the Neighbourhood Gardener Pioneers. Jackie Humberstone, Neighbourhood Gardener Pioneer working on the Broomfield Secret Garden says:

"Before I became involved with this scheme, I felt my life lacked direction. I now have a new found confidence and I'm looking forward to fresh opportunities. I even hope to pursue a career in gardening in the future."

For information on how to get involved in BBC Neighbourhood Gardener in your area
call 08000 150 950
email neighbourhood.gardener@bbc.co.uk or
visit the website bbc.co.uk/neighbourhoodgardener

Broomfield Primary School project.
Back row L-R:
Rene Latta, John Bowers, Angela Falconer.
Front row L-R:
Julie MacKinder, Chris Beardshaw,
Jackie Humberstone (Group Co-ordinator)

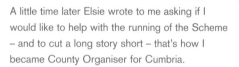

Linda Orchant

Garden opener and County Organiser for Cumbria

Unsung heroes

After helping a neighbour with the teas for her garden open day, it was suggested to me that I might like to think about opening my garden too. After much deliberation I rang the County Organiser who duly came to visit…..

I had envisaged a terrifying Miss Marple look-alike in tweedy suit and stout shoes trying not to show disdain for my horticultural efforts and searching for words to refuse me gently. No such thing, Elsie Tongue was kind and charming and best of all my garden was accepted into the fold. I was thrilled!

A little time later Elsie wrote to me asking if I would like to help with the running of the Scheme – and to cut a long story short – that's how I became County Organiser for Cumbria.

Now much is said of our wonderful garden owners who, with months of sheer hard work and dedication, prepare their gardens for an open day. All things domestic take second place when family and friends come laden with home made cakes and helpers rearrange the kitchen with smart little boxes of Jackson's teas. Visitors arrive in a steady stream and I answer questions from keen and interested gardeners and finally at the end of a wonderful day we put our feet up, relax and marvel at what we raised for the NGS and its charities. However there is also a small group of not often mentioned folk who ensure that each County runs like clockwork, giving support to garden owners – the County Team. Assistant COs work tirelessly finding new gardens and ensuring that old and new have successful open days. Press and Publicity Officers spend many a winter's night planning their campaigns for the following year and the Treasurers take care of all things monetary. Giving the most precious commodity of time, they juggle NGS work to fit in with their busy lives. I personally feel privileged to work with such a fine bunch of people who help run The National Gardens Scheme. They are my unsung heroes.

Linda's garden: High Cross Lodge
(see Cumbria county section)
Photograph: Brian Adams

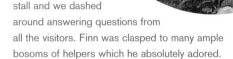

Emma Duncan

Garden opener and young mother

All in the family

I blame it entirely on Mum and Dad. We had always had a beautiful garden at home where we spent most of our free time and it seemed a natural progression for my parents to open it for The National Gardens Scheme when they retired. So when my husband Seb and I bought our own house it seemed certain that the garden would be important in our lives.

Five years later, inspired by my parents we approached our local NGS Assistant County Organiser to see if our garden might be suitable. It's not a big garden but it had enough interest to appeal to visitors and consequently a day in August the following year was set.

Preparations started early and it was shortly after we were accepted that I discovered that I was expecting a baby, about the same time the exotic borders needed to be planted out!

Finn was born in the second week of May. He received a warm welcome from the County Organisers having been christened "the youngest gardener in the NGS" by them. The exotics were planted out the following week!

Despite awful weather for most of August our first open day was held in bright sunshine. Mum and Dad manned the gate and the plant stall and we dashed around answering questions from all the visitors. Finn was clasped to many ample bosoms of helpers which he absolutely adored.

Sometimes people are surprised that we have a young family and a garden in The National Gardens Scheme but if you love gardening and enjoy sharing that passion with other people then, believe me, it is a fantastic experience to open your garden.

Emma's garden: Hollycroft
(see Norfolk county section)

ngs gardens open for charity

Royal Frogmore, Windsor

A record day for the NGS

Dazzling sunshine on a May summer's day heralded the most successful day yet at Frogmore House Garden. Thanks to the continuing generosity and kindness of Her Majesty The Queen, Frogmore House Garden was again opened in aid of The National Gardens Scheme on Tuesday 18 May last year raising a record £5,000 for the NGS beneficiary charities.

The gardens are only open to the public for a few days of the year and thousands took advantage of this unique opportunity to view the beautiful parkland gardens and lake as well as the famous Mausoleum, resting place of Queen Victoria and Prince Albert.

Pre-booked tours of the gardens were again a popular feature led by Neil Dodds, Head Gardener. Refreshments were available and picnics welcome. The NGS County Team, led by Jeremy Bayliss and Fenja Anderson, were on hand to make it such a success (see pictured above with Neil Dodds, centre). Well done to everyone involved and especially the Royal Parks & Gardens and the Royal Collection to whom we are indebted for their support and assistance. We look forward to Tuesday May 17 this year and another successful opening which will celebrate the 60th year for the NGS at Frogmore Gardens.

Tickets can be booked in advance nearer the time by telephoning the ticket Sales & Information Office at Buckingham Palace on 020 7766 7305 or visit www.royal.gov.uk. Tickets will be available too through www.ngs.org.uk where you will also find further information.

28 ◆ Spains Hall, Finchingfield ♿🐕
(Sir John Ruggles-Brise) *1m N of
Finchingfield. From Finchingfield
village green war memorial cross over
bridge take 1st L. After windmill on
RH-side take 1st L to Helions
Bumpstead. After ¾m at top of hill
white gateposts on RH-side.* Classic
mature garden in same family's
ownership since 1760. House
Elizabethan/Georgian (not open) with
partial moat, overlooking formal rose
garden, C17 cedar tree, topiary,
lawns, herbaceous/shrub borders,
walled garden, glasshouses. Lakeside
walk. Extensive programme of
renovation and new planting.
Featured in 'Essex Life' 2003. Home-
made TEAS (6 July only). *Adm £2,
chd 50p. Mons to Thurs Mar to Aug
(10-4); Suns June to Aug (2-5).* **For
NGS:** *Wed 6 July (10-4).* Tel 01371
810232 *rb.spains@btopenworld.com*

**29 Springvale, Beach Road, St
Osyth** ♿🐕
(Mr & Mrs M A Roberts) *4m W of
Clacton-on-Sea. 500yds S of Xrds in
village, towards Seawick, just across
the brook.* An unusual sloping 1-acre
garden, designed in 'rooms', with a
large variety of shrubs, perennials,
roses, clematis and grasses for long
term interest. Areas and pond for
wildlife. Old farming items, garden
memorabilia in the Roman temple.
July open days with herb theme. Free
art exhibition and demonstrations.
TEAS. *Adm £2, chd free. Sat, Sun 16,
17 July (11-5). Private visits welcome
by appt, 12+ Apr to July, can be
combined with guided tour of
beautiful Tudor church, both £3.50
(share to Friends of the Church).*
Tel 01255 822310
roberts.stosyth@tesco.net

**30 Tudor Roost, 18 Frere Way,
Fingringhoe** 🐕
(Chris & Linda Pegden) *5m S of
Colchester. In centre of village by
Whalebone PH. Follow sign to*

*Ballast Quay, after ½m turn R into
Brook Hall Rd, then 1st L into Frere
Way.* Set in delightful village,
compact, 135ft x 60ft enthusiast's
garden, offering an abundance of yr-
round colour, foliage and the exotic.
A koi carp pond (tame koi - 2') being
the central feature surrounded by
borders and walkways. Rose and
clematis covered pergola and pillars.
Nature reserve within 1m. Featured
in 'Essex Life' 2004. Home-made
TEAS. *Adm £2, chd free. Suns 17
Apr; 29, Mon 30 May; Weds, 8 June
to 29 June; Suns 24 July; 14 Aug
(2-5.30). Private visits welcome by
appt.* Tel 01206 729831

31 Ulting Wick, Ulting ♿🐕
(Mr & Mrs B Burrough) *3m NW of
Maldon. Take turning to Ulting
(Ulting Lane) off B1019 at Langford,
after 2.2m at T-junction, garden is
opp.* 4 acre garden set around C16
farmhouse (not open) and barns (C17
barn open) undergoing major changes
with emphasis on colour. Herbaceous
borders, winter, spring and cutting
garden provide yr-round interest.
Natural pond and stream bordered
by mature willows and beds
containing moisture and shade loving
plants. New for 2005, vegetable
garden with Victorian style
glasshouse and 2 further gardens
(hopefully complete!). Home-made
TEAS in aid of All Saints, Ulting.
*Adm £2.50, chd free. Sun 22 May
(2-5). Private visits welcome by appt.*
Tel 01245 380216

**32 ◆ Westlands, Chalk Street,
Rettendon** ♿🐕
(Keith & Sally Player) *7m SE of
Chelmsford, 6m NE of Wickford. At
Rettendon Bell junction, head for
Hanningfield Reservoir (opp turning
for Hyde Hall) 1st L into Chalk St,
¼m on L.* An enthusiast's garden full
of surprises in attractive rural setting.
Informal borders of perennials,
shrubs and grassess in colour-themed
areas. 2 acres, incl ponds, pergolas,

water features, gravel garden, stone
circle. New-planted woodland walk,
duck pond and meadow walk.
Adjacent hardy plant nursery. Home-
made TEAS. *Adm £2, chd under 16
free. Weds to Suns 1 May to 30 Sept.*
For NGS: *Sun 12 June; Weds 4 May to
28 Sept; (10-5).* Tel 01245 400902
www.westlandsnursery.co.uk

33 Wickets, Langley Upper Green ♿🐕
(Mr & Mrs D Copeland) *10m N of
Bishops Stortford. Turn W off B1383
(old A11) at Newport. After 5m turn
R off B1038 at Clavering, signed
Langley. Drive over ford, Upper
Green 3m further on. Last house on
R of cricket green.* 15yr old romantic
country garden approx 1½ acres,
designed by Susan Copeland, divided
into themed areas. Mixed borders
with emphasis on shrub roses, gravel
garden, landscaped meadow, natural
pond with water lilies, sculptures and
extensive views. Home-made TEAS.
*Adm £2.50, chd free. Suns, Mon 29,
30 May; 5, 12, 19 June (2-5). Private
visits welcome by appt.* Tel 01799
550553 *sgardesign@aol.com*

**34 Wickham Place Farm, Station
Road, Wickham Bishops** ♿🐕
(Mrs J Wilson) *2½m SE of Witham.
On B1018. Take B1018 from
Witham to Maldon. After going
under A12 take 3rd L (Station Rd).
1st house on L.* 2-acre walled garden
with huge climbers and roses filled by
shrubs, perennials and bulbs.
Renowned for stunning wisteria in
May/June, one now 250ft long. 12
acres of mixed woodland, incl rabbit-
resistant plants and bulbs, features
lovely walks. Yr-round colour; knot
garden. Home-made TEAS. *Adm
£2.50, chd 50p over 5 (share to
Farleigh Hospice). Fris 29 Apr to 29
July; 2 to 30 Sept (11-4). Private
visits welcome by appt,groups &
coaches permitted.* Tel 01621
891282

③⑤ NEW Woolards Ash & Little Hallingbury Gardens
TEAS at Beggars Hall & Woolards Ash. *No combined adm. Mon 30 May (2-6)*

NEW Beggars Hall, Great Hallingbury 🅰️🐕 *(Mr & Mrs Andrew Streeter) 1½m from Hallingbury. Take B1256 from M11 J8 towards Takeley, turn opp Esso garage R signed Great Hallingbury. Approx 1m turn L at Hop Poles PH - take RH-side fork to Beggars Hall.* Small enclosed garden of mixed beds; courtyard with roses, adjoining Hatfield Forest. *Adm £2.50, chd free*

NEW Gaston House, Gaston Green, Little Hallingbury 🅰️ *(Mr & Mrs Roger Graham) From London exit M11 J7 go N A414 then A1184 to Sawbridgeworth, at 2 mini-roundabouts - turn R down hill to station - level-Xng after 150 metres L, 1½m along twisty lane to Gaston Green (signed), garden on L. From N & E exit M11 J8, L on B1254 towards Takeley after 150 metres R (opp*

Esso garage) towards The Hallingburys through Great Hallingbury over M11, at T-junction L towards Hatfield Heath and Little Hallingbury (signed), 2nd turning on R signed Gaston Green, garden 150yds on R. Knot garden leading to terrace. Fine formal and water gardens; raised vegetable beds, parterre enclosed by pleached limes. Re-designed pool garden. *Adm £2.50, chd free*

Woolards Ash, Hatfield Broad Oak
🅰️🐕 *(Mr & Mrs Le Q Herbert) 6m SW of Gt Dunmow & 6m SE of Bishops Stortford. From Hatfield Broad Oak follow B183 N (towards Takeley). After ¾m take 1st R (signed to Taverners Green & Broomshawbury), then 2nd R to Woolards Ash. From Takeley, B183 S (towards Hatfield Broad Oak). After ¾m 1st L (signed Cranfield & High Roding), then 2nd L to Woolards Ash.* 2½ acres of subtly-planted borders divided by beech and yew hedges. Mature trees, shrubs and old roses set in pastoral

landscape. TEAS. *Adm £3.50, chd free*

③⑥ Writtle College, Writtle 🅰️⊕
(Mr G Allen - Curator) 4m W of Chelmsford. On A414, nr Writtle village, clearly signed. Approx 15 acres; informal lawns with naturalised bulbs in spring and wild flowers in summer, large tree collection, mixed shrub and herbaceous borders, heathers and alpines. Landscaped gardens designed and built by students including 'Centenary' garden and sub-tropical 'Hot 'n' Spicy' garden. Development of new 13-acre parkland area. Orchard meadows, recently started on the site of an old apple orchard. Landscaped glasshouses. Light refreshments and TEAS. *Adm £3, chd free, concessions £2. Suns 13 Mar; 12 June; 25 Sept (10-4). Private visits welcome by appt. Tel 01245 424200 www.writtle.ac.uk*

Evening Opening (See also garden description)	
Barnards Farm	5 May

help the hospices

"If you took all the love and companionship given by the nurses and staff here, put it in a light bulb under the Millennium Dome, you would see it in Sydney."

David, a Day Care patient at a hospice

Hospice care is based on the simple idea that a dying patient is a living person; someone who deserves peace, respect and calm until the very end of their life. Hospice staff and volunteers seek to help people live life to the full, for whatever time they have left – no matter how long or how short. All hospice care is given free of charge.

Help the Hospices is the national charity for the hospice movement. Our role is to complement and enhance the wonderful care hospices give to patients and their loved ones. We do this by making grants to fund training of hospice staff particularly doctors and nurses; support new services; offer hospices advice and information and promote the issues affecting them and those who need their care to government and the media and running fundraising campaigns to support hospice care. Funds raised by the National Gardens Scheme are a vital source of income to help us in our work.

For further information, please call us on 020 7520 8200; www.helpthehospices.org.uk

Flintshire & Wrexham
See separate Welsh section on page 453

Glamorgan
See separate Welsh section on page 458

Gloucestershire North & Central

County Organiser:	Mrs Stella Martin, Dundry Lodge, France Lynch, Stroud, Gloucestershire GL6 8LP Tel 01453 883419
Assistant County Organisers:	Mrs Barbara Adams, Warners Court, Charfield, Wotton under Edge, Gloucestershire GL12 8TG Tel 01454 261078
	Mrs Lisa Fellows, The Holme House, Jubilee Road, Mitcheldean, Gloucestershire GL17 0EE Tel 01594 543875
	Mrs Meryl King, Springfield, Lower Chedworth, Cheltenham, Gloucestershire GL54 4AN Tel 01285 720278
	Mrs Rosemary Lyons, The Granary, Willington Court, Sandhurst, Gloucester GL2 9NZ Tel 01452 730228
	Mr Tony Marlow, Greenedge, 32 Dr Browns Road, Minchinhampton, Gloucestershire GL6 9BT Tel 01453 883531
	Miss Anne Palmer, 10 Vineyard Street, Winchcombe, Gloucestershire GL54 5LP Tel 01242 603761
County Treasurer:	Mr Graham Baber, 11 Corinium Gate, Cirencester, Gloucestershire GL7 2PX Tel 01285 650961

Maps: Numbers shown next to each garden entry refer to that garden's entry on the county map. This position is approximate; distance and directions from the nearest main town are generally shown in the garden text.
A precise location is available for those gardens featured on the NGS website by visiting www.ngs.org.uk.

Symbols: Information relating to symbols is given on page 21

DATES OF OPENING

Evening openings
See end of county listing

Private gardens open regularly for NGS
25 Bowling Green Road, Cirencester *(9)*
Ewen Manor, Ewen Village, nr Cirencester *(19)*
Green Cottage, Lydney *(24)*
Tinpenny Farm, Fiddington *(72)*
Trench Hill, Sheepscombe *(73)*
Willow Lodge, nr Longhope *(79)*

Gardens open to the public
For details see garden description
Bourton House Garden, Bourton-on-the-Hill *(8)*
Cerney House Gardens, North Cerney *(12)*
Colesbourne Park, Colesbourne *(15)*
Eastleach House, Eastleach Martin *(18)*
Hidcote Manor Garden, Chipping Campden *(25)*
Hunts Court, North Nibley *(34)*
Kempsford Manor, Kempsford *(36)*
Kiftsgate Court, nr Chipping Campden *(38)*
Lydney Park Spring Garden, Lydney *(41)*
The Matara Garden (formally Maheo), Kingscote *(42)*
Mill Dene Garden, Blockley *(43)*
Misarden Park, Miserden *(44)*
Painswick Rococo Garden, Painswick *(50)*
Rodmarton Manor, Cirencester *(60)*
Sezincote, nr Moreton-in-Marsh *(64)*
Snowshill Manor, nr Broadway *(66)*
Stanway Fountain & Water Garden, nr Winchcombe *(68)*
Westbury Court Garden, Westbury-on-Severn *(77)*
Westonbirt School Gardens, Westonbirt *(78)*

By appointment only
For telephone number and other details see garden description.
Private visits welcomed
Alderley Grange, Alderley *(2)*
The Chipping Croft, Tetbury *(14)*
Througham Court, Througham *(71)*

January 30 Sunday
Home Farm, Huntley *(30)*

February 13 Sunday
Home Farm, Huntley *(30)*
Trench Hill, Sheepscombe *(73)*

February 14 Monday
The Old Rectory, Duntisbourne Rous *(48)*

February 20 Sunday
Tinpenny Farm, Fiddington *(72)*
Trench Hill, Sheepscombe *(73)*

March 5 Saturday
Redwood, Bussage *(58)*

March 6 Sunday
Redwood, Bussage *(58)*

March 13 Sunday
Sheephouse, Painswick *(65)*

March 14 Monday
The Old Rectory, Duntisbourne Rous *(48)*

March 20 Sunday
Pear Tree Cottage, Gotherington *(52)*
Tinpenny Farm, Fiddington *(72)*

March 27 Sunday (Easter)
Beverston Castle, nr Tetbury *(5)*
Trench Hill, Sheepscombe *(73)*

March 28 Monday (Easter)
Beverston Castle, nr Tetbury *(5)*
The Old Vicarage, Maisemore *(49)*
Trench Hill, Sheepscombe *(73)*

April 3 Sunday
Highnam Court, Highnam *(26)*

Home Farm, Huntley *(30)*
Mill Dene Garden, Blockley *(43)*
Misarden Park, Miserden *(44)*

April 10 Sunday
Abbotswood, Stow-on-the-Wold *(1)*
The Bungalow, nr Newent *(10)*
Hodges Barn, Shipton Moyne *(28)*
The Old Chequer, Draycott *(47)*
Rosemary Cottage, Frocester *(62)*
Stanway Fountain & Water Garden, nr Winchcombe *(68)*

April 11 Monday
Hodges Barn, Shipton Moyne *(28)*

April 14 Thursday
Barnsley House, nr Cirencester *(4)*

April 15 Friday
Colesbourne Park, Colesbourne *(15)*

April 17 Sunday
Home Farm, Huntley *(30)*
Pigeon House, Southam *(54)*
Tinpenny Farm, Fiddington *(72)*
Willow Lodge, nr Longhope *(79)*

April 18 Monday
Willow Lodge, nr Longhope *(79)*

April 20 Wednesday
Lydney Park Spring Garden, Lydney *(41)*

April 24 Sunday
Cotswold Farm, nr Duntisbourne Abbots, Cirencester *(16)*
Kestrel Cottage, Brand Green *(37)*
Rosemary Cottage, Frocester *(62)*
Stone House, Wyck Rissington *(69)*
Willow Lodge, nr Longhope *(79)*

April 25 Monday
Kestrel Cottage, Brand Green *(37)*
Willow Lodge, nr Longhope *(79)*

GLOUCESTERSHIRE NORTH & CENTRAL

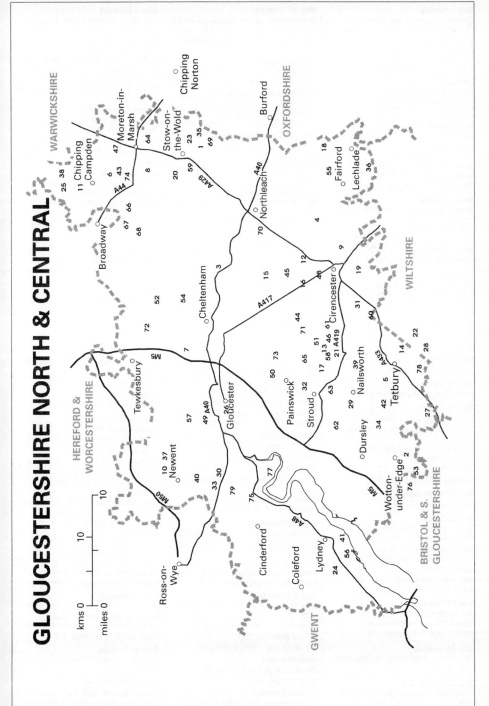

WARWICKSHIRE

OXFORDSHIRE

WILTSHIRE

HEREFORD &
WORCESTERSHIRE

BRISTOL & S.
GLOUCESTERSHIRE

GWENT

Chipping
Norton

Burford

Moreton-in-
Marsh

Stow-on-
the-Wold

Chipping
Campden

Fairford

Lechlade

Northleach

Broadway

Cheltenham

Cirencester

Tewkesbury

Gloucester

Painswick

Nailsworth

Stroud

Tetbury

Newent

Dursley

Wotton-
under-Edge

Ross-on-
Wye

Cinderford

Coleford

Lydney

kms 0   10

miles 0   10

25 38
11
6 43
74
A44
66
67
68
47
64
8
20
59
A429
A40
23
1 35
69
55
18
36
70
4
9
12
15
45
16
40
19
A417
52
54
3
72
7
M5
44
71
51
46
61
A419
31
60
21
5 A433
22
14
28
78
27
50 73
65
17 58 13
63
39
42
34
57
49 A40
26
29
62
2
76 53
79
30
33
40
10 37
M50
75
77
A48
56 41
24
M5

May 1 Sunday
Eastcombe, Bussage and Brownshill Gardens *(17)*
Green Cottage, Lydney *(24)*
Highnam Court, Highnam *(26)*
Home Farm, Huntley *(30)*
Humphreys End House, Randwick, nr Stroud *(32)*
Huntley Manor, Huntley *(33)*
Warners Court, Charfield *(76)*
Willow Lodge, nr Longhope *(79)*

May 2 Monday (Bank Hol)
Eastcombe, Bussage and Brownshill Gardens *(17)*
Home Farm, Huntley *(30)*
Huntley Manor, Huntley *(33)*
Warners Court, Charfield *(76)*
Willow Lodge, nr Longhope *(79)*

May 3 Tuesday
Lydney Park Spring Garden, Lydney *(41)*

May 4 Wednesday
Kiftsgate Court, nr Chipping Campden *(38)*

May 7 Saturday
Rookwoods, Waterlane, nr Bisley *(61)*

May 8 Sunday
Abbotswood, Stow-on-the-Wold *(1)*
Cerney House Gardens, North Cerney *(12)*
Green Cottage, Lydney *(24)*
Kestrel Cottage, Brand Green *(37)*
The Old Vicarage, Maisemore *(49)*
Ramblers, Aylburton, nr Lydney *(56)*
Upton Wold, nr Moreton-in-Marsh *(74)*

May 9 Monday
The Old Rectory, Duntisbourne Rous *(48)*

May 10 Tuesday
Kestrel Cottage, Brand Green *(37)*

May 15 Sunday
Green Cottage, Lydney *(24)*
The Red House, Staunton, nr Gloucester *(57)*
Stanway Fountain & Water Garden, nr Winchcombe *(68)*
Stowell Park, Northleach *(70)*
Tinpenny Farm, Fiddington *(72)*

May 18 Wednesday
France Lynch, nr Stroud *(21)*

May 22 Sunday
Green Cottage, Lydney *(24)*
Hodges Barn, Shipton Moyne *(28)*
Kestrel Cottage, Brand Green *(37)*
The Matara Garden (formally Maheo), Kingscote *(42)*
Pear Tree Cottage, Gotherington *(52)*
Willow Lodge, nr Longhope *(79)*

May 23 Monday
Hodges Barn, Shipton Moyne *(28)*
Kestrel Cottage, Brand Green *(37)*
Willow Lodge, nr Longhope *(79)*

May 24 Tuesday
Ewen Manor, Ewen Village, nr Cirencester *(19)*

May 25 Wednesday
Ewen Manor, Ewen Village, nr Cirencester *(19)*
Lower Farm House, Cliffords Mesne *(40)*

May 26 Thursday
Bourton House Garden, Bourton-on-the-Hill *(8)*
Ewen Manor, Ewen Village, nr Cirencester *(19)*

May 29 Sunday
Boddington Manor, Boddington *(7)*
Green Cottage, Lydney *(24)*
Mill Dene Garden, Blockley *(43)*
The Old Vicarage, Maisemore *(49)*
Pemberley Lodge, Old Charfield *(53)*
Westonbirt School Gardens, Westonbirt *(78)*

May 30 Monday (Bank Hol)
The Bungalow, nr Newent *(10)*

May 31 Tuesday
Ewen Manor, Ewen Village, nr Cirencester *(19)*

June 1 Wednesday
Ewen Manor, Ewen Village, nr Cirencester *(19)*
Lower Farm House, Cliffords Mesne *(40)*
Trench Hill, Sheepscombe *(73)*

June 2 Thursday
Ewen Manor, Ewen Village, nr Cirencester *(19)*

June 4 Saturday
The Old Chapel, Chalford Vale *(46)*

June 5 Sunday
The Bungalow, nr Newent *(10)*
Green Cottage, Lydney *(24)*
Highnam Court, Highnam *(26)*
Holcombe Glen Cottage, Minchinhampton *(29)*
Kestrel Cottage, Brand Green *(37)*
Lammas Park, Minchinhampton *(39)*
The Old Chapel, Chalford Vale *(46)*
Pigeon House, Southam *(54)*
Ramblers, Aylburton, nr Lydney *(56)*
Westonbirt School Gardens, Westonbirt *(78)*
Willow Lodge, nr Longhope *(79)*

June 6 Monday
The Old Chapel, Chalford Vale *(46)*
Willow Lodge, nr Longhope *(79)*

June 7 Tuesday
Ewen Manor, Ewen Village, nr Cirencester *(19)*
Kestrel Cottage, Brand Green *(37)*
The Old Chapel, Chalford Vale *(46)*

June 8 Wednesday
Campden House, Chipping Campden *(11)*
Ewen Manor, Ewen Village, nr Cirencester *(19)*
Green Cottage, Lydney *(24)*
The Old Chapel, Chalford Vale *(46)*
Trench Hill, Sheepscombe *(73)*

June 9 Thursday
Ewen Manor, Ewen Village, nr Cirencester *(19)*
Humphreys End House, Randwick, nr Stroud **(Evening)** *(32)*
The Old Chapel, Chalford Vale *(46)*

June 10 Friday
The Old Chapel, Chalford Vale *(46)*

June 11 Saturday
Chalford Gardens *(13)*
Hullasey House, Tarlton *(31)*
The Old Chapel, Chalford Vale *(46)*

June 12 Sunday
Barn House, Sandywell Park, Whittington *(3)*
Blockley Gardens *(6)*
Chalford Gardens *(13)*
Eastleach House, Eastleach Martin *(18)*
The Glebe House, Shipton Moyne *(22)*
Green Cottage, Lydney *(24)*
Hillesley House, Hillesley, nr Wotton-under-Edge *(27)*
Hullasey House, Tarlton *(31)*
Hunts Court, North Nibley *(34)*
The Old Chapel, Chalford Vale *(46)*
Ramblers, Aylburton, nr Lydney *(56)*
The Red House, Staunton, nr Gloucester *(57)*

June 13 Monday
The Glebe House, Shipton Moyne *(22)*
Hullasey House, Tarlton *(31)*
The Old Chapel, Chalford Vale *(46)*

June 14 Tuesday
Ewen Manor, Ewen Village, nr Cirencester *(19)*
The Old Chapel, Chalford Vale *(46)*

June 15 Wednesday
Campden House, Chipping Campden *(11)*
Ewen Manor, Ewen Village, nr Cirencester *(19)*
Eyford Gardens *(20)*
Green Cottage, Lydney *(24)*
The Old Chapel, Chalford Vale *(46)*
Rockcliffe, nr Lower Swell *(59)*
Trench Hill, Sheepscombe *(73)*

June 16 Thursday
Ewen Manor, Ewen Village, nr Cirencester *(19)*
The Old Chapel, Chalford Vale *(46)*

June 17 Friday
The Old Chapel, Chalford Vale *(46)*

June 18 Saturday
The Old Chapel, Chalford Vale *(46)*
The Vicarage, Westbury on Severn *(75)*

June 19 Sunday
25 Bowling Green Road, Cirencester *(9)*
The Bungalow, nr Newent *(10)*
Grange Farm, Evenlode, nr Moreton-in-Marsh *(23)*
Green Cottage, Lydney *(24)*
Hunts Court, North Nibley *(34)*
Kestrel Cottage, Brand Green *(37)*
The Old Chapel, Chalford Vale *(46)*
Stanton Gardens, nr Broadway *(67)*
Stowell Park, Northleach *(70)*
Tinpenny Farm, Fiddington *(72)*
The Vicarage, Westbury on Severn *(75)*
Willow Lodge, nr Longhope *(79)*

June 20 Monday
25 Bowling Green Road, Cirencester *(9)*
Kestrel Cottage, Brand Green *(37)*
The Old Rectory, Duntisbourne Rous *(48)*
Willow Lodge, nr Longhope *(79)*

June 21 Tuesday
Ewen Manor, Ewen Village, nr Cirencester *(19)*

June 22 Wednesday
25 Bowling Green Road, Cirencester *(9)*
Ewen Manor, Ewen Village, nr Cirencester *(19)*

Eyford Gardens *(20)*
Green Cottage, Lydney *(24)*
Rockcliffe, nr Lower Swell *(59)*
Trench Hill, Sheepscombe *(73)*

June 23 Thursday
Barnsley House, nr Cirencester *(4)*
Ewen Manor, Ewen Village, nr Cirencester *(19)*
Rockcliffe, nr Lower Swell *(59)*

June 26 Sunday
Barn House, Sandywell Park, Whittington *(3)*
25 Bowling Green Road, Cirencester *(9)*
Green Cottage, Lydney *(24)*
Hunts Court, North Nibley *(34)*
Icomb Place, nr Stow-on-the-Wold *(35)*
Misarden Park, Miserden *(44)*
Quenington Gardens, nr Fairford *(55)*
The Red House, Staunton, nr Gloucester *(57)*
Upton Wold, nr Moreton-in-Marsh *(74)*

June 27 Monday
25 Bowling Green Road, Cirencester *(9)*

June 28 Tuesday
Ewen Manor, Ewen Village, nr Cirencester *(19)*

June 29 Wednesday
25 Bowling Green Road, Cirencester *(9)*
Ewen Manor, Ewen Village, nr Cirencester *(19)*
Snowshill Manor, nr Broadway *(66)*
Trench Hill, Sheepscombe *(73)*

June 30 Thursday
Bourton House Garden, Bourton-on-the-Hill *(8)*
Ewen Manor, Ewen Village, nr Cirencester *(19)*
Moor Wood, Woodmancote *(45)*

July 2 Saturday
Rookwoods, Waterlane, nr Bisley *(61)*

July 3 Sunday
Beverston Castle, nr Tetbury *(5)*
25 Bowling Green Road, Cirencester *(9)*
The Bungalow, nr Newent *(10)*
Highnam Court, Highnam *(26)*
Sezincote, nr Moreton-in-Marsh *(64)*
Willow Lodge, nr Longhope *(79)*

July 4 Monday
Beverston Castle, nr Tetbury *(5)*
25 Bowling Green Road, Cirencester *(9)*
Hodges Barn, Shipton Moyne *(28)*
Willow Lodge, nr Longhope *(79)*

July 5 Tuesday
Ewen Manor, Ewen Village, nr Cirencester *(19)*
Hodges Barn, Shipton Moyne *(28)*

July 6 Wednesday
25 Bowling Green Road, Cirencester *(9)*
Ewen Manor, Ewen Village, nr Cirencester *(19)*

July 7 Thursday
Ewen Manor, Ewen Village, nr Cirencester *(19)*

July 8 Friday
Hodges Barn, Shipton Moyne *(28)*

July 10 Sunday
25 Bowling Green Road, Cirencester *(9)*
Selsley Gardens *(63)*

July 11 Monday
25 Bowling Green Road, Cirencester *(9)*

July 13 Wednesday
25 Bowling Green Road, Cirencester *(9)*

July 17 Sunday
25 Bowling Green Road, Cirencester *(9)*
The Matara Garden (formally Maheo), Kingscote *(42)*
Rosemary Cottage, Frocester *(62)*
Tinpenny Farm, Fiddington *(72)*
Trench Hill, Sheepscombe *(73)*
Willow Lodge, nr Longhope *(79)*

July 18 Monday
25 Bowling Green Road, Cirencester *(9)*
Willow Lodge, nr Longhope *(79)*

July 20 Wednesday
25 Bowling Green Road, Cirencester *(9)*

July 24 Sunday
25 Bowling Green Road, Cirencester *(9)*

July 25 Monday
25 Bowling Green Road, Cirencester *(9)*

July 27 Wednesday
25 Bowling Green Road, Cirencester *(9)*

July 28 Thursday
Bourton House Garden, Bourton-on-the-Hill *(8)*
Mill Dene Garden, Blockley *(43)*

July 30 Saturday
Home Farm, Huntley *(30)*

July 31 Sunday
25 Bowling Green Road, Cirencester *(9)*
Paulmead, Bisley *(51)*
Willow Lodge, nr Longhope *(79)*

August 1 Monday
Willow Lodge, nr Longhope *(79)*

August 7 Sunday
Highnam Court, Highnam *(26)*
Rosemary Cottage, Frocester *(62)*

August 10 Wednesday
Kiftsgate Court, nr Chipping Campden *(38)*

August 11 Thursday
Barnsley House, nr Cirencester *(4)*

August 14 Sunday
Trench Hill, Sheepscombe *(73)*
Willow Lodge, nr Longhope *(79)*

August 15 Monday
Willow Lodge, nr Longhope *(79)*

August 21 Sunday
Cotswold Farm, nr Duntisbourne Abbots, Cirencester *(16)*

August 25 Thursday
Bourton House Garden, Bourton-on-the-Hill *(8)*

August 28 Sunday
Rodmarton Manor, Cirencester *(60)*
Trench Hill, Sheepscombe *(73)*

September 4 Sunday
Highnam Court, Highnam *(26)*
Hunts Court, North Nibley *(34)*
Westbury Court Garden, Westbury-on-Severn *(77)*

September 11 Sunday
Blockley Gardens *(6)*
Hunts Court, North Nibley *(34)*
Trench Hill, Sheepscombe *(73)*

September 18 Sunday
Tinpenny Farm, Fiddington *(72)*

September 25 Sunday
Hidcote Manor Garden, Chipping Campden *(25)*
The Matara Garden (formally Maheo), Kingscote *(42)*

September 29 Thursday
Bourton House Garden, Bourton-on-the-Hill *(8)*

October 16 Sunday
Tinpenny Farm, Fiddington *(72)*

October 27 Thursday
Bourton House Garden, Bourton-on-the-Hill *(8)*

2006

February 19 Sunday
Tinpenny Farm, Fiddington *(72)*

DESCRIPTIONS OF GARDENS

◆ **Abbey House Gardens, Malmesbury Town Centre** ♿️✂️☺
See Wiltshire.

❶ Abbotswood, Stow-on-the-Wold ♿️
(Mr R Scully) *1m W of Stow-on-the-Wold. On B4068 nr Lower Swell or B4077 nr Upper Swell.* Massed plantings of spring bulbs, heathers, flowering shrubs and rhododendrons in dramatic, landscaped hillside stream gardens; fine herbaceous planting in elegant formal gardens with lily pond, terraced lawn and fountain created by Sir Edwin Lutyens. Partially suitable for wheelchairs, dogs on leads. TEAS. *Adm £3, chd free. Suns 5 June; 3 July; 7 Aug; 11 Sept.* **For NGS:** *Suns 10 Apr; 8 May (1.30-6)*

❷ Alderley Grange, Alderley ♿️✂️
(Mr Guy & the Hon Mrs Acloque) *2m S of Wotton-under-Edge. Turn NW off A46 Bath to Stroud rd, at Dunkirk.* Walled garden with fine trees, roses; herb gardens and aromatic plants. *Adm £3.50, chd free. Private visits welcome by appt June only. Tel 01453 842161*

❸ Barn House, Sandywell Park, Whittington ✂️
(Shirley & Gordon Sills) *5m E of Cheltenham. On A40 between Cheltenham & Andoversford. Near sign to Whittington.* Plantaholic designer's own 2-acre walled garden, developed from blank canvas over 16yrs by current owners with particular emphasis on attracting

wildlife. Variety of heavily planted rooms - both formal and informal, incl scented garden, yellow garden, stream garden with wildlife pool, formal water features and small arboretum area. *Adm £2.50. Suns 12, 26 June (2-5)*

❹ Barnsley House, nr Cirencester 🚻
(Mr Tim Haigh & Mr Rupert Pendered) *4m NE of Cirencester. On B4425.* Mature family garden, created by the late Rosemary Verey, with interesting collection of shrubs and trees; ground cover; herbaceous borders; pond garden; laburnum walk; knot and herb gardens; potager; C18 summerhouses. C17 house (not open). Garden open to the public on only seven days during the year. Home-made TEAS. *Adm £5. Thurs 14 Apr; 23 June; 11 Aug (11-5). Private visits welcome by appt, min 10, max 50. Tel 01285 740000 www.barnsleyhouse.com*

Barton House, Barton-on-the-Heath 🚻🌀🏵
See Warwickshire & part of West Midlands.

❺ Beverston Castle, nr Tetbury 🚻🏵
(Mrs A L Rook) *2m W of Tetbury. On A4135 rd to Dursley between Tetbury & Calcot Xrds.* Overlooked by romantic C12-C17 castle ruin (not open), overflowingly planted paved terrace leads from C18 house (not open) across moat to sloping lawn with spring bulbs in abundance, and full herbaceous and shrub borders. Large walled kitchen garden and greenhouses, orchids. Exhibition by local artists of botanical works at Easter. Home-made TEAS Suns only. *Adm £3, chd £2 14 to 18 under 14 free, OAP £2. Suns, Mons 27, 28 Mar (2-5); 3, 4 July (2-6). Private visits welcome by appt ejarook1@btinternet.com*

❻ Blockley Gardens
3m NW of Moreton-in-Marsh. Take A44 Moreton to Broadway rd; turning E. Popular Cotswold hillside village with great variety of high quality gardens; some walking necessary and some gardens not safe for small children. Bus provided. Home-made TEAS at St George's Hall. *Combined adm £5, chd free. Suns 12 June; 11 Sept (2-6)*

Colebrook House, Lower Street Mature garden approx 2½ acres, divided into numerous 'rooms' on different levels with many mature trees and shrubs, box hedges, kitchen garden, lawns and

herbaceous borders. 2 streams cross the garden, providing pretty water features. *Not open Sun 11 Sept*

3 The Dell 🏵 (Ms E Powell) Very small garden situated on the side of Blockley Brook. Restricted entry. *Not open Sun 11 Sept*

4 The Dell (Mr & Mrs B Stubbs) Fairly small garden, sloping down to Blockley Brook. *Not open Sun 11 Sept*

NEW Grange Cottage 🏵 (Alison & Guy Heitmahn) New owners have redesigned this multi-layered garden, with interest from May to Oct. Mixture of traditional and contemporary, from lush perennial plantings to cool green spaces.

NEW Keepers Cottage 🚻 (Paul Williams) Young garden with wide range of unusual plants, Sept especially good. *Private visits welcome by appt. Tel 01386 701048*

Malvern Mill 🌀🏵 (Mr & Mrs J Bourne) Old water mill with pond and brook; kitchen garden and orchard; cottage flower garden. Featured in 'Cotswold Life' 2004. *Not open Sun 11 Sept*

The Manor House 🚻 (George & Zoe Thompson) Top garden with lawn, roses, lavender and pergola. Lower garden beneath listed wall terraced with borders, box hedging and lawn leading to brook. Separate vegetable and herb garden with espaliered and cordoned fruits.

Mill Dene Garden, School Lane (Mr & Mrs B S Dare) (See separate entry).

The Old Chequer 🚻🌀🏵 (Mr & Mrs Linley) (See separate entry).

Pear Trees 🏵 (Mrs J Beckwith) Charming long narrow garden with entrance at rear and sunny gravel front garden.

Porch House 🏵 (Mr & Mrs C Johnson) Centrally located village garden with countryside views. Pear tree walk, knot garden and mixed borders. Redevelopment in progress.

❼ Boddington Manor, Boddington 🚻🏵
(Robert Hitchins Ltd) *3m W of Cheltenham. Off A4019 Cheltenham to Tewkesbury rd. After crossing M5, take first turning L, signed to Boddington.* Old garden sympathetically restored since 1985 incl wild flower woodland walk, mature specimen trees, extensive lawns and lakes; established pinetum

and bog garden. New planting of acers, birches, liquidambars in meadow setting. Neo-gothic manor house (not open). Country Garden Market. Light refreshments and TEAS in aid of Church of St Mary Magdalene. *Adm £2.50, chd free. Sun 29 May (11-5)*

❽ ◆ Bourton House Garden, Bourton-on-the-Hill 🚻🌀🏵
(Mr & Mrs R Paice) *2m W of Moreton-in-Marsh. On A44.* Intensively planted 3 acres with topiary, knot garden, potager, colour and herbaceous borders, water features and C16 tithe barn. Imaginative containers, vast range of unusual plants incl tender and half hardy, providing lots of late season interest; a plantsman's paradise. Featured in 'The English Garden' 2003 & 'Cotswold Life' 2004. Light refreshments and TEAS. *Adm £5, chd free, concessions £4.50. Weds to Fris 25 May to 31 Aug; Thurs, Fris, Sept to end Oct; Bank Hols Sun, Mon end May & Aug.* **For NGS:** *Thurs 26 May; 30 June; 28 July; 25 Aug; 29 Sept; 27 Oct (10-5). Tel 01386 700754 www.bourtonhouse.com*

❾ 25 Bowling Green Road, Cirencester 🏵
(Fr John & Susan Beck) *Take A417 to Gloucester just to T-lights, cross or turn R into The Whiteway then 1st L to No 25 on R of rd bend. Please respect neighbours' driveways, no pavement parking.* 400 (and still counting!) delightful, daring and different daylilies vie for space with plentiful priceless perennials, rambling roses, curvaceous clematis, graceful grasses, hopeful hostas, slim-line lawns and friendly frogs around paths, pools, pots and pergolas in their over-enthusiastic owners' Hemerocallis Heaven. *Adm £2, chd under 16 free. Mons, Weds, Suns, 19 June to 31 July (Suns 2-5) (Mons, Weds 11-4). Private visits welcome by appt mid June to end July, also groups. Tel 01285 653778 sjb@beck-hems.org.uk*

Broughton Poggs & Filkins Gardens
See Oxfordshire.

❿ The Bungalow, Birches Lane, nr Newent 🌀🏵
(Mrs Sue Clive) *1½m N of Newent. Off B4215, half-way between Newent & Dymock, signposted Botloes Green & Pool Hill. The Bungalow is first on L on edge of Three Choirs Vineyard.* With the Malvern Hills as a backdrop this ½-acre garden takes an individual

approach. Herbaceous cottage and wild flowers, hard and soft fruits and unusual custom-built water and architectural features are brought together with artistic intent. Home-made TEAS not Apr. *Adm £2, chd free (share to Downs Syndrome Assoc). Sun 10 Apr; Mon 30 May; Suns 5, 19 June; 3 July (1.30-5). Private visits welcome by appt May, June & July, also groups. Tel 01531 821640/020 7834 8233*

⑪ Campden House, Chipping Campden &
(The Hon Philip & Mrs Smith) ½m SW of Chipping Campden. Entrance on Chipping Campden to Weston Subedge rd, approx ¼m SW of Campden, 1¼m drive. 2 acres featuring mixed borders of plant and colour interest around house and C17 tithe barn (neither open). Set in fine parkland in hidden valley. Woodland walk, vegetable garden. *Adm £3, chd free. Weds 8, 15 June (2-6)*

⑫ ◆ Cerney House Gardens, North Cerney &⊗☺
(Sir Michael & Lady Angus) 4m NW of Cirencester. On A435 Cheltenham rd. Turn L opp Bathurst Arms, past church up hill, pillared gates on R. Romantic walled garden filled with old-fashioned roses and herbaceous borders. Working kitchen garden, scented garden, well-labelled herb garden, Who's Who beds and genera borders. Spring bulbs in abundance all around the wooded grounds. Bothy pottery. Cream TEAS. *Adm £3, chd £1. Tues, Weds, Fris, Suns Easter to July (10-5). For NGS: Sun 8 May (10-5). Tel 01285 831300 www.cerneygardens.com*

⑬ Chalford Gardens
4m E of Stroud. On A419 to Cirencester. Gardens are high above Chalford Vale & reached on foot by steep climb from car park on main rd or from High St. Hillside village with many quaint lanes, S-facing. Home-made TEAS at Marle Hill House (2-5). *Combined adm £4, chd free. Sat, Sun 11, 12 June (11-5)*

Marle Hill House ⊗ (Mike & Leslie Doyle-Davidson) 1-acre recently reclaimed Victorian woodland garden, containing a number of interlinked secret, formal and natural areas on steep terraced hillside with ponds, folly, nut tunnel and moongate.

The Old Chapel, Marle Hill ⊗ (F J & F Owen) (See separate entry).

The Rock House ⊗ (Mr & Mrs George Edwards) 1-acre, S-facing old garden. Dramatic 40ft cliff

and cave provide backdrop for climbing roses, clematis, shrubbery, rockery, lawn and herbaceous borders.

Chastleton Gardens
See Oxfordshire.

⑭ The Chipping Croft, 26 The Chipping, Tetbury &☺
(Dr & Mrs P W Taylor) 10m W of Cirencester. At bottom of Chipping Hill approached downhill from The Chipping market place. Up private drive after black door in wall. Free long-term car park 250yds: entrance nr Royal Oak PH. 2-acre, secluded, walled town garden on three levels, with mature trees, shrubs, herbaceous borders, rose beds and unusual plants; spring blossom and bulbs. Series of formal gardens, incl fruit and vegetable/flower potager all informally planted; also water garden. C17 Cotswold house (not open). Featured in 'Gloucester Citizen/Echo' 2004. *Adm £3.50, chd free. Private visits welcome by appt Apr to Sept. Tel 01666 503178*

⑮ NEW ◆ Colesbourne Park, Colesbourne &☺
(Mr & Mrs H W G Elwes) 8m S of Cheltenham. On A435 midway between Cheltenham & Cirencester. 10 acre garden famous for massed displays of rare snowdrops and other bulbs in spring. Currently undergoing restoration to reflect plantmanship of H J Elwes. Garden comprises woodland and lakeside walks, spring garden, herbaceous borders, formal lawns and terraces. Adjacent park, aboretum and church also open. Featured in 'Daily Telegraph' & 'Homes & Gardens' 2004. TEAS. *Adm £5. Fri to Sun 4 to 20 Feb; Sat to Mon 26 27, 28 Mar; Sats, Sun 16, 17 30 Apr; Sun, Mon 1,2 May. For NGS: Fri 15 Apr (1- last entry 4.30). Tel 01242 870567 www.colesbournegardens.org.uk*

⑯ Cotswold Farm, nr Duntisbourne Abbots, Cirencester ☺
(Mrs Mark Birchall) 5m NW of Cirencester. Off the old A417. From Cirencester turn L signed Duntisbourne Abbots Services, then immed R & R again into underpass. Private drive straight ahead. From Gloucester turn L signed Duntisbourne Abbots Services. Pass services; private drive on L. Cotswold garden in lovely position overlooking quiet valley on different levels with terrace designed by Norman Jewson in 1938; shrubs and trees, mixed borders, alpine border, shrub roses.

Croquet and toys for children on lawn. Walled kitchen garden. Snowdrops in Feb (by appt). Home-made TEAS in aid of WI. *Adm £3, chd free. Suns 24 Apr; 21 Aug (2-6). Private visits welcome by appt. Tel 01285 821857*

Dauntsey Gardens
See Wiltshire.

⑰ Eastcombe, Bussage and Brownshill Gardens
3m E of Stroud. 2m N of A419 Stroud to Cirencester rd on turning sign-posted to Bisley & Eastcombe. A group of gardens, large and small, set in a picturesque hilltop location. Some only approachable by foot. Exhibition of botanical art by Sally Birch. Jewellery and hand-painted silk scarves by Jean French. Home-made TEAS at Eastcombe Village Hall. *Combined adm £3.50, chd free (share to Cotswold Care Hospice, Cobalt Unit Appeal Fund Cheltenham, & Victim Support Glos). Sun, Mon 1, 2 May (2-6)*

Beechcroft, Beech Lane, Brownshill & (Mr & Mrs R H Salt) Traditional garden surrounding an Edwardian house (not open) with a cottage garden feel. Mature trees, shrubs, herbaceous borders, wild area, herb garden, conservatory, potting shed, vegetable garden and greenhouse.

NEW 26 Ferris Court View, Bussage &⊗ (Mr & Mrs Peter Brook) Small easy-care retirement garden.

Five One Two, Beech Lane, Brownshill ⊗ (Pamela Woods & James Showers) Newly-developed garden created by designer and plantswoman Pamela Woods, consisting of Mediterranean garden with pool and woodland garden with unusual shrubs. Unique timber features, such as a moongate created by James Showers. Featured with Chris Beardshaw on BBC Heaven & Earth 2004. *Private visits welcome by appt also groups. Tel 01453 885903*

NEW 1 The Laurels, Eastcombe ⊗ (Andrew & Ruth Fraser) Terraced garden on several levels joined by flights of steps with herbaceous borders, shrubs, small pond and terraced vegetable garden, largely reconstructed by present owners. Not suitable for the infirm.

NEW Little Dormers, 64 Lypiatt View, Bussage &⊗ (Bernadette Scahill) Small terraced garden with a mixture of unusual acid loving plants and waterfall feature.

NEW **Mount Pleasant Cottage, Eastcombe** &⃝ (Mr & Mrs R Peyton) Large garden with formal lawns and borders. Informal lower garden near woodland with small natural pond.

NEW **Normandie Cottage, Fidges Lane, Eastcombe** & (Anita Heywood) Cottage garden where flowers grow in unexpected places. Child and dog friendly. Huge willow tree and small orchard of fruit trees.

Redwood, Bussage &⃝ (David & Rita Collins) Terraced garden with a variety of hard landscaping, pergolas and screens together with ponds, lawns, vegetable garden and cordon fruit trees. Unusual plants and spring bulbs with many double hellebores.

NEW **Rose Cottage, The Street** & (Mrs J Shipman) Old-fashioned walled cottage garden, terraced to take advantage of hillside site and beautiful views.

18 ♦ **Eastleach House, Eastleach Martin** &⃝
(Mrs David Richards) *5m NE of Fairford. From Fairford on A417, signed to Eastleach on L. 4m to village, turn R down hill towards bridge. Entrance to garden by church gates. No access for coaches - drop visitors at gate and park outside village. Limted parking at house for disabled.* Large traditional all-yr-round garden. Wooded hilltop position with long views S and W. New parkland, lime avenue and arboretum. Wild flower walk, wildlife pond, lawns, walled and rill gardens, with modern herbaceous borders, yew and box hedges, iris and peony borders, lily ponds, formal herb, topiary and knot gardens. Rambling roses into trees. Steep entrance drive and gravel paths. Featured in 'Country Life' 2003. Home-made TEAS in village hall (NGS day only). *Adm £5, chd under 16 free (share to Eastleach PCC, Church Fabric fund). Fris June & July.* **For NGS:** *Sun 12 June (2-5) sreastleach@onetel.com*

19 **Ewen Manor, Ewen Village, nr Cirencester** &
(Lady Gibbs) *4m SW of Cirencester. Via A429 3m from Cirencester turn at signpost Ewen 1m.* Profusely planted series of gardens with architectural features, yew hedges, pattern-mown lawn, terrace and

containers, lily pool, cedar trees over 200yrs old; woodland area all around. Spring bulbs and blossom. Georgian Cotswold manor (not open). *Adm £2.50. Tues, Weds, Thurs, 24 May to 7 July (11-4)*

20 **Eyford Gardens**
3m W of Stow on the Wold. On the B4068 (formerly A436), signed Lower Swell & Naunton. 2 gardens near to each other, just outside village. *Combined adm £3. Weds 15, 22 June (2-6)*

> **Eyford House** (Mrs C A Heber Percy) *Stone Lodge on R, with white iron gates & cattle grid.* 1½-acre sloping N garden, ornamental shrubs and trees. Laid out originally by Graham Stuart Thomas, 1976. West garden and terrace, red border, walled kitchen garden, two lakes with pleasant walks and views (boots needed).

> **Eyford Knoll** (Mrs S Prest) *At Xrds turn R for Cotswold Farm Park, entrance 400yds on R.* Cottage garden, with C18 fountain from Faringdon House, gardens redesigned 8yrs ago by Lady Aird.

21 **France Lynch, nr Stroud**
5m E of Stroud. Turn off A419 at Chalford signed Chalford Lynch. Follow signs to France Lynch. Parking in village limited. Car park at Highfield Sports Club. Hillside village of old cottages and pretty lanes, with views across valley. Home-made TEAS at Orchard Cottage in aid of NSPCC. *Combined adm £3.50. Wed 18 May (2-6)*

> **NEW** **The Anchorage, Brantwood Road** ⃝ (Simon & Carol Smith) Small landscaped garden with gravel paths, pond and mixed borders of herbaceous perennials.

> **Dundry Lodge, Lynch Road** ⃝ (David & Stella Martin) Walled secluded, ½-acre garden evolved over past 30yrs, planned to use structure and form as well as colour. Terraced vegetable garden with 2 greenhouses aimed to produce yr-round crops. *Private visits welcome by appt. Tel 01453 883419*

> **Lilac Cottage, Sturmyes Road** ⃝⃝ (Mr & Mrs Malcolm Heath) Small cottage garden. Roses, clematis, some tender perennials. Lots of colour.

> **NEW** **Little Oaks, Coppice Hill** ⃝ (Mrs Jane Calvert) E-facing sloping garden with curved mixed borders to complement the

undulations of the surrounding countryside.

Orchard Cottage, Lynch Road ⃝ (Charles & Pat Willey) Large cottage garden in the process of reclamation over the last 4yrs; mixed flower borders with emphasis on pinks and blues; also developing vegetable and fruit areas. Woodland.

The Tyning, Highfield Way ⃝⃝ (Michael & Maureen Dewhurst) ½-acre garden evolved over past 9yrs. Approx 80 mature and new trees and shrubs with herbaceous borders. Beyond the house (not open) is a 'wildwood' underplanted with bulbs and shade-loving plants.

Gadfield Elm House, Malvern Road, Staunton &
See Worcestershire.

22 **The Glebe House, Shipton Moyne** &
(Mr & Mrs Richard Boggis-Rolfe) *2½m S of Tetbury. In Shipton Moyne. Next to church.* Medium-sized garden surrounding former rectory (not open). Mixture of formal and informal planting. Walled kitchen garden, mown walks through orchard and woodland planted with bulbs. Double herbaceous border newly planted and designed. TEAS. *Adm £2.50. Sun, Mon 12, 13 June (2-6)*

23 **Grange Farm, Evenlode, nr Moreton-in-Marsh** &⃝⃝
(Lady Aird) *3m N of Stow-on-the-Wold. E of A429 Fosseway & 1½m from Broadwell.* This imaginative, well-planted garden is subdivided and the areas flow easily from one to another. The route from herbaceous borders and lawn to the water garden overhung with ancient apple trees and on through the yew circle and sunk garden are inviting and interesting and children seem to love it. There is a productive vegetable garden and shady, tranquil places to sit. TEAS in aid of St Edward's Church, Evenlode. *Adm £2.50, chd free. Sun 19 June (11-5). Private visits welcome by appt May & June. Tel 01608 650607 meaird@aol.com*

24 **Green Cottage, Lydney** &⃝ NCCPG
(Mr & Mrs F Baber) *¼m SW of Lydney. Approaching Lydney from Gloucester, keep to A48 through Lydney. Leaving Lydney turn R into narrow lane at de-limit sign. Garden 1st R. Shady parking.* 1½-acre country garden planted for seasonal

interest and wildlife. Mature trees, stream, duckpond and bog garden. Developing woodland area and banks, planted with ferns, hellebores, daphnes and other shade lovers. Cottage garden. Herbaceous peonies featured throughout the garden, incl National Collection of rare Victorian and Edwardian cultivars of peonies (best in June), others in May. Home-made TEAS (Suns only). Adm £2, chd free. Suns 1 May to 26 June; Weds 8, 15, 22 June (2-5)

◆ **Hellens, Much Marcle** &⊕
See Herefordshire.

㉕ ◆ **Hidcote Manor Garden, Chipping Campden** ⊗⊕
(The National Trust) 4m NE of Chipping Campden. Off B4081, close to the village of Mickleton. One of England's great gardens, 10½-acre 'Arts and Crafts' masterpiece created by the Major Lawrence Johnston. Series of outdoor rooms, each with a different character and separated by walls and hedges of many different species. Many rare trees and shrubs, outstanding herbaceous borders and unusual plant species from all over the world. Light refreshments and TEAS in Al-Fresco Tea Bar & Garden Restaurant. Adm £6.60, chd £3.30. Sats to Weds 19 Mar to 30 Oct (10.30-5), from 3 Oct (10.30-last adm 4). For NGS: Sun 25 Sept (10.30-5). Tel 01386 438333 www.nationaltrust.org.uk/hidcote

㉖ **Highnam Court, Highnam** &
(Roger Head) 2m W of Gloucester. Leave Gloucester on A40 towards Ross on Wye. DO NOT take Newent turning, but proceed to next big Highnam roundabout. Take R exit for Highnam Court entrance directly off roundabout. 40 acres of Victorian landscaped gardens surrounding magnificent Grade I house (not open), set out by the artist Thomas Gambier Parry. Lakes, shrubberies and listed Pulhamite water gardens with grottos and fernery. Exciting ornamental lakes, and woodland areas. New extensive 1-acre rose garden. TEAS. Adm £3, chd free. Suns 3 May; 1 May; 5 June; 3 July; 7 Aug; 4 Sept (11-5). Private visits welcome by appt, coaches permitted, groups of 15+. Tel 01452 308251

㉗ **Hillesley House, Hillesley, nr Wotton-under-Edge** &⊕
(Fiona & Jeremy Walsh) 3m from Wotton-under-Edge. On rd to Hawkesbury Upton & A46 from Wotton-under-Edge. Extensive revamping and planting of 4 acres of walled, secret and open garden, plus

vegetable garden and arboretum. Unusual topiary. Rose beds and borders. Plenty of exciting ideas are being continued this yr. Open this yr by appt for the first time for viewing of mass daffodil show, also May for wisteria flowering. Light refreshments and TEAS. Adm £3, chd free. Sun 12 June (2-6). Private visits welcome by appt, Mar, Apr; 9 to 27 May; 13 June to 12 Aug (not Suns prefer weekdays). Tel Stewart (Head Gardener) - 07971 854260/01453 842332

㉘ **Hodges Barn, Shipton Moyne** &
(Mrs C N Hornby) 3m S of Tetbury. On Malmesbury side of village. Very unusual C15 dovecote converted into family home (not open). Cotswold stone walls act as host to climbing and rambling roses, clematis, vines, hydrangeas, and together with yew, rose and tapestry hedges create formality around house. Mixed shrub and herbaceous borders, shrub roses; water garden; woodland garden planted with cherries, magnolias and spring bulbs. Also open for NGS, adjoining garden of **Hodges Farmhouse** by kind permission of Mrs Clive Lamb. Featured in BBC 2 Gardeners World 2004. Adm £5, chd free. Suns, Mons 10, 11 Apr; 22, 23 May; Mon, Tues, Fri 4, 5, 8 July (2-6). Private visits welcome by appt. Tel 01666 880202

㉙ **Holcombe Glen Cottage, Minchinhampton** &⊕
(Christine & Terry Sharpe) 1m E of Nailsworth. From Nailsworth take Avening Rd B4014. Turn L at Weighbridge Inn. Turn L 100yds into Holcombe Glen. 1st house on L. From Minchinhampton 1¼m via Well Hill or New Rd. 3 acres incl springs and ponds. Small waterfalls feed river and stream giving bog and meadow areas full of wildlife and wild flowers. Above these terraced walled garden for vegetables and herbaceous plants. TEAS in aid of Cobalt Unit Appeal Fund. Adm £3, chd free. Sun 5 June (11-5)

㉚ **Home Farm, Huntley** ⊗
(Mrs T Freeman) 4m S of Newent. On B4216 ½m off A40 in Huntley travelling towards Newent. Set in elevated position with exceptional views. 1m walk through woods and fields to show carpets of spring flowers. Enclosed garden with fern border, sundial and heather bed. White and mixed shrub borders. Stout footwear advisable in winter. Home-made TEAS in aid of Riding for the Disabled. Adm £2 single gdn,

combined £4.50 with **Huntley Manor**1, 2 May, chd free. Suns 30 Jan; 13 Feb; 3, 17 Apr; 1, 2 May (2-5); Sat 30 July (11-6 for Glos Catherdral Flower Show). Private visits welcome by appt. Tel 01452 830209 torill@ukgateway.net

㉛ **Hullasey House, Tarlton** &⊗
(Jonathan & Gail Taylor) 5m SW of Cirencester. Off A433. Cotswold garden with exceptional views. Stone walls, many old roses, gravel gardens round house (not open). Walled herb and fruit potager; walled mixed shrub and herbaceous garden. Adm £2.50, chd free. Sat, Sun, Mon 11, 12, 13 June (2-6). Private visits welcome by appt mid May - mid July. Tel 01285 770132

㉜ **Humphreys End House, Randwick, nr Stroud** ⊗⊕
(Pat & Jim Hutton) 2m NW of Stroud. M5 J13, follow signs to Cashes Green & Randwick. At Townsend, turn R. Parking at Rose Cottage opp. Different areas of contrasting mood and interesting planting in 1-acre garden surrounding listed C16 farmhouse (not open). Wildlife pond, herbs, old roses, grasses. Organic vegetables. Cream TEAS (Sun). Adm £2, chd free. Sun 1 May (2-6). Evening Opening £2, wine, Thur 9 June (5-9). Private visits welcome by appt, May, June & July. Tel 01453 765401

㉝ NEW **Huntley Manor, Huntley** &⊗
(Prof & Mrs Tim Congdon) 4m S of Newent. On B4216 ½m off A40 in Huntley travelling towards Newent. Park-like grounds surround the gothic 'French Chateau' style house (not open) built in 1862 by S S Teulon. Informal beds of mature shrubbery and rare specimen trees (tulip tree reputed to be tallest in the country after Kew), intersperse with sweeping lawns down to lake. Woodland walk with giant redwoods; exotic waterfowl and peacocks roam the grounds. Artists/painters welcome. Featured in The Country Houses of Gloucestershire vol 3 & Pevsner. Picnic Boxes in aid of Sophie's Silver Lining Fund. Adm £3 single gdn, combined £4.50 with **Home Farm** 1, 2 May. Private visits welcome by appt apply in writing Mrs Dorianne Congdon/Mr Alex Woods Huntley Manor, Huntley GL19 3HQ

㉞ ◆ **Hunts Court, North Nibley** &⊗⊕
(Mr & Mrs T K Marshall) 2m NW of Wotton-under-Edge. From Wotton

B4060 Dursley rd turn R in North Nibley at Black Horse; fork L after ¼m. A plant lover's garden with unusual shrubs, 450 varieties old roses, large collection of penstemons and hardy geraniums in peaceful 2½-acre garden set against tree-clad hills and Tyndale monument. Recently planted mini-arboretum. House (not open) possible birthplace of William Tyndale. Picnic area. Featured in 'English Garden' 2003 & 'The Times' 2004. Home-made TEAS (NGS days) in aid of St Martin's Church & Mothers' Union. *Adm £3, chd free. Tues to Sats all yr except Aug (9-12.30 - 1.45 - 5).* **For NGS:** *Suns 12, 19, 26 June; 4, 11 Sept (2-6). Tel 01453 547440 keith@huntscourt.fsnet.co.uk*

㉟ Icomb Place, nr Stow-on-the-Wold ⌦
(Mr & Mrs T L F Royle) *4m S of Stow. After 2m on A424 Burford rd turn L to Icomb village.* Over 100-yr-old garden (one of the original gardens open under the NGS) featuring woodland walk through mature and young trees in arboretum; hydrangeas, rhododendrons and azaleas in season; grotto; pools, stream and water garden; potager; lawned garden with extensive views. C14 manor house (not open). Home-made TEAS in aid of village hall. *Adm £3, chd £1.50. Sun 26 June (2-6)*

"You can come down now Henry, they've all gone!"

㊱ ◆ Kempsford Manor, Kempsford ⌦⌦
(Mrs Z I Williamson) *3m S of Fairford. Take A419 from Cirencester or Swindon. Kempsford is signed 10m (approx) from each. The Manor is in the centre of village.* Early spring garden with snowdrops, winter aconites, followed by crocuses, anemones, daffodils and narcissi. Snowdrop walk along canal to orchard and vegetable garden. Summer garden of herbaceous borders and roses; adjacent to village cricket field. Outdoor games for children. Peaceful, expansive garden for relaxation. Live music on some occasions. Accommodation. Home-made TEAS. *Adm £3, chd free. Suns, Bank Hol Mons 16 Feb to 25 Sept, except 20 Mar; 3 Apr; 15 May; 3 July. Open Weds 16, 23 Feb; 8, 15, 22 June; 17, 24 Aug (2-5); Sun 19 June Flower Festival and Jazz, adm £6 (2-9). Tel 01285 810131 www.members.lycos. co.uk/kempsford_manor*

Kencot Gardens, nr Lechlade
See Oxfordshire.

㊲ Kestrel Cottage, Brand Green ⌦⌦
(Jo & Mike Howe) *2½m NE of Newent. From Gloucester take A40 W. Turn R onto B4215. After 3½m, turn R signed Hartpury & Upleadon. Proceed 2¾m, over Xrds & after 1¼m park at village hall (Pauntley), garden 200yds on R.* ½-acre, sloping plantsman's garden . Pretty half-timbered cottage (not open), beautiful views over Severn Vale. Unusual plants, mixed and herbaceous borders, dappled shade area, pond, stone troughs and alpines. Ferns, trilliums, hardy orchis, erythroniums, roscoea, iris, epimediums, clematis, euphorbias, roses, violas, lavenders and arisaemas feature. TEAS at Pauntley Village Hall (Suns only). *Adm £2 , chd free. Suns, Mons, Tues 24, 25 Apr; 8, 10, 22, 23 May; 5, 7, 19, 20 June (2-5). Private visits welcome by appt. Tel 01531 821055*

㊳ ◆ Kiftsgate Court, nr Chipping Campden ⌦⌦
(Mr & Mrs J G Chambers) *4m NE of Chipping Campden. Adjacent to Hidcote National Trust Garden. 1m E of B4632 & B4081.* Magnificent situation and views; many unusual plants and shrubs; tree peonies, hydrangeas, abutilons, species and old-fashioned roses, but largest rose in England, *Rosa filipes* 'Kiftsgate'. Winner Garden of the Year award, HHA/Christie's 2003. Home-made TEAS. *Adm £5, chd £1.50. Weds,*

Thurs, Suns, Bank Hol Mons Apr, May, Aug, Sept (2-6); Mons, Weds, Thurs, Sats, Suns June, July (12-6). **For NGS:** *Weds 4 May; 10 Aug (2-6). Tel 01386 438777 www.kiftsgate. co.uk*

◆ Kingstone Cottages, Weston under Penyard, nr Ross-on-Wye ⌦⌦ NCCPG
See Herefordshire.

㊴ Lammas Park, Cuckoo Row, Minchinhampton ⌦
(Mr P Grover) *4m SE of Stroud. From Market Sq down High St for 100yds, turn R at Xrds. After 300yds turn L, Lammas Park 100yds on L.* 2½ acres around Cotswold 'Arts and Crafts' style house (not open). Herbaceous borders, pleached lime allee, wild garden, alpines, restored C17 'hanging gardens' with tunnel. Superb views. Home-made TEAS in aid of Minchinhampton Centre for the Elderly. *Adm £2, chd free. Sun 5 June (2-5). Private visits welcome by appt. Tel 01453 886471*

The Long Barn, Eastnor ⌦⌦
See Herefordshire.

㊵ Lower Farm House, Cliffords Mesne ⌦⌦
(Gareth & Sarah Williams) *2m S of Newent. From Newent follow signs to Cliffords Mesne & Birds of Prey Centre (1½m). Approx ½m beyond 'centre', turn L at Xrds. Signed Kents Green. Garden 150yds down hill on bend.* Car park (limited if wet). 2-acre garden developed over 12yrs, incl woodland, stream and large natural lily pond with rockery and bog garden. Herbaceous borders, pergola walk, terrace with ornamental fishpond, kitchen and herb garden; many interesting and unusual trees and shrubs. TEAS. *Adm £2.50, chd free. Weds 25 May; 1 June (2-6)*

㊶ ◆ Lydney Park Spring Garden, Lydney ⌦⌦
(The Viscount Bledisloe) *½m SW of Lydney. On A48 Gloucester to Chepstow rd between Lydney & Aylburton. Drive is directly off A48.* Spring garden in 8-acre woodland valley with lakes, profusion of rhododendrons, azaleas and other flowering shrubs. Formal garden; magnolias and daffodils (April). Picnics in deer park which has fine trees. Important Roman Temple site and museum. Teas in family dining room (otherwise house not open), . Dogs on leads. Home-made TEAS. *Adm £4, chd 50p, concessions £3 (Weds only). Weds, Suns, Bank Hols*

20 Mar to 5 June; Every day 2 to 8 May & 30 May to 5 June. **For NGS:** Wed 20 Apr; Tue 3 May (11-6). Tel 01594 842844

42 ◆ The Matara Garden (formally Maheo), Kingscote &🚫⊕
(Herons Mead Ltd) 5½m NW of Tetbury. On A4135 towards Dursley. At the Hunters Hall Inn turn R into Kingscote village. Enter Park at 1st gate on R. A unique meditative garden alive with inspiration from around the world. Labyrinths, medicine wheel, ponds, sculptures and walled ornamental vegetable garden. We are developing an Eastern woodland walk and wild flower meadow. Matara is a spiritual garden dedicated to the full expression of the human spirit. All set within a 28-acre parkland. Partially suitable for wheelchairs. Light refreshments and TEAS (NGS days). Adm £3, chd free. Weds, Fris, Suns May to Sept. **For NGS:** Suns 22 May; 17 July; 25 Sept (1-5). Tel 01453 860084 www.matara.co.uk

43 ◆ Mill Dene Garden, School Lane, Blockley &🚫⊕
(Mr & Mrs B S Dare) 3m NW of Moreton-in-Marsh. From A44, follow brown signs from Bourton-on-the-Hill, to Blockley. 1½m down hill turn L behind village gates. Parking for 8 cars. This garden surrounds a Cotswold stone water-mill, set in a tiny steep sided valley. It seems to have evolved naturally in English 'country garden' style. A millpond, stream, grotto, potager and trompe l'oeil all contribute to the owner's design for surprise, concealment, scent, colour and, above all, fun. Accommodation. Featured in 'Essential Water Garden', Het & Bolig', 'Sunday Telegraph', 2003, 'Leisure Painter', 'Sondagsavisen', NHK TV - Japan 2004. Light refreshments and TEAS. Adm £5, chd £1, concessions £4.50. Tues to Fris 5 Apr to 28 Oct (10-5.30); . **For NGS:** Suns 3 Apr; 29 May; Thur 28 July (2-5). Also opening with **Blockley Gardens** 12 June, 11 Sept. Tel 01386 700457 www.milldenegarden.co.uk

44 ◆ Misarden Park, Miserden &🚫⊕
(Major M T N H Wills) 6m NW of Cirencester. Follow signs off A417 or B4070 from Stroud. Spring flowers, shrubs, fine topiary (some designed by Sir Edwin Lutyens) and herbaceous borders within walled garden; roses; fine specimen trees; rill and parterre; C17 manor house (not open) standing high overlooking

Golden Valley. Adjacent nursery. Featured in 'Western Gazette' & 'Gloucestershire Echo' 2004. Home-made TEAS (NGS days). Adm £3.50, chd free (share to Gloucestershire Cathedral Trust, NGS days only). Tues, Weds,Thurs Apr to Sept (10-5). **For NGS:** Suns 3 Apr; 26 June (2-6). Tel 01285 821303

45 Moor Wood, Woodmancote 🚫NCCPG
(Mr & Mrs Henry Robinson) 3½m NW of Cirencester. Turn L off A435 to Cheltenham at North Cerney, signed Woodmancote 1¼m; entrance in village on L beside lodge with white gates. 2 acres of shrub, orchard and wild flower gardens in isolated valley setting. Holder of the National Collection of rambler roses. Home-made TEAS. Adm £2.50. Thur 30 June (2-6). Private visits welcome by appt. Tel 01285 831397

46 The Old Chapel, Marle Hill, Chalford Vale
(F J & F Owen) 4m E of Stroud. On A419 to Cirencester. Above Chalford Vale, steep climb from car park on main rd, up Marle Hill. 1-acre Victorian chapel garden on precipitous hillside. A tiered tapestry of herbaceous borders, formal potager, small orchard, pond and summerhouse, old roses. Gothic pergola and rose tunnel, all laid out on terraced S-facing Marle Cliff. Art Exhibition in studio. Adm £3, chd free. Sat 4 June to Sun 19 June (10-5). Also opening with **Chalford Gardens** 11, 12 June

47 The Old Chequer, Draycott
(Mr & Mrs H Linley) 2m NE of Moreton-in-Marsh. Nr Blockley. 2-acre garden planted for all-yr interest. Distinct areas: gravel; island beds; mixed shrubs and herbaceous, alpines, unusual plants, kitchen garden, old orchard and croquet lawn. Accommodation. Featured in Japanese 'NHK Gardening' magazine & Japanese version of Gardeners' World TV. TEAS. Adm £2, chd free. Sun 10 Apr (11-4.30). Also opening with **Blockley Gardens** 12 June 11 Sept. Private visits welcome by appt, Apr to July only. Tel 01386 700647

The Old Corn Mill, Aston Crews 🚫⊕
See Herefordshire.

48 The Old Rectory, Duntisbourne Rous
(Charles & Mary Keen) 4m NW of Cirencester. At Daglingworth take valley rd for the Duntisbournes. After

½m no-through rd joins from R at entrance to Old Rectory. Can also be approached via Duntisbourne Leer off A417; turn L (after crossing ford) at T junction. Writer and designer's own 1½-acre Cotswold family garden. Beautiful setting nr Saxon church. Planted for atmosphere and all-yr interest, this small garden has ten distinct areas and moods. Winter flowers, 100+ auriculas under cover, tender plants and unusual pelargoniums a speciality. Plants for sale occasionally. 'House & Garden' feature 2003. Adm £3.50, chd free. Mons 14 Feb; 14 Mar; 9 May; 20 June (11-5). Private visits welcome by appt for groups Written or email appt The Old Rectory, Duntisbourne Rous GL7 7AP mary@keengardener.com

49 The Old Vicarage, Maisemore &🚫⊕
(Mr & Mrs George Hayter) 2m NW of Gloucester. Take the A417 from Gloucester towards Ledbury. Cross the R Severn in Maisemore. Take 2nd turning on R, at the church bear L, at Xrds turn R. Car park approx 400yds on R. Easy access and parking. Garden approx 2 acres. Delightful rose garden edged with lavender; richly planted herbaceous borders with many unusual plants interspersed with shrubs; potager with flowers, fruit and vegetables. Knot garden which leads to large rock garden. Beside the rock garden is 'Pooh Corner' where within an old ash tree is a tree house and play-ship. Cream TEAS in aid of Gloucester Cathedral Flower Guild. Adm £2.50, chd £1. Mon 28 Mar; Suns 8, 29 May (2-6)

50 ◆ Painswick Rococo Garden, Painswick ⊕
(Painswick Rococo Garden Trust) ¼m N of Painswick. ½m outside village on B4073. Unique C18 garden from the brief Rococo period, combining contemporary buildings, vistas, ponds, kitchen garden and winding woodland walks. Recently planted maze. Light refreshments and TEAS in The Coach House. Adm £4, chd £2, concessions £3.50. Daily 10 Jan to 31 Oct (11-5). Tel 01452 813204 prm@rococogarden.co.uk

Park Farm, Alderley &🚫⊕
See Bristol & South Gloucestershire.

51 Paulmead, Bisley &🚫
(Judy & Philip Howard) 5m E of Stroud. On S edge of Bisley at head of Toadsmoor Valley. 5m E of Stroud on top of Cotswolds. Garden & car park well signed in Bisley village. Approx 1-acre landscaped garden

constructed in stages over last 15yrs. Terraced in three main levels: natural stream garden; formal herbaceous and shrub borders; yew and beech hedges; formal vegetable garden; lawns; summerhouse with exterior wooden decking by pond and thatched roof over well head. New unusual tree house. *Adm £3, chd free (share to Gloucester Cathedral Trust). Sun 31 July (2-6.30)*

52 Pear Tree Cottage, 58 Malleson Road, Gotherington 🔲
(Mr & Mrs E Manders-Trett) *4m N of Cheltenham. A435 N of Cheltenham. Turn R into Gotherington 1m after end of Bishop's Cleeve bypass. Garden is on L approx 100yds past Shutter Inn.* Mainly informal country garden approx ½-acre with pond and gravel garden, grasses and herbaceous borders, trees and shrubs surrounding lawns. Wild garden and orchard lead to greenhouses, herb and vegetable gardens. Spring bulbs and early summer perennials and shrubs particularly colourful. TEAS. *Adm £2.50, chd free. Suns 20 Mar; 22 May (2-5). Private visits welcome by appt, also groups of 10+. Tel 01242 674592 edandmary@emanders-trett. freeserve.co.uk*

53 NEW Pemberley Lodge, Churchend Lane, Old Charfield 🔲🔲
(Rob & Yvette Andrewartha) *3½m SW of Wotton-under-Edge. Off B4058 from Wotton-under Edge through Charfield Village. At top of Charfield Hill, turn L. 2m from M5 J14, at Xrds on B4509 go straight across into Churchend Lane.* Small private garden designed and planted in 2002 by Lesley Rosser. Densly planted for all-yr-round interest, maturing well. Incoporates trees, shrubs, perennials, grasses, water, gravel and hard landscaping to give an informal peaceful feel. *Adm £2, chd under 12 free. Sun 29 May (2-5)*

54 Pigeon House, Southam Lane, Southam 🔲🔲
(Mr & Mrs Julian Taylor) *3m NE of Cheltenham. Off B4632 toward Winchombe. Parking available adjacent to Southam Tithe Barn.* 2-acre garden surrounding Cotswold stone manor (not open) of medieval origin. Small lake with island and separate water garden with linked pools featuring water margin and bog plants. Extensive lawns on several levels; wide range of flowering shrubs and borders designed to create a multitude of vistas; woodland area with shade-loving plants and many

spring bulbs. TEAS. *Adm £2, chd free. Suns 17 Apr; 5 June (2-5). Private visits welcome by appt. Tel 01242 529342 juliantaylor@pigeonhouse. freeserve.co.uk*

55 Quenington Gardens, nr Fairford
8m NE of Cirencester. A rarely visited Coln Valley village delighting its infrequent visitors with C12 Norman church and C17 stone cottages (not open). An opportunity to discover the horticultural treasures behind those Cotswold stone walls and visit 6 very different but charming gardens incorporating everything from the exotic and the organic to the simple cottage garden; a range of vistas from riverside to seclusion. Sculpture Show at The Old Rectory. TEAS at The Old Rectory in aid of Hatherop Primary School. *Combined adm £4. Sun 26 June (2-6)*

Bank View (Mrs J A Moulden) Terraced garden with wonderful views over the R Coln.

Old Post House (Mrs D Blackwood) Terraced garden. Full of colour, and a wonderful conservatory.

The Old Rectory 🔲🔲 (Mr & Mrs D Abel Smith) On the banks of the mill race and the R Coln, this is an organic garden of variety. Mature trees and new plantings, large vegtable garden, herbaceous, shade, pool and bog gardens. Host to biennial sculpture show.

Pool Hay (Mrs E A Morris) Small beautiful riverside garden - old-fashioned roses a feature.

Yew Tree Cottages (Mr J Lindon) Quintessential cottage garden.

56 Ramblers, Lower Common, Aylburton, nr Lydney 🔲🔲
(Jane & Leslie Hale) *1½m W of Lydney. Off A48 Gloucester to Chepstow Rd. From Lydney through Aylburton, out of de-limit turn R signed Aylburton Common, ¾m along lane.* Peaceful medium-sized country garden with informal cottage planting, herbaceous borders and small pond looking through hedge 'windows' onto wild flower meadow. Front woodland garden with shade-loving plants and topiary. Large productive vegetable garden. Recently planted apple orchard. Steps to entrance and terracing. Featured in HTV Roots & Shoots 2003. TEAS. *Adm £2.50, chd free. Suns 8 May; 5, 12 June (2-6)*

57 The Red House, Staunton, nr Gloucester 🔲🔲
(Mr & Mrs W K Turner) *8m NW of Gloucester. Pillows Green. On A417 from Staunton Xrds, ½m off B4208.* Split-level 2-acre organic and wildlife garden with herbaceous borders, containing many native wild plants, ponds; gravel garden and terrace with containers; parterre; also flower meadow. C17 house open by appt. Garden designed and maintained by owners. TEAS. *Adm £2, chd free. Suns 15 May; 12, 26 June (2-6). Private visits welcome by appt. Tel 01452 840505 keith@redhouse.ip.uk.com*

58 Redwood, Bussage 🔲
(David & Rita Collins) *3m E of Stroud. 2m N of A419 Stroud to Cirencester on turning signed to Bisley & Eastcombe. Please park with consideration.* Terraced garden with a variety of hard landscaping, pond, fruit and vegetable garden. Many unusual early blooming flowers especially double hellebores. Hellebores for sale on Sat (& Sun if supplies last). TEAS. *Adm £2, chd under 14 free. Sat, Sun 5, 6 Mar (1-4). Also opening with Eastcombe, Bussage & Brownshill Gardens 1, 2 May*

59 Rockcliffe, nr Lower Swell 🔲🔲
(Mr & Mrs Simon Keswick) *2m SW of Stow-on-the-Wold. On B4068. From Stow-on-the-Wold go through Lower Swell, 1½m turn R into signed driveway.* Large traditional English garden 7 acres incl pink, white and blue gardens, herbaceous border, rose terrace; walled kitchen garden and orchard; greenhouses and new stone dovecot with pathway of topiary birds leading up to it. Home-made TEAS in aid of Kates Home Nursing. *Adm £3.50. Weds 15, 22, Thur 23 June (12-5)*

60 ◆ Rodmarton Manor, Cirencester 🔲🔲
(Mr & Mrs Simon Biddulph) *5m NE of Tetbury. Off A433. Between Cirencester & Tetbury.* The 8-acre garden of this fine 'Arts and Crafts' house is a series of 'outdoor rooms' each with its own distinctive character. Leisure garden, winter garden, troughery, topiary, hedges, lawns, rockery, containers, wild garden, kitchen garden, magnificent herbaceous borders. Snowdrop collection. *House and Garden adm £7, chd £3.50 (5-15yrs), Garden only adm £4, chd £1 (5-15yrs). Suns 13, 20, Thurs 17 Feb (gdn only) (1.30-5);*

(hse & gdn) Weds, Sats, Bank Hol 2 May to 17 Sept (2-5). **For NGS:** *Sun 28 Aug (2-5). Tel 01285 841253 www.rodmarton-manor.co.uk*

61 Rookwoods, Waterlane, nr Bisley ⊕
(Mr & Mrs Des Althorp) *5m E of Stroud. Between Sapperton & Bisley. Turn down No Through Rd in Waterlane then follow signs.* 3-acre, well structured garden with herbaceous borders to colour themes. Pleached whitebeam around pool area. Wide variety of old-fashioned and modern climbing and shrub roses (labelled), water gardens and outstanding views. Home-made TEAS. Adm £2, chd free. Sats 7 May; 2 July (2-6)

62 Rosemary Cottage, 8 Peter Street, Frocester ⓖⓧⓔ NCCPG
(Eric & Madeline Sadler) *4m SW of Stroud. Junction 13 M5. A419 towards Stroud, turn R at 1st roundabout to Eastington. Next roundabout turn L to Frocester. At Xrds turn R down beside The George PH. Park in field 200yds on L. Cottage further 200yds on R.* ½-acre on gentle S-facing slope. Tiny wood with pond for wildlife. Lots of mixed borders and paths - sorry no room for a lawn. National Collection of *Rosmarinus officinalis*best viewed in April. Plant sales to WSPA. Featured in 'Gardeners' World' 2003, & 'Gloucestershire Citizen' 2004. TEAS. Adm £2, chd free. Suns 10, 24 Apr; 17 July; 7 Aug (2-6). Private visits welcome by appt. Tel 01453 827607 rosemarycottage@supanet.com

Salford Gardens, nr Chipping Norton
See Oxfordshire.

63 Selsley Gardens
2m SW of Stroud Centre. On B4066 to Dursley. Signed from A419 at Sainsbury Roundabout. Home-made TEAS at The Old Post Office. Combined adm £3. Sun 10 July (2-6)
 The Green ⓖⓔ (Mr & Mrs Jolyon Gardiner) Approx 1-acre garden round C17 house (not open). Fresh water pond, secret garden and large vegetable garden; orchard, patio, many interesting plants. Well kept lawns; real family garden. Wheelchair access to top patio.
 The Old Post Office, Pooles Lane ⓧⓔ (Mr & Mrs C Verey) Approx ½-acre cottage garden overflowing with a wide range of plants incl fruit and vegetables.

The sloping site divides naturally into different areas with pond, orchard and terrace.
 Wild Acre ⓖⓧⓔ (Mr & Mrs B Thacker & Miss J Sansom) Informal ¾ acre garden; shrub and herbaceous borders; large fish pond with waterlilies. Rose and clematis pergola, shrub roses; formal kitchen garden. Ornamental and fruit trees.

64 ◆ Sezincote, nr Moreton-in-Marsh ⓖⓧ
(Mr & Mrs D Peake) *3m SW of Moreton-in-Marsh. From Moreton-in-Marsh turn W along A44 towards Evesham; after 1½m (just before Bourton-on-the-Hill) take turn L, by stone lodge with white gate.* Exotic oriental water garden by Repton and Daniell with lake, pools and meandering stream, banked with massed perennials. Large semi-circular orangery, formal Indian garden, fountain, temple and unusual trees of vast size in lawn and wooded park setting. House in Indian manner designed by Samuel Pepys Cockerell. Home-made TEAS (NGS day only). *House (not open for NGS)and garden adm £6, Garden only adm £4, chd £1.50. Thurs, Fris, Bank Hol Mons except Dec.* **For NGS:** *Sun 3 July (2-6). Tel 01386 700444*

65 Sheephouse, Stepping Stone Lane, Painswick ⓖⓧ
(Lawrence & Lindsay Gardiner) *¼m E of Painswick. From A46 through Painswick take Stamages Lane (below car park) & follow signs. Parking in Painswick will assist parking at house & provide lovely partly steep 1m walk.* 1¼-acre garden surrounding C15, C17 and C19 country house (not open). Extensively re-designed and developed. Formal holly and clipped yew drive; water feature with weir; knot garden; formal potager designed by Robert Bryant. 40,000 spring bulbs; hellebores; beautiful mature trees. Featured in '25 Beautiful Gardens' 2004. TEAS. Adm £2.50, chd free, concessions £2 (share to The Willow Trust, Cirencester). Sun 13 Mar (2-5)

66 ◆ Snowshill Manor, nr Broadway ⓧⓔ
(The National Trust) *2½m S of Broadway. Off A44 bypass into Broadway village.* Small terraced garden in which organic and natural methods only are used. Highlights incl tranquil ponds, old roses, old-fashioned flowers and herbaceous borders rich in plants of special interest. House open with fine collections. Light refreshments and

TEAS. *House and Garden adm £7, chd £3.50, Garden only adm £4, chd £2. Thurs to Suns 4 May to 2 May; Weds to Suns 4 May to 30 Oct & Bank Hols Mons.* **For NGS:** *Wed 29 June (11-5.30). Tel 01386 852410 snowshillmanor@nationaltrust.org.uk*

67 Stanton Gardens, nr Broadway ⓖⓔ
(Mr K J Ryland) *3m SW of Broadway. Off B4632, between Broadway (3m) & Winchcombe (6m).* One of the most picturesque and unspoilt C17 Cotswold villages with many gardens to explore (24 open in 2004) ranging from charming cottage to large formal gardens of appeal to visitors of all tastes. TEAS in aid of Stanton Church. Adm £4, chd free. Sun 19 June (2-6). Details from Charity Farm, Stanton WR12 7NE

68 ◆ Stanway Fountain & Water Garden, nr Winchcombe
(Lord Neidpath) *9m NE of Cheltenham. 1m E of B4632 Cheltenham to Broadway rd or B4077 Toddington to Stow-on-the-Wold rd.* 20 acres of planted landscape in early C18 formal setting. Recent restoration of canal, upper pond and 165ft high fountain have re-created one of the most interesting baroque water gardens in Britain. Striking C16 manor with gatehouse, tithe barn and church. Britain's highest fountain, the world's highest gravity fountain. Light refreshments and TEAS. *House and Garden adm £6 chd £1.50, concessions £4.50, Garden only adm £4, chd £1, concessions £3. House & Garden Tues, Thurs July to end Sept ; Garden only Sats July to end of Sept.* **For NGS:** *Suns 10 Apr; 15 May (2-5). Tel 01386 584528 www.stanwayfountain.co.uk*

69 Stone House, Wyck Rissington ⓧ
(Mr & Mrs Andrew Lukas) *3m S of Stow-on-the-Wold. Off A429 between Bourton-on-the-Water & Stow-on-the-Wold. Last house in village behind high bank on R.* 2 acres full of unusual bulbs, shrubs and herbaceous plants. Crab apple walk, rose borders, herb and water garden, meadow walk. Plantwoman's garden with yr-round interest. Home-made TEAS in aid of village hall. Adm £4, chd free. Sun 24 Apr (2-5). Private visits welcome by appt March to Oct. Tel 01451 810337 katelukas@global.net.co.uk

70 Stowell Park, Northleach ♿☒☻
(The Lord & Lady Vestey) *8m NE of Cirencester. Off Fosseway A429 2m SW of Northleach.* Magnificent lawned terraces with stunning views over Coln Valley. Fine collection of old-fashioned roses and herbaceous plants, with pleached lime approach to C14 house (not open). Two large walled gardens containing vegetables, fruit, cut flowers and range of greenhouses. Long rose pergola and wide, plant-filled borders divided into colour sections. Garden has opened for 41yrs., Plant Sale - 15 May. Home-made TEAS in aid of Yanworth & Stowell Churches (May) & Royal British Legion (June). *Adm £4. Suns 15 May; 19 June (2-5). Private visits welcome by appt. Tel 01285 720610*

71 NEW Througham Court, Througham ☒☻
(Dr Christine Facer Hoffman) *8m W of Cirencester. From Birdlip, follow B4070 taking turn signed The Camp, then 1st L to Througham, 2nd L (down hill). House and garden immed on R. Park where signed.* Scientist and landscape designer's own 2½ acre garden in peaceful valley. Jacobean House (not open) surrounded by contrasting 'traditional ' and new contemporary garden areas. Former incl historical yew/box topiary; walled kitchen garden; sunken Elizabethan garden. Herbaceous borders. Contemporary garden design inspired by scientific facts/theories and incl garden of cosmic evolution; chaos gate; black bamboo maze; new perennial planting; slate black pool; Fibonacci's walk. Short guided tour by owner (groups only - fee negotiable). No cameras. Featured BBC Radio 4 Growing Spaces' HTV-West TV Roots & Shoots & TV Discovery Channel 2003. TEAS Sats & Suns (if fine). *Adm £4 (negotiable for groups), chd free. Private visits welcome by appt May to Aug, groups up to 15, coaches permitted. Tel 01285 821215 cafacer@netcomuk.co.uk*

72 Tinpenny Farm, Fiddington ♿☒☻
(E S Horton) *2½m SE of Tewkesbury. From M5 J9 take A46 exit towards Evesham. Just after T-lights turn R to Fiddington. After 1½m turn R to Walton Cardiff. Entrance 1st on R.* Amazing collection of plants incl hellebores, iris, hemerocallis, hostas. Do not expect a weed-free zone! But to see what can be achieved with a wind-swept site on impenetrable clay, please do visit. *Adm £2. Thurs all yr. Suns 20 Feb; 20 Mar; 17 Apr; 15 May; 19 June; 17 July; 18 Sept; 16 Oct; (12-5); Sun 19 Feb 2006. Private visits welcome by appt. Tel 01684 292668*

73 Trench Hill, Sheepscombe ♿☒☻
(Celia & Dave Hargrave) *1½m E of Painswick. On A46 to Cheltenham after Painswick, turn R to Sheepscombe. Approx 1½m (before reaching village) turn L by telegraph poles, Trench Hill at top of lane.* Approx 3 acres set in small woodland with panoramic views. Variety of herbaceous and mixed borders, rose garden, extensive vegetable plots, wild flower areas, plantings of spring bulbs, woodland walk, 2 small ponds, waterfall and larger conservation pond. Interesting wooden sculptures. Run on organic principles. Featured in 'A Secret Garden' a book by Annie Bullen 2004. Home-made TEAS. *Adm £2.50, chd free. Suns 13, 20 Feb (11-5); Sun 27, Mon 28 Mar; Suns 17 July; 14, 28 Aug; 11 Sept (11-6); Weds, 1 June to 29 June (2-6). Private visits welcome by appt. Tel 01452 814306 celia@trenchhill. freeserve.co.uk*

74 Upton Wold, nr Moreton-in-Marsh ☒☻
(Mr & Mrs I R S Bond) *3½m W of Moreton-in-Marsh. On A44 1m past A424 junction at Troopers Lodge Garage.* Ever-developing and changing garden, architecturally and imaginatively laid out around C17 house (not open) with commanding views. Yew hedges; old shrub roses; herbaceous walk; some unusual plants and trees; vegetables; pond and woodland gardens. TEAS. *Adm £4, chd free. Suns 8 May; 26 June (10-6). Private visits welcome by appt May to July (£6). Tel 01386 700667*

75 The Vicarage, High Street, Westbury on Severn ♿☻
(Rev & Mrs Clive Edmonds) *9m SW of Gloucester. On A48 Chepstow rd at end of village high st on RH-side,*

adjacent to Court Farm. Walled garden of approx ½-acre, surrounding the vicarage, restored over the last 3yrs with large collection hardy geraniums, salvias, unusual perennial plants, new beds, borders; very much a plantsman's garden. Featured on HTV Roots & Shoots 2003. Light refreshments and TEAS. *Adm £2, chd free (share to churches in benefice). Sat 18 (11-5), Sun 19 June (2-6). Private visits welcome by appt June only. Tel 01452 760592*

76 Warners Court, Charfield ♿☒☻
(Mr & Mrs M Adams) *3m SW of Wotton-under-Edge. On B4058 (from Wotton-under-Edge & 2½m from M5 junction 14), in main st of Charfield.* 1 acre, with small points of colour and foliage as the guidelines for the mixed informal planting within a gently structured framework. Vegetables grown in organic, raised bed system using 'no dig' principles. Large tranquil pond area. TEAS in aid of Cotswold Care Hospice. *Adm £3, chd free. Sun, Mon 1, 2 May (2-5)*

◆ Waterpump Farm, Ryeford ♿☒☻
See Herefordshire.

77 ◆ Westbury Court Garden, Westbury-on-Severn ♿☻
(The National Trust) *9m SW of Gloucester. On A48.* Formal Dutch-style water garden, earliest remaining in England; canals, summerhouse, over 100 species of plants grown in England and recreated vegetable plots, growing crops all from before 1700. The walled garden will be closed in 2005 for replanting. *Adm £3.75, chd £1.85.* **For NGS:** *Sun 4 Sept (10-4). Tel 01452 760461 jerry.green@nationaltrust.org.uk*

Weston Mews, Weston under Penyard ♿☒☻
See Herefordshire.

78 ◆ Westonbirt School Gardens, Westonbirt ♿
(Westonbirt School) *3m SW of Tetbury. Opp Westonbirt Arboretum, on the A433 (follow brown tourist information signs).* 22 acres. Former private garden of Robert Holford, founder of Westonbirt Arboretum. Formal Victorian gardens incl walled Italian garden, terraced pleasure garden, rustic walks, lake, statuary and grotto. Rare, exotic trees and shrubs. Beautiful views of Westonbirt House, now Westonbirt School (not open). Cold drinks available (NGS days).

House and Garden £6 (by appt only), Garden only adm £3.50, chd £2. Daily 20 Mar to 10 April; 10 July to 3 Sept; 22 Oct to Oct. **For NGS:** *Suns 29 May; 5 June (1-4.30). Tel   01666 881338 Jack Doyle doyle@westonbirt.gloucs.sch.uk*

Westwell Manor, nr Burford ⌘⌘
See Oxfordshire.

Whitehill Farm, nr Burford ⌘⌘
See Oxfordshire.

79 Willow Lodge, nr Longhope
⌘⌘⌘
(John & Sheila Wood) *10m W of Gloucester, 6m E of Ross-on-Wye. On A40 between May Hill & Longhope.* Plantsman's garden with unusual and rare plants, herbaceous borders, shrubs and alpine garden. Many woodland plants incl trilliums, erythroniums, hellebores etc. Greenhouses and vegetable plot. Large bog garden with marginals and Asiatic primulas. Fish pond and stream. Exceptional arboretum containing approx 400 different trees and shrubs, from all over the temperate world. Areas of wild

flowers in 4-acre grounds. Plants labelled. Featured in 'The Lady' & RHS 'Garden Finder', 2004. TEAS. *Adm £2.50, chd free. Suns, Mons 17,18, 24, 25 Apr; 1, 2, 22, 23 May; 5, 6, 19, 20 June; 3, 4, 17, 18, 31 July; 1, 14, 15 Aug (1-5). Private visits welcome by appt. Tel 01452 831211   www.willowgardens.fsnet. co.uk*

Evening Opening (See also garden description)
Humphreys End House
9 June

Gwent
See separate Welsh section on page 462

Gwynedd
See separate Welsh section on page 467

Hampshire

County Organiser:
(Central West)

Mrs Patricia Elkington, Little Court, Crawley, Winchester, Hampshire SO21 2PU
Tel 01962 776365 email elkslc@onetel.com

Assistant County Organisers:
(East)
(North)

Mrs R Macpherson, Stedham House, Droxford, Southampton SO32 3PB Tel 01489 877006
Mrs Cynthia Oldale, Little Coopers, Coopers Hill, Eversley, Hampshire RG27 0QA
Tel 01252 872229

(North-East)

Mrs Elizabeth Powell, Broadhatch House, Bentley, nr Farnham, Surrey GU10 5JJ
Tel 01420 23185

(North-West)
(Central-East)
(West)

Miss Carol Pratt, Field House, Monxton, Andover, Hampshire SP11 8AS Tel 01264 710305
Mrs W F Richardson, Hill House, Old Alresford, Hampshire SO24 9DY Tel 01962 732720
Mr Christopher Stanford, Oakdene, Sandleheath, Fordingbridge, Hampshire SP6 1PA
Tel 01425 652133

(South)

Mrs Barbara Sykes, The Cottage, 16 Lakewood Road, Chandlers Ford, Hampshire
SO53 1ES Tel 02380 254521

(South-West)

Mrs Sybil Warner, Birchwood House, Cadnam, Southampton, Hampshire SO40 2NR
Tel 02380 813400

County Treasurer:

Mr Richard Morcom, White Poplars, Station Road, Chilbolton, Hampshire SO20 6AW
Tel 01264 860125

Maps: Numbers shown next to each garden entry refer to that garden's entry on the county map. This position is approximate;
distance and directions from the nearest main town are generally shown in the garden text.
A precise location is available for those gardens featured on the NGS website by visiting www.ngs.org.uk.
Symbols: Information relating to symbols is given on page 21

DATES OF OPENING

Evening openings
See end of county listing

Private gardens open regularly for NGS
Beechenwood Farm, Odiham *(11)*
Elbow Corner, Basingstoke *(38)*
2 Warren Farm Cottages, nr West Tytherley
(112)
Whistlers, Buriton *(116)*

Gardens open to the public
For details see garden description
Alverstoke Crescent Garden, Gosport *(3)*
Apple Court, Lymington *(5)*
Coles, Privett *(29)*
Exbury Gardens & Steam Railway,
Southampton *(40)*
Hinton Ampner, Alresford *(52)*
Longthatch, Warnford *(67)*
Macpennys Woodland Garden & Nurseries,
Bransgore *(69)*
Mottisfont Abbey & Garden, Romsey *(80)*
Spinners, Boldre *(99)*
The Vyne, Sherborne St John *(107)*

By appointment only
For telephone number and other
details see garden description.
Private visits welcomed
Broadhatch House, Bentley *(18)*
Clibdens, Chalton *(24)*
White Barn, Crow Hill, Ringwood *(117)*

February 5 Saturday
Brandy Mount House, Alresford *(16)*

February 13 Sunday
Bramdean House, Bramdean *(15)*
Conholt Park, Chute *(30)*
Little Court, Crawley, nr Winchester *(63)*

February 20 Sunday
Little Court, Crawley, nr Winchester *(63)*
The White Cottage, Beech, Alton *(118)*

February 21 Monday
Little Court, Crawley, nr Winchester *(63)*

February 22 Tuesday
Little Court, Crawley, nr Winchester *(63)*

March 6 Sunday
Brandy Mount House, Alresford *(16)*
Heathlands, Locks Heath, nr Fareham *(48)*
Longthatch, Warnford *(67)*

March 13 Sunday
Longthatch, Warnford *(67)*
The White Cottage, Beech, Alton *(118)*

March 19 Saturday
Houghton Lodge Garden, nr Stockbridge
(55)

March 20 Sunday
Houghton Lodge Garden, nr Stockbridge
(55)
Little Court, Crawley, nr Winchester *(63)*
Longthatch, Warnford *(67)*
Mittens, Mapledurwell *(78)*

March 22 Tuesday
Little Court, Crawley, nr Winchester *(63)*

March 25 Friday (Easter)
Greatham Mill, Greatham, nr Liss *(46)*
2 Warren Farm Cottages, nr West Tytherley
(112)
Whistlers, Buriton *(116)*

March 26 Saturday (Easter)
Greatham Mill, Greatham, nr Liss *(46)*

March 27 Sunday (Easter)
Appleshaw Manor, nr Andover *(6)*
Bramdean House, Bramdean *(15)*
Durmast House, Burley *(36)*
Greatham Mill, Greatham, nr Liss *(46)*

March 28 Monday (Easter)
Appleshaw Manor, nr Andover *(6)*
The Deanery, Winchester *(35)*

March 30 Wednesday
Beechenwood Farm, Odiham *(11)*

April 1 Friday
Beechenwood Farm, Odiham *(11)*
2 Warren Farm Cottages, nr West Tytherley
(112)
Whistlers, Buriton *(116)*

April 3 Sunday
Crawley Gardens, nr Winchester *(33)*
East Lane, Ovington *(37)*
Flintstones, Durley *(42)*

April 4 Monday
Crawley Gardens, nr Winchester *(33)*

April 6 Wednesday
Beechenwood Farm, Odiham *(11)*

April 8 Friday
2 Warren Farm Cottages, nr West Tytherley
(112)
Whistlers, Buriton *(116)*

April 15 Friday
Beechenwood Farm, Odiham *(11)*
Lake House, Northington *(59)*
2 Warren Farm Cottages, nr West Tytherley
(112)
Whistlers, Buriton *(116)*

April 16 Saturday
Lake House, Northington *(59)*

Treetops, Upper Froyle *(102)*
Walbury, Lower Froyle *(109)*
April 17 Sunday
Bramdean House, Bramdean *(15)*
Hambledon House, Hambledon *(47)*
Lake House, Northington *(59)*
'Selborne', East Worldham *(97)*
St Christopher's, Whitsbury *(100)*
Tylney Hall Hotel, Rotherwick *(104)*
2 Warren Farm Cottages, nr West Tytherley *(112)*
April 18 Monday
'Selborne', East Worldham *(97)*
April 20 Wednesday
Beechenwood Farm, Odiham *(11)*
April 22 Friday
2 Warren Farm Cottages, nr West Tytherley *(112)*
Whistlers, Buriton *(116)*
April 24 Sunday
80 Abbey Road, Fareham *(2)*
Forest Edge, Andover Down *(43)*
Hinton Ampner, Alresford *(52)*
60 Lealand Road, Drayton, Portsmouth *(60)*
Longthatch, Warnford *(67)*
Rowans Wood, Ampfield *(94)*
St Christopher's, Whitsbury *(100)*
Valentine Cottage, Newnham, nr Basingstoke *(106)*
April 25 Monday
Hinton Ampner, Alresford *(52)*
April 29 Friday
Beechenwood Farm, Odiham *(11)*
2 Warren Farm Cottages, nr West Tytherley *(112)*
Whistlers, Buriton *(116)*
May 1 Sunday
Abbey Cottage, Itchen Abbas *(1)*
Bluebell Cottage, Froxfield *(13)*
Closewood House, Denmead *(26)*
The Cottage, Chandler's Ford *(31)*
53 Ladywood, Eastleigh *(58)*
Little Coopers, Eversley *(61)*
Marlands, Headbourne Worthy *(72)*
The Old House, Silchester *(85)*
Rotherfield Park, East Tisted *(92)*
Rowans Wood, Ampfield *(94)*
May 2 Monday (Bank Hol)
Abbey Cottage, Itchen Abbas *(1)*
Bluebell Cottage, Froxfield *(13)*
Closewood House, Denmead *(26)*
The Cottage, Chandler's Ford *(31)*
Marlands, Headbourne Worthy *(72)*
Rowans Wood, Ampfield *(94)*
May 4 Wednesday
Beechenwood Farm, Odiham *(11)*
May 6 Friday
2 Warren Farm Cottages, nr West Tytherley *(112)*
Whistlers, Buriton *(116)*
May 7 Saturday
Lower Spinney, Warsash *(68)*
Pennington House, Lymington *(87)*
May 8 Sunday
Lower Spinney, Warsash *(68)*
Pennington House, Lymington *(87)*
Shaw Trust Horticulture, Portsmouth *(98)*

Tylney Hall Hotel, Rotherwick *(104)*
White Windows, Longparish *(120)*
May 9 Monday
White Windows, Longparish *(120)*
May 13 Friday
Beechenwood Farm, Odiham *(11)*
2 Warren Farm Cottages, nr West Tytherley *(112)*
Whistlers, Buriton *(116)*
May 15 Sunday
The Cottage, Chandler's Ford *(31)*
Hambledon House, Hambledon *(47)*
Hordle Walhampton School, Lymington *(54)*
The House in the Wood, Beaulieu *(56)*
Little Court, Crawley, nr Winchester *(63)*
Mount Joy, nr Cadnam *(81)*
The Old House, Silchester *(85)*
Pylewell Park, Lymington *(89)*
Rowans Wood, Ampfield *(94)*
2 Warren Farm Cottages, nr West Tytherley *(112)*
May 16 Monday
The Cottage, Chandler's Ford *(31)*
Mount Joy, nr Cadnam *(81)*
May 17 Tuesday
Little Court, Crawley, nr Winchester *(63)*
May 18 Wednesday
Beechenwood Farm, Odiham *(11)*
May 20 Friday
2 Warren Farm Cottages, nr West Tytherley *(112)*
Whistlers, Buriton *(116)*
May 21 Saturday
6 Breamore Close, Eastleigh *(17)*
Littlewood, Hayling Island *(64)*
Wisteria Cottage, Fareham *(122)*
May 22 Sunday
6 Breamore Close, Eastleigh *(17)*
Enchanted Cottage, Hayling Island *(39)*
60 Lealand Road, Drayton, Portsmouth *(60)*
Littlewood, Hayling Island *(64)*
Pylewell Park, Lymington *(89)*
'Selborne', East Worldham *(97)*
Tylney Hall Hotel, Rotherwick *(104)*
The White Cottage, Beech, Alton *(118)*
Wisteria Cottage, Fareham *(122)*
May 23 Monday
'Selborne', East Worldham *(97)*
May 25 Wednesday
23 Anglesey Road, Aldershot *(4)*
Appletree House, Soberton *(7)*
Hambledon House, Hambledon *(47)*
May 27 Friday
Beechenwood Farm, Odiham *(11)*
2 Warren Farm Cottages, nr West Tytherley *(112)*
Whistlers, Buriton *(116)*
May 28 Saturday
Froyle Cottage Gardens *(45)*
May 29 Sunday
Bury Farm, Marchwood *(21)*
Chilland House, Martyr Worthy *(22)*
Conholt Park, Chute *(30)*
Froyle Cottage Gardens *(45)*
Longparish Gardens, nr Andover *(65)*
Longthatch, Warnford *(67)*

20 Magdalene Way, Locks Heath, nr Fareham *(70)*
Monxton Gardens *(79)*
Mount Joy, nr Cadnam *(81)*
Romsey Gardens *(91)*
Waldrons, Brook *(110)*
West Silchester Hall, Silchester *(113)*
May 30 Monday (Bank Hol)
Alverstoke Crescent Garden, Gosport *(3)*
Chilland House, Martyr Worthy *(22)*
The Deanery, Winchester *(35)*
Longparish Gardens, nr Andover *(65)*
Longthatch, Warnford *(67)*
20 Magdalene Way, Locks Heath, nr Fareham *(70)*
Monxton Gardens *(79)*
Mount Joy, nr Cadnam *(81)*
Romsey Gardens *(91)*
Waldrons, Brook *(110)*
West Silchester Hall, Silchester *(113)*
June 1 Wednesday
Beechenwood Farm, Odiham *(11)*
June 3 Friday
71 Church Close, Northington *(23)*
Meadow Lodge, Swarraton *(75)*
2 Warren Farm Cottages, nr West Tytherley *(112)*
Whistlers, Buriton *(116)*
June 4 Saturday
71 Church Close, Northington *(23)*
The Clock House, nr Sparsholt, Winchester *(25)*
Meadow Lodge, Swarraton *(75)*
June 5 Sunday
Barncroft Gardens, Appleshaw *(9)*
71 Church Close, Northington *(23)*
The Clock House, nr Sparsholt, Winchester *(25)*
Flintstones, Durley *(42)*
Meadow Lodge, Swarraton *(75)*
Meon Orchard, N of Wickham *(76)*
The Vyne, Sherborne St John *(107)*
June 6 Monday
Barncroft Gardens, Appleshaw *(9)*
Flintstones, Durley *(42)*
June 8 Wednesday
Appletree House, Soberton *(7)*
Hambledon House, Hambledon *(47)*

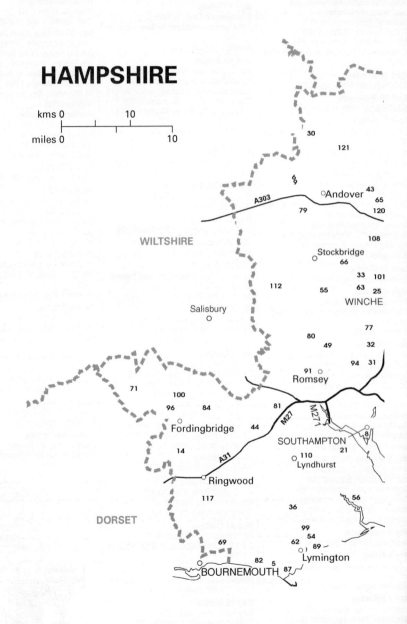

HAMPSHIRE

kms 0   10

miles 0   10

30

121

6
9

A303   ○Andover   43

65

79   120

WILTSHIRE   108

○Stockbridge

66

33   101

112   55   63   25

WINCHE

Salisbury   77
○

80   49   32

94   31

91 ○

Romsey

71

100   81

96   84   M27   M271

○   8

Fordingbridge   44   SOUTHAMPTON

14   A31   21

○ 110

Lyndhurst

○Ringwood

117   56

DORSET   36

99

54

62   89

69   ○ Lymington

82   5

BOURNEMOUTH   87

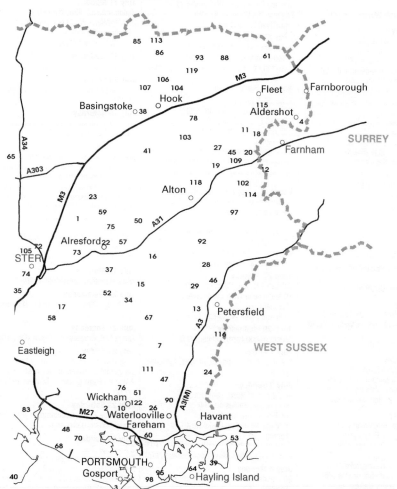

June 10 Friday
Beechenwood Farm, Odiham *(11)*
2 Warren Farm Cottages, nr West Tytherley *(112)*
Whistlers, Buriton *(116)*

June 11 Saturday
Bentley Village Gardens *(12)*
The Manor House, Martin, Fordingbridge *(71)*
The Mathom House, Winchester *(74)*

June 12 Sunday
Bentley Village Gardens *(12)*
Closewood House, Denmead *(26)*
Cranbury Park, Otterbourne *(32)*
Enchanted Cottage, Hayling Island *(39)*
Forest Edge, Andover Down *(43)*
The Homestead, Hayling Island *(53)*
The Manor House, Martin, Fordingbridge *(71)*
Marlands, Headbourne Worthy *(72)*
Martyr Worthy Gardens *(73)*
The Mathom House, Winchester *(74)*
Oakdene, Fordingbridge *(84)*
Valentine Cottage, Newnham, nr Basingstoke *(106)*
The Walled House, Droxford *(111)*

June 13 Monday
Marlands, Headbourne Worthy *(72)*

June 14 Tuesday
The Little Cottage, Lymington *(62)*

June 15 Wednesday
Beechenwood Farm, Odiham *(11)*
The Clock House, nr Sparsholt, Winchester *(25)*
The Walled House, Droxford *(111)*

June 17 Friday
Greatham Mill, Greatham, nr Liss *(46)*
2 Warren Farm Cottages, nr West Tytherley *(112)*
Whistlers, Buriton *(116)*

June 18 Saturday
Brocas Farm, Lower Froyle *(19)*
Greatham Mill, Greatham, nr Liss *(46)*
The Mathom House, Winchester *(74)*
Mulberry House, Barton-on-Sea *(82)*

June 19 Sunday
Bramdean House, Bramdean *(15)*
Brocas Farm, Lower Froyle *(19)*
Closewood House, Denmead *(26)*
Conholt Park, Chute *(30)*
Farleigh House, nr Basingstoke *(41)*
Greatham Mill, Greatham, nr Liss *(46)*
Longstock Park Water Garden, nr Stockbridge *(66)*
Longthatch, Warnford *(67)*
20 Magdalene Way, Locks Heath, nr Fareham *(70)*
The Mathom House, Winchester *(74)*
Oakdene, Fordingbridge *(84)*
Old Meadows, Silchester *(86)*
Wades House, Barton Stacey *(108)*
2 Warren Farm Cottages, nr West Tytherley *(112)*

June 20 Monday
20 Magdalene Way, Locks Heath, nr Fareham *(70)*

June 21 Tuesday
Mulberry House, Barton-on-Sea *(82)*
Wades House, Barton Stacey *(108)*

June 22 Wednesday
The Clock House, nr Sparsholt, Winchester *(25)*
Dean House, Kilmeston *(34)*

June 23 Thursday
Crawley Gardens, nr Winchester *(33)*
Windmill Hill Gardens, Ibthorpe, Hurstbourne Tarrant *(121)*

June 24 Friday
Beechenwood Farm, Odiham *(11)*
Crawley Gardens, nr Winchester *(33)*
2 Warren Farm Cottages, nr West Tytherley *(112)*
Whistlers, Buriton *(116)*

June 26 Sunday
Colemore House, Colemore *(28)*
Durmast House, Burley *(36)*
Fritham Lodge, Fritham *(44)*
Hambledon House, Hambledon *(47)*
53 Ladywood, Eastleigh *(58)*
60 Lealand Road, Drayton, Portsmouth *(60)*
20 Magdalene Way, Locks Heath, nr Fareham *(70)*
Mottisfont Abbey & Garden, Romsey *(80)*
Mulberry House, Barton-on-Sea *(82)*
Quoin Cottage, Denmead *(90)*
'Selborne', East Worldham *(97)*
The White Cottage, Beech, Alton *(118)*
White Gables, Sherfield-on-Loddon *(119)*
Windmill Hill Gardens, Ibthorpe, Hurstbourne Tarrant *(121)*

June 27 Monday
Colemore House, Colemore *(28)*
20 Magdalene Way, Locks Heath, nr Fareham *(70)*
'Selborne', East Worldham *(97)*

June 29 Wednesday
Beechenwood Farm, Odiham *(11)*

July 1 Friday
2 Warren Farm Cottages, nr West Tytherley *(112)*

July 3 Sunday
19 Barnwood Road, Fareham *(10)*
Dean House, Kilmeston *(34)*
The Hedges, Timsbury *(49)*
20 Magdalene Way, Locks Heath, nr Fareham *(70)*
Tunworth Old Rectory, nr Basingstoke *(103)*
Whispers, Chatter Alley, Dogmersfield *(115)*

July 4 Monday
20 Magdalene Way, Locks Heath, nr Fareham *(70)*

July 5 Tuesday
The Hedges, Timsbury *(49)*
The Little Cottage, Lymington *(62)*

July 8 Friday
80 Abbey Road, Fareham **(Evening)** *(2)*
Beechenwood Farm, Odiham *(11)*
2 Warren Farm Cottages, nr West Tytherley *(112)*

July 9 Saturday
Ulvik, Winchester *(105)*

July 10 Sunday
Bury Court, Bentley *(20)*

Farleigh House, nr Basingstoke *(41)*
Hinton Ampner, Alresford *(52)*
20 Magdalene Way, Locks Heath, nr Fareham *(70)*
Rotherwick Gardens *(93)*
Sandle Cottage, Sandleheath *(96)*
Ulvik, Winchester *(105)*
West Silchester Hall, Silchester *(113)*

July 11 Monday
Hinton Ampner, Alresford *(52)*
20 Magdalene Way, Locks Heath, nr Fareham *(70)*
Ulvik, Winchester *(105)*

July 13 Wednesday
Beechenwood Farm, Odiham *(11)*

July 15 Friday
2 Warren Farm Cottages, nr West Tytherley *(112)*

July 16 Saturday
The Coach House, South Warnborough *(27)*
1 Lower Spinney, Warsash *(68)*

July 17 Sunday
Bramdean House, Bramdean *(15)*
The Coach House, South Warnborough *(27)*
1 Lower Spinney, Warsash *(68)*
49 Newtown Road with 26 & 29 Weston Allotments, Woolston *(83)*
The Priors Farm, Mattingley *(88)*
Valentine Cottage, Newnham, nr Basingstoke *(106)*
2 Warren Farm Cottages, nr West Tytherley *(112)*
White Windows, Longparish *(120)*

July 18 Monday
White Windows, Longparish *(120)*

July 20 Wednesday
2 Ashridge Close, Southampton **(Evening)** *(8)*

July 21 Thursday
Tanglefoot, Crawley, nr Winchester *(101)*

July 22 Friday
Beechenwood Farm, Odiham *(11)*
Tanglefoot, Crawley, nr Winchester *(101)*
2 Warren Farm Cottages, nr West Tytherley *(112)*

July 23 Saturday
2 Ashridge Close, Southampton *(8)*
Elbow Corner, Basingstoke *(38)*

July 24 Sunday
2 Ashridge Close, Southampton *(8)*
Elbow Corner, Basingstoke *(38)*
Merdon Manor, Hursley *(77)*
49 Newtown Road with 26 & 29 Weston Allotments, Woolston *(83)*
The Priors Farm, Mattingley *(88)*
28 St Ronan's Avenue, Southsea *(95)*
Sandle Cottage, Sandleheath *(96)*

July 25 Monday
Elbow Corner, Basingstoke *(38)*

July 26 Tuesday
Elbow Corner, Basingstoke *(38)*

July 27 Wednesday
Beechenwood Farm, Odiham *(11)*
Elbow Corner, Basingstoke *(38)*
The Vyne, Sherborne St John **(Evening)** *(107)*

July 28 Thursday
Elbow Corner, Basingstoke *(38)*

July 29 Friday
Elbow Corner, Basingstoke *(38)*
2 Warren Farm Cottages, nr West Tytherley *(112)*

July 30 Saturday
Elbow Corner, Basingstoke *(38)*

July 31 Sunday
Braemoor, Fordingbridge *(14)*
Elbow Corner, Basingstoke *(38)*
Hill House, Old Alresford *(50)*
Meon Orchard, N of Wickham *(76)*
Sandle Cottage, Sandleheath *(96)*
Ulvik, Winchester *(105)*
West Silchester Hall, Silchester *(113)*

August 1 Monday
Elbow Corner, Basingstoke *(38)*
Ulvik, Winchester *(105)*

August 2 Tuesday
Elbow Corner, Basingstoke *(38)*
Hill House, Old Alresford *(50)*
The Little Cottage, Lymington *(62)*

August 3 Wednesday
Elbow Corner, Basingstoke *(38)*

August 4 Thursday
Elbow Corner, Basingstoke *(38)*

August 5 Friday
Elbow Corner, Basingstoke *(38)*
2 Warren Farm Cottages, nr West Tytherley *(112)*

August 6 Saturday
Elbow Corner, Basingstoke *(38)*

August 7 Sunday
Braemoor, Fordingbridge *(14)*
Bury Court, Bentley *(20)*
Elbow Corner, Basingstoke *(38)*
The Hyde, Old Alresford *(57)*
'Selborne', East Worldham *(97)*
The White Cottage, Beech, Alton *(118)*

August 8 Monday
Elbow Corner, Basingstoke *(38)*
'Selborne', East Worldham *(97)*

August 9 Tuesday
Elbow Corner, Basingstoke *(38)*

August 10 Wednesday
Elbow Corner, Basingstoke *(38)*

August 11 Thursday
Elbow Corner, Basingstoke *(38)*

August 12 Friday
Elbow Corner, Basingstoke *(38)*
2 Warren Farm Cottages, nr West Tytherley *(112)*

August 13 Saturday
Elbow Corner, Basingstoke *(38)*
Wheatley House, between Binsted and Kingsley *(114)*

August 14 Sunday
Bramdean House, Bramdean *(15)*
Elbow Corner, Basingstoke *(38)*
Enchanted Cottage, Hayling Island *(39)*
Hillside Cottages, North Boarhunt *(51)*
Wheatley House, between Binsted and Kingsley *(114)*

August 19 Friday
2 Warren Farm Cottages, nr West Tytherley *(112)*

August 20 Saturday
Mulberry House, Barton-on-Sea *(82)*

August 21 Sunday
Heathlands, Locks Heath, nr Fareham *(48)*
2 Warren Farm Cottages, nr West Tytherley *(112)*

August 26 Friday
2 Warren Farm Cottages, nr West Tytherley *(112)*

August 28 Sunday
Abbey Cottage, Itchen Abbas *(1)*
Rotherfield Park, East Tisted *(92)*

August 29 Monday (Bank Hol)
Abbey Cottage, Itchen Abbas *(1)*

September 2 Friday
2 Warren Farm Cottages, nr West Tytherley *(112)*

September 4 Sunday
Bury Court, Bentley *(20)*
Meon Orchard, N of Wickham *(76)*
Mittens, Mapledurwell *(78)*
28 St Ronan's Avenue, Southsea *(95)*

September 6 Tuesday
The Little Cottage, Lymington *(62)*

September 9 Friday
2 Warren Farm Cottages, nr West Tytherley *(112)*

September 10 Saturday
Hinton Ampner, Alresford *(52)*

September 11 Sunday
Bramdean House, Bramdean *(15)*
Hinton Ampner, Alresford *(52)*

September 16 Friday
2 Warren Farm Cottages, nr West Tytherley *(112)*

September 18 Sunday
The Coach House, South Warnborough *(27)*
Hambledon House, Hambledon *(47)*
2 Hillside Cottages, North Boarhunt *(51)*
2 Warren Farm Cottages, nr West Tytherley *(112)*

September 19 Monday
Hambledon House, Hambledon *(47)*

September 21 Wednesday
23 Anglesey Road, Aldershot *(4)*

September 23 Friday
2 Warren Farm Cottages, nr West Tytherley *(112)*

September 25 Sunday
Abbey Cottage, Itchen Abbas *(1)*
Shaw Trust Horticulture, Portsmouth *(98)*

September 30 Friday
2 Warren Farm Cottages, nr West Tytherley *(112)*

October 2 Sunday
2 Warren Farm Cottages, nr West Tytherley *(112)*

October 9 Sunday
Rowans Wood, Ampfield *(94)*

2006

February 12 Sunday
Little Court, Crawley, nr Winchester *(63)*

February 19 Sunday
Bramdean House, Bramdean *(15)*
Little Court, Crawley, nr Winchester *(63)*
The White Cottage, Beech, Alton *(118)*

February 20 Monday
Little Court, Crawley, nr Winchester *(63)*

February 21 Tuesday
Little Court, Crawley, nr Winchester *(63)*

DESCRIPTIONS OF GARDENS

❶ Abbey Cottage, Itchen Abbas
(Colonel P J Daniell) *2½m W of Alresford. On B3047.* Inspiring 1½ acres of walled garden and meadow on alkaline soil, designed and created on different levels, and maintained organically by owner. Trees, hedges, walls and various features provide a strong framework within which a wide range of shrubs, plants and fruit trees flourish and provide yr-round interest. Finalist ITV Britain's Best Back Gardens 2004. Home-made TEAS. *Adm £2.50, chd free. Suns, Mons 1, 2 May; 28, 29 Aug; Sun 25 Sept (12-5)*

❷ 80 Abbey Road, Fareham
(Brian & Vivienne Garford) *From M27 J9 take A27 towards Fareham. At top of hill past Titchfield gyratory, turn L at T-lights into Highland Rd. Turn 4th R into Blackbrook Rd. Abbey Rd 4th turning on L.* Very small garden with extensive collection of herbs, also unusual plants, many of botanical and historical interest. 2 small ponds, minuscule meadow area, but no lawn. Planting throughout attracts wide range of butterflies. Many original ideas for small gardens. Some new hard landscaping for 2005. Home-made TEAS. *Adm £2, chd free. Sun 24 Apr (11-5)*; **Evening Opening** *£3, wine, Fri 8 July (6-9). Private visits welcome by appt, 80 Abbey Road, Fareham, PO15 5HW*

❸ ◆ Alverstoke Crescent Garden, Gosport
(Gosport Borough Council) *1m S of Gosport. From A32 & Gosport follow signs for Stokes Bay. Continue beside bay until small roundabout, turn L into Anglesey Rd. Crescent Garden signed 50yds on R.* Rare example of a recreated Regency garden. 1.3 acres opp 1826 Grade II* Crescent. Partnership between community and Council. Vistas through tranquil shrubbery walk, Reptonian flower baskets, tulip trees, cedars and mulberry. Sparkling dolphin fountain at its heart, surrounded with flowers, scents of

old roses. Friendly Green Team often at work. RHS 'The Garden' feature, 2003. Best public park and Chairman's special prize, S England in Bloom 2004. Green Flag award 2004. Plant sale for NGS & home-made Elevenses Mon 30 May (10-1). *Adm by donation. Open daily all yr*

4 NEW **23 Anglesey Road, Aldershot** ✿⊕

(Adrian & Elizabeth Whiteley) *On E edge of Aldershot. From A331 take A323 towards Aldershot. Keep in R-hand lane and turn R at T-lights into North Lane, then immed R into Lower Newport Rd. Round bend turn immed R into Newport Rd, 1st R into Wilson Rd. Round L-hand bend turn immed R into Roberts Rd, Anglesey Rd 1st on L. Please park considerately in local rds.* Botanist's untypical suburban garden, 48ft x 28ft (combined front and back), now in its 7th yr. An eclectic mix of rare, unfamiliar and everyday plants gives yr-round interest. Unusually-shaped plot echoed in strongly geometric, densely-planted beds. Small pond, greenhouse, fern border and seating areas complete the picture. TEAS. *Adm £1.50, chd free. Weds 25 May; 21 Sept (1-5). Private visits welcome by appt. Tel 01252 677623*

5 ◆ **Apple Court, Lymington** ⊕✿⊕

(Charles & Angela Meads) *From A337 between Lymington & New Milton, turn into Hordle Lane at Royal Oak at Downton Xrds.* 1½-acre formally designed and exuberantly planted sheltered walled garden. Theatrical white garden, extensive ornamental grass plantings, subtropical borders. 70 metre hosta walk. International display gardens of day lilies, fern walk, Japanese-style garden with koi pond. Featured in 'Koi Ponds & Water Gardens' 2004, 'Amateur Gardening' 2003/4 and 'Country Living' 2003. TEAS. *Adm £2.50, chd free. Fris, Sats, Suns & Bank Hol Mons 4 Mar to 30 Oct (10-5). Tel 07711 000004 www.applecourt.com*

6 **Appleshaw Manor, nr Andover** ⊕✿⊕

(Mr & Mrs Patrick Walker) *5m NW of Andover. Take A342 Andover/Marlborough rd. Turn to Appleshaw 1m W of Weyhill. Fork L at playing field, on R after ½m, nr church.* 7 acres, walled garden and grounds. Spring flowers, kitchen garden, wood garden and arboretum. Notable beech and yew hedges. Home-made TEAS in aid of St Peter in the Wood Church. *Adm £2.50,*

chd free. Sun, Mon 27, 28 Mar (2-5). Private visits welcome by appt. Tel 01264 772255 the6walkers@aol.com

7 **Appletree House, Station Road, Soberton** ✿⊕

(Mrs J Dover) *10m N of Fareham. A32 N to Droxford, at Xrds turn R B2150. Turn R under bridge into Station Rd, garden 1m. Parking in lay-by 300yds or in rd.* Romantic, small woodland-style country garden 40yds x 14yds with richly-planted island beds set in a meandering lawn. Trees, rare shrubs, unusual roses and clematis join with bulbs, grasses and herbaceous perennials in variety to give yr-round interest. Also hosta corner, small fernery and a Mediterranean sitting area. Home-made TEAS in aid of Rowans Hospice. *Adm £2, chd free. Weds 25 May; 8 June (1.30-5). Private visits welcome by appt. Tel 01489 877333*

Ashley Park Farm, Damerham ⊕
See Dorset.

8 NEW **2 Ashridge Close, Northlands Road, Southampton** ✿

(Chris & Gill Hayes) *½m N of Southampton city centre. From M3 J14, continue down A33 into Southampton. Turn R into Northlands Rd after Cowherds PH, 500yds on R.* Very colourful small town garden, good use of different areas with beds, baskets, pots and immaculate lawns. Southampton in Bloom joint 3rd Best Private Garden 2004. Home-made TEAS. *Adm £2, chd free.* **Evening Opening** *£3, wine, Wed 20 July (6-8). Sat, Sun 23, 24 July (2-5)*

9 NEW **Barncroft Gardens, Appleshaw**

5m NW of Andover. Take A342 Andover to Marlborough rd. Turn to Appleshaw 1m W of Weyhill. After ½m park on R in field. Small pretty village, population approx 500. Lovely church, pub and village green. Home-made TEAS at Haleakala. *Combined adm £3, chd free. Sun, Mon 5, 6 June (2-5.30)*

NEW **Haleakala** ✿⊕ (Jenny & Roger Bateman) Half-acre 4yr-old shrub and herbaceous garden, designed by owners for yr-round colour and interest. Winding paths, large pond and rockery, summerhouse, gravel garden, secret sitting places, unusual plants. Plant sales in aid of St Peter in the Wood Church.

NEW **The Jays** ✿⊕ (Mr & Mrs A Clarke) Half-acre garden

redesigned and restored in past 4yrs. Various fruit and flowering trees, mixed borders, rockeries, fish pond and bog garden. Plant sales in aid of St Peter in the Wood Church.

10 **19 Barnwood Road, Fareham** ✿⊕

(Jill & Michael Hill) *From M27 J9 take A27 towards Fareham. At top of hill past Titchfield Mill PH turn L at T-lights into Highlands Rd. Take 4th turning R into Blackbrook Rd, Meadow Bank is 4th turning on R. Barnwood is off Meadow Bank.* Small plot, mostly perennials and shrubs, with winding paths and surprising vistas. Double pond with bridge. Interesting use of colour in planting schemes and structural features, thatched summerhouse. Winner Plantsman's Garden, Fareham in Bloom 2003. Home-made TEAS. *Adm £2, chd free. Sun 3 July (11-5). Private visits welcome by appt for groups of 10+, 19 Barnwood Road, Fareham, PO15 5LA*

11 **Beechenwood Farm, Odiham** ⊕✿⊕

(Mr & Mrs M Heber-Percy) *5m SE of Hook. Turn S into King St from Odiham High St. Turn L after cricket ground for Hillside. Take 2nd turn R after 1½m, modern house ½m.* 2-acre garden in many parts incl woodland garden, rock garden, pergola, conservatory, herb garden with exuberant planting, belvedere with spectacular views over Odiham. Recently planted wood of 8 acres. Home-made TEAS in aid of Odiham Cottage Hospital. *Adm £2.50, chd free. Weds 30 Mar; 6, 20 Apr; 4, 18 May; 1, 15, 29 June; 13, 27 Jul. Fris 1, 15, 29 Apr; 13, 27 May; 10, 24 Jun; 8, 22 Jul (2-5). Private visits welcome by appt. Tel 01256 702300*

12 NEW **Bentley Village Gardens**

4m NE of Alton off A31 (Bentley by-pass). Turn off A31 into village. At X-rds, Main Road, 2 gardens to R, one to L. Follow signs. Three small gardens, each very different, in Bentley village. Maps given to all visitors. Home-made TEAS at Bay Tree Cottage. *Combined adm £3, chd free. Sat, Sun 11, 12 June (2-6)*

NEW **Avenue Cottage** ⊕✿⊕ (David & Rosie Darrah) *At Main Rd turn R, ½m on R.* Very pretty cottage garden with formal herb garden and potager.

NEW **Bay Tree Cottage** ⊕✿ (Andrew & Mary Thomson) *At Main Road turn R, approx ¼m on R. Opp playing field.* Cottage garden covering approx ¼ acre.

Incl herbaceous, shrubbery, herb garden, vegetables, soft fruit, and colourful hens in separate enclosure.

NEW **The Kilns** 🖉 (Mascha & Richard Tyrrell) *L at X-rds, 200yds on R is lane marked Bentley Garden Farm. Last house down lane on R.* Garden reclaimed from a concrete wasteland 7yrs ago. Unusual plants in mixed herbaceous borders; courtyard and lawns. *Private visits welcome by appt. Tel 01420 520377*

⓭ Bluebell Cottage, Broadway, Froxfield 🖉
(Mr & Mrs T Clarke) *3½m NW of Petersfield. Between top of Stoner Hill & Froxfield Green, or take sign to Froxfield off A272 opp Bordean House & follow yellow signs.* 1 acre incl natural woodland with prolific bluebells and ferns. Mixed borders, kitchen garden with raised beds, fruit and greenhouse. Conservatory, pool. Places to sit in sun or shade. *Adm £2, chd free. Sun, Mon 1, 2 May (2-6)*

⓮ NEW Braemoor, Harbridge, Fordingbridge 🖕🖉🏵
(Tracy & John Netherway & Judy) *2½m S of Fordingbridge. 1m S of Alderholt on Ringwood rd. ¾-acre* garden of mixed herbaceous borders and shrubs with a small stream and pond; patio areas with pots and containers; grasses in gravel scree; 2 greenhouses with a collection of cacti and carnivorous plants; many unusual plants; vegetable garden. Fancy bantams. Home-made TEAS. *Adm £2, chd free. Suns 31 July; 7 Aug (2-5.30). Private visits welcome by appt. Tel 01425 652983 jnetherway@btinternet.com*

⓯ Bramdean House, Bramdean 🖕🖉🏵
(Mr & Mrs H Wakefield) *4m S of Alresford. In centre of village on A272.* Traditional 6-acre garden on chalk, famous for mirror-image herbaceous borders. Very many unusual plants incl collection of old-fashioned sweet peas. Carpets of bulbs in the spring and 1-acre kitchen garden featuring prizewinning vegetables, fruit and flowers. BBC2 Flying Gardener & 'The Times' feature 2003, Saturday 'Telegraph' 2004. *Adm £3, chd free (share to RHS). Suns 13 Feb; 27 Mar; 11 Apr; 19 June; 17 July; 14 Aug; 11 Sept (2-5); 19 Feb 2006. Private visits welcome by appt. Tel 01962 771214*

⓰ Brandy Mount House, Alresford 🖕🏵 **NCCPG**
(Caryl & Michael Baron) *nr Alresford centre. From centre, 1st R in East St before Sun Lane. Please leave cars in Broad St or station car park.* 1-acre, informal plantsman's garden. Spring bulbs, hellebores, species geraniums. National Collections of snowdrops and daphnes. European primulas, expanding collection of dwarf narcissi, herbaceous and woodland plants. Featured in 'Amateur Gardening', 'Countryside Magazine', 'Gardens Illustrated' 2004. Home-made TEAS Sun 6 Mar only. *Adm £2, chd free. Sat 5 Feb (11-4); Sun 6 Mar (2-5) www.brandymount.co.uk*

⓱ 6 Breamore Close, Eastleigh 🖕🖉🏵
(Mr & Mrs R Trenchard) *1m N of Eastleigh. Leave M3 J12. Follow signs to Eastleigh. Turn R at roundabout into Woodside Ave, then 1st L into Broadlands Ave. Breamore Close is 3rd on L. Park in Broadlands Ave.* Delightful ½-acre garden with distinctive planting themes in different areas. Shrubs, trees and herbaceous plants give good spring and early summer colour, with magnificent wisteria display (flowers 3ft-4ft long) intermingled with clematis and roses over pergola. Home-made TEAS. *Adm £2. Sat, Sun 21, 22 May (1-5.30)*

⓲ Broadhatch House, Bentley 🖕🖉🏵
(Bruce & Lizzie Powell) *4m NE of Alton. Turn off A31 (Bentley bypass), R through village up School Lane. R to Perrylands, after 300yds drive on R. 3½* acres divided by yew hedges into different gardens: spring, rose, sunken etc. Formal pools and large herbaceous borders for long seasonal interest. Semi-walled ex-vegetable garden. Wide range of plants. *Private visits welcome by appt, June & July. Tel 01420 23185 lizzie.powell@btconnect.com*

⓳ Brocas Farm, Lower Froyle 🖕🖉
(Mr & Mrs J Dundas) *5m NE of Alton. Access to Lower Froyle from A31 between Alton & Farnham at Bentley. Parking in field.* Grade II listed house (not open). Medium-sized, mature garden with herbaceous borders, kitchen garden, orchard and small arboretum. TEAS. *Adm £2, chd under 10 free. Sat, Sun 18, 19 June (2-6)*

⓴ Bury Court, Bentley 🖕🖉🏵
(John Coke) *5m NE of Alton. 1m N of Bentley. Take Hole Lane, then follow signs towards Crondall.* New garden, designed in cooperation with Piet Oudolf, created from old farmyard. Currently the only pure example of continental 'naturalistic' style, making heavy use of grasses in association with perennials selected for an extended season of interest. Recently completed area designed by Christopher Bradley-Hole in minimalist style, featuring grid of gravel paths bisecting chequerboard of naturalistically planted raised squares edged in rusted steel. Featured in Saturday 'Telegraph' 2004. Light refreshments and TEAS. *Adm £2.50, chd 50p. Suns 10 July; 7 Aug; 4 Sept (12-6)*

㉑ Bury Farm, Marchwood 🖕🖉🏵
(Mr & Mrs Barker-Mill) *6m W of Southampton. Off A326 between Totton & Marchwood. Follow yellow signs.* Contemporary organic garden of large sculpture and shrubs, started in 1983. Walled circular kitchen garden in potager style with 4-colour garden and well-head pool at centre. Spiral yew maze. Mystery passage leads to octagonal plunge pool with sun pavilion. Home-made TEAS. *Adm £2, chd free. Sun 29 May (11-5)*

㉒ Chilland House, Martyr Worthy 🖕
(Mr & Mrs Andrew Impey) *7m NE of Winchester. On B3047 between Martyr Worthy & Itchen Abbas, signed Chilland.* 4 acres with stream overlooking R Itchen and watermeadows, woods and farmland beyond. Large collection of mature shrubs planned for yr-round colour effects. Many fine trees and shrubs incl huge plane and ancient mulberry, nutwalk, spring bulbs, clematis, herbaceous borders and flowering shrubs. *Adm £2, chd free. Sun, Mon 29, 30 May (2-5.30)*

㉓ 71 Church Close, Northington
(Mr & Mrs Swithinbank) *4m N of Alresford. Follow B3046 N from Alresford to Northington. From Basingstoke or Winchester take the A33, turning at the Lunnways Inn to Northington. Park in church car park.* There is a peaceful view across the Candover Valley from this mature cottage garden. The garden is on chalk and falls away from a terraced cottage on a ⅓-acre sloping site. The garden will inspire you with its planting, use of colour and delightful features such as a circular potager,

old apple trees and hazel arches supporting clematis, honeysuckle, sweet peas, climbing roses and hydrangea. Home-made TEAS in aid of Riding for the Disabled. *Adm £1.50, chd free. Fri, Sat, Sun 3, 4, 5 June (1.30-5.30). Also open* **Meadow Lodge**

㉔ Clibdens, Chalton &🐾
(Mrs Jacqueline Budden) 6m S of Petersfield. Turn L off A3 N of Horndean then directly R to Chalton. Clibdens is 1st turning on L in village, directly before Chalton village sign. 1-acre garden surrounding farm with fine views to Windmill Hill. Chalk garden with 4 rooms of lawn, shrubs and herbaceous plants. Terrace with stone pots of agapanthus, box, lavender and yew topiary. Gravel garden, stump garden and wild life pond. Rose garden with oak posts and rope arches. Home-made TEAS. *Adm £2.50, chd free. Private visits welcome by appt May & June only, groups welcome. Please phone. Tel 02392 592172*

㉕ The Clock House, nr Sparsholt, Winchester &🐾🌳
(Mr & Mrs Robert Harman) 3½m W of Winchester. Off B3049 between Winchester & Stockbridge (3½m & 6½m). Watch for staggered sign with bend on B3049 & turn N up farm lane opp hoardings to Sparsholt College. After 300yds turn L & go to end. Avoid signs to Sparsholt village. Parking in field. 2 acres incl large walled garden with traditional herbaceous borders and climbing roses. Wisteria and laburnum arch. Mature specimen trees. Pond and extensive views. Large greenhouse, well stocked. Home-made TEAS. *Adm £2.50, chd free. Sat, Sun 4, 5, Weds 15, 22 June (2-5.30) . Private visits welcome by appt June & July only for groups of 10+. Tel 01962 776461*

㉖ Closewood House, Newlands Lane, Denmead &
(Mr & Mrs Peter Clowes) 1m W of Waterlooville. Take Closewood Rd to W of B2150 between Waterlooville & Denmead. Turn L at T-junction after ½m. Signs to car park after 330yds. 4½ acres. Collection of

scented roses incl large climbers and shrubs with good vistas between sections. 200 different specimen trees and grass walk. Box parterre, fishpond and large abstract sculpture. Picnics welcome by stream. Home-made TEAS. *Adm £3, chd free. Sun, Mon 1, 2 May; Suns 12, 19 June (2-5). Private visits welcome by appt for groups of 15+. Tel 02392 264213 pjclowes@onetel.com*

㉗ The Coach House, South Warnborough &🐾
(John & Sarah Taylor) 5m N of Alton on B3349. In the middle of village opp village shop/post office. Car parking in lay-by opp. ¾-acre semi-walled garden almost entirely given over to plantings of perennials and grasses in a naturalistic and informal style. Gravel planting and deep generous beds with an emphasis on height and proximity to plants. Home-made TEAS. *Adm £2, chd free. Sat, Sun 16, 17 July; Sun 18 Sept (2-6). Private visits welcome by appt. Tel 01256 862782 johntaylormw@hotmail.com*

㉘ Colemore House, Colemore &🐾🌳
(Mr & Mrs Simon de Zoete) 5m S of Alton. Take A32 towards Petersfield then L to Colemore just beyond East Tisted. Situated in beautiful unspoilt country, 2½ acres with wide variety of unusual plants. Yew and box hedges, mixed herbaceous and shrub borders, yellow and blue garden, rose walk and excellent lawns. Garden is being constantly developed and incl spectacular new water rill, swimming pool garden and the creation of a wild flower, tree and shrub area. Many different roses, salvias, penstemons and tender plants and bulbs. TEAS. *Adm £2.50, chd free. Sun, Mon 26, 27 June (2-6). Private visits welcome by appt. Tel 01420 588202*

㉙ ◆ Coles, Privett 🌳🌼
(Mrs Tim Watkins) 6m NW of Petersfield. Nr Alton & Petersfield. Between Privett & High Cross. From A32, S of Alton between East Tisted & West Meon Hut, turn E to Froxfield at Pig & Whistle/Lawns PH. After ¼m turn L at T-junction & continue for ¾m, entrance on L. 26

acres specialising in rhododendrons and azaleas, set amongst mixed woodland with rare specimens. Walks, clearings and decorative ponds. Spring bluebells, autumn leaf colours. Home-made TEAS. *Adm £4, chd 50p, concessions £3.50. Mons 28 Mar; 2, 30 May. Suns 1 May to 29 May incl; 16, 23 Oct (2-5). Tel 01730 828050 sara@sarawalker.com*

㉚ Conholt Park, Chute 🌼
(Professor Caroline Tisdall) 7m N of Andover. Turn N off A342 Andover to Devizes rd at Weyhill Church. Proceed 5m N through Clanville & Tangley Bottom. Turn L at Conholt ½m on R, just off Chute causeway. 10 acres surrounding Regency house (not open), rose 'Calor', Shakespeare, winter and secret gardens. Restored 1½-acre walled garden with potager, berry wall, rare fruit orchard, white border, mahonia, hardy geraniums and allium collections. All completely organic. Romantic Edwardian Ladies' Walk and possibly longest maze in Britain. Ornate copper rose fountain. On farm unusual animals incl bison, wild boar and a shire horse. Home-made TEAS. *Adm £3, chd free. Suns 13 Feb (2-4); 29 May; 19 June (11-5). Private visits welcome by appt, Jun & July only, groups & coaches permitted. Tel 07803 021208 carolehaynes@tiscali.co.uk*

㉛ The Cottage, 16 Lakewood Road, Chandler's Ford 🌳🌼
(Hugh & Barbara Sykes) 2m NW of Eastleigh. Leave M3 at J12, follow signs to Chandler's Ford. At King Rufus PH on Winchester Rd, turn R into Merdon Ave, then 3rd rd on L. The Cottage was built 100yrs ago amongst mature oaks and pines, ideal for rhododendrons, azaleas, camellias, spring bulbs and trilliums. The ¾-acre garden, begun in 1950, is maintained by owners and planted for yr-round interest with herbaceous borders, kitchen area, spring-fed bog garden and ponds. Bantams. Children's quiz. Honey. Home-made TEAS. *Adm £2, chd 50p. Suns, Mons 1, 2, 15, 16 May (2-6)*

㉜ Cranbury Park, Otterbourne &🌼
(Mr & Mrs Chamberlayne-Macdonald) *3m SW of Eastleigh. Main entrance on old A33 between Winchester and Southampton, by bus stop at top of Otterbourne Hill. Entrances also in Hocombe Rd, Chandler's Ford and next to church in Otterbourne.* Extensive pleasure grounds laid out in late C18 and early C19 by

Papworth; fountains, rose garden, specimen trees and pinetum, lakeside walk and fern walk. Family carriages and collection of prams will be on view. Home-made TEAS. *Adm £4, chd 50p (share to St Matthew's Church, Otterbourne). Sun 12 June (2-6)*

㉝ Crawley Gardens, nr Winchester
5m NW of Winchester. Off A272 or A3049 Winchester-Stockbridge rd. Parking at top of village nr church or in Littleton Rd. Very pretty unspoilt small village with thatched houses, C14 church and village pond. Home-made TEAS. *Combined adm £3.50, chd free (share to Crawley Village Hall). Sun, Mon 3, 4 Apr; Thur, Fri 23, 24 June (2-5.30)*

Glebe House, Littleton Road 🚻 (Lt Col & Mrs J Andrews) *Parking in rd outside garden, at opp end of village to Church. 1½ acres. Bulbs and shrubs incl eucalyptus collection. Not open 23, 24 June*

Little Court (Prof & Mrs A R Elkington) (See separate entry).

Paige Cottage 🌿 (Mr & Mrs T W Parker) 1 acre of traditional English country garden incl grass tennis court (not open) and walled Italian-style swimming pool (not open); roses climbing into apple trees.

Tanglefoot 🚻🌿 (Mr & Mrs F J Fratter) (See separate entry). *Not open 3, 4 Apr*

㉞ Dean House, Kilmeston 🚻
(Mr P H R Gwyn) *5m S of Alresford. Via village of Cheriton or off A272 signed at Cheriton Xrds. 7 acres; orchard, paddock with small, formal pond, spacious lawns, mixed and herbaceous borders surrounding symmetrical rose garden, planted tunnel, working walled kitchen garden and generously stocked glasshouses. Adm £2.50, chd free. Wed 22 June; Sun 3 July (10-4)*

㉟ The Deanery, The Close, Winchester 🚻🌿
The Dean & Mrs Michael Till) *Central Winchester. S side of Winchester Cathedral. 3 hidden acres compose their own views of Winchester Cathedral. Trout stream where Izaac Walton 'studied to be quiet') separates Deanery and Bishop's gardens. Charles II, Philip of Spain and Henry VII also walked here. Adm £2.50, chd 50p. Mons 28 Mar; 30 May (2-5.30). Private visits welcome by appt. Tel 01962 853738 essa.till@tesco.net*

Dormers, West Marden 🚻🌿
See Sussex.

㊱ Durmast House, Burley 🚻
(Mr & Mrs P E G Daubeney) *5m SE of Ringwood. Off Burley to Lyndhurst rd, nr White Buck Hotel. 4 acres designed by Gertrude Jekyll in 1907, in process of being restored from original plans. Formal rose garden edged with lavender, 130yr-old Monterey pine, mimosa tree, Victorian rockery, coach house. New Lutyens-style summerhouse on original site and Jekyll herbaceous borders. Restored azalea walk. Listed in Hampshire register of historic gardens. Cream TEAS. £2.50, chd 50p (share to Delhi Commonwealth Women's Association Clinic, 27 Mar; Harrison Heart Foundation, 26 June). Suns 27 Mar; 26 June (2-5). Private visits welcome by appt, gardening clubs welcome. Tel 01425 403527 philip@daubeney.co.uk*

㊲ East Lane, Ovington 🌿
(Sir Peter & Lady Ramsbotham) *1m W of Alresford. Take A31 from Winchester towards Alresford. Immed after roundabout, 1m W of Alresford, small sign to Ovington, turn sharp L up incline, down small country rd to Ovington. East Lane is only house on L, 500yds down hill towards Bush Inn. 5-acre charming woodland garden. Large lawn leading up to white gazebo and arboretum with fine views. Collection of mature shrubs interspersed with an acre of spring bulbs. Herbaceous borders. Walled rose garden. Large terraced water garden overlooking water meadows with stream flowing through. Adm £2.50, chd free. Sun 3 Apr (2.30-5.30)*

㊳ Elbow Corner, Basingstoke 🚻
(Mr & Mrs M Penfold) *Off Church Square. Car park opp Anvil Theatre, Churchill Way in centre of Basingstoke. Walk via Lower Church St or through park from car park to Elbow Corner, adjacent to St Michael's Church. Very unusual. Small terraced front gardens in a short row of Victorian cottages in the heart of old Basingstoke. Planted out with hundreds of hanging baskets and containers providing a riot of colours. Water feature. Featured in 'Hampshire County' magazine 2004. TEAS in aid of Naomi House Children's Hospice. Adm £2, chd free. Sat 23 July to Sun 14 Aug incl (10-5). Private visits welcome by appt July & Aug. Tel 01256 331029*

㊴ NEW Enchanted Cottage, 242 Havant Road, Hayling Island 🌿
(Mr & Mrs Graham) *1m S of Havant. From A27 Havant/Hayling junction travel S 1m. House on L. ⅓-acre romantic cottage garden with many interesting features. An abundance of plants, rambling roses and clematis cover a long arbour. Gravel areas planted with herbs, and pots. Plenty of seating. A magical garden for children with an adventure playground for cats! Home-made TEAS. Adm £2, chd free. Suns 22 May; 12 June; 14 Aug (11-5). Also open 12 June* **The Homestead**

㊵ ◆ Exbury Gardens & Steam Railway, Southampton 🚻
(Edmund de Rothschild Esq) *16m S of Southampton. 4m Beaulieu. Exbury 20mins M27 J2. 200-acre woodland garden with world-famous displays of rhododendrons, azaleas, camellias and magnolias. Rock garden, exotic garden, herbaceous gardens, ponds, cascades, river walk and seasonal trails. Steam railway and Summer Lane Garden are popular favourites. In 2005 Exbury celebrates 50th anniversary of first opening to the public. 'Daily Mail' coverage of Queen's visit in 2004. Light refreshments and TEAS. Adm high season (21 Mar to 5 June) £7, concessions £6.50 (OAP £6 Tues, Weds, Thurs), chd £1.50. Low season £5, concessions £4.50, chd £1. Daily 26 Feb to 6 Nov 10-5.30. Tel 02380 891203 www.exbury.co.uk*

㊶ NEW Farleigh House, Farleigh Wallop, nr Basingstoke 🚻
(The Earl & Countess of Portsmouth) *3m SE of Basingstoke. Off B3046 Basingstoke to Preston Candover rd. Contemporary garden of great tranquillity designed by Georgia Langton, surrounded by wonderful views. 3-acre walled garden in three sections: ornamental potager, formal rose garden and wild rose garden. Greenhouse full of exotics, serpentine yew walk, contemplative pond garden and lake with planting for wildlife. Approx 10 acres and 1 hour to walk around. Home-made TEAS. Adm £3, chd free. Suns 19 June; 10 July (11-5)*

㊷ Flintstones, Sciviers Lane, Durley 🚻
(June & Bill Butler) *5m E of Eastleigh. From M3 J11 follow signs for Marwell Zoo. From B2177 turn R opp Woodman PH. From M27 J7 follow signs for Fair Oak then Durley, turn L at Robin Hood PH. ¾ acre designed and developed entirely by owners. Plantswoman's garden*

densely planted on clay, with many unusual and interesting plants, providing a pleasing tapestry effect of texture and colour, for all-yr interest. TEAS 3 Apr, Home-made TEAS 5, 6 June. *Adm £2, chd free. Suns 3 Apr; 5 June; Mon 6 June (2-6). Private visits welcome by appt May to September. Tel 01489 860880 butlerbilljune@flintstones5.fsnet. co.uk*

Folly Farm, Sulhamstead 👆🌸🏵
See Berkshire.

❸ Forest Edge, Andover Down 👆🌸
(Annette & David Beeson) *2m E of Andover. On B3400 to Whitchurch. Watch for B&B sign. Please avoid parking on brow of hill.* 1-acre eco-friendly garden adjacent to Harewood Forest. Succession of wild daffodils, cowslips, meadow saxifrages and buttercups in spring meadow. Summer meadow rich in native species incl orchids. Wild pond and hedges. Wild flower herbaceous bed. Shrub borders with exotic and British herbaceous plants. Dwarf conifers in gravel areas. Accommodation. Featured on BBC Gardeners' World 2004. Home-made TEAS. *Adm £2, chd free. Suns 24 Apr; 12 June (2-6). Private visits welcome by appt. Tel 01264 364526 www.forest-edge.co.uk*

❹ Fritham Lodge, Fritham 👆🏵
(Mr & Mrs Christopher Powell) *6m N of Lyndhurst. 3m NW of M27 J1 Cadnam. Follow signs to Fritham.* Set in heart of New Forest in 18 acres; with 1-acre old walled garden round Grade II listed C17 house (not open) originally one of Charles II hunting lodges. Parterre of old roses, potager with wide variety of vegetables, herbs and fruit trees, pergola, herbaceous and blue and white mixed borders, ponds, walk across hay meadows to woodland and stream, with ponies, donkeys, sheep, ducks and rare breed hens. Featured in 'English Gardens' 2003. Cream TEAS. *Adm £2.50, chd free. Sun 26 June (2-5). Private visits welcome by appt. Tel 02830 812650 chris.powell@ddblondon.com*

❺ Froyle Cottage Gardens
2m E of Alton. Access to Lower Froyle from A31 between Alton & Farnham, at Bentley. Follow signs from Lower Froyle to Upper Froyle. 'The Village of Saints'. Maps given to all visitors. Home-made TEAS at Froyle Village Hall. *Combined adm £3, chd free. Sat, Sun 28, 29 May (2-6)*

The Cottage, Lower Froyle 🌸 (Mr & Mrs Carr) Not only plants but a collection of animals frequently associated with a true cottage garden.

Oklahoma, Lower Froyle 👆🌸🏵
(Mr & Mrs Figgins) Real English garden with foreign-sounding name. Recycled items used to make garden structures. 3 well-stocked greenhouses. Productive vegetable garden and fruit cage. Collection of streptocarpus and miniature poultry. *Private visits welcome by appt. Tel 01420 22220*

The Old School, Upper Froyle 👆🌸
(Nigel & Linda Bulpitt) Mature garden, mainly perennials with climbing roses and shrubs. Small wild area making a foil between garden and countryside.

Treetops, Upper Froyle 🌸🏵 (Mr & Mrs J Cresswell) (see separate entry).

Walbury, Lower Froyle 👆🏵 (Mr & Mrs Milam) (see separate entry).

Warren Cottage, Lower Froyle 👆🌸🏵 (Mrs A A Robertson) Garden surrounds C18 cottage (not open). Many interesting plants and lovely views.

❻ Greatham Mill, Greatham, nr Liss 👆🌸🏵
(Mr & Mrs J Graves) *5m N of Petersfield. From A3 roundabout ⅔m on B3006 towards Selborne. Down lane at junction with Snailing Lane.* 5 acres beside R Rother with views to the Hangers. Spring meadow with island beds of naturalised narcissi. 2½ acres of cottage-style garden undergoing continued restoration, full of interesting trees, shrubs, roses, herb garden, pond, mill and millrace. If wet, wear boots. TEAS. *Adm £2.50, chd free (share to Alzheimer's Society). Fris, Sats, Suns Easter w/end 25, 26, 27 Mar; 17, 18, 19 June (11-4)*

❼ Hambledon House, Hambledon 🌸🏵
(Capt & Mrs David Hart Dyke) *8m SW of Petersfield, 5m NW of Waterlooville. In village centre.* 2 acres partly walled plantsman's garden for all seasons. Large borders filled with wide variety of unusual shrubs and imaginative plant combinations. Large collection of salvias, hardy geraniums and ornamental grasses. Hidden, secluded areas reveal surprise views of garden and village rooftops. Featured in 'Hampshire Society' 2003 & '25 Beautiful Gardens' 2004. Home-

made TEAS. *Adm £2.50, chd free. Suns 17 Apr; 15 May; 26 June; Sun, Mon 18, 19 Sept. Weds 25 May; 8 June (2-5.30). Private visits welcome by appt for individuals & groups. Tel 02392 632380*

❽ Heathlands, 47 Locks Road, Locks Heath, nr Fareham 👆🏵 NCCPG
(Dr & Mrs John Burwell) *5m W of Fareham. From M27 J9, travel W on A27 towards Southampton. After 1m in Parkgate turn L into Locks Rd after pelican crossing. It is 1m down on RH-side.* 1-acre plantsman's garden designed and developed by owner since 1967. Yr-round interest against background of evergreens and mature trees. Spring bulbs, rhododendrons, paulownias, cyclamen, ferns and many unusual plants. Topiary peacock, small herbaceous border, scree and moss beds. National Collection of Japanese anemones. Home-made TEAS. *Adm £2.50, chd under 14 free. Suns 6 Mar; 21 Aug (2-5.30)*

❾ The Hedges, Chapel Lane, Timsbury 👆🌸🏵
(Betty & Tony Rackham) *2½m N of Romsey. From Romsey proceed on A3057 Stockbridge Rd to middle of Timsbury, turn R towards Michelmersh along New Rd. Chapel Lane is gravel track 400yds along New Rd on R. 1st bungalow on R along lane.* 2 acres. Botanists' garden of gravel beds, ponds, formal beds and many natural areas with varied plant collection incl many oenothera species and unusual perennials. Meadow and woodland areas are managed to encourage wild flowers, incl orchid species. Interesting vegetable garden and greenhouses. Photographic exhibition. Featured on ITV The Garden Makers 2004. Home-made TEAS. *Adm £2, chd free. Sun, Tue 3, 5 July (2-5.30)*

❿ Hill House, Old Alresford 👆
(Major & Mrs W F Richardson) *1m W of Alresford. From Alresford 1m along B3046 towards Basingstoke, then R by church.* 2 acres with large old-fashioned herbaceous border, established in 1938, and shrub beds set around large lawn; large kitchen garden. Dried flowers. Dexter cows and chickens. Home-made TEAS. *Adm £2, chd free. Sun 31 July; Tue 2 Aug (1.30-5)*

⓫ NEW 2 Hillside Cottages, Trampers Lane, North Boarhunt 👆 NCCPG
(John & Lynsey Pink) *5m N of Fareham. 3m E of Wickham. From*

A32 at Wickham take B2177 E.
Trampers Lane 2nd on L (approx
2m). Hillside Cottages approx ½m on
L. An acre of plantman's garden with
sweeping mixed borders. An island
bed annually planted with exotic
plants and salvias dominates the view
from the house. Holders of the
National Collection of salvia sp.
which are planted throughout the
garden along with many unusual
shrubs and herbaceous plants. TEAS.
Adm £2, chd free. Suns 14 Aug; 18
Sept (1-5). Private visits welcome by
appt. Tel 01329 832786

52 ◆ Hinton Ampner, Alresford
&⚘
(The National Trust) 3½m S of
Alresford. S on A272 Petersfield to
Winchester rd. 12 acres; C20 shrub
garden designed by Ralph Dutton.
Strong architectural elements using
yew and box topiary; spectacular
views. Bold effects using simple
plants, restrained and dramatic
bedding. Orchard with spring wild
flowers and bulbs within formal box
hedges; magnolia and philadelphus
walks. Dell garden made from chalk
pit. Shrub rose border dating from
1950s. Light refreshments and TEAS.
Adm £5, chd £2.50. For NGS: Suns,
Mons 24, 25 Apr; 10, 11 July; Sat,
Sun 10, 11 Sept (12-5). Tel 01962
771305
hintonampner@nationaltrust.org.uk

53 The Homestead, Northney
Road, Hayling Island &
(Stan & Mary Pike) 3m S of Havant.
From A27 Havant/Hayling Island
roundabout, travel S over Langstone
Bridge & turn immed L into
Northney Rd. 1st house on R after
Langstone Hotel. Owner-maintained
½-acre garden with views to
Chichester harbour and beyond.
Features incl pleached lime walk,
pergola, arbour, ponds and tennis
court bordered by alpine beds and
box hedging. Recently reconstructed
barn with small walled garden
containing trained fruit trees, formal
herb garden and vegetables. Home-
made TEAS. Adm £2, chd free. Sun
2 June (2-5.30). Also open
Enchanted Cottage

54 Hordle Walhampton School,
Beaulieu Road, Lymington &⚘
(Hordle Walhampton School Trust
Ltd) 1m E of Lymington. From
Lymington follow signs to Beaulieu
(B3054) for 1m & turn R in to main
entrance at 1st school sign 200yds
after reaching top of hill. 97-acre
grounds of C18/19 manor.
Landscape: naturalistic derived from
C18 formal and English styles and

influence of Capability Brown.
Garden styles/origins: late C19/early
C20 Italianate revival with influence
of Harold Peto; early C20 Arts and
Crafts with designs by Thomas
Mawson; early C19
picturesque/gothic. Features: manor
(not open), lakes, canal, mount,
banana house, shell grotto, C19 trees,
mature shrubs, terraces, vistas and
views of Isle of Wight. Guided tours.
TEAS. Adm £3, chd 50p (share to
Boldre Church). Sun 15 May (2-6)

55 Houghton Lodge Garden, nr
Stockbridge &⚘
(Captain M W Busk) 1½m S of
Stockbridge. From A30 at
Stockbridge take minor rd S to
Houghton village. Haven of peace
above the natural beauty of R Test. 5
acres (Grade II*) with fine trees
surround C18 Cottage Orné.
Traditional walled kitchen garden,
ancient espaliers, herbs, parterre,
topiary (beware the snorting
'dragon'!). Heated greenhouses,
tropical orchid collection. Prolific
daffodils. German TV 2004. TEAS.
Adm £5, chd free. Sat, Sun 19, 20
Mar (10-5) www.houghtonlodge.
co.uk

56 The House in the Wood,
Beaulieu
(Victoria Roberts) 8m NE of
Lymington. Leaving the entrance to
Beaulieu motor museum on your R
(B3056) take the next R turn signed
Ipley Cross. Take 2nd gravel drive on
RH-bend, approx ½m. Charming
woodland garden set in 12 acres
specialising in rhododendrons and
azaleas. Large lawn, views and walk
down to a lake at the bottom. The
area was used during the war to train
the Special Operations Executive.
Cream TEAS. Adm £3, chd 50p. Sun
15 May (2-6)

57 NEW The Hyde, Old Alresford
&⚘
(Sue Alexander) 1m W of Alresford.
From Alresford 1m along B3046
towards Basingstoke. House in centre
of village, opp village green. Tucked
away behind an old field hedge, an
unexpected and delightful ¾-acre
garden on two levels created by the
owner. The flowing borders and
mixed planting reflect a flower
arranger's passion for colour and
texture and incl a lush bog garden,
vegetable parterre, shady woodland
corners, new meadows and wildlife
pool. Home-made TEAS. Adm £2,
chd free. Sun 7 Aug (1.30-5)

Kent House, East Harting &⚘
See Sussex.

58 53 Ladywood, Eastleigh ⚘&
(Mr & Mrs D Ward) 1m N of
Eastleigh. Leave M3 J12. Follow
signs to Eastleigh. Turn R at
roundabout into Woodside Ave, then
2nd R into Bosville. Ladywood is 5th
on R. Park in Bosville. 45ft x 45ft
giving ideas for the small garden.
Over 1,800 different plants labelled.
Trellis fences give vertical space for
many clematis and unusual climbers.
Special interest in foliage plants,
hardy geraniums, phlox and
pulmonarias, all designed to create
peace and harmony in a town garden.
Featured in BBC 'Easy Gardening'
and 'Garden Answers' 2004. Home-
made TEAS (donation to NGS). Adm
£2.50, chd £1. Suns 1 May; 26 June
(11-5). Private visits welcome by
appt, Tues Apr to July (2-5).
Tel 02380 615389

59 Lake House, Northington
(Lord Ashburton) 4m N of Alresford.
Off B3046. Follow English Heritage
signs to The Grange, then directions.
2 large lakes in Candover Valley set
off by mature woodland with
waterfalls, abundant bird life, long
landscaped vistas and folly. 1½-acre
walled garden, mixed borders, long
herbaceous border, rose pergola
leading to moon gate. Formal kitchen
garden, flowering pots, conservatory
and greenhouses. Picnicking by lakes.
Home-made TEAS. Adm £3, chd free
(share to St John's Church,
Northington). Fri, Sat, Sun 15, 16, 17
Apr (1.30-5.30). Private visits
welcome by appt for small groups
only, Lake House, Northington,
Alresford SO24 9TG

60 60 Lealand Road, Drayton,
Portsmouth &⚘
(Mr F G Jacob) 2m E of Cosham.
Old A27 (Havant Rd) between
Cosham & Bedhampton.
Prizewinning garden, with a
difference, created by the owner since
1969. Plants from around the world
incl palms, yuccas, echiums and
cannas. Designed for maximum effect
with lily ponds and rockery. Incl
collection of bamboos and grasses,
also cacti and other exotics in
greenhouse. Home-made TEAS. Adm
£2, chd free. Suns 24 Apr; 22 May;
26 June (1-5.30). Private visits
welcome by appt. Tel 02392 370030

61 Little Coopers, Coopers Hill,
Eversley &⚘
(Mr & Mrs J K Oldale) 4m N of
Fleet. On B3016, signed from A30
(W of Blackbushe Airport) and from
B3272 (E of Eversley cricket ground).
Signed car parking at Westfield Farm,
100yds from garden. 10 acres. A

walk will take you through woodland carpeted with bluebells. Rhododendrons, azaleas, many unusual shrubs. Water and bog gardens; extensive lawn with conifers; heathers; Mediterranean, rose, small Japanese and dry gardens. Cream TEAS in aid of St Mary's Church, Eversley. *Adm £2.50, chd free. Sun 1 May (2-5.30)*

62 The Little Cottage, Southampton Road, Lymington 🌚 (Peter & Lyn Prior) *On N edge of Lymington on A337 opp Toll House Inn.* Garden of unique and artistic design using unusual and interesting plants arranged to form pictures with arches, arbours and urns in secret rooms. Each room is hidden from the next and contrasts sharply in style and colour to stimulate or calm, excite or amaze. Unsuitable for children. *Adm £2. Tues 14 June; 5 July; 2 Aug; 6 Sept (10-1 & 2-5). Private visits welcome by appt 14 June to 6 Sept. Tel 01590 679395*

63 Little Court, Crawley, nr Winchester 🚻🌚 (Prof & Mrs A R Elkington) *5m NW of Winchester. Off A272 or B3049 in Crawley village; 300yds from either village pond or church.* 1½-acre, walled old country garden of great tranquillity. Carpets of spring bulbs; climbers and perennials in related colours and naturalistic style, many hellebores, geraniums, clematis and eryngiums. Walled traditional kitchen garden. Large tree house and deck, suitable for all ages, with beautiful view. Grass labyrinth. Featured in 'The Times' 2004 and on ITV The Garden Makers 2004. Home-made TEAS. *Adm £3, chd free (share to Crawley Village Hall). Suns 13, 20, Mon, Tue 21, 22 Feb; Suns, Tues 20, 22 Mar: 15, 17 May (2-5.30) Suns 12, 19, Mon, Tue 20, 21 Feb 2006. Also opening with* **Crawley Gardens** *Sun, Mon 3, 4 Apr; Thur, Fri 23, 24 June. Private visits welcome by appt until September. Tel 01962 776365 elkslc@onetel.com*

64 Littlewood, West Lane, Hayling Island 🚻🌚 (Mr & Mrs Steven Schrier) *3m S of Havant. From A27 Havant/Hayling Island junction, travel S for 2m, turn R into West Lane and continue 1m. House set back from rd in wood. Disabled should drive to very top of drive.* 2½-acre woodland garden surrounded by fields and near sea, protected from sea winds by multi-barrier hedge. Rhododendrons, azaleas, camellias and many other shrubs. Woodland walk to full size

tree house. Features incl pond, bog garden watered from roof of conservatory, house plants, summerhouse and many places to sit outside and under cover. Picnickers welcome. Home-made TEAS. *Adm £2.50, chd free. Sat, Sun 21, 22 May (11-5)*

65 Longparish Gardens, nr Andover *7m E of Andover. Off A303. To village centre on B3048. Parking at Lower Mill only, except for disabled.* Home-made TEAS at Longmead House in aid of Longparish School and Community Project. *Combined adm £4, chd 50p. Sun, Mon 29, 30 May (2-6)*

Longmead House 🚻🌚 (Mr & Mrs J H Ellicock) 2½-acre organic and wildlife garden. Large, hedged vegetable garden with deep beds, polytunnel, fruit cage and composting display. Fish pond, wildlife pond. Wild flower meadow. Herbaceous and shrub borders, woodland walk. Conservatory and greenhouse. *Private visits welcome by appt, June & July only for groups of 10+. Tel 01264 720386 jhe@waitrose.com*

Lower Mill 🌚 (Mr & Mrs A W Dinesen) Spacious garden with enormous variety of design and planting incl courtyard and water garden. Tranquil natural walks beside the R Test. Approx 15 acres.

66 Longstock Park Water Garden, nr Stockbridge 🚻🌚 NCCPG (Leckford Estate Ltd, part of John Lewis Partnership) *4m S of Andover. From A30 turn N on to A3057; follow signs to Longstock.* Famous water garden with extensive collection of aquatic and bog plants set in 7 acres of woodland with rhododendrons and azaleas. A walk through park leads to National Collection of *Buddleia* and *Clematis viticella*, arboretum, herbaceous border. Home-made TEAS provided by, and in aid of, local churches. *Adm £4, chd 50p. Sun 19 June (2-5) www.longstockpark.co.uk*

67 ◆ Longthatch, Upper Lane, Warnford 🚻🌚 NCCPG (Peter & Vera Short) *12m N of Fareham. On A32, turn R from N or L from S at George & Falcon PH. After 100yds turn R at T-junction, continue for ¼m; thatched C17 house on R. Parking opp.* 3½ acres, plantsman's garden on R Meon. Rare trees and shrubs. Part of National Collection of *Helleborus*. Fine lawns,

herbaceous borders, island beds and bog gardens. Spring-fed ponds, woodland area with hellebores, primulas and shade-loving plants. Featured on BBC TV How to be a Gardener 2003. Home-made TEAS, Apr, May & June. *Adm £2.50, chd free. Weds in March.* **For NGS:** *Suns 6, 13, 20 Mar; 24 Apr; 29 May; 19 June; Mon 30 May (2-5). Tel 01730 829285*

NEW **Lowder Mill, Bell Vale Lane, Fernhurst** 🌚🌚 See Sussex.

Lower House, Whiteparish 🚻🌚 NCCPG See Wiltshire.

68 1 Lower Spinney, Warsash 🌚🌚 (Pam & Ben Whitfield) *7m W of Fareham. A27 Sarisbury Green (E of R Hamble). Turn into Barnes Lane signed Warsash. In village centre straight into Newtown Rd then 3rd L, Pitchponds Rd 1st R.* ⅓-acre steeply sloping site. Patio with planted containers, water feature, ornamental pond with cascade. Winding paths through trees and shrubs. Plants incl rhododendrons, azaleas, pieris, foxgloves, primulas, herbaceous perennials, hydrangeas, fuchsias and annuals. For walkers the Solent Way and Hook with Warsash Nature Reserve are 400 yds away. Fareham in Bloom winner, Gold and Best in Category 2004. Home-made TEAS. *Adm £2, chd free. Sats, Suns 7, 8 May; 16, 17 July (2-5)*

69 ◆ Macpennys Woodland Garden & Nurseries, Burley Road, Bransgore 🌚 (Mr & Mrs T M Lowndes) *6m S of Ringwood. Halfway between Christchurch & Burley. At Xrds by The Crown Bransgore turn R & proceed ¼m. From A31 (travelling towards Bournemouth) L at Picket Post, signed Burley, then R at Burley Cross. Garden on L after 2m.* 12 acres; 4-acre gravel pit converted into woodland garden; many unusual plants. Silver Gilt award in Trees and Shrubs at New Forest Show 2003. *Adm by donation. Mons to Sats (9-5), Suns (10-5) 2 Jan to 24 Dec. Tel 01425 672348 www.macpennys.co.uk*

70 20 Magdalene Way, Locks Heath, nr Fareham 🌚🌚 (Roy Dorland) *3m W of Fareham. Leave M27, J9 (Fareham W). Follow signs to Park Gate on A27. Turn L a Hunts Pond Rd, then R into Absbot Rd, 1st L into Cambridge Green*

leading to Magdalene Way.
Interesting plantsman's garden, 45ft ×
25ft, with many ideas for the small
garden, incl fernery, water feature
and winding paths to several seating
areas. Special interest in foliage
plants. Hostas, grasses, tiarellas,
heucheras, hardy geraniums and
phlox. Soft colours chosen for
relaxation. Regret not suitable for
children. Featured in Hampshire
Society 2004. Home-made TEAS
Suns only. *Adm £2. Suns (1-5), Mons
(11-4) 29, 30 May; 19, 20, 26, 27
June; 3, 4, 10, 11 July . Private visits
welcome by appt, June and July only.
Tel 01489 571788*
roy@dorland54.fsnet.co.uk

**71 The Manor House, Martin,
Fordingbridge** 🅰🚫🏠
*(Sir Michael & Lady Cobham) 6m
NW of Fordingbridge. From
Fordingbridge take rd to Damerham.
Turn R to Martin. Manor House is in
village centre.* Peaceful walled garden
of 1½ acres adjoining C15 Manor
House (not open). Spacious lawns
with interesting peripheral planting,
rose-covered pergola and pond. 3
garden gates lead to stable yard with
outlying paddocks, grazing mares,
foals and cattle. Home-made TEAS.
*Adm £2.50, chd free. Sat, Sun 11, 12
June (2-5.30). Private visits welcome
by appt. Tel 01725 519232*

NEW Manor House, Stratford Tony
🅰🚫🏠
See Wiltshire.

**72 NEW Marlands, London Road,
Headbourne Worthy** 🅰🏠
(Mike and Sally Humphries) *1½m
NW of Winchester. 1st house N of
Bedfield Lane junction, 300yds S of
flyover.* Contemporary garden
surrounds Victorian house, 1 acre
planted for green, foliage effect with
sculpture, and still developing. Raised
vegetable beds. Old rainwater
collection chamber pumped up for
irrigation. TEAS Suns only. *Adm £2,
chd free. Suns, Mons 1, 2 May; 12,
3 June (2-5)*

3 Martyr Worthy Gardens
5m NE of Winchester. On B3047. 2
different but complementary gardens
1m apart. Joined by lovely walk
along Pilgrims Way through Itchen
Valley. Home-made TEAS at & in
aid of Village Hall. *Adm £2 each
garden, chd free. Sun 12 June (2-6)*

Cygnet House 🅰🏠 (Mr & Mrs
Shane Chichester) Terraced
garden of 1½ acres with a large
number of old-fashioned roses,
shrubs, climbers and interesting

perennials. Lovely views over
valley.

The Manor House 🅰 (Sir Miles &
Lady Rivett-Carnac) Large
garden, roses, mixed borders,
lawns, shrubs and fine trees, next
to C12 church and footbridge
over R Itchen.

**74 NEW The Mathom House, 17
Bereweeke Road, Winchester**
🅰🏠
(Eric Eisenhauer) *½m from
Winchester station. In NW
Winchester between B3420 and
B3049. Walk from station approx 8
mins.* Nearly one acre, professionally
designed in 1997. Features parterre
'Pleasaunce Garden' in classical C17
design with old roses, flowering herbs
and hedged by 300 lavenders. Small
ornamental fruit garden with fanned
apple, pear, fig and peach. 100yr old
Judas tree. Significant bamboo hedge.
Specimen shrubs, climbers and
herbaceous borders. Home-made
TEAS. *Adm £2.50, chd free. Sats,
Suns 11, 12, 18, 19 June (12-6)*

Meadow House, Ashford Hill
🅰🚫🏠
See Berkshire.

75 Meadow Lodge, Swarraton
🅰🏠
(Mr & Mrs D Hardy) *3½m N of
Alresford. Off B3046 close to the
main entrance to the Grange. Follow
English Heritage signs to the Grange.*
Cottage garden of approx ⅓ acre with
herbaceous borders, varieties of
fuchsia, hanging baskets, outdoor
containers, water feature, pergola,
small fruit and vegetable plot. Horse,
sheep and various breeds of chickens.
Home-made TEAS at 71 Church
Close. *Adm £1.50, chd free. Fri, Sat,
Sun 3, 4, 5 June (1.30-5.30). Also
open **71 Church Close***

**76 Meon Orchard, Kingsmead, N
of Wickham** 🅰🏠 NCCPG
(Doug & Linda Smith) *5m N of
Fareham. From Wickham take A32
N for 1½m. Turn L at Roebuck Inn.
Continue ½m.* 1½-acre garden
designed and constructed by current
owners. An exceptional range of rare,
unusual and architectural plants incl
National Collection of Eucalyptus.
Much use made of dramatic foliage
plants from around the world, both
hardy and tender, big bananas, huge
taros, tree ferns, cannas, hedychiums
and palms. Streams and ponds,
combined with an extensive range of
planters, complete the display.
Owners available to answer
questions. Special plant sale of the
exotic and rare Sun 4 Sept. TEAS.

*Adm £2.50, chd 50p. Suns 5 June; 31
July; 4 Sept (2-6). Private visits
welcome by appt, groups welcome.
Tel 01329 833253*
doug.smith@btinternet.com

77 Merdon Manor, Hursley
🅰🚫🏠
(Mr & Mrs J C Smith) *5m SW of
Winchester. From A3090 Winchester
to Romsey rd, turn R at Standon
onto rd to Slackstead; proceed 1½m.*
5 acres with panoramic views;
herbaceous border, water lilies,
selection of roses; fruit-bearing lemon
trees and small secret walled water
garden. Ha-ha and black (St Kilda)
sheep. Home-made TEAS. *Adm £3,
chd free. Sun 24 July (2-6). Private
visits welcome by appt. Tel 01962
775215 vronk@freeuk.com*

Mitchmere Farm, Stoughton
🅰🚫🏠
See Sussex.

78 Mittens, Mapledurwell 🚫🏠
(Mr & Mrs David Hooper) *3½m E
of Basingstoke. Off A30 at Hatch,
signed Mapledurwell. Over M3
bridge take 2nd R, Frog Lane, to
Xrds at pond. 300yds up rd to
Tunworth.* 1½ acres. Created from
farmland in conservation area; spring
bulbs, children's garden with rill and
ivy house, secret garden with pool,
pergola, nut arch, purple border, 2
major borders of red and yellow with
colour from dahlias, cannas, gladioli
and roses and hedges forming rooms.
Home-made TEAS in aid of St
Mary's Church Mapledurwell. *Adm
£2.50, chd 50p. Suns 20 Mar; 4 Sept
(2-5.30). Private visits welcome by
appt. Tel 01256 321838*
david.hooper@futurescope.co.uk

79 Monxton Gardens
*3m W of Andover. Between A303 &
A343; parking at Field House.* Cream
TEAS at village hall in aid of St
Mary's Church. *Combined adm £3,
chd free. Sun, Mon 29, 30 May
(2-5.30)*

Field House 🅰🚫🏠 (Pratt
Family) 2 acres created by
owners, with herbaceous borders,
orchard, kitchen garden and dell
with winding paths and pond,
creating an air of tranquillity.

Hutchens Cottage 🅰🏠 (Mr &
Mrs R A Crick) ¾-acre cottage
garden with interesting scented
plants: old roses, clematis, shrubs
incl daphnes, mature trees, small
orchard; mixed thyme patch and
kitchen garden with developed
compost and leaf mould systems.

White Gables 🚻🚫😊 (Mr & Mrs D Eaglesham) Cottage-style garden of ⅓ acre, leading down to Pill Hill Brook. Interesting shrubs, old roses and herbaceous plants.

80 ◆ **Mottisfont Abbey & Garden, Romsey** 🚻🚫😊 NCCPG (The National Trust) 4½m NW of Romsey. From A3057 Romsey to Stockbridge turn W at sign to Mottisfont. 6 wheelchairs & battery car service available at garden. Built C12 as Augustinian priory, now house of some note. 30-acre landscaped garden incl spring or 'font' from which house derives its name, magnificent ancient trees, tributary of R Test and walled gardens with National Collection of old-fashioned roses. Light refreshments and TEAS. Adm £7, chd £3.50. Opening days & times vary according to season; please phone or visit website for details. *For NGS: Sun 26 June (11-8.30).* Tel 01794 340757 *mottisfontabbey@nationaltrust .org.uk*

81 **Mount Joy, Newbridge Village, nr Cadnam** 🚻🚫😊 NCCPG (Mr Glyndwr Marsh) 3m SW of Romsey. ¾m NE of Cadnam roundabout on A31, L into Newbridge Rd at Copythorne Xrds. ¾m to Newbridge village. 5½ acres, incl garden of several collections of primulas, meconopsis, dwarf conifers, bearded iris. Arboretum of 116 trees incl 28 species of sorbus. Provisional National Collection holder of native sorbus. Badger-faced sheep and lambs. Home-made TEAS. Adm £2, chd free. Suns, Mons 15, 16, 29, 30 May (2-5)

82 NEW **Mulberry House, 7 Moorland Avenue, Barton-on-Sea** 🚻🚫😊 (Rosemary & John Owen) 6m W of Lymington. From the A337 (S of New Milton), going W, take L turn into Barton Court Ave and 4th R into Moorland Ave. Pretty family garden of ¼ acre with summer-flowering and modern roses, a scramble of clematis, traditional fruit trees and herb and vegetable areas. Late summer colour incl a number of viticella clematis, salvias and penstemon. Relaxed, principally organic, garden with much native planting to attract insect and bird life. Home-made TEAS. Adm £2, chd free (share to Oakhaven Hospice). Sat, Tue, Sun 18, 21, 26 June; Sat 20 Aug (2-5). Private visits welcome by appt. Tel 01425 612066 rojowen@btinternet.com

Newland, Lodge Drove, Woodfalls 🚫 See Wiltshire.

83 NEW **49 Newtown Road with 26 & 29 Weston Allotments, Woolston** 🚫😊 (Mrs Belinda Hayes) 3m E of Southampton City Centre. Leave M27 J8, follow signs for Hamble-le-Rice and at Windhover roundabout, take 2nd exit past Tesco into Hamble Lane B3397. R into Portsmouth Rd, 1m L at 2nd mini roundabout into Upper Weston Lane, 2nd L into Newtown Rd. Disabled parking only at allotments, other parking on public rd. 9 houses between garden and allotments. Long narrow garden with patio, pool, unusual perennials, lawn, climbers, many containers and hanging baskets with bedding plants. Allotments packed with vegetables, fruit and flowers for floral art. Southampton in Bloom joint 3rd Best Private Garden 2004. Home-made TEAS. Adm £2.50, chd free. Suns 17, 24 July (2-6)

84 **Oakdene, Sandleheath, Fordingbridge** 🚻🚫😊 (Shirley & Chris Stanford) 1½m W of Fordingbridge. Adjacent to St Aldhelm's Church. 2-acre garden for rose lovers with more than 400 in formal beds, mixed borders, on long pergola and walls and climbing through fruit trees. Orchard, children's playhouses, walled organic kitchen garden with apple and pear arches and an abundance of flowers, fruit and vegetables. Greenhouses, dovecotes with resident doves. Free range hens. New planting and features always in progress. Featured on ITV The Garden Makers and BBC UK TV Style 2004. Cream TEAS. Adm £2.50, chd free (share to Friends of Western Downland Primary School). Suns 12, 19 June (2-5.30) . Private visits welcome by appt. Tel 01425 652133

85 **The Old House, Bramley Road, Silchester** 🚻😊 (Mr & Mrs M Jurgens) 7m N of Basingstoke. 7m S of Reading. Next to Roman Museum. Large garden, dating from 1920s, surrounding a Queen Anne rectory (not open) with swathes of daffodils in the spring; camellias and rhododendrons from January to June. The woodland garden is carpeted with bluebells. Fine selection of rare and unusual trees, incl magnolias and a handkerchief tree, azaleas, climbing roses and clematis. A relaxed garden in a natural setting. Cream TEAS in aid of St Mary's Church Silchester.

Adm £2.50, chd 50p. Suns 1, 15 May (2-6). Private visits welcome by appt Mar to June, groups of 10+, coaches permitted. Tel 0118 970 0240

86 **Old Meadows, Bramley Road, Silchester** 🚻🚫😊 (Dr & Mrs J M Fowler) 7m N of Basingstoke. 7m S of Reading. Off A340 between Reading & Basingstoke, on rd to Bramley. 5 acres incl unploughed, wild flower meadow. Walled garden with diverse plants and vegetables, bed of American annuals, beautiful rose garden. Carpets of old-fashioned spring bulbs. Hand-made living willow/hazel seats and arches. Rare geese, peacocks and hens. Recently restored C17 barn. Children very welcome. Plant sale in aid of the Lone Twin Network. Home-made TEAS. Adm £3, chd free. Sun 19 June (2-6). Private visits welcome by appt, coaches permitted. Tel 01256 881450 elizabeth@silchester.org

The Old Rectory, Ham 🚻🚫😊 See Wiltshire.

87 **Pennington House, Ridgeway Lane, Lymington** 🚻😊 (Sue Stowell & John Leach) 1½m S of Lymington. S on A337 from Lymington approx ½m to Pennington roundabout. Turn L & immed fork L into Ridgeway Lane, signed Riverside Marinas. Continue for ½m until Chequers PH. Turn R immed by post box into private drive 7 acres. Created around 1910. Substantial rockery of mature acers. Stream and pond area. Italian sunken garden, rose garden, organic ½-acre walled Victorian kitchen garden in full use. Magnificent wisteria on the house. Adm £3, chd free. Sat, Sun 7, 8 May (2-5.30)

88 **The Priors Farm, Reading Road, Mattingley** 🚻🚫 (Mr & Mrs Miles Hudson) 2m N of Hook. On B3349 Reading rd. Parking on green just N of Leather Bottle PH. Entrance by gate on green parking area. Mixed border garden, rose garden and orchard area with cedar and other trees. Bog garden area and swimming pool area. C15 granary and goatery. Herb bed. Statuary. 3½ acres. Home-made TEAS. Adm £2.50, chd free. Suns 17, 24 July (2-5.30). Private visits welcome by appt. Tel 0118 932 6262

89 Pylewell Park, Lymington 🚭
(Lord Teynham) *2m E of Lymington.*
Beyond IOW car ferry. Very large
garden of botanical interest, dating
from 1900. Fine trees, flowering
shrubs, rhododendrons, with walk
beside the lakes and seashore. *Adm
£3, chd free. Suns 15, 22 May (2-5)*

**90 Quoin Cottage, Southwick
Road, Denmead** 🚭
(Mrs N Vernon-Harcourt) *3m NW of
Waterlooville. 200yds from village
green on Southwick Rd off B2150.*
Fine example of what can be achieved
in small garden. Imaginative mixture
of colourful shrubs intermingle with
climbing and shrub roses and little
paths lead to hidden and secluded
corners. Home-made TEAS. *Adm £2,
chd free. Sun 26 June (2-5.30)*

**The Red House, Daggons Road,
Alderholt** 🚭🌣
See Dorset.

91 Romsey Gardens
*All within walking distance of
Romsey Abbey.* Small attractive
market town with notable Norman
C12 Abbey. TEAS at King John's
House. *Combined adm £3, chd free.
Sun, Mon 29, 30 May (11-5.30)*

King John's Garden, Church Street
🚭🌣☺ (Friends of King John's
Garden & Test Valley Borough
Council) Listed C13 house (not
open). Historic garden planted
with material available up to
1700. Award-winning Victorian
garden and North Courtyard
with water features.

The Lake House, 64 Mill Lane
(David & Lorraine Henley) *At
very bottom of Mill Lane on LH-
side.* Garden is set in 4½ acres of
beautiful parkland incl large lake.
Recently reclaimed from
meadow. Redesigned with large
borders containing shrubs, trees
and perennials. Superb views
from all parts of garden.

4 Mill Lane ☺ (Miss J Flindall)
Small, long, floriferous town
garden. S-facing. Backdrop
Romsey Abbey; original sculpture
and attractive hard landscaping.
Featured on ITV The Garden
Makers 2004 and in
'Inspirations' magazine 2003.
*Private visits welcome by appt.
Tel 01794 513926*

92 Rotherfield Park, East Tisted
🚭🌣
(Sir James & Lady Scott) *4m S of
Alton on A32.* Take some ancient
ingredients: ice house, ha-ha, lime
avenue; add a walled garden, fruit

and vegetables, trees and hedges; set
this 12-acre plot in an early C19 park
(picnic here from noon) with views to
coin clichés about. Mix in a bluebell
wood in May and apple-picking in
September. Featured on BBC TV
How to be a Gardener, Series 2, part
1. Home-made TEAS in aid of
nominated local charities. *Adm
£2.50. Suns 1 May; 28 Aug (2-5).
Private visits welcome by appt, May
& Sept only. Tel 01420 588207*

93 Rotherwick Gardens
*2½m N of Hook. M3 J5 or M4 J11
via B3349.* Tickets at each garden.
TEAS at Rotherwick village hall in
aid of Whitewater School PTA.
*Combined adm £3, chd free. Sun 10
July (2-5.30)*

Tylney House 🚭🌣☺ (Mr & Mrs
A E M Barlow) *Approx ¾m S of
village. Opp Tylney Hall Hotel.*
Tylney House (not open), Arts
and Crafts design after the style
of Voysey, once part of Tylney
Estate. 1-acre garden features
large lawn; established well-
stocked herbaceous borders with
many specialist plants; rose
pergola, cornus, conifers and
large shrubbery. Unusual
dovecote in paddock.

1 Wogsbarne Cottages 🚭🌣☺
(Mr R & Miss S Whistler)
Cottage garden with flowers,
vegetables and ornamental pond.
Alpine garden.

**94 Rowans Wood, 28 Straight
Mile, Ampfield** 🚭☺
(Mrs D C Rowan) *2m E of Romsey.
Straight Mile, on A3090 (old A31), S
side. 2m W of Potters Heron Hotel.*
Parking on service rd. Woodland
garden developed since 1962 and
planted for yr-round interest.
Camellias, rhododendrons, flowering
trees, spring bulbs followed by
azaleas, hostas and other perennials.
Autumn colour, views. Home-made
TEAS. *Adm £2.50, chd free,
concessions (Oct) £1.50. Sun 24 Apr
(2-5); Suns 1, 15, Mon 2 May (2-6);
Sun 9 Oct (2-5). Private visits
welcome by appt. Tel 01794 513072*

**95 28 St Ronan's Avenue,
Southsea** 🌣
(Mr I Craig) *Follow signs to
Portsmouth & Southsea from
M27/A27. St Ronan's Ave is a cul-de-
sac off St Ronan's Rd. Turn into St
Ronan's Rd from Albert Rd at
junction opp Trinity Methodist
Church.* Alternatively, follow signs to
seafront and then follow yellow NGS
signs from canoe lake and Eastern
Parade. Park at Craneswater School.
145ft x 25ft town garden. Created

from derelict land. Newly planted in
1999. Bold planting incl ferns,
cannas, bananas, wild flower area,
herbaceous borders, bog garden,
vegetable beds and dry garden.
Sculpture made by owner from
recycled materials. Winner Southsea
Town Council Special Category
2003. Featured in 'Garden Answers'
2003, 'Woman's Weekly' home series
2004. TEAS. *Adm £1.50, chd free.
Suns 24 July; 4 Sept (2-6)*

NEW Sandhill Farm House, Rogate
🚭🌣
See Sussex.

96 Sandle Cottage, Sandleheath
🌣☺
(Peter & Yo Beech) *2m W of
Fordingbridge.* Turn R at
Sandleheath Xrds. *Entrance 50yds on
L.* Ample parking in owner's field.
2½-acre garden designed and
maintained by the owners with
displays of dahlias, bedding plants
and sweet peas. Features incl unusual
sunken garden, small lake with
cascading waterfall and bridge over
stream. Traditional walled kitchen
garden. Feature summerhouse in own
cottage garden. New for 2005
campanula terrace and other
developments. Home-made TEAS in
aid of Fordingbridge United
Reformed Church. *Adm £2.50, chd
free. Suns 10, 24, 31 July (1.30-5.30).
Private visits welcome by appt
coaches permitted. Tel 01425
654638 www.sandlecottage.com*

**97 'Selborne', Caker Lane, East
Worldham** 🚭☺
(Mr & Mrs Brian Jones) *2m SE of
Alton. On B3004 at edge of East
Worldham at Alton end (please note,
NOT in the village of Selborne).* ½-
acre mature garden with old
established orchard of named
varieties. Meandering paths provide
changing vistas. Mixed borders
featuring a large collection of hardy
geraniums with alliums, euphorbias
and other herbaceous plants and
shrubs designed for yr-round effect.
Shrubbery, vegetable and soft fruit
garden with greenhouse feature,
metal sculptures, containers,
summerhouse and small
conservatory. Teas in the shade of the
orchard, comfortable on warm
summer days. Home-made TEAS.
*Adm £2, chd free (share to Harare
Children's Home 17, 18 Apr; East
Worldham Church Fabric Fund 26,
27 June; Tafara Mission Zimbabwe
7, 8 Aug). Suns, Mons 17, 18 Apr;
22, 23 May; 26, 27 June; 7, 8 Aug
(2-6). Opening with White Cottage,
Beech Suns 22 May, 26 June, 7 Aug.*

Private visits welcome by appt May to early Aug. Tel 01420 83389 mtrigwelljones@talk21.com

98 Shaw Trust Horticulture, St James Hospital grounds, Portsmouth 👤♿

(Shaw Trust) *4m E of Portsmouth. From A27 or M27 take A2030 into Portsmouth, at T-lights rd curves R. Continue to Velder Ave until roundabout. Take L turn into Milton Rd (A288), hospital is signed at top of Lockway Rd, 8th rd from roundabout. Shaw Trust Horticulture Training Therapy centre signed in hospital grounds.* Approx ⅔ acre. Display beds of all kinds, incl vegetables, nature and ornamental ponds, polytunnels and greenhouses. Training display plots. Silver Medal winner Hampton Court Flower Show 2003, Silver Gilt Southsea Show 2004. TEAS. *Adm £1.50, chd free. Suns 8 May (11-5); 25 Sept (11-3). Private visits welcome by appt. Tel 02392 737724*

Simms Farm House, Mortimer 👤♿☕
See Berkshire.

South Harting Gardens
See Sussex.

99 ◆ Spinners, Boldre ♿☕
(Peter Chappell) *2½m N of Lymington. Signed off A337 Brockenhurst to Lymington rd, (do not take sign to Boldre Church).* Azaleas, rhododendrons, hydrangeas, maples and other rare shrubs interplanted with huge range of plants and woodland bulbs, especially erythroniums and trilliums. New plantings of Teller lace-cap hydrangeas and a range of the newer magnolias. Visited by people from all over the temperate world. *Adm £2.50 Apr-July, £2 Aug & Sept, chd under 6 free. Tues to Sats 1 Apr to 14 Sept (10-5). Tel 01590 673347*

100 St Christopher's, Whitsbury ♿☕
(Christine Southey & David Mussell) *3½m NW of Fordingbridge. In village centre, 200yds down from Cartwheel PH.* Long ¾-acre alkaline and acidic garden sloping uphill with superb views. Alpines in scree, dwarf and unusual bulbs, daffodils, narcissi and spring blossom, shrubs and fruit trees. Wild area, mature oaks. Conservatory with unusual plants. TEAS. *Adm £2, chd free (share to Whitsbury Church Fabric Fund). Suns 17, 24 Apr (2-5.30). Private visits welcome by appt. Tel 01725 518404*

101 Tanglefoot, Crawley, nr Winchester 👤♿
(Mr & Mrs F J Fratter) *5m NW of Winchester. Private lane beside entrance to Crawley Court (NTL). Drop-off & disabled parking only at house, other parking on public rd.* Approx ½ acre on chalk, designed and developed by owners, with mature shrubs, colour-themed herbaceous and mixed borders, raised lily pond, herb wheel and developing wild flower area. Divided into areas by the planting, and bounded on one side by a magnificent Victorian wall, covered with trained top fruit, protecting a compact productive kitchen garden and greenhouse. Cold drinks. *Adm £2, chd free. Thu, Fri 21, 22 July (2-5.30). Opening with* **Crawley Gardens** *Thur, Fri 23, 24 June*

102 Treetops, Upper Froyle ♿☕
(Mr & Mrs J Cresswell) *3m E of Alton on A31. On lane to Upper Froyle, just behind Hen & Chicken Inn. Continue up lane to Lower Froyle where* **Walburly** *is also open.* Medium-sized garden, richly planted with many unusual plants, herbaceous borders, shrubs and pond. Home-made TEAS. *Adm £1.50, chd free. Sat 16 Apr (2-6). Opening with* **Froyle Cottage Gardens** *Sat, Sun 28, 29 May*

Trotton Old Rectory, Trotton ♿☕
See Sussex.

103 Tunworth Old Rectory, nr Basingstoke 👤☕
(The Hon Mrs Julian Berry) *4m SE of Basingstoke. Turn S off A30 at sign to Tunworth.* Laid out with yew hedges, enclosing different aspects. Double herbaceous border; white garden; ruby wedding garden; pleached hornbeam walk; lime avenue; ornamental pond; interesting trees incl beech-lined walk to church. Decorative pots. Walks in park. Cream TEAS in aid of All Saints Church Tunworth. *Adm £2, chd free. Sun 3 July (2-5.30). Private visits welcome by appt. Tel 01256 471436*

104 Tylney Hall Hotel, Ridge Lane, Rotherwick ♿☕
(The Manager) *3m NW of Hook. From M3 J5 via A287 & Newnham, M4 J11 via B3349 & Rotherwick.* Large garden of 67 acres with extensive woodlands and fine vistas being restored with new planting. Fine avenues of wellingtonias; rhododendrons and azaleas; Italian garden; lakes, large water and rock garden, dry stone walls originally designed with assistance of Gertrude

Jekyll. TEAS. *Adm £2, chd free. Suns 17 Apr; 8, 22 May (10-5)*

105 Ulvik, 114 Harestock Road, Winchester 👤♿
(Mr & Mrs G G Way) *1m N of Winchester. 5th house on L in Harestock Rd off A3049 (old A272).* Long narrow site of ½ acre designed to create unfolding and interesting sinuous shapes, views and nooks and crannies. Mixed herbaceous borders and shrubberies, ornamental grasses and prairie-style borders, small vegetable garden, ponds and wooded areas for shade-loving plants. Fun sculptures and features. Featured on ITV The Garden Makers 2004. Cold drinks. *Adm £2, chd free. Sat, Sun, Mon 9, 10, 11 July; Sun 31 July; Mon 1 Aug (2-6). Private visits welcome by appt June and July only. Tel 01962 852361*

◆ Uppark, South Harting 👤♿
See Sussex.

106 Valentine Cottage, Newnham, nr Basingstoke 👤♿☕
(Mr & Mrs P Brown) *2m NW of Hook. From Hook follow A30 towards Basingstoke. After approx 1m turn R at Dorchester Arms into Old School Rd, passing Newnham. At end of Old School Rd turn L into Newnham Rd.* Exuberant cottage garden of ⅔ acre, specialising in clematis; laid out into individual smaller gardens. Featured in 'Homes & Gardens' and RHS 'The Garden' 2004. TEAS. *Adm £2.50, chd 50p. Suns 24 Apr; 12 June; 17 July (2-5.30). Private visits welcome by appt. Tel 01256 762049*

107 ◆ The Vyne, Sherborne St John 👤♿☕
(The National Trust) *4m N of Basingstoke. Between Sherborne St John & Bramley. From A340 turn E at NT signs.* 13 acres with extensive lawns, lake, fine trees, herbaceous border and Edwardian-style summerhouse garden. Extensive woodland and parkland walks. Light refreshments and TEAS. *House and garden adm £7, chd £3.50. Garden only £4, chd £2. 23 Mar to 30 Oct (11-5) not Thurs, Fris. For NGS: Sun 5 June (11-5).* **Evening Picnic** *£4, Wed 27 July (5-9). Tel 01256 883858 nick.lightfoot@nationaltrust.org.uk*

108 Wades House, Barton Stacey 👤♿☕
(Mr & Mrs Antony Briscoe) *Midway between A303 & A30 nr Andover. Approached from S entrance to village.* 2-acre garden on chalk with commanding views. Large herbaceous

borders, well maintained lawns. Rose pergola and old-fashioned rose garden. Kitchen garden, greenhouses and orchard. Diverse planting in containers on terrace. Home-made TEAS. *Adm £2.50, chd free (share to All Saints Church, Barton Stacey). Sun, Tue 19, 21 June (2-5) . Private visits welcome by appt. Tel 01962 760516 roo@andover.co.uk*

109 Walbury, Lower Froyle 🚹♿🏵
(Mr & Mrs E Milam) *3m E of Alton. Access to Lower Froyle from A31 between Alton and Farnham at Bentley. Walbury is nr village hall where parking is available. Follow signs to Upper Froyle where* **Treetops** *is also open.* Cottage garden atmosphere with small pond. Lower area is a small, formal, colour-themed garden, informally planted with many unusual plants. Home-made TEAS. *Adm £1.50, chd free. Sat 16 Apr (2-6). Opening with* **Froyle Cottage Gardens** *Sat, Sun 28, 29 May*

110 Waldrons, Brook 🚹🐕🏵
(Major & Mrs J Robinson) *4m N of Lyndhurst. On B3079 1m W from J1 M27. 1st house L past Green Dragon PH & directly opp Bell PH.* 1-acre garden of C18 listed cottage (not open). Conservatory; mixed planting of conifers, shrubs and herbaceous plants around old orchard trees; raised alpine garden, rose beds, arbour, trellis and arches. Small stableyard; herb garden and many original garden ideas. Seating throughout. Home-made TEAS. *Adm £2, chd free. Sun, Mon 29, 30 May (2-5)*

111 The Walled House, Midlington Hill Lane, Droxford 🚹♿
(Mr & Mrs Cornell) *10m N of Fareham. ½m S of Droxford off A32. At Midlington Xrds on A32 turn off towards Swanmore. After 100yds keep R & follow signs.* Walled garden of ¾ acre created by owners in last 7yrs. Sloping, S-facing lawns with distant views in magnificent setting in Meon Valley. All-yr interest with some unusual shrubs, climbers and plants. Roses and clematis underplanted with a variety of bulbs. New grass setting for shrubs and bulbs. Home-made TEAS in aid of Rowans Hospice. *Adm £2.50, chd free. Sun 12, Wed 15 June (2-6). Private visits welcome by appt. Tel 01489 877261 shenacornell@aol.com*

112 2 Warren Farm Cottages, nr West Tytherley 🐕🏵
(Dr & Mrs J G Mitchell) *4½m W of Stockbridge, follow yellow signs off*

A30. *Proceed 1¾m along The Warren. Please park in lay-by.* Half-acre cotttage garden with many special plants as well as old favourites. Hardy geraniums, poppies, phlox, heleniums, Michaelmas daisies. Wildlife pond and gazebo. Late season interest. Featured in 'Amateur Gardening' 2004. *Adm £1.50. Nursery open most days. Please ring before you come. Fris 25 Mar to 30 Sept; Suns 17 Apr; 15 May; 19 June; 17 July; 21 Aug; 18 Sept; 2 Oct (10-5). Tel 01980 863101*

113 West Silchester Hall, Silchester 🚹♿
(Mrs Jenny Jowett) *7m N of Basingstoke. 7m S of Reading, off A340 (signed from centre of village).* 1½ acres, plantsman artist's garden with interest over a long period. Good herbaceous borders, rose and shrub borders, rhododendrons and many acid-loving plants. Small pond and bog garden, kitchen garden, interesting display of half hardies. Studio open with exhibition of paintings and cards by owners. Home-made TEAS in aid of Basingstoke Hospice. *Adm £2.50, chd free. Sun, Mon 29, 30 May; Suns 10, 31 July (2-6). Private visits welcome by appt, groups only, coaches permitted. Tel 0118 970 0278*

114 Wheatley House, between Binsted and Kingsley 🚹🐕🏵
(Mr & Mrs Michael Adlington) *4m E of Alton, 5m SW of Farnham. From Alton follow signs to Holybourne & Binsted. At end of Binsted turn R signed Wheatley. ¾m down lane on L.* Magnificent setting with panoramic views over fields and forests. Sweeping mixed borders, shrubberies, roses and grasses. 1½ acres, designed by artist-owner, with particular emphasis on colour and form. Sale of local crafts in old barn. Home-made TEAS. *Adm £2.50, chd free. Sat 13 (2-6), Sun 14 Aug (11-5.30). Private visits welcome by appt. Tel 01420 23113*

115 NEW Whispers, Chatter Alley, Dogmersfield 🐕🏵
(Mr & Mrs John Selfe) *3m W of Fleet. Turn N off A287 Odiham to Farnham rd. Turn L by Queen's Head PH.* Spectacular waterfall cascades towards an impressive terrace of Indian sandstone. 2 flights of steps lead upwards to the wide sweeping lawn with gazebo and rockstone seat. Mature trees have been transplanted to form the main structure of this new 2-acre garden.

Borders full of eye-catching colour, incl blue spruce, nandina, gingko, eucalyptus, tree ferns and acers. Home-made TEAS. *Adm £2.50, chd free (share to Samantha Dickson Research Trust). Sun 3 July (12-5)*

116 Whistlers, Buriton 🚹🐕🏵
(Sir William & Lady Vincent) *2m S of Petersfield. Take 1st exit off A3M, S of Petersfield (marked Buriton), follow signs into village until you reach village pond. Park on far side of pond & walk up South Lane, following signs. Disabled access through car park.* Undulating grounds sheltered by woodland. Small lake with path and seating on far bank has island, black swans, ornamental water fowl. Two waterfalls gush down into lower streams bounded by tree ferns, lush planting, gunnera, astilbe, petasites, etc. Huge roses drape trees, pergola and Palladian folly. Formal white 'Breakthrough' garden. Peacocks, pheasants and more. Not for the tidy-minded! Disabled or elderly people should be driven into car park and enter garden from driveway. TEAS. *Adm £2.50, chd free. Every Fri 25 Mar to 24 June (2-5) www.whistlersgarden.co.uk*

117 White Barn, Woodend Road, Crow Hill, Ringwood 🚹🐕🏵
(Marilyn & Barrie Knight) *2m SE of Ringwood. From Ringwood take B3347 Christchurch rd. After 1m turn L for Burley & proceed 1m. Woodend Rd on L.* ½ acre with lovely views. English country garden with well-planned and sympathetic mix using large variety of unusual plants. Semi-formal layout in cottage style planting creating an enchanting and delightfully relaxing garden with good colour. Roses and clematis abound. Pond. Light refreshments and TEAS in aid of local Methodist Church. *Adm £2.50, chd free. Private visits welcome by appt Apr to July. Please telephone. Tel 01425 473527*

118 The White Cottage, 35 Wellhouse Road, Beech, Alton 🚹🐕🏵
(Mr & Mrs P Conyers) *2m N of Alton. Leave Alton on Basingstoke Rd A339. After approx 1m turn L to Medstead & Beech. Wellhouse Rd is 2nd turning on R. Parking at village hall at bottom of rd, limited parking at house.* 1-acre chalk garden with wide range of shrubs and plants; colourful herbaceous borders and large collection of hellebores and bulbs. Greenhouses, conservatory with exotics, scree bed and new pebble area with water feature.

TEAS. *Adm £2, chd free. Suns 20 Feb; 13 Mar (11-5); 22 May; 26 June; 7 Aug (2-5); 19 Feb 2006. Also open 'Selborne' Suns 22 May, 26 June, 7 Aug. Private visits welcome by appt. Tel 01420 89355*

119 White Gables, Breach Lane, Sherfield-on-Loddon ♿✿☺
(Terry & Brian Raisborough) *6m N of Basingstoke. From Basingstoke follow A33 towards Reading for approx 6m. Breach Lane is unmade lane immed before Sherfield-on-Loddon roundabout on R. Limited parking for disabled by house. Main parking in 2 free signed car parks in main village. Short walk to garden.* Plantaholic's paradise, 110ft x 95ft with mass planting of tropical plants, unusual shrubs, perennials and roses. Oriental border with arbour, raised banana bed, gravel garden with 3 small ponds, conifer bed, tropical border, numerous tender plants in pots on patio. Raised vegetable garden. Winner Flower Gardener of the Year, featured in 'Gardens Monthly' 2003. Runner up in final of BBC Gardener of the Year 2004, featured on BBC TV 2004. Home-made TEAS in aid of Sherfield-on-Loddon village hall. *Adm £2.50, chd free. Sun 26 June (12-5). Private visits welcome by appt. Tel 01256 882269*

120 White Windows, Longparish ♿✿☺NCCPG
(Mr & Mrs B Sterndale-Bennett) *6m E of Andover. Off A303, to village centre on B3048. ⅔-acre country garden with mixed borders filled with* glorious range of hardy perennials, trees and shrubs. Planted for yr-round foliage interest and subtle colour blendings. Particularly wide range of perennials incl many hellebores, hardy geraniums, pulmonarias, euphorbias, asters and grasses. Part of National Collection of hellebores. Finalist 'Gardening Which' Favourite Gardens 2003. Home-made TEAS. *Adm £2, chd 50p. Suns, Mons 8, 9 May; 17, 18 July (1.30-5.30). Private visits welcome by appt, Weds pm Apr to Sept. Tel 01264 720222*

121 NEW Windmill Hill Gardens, Ibthorpe, Hurstbourne Tarrant
5m N of Andover. Off A343 at top of Hurstbourne Hill, signed The Chutes and Tangley. 1st turning on R. Tranquil gardens, elevated and with glorious views. Nearby woodland may be visited. TEAS at Windmills. *Combined adm £3, chd free. Thu 23, Sun 26 June (2-5.30)*

NEW Ibthorpe Tower ♿✿☺ (Mr & Mrs P Gregory) *3½ acres of* garden planted in contemporary style, focusing on colour and texture. Large wildlife pond, woodland garden, potager and long banks planted with hardy perennials.

NEW Windmill Farmhouse ♿✿
(Gwen & Pete Zaslawsky) 1-acre cottage garden set around C18 thatched farmhouse (not open) neighbouring woodland. Roses, herbaceous borders and kitchen garden.

NEW Windmills ♿✿ (Mr & Mrs J A Harvie) Edwardian garden and parkland with 4-acre woodland walk. Arboretum, roses, herbaceous borders, kitchen garden and far-reaching views.

122 Wisteria Cottage, 15 Gudge Heath Lane, Fareham ☺
(Gill & Colin Gittins) *From Fareham take A27 direction Southampton. At T-lights immed after railway station bridge, turn R into Gudge Heath Lane. No 15 is approx 100yds on RH-side (parking for disabled badge holders only). Suggested parking, railway station, 4 mins walk.* ½-acre gardens incorporating a number of varied features: decking area which leads through the wisteria walk to sun terrace, beach garden and Japanesque area. Across the Monet-style bridge are the lower garden and woodland walk which meanders up through high pines to viewing point, from which the entire garden can be appreciated. New summerhouse on stilts surrounded by dry garden. Home-made TEAS. *Adm £2, chd free. Sat, Sun 21, 22 May (10.30-5.30)*

Evening Opening (See also garden description)	
80 Abbey Road	8 July
2 Ashridge Close	20 July
The Vyne	27 July

Crossroads – *Caring For Carers*
1974-2004 30 years of caring

*1984
30
Years of
Caring
2004*

Crossroads is the leading national charity providing practical support to Carers giving them a regular break from their caring responsibilities.
"Time to be Themselves"
The continued support of the National Gardens Scheme helps us to continue our vital work with Carers as our services are as relevant today as they were when we were founded thirty years ago.

For more information please contact:
Crossroads-Caring For Carers, 10 Regent Place, Rugby CV21 2PN
www.crossroads.org.uk   Telephone 0845 450 0350   E-mail information@crossroads.org.uk

Herefordshire

County Organiser: Lady Curtis, South Parade House, Ledbury, Herefordshire HR8 2HB
Assistant County Organisers: Dr J A F Evans, 7 St Margaret's Road, Hereford HR1 1TS Tel 01432 273000
Press & Publicity Officer: Mrs Sue Evans, The Nest, Moreton, Eye, nr Leominster HR6 0DP Tel 01568 614501
Mr Graham Spencer, 2 Bramley Court, King's Acre Road, Hereford HR4 0SB
Tel 01432 267744
County Leaflet: Mrs R Verity, Crowards Mill, Eyton, Leominster HR6 0AD Tel 01568 615200
County Treasurer: Mr Michael Robins, Newsholme, 77 Bridge Street, Ledbury HR8 2AN Tel 01531 632232

Maps: Numbers shown next to each garden entry refer to that garden's entry on the county map. This position is approximate; distance and directions from the nearest main town are generally shown in the garden text.
A precise location is available for those gardens featured on the NGS website by visiting www.ngs.org.uk.
Symbols: Information relating to symbols is given on page 21

DATES OF OPENING

Evening openings
See end of county listing

Private gardens open regularly for NGS
The Long Barn, Eastnor *(31)*
The Orchards, Bishops Frome *(40)*
The Picton Garden, Colwall *(41)*

Gardens open to the public
For details see garden description
Abbey Dore Court Garden, Abbey Dore *(1)*
Arrow Cottage Garden, nr Weobley *(2)*
Aulden Farm, Leominster *(3)*
The Bannut, Bringsty *(4)*
Berrington Hall, Leominster *(6)*
Broadfield Court Gardens & Vineyard, Bodenham *(7)*
Bryan's Ground, Stapleton, nr Presteigne *(8)*
Croft Castle, Leominster *(12)*
Hellens, Much Marcle *(18)*
The Henry Weston Garden, Much Marcle *(19)*
Hergest Croft Gardens, Kington *(20)*
How Caple Court, How Caple *(22)*
Ivy Croft, Ivington Green, Leominster *(24)*
Kingstone Cottages, Weston under Penyard, nr Ross-on-Wye *(26)*
Lawton Hall Herbs, Eardisland *(28)*
Moors Meadow, Collington *(36)*
Shipley Gardens, Holme Lacy *(43)*
Staunton Park, Staunton Green *(44)*
Stockton Bury Gardens Ltd, Kimbolton *(45)*
Waterpump Farm, Ryeford *(49)*
Westonbury Mill Water Garden, Pembridge *(52)*
The Wiggly Garden, Blakemere *(54)*

By appointment only
*For telephone number and other details see garden description.
Private visits welcomed*
Chennels Gate, Eardisley *(10)*
Ivy Cottage, Kinsham *(23)*
Lakeside, Whitbourne *(27)*
Little Llanavon, Dorstone *(29)*
The View, Ochre Hill, Wellington Heath *(48)*
Well Cottage, Blakemere *(50)*

February 3 Thursday
Ivy Croft, Ivington Green, Leominster *(24)*
February 10 Thursday
Ivy Croft, Ivington Green, Leominster *(24)*
February 17 Thursday
Ivy Croft, Ivington Green, Leominster *(24)*
February 24 Thursday
Ivy Croft, Ivington Green, Leominster *(24)*
March 19 Saturday
Moors Meadow, Collington *(36)*
March 25 Friday (Easter)
The Old Corn Mill, Aston Crews *(38)*
April 3 Sunday
Lower Hope, Ullingswick *(33)*
April 6 Wednesday
The Old Corn Mill, Aston Crews *(38)*
April 8 Friday
Hope End House, Hope End *(21)*
April 9 Saturday
Hope End House, Hope End *(21)*
April 10 Sunday
Arrow Cottage Garden, nr Weobley *(2)*
Hope End House, Hope End *(21)*
Ivy Croft, Ivington Green, Leominster *(24)*
April 11 Monday
Hope End House, Hope End *(21)*
April 12 Tuesday
Hope End House, Hope End *(21)*
April 13 Wednesday
Hope End House, Hope End *(21)*
April 14 Thursday
Hope End House, Hope End *(21)*
April 15 Friday
Hope End House, Hope End *(21)*
April 16 Saturday
Hope End House, Hope End *(21)*
April 17 Sunday
Garnstone House, Weobley *(14)*
Hope End House, Hope End *(21)*
April 18 Monday
Hope End House, Hope End *(21)*
April 19 Tuesday
Hope End House, Hope End *(21)*
April 20 Wednesday
Hope End House, Hope End *(21)*

April 21 Thursday
Hope End House, Hope End *(21)*
April 22 Friday
Hope End House, Hope End *(21)*
April 23 Saturday
Hope End House, Hope End *(21)*
Moors Meadow, Collington *(36)*
April 24 Sunday
Caves Folly Nursery, Colwall *(9)*
Hope End House, Hope End *(21)*
Longacre, Colwall Green *(32)*
April 25 Monday
Hope End House, Hope End *(21)*
April 26 Tuesday
Hope End House, Hope End *(21)*
April 27 Wednesday
Hope End House, Hope End *(21)*
April 28 Thursday
Hope End House, Hope End *(21)*
April 29 Friday
Hope End House, Hope End *(21)*
April 30 Saturday
Hope End House, Hope End *(21)*
May 1 Sunday
Hope End House, Hope End *(21)*
The Nest, Moreton, Eye *(37)*
May 2 Monday (Bank Hol)
Hope End House, Hope End *(21)*
The Nest, Moreton, Eye *(37)*
May 3 Tuesday
Hope End House, Hope End *(21)*
May 4 Wednesday
Hope End House, Hope End *(21)*
The Old Corn Mill, Aston Crews *(38)*
May 5 Thursday
Hope End House, Hope End *(21)*
May 6 Friday
Hope End House, Hope End *(21)*
Waterpump Farm, Ryeford *(49)*
May 7 Saturday
Hope End House, Hope End *(21)*
Waterpump Farm, Ryeford *(49)*
May 14 Saturday
The Griggs, Newton St Margarets *(17)*

SHROPSHIRE

HEREFORDSHIRE

WORCESTERSHIRE

POWYS

GLOUCESTERSHIRE

kms 0   10

miles 0   10

May 15 Sunday
The Bannut, Bringsty *(4)*

May 18 Wednesday
The Long Barn, Eastnor *(31)*

May 19 Thursday
The Long Barn, Eastnor *(31)*

May 20 Friday
The Long Barn, Eastnor *(31)*

May 21 Saturday
Stockton Bury Gardens Ltd, Kimbolton *(45)*

May 22 Sunday
Batch Cottage, Almeley *(5)*
Kilima Lodge, Colwall *(25)*
Lower Hope, Ullingswick *(33)*
The Old Quarry, Eardisley *(39)*
The Orchards, Bishops Frome *(40)*
Shipley Gardens, Holme Lacy *(43)*
Whitfield, Wormbridge *(53)*

May 24 Tuesday
Bryan's Ground, Stapleton, nr Presteigne *(8)*

May 25 Wednesday
The Long Barn, Eastnor *(31)*

May 26 Thursday
The Long Barn, Eastnor *(31)*

May 27 Friday
The Long Barn, Eastnor *(31)*
Waterpump Farm, Ryeford *(49)*

May 28 Saturday
Monnington Court, Hereford *(35)*
Moors Meadow, Collington *(36)*
Waterpump Farm, Ryeford *(49)*

May 29 Sunday
Aulden Farm, Leominster *(3)*
Berrington Hall, Leominster *(6)*
Caves Folly Nursery, Colwall *(9)*
Ivy Croft, Ivington Green, Leominster *(24)*
Longacre, Colwall Green *(32)*
Monnington Court, Hereford *(35)*
The Nest, Moreton, Eye *(37)*

May 30 Monday (Bank Hol)
Monnington Court, Hereford *(35)*
The Nest, Moreton, Eye *(37)*

June 1 Wednesday
The Long Barn, Eastnor *(31)*
The Old Corn Mill, Aston Crews *(38)*

June 2 Thursday
The Long Barn, Eastnor *(31)*

June 3 Friday
The Long Barn, Eastnor *(31)*

June 4 Saturday
Arrow Cottage Garden, nr Weobley *(2)*
The Griggs, Newton St Margarets *(17)*
Stoney Croft, Byton *(46)*

June 5 Sunday
How Caple Court, How Caple *(22)*
Stoney Croft, Byton *(46)*
The Wiggly Garden, Blakemere *(54)*

June 7 Tuesday
The Orchards, Bishops Frome *(40)*

June 8 Wednesday
The Long Barn, Eastnor *(31)*
June 9 Thursday
The Long Barn, Eastnor *(31)*
June 10 Friday
The Long Barn, Eastnor *(31)*
Waterpump Farm, Ryeford *(49)*
June 11 Saturday
The Nest, Moreton, Eye *(37)*
Waterpump Farm, Ryeford *(49)*
June 12 Sunday
Batch Cottage, Almeley *(5)*
Broadfield Court Gardens & Vineyard,
Bodenham *(7)*
Croose Farm, Woolhope *(13)*
Grantsfield, nr Kimbolton *(15)*
Hergest Croft Gardens, Kington *(20)*
Lawton Hall Herbs, Eardisland *(28)*
Llandinabo Court, Hereford *(30)*
The Nest, Moreton, Eye *(37)*
Upper Tan House, Stansbatch *(47)*
Westonbury Mill Water Garden, Pembridge
(52)
June 14 Tuesday
Michaelchurch Court, St Owens Cross *(34)*
The Orchards, Bishops Frome *(40)*
June 15 Wednesday
The Long Barn, Eastnor *(31)*
Michaelchurch Court, St Owens Cross *(34)*
June 16 Thursday
The Long Barn, Eastnor *(31)*
June 17 Friday
The Long Barn, Eastnor *(31)*
June 18 Saturday
Lawton Hall Herbs, Eardisland *(28)*
Michaelchurch Court, St Owens Cross *(34)*
Moors Meadow, Collington *(36)*
Weston Mews, Weston under Penyard *(51)*
June 19 Sunday
The Great House, Dilwyn *(16)*
Lawton Hall Herbs, Eardisland *(28)*
The Orchards, Bishops Frome *(40)*
Shipley Gardens, Holme Lacy *(43)*
Weston Mews, Weston under Penyard *(51)*
June 21 Tuesday
Lawton Hall Herbs, Eardisland *(28)*
The Orchards, Bishops Frome *(40)*
June 22 Wednesday
The Long Barn, Eastnor *(31)*
June 23 Thursday
The Long Barn, Eastnor *(31)*
June 24 Friday
Croft Castle, Leominster *(12)*
Hellens, Much Marcle *(18)*
The Long Barn, Eastnor *(31)*
Stoney Croft, Byton *(46)*
Waterpump Farm, Ryeford *(49)*
June 25 Saturday
Shieldbrook, Kings Caple *(42)*
Stoney Croft, Byton *(46)*
Waterpump Farm, Ryeford *(49)*
June 26 Sunday
Caves Folly Nursery, Colwall *(9)*
Longacre, Colwall Green *(32)*
Shieldbrook, Kings Caple *(42)*
The Wiggly Garden, Blakemere *(54)*

June 28 Tuesday
The Orchards, Bishops Frome *(40)*
June 29 Wednesday
The Long Barn, Eastnor *(31)*
June 30 Thursday
The Long Barn, Eastnor *(31)*
July 1 Friday
Hellens, Much Marcle *(18)*
The Long Barn, Eastnor *(31)*
July 3 Sunday
Aulden Farm, Leominster *(3)*
Ivy Croft, Ivington Green, Leominster *(24)*
Staunton Park, Staunton Green *(44)*
The Wiggly Garden, Blakemere *(54)*
July 5 Tuesday
The Orchards, Bishops Frome *(40)*
July 6 Wednesday
The Long Barn, Eastnor *(31)*
July 7 Thursday
The Long Barn, Eastnor *(31)*
July 8 Friday
The Long Barn, Eastnor *(31)*
July 9 Saturday
The Griggs, Newton St Margarets *(17)*
July 10 Sunday
Lower Hope, Ullingswick *(33)*
July 12 Tuesday
The Orchards, Bishops Frome *(40)*
July 13 Wednesday
The Long Barn, Eastnor *(31)*
July 14 Thursday
The Long Barn, Eastnor *(31)*
July 15 Friday
The Long Barn, Eastnor *(31)*
July 17 Sunday
The Bannut, Bringsty *(4)*
The Orchards, Bishops Frome *(40)*
July 19 Tuesday
The Orchards, Bishops Frome *(40)*
July 20 Wednesday
The Long Barn, Eastnor *(31)*
July 21 Thursday
The Long Barn, Eastnor *(31)*
July 22 Friday
The Long Barn, Eastnor *(31)*
July 23 Saturday
Moors Meadow, Collington *(36)*
July 26 Tuesday
The Orchards, Bishops Frome *(40)*
July 27 Wednesday
The Long Barn, Eastnor *(31)*
July 28 Thursday
The Long Barn, Eastnor *(31)*
July 29 Friday
The Long Barn, Eastnor *(31)*
August 2 Tuesday
The Orchards, Bishops Frome *(40)*
August 3 Wednesday
The Long Barn, Eastnor *(31)*
The Picton Garden, Colwall *(41)*
August 4 Thursday
The Long Barn, Eastnor *(31)*
The Picton Garden, Colwall *(41)*

August 5 Friday
The Long Barn, Eastnor *(31)*
The Picton Garden, Colwall *(41)*
August 6 Saturday
The Picton Garden, Colwall *(41)*
August 7 Sunday
The Bannut, Bringsty *(4)*
Caves Folly Nursery, Colwall *(9)*
Coddington Vineyard, Coddington *(11)*
Longacre, Colwall Green *(32)*
The Picton Garden, Colwall *(41)*
August 9 Tuesday
The Orchards, Bishops Frome *(40)*
August 10 Wednesday
The Long Barn, Eastnor *(31)*
The Picton Garden, Colwall *(41)*
August 11 Thursday
The Long Barn, Eastnor *(31)*
The Picton Garden, Colwall *(41)*
August 12 Friday
The Long Barn, Eastnor *(31)*
The Picton Garden, Colwall *(41)*
August 13 Saturday
The Picton Garden, Colwall *(41)*
August 14 Sunday
The Orchards, Bishops Frome *(40)*
The Picton Garden, Colwall *(41)*
August 16 Tuesday
The Orchards, Bishops Frome *(40)*
August 17 Wednesday
The Long Barn, Eastnor *(31)*
The Picton Garden, Colwall *(41)*
August 18 Thursday
The Long Barn, Eastnor *(31)*
The Picton Garden, Colwall *(41)*
August 19 Friday
The Long Barn, Eastnor *(31)*
The Picton Garden, Colwall *(41)*
August 20 Saturday
Moors Meadow, Collington *(36)*
The Picton Garden, Colwall *(41)*
August 21 Sunday
The Picton Garden, Colwall *(41)*
Upper Tan House, Stansbatch *(47)*
August 23 Tuesday
The Orchards, Bishops Frome *(40)*
August 24 Wednesday
The Long Barn, Eastnor *(31)*
The Picton Garden, Colwall *(41)*
August 25 Thursday
The Long Barn, Eastnor *(31)*
The Picton Garden, Colwall *(41)*
August 26 Friday
The Long Barn, Eastnor *(31)*
The Picton Garden, Colwall *(41)*
Waterpump Farm, Ryeford *(49)*
August 27 Saturday
Arrow Cottage Garden, nr Weobley *(2)*
The Picton Garden, Colwall *(41)*
Waterpump Farm, Ryeford *(49)*
August 28 Sunday
Ivy Croft, Ivington Green, Leominster *(24)*
The Picton Garden, Colwall *(41)*
August 30 Tuesday
The Orchards, Bishops Frome *(40)*

August 31 Wednesday
The Long Barn, Eastnor (31)
The Picton Garden, Colwall (41)

September 1 Thursday
The Long Barn, Eastnor (31)
The Picton Garden, Colwall (41)

September 2 Friday
The Long Barn, Eastnor (31)
The Picton Garden, Colwall (41)

September 3 Saturday
The Picton Garden, Colwall (41)

September 4 Sunday
The Picton Garden, Colwall (41)

September 5 Monday
The Picton Garden, Colwall (41)

September 6 Tuesday
The Picton Garden, Colwall (41)

September 7 Wednesday
The Long Barn, Eastnor (31)
The Old Corn Mill, Aston Crews (38)
The Picton Garden, Colwall (41)

September 8 Thursday
The Long Barn, Eastnor (31)
The Picton Garden, Colwall (41)

September 9 Friday
The Long Barn, Eastnor (31)
The Picton Garden, Colwall (41)
Waterpump Farm, Ryeford (49)

September 10 Saturday
The Picton Garden, Colwall (41)
Waterpump Farm, Ryeford (49)

September 11 Sunday
Broadfield Court Gardens & Vineyard,
 Bodenham (7)
The Picton Garden, Colwall (41)

September 12 Monday
The Picton Garden, Colwall (41)

September 13 Tuesday
The Picton Garden, Colwall (41)

September 14 Wednesday
The Long Barn, Eastnor (31)
The Picton Garden, Colwall (41)

September 15 Thursday
The Long Barn, Eastnor (31)
The Picton Garden, Colwall (41)

September 16 Friday
The Long Barn, Eastnor (31)
The Picton Garden, Colwall (41)

September 17 Saturday
The Picton Garden, Colwall (41)
Stockton Bury Gardens Ltd, Kimbolton (45)

September 18 Sunday
Ivy Croft, Ivington Green, Leominster (24)
The Picton Garden, Colwall (41)

September 19 Monday
The Picton Garden, Colwall (41)

ngs gardens open for charity

Look out for the NCCPG
National Plant
Collections at some
of our gardens

September 20 Tuesday
The Picton Garden, Colwall (41)

September 21 Wednesday
The Long Barn, Eastnor (31)
The Picton Garden, Colwall (41)

September 22 Thursday
The Long Barn, Eastnor (31)
The Picton Garden, Colwall (41)

September 23 Friday
The Long Barn, Eastnor (31)
The Picton Garden, Colwall (41)

September 24 Saturday
The Picton Garden, Colwall (41)

September 25 Sunday
The Picton Garden, Colwall (41)

September 26 Monday
The Picton Garden, Colwall (41)

September 27 Tuesday
The Picton Garden, Colwall (41)

September 28 Wednesday
The Long Barn, Eastnor (31)
The Picton Garden, Colwall (41)

September 29 Thursday
The Long Barn, Eastnor (31)
The Picton Garden, Colwall (41)

September 30 Friday
The Long Barn, Eastnor (31)
The Picton Garden, Colwall (41)

October 1 Saturday
The Picton Garden, Colwall (41)

October 2 Sunday
Lower Hope, Ullingswick (33)
The Picton Garden, Colwall (41)

October 3 Monday
The Picton Garden, Colwall (41)

October 4 Tuesday
The Picton Garden, Colwall (41)

October 5 Wednesday
The Old Corn Mill, Aston Crews (38)
The Picton Garden, Colwall (41)

October 6 Thursday
The Picton Garden, Colwall (41)

October 7 Friday
The Picton Garden, Colwall (41)

October 8 Saturday
The Picton Garden, Colwall (41)

October 9 Sunday
Hergest Croft Gardens, Kington (20)
The Picton Garden, Colwall (41)

October 10 Monday
The Picton Garden, Colwall (41)

October 11 Tuesday
The Picton Garden, Colwall (41)

October 12 Wednesday
The Picton Garden, Colwall (41)

October 13 Thursday
The Picton Garden, Colwall (41)

October 14 Friday
The Picton Garden, Colwall (41)

October 15 Saturday
The Picton Garden, Colwall (41)

October 16 Sunday
The Picton Garden, Colwall (41)

October 23 Sunday
Longacre, Colwall Green (32)

2006

February 2 Thursday
Ivy Croft, Ivington Green, Leominster (24)

February 9 Thursday
Ivy Croft, Ivington Green, Leominster (24)

February 16 Thursday
Ivy Croft, Ivington Green, Leominster (24)

February 23 Thursday
Ivy Croft, Ivington Green, Leominster (24)

DESCRIPTIONS OF GARDENS

❶ ◆ Abbey Dore Court Garden, Abbey Dore 🚻🐕🌳
(Mrs Charis Ward) *11m SW of Hereford. From A465 midway Hereford-Abergavenny turn W, signed Abbey Dore, then 2½m.* 6-acre garden. Walled garden which has been substantially altered. Long purple, gold and silver borders, together with cottage garden and a new area which was field; gazebo. Riverside walk leading to bridge across R Dore and meadow planted with trees. The garden is full of trees, shrubs and interesting herbaceous perennials, especially hellebores, peonies, pulmonaria, astrantia and crocosmia. Adjacent nursery. Sedum article in 'Gardening Which' 2004. Light Refreshments and TEAS. *Adm £3.50, chd 50p. Tues, Thurs, Sats, Suns & Bank Hol Mons 26 Mar to 2 Oct. Tel 01981 240419 www.abbeydorecourt.co.uk*

❷ ◆ Arrow Cottage Garden, Ledgemoor, nr Weobley 🐕
(David & Janet Martin) *8m SE of Kington. From Weobley take unclassified rd direction Wormsley (Kings Pyon-Canon Pyon), after 1m, turn L signed Ledgemoor. 2nd R (no through rd). 1st house on L.* Set amidst an idyllic landscape in rural countryside, this romantic 2-acre garden combines formal design, follies, water features and topiary with exuberant and imaginative planting. The 23 separate rooms each stand alone, whilst combining to make a truly fascinating, cohesive garden. Coaches permitted. TEAS. *Adm £3.50, chd £1. Weds, Sats & Suns Apr to Sept incl.* **For NGS:** *Sun 10 Apr; Sats 4 June; 27 Aug (11-4). Tel 01344 622181 www.arrowcottagegarden.co.uk*

❸ NEW ◆ Aulden Farm, Aulden, Leominster 🚻🐕🌳
(Alun & Jill Whitehead) *4m SW of Leominster. From Leominster take Ivington/Upper Hill Rd. ¾m after Ivington Church, turn R (signed*

Aulden), garden 1m on R. From A4110 signed Ivington. After ¾m turn R opp tel box, garden ¾m on L. Informally-planted country garden and nursery surrounding old farmhouse. Many different aspects to enjoy, all in a garden of 2 acres. Numerous iris incl ditch containing ensatas and natural pond surrounded by sibiricas. Hemerocallis also strongly represented. Garden started from scratch in 1997 and still evolving. TEAS at Ivy Croft on NGS days only. *Adm £2.50, chd free. Tues & Thurs 5 Apr to 30 Aug (10-5).* **For NGS:** *combined adm with* **Ivy Croft** *£4, chd free. Suns 29 May; 3 July (2-5). Tel 01568 720129 www.auldenfarm.co.uk*

❹ ◆ The Bannut, Bringsty 🏵️🐕🍴
(Daphne & Maurice Everett) *2½m E of Bromyard. On A44 Worcester Rd, ½m E of entrance to National Trust, Brockhampton.* 2½ acres of formal and informal gardens, interest throughout the yr, with lovely views to the Malvern Hills. Manicured hedges divide garden rooms, which incl a yellow and white garden, romantic arbour garden, secret garden and unusual knot garden. There are rhododendrons, azaleas, camellias, magnolias, pieris etc and masses of cowslips in the spring, as well as many other interesting trees and shrubs and a colourful heather garden. Featured in 'The English Garden' 2003 and 'Herefordshire & Monmouthshire Life' 2004. Light refreshments and TEAS (NGS days). *Adm £3, chd £1.50. Weds, Sats, Suns, Bank Hols Easter to Sept.* **For NGS:** *Suns 15 May; 17 July; 7 Aug (12.30-5). Tel 01885 482206 www.bannut.co.uk*

❺ Batch Cottage, Almeley 🏵️🐕🍴
(Jeremy & Elizabeth Russell) *16m NW of Hereford. 2m off A438-A4111 to Kington, turn R at Eardisley.* Maturing conservation-oriented garden of some 2½ acres with streams and large pond, set in a natural valley, surrounded by woodland and orchard. Over 360 labelled trees and shrubs, mixed borders, fern and bog beds, wild flower bank, stumpery, woodland walk and wooden sculptures. Cream TEAS in aid of St Mary's Church, Almeley. *Adm £3, chd free. Suns 22 May; 12 June (2-5.30). Private visits welcome by appt, club and association outings welcome. Tel 01544 327469*

❻ ◆ Berrington Hall, Leominster 🏵️🐕🍴
(The National Trust) *3m N of Leominster. On A49, signed. Buses: Midland Red (W) 92, 292 alight Luston 2m.* Extensive views over Capability Brown park; formal garden; wall plants, unusual trees, camellia collection, herbaceous plants, wisteria. Woodland walk, rhododendrons, walled garden with historic apple collection. Light refreshments and TEAS. *House & garden adm £5. Garden only £3.50. Sats, Suns 5 to 18 Mar & 5 Nov to 18 Dec; Sats to Weds 19 Mar to 30 Oct.* **For NGS:** *Sun 29 May (12-5). Tel 01568 615721 berrington@nationaltrust.org.uk*

Birtsmorton Court, nr Malvern 🏵️🐕🍴
See Worcestershire.

❼ ◆ Broadfield Court Gardens & Vineyard, Bodenham 🏵️🍴
(Mrs Keith James) *7m SE of Leominster. A49 from Leominster or Hereford & A417 to Bodenham, turn L at Risbury signed at Bodenham.* Domesday Manor House (not open). 4 acres of old English gardens; yew hedges; spacious lawns; herbaceous. Rose garden designed by David Austin. Picnic area. 14 acres of vineyard; wine tasting incl in entrance charge. Working kitchen garden incl 300 varieties of fruit and vegetables. Light refreshments and TEAS. *Adm £3, chd 50p. Open all yr, except 2 wks after Christmas.* **For NGS:** *Suns 12 June; 11 Sept (10-4.30). Tel 01568 797483 info@broadfieldcourt.co.uk*

❽ ◆ Bryan's Ground, Stapleton, nr Presteigne 🏵️🐕🍴
(David Wheeler & Simon Dorrell) *12m NW of Leominster. Between Kinsham & Stapleton. At Mortimers Cross take B4362 signed Presteigne. At Combe, follow signs.* Beautiful 8-acre garden. Yew and box topiary, parterres, sunk garden, formal herb garden, partly-walled kitchen garden. Colour-themed flower and shrub borders with 'Sulking House'. Shrubbery with spring bulbs, Heritage apple orchard, formal pools, belvedere, lighthouse, dovecote and Edwardian greenhouse. Arboretum. Home of Hortus, The International Garden Journal. One of 'The Independent's' 10 best contemporary British gardens 2003. TEAS. *Adm £4, chd £1, OAP £3.50. Suns, Mons 25 Mar to 29 Aug. Daily 31 May to 4 June.* **For NGS:** *Tue 24 May (2-5). Tel 01544 260001 www.bryansground.co.uk*

❾ Caves Folly Nursery, Evendine Lane, Colwall 🏵️🐕🍴
(Wil Leaper & Bridget Evans) *1¼m NE of Ledbury. Evendine Lane, off Colwall Green. B4218. Between Malvern & Ledbury. Car parking at Caves Folly.* Organic nursery established 19yrs specialising in alpines, herbaceous perennials and grasses, some unusual. All plants peat-free and grown organically with Soil Association symbol. Herbaceous borders, solar powered water features and display gardens. Meadow walk with pond, chickens and ducks and 'willow dome'. Organic shop selling fruit and vegetables. Organic ice creams. Home-made TEAS. *Combined adm with* **Longacre** *£3, chd free. Suns 24 Apr; 29 May; 26 June; 7 Aug (2-5). Private visits welcome by appt at any time, for groups of 10+. Tel 01684 540631 www.cavesfolly.com*

❿ Chennels Gate, Eardisley 🏵️🐕🍴
(Mrs Una Dawson) *5m S of Kington. A438 to Eardisley. Opp PH turn W signed Woodseaves. ½m house & nursery on L.* 2-acre plantsman's garden divided into areas of interest: Victorian cottage garden, parterre, sunken garden with pond and folly, native woodland with paths. Orchard with wild flowers, chickens and Victorian piggery. Home-made TEAS. *Adm £2.50, chd free. Private visits welcome by appt May to July, coaches permitted. Tel 01544 327288*

⓫ ◆ Coddington Vineyard, Coddington 🏵️🍴
(Denis & Ann Savage) *4m NE of Ledbury. From Ledbury to Malvern rd A449, follow brown signs to Coddington Vineyard.* 5 acres incl 2-acre vineyard, listed farmhouse, threshing barn and cider mill. Garden with terraces, woodland with tree ferns, pond and stream. Unusual perennials, trees and shrubs. Winery on view. Wine tasting incl. Home-made TEAS. *Adm £3, chd £1, under 12 free. Sun 7 Aug (2-5)*

⓬ ◆ Croft Castle, Leominster 🏵️🐕
(The National Trust) *5m NW of Leominster. On B4362 (off B4361, Leominster to Ludlow rd).* Large garden; borders; walled garden; landscaped park and walks in Fishpool Valley; fine old avenues. Light refreshments and TEAS. *House and garden adm £4.60. Garden only £3.20.* **For NGS:** *Fri 24 June (12-5). Tel 01568 780246*

⑬ Croose Farm, Woolhope
(Mr & Mrs R Malim) *5m N of Ross-on-Wye. Woolhope is E of the B4224 halfway between Ross-on-Wye & Hereford. From centre of village take rd opp church signed Sollars Hope & The Hyde. Garden is ¾m on L.* 2½ acres of well-established garden, developed over 16yrs. Formal and informal areas incl a 'hot bed', roses, white garden, lime walk, courtyards, knot garden and water garden. Many unusual plants, trees and shrubs. Home-made TEAS. *Adm £3, chd free. Sun 12 June (2-6)*

⑭ Garnstone House, Weobley ✗☯☺
(Michael & Dawn MacLeod) *8m W of Leominster. From village of Weobley follow B4230 for 1m. On LH-side take private turning beneath large trees.* Garnstone House is 2nd on L. 1-acre garden with an extensive woodland fringe containing specimen trees. Large collection of clematis and many container plants. Various well stocked herbaceous borders; small kitchen garden; outlook over parkland. Accommodation. *Adm £2.50, chd under 12 free. Sun 17 Apr (2-6)*

⑮ Grantsfield, nr Kimbolton ☺✗☯☺
(Colonel & Mrs J G T Polley) *3m NE of Leominster. A49 N from Leominster, A4112 turn R & follow signs. No parking for coaches - drop & collect visitors in village; (minibus acceptable). A44 W to Leominster. Turn R at Drum Xrds (notice up).* Contrasting styles in gardens of old stone farmhouse; wide variety of unusual plants, trees and shrubs, old roses, climbers, herbaceous borders, superb views. 1½-acre orchard and kitchen garden with flowering and specimen trees and shrubs. Spring bulbs. TEAS. *Adm £2.50, chd under 16 free (share to Hamnish Village Hall Charity). Sun 12 June (2-5.30). Private visits welcome by appt. Tel 01568 613338*

⑯ The Great House, Dilwyn ☺✗☺
(Tom & Jane Hawksley) *7m W of Leominster. A44 from Leominster joining A4112 (signed Brecon). Turn L into Dilwyn village. House on RH-side opp village green.* 1½-acre all-yr garden, designed and created by owners over the last 8yrs. Spring bulbs, traditional rose gardens, yew and beech hedging, raised knot garden, decorative stone and brickwork. 40ft reflecting pool and pleached hornbeams lining the drive all add interest to this country garden which is fronted by wonderful C18 wrought iron gates. Accommodation. Home-made TEAS in aid of St Michael's Hospice. *Adm £2.50, chd under 12 free. Sun 19 June (2-5) www.herefordshireaccommodation.com*

⑰ The Griggs, Newton St Margarets ☺✗
(John & Bridget Biggs) *14m SW of Hereford. Take B4348 to Vowchurch, turn L through Turnastone & follow NGS signs. Signs will also be posted for those approaching from Longtown or Abbey Dore via Bacton.* Located in a remote scenic setting between the Golden Valley and the Black Mountains, a floriferous country garden of 1½ acres, managed organically and incl extensive mixed borders, wild flower meadows, wildlife ponds and large productive kitchen garden. A garden to lose oneself in. Home-made TEAS. *Adm £2.50, chd free (share to Community Action, Nepal). Sats 14 May; 14 June; 9 July (2-6). Private visits welcome by appt 1 Apr to 7 Aug. Tel 01981 510629*

⑱ ♦ Hellens, Much Marcle ☺☺
(Pennington Mellor Munthe Charity Trust) *4m SW of Ledbury. 6m from Ross-on-Wye, off A449.* Hellens is an interesting manor house which is open to visitors. The gardens are being actively redeveloped to reflect the C17 ambience of the house. They incorporate a rare octagonal dovecote, two knot gardens and young yew labyrinth. Lawns, herb and kitchen gardens; short woodland and pond walk. Home-made TEAS. *Adm £2.50, chd free. For NGS: Fris 24 June; 1 July (2-5). Tel 01531 660504 hellensmanor@tiscali.co.uk*

⑲ ♦ The Henry Weston Garden, Much Marcle ☺
(The Weston Family) *5m W of Ledbury. On A449 Ledbury to Ross-on-Wye.* Courtyard garden with water feature designed by John

Rutledge and Rachel Hardwick. Planted for yr-round interest on raised beds using old bricks and local stone. RHS Hampton Court Palace Show garden transferred to present site. Light refreshments and TEAS. *Adm free. Open daily (closed Christmas). Tel 01531 660108 www.westons-cider.co.uk*

⑳ ♦ Hergest Croft Gardens, Kington ☺☺NCCPG
(Mr W L Banks) *½m W of Kington. ½m off A44 on Welsh side of Kington. 20m NW of Hereford. Turn L at Rhayader end of bypass; then 1st R; gardens ¼m on L.* 50 acres of garden owned by Banks family for 4 generations. Edwardian garden surrounding house; Park Wood with rhododendrons up to 30ft tall; old-fashioned kitchen garden with spring and herbaceous borders. One of finest private collections of trees and shrubs, selected to hold National Collections of maples, birches and zelkova. Hergest Croft celebrated its centenary in 1996. Light refreshments and TEAS. *Adm £5, chd free. Open Mar weekends; daily 25 Mar to 30 Oct (12.30-5.30, May & June 12-6). For NGS: Suns 12 June; 9 Oct. Tel 01544 230160 www.hergest.co.uk*

㉑ Hope End House, Raycombe Lane, Hope End
(Mrs P J Maiden) *2m NE of Ledbury. From Ledbury, take Bromyard rd N. ½m from station turn R signed Wellington Heath & Hope End, uphill for 1½m to T-junction, turn R. Continue for ½m. Turn into Raycombe Lane, entrance from this lane on R. Signed after 1m. Parking in woodland & lane.* Woodland walk through 30 acres parkland, Oyster Hill originally laid out in the early C19. 6-acre bluebell walk through Cockshute. Perfect for picnics. *Adm £2.50. Fri 8 Apr to Sat 7 May incl (10-4). Private visits welcome by appt. Tel 01531 635890*

㉒ ♦ How Caple Court, How Caple
(Mr & Mrs Roger Lee) *5m N of Ross-on-Wye. 10m S of Hereford. On B4224; turn R at How Caple Xrds, garden 400yds on L.* 11 acres. Edwardian gardens set high above R Wye in park and woodland; formal terraces; yew hedges, statues and pools; sunken Florentine water garden; woodland walks; herbaceous and shrub borders; shrub roses; mature trees. Medieval church with restored C16 diptych. Cream TEAS. *Adm £2.50, chd free. Daily 14 Mar to 16 Oct. For NGS: Sun 5 June*

(10-5). Tel 01989 740626
how.caple@clara.co.uk

㉓ Ivy Cottage, Kinsham 🏠⊕
(Jane & Richard Barton) *12m NW of
Leominster. From Mortimers Cross
take B4362 towards Presteigne. Turn
R at Combe towards Lingen for 1m.
Easy parking.* Charming cottage
garden developed over 12yrs. Mixed
borders planted for colour, scent and
all-yr interest. Shrub roses, clematis
and wide range of perennials, some
unusual, incl many hardy geraniums,
astrantias, campanulas and asters.
Shade areas, pergolas, vegetable
garden and fruit trees in ½-acre
setting. Featured in 'Woman's
Weekly' 2004. *Adm £2.50, chd free.
Private visits welcome by appt Apr to
Sept, coaches permitted, groups
welcome. Tel 01544 267154
jane@barton3.freeserve.co.uk*

**㉔ ◆ Ivy Croft, Ivington Green,
Leominster** 🏠⊕
(Sue & Roger Norman) *3m SW of
Leominster. From Leominster take
Ryelands Rd to Ivington. Turn R at
church, garden ¾m on R. From
A4110 signed Ivington, garden 1¾m
on L.* Garden created since 1997
surrounds C17 cottage in 4 acres of
rich grassland. Plant lovers' garden
designed for all-yr interest. Raised
beds, mixed herbaceous borders,
trees, alpines, troughs, formal
vegetable garden framed by trained
fruit trees; collections of ferns,
willows and snowdrops. TEAS Suns
only. *Adm £2.50, chd free. Weds and
Thurs Mar to Sept.* **For NGS:** *Every
Thurs 3 to 24 Feb (9-1, 2-4). Suns 10
Apr; 29 May; 3 July; 28 Aug; 18 Sept
(2-5). Thurs 2 to 23 Feb 2006.
Combined adm £4, chd free with
Aulden Farm 29 May, 3 July. Private
visits welcome by appt all yr, for
NGS. Tel 01568 720344
www.ivycroft.freeserve.co.uk*

**㉕ Kilima Lodge, Evendine Lane,
Colwall** 🏠⊕
(Mr & Mrs W B Stallard) *1¼m NE
of Ledbury. Evendine Lane off
Colwall Green. Take A449 S from
Malvern, R on to B4218 to Colwall,
L just before Yew Tree PH. Garden
on R past Caves Folly Nursery.* 2-
acre garden which has evolved over
the last 9yrs with a background of
established trees and shrubs and
dramatic views of the Malvern Hills.
Mixed borders of shrubs and
herbaceous plants with the accent on
foliage and the unusual; water feature
with mixed planting. Home-made
TEAS. *Adm £2.50, chd free. Sun 22
May (2-5)*

**㉖ ◆ Kingstone Cottages, Weston
under Penyard, nr Ross-on-Wye**
🏠⊕ NCCPG
(Mr & Mrs M Hughes) *2m E of
Ross-on-Wye. A40 Ross to
Gloucester, turn off at Weston Cross
PH to Linton, then 2nd L to Rudhall.*
Informal 1½-acre cottage garden
containing National Collection of old
pinks and carnations and other
unusual plants. Terraced beds, ponds,
grotto, summerhouse, lovely views.
Separate parterre garden containing
the collection. Much of the garden
replanted 2004. Featured in
'Hereford Times', 'Amateur
Gardening', 'Garden Design'
(Holland) and on Dutch TV 2004.
Home-made TEAS (Suns only). *Adm
£2, chd free. Daily 2 May to 8 July
(10-5). Tel 01989 565267*

**㉗ Lakeside, Gaines Road,
Whitbourne** 🏠🏠
(Mr D Gueroult) *9m W of Worcester.
Off A44 at County boundary sign
(ignore sign to Whitbourne village)
400yds along Gaines Rd on L.* 6
acres, large walled garden with many
mixed beds and borders, spring
bulbs, climbers, small maturing
pinetum, heather garden, bog garden,
medieval carp lake. Steep steps and
slopes, partial wheelchair access.
Home-made TEAS in aid of St
Michael's Hospice. *Adm £3, chd free.
Private visits welcome by appt Apr to
June (2-5), for groups of 10+.
Tel 01886 821119*

**㉘ ◆ Lawton Hall Herbs,
Eardisland** ⊕
(Alex & Duncan Fox) *2½m W of
Leominster. From Leominster follow
A44 W. Fork R on to B4529,
continue 2½m to Lawton. Nursery
on L.* Herb gardens with low box and
brick edging, created in 2001 with
extensive range of culinary, medicinal
and scented plants. Set in traditional
S-facing garden with high beech
hedging and lovely views. Lawns, ha-
ha and abandoned 1-acre garden in
outstanding position across field.
Home-made TEAS (NGS days). *Adm
£2.50, chd free. Weds to Mons Easter
to mid-Oct (10.30-5.30).* **For NGS:**
*Sun 12, Sat, Sun 18, 19, Tues 21 June
(11-5). Tel 01568 709215
www.lawtonhall.co.uk*

㉙ Little Llanavon, Dorstone
🏠🏠⊕
(John & Jenny Chippindale) *2m N of
Peterchurch. In the Golden Valley,
15m W of Hereford on B4348, ½m
towards Peterchurch from Dorstone.*
½-acre S-facing cottage-style walled
garden in lovely rural location.
Meandering paths among shrubs in

shady spring garden. Hot gravel area
and herbaceous borders closely
planted with select perennials and
grasses, many unusual. Good late
colour. *Adm £2.50, chd free. Private
visits welcome by appt May to Sept.
Tel 01981 550984
john.chippindale@virgin.net*

㉚ Llandinabo Court, Hereford
🏠🏠⊕
(Peter & Jane Symonds) *6m SE of
Hereford. Located off A49
equidistant between Ross-on-Wye &
Hereford. Entrance opp B4348 off
A49 signed Hay-on-Wye.* Traditional
Victorian-type garden with
herbaceous borders, rose gardens,
lake and well-stocked vegetable patch
with fruit trees. Modern greenhouse
containing a vine, small orchid house,
peaches and nectarines. Within the
grounds is the Parish Church of
Llandinabo surrounded by a circular
wall. This area is landscaped with old
roses and small pond. Home-made
TEAS. *Adm £2.50, chd free. Sun 12
June (2-5). Private visits welcome by
appt. Tel 01989 730435
peter.symonds@llandinabofarms.
co.uk*

㉛ The Long Barn, Eastnor 🏠⊕
(Fay & Roger Oates) *2m E of
Ledbury. On A438 Ledbury to
Tewkesbury rd. From Ledbury take
Malvern rd & turn R after 1¼m
towards Eastnor-Tewkesbury. Roger
Oates Studio ¾m along rd, on LH-
side. Parking in car park.* New
garden planted over last 10yrs, made
for owners' pleasure. Strong design
structure with mixed, natural
crowded plantings of perennials and
herbaceous plants, selected for
fragrance and texture. Sitting in the
landscape, garden is small, less than ⅓
acre, and enclosed, set by edge of 3-
acre orchard. Situated behind the
design studio of Roger Oates Design
Co. *Adm £2.50, chd free. Every Wed,
Thur & Fri 18 May to 30 Sept (11-5).
Private visits welcome by appt.
Tel 01531 632718
roger@rogeroates.com*

**㉜ Longacre, Evendine Lane,
Colwall Green** 🏠🏠
(Mr D M Pudsey) *3m S of Malvern.
Off Colwall Green. Off B4218. Car
parking at Caves Folly Nursery.* 3-
acre garden-cum-arboretum
developed since 1970. Island beds of
trees and shrubs, half of them
underplanted with bulbs and
herbaceous perennials, present a
sequence of pictures and views
through the seasons. Sense of
spaciousness and of being led on and
in is generated by long paths and

avenues that connect half a dozen focal points and open lawns. Over 50 types of conifer provide the background against which are displayed maples, rhododendrons, azaleas, dogwoods, eucryphias etc. Home-made TEAS at Caves Folly. *Combined adm £3, chd free with* **Caves Folly Nursery** *Suns 24 Apr; 29 May; 26 June; 7 Aug (2-5).* **Longacre** *only Sun 23 Oct, adm £2 chd free. Private visits welcome by appt. Tel 01684 540377*

㉝ Lower Hope, Ullingswick 🔗🌿🖥

(Mr & Mrs Clive Richards) *5m S of Bromyard. From Hereford take A465 N to Bromyard. After 6m turn L at Burley Gate on A417 signed Leominster. Approx 2m take 3rd turning on R signed Lower Hope & Pencombe, ½m on LH-side.* 5-acre garden facing S and W. Herbaceous borders, rose walks and gardens, laburnum tunnel, Mediterranean garden, bog gardens. Lime tree walk, lake landscaped with wild flowers; streams, ponds. Conservatories and large glasshouse with exotic species orchids, bougainvilleas. Prizewinning herd of pedigree Hereford cattle, flock of pedigree Suffolk sheep. TEAS served 2.30-5. *Adm £3, chd £1. Suns 3 Apr; 22 May; 10 July; 2 Oct (2-6)*

Lower House, Cusop, Hay-on-Wye 🌿🖥
See Powys.

Maesllwch Castle, Glasbury-on-Wye 🖥
See Powys.

㉞ Michaelchurch Court, St Owens Cross 🌿
(Dr & Mrs D J L Smith) *7m N of Ross-on-Wye. On A49, turn L onto B4521 signed Abergavenny; turn R at Xrds. After ¼m turn L at 1st opportunity into narrow rd to Michaelchurch Court. From Hereford approx 12m S on A49; approx ¼m after Harewood End turn R signed Orcop; 1st minor Xrds turn L . At next minor Xrds turn L into narrrow rd to Michaelchurch Court.* C17 farmhouse (not open), in open countryside near Norman church. Approx 3 acres incl large pond, stream with flower border. Old-fashioned roses and herbaceous borders set amongst lawns, one long border backed by high wall covered with climbing roses, honeysuckle. Long pergola covered with roses, honeysuckle, clematis and wisteria leads to sunken garden with water feature and seating area. Climbing roses and hydrangeas over 20ft high

cover house. Arboretum and wild flower meadow planted 2001. Featured in 'The English Garden' 2003. TEAS. *Adm £2.50, chd free. Tues, Wed, Sat 14, 15, 18 June (2.30-6)*

㉟ Monnington Court, Monnington-on-Wye, Hereford 🔗
(Mr & Mrs Bulmer) *9m W of Hereford. S off A438. Monnington-on-Wye. Lane to village & Monnington Court.* 20 acres, lake, river, sculpture garden (Mrs Bulmer is sculptor Angela Conner). Famous mile-long avenue of pines and yews, favourite of Sir John Betjeman and in Kilvert's Diary. Lake and river. Foundation Farm of British Morgan Horse, living replicas of statues in Trafalgar Square, etc, cider press. C13 Moot Hall, C15 and C17 house. Horse display 3.30. Featured on BBC and local radio, 'Hereford Times' 2004. Home-made TEAS (10-7), BBQ (11-7). *Garden & display adm £5 (chd £3). House, garden & display £6 (chd £3.50). Sat, Sun, Mon 28, 29, 30 May (10-7)*

㊱ ◆ Moors Meadow, Collington 🌿🖥
(Ros Bissell) *4½m N of Bromyard. On B4214 turn L up lane, over two cattle grids turn R.* Intriguing plantsman's garden of great appeal. 7-acre organic hillside site rich in unusual plants and trees. Extensive shrubberies and woodland provide yr-round interest alongside water features, grass garden, fernery, wild flower meadow, spring bulbs and large kitchen garden. Abundant wildlife to be seen. Strong shoes advisable, WC. *Adm £3, chd free. Open Fri to Tue Mar to end Sept. For NGS: Sats 19 Mar; 23 Apr; 28 May; 18 June; 23 July; 20 Aug (11-5). Tel 01885 410318*

㊲ The Nest, Moreton, Eye 🔗🌿🖥
(Sue Evans & Guy Poulton) *3m N of Leominster. A49. L in Ashton. 1m on L signed The Nest Cottage Garden.* Drive entrance between Stourport-Leominster canal remnant and 3-acre wild flower meadow. 1530s yeoman's timber-framed house (not open). Potager, soft and hard fruits. Rockeries, scree and gravel gardens. Shrubberies and summer garden with water feature. Wet area with primulas. Ferns, 42 varieties. Pond, waterfall and Mediterranean area. Lots of pots. Home-made TEAS. *Adm £2.50, chd free. Suns, Mons 1, 2, 29, 30 May; Sat, Sun 11, 12 June (2-5). Private visits welcome by appt,*

coaches welcome. Tel 01568 614501 sue@thenest99.freeserve.co.uk

㊳ The Old Corn Mill, Aston Crews 🌿🖥
(Mrs Jill Hunter) *5m E of Ross-on-Wye. A40 Ross to Gloucester. Turn L at T-lights at Lea Xrds onto B4222 signed Newent. Garden ½m on L.* Tranquil garden in wooded valley. Native trees, streams, meadow areas and small orchard, informal flower and shrub beds providing yr-round interest. Picnics welcome. *Adm £2.50, chd free. Fri 25 Mar; Weds 6 Apr; 4 May; 1 June; 7 Sept; 5 Oct (11-5). Private visits welcome by appt all yr for individuals and small groups. Tel 01989 750059*

㊴ NEW The Old Quarry, Almeley Road, Eardisley 🔗🖥
(John & Anne Davis) *16m NW of Hereford. ¾m off A438-A4111 to Kington, turn R at Eardisley.* Gently-sloping garden of 2½ acres, laid out in the 1930s now being renovated and developed. Terraces and old quarry gardens with rhododendrons and mature trees, new parterre, vegetable garden and herbaceous beds. Far-reaching views of Black Mountains and Hay Bluff. Home-made TEAS in aid of St Mary's Church, Almeley. *Adm £3, chd free. Sun 22 May (2-5)*

㊵ The Orchards, Golden Valley, Bishops Frome 🌿🖥
(Mr & Mrs Robert Humphries) *14m E of Hereford. A4103 turn L at bottom of Fromes Hill, through village of Bishops Frome on B4214. Turn R immed after de-regulation signs along narrow track for 250yds. Park in field by garden.* 1-acre garden designed in areas on various levels. 15 water features incl Japanese water garden and tea house, Mediterranean area, rose garden with rill, also aviary. Large rose, clematis, fuchsia and dahlia collections. Seating areas on all levels. New projects every yr. Featured in 'Amateur Gardening' 2003. Home-made TEAS. *Adm £2.50, chd 50p. Every Tues 7 June to 30 Aug. Suns 22 May: 19 June; 17 July; 14 Aug (2-6). Private visits welcome by appt for parties & coaches. Tel 01885 490273*

Pen-y-Maes, Hay-on-Wye 🔗🖥
See Powys.

㊶ The Picton Garden, Old Court Nurseries, Colwall 🔗🌿🖥 NCCPG
(Mr & Mrs Paul Picton) *3m W of Malvern. On B4218 (Walwyn Rd) N of Colwall Stone. Turn off A449 from Ledbury or Malvern.* 1½ acres W of Malvern Hills. Plantsman's

garden specialising in summer and autumn colour. Wide range of interesting herbaceous perennials precede Sept/Oct flowering of National Collection of autumn-flowering asters (Michaelmas daisies). Many unusual plants to be seen. Featured in 'Garden Life' and 'Gardens Illustrated' 2004. *Adm £2.50, chd free. Weds to Suns in Aug; daily 1 Sept to 16 Oct (11-5), by appt only 17-31 Oct. Tel 01684 540416 www.autumnasters.co.uk*

The Red House, Staunton, nr Gloucester 🚻♿

See Gloucestershire North & Central.

㊷ Shieldbrook, Kings Caple 🚻♿

(Sue & Oliver Sharp) *7m S of Hereford. Take A49 from Hereford or Ross. Take 1st rd signed to Hoarwithy (there are 3). Go past New Harp PH on R, then next R over R Wye. Up the hill take 2nd R into Kings Caple, down hill over Xrds then Shieldbrook ½m on L.* 1-acre country garden planted for yr-round interest featuring grasses, shrubs and perennials. Rose garden and orchard, healing garden with pond and rockery. Sculpture garden of local sculptor's work is of special interest. Stream runs through the garden and there are many secret corners. Garden managed organically. Home-made TEAS. *Adm £3, chd free, concessions £2. Sat, Sun 25, 26 June (2-5). Private visits welcome by appt. Tel 01432 840670*

㊸ ◆ Shipley Gardens, Holme Lacy 🚻♿⊞

(R I & S L Macadie) *5m SE of Hereford. From Hereford-Fownhope B4224, cross over Wye bridge & take B4399 to Holme Lacy village. Garden entrance on L as you enter village.* Several acres of gardens set within an idyllic and secluded aspect of the Wye valley. Combinations of annual and perennial flowers woven among tapestries of ornamental conifers, shrubs, bulbs and garden trees to exploit harmonies and contrasts of colour shape, texture and perfume. A haven for butterflies, birdlife, peacocks and white pigeons. Home-made TEAS. *Adm £3.50, chd free. Open daily 31 Mar-31 Oct (10-6).* **For NGS:** *Suns 22 May; 19 June (11-5)*

Shuttifield Cottage, Birchwood, Storridge ♿⊞

See Worcestershire.

㊹ ◆ Staunton Park, Staunton Green 🚻♿⊞

(Susan Fode) *3m N of Pembridge. At Pembridge (on A44) take rd signed Presteigne, Shobdon. After 3m look out for red phone box on R. Staunton Park is 150yds on L. Do not go to Staunton-on-Arrow.* 10-acre garden and grounds incl drive with stately wellingtonias, rose garden, separate kitchen garden, herbaceous borders and Victorian rock garden, lake and lakeside walk. Specimen trees incl mature monkey puzzle, gigantic liriodendron, *Davidia involucrata*, *ginkgo bilobas* and several ancient oaks. Home-made TEAS (NGS day only) by and in aid of WI. *Adm £2.50, chd free. Every Thurs 17 May to 18 Aug (11-5).* **For NGS:** *Sun 3 July (2-5.30)*

㊺ ◆ Stockton Bury Gardens Ltd, Kimbolton 🚻♿⊞

(Raymond G Treasure Esq) *2m N of Leominster. On A49. Turn R onto A4112 Kimbolton rd. Gardens are 300yds on R.* Superb, sheltered 4-acre garden with a very long growing season giving colour and interest all yr. Extensive collection of plants, many rare and unusual set amongst medieval buildings, a real kitchen garden. Pigeon house; tithe barn; grotto; cider press; pools; ruined Chapel and rill, all surrounded by unspoilt countryside. Unsuitable for children. *Adm £4. Weds to Suns & Bank Hols 1 Apr to 30 Sept.* **For NGS:** *Sats 21 May, 17 Sept (12-5). Tel 01568 613432*

㊻ [NEW] Stoney Croft, Church Road, Byton ♿

(Alan & Jenifer Grigg) *4m E of Presteigne, 6m N of Kington. B4362 Mortimer's Cross to 4m E of Presteigne, take sign to Byton. Drive approx ½m passing farm buildings, R to Church cul-de-sac. Stoney Croft 500yds from Church car park. More parking at garden, follow directions to orchard.* Family cottage garden of 3½ acres with orchard and hill pasture. Magnificent views of mid Lugg Valley to Radnor Forest. 50 varieties of roses, peonies, clematis, magnolias; trees, shrubs, herbaceous borders, vegetables, soft fruits. Pond with great crested newts. 40 varieties of apple, pear, plum, damson, black and white mulberry, medlar, walnut. Home-made TEAS in aid of St Mary's Church, Byton. *Adm £2.50, chd £1. Sat, Sun 4, 5, Fri, Sat 24, 25 June (2-5)*

㊼ Upper Tan House, Stansbatch 🚻⊞

(Mr & Mrs James Weymouth) *12m W of Leominster. From Leominster take A44 to Rhayader. In middle of Pembridge turn R signed Shobdon & Presteigne. Stansbatch is 4m on this rd.* 1½-acre, S-facing, informal garden in beautiful setting. Deep borders sloping down to lawn and brook. Interesting collection of herbaceous plants and shrubs; good late summer colour. Pond and bog garden. Formal vegetable garden. Natural wild flower meadow incl orchids in June. Reed beds. *Adm £2.50, chd free. Suns 12 June; 21 Aug (2-5)*

㊽ The View, Ochre Hill, Wellington Heath 🚻♿⊞

(Mr & Mrs David Evans) *1m N of Ledbury. From Ledbury take Bromyard rd, 1st turning R after railway bridge signed Wellington Heath. Turn R at next T-junction (oak tree with seat round it). After 40yds turn R down The Common. Ochre Hill on L, The View is at top of hill. Limited parking available.* 2-acre sloping garden, part terraced, planted to encourage wildlife. Mixed beds, herb garden, ponds, summerhouse and other features. Orchard planted with old varieties; vegetable garden; small woodland walk. Cider mill and press. Most hard landscaping recycled from material on site. Magnificent views. Always changing. *Adm £2.50, chd free. Private visits welcome by appt. Tel 01531 632644*

The Walled Garden, Knill 🚻⊞

See Powys.

㊾ ◆ Waterpump Farm, Ryeford 🚻♿⊞

(Mrs Liz Sugden) *3m SE of Ross-on-Wye. On A40 to Gloucester.* 3-acre naturalistic style, wildlife-friendly garden. Informal beds of unusual plants. Some beds replanted, with new area for hardy geranium collection and fruit and vegetables in raised beds. Ponds and lake with waterfowl. Further 5 acres of walk on mown paths. Pet llamas and miniature horses in paddock. Hardy geraniums and pond plants for sale. Limited wheelchair access. TEAS. *Adm £2.50, chd free.* **For NGS:** *Fris, Sats 6, 7, 27, 28 May; 10, 11, 24, 25 June; 26, 27 Aug; 9, 10 Sept (12-4). Tel 01989 750177*

㊿ Well Cottage, Blakemere 🚻

(Mrs V M S Gordon) *10m W of Hereford. Leave Hereford on A465 (Abergavenny rd). After 3m turn R towards Hay B4349 (B4348). At*

Clehonger keep on B4352. Well Cottage is on L by tel box in Blakemere. 1¾-acre garden of mixed planting, specially designed to blend with surrounding hills and fields. Many seating areas: on terrace, upper and lower lawns, by pool and meadow. Summerhouse. All to encourage relaxed enjoyment of garden and views beyond. *Adm £2.50, chd free. Private visits welcome by appt April to July. Tel 01981 500475*

NEW Weobley Cross Cottage, South End Lane, Mathon, nr Malvern ⚘
See Worcestershire.

51 Weston Mews, Weston under Penyard ⚘⚘⚘
(Ann Rothwell & John Hercock) *2m E of Ross-on-Wye. Going towards Gloucester on A40, continue approx 100yds past the Weston Cross PH and turn R into grey brick-paved courtyard.* Walled ex-kitchen garden of approx ½ acre divided by clipped yew and box hedges. Broad range of herbaceous flowers and shrubs in beds and borders at different levels. Large lean-to Victorian vine house on rear of what was a stable and coach

house. Small kitchen garden. Home-made TEAS in aid of St Michael's Hospice. *Adm £3, chd free. Sat 18 (11-5), Sun 19 June (1-5). Private visits welcome by appt. Tel 01989 563823*

52 ◆ **Westonbury Mill Water Garden, Pembridge** ⚘⚘
(Richard Pim) *8m W of Leominster. On A44 1½m W of village of Pembridge, L into signed drive.* 2-acre water mill garden situated amid fields and orchards. Colourful waterside plantings of bog and moisture-loving plants around a tangle of streams and ponds, together with a natural bog garden in the area of the Old Mill pond. Unusual water features incl stone tower with water wheel. Featured on BBC TV Gardeners' World 2003. TEAS. *Adm £2.50, chd 50p. Thurs to Mons Easter to 30 Sept.* **For NGS:** *Sun 12 June (11-5). Tel 01544 388650*

53 Whitfield, Wormbridge ⚘
(Mr & Mrs Edward Clive) *8m SW of Hereford. On A465 Hereford to Abergavenny rd.* Parkland, wild flowers, ponds, walled garden, many flowering magnolias (species and hybrids), 1780 ginkgo tree, 1½m

woodland walk with 1851 redwood grove. Picnic parties welcome. Home-made TEAS. *Adm £3, chd free (share to Dore Abbey Restoration Fund). Sun 22 May (2-6). Private visits welcome by appt. Tel 01981 570727 tboyd@globalnet.co.uk*

54 NEW ◆ **The Wiggly Garden, Wiggly Wigglers, Blakemere** ⚘⚘
(Duchy of Cornwall) *9m W of Hereford. On B4352, halfway between Hereford and Hay-on-Wye.* Walled oasis for wildlife, built around a wildlife pond and filled with British native trees, hedging, shrubs and wild flowers. We use the garden to 'test drive' the range of composters, wildlife feeders and habitats that we sell: from wormeries to bird feeders you'll find them all on show here. RHS Silver Gilt medal & Best in Show Malvern 2004. Featured in 'The Telegraph' and on BBC TV Gardeners' World 2004. Home-made TEAS on NGS days. *Adm £2.50, chd free.* **For NGS:** *Suns 5, 26 June; 3 July (2-5). Tel 01981 500391 www.wigglywigglers.co.uk*

Willow Lodge, nr Longhope ⚘⚘⚘
See Gloucestershire North & Central.

Hertfordshire

County Organiser:	Mrs Virginia Newton, Moat Farm House, Much Hadham SG10 6AE
	Tel 01279 843232 email vnewton@moatfarmhouse.co.uk
Assistant County Organisers:	Mr Michael Belderbos, 6 High Elms, Hatching Green, Harpenden AL5 2JU
	Tel 01582 712612
	Mrs Gail Fox, Jenningsbury, London Road, Hertford SG13 7NS
	Tel: 01992 583978 email foxgail@jenningsbury.co.uk
	Mrs Marigold Harvey, Upwick Hall, Little Hadham, Ware SG11 2JY
	Tel 01279 771769 email marigold.harvey@btinternet.com
	Mrs Jan Marques, Cockhamsted, Braughing, Ware SG11 2NT Tel 01279 771312
	Mr Christopher Melluish, Thundridge Hill House, Cold Christmas Lane, Ware SG12 0UF
	Tel 01920 462500
	Mrs Edwina Robarts, Bromley Hall, Standon, Ware SG11 1NY
	Tel 01279 842422 email edwina.robarts@btinternet.com
	Mrs Julie Wise, Rustling End Cottage, Rustling End, Nr Codicote SG4 8TD
	Tel 01438 821509 email juliewise@f2s.com
County Treasurer:	Mrs Rösli Lancaster, Manor Cottage, Aspenden, Buntingford SG9 9PB Tel 01763 271711

Maps: Numbers shown next to each garden entry refer to that garden's entry on the county map. This position is approximate; distance and directions from the nearest main town are generally shown in the garden text.
A precise location is available for those gardens featured on the NGS website by visiting www.ngs.org.uk.

Symbols: Information relating to symbols is given on page 21

DATES OF OPENING

Evening openings
See end of county listing

Gardens open to the public
For details see garden description
Benington Lordship, nr Stevenage *(4)*
Capel Manor Gardens, Enfield, Middlesex *(7)*
Hopleys, Much Hadham *(13)*
Knebworth House Gardens, Knebworth *(16)*
Shaw's Corner, Ayot St Lawrence *(29)*

April 3 Sunday
Brent Pelham Gardens *(5)*

April 17 Sunday
St Paul's Walden Bury, Hitchin *(26)*

May 1 Sunday
The Abbots House, Abbots Langley *(1)*
20 Park Avenue South, Harpenden *(20)*
Patchwork, Berkhamsted *(21)*

May 8 Sunday
Brent Pelham Gardens *(5)*
St Paul's Walden Bury, Hitchin *(26)*

May 15 Sunday
West Lodge Park, Hadley Wood *(34)*

May 22 Sunday
Cockhamsted, Braughing *(9)*

May 29 Sunday
Great Sarratt Hall, Sarratt, Rickmansworth *(12)*
Kettle Green Gardens, Kettle Green, Much Hadham *(15)*
Odsey Park, Ashwell *(18)*
Queenswood School, Hatfield *(22)*

May 30 Monday (Bank Hol)
Queenswood School, Hatfield *(22)*

June 1 Wednesday
Rustling End Cottage, Rustling End *(24)*

June 5 Sunday
Bromley Hall, Standon, Ware *(6)*
St Mary's Croft, Elstree *(25)*
St Paul's Walden Bury, Hitchin *(26)*

June 11 Saturday
Shaw's Corner, Ayot St Lawrence **(Evening)** *(29)*

June 12 Sunday
207 East Barnet Road, New Barnet *(10)*
Jenningsbury Gardens, Hertford Heath *(14)*
Moor Place, Much Hadham *(17)*

June 16 Thursday
St Mary's Croft, Elstree **(Evening)** *(25)*

June 19 Sunday
Ashridge, Berkhamsted *(2)*
Serge Hill Gardens *(28)*
Thundridge Hill House, Ware *(31)*

June 21 Tuesday
Capel Manor Gardens, Enfield, Middlesex **(Evening)** *(7)*

June 25 Saturday
Benington Lordship, nr Stevenage *(4)*

June 26 Sunday
Benington Lordship, nr Stevenage *(4)*
Ragged Hall, nr Hemel Hempstead *(23)*
Waterdell House, Croxley Green *(33)*

July 3 Sunday
The Abbots House, Abbots Langley *(1)*
Tudor Cottage, Nr Albury *(32)*

July 8 Friday
4 School Cottages, Ley Green **(Evening)** *(27)*

July 10 Sunday
8 Gosselin Road, Bengeo, Hertford *(11)*
4 School Cottages, Ley Green *(27)*

July 17 Sunday
The Old Walled Gardens of Aston House, Aston, Nr Stevenage *(19)*
20 Park Avenue South, Harpenden *(20)*

July 24 Sunday
Stresa, Rickmansworth *(30)*

July 31 Sunday
Rustling End Cottage, Rustling End *(24)*

August 5 Friday
Rustling End Cottage, Rustling End **(Evening)** *(24)*

August 6 Saturday
Chusan, Watford **(Evening)** *(8)*

August 7 Sunday
The Barn, Bovingdon *(3)*
Hopleys, Much Hadham *(13)*

August 14 Sunday
Patchwork, Berkhamsted *(21)*

August 28 Sunday
The Abbots House, Abbots Langley *(1)*

September 4 Sunday
8 Gosselin Road, Bengeo, Hertford *(11)*

September 5 Monday
Knebworth House Gardens, Knebworth *(16)*

October 16 Sunday
West Lodge Park, Hadley Wood *(34)*

October 30 Sunday
Capel Manor Gardens, Enfield, Middlesex *(7)*

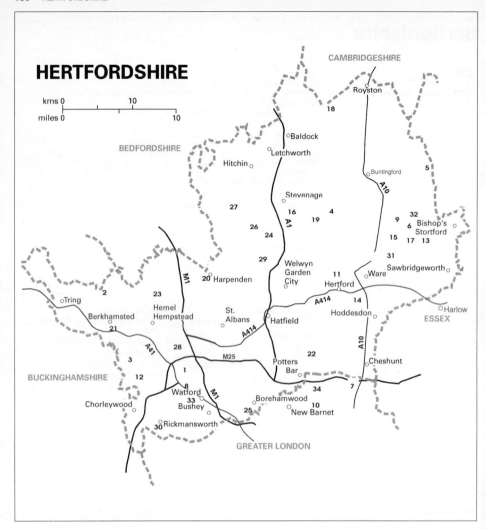

HERTFORDSHIRE

kms 0 ___ 10
miles 0 ___ 10

CAMBRIDGESHIRE

Royston
18

BEDFORDSHIRE

Baldock
Letchworth
Hitchin

Buntingford
5
A10

Stevenage
27   16   4
26   19
24   A1

32
9   6 Bishop's
Stortford
15   17 13

29   Welwyn
Garden
City
31
11   Sawbridgeworth
Ware
Hertford

20 Harpenden
M1
2   23

Tring
Berkhamsted
21
Hemel
Hempstead
St.
Albans
A414
Hatfield
A414   14
Hoddesdon
Harlow
ESSEX

A41
28   M25
3   1
12

Potters
Bar
22   A10
Cheshunt

BUCKINGHAMSHIRE

Chorleywood
Watford
33
Bushey
M1
8
34   7
Borehamwood
25   10
New Barnet

30 Rickmansworth

GREATER LONDON

DESCRIPTIONS OF GARDENS

❶ The Abbots House, 10 High Street, Abbots Langley 🔥🖌️✿
(Peter & Sue Tomson) *5m NW of Watford. Exit at J20 on M25. Take A4251 signposted Kings Langley. R at 1st roundabout (Home Park Industrial Estate). R at T-junction. Follow rd, under railway bridge and the yellow signs will become apparent. Free parking in village car park.* 1¾-acre garden with interesting trees, shrubs, mixed borders, sunken garden, pond, annual flower meadow, conservatory. Exotic garden. A garden of 'rooms' with different styles and moods. Many

half-hardy plants. Plants propagated from the garden. Home-made TEAS. *Adm £3 (share to Friends of St Lawrence Church). Suns 1 May; 3 July; 28 Aug (2-5). Private visits welcome by appt. Tel 01923 264946 peter.tomson@btinternet.com*

❷ Ashridge, Berkhamsted 🔥
(Ashridge (Bonar Law Memorial) Trust) *3m N of Berkhamsted.* Approx 200 acres. The pleasure gardens designed by Repton and modified by Wyatville. Rosary, Italian garden, skating pond, armorial garden, grotto. Avenues of trees from Victorian period with rhododendron walk. Cream TEAS.

Adm £3, chd £1.50, concessions £1.50. Sun 19 June (2-6)

❸ The Barn, Stoney Lane, Bovingdon 🖌️
(Richard Daynes) *3m SW of Hemel Hempstead. At lower end of Bovingdon High St turn into Church St, Bull PH on corner, car park 60yds on L, short walk to garden.* Recently established medium-sized garden around converted agricultural building in 16 acres. Garden divided into rooms; roses along with clematis, honeysuckle, topiary, water features and woodland. Wild flower meadow and pond being developed along with new small orchard and revised

planting. TEAS. *Adm £2.50, chd free (share to St Lawrence Church). Sun 7 Aug (2-6)*

④ ◆ Benington Lordship, nr Stevenage 🌿
(Mr & Mrs R R A Bott) *5m E of Stevenage. In Benington Village, signs off A602. Next to church.* 7-acre garden incl historic buildings, kitchen garden, lakes, roses. Spectacular borders, unspoilt panoramic views. Children's trail. Limited wheelchair access. Home-made TEAS in village hall at entrance on NGS days only. *Adm £3.50, chd free, wheelchair users free. Open daily (2-5) 27 June to 3 July, also spring & summer Bank Hols, Suns (2-5), Mons (12-5). By request all yr.* **For NGS:** *Sat, Sun 25, 26 June (12-6). Tel 01438 869228, Mrs Bott www.beningtonlordship.co.uk*

⑤ Brent Pelham Gardens
8 m NW of Bishops Stortford. On B1038 by the church and on E side of village. TEAS at Pelham House in aid of Isabel Hospice. Combined adm *£3.50, chd free. Suns 3 Apr; 8 May (1-5)*

Church Cottage 🚹🌿 (Mr & Mrs G D Clark) Semi-woodland garden with mature trees. Extensive planting around large natural pond, many unusual plants.

Pelham House 🚹🏠 (Mr & Mrs D K Haselgrove) 3½-acre informal garden on alkaline clay started by present owner in 1986. Plenty of interest to the plantsman. Wide variety of trees and shrubs especially birches and oaks. Bulb frames, raised beds with alpines and acid-loving plants and small formal area with ponds. Many daffodils and tulips.

⑥ Bromley Hall, Standon, Ware 🚹🌿🏠
Julian & Edwina Robarts) *6m W of Bishop's Stortford. On Standon to Much Hadham rd.* Mature 4½-acre garden surrounding C16 farmhouse not open). It is both an architectural and a plantsman's garden with an immaculate kitchen garden. On a windy site, good use has been made of walls and hedges to shelter borders filled with a mixture of shrubs, foliage plants and unusual and elegant perennials. Home-made TEAS in aid of St Elizabeth's Centre. *Adm £3.50, chd free. Sun 5 June (2-5.30)*

⑦ ◆ Capel Manor Gardens, Bullsmoor Lane, Enfield, Middlesex 🚹🏠
(Capel Manor Charitable Corporation) *2m from Cheshunt. 3 mins from M25 junction M25/A10.* 30 acres of historical and modern theme gardens, Japanese garden, large Italian style maze, rock and water features. Walled garden with rose collection and woodland walks. Also trial and demonstration gardens run by 'Gardening Which?' together with small model gardens designed to inspire and provide ideas. Light refreshments and TEAS. *Adm £5, chd £2, concessions £4. Open daily Mar to Oct (10-6, last entry 4.30).* **For NGS: Evening Opening** *£5, wine, Tue 21 June (6.30-9); Sun 30 Oct (10-6). Tel 020 8366 4442 www.capel.ac.uk*

Cheddington Gardens
See Buckinghamshire.

⑧ Chusan, 69 The Ridgeway, Watford 🌿🏠
(Marion Joel & Richard Baldwin) *2m NW of Watford Town Centre. A411 NW. 1 ½m R into Courtlands Dr, 2nd L or M25 clockwise J19, A411 Hempstead rd, 1st L into Courtlands Dr, 2nd L or M25 anticlockwise J20, A41 Watford, A411 Watford, then as above .* Exotic suburban garden. 90ft x 40ft. Mature architectural plants such as palms, bananas, tree ferns, bamboos and echiums. Water features, folly, driftwood and sculptures. **Evening Opening** *cheese and wine, Adm £2, chd free, Sat 6 Aug (7-10)*

Clavering Gardens
See Essex.

⑨ Cockhamsted, Braughing 🚹🌿🏠
(David & Jan Marques) *7m N of Ware. W of Bishops Stortford. 2m E of village towards Braughing Friars. 1st turn L in Friars Rd.* Lovely garden surrounded by open fields. 2 acres of informal planting. Alliums, grasses, tree paeonies, early roses. Island surrounded by C14 moat. Remote and romantic. Home-made TEAS in aid of Leukaemia Research. *Adm £3, chd free. Sun 22 May (2-6)*

⑩ 207 East Barnet Road, New Barnet 🌿🏠
(Margaret Arnold) *M25 J24 then A111 to Cockfosters. Underground stations High Barnet or Cockfosters. On bus route 184, 307 & 326.* Delightful example of minute courtyard garden 25ft x 30ft. High fences are covered with clematis,

honeysuckle and passion flowers, roses and vines scramble over an arch above a seat. Small pond with goldfish and water plants. Many interesting and unusual plants, mainly in pots. Home-made TEAS. *Adm £1.50, chd 50p. Sun 12 June (2-5). Private visits welcome by appt. Tel 020 8440 0377 magg1ee@hotmail.com*

⑪ 8 Gosselin Road, Bengeo, Hertford 🌿🏠
(Anne Godfrey) *N of Hertford on B158 signposted Bengeo. Follow up Port Hill & take 2nd R past White Lion PH.* 100ft x 30ft professional designer's garden featuring as many interesting and unusual plants, mainly herbaceous, as can be crammed in. Garden changes from week to week with interest all yr. *Adm £2, chd 50p. Suns 10 July; 4 Sept (12-5). Private visits welcome by appt for groups of 6+. Tel 01992 582401 www.daisyroots.com*

⑫ Great Sarratt Hall, Sarratt, Rickmansworth 🚹🌿🏠
(Mr H M Neal) *5m N of Rickmansworth. From Watford N via A41 (or M1 J5) to Kings Langley; left (W) to Sarratt; garden is 1st on R after village sign.* 4 acres. Herbaceous and mixed shrub borders; pond, moisture-loving plants and trees; walled kitchen garden; rhododendrons, magnolias, camellias; new planting of specialist conifers and rare trees. Home-made TEAS. *Adm £3.50, chd free. Sun 29 May (2-6)*

⑬ ◆ Hopleys, Much Hadham 🚹🌿🏠
(Mr Aubrey Barker) *5m W of Bishop's Stortford. On B1004. M11 (J8) 7m or A10 (Puckeridge) 5m via A120. 50yds N of Bull PH in centre of Much Hadham.* 3½ acres of constantly developing garden; trees, shrubs, herbaceous and alpines; island beds with mixed planting in parkland setting; pond recently refurbished. Home-made TEAS in aid of Isabel Hospice. *Adm £2, chd free. Open every Mon, Wed to Sun (9-5), Sun (2-5), Mar to Oct.* **For NGS:** *Sun 7 Aug (2-5). Tel 01279 842509 www.hopleys.co.uk*

⑭ Jenningsbury Gardens, Hertford Heath
1m SE of Hertford towards Hertford Heath. From A414 between A10 & Hertford take B1197, to Hertford Heath & Haileybury College, (Foxholes roundabout, Lancaster Mercedes garage) ½m on RH-side at post and rail fencing. A pair of

contrasting gardens surrounding C17 house and converted barn. Home-made TEAS at Jenningsbury in aid of Isabel Hospice, Welwyn Garden City. *Combined adm £3.50, chd free. Sun 12 June (2-6)*

Far End Barn, 4 Jenningsbury Court 🚻✿ (Mr & Mrs Richard Conyers) Colourful family garden running down to the moat.

Jenningsbury 🚻✿⊕ (Mr & Mrs Barry Fox) Listed, partly-moated farm house (not open) with wild flower meadows designed by Julie Toll. Ponds and borders created to attract wildlife. More formal garden surrounds the house. About 3 acres.

⑮ Kettle Green Gardens, Kettle Green, Much Hadham
¾m W of Much Hadham. Two contrasting gardens, one traditional and one modern. Home-made TEAS at Moat Farm House in aid of Isabel Hospice. *Combined adm £3, chd free. Sun 29 May (2-5)*

Kettle Barn (Mr & Mrs John Wiseman) Unusual courtyard garden designed and planted by the artist owner. Pond, spectacular architectural plants, trees and sculptures by Bernard Sindall.

Moat Farm House, Kettle Green 🚻✿⊕ (Mr & Mrs Hedley Newton) C17 moated farmhouse (not open) on island with ancient mulberry tree, mixed borders and orchard. Approx 1 acre.

⑯ ◆ Knebworth House Gardens, Knebworth 🚻✿⊕
(The Hon Henry Lytton Cobbold) 28m N of London. Direct access from A1(M) J7 at Stevenage. Station & bus stop: Stevenage 3m. Historic home of Bulwer Lytton, Victorian

novelist and statesman. Knebworth's magnificent gardens were laid out by Lutyens in 1910. Lutyens' pollarded lime avenues, Gertrude Jekyll's herb garden, the newly restored maze, yew hedges, roses and herbaceous borders are key features of the formal gardens with peaceful woodland walks beyond. Gold garden, green garden, brick garden, walled vegetable and herb garden. Light refreshments and TEAS. *Adm £3, chd £2, concessions £2.* **For NGS:** *Mon 5 Sept (11-4.30). Tel 01438 812661 www.knebworthhouse.com*

⑰ Moor Place, Much Hadham 🚻✿⊕
(Mr & Mrs B M Norman) 5m W of Bishop's Stortford. Entrance either at war memorial or at Hadham Cross. 2 C18 walled gardens. Herbaceous borders. Large area of shrubbery, lawns, hedges and trees. 2 ponds. Approx 10 acres. Home-made TEAS. *Adm £3.50, chd free. Sun 12 June (2-5.30)*

⑱ Odsey Park, Ashwell 🚻✿⊕
(Mr & The Hon Mrs Jeremy Fordham) 4½m E of Baldock. On A505 equidistant from Royston & Baldock. Enter by Lodge on the N carriageway of A505 (going towards Royston), over cattle grid, follow signs to parking area. A505 is fast rd so take care when both entering and leaving. Sign on N carriageway 350yds before Lodge indicating Odsey Park. Re-modelled 4-acre Victorian garden. Lawns, walled garden, good roses, parterre, herbaceous and shrub borders, iris garden and yew walks. New parkland landscaping. TEAS in aid of Ashwell Church. *Adm £3, chd under 10 free. Sun 29 May (2-5.30)*

⑲ The Old Walled Gardens of Aston House, Aston, Nr Stevenage
4m E of Stevenage. From A1 take J7, follow A602 towards Ware, turn L to Aston (signed) opp Van Hage garden centre, bear L after golf club. 2 gardens inside and outside an old C18 wall. Cream TEAS at 16 Yeomans Dr. *Combined adm £2.50, chd under 12 free (share to St Mary's Church, Aston). Sun 17 July (12-6.30)*

14 Yeomans Drive 🚻✿⊕ (Mr John Catherall) Part of walled garden with borders, vegetables, soft and tree fruits.

16 Yeomans Drive 🚻✿⊕ (Mrs Rosemary Stille) Many interesting trees and shrubs, mixed borders, pond and water gardens.

⑳ 20 Park Avenue South, Harpenden ✿⊕
(Miss Isobel M Leek) 6m N of St Albans. Off A1081 turn W by The Cock Inn & War Memorial up Rothamsted Ave; 3rd on L. ½-acre plantsman's garden with trees, shrub and herbaceous borders, gravel beds, topiary animals, pond and bog garden, all planted for yr-long interest and colour; aviary, conservatory. 1st prize Harpenden in Bloom Competition 2004. TEAS. *Adm £2.50, chd free. Suns 1 May; 17 July (2-5)*

㉑ Patchwork, 22 Hall Park Gate, Berkhamsted ⊕
(Jean & Peter Block) 3m W of Hemel Hempstead. Entering E side of Berkhamsted on A4251, turn L 200yds after 40mph sign. ¼-acre garden with lots of yr-round colour, interest and perfume; a riot of colour on opening days. Sloping site with rockeries, two small ponds, patios, shrubs and trees, spring bulbs, herbaceous border, roses, bedding, fuchsias, sweet peas, dahlias, patio pots and tubs galore and hanging baskets. Featured in 'Woman's Weekly' 2004. TEAS in aid of Berkhamsted Lions Club Charitable Trust. *Adm £2, chd free. Suns 1 May; 14 Aug (2-5). Private visits welcome by appt Mar to Oct incl. Tel 01442 864731*

㉒ Queenswood School, Shepherds Way, Brookmans Park, Hatfield 🚻✿
From S: M25 J24 signposted Potters Bar. In ½m at lights turn R onto A1000 signposted Hatfield. In 2m turn R onto B157. School is ½m on R. From N: A1000 from Hatfield. In 5m turn L onto B157. 120 acres of informal gardens and woodlands.

"Kenneth is a bit of a perfectionist when it comes to lawncare!"

Rhododendrons, fine specimen trees, shrubs and herbaceous borders. Glasshouses. Fine views to Chiltern Hills. Picnic area. Light refreshments and TEAS. *Adm £2.50, chd £1.50, concessions £1. Sun, Mon 29, 30 May (11-6)*

㉓ Ragged Hall, Gaddesden Row, nr Hemel Hempstead ♿✂☺
(Mr & Mrs Anthony Vincent) *4m N of Hemel Hempstead. Take A4146 to Water End. Turn R up hill for 2m, turn R at T-junction. House is 3rd L, ½m.* Garden of 1½ acres. Some new landscaping and new late summer border. Mixed borders. Some unusual plants. Pond garden and cutting garden. Potager with vegetables and flowers. Brass band will play throughout afternoon. Home-made TEAS. *Adm £3. Sun 26 June (2-5.30)*

㉔ Rustling End Cottage, Rustling End ✂☺
(Julie & Tim Wise) *1m N of Codicote. From B656 turn L into '3 Houses Lane' then R to Rustling End. House is 2nd on L.* Attractive early C18 cottage (not open) surrounded by fields and woodland. ½-acre plantswoman's garden, continually evolving. Planting incl sunny gravel garden, N-facing shady borders. Wildlife pond with bog planting, late flowering deep herbaceous borders and small kitchen garden. *Adm £2.50, chd 50p. Wed 1 June; Sun 31 July (12-6).* **Evening Opening** *£2.50, wine, Fri 5 Aug (6-9). Tel 01438 821509 www.rustlingend.com*

㉕ St Mary's Croft, Fortune Lane, Elstree ♿☺
(Hilde & Lionel Wainstein) *2m SW of Borehamwood. Off A411 Barnet Lane. Leave M25 at J23, then take A1 London. R at first roundabout, L at next roundabout into Barnet Lane, Fortune Lane is on L in Elstree Village. Careful parking on Barnet Lane and in Fortune Lane (L only).* 1-acre designer/plantswoman's garden, continually being developed. Modern grass and perennial plantings, wildflower meadow, large wildlife pond, bog garden, herb garden, rock garden, woodland, summerhouse. Many unusual plants for sale, most propagated from garden. Light refreshments and TEAS served in large conservatory. *Adm £2.50, chd £1 (share to Abbeyfield Camden Ltd (sheltered housing charity)). Sun 5 June (11-6).* **Evening Opening** *£2.50, wine, Thur 16 June '6-9.30). Private visits welcome by appt. Tel 020 8953 3022 ildewainstein@aol.com*

㉖ St Paul's Walden Bury, Hitchin ♿
(Mr & Mrs Simon Bowes Lyon) *5m S of Hitchin. On B651; ½m N of Whitwell.* Childhood home of The Queen Mother. Formal woodland garden listed Grade 1. Laid out about 1730, influenced by French tastes. Long rides and avenues span about 40 acres, leading to temples, statues, lake and ponds. Also more recent flower gardens and woodland garden with rhododendrons, azaleas and magnolias. Sun 5 June opening followed by a Lakeside Concert. TEAS 17 Apr, 8 May only in aid of St Paul's Walden Church. *Adm £3.50, chd 50p, concessions £2. Suns 17 Apr; 8 May (2-7); 5 June (12-3.30, followed by lakeside concert). Private visits welcome by appt. Tel 01438 871218 spw@boweslyon.demon. co.uk*

㉗ 4 School Cottages, Ley Green ✂☺
(Mrs Barbara Millard) *4m SW of Hitchin. Take A505 from Hitchin to Luton. Turn off to Great Offley. In Great Offley take 1st L signposted Kings Walden. After 1¼m follow 'Garden Open' signs.* Country setting for a ¾-acre plantswoman's garden on sloping site planted for yr-round interest. Trees, shrubs, perennials, bog gardens, 2 ponds, rockery, raised vegetable beds, 2 pergolas with climbers. Home-made TEAS Sun only. *Adm £2.50, chd 50p. Sun 10 July (2-6).* **Evening Opening** *£2.50, wine, Fri 8 July (6-9)*

㉘ Serge Hill Gardens
½m E of Bedmond. Past White Hart PH, in Bedmond, then ½m on, down Serge Hill Lane. Home-made TEAS at Serge Hill. Combined adm £4, chd £1, concessions £2. Sun 19 June (2-5)
 The Barn (Tom Stuart-Smith & family) 1-acre garden. Small sheltered courtyard planted with unusual shrubs and perennials, contrasts with more open garden with views over wild flower meadow.
 Serge Hill ✂ (Sir Murray & Lady Stuart-Smith) Regency house (not open) in parkland setting with fine kitchen garden of ½ acre. A range of unusual wall plants, mixed border of 100yds.

㉙ ◆ Shaw's Corner, Ayot St Lawrence ♿✂☺
(The National Trust) *2m NE of Wheathampstead. At SW end of village, approx 2m from B653 (A1 J4 - M1 J10). Signposted from B653 (Shaw's Corner/The Ayots).* Approx 4 acres with richly planted borders,

orchard, small meadow, wooded areas and views over the Hertfordshire countryside. Historical garden, belonging to George Bernard Shaw from 1906 until his death in 1950. Hidden among the trees is the revolving summerhouse where Shaw retreated to write. *House and Garden Adm £4, chd £2. 19 Mar to 30 Oct Weds to Suns incl & Bank Hols Mons (12-5.30).* **For NGS: Evening Opening** *£3.50, chd £1.50, wine, Sat 11 June (6-9). Tel 01438 820307 shawscorner@nationaltrust.org.uk*

㉚ Stresa, 126 The Drive, Rickmansworth ✂☺
(Roger & Patt Trigg) *1m NW of Rickmansworth. From M25 junction 18 take A404 towards Rickmansworth for 200yds, turn R into The Clump, then 1st L into The Drive. From Rickmansworth take A404 toward Amersham for approx ½m, L into Valley Road, 1st L into The Drive.* Approx ½ acre, herbaceous perennials and shrubs, particularly hostas and shade loving plants; euphorbias, rhododendrons, phlox, heucheras; conservatory. Recently re-designed front garden with gravel beds and renewed grasses bed. Home-made TEAS. *Adm £2, chd free. Sun 24 July (2-5.30). Private visits welcome by appt May to early Sept for groups of 10 to 20. Tel 01923 774293 roger.trigg@tiscali.co.uk*

㉛ Thundridge Hill House, Cold Christmas Lane, Ware ♿☺
(Mr & Mrs Christopher Melluish) *2m NE of Ware. ¾m from The Sow & Pigs PH off the A10 down Cold Christmas Lane, (crossing new bypass).* Well-established garden of approx 2½ acres; good variety of plants, shrubs and roses. Fine views down to the Rib Valley. Cream TEAS in aid of St Marys Church, Thundridge. *Adm £3, chd free. Sun 19 June (2-5.30). Private visits welcome by appt, coaches permitted. Tel 01920 462500 c.melluish@btopenworld.com*

㉜ NEW Tudor Cottage, Upwick Green, Nr Albury ♿✂☺
(Delphine Hill) *4m W of Bishops Stortford. A120 to Little Hadham T-lights. Turn N signposted Albury and The Pelhams. After 1m turn R to Upwick Green. Tudor Cottage is 1st house on R after approx ½m.* Listed Tudor cottage (not open) sited in approx 1½-acre garden which was started from scratch by owner who is professional garden designer. Extensive views, natural and formal water features, mixed borders,

herbaceous and secret garden. Planted for all-yr-round interest. Plant stalls and sculpture display. Home-made TEAS in aid of Isabel Hospice. *Adm £3, chd free. Sun 3 July (2-6)*

③ Waterdell House, Little Green Lane, Croxley Green 🅑🍴🎪 (Mr & Mrs Peter Ward) *1½m NE of Rickmansworth. M25, J18, direction Rickmansworth to join A412 towards Watford. From A412 turn L signed Sarratt, along Croxley Green, fork R past Coach & Horses, cross Baldwins Lane into Little Green Lane, then L at top. 1½-acre walled garden systematically developed over 50yrs by present owner/gardener: mature and young trees, topiary holly*

hedge, herbaceous borders, modern island beds of shrubs, old-fashioned roses, pelargoniums, grasses and pond gardens. Spring visits also recommended. Cream TEAS in aid of Macmillan Cancer Relief 26 June only. *Adm £3, chd free, concessions £2. Sun 26 June (2-5.30). Private visits welcome by appt. Tel 01923 772775*

④ West Lodge Park, Cockfosters Road, Hadley Wood 🅑🍴🎪 NCCPG (Beales Hotels) *2m S of Potters Bar. On A111. J24 from M25 signed Cockfosters.* 10-acre Beale Arboretum consists of over 700 varieties of trees and shrubs, incl National Collections of *Elaeagnus* and hornbeam cultivars, with a good

selection of conifers, oaks, maples and mountain ash. A network of paths has been laid out, and most specimens are labelled. Light refreshments and TEAS. *Adm £2.50, chd free. Suns 15 May (2-5); 16 Oct (1-4)*

Evening Opening (See also garden description)

Shaw's Corner	11 June
St Mary's Croft	16 June
Capel Manor Gardens	
	21 June
4 School Cottages	8 July
Rustling End Cottage	
	5 August
Chusan	6 August

---

ngs **The Yellow Book 2006** £7.99 *including UK p&p*

gardens open for charity

Available through **www.ngs.org.uk** or by enquiry to the NGS.
T +44 (0)1483 211535 **F** +44 (0)1483 211537 **E**mail ngs@ngs.org.uk
Cheques should be in £ sterling, made payable to The National Gardens Scheme and sent to:

The National Gardens Scheme, Hatchlands Park, East Clandon, Guildford, Surrey GU4 7RT

The book will be posted on publication (Feb/Mar 2006)

Marie Curie Cancer Care

Research has shown that 75% of people seriously ill with cancer would like to be cared for at home. Every year, Marie Curie Nurses make that wish possible for thousands of cancer patients in cities, towns and villages across the UK. Marie Curie Nurses provide expert hands-on care, as well as comfort and emotional support to the family.

"You were all wonderful. You gave him three special days when he was able to go out into the garden to enjoy the sun and air." Jan

Thanks to supporters such as The National Gardens Scheme, our care is always free of charge.

Find out more at **www.mariecurie.org.uk**

Charity Reg. No. 207994

Marie Curie Cancer Care
Devoted to Life

ngs gardens open for charity

Every time you visit a garden which opens for the NGS you are helping to raise money for:

- Macmillan Cancer Relief
- Marie Curie Cancer Care
- Help the Hospices
- Crossroads – Caring for Carers
- The Queen's Nursing Institute
- The Nurses Welfare Service
- The Royal Gardeners' Orphan Fund
- NGS Gardeners' Bursaries – The National Trust Careership Scheme
- Perennial – Gardeners' Royal Benevolent Society
- County Nursing Associations

Additional charities nominated by owners

THE QUEEN'S NURSING INSTITUTE

George is 76. His leg ulcer was making life misery and he feared that one more would incapacitate him. Then, his local district nurse developed a programme of education and exercise, which has helped George's ulcer heal quickly and should prevent him from getting another. It was the Queen's Nursing Institute, which provided the funding for this work, through its Innovation and Creative Practice Award.

Each year throughout England, Wales and Northern Ireland, similar projects, developed and led by community nurses, are transforming the lives of thousands of people like George. Many of them focus on the needs of elderly people. Others are helping new mums with their babies, young people with learning difficulties and teenagers coping with the pressures of modern life.

The award scheme, which is open to school nurses, district nurses, practice nurses, midwives, health visitors and community psychiatric nurses is supported by the generosity of The National Garden Scheme.

For more information contact the QNI
Tel: 020 7490 4227   Website: www.qni.org.uk

Isle of Wight

County Organiser: Mrs Bunny Cove, The Old Rectory, St James Street, Yarmouth, Isle of Wight PO41 0NU Tel 01983 760555

Assistant County Organisers: Mrs R Hillyard, The Coach House, Duver Road, St Helens, Ryde, Isle of Wight PO33 1XY Tel 01983 875163

Mrs M Peplow, Dog Kennel Cottage, Broad Lane, Thorley, Isle of Wight PO41 0UH Tel 01983 756712

Mrs K Wolley Dod, Bakers Farmhouse, Gate Lane, Freshwater Bay, Isle of Wight PO40 9QD Tel 01983 752040

County Treasurer: Mr Peter Cove, The Old Rectory, St. James Street, Yarmouth, Isle of Wight PO41 0NU Tel 01983 760555

Maps: Numbers shown next to each garden entry refer to that garden's entry on the county map. This position is approximate; distance and directions from the nearest main town are generally shown in the garden text.

A precise location is available for those gardens featured on the NGS website by visiting www.ngs.org.uk.

Symbols: Information relating to symbols is given on page 21

DATES OF OPENING

Evening openings
See end of county listing

Gardens open to the public
For details see garden description
Afton Park, Freshwater *(1)*
Mottistone Manor Garden, Mottistone *(12)*

By appointment only
For telephone number and other details see garden description.
Private visits welcomed
Highwood, Cranmore *(10)*

March 27 Sunday (Easter)
Kings Manor, Freshwater *(11)*

April 24 Sunday
Badminton, Clatterford Shute *(3)*

May 1 Sunday
Northcourt Gardens, Shorwell *(13)*

May 29 Sunday
Afton Park, Freshwater *(1)*

June 5 Sunday
Nunwell House, Brading *(14)*

June 9 Thursday
Pitt House, Bembridge *(15)*

June 11 Saturday
Hamstead Grange, Yarmouth **(Evening)** *(9)*

June 12 Sunday
Clatterford House, Clatterford Shute *(6)*

June 19 Sunday
Thorley Manor, Yarmouth *(16)*

June 26 Sunday
The Barn, Shorwell *(4)*

July 2 Saturday
Ashknowle House, Whitwell *(2)*

July 3 Sunday
Ashknowle House, Whitwell *(2)*

July 7 Thursday
Mottistone Manor Garden, Mottistone *(12)*
Pitt House, Bembridge *(15)*

July 10 Sunday
Brighstone Village Gardens *(5)*

August 11 Thursday
Pitt House, Bembridge *(15)*

August 14 Sunday
Crab Cottage, Shalfleet *(7)*

August 21 Sunday
4 Greenway, Binstead *(8)*

DESCRIPTIONS OF GARDENS

❶ ◆ Afton Park, Freshwater

(Mr & Mrs C Barnes) *On B3399 Newport to Freshwater rd. Nr junction of A3055 close to Freshwater Bay.* Developing garden set in a 6-acre apple orchard with lovely views to Tennyson and East Afton Downs. Cottage garden, coastal seaside garden, large gravel garden celebrating drought-resistant planting. Summer garden with large drifts of grasses and perennials in a naturalistic style. Meadow walk with access on to Tennyson trail. Living willow story house with children's trail. Light refreshments and TEAS from local produce. *Adm £1.50, chd free.* **For NGS:** *Sun 29 May (10.30-4.30). Tel 01983 755774 www.aftonpark.co.uk*

❷ Ashknowle House, Whitwell

(Mr & Mrs K Fradgley) *4m W of Ventnor. From Ventnor rd turn for Ashknowle Lane next to Old Rectory. Lane is unmarked & unmade. Car parking in village but field parking available, except when wet.* 3 acres. Mature but developing garden with trees, shrubs and lawned areas. 2 ponds and small cascade. Of special interest is the fruit and vegetable garden with tunnels, glasshouses and cages. Raised beds in cropping area a particular feature.

Recent addition is an area of young woodland and newly-planted trees. TEAS. *Adm £2.50, chd free. Sat, Sun 2, 3 July (2-5).*

❸ Badminton, Clatterford Shute

(Mr & Mrs G S Montrose) *1½m SW of Newport. Free parking in Carisbrooke Castle car park. Public footpath to Millers Lane in corner of car park leads down to garden, approx 200yds. Parking for disabled can be arranged; please telephone prior to opening.* ¾-acre garden with natural chalk stream. Mixed borders planted by owners during last 25yrs for all-yr interest. Kitchen garden. Lovely views. Continuing development of parts of garden. Home-made TEAS. *Adm £2.50, chd 50p. Sun 24 Apr (2-5). Tel 01983 526143*

❹ The Barn, Dungewood Lane, Shorwell

(Mr & Mrs Mount) *Approx 1½m from Shorwell village. From Shorwell turn into Farriers Way at the mini-roundabout. 2nd R at the forge into Corve Hill. At top, L into Park Lane, signed Chale and Atherfield Green. Dungewood Lane 1st L, The Barn entrance immed L.* Developing garden on 3½-acre site exposed to salt-laden winds compensated by superb views of the surrounding countryside. Gardened for all-yr interest by plantaholic whose plant associations may challenge received wisdom. Herbaceous borders with interesting and unusual plants; fruit and vegetables; greenhouse; pond; field full of butterflies and bees. Some wheelchair access. TEAS. *Adm £2.50, chd free. Sun 26 June (2-5). Private visits welcome by appt, group visits welcome. Tel 01983 551322*

ISLE OF WIGHT

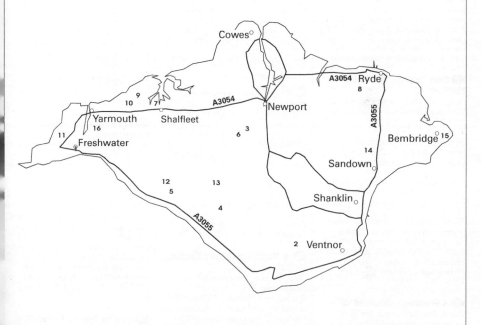

```
kms 0        10
miles 0              10
```

Cowes
A3054 Ryde
       8
A3054   Newport
Yarmouth Shalfleet
16   6 3   A3055
11   Bembridge 15
Freshwater   14
                    Sandown
        12   13
        5   Shanklin
            4
     A3055
            2 Ventnor

5 NEW **Brighstone Village Gardens**

7m from both Newport and Freshwater. B3399 from Newport or turn off Military Rd at Grange Farm, signed to Brighstone. Attractive large village with interesting church. Tickets available at both village shops, The Elms and Yultide. Village map given to visitors. Picnic in some gardens. Home-made TEAS at the Brighstone Scout Hut in aid of Brighstone Sea Scouts. *Combined adm £3, chd free. Sun 10 July (12-5)*

NEW **The Elms** ♿✖ (David & Alison Harding) An attempt to grow everything in a small garden: vegetables, fruit, flowers, topiary and greenhouse. Some wheelchair access.

NEW **Greens Butt** ✖ (Mag Ratcliffe) One woman's garden - developed over 18yrs from a wilderness of weeds.

NEW **Kiplings** ✖ (Margaret & David Williamson) Gently sloping small garden planted for all-yr interest, with mixed borders, pond, rockery, vegetable patch and unusual double-skinned greenhouse.

NEW **Little Shate** ♿✖ (David & Julia Cooper) Terraced stream-side garden, planted over the last 7yrs with a wide variety of flowering trees, shrubs and perennials, with spring bulbs and summer annuals for extra colour. Some wheelchair access.

NEW **Medavale** ♿✖ (George & Joyce Trickett) Flowers, fruit and vegetables expertly grown with a lifetime's experience. Some wheelchair access.

NEW **Miller's Cottage** ✖ (Jean Renouf) Difficult sloping site on builder's spoil and clay planted in tiers with shrubs, grasses and perennials for easy maintenance.

NEW **The Old Rectory** ✖ (John & Jillo Waddington-Ball) Atmospheric old rectory garden under sensitive ongoing restoration. Some wheelchair access.

NEW **Yultide** ✖ (Joan & Rob Snow) Home of the gnome and the Brighstone bean! The Good Life garden.

⑥ Clatterford House, Clatterford Shute 🚻♿⌂
(Sylvia Clare & David Hughes) 1½m SW of Newport. Public footpath from Carisbrooke Castle car park or 20ft from Clatterford Rd. Park at Castle or in Clatterford Rd. Developing garden, reclaimed in 2000 from derelict and overgrown property. Design and layout have mystical or healing significance, fully organically managed. Fantastic views enhance the naturalistic planting. Residential courses and accommodation available. Home-made TEAS in aid of Watchbell Natural Therapies Trust. Adm £2.50, chd 50p. Sun 12 June (2-5). Private visits welcome by appt. Tel 01983 537338 www.claritybooks.co.uk

⑦ Crab Cottage, Mill Road, Shalfleet 🚻⌂
(Mr & Mrs Peter Scott) 3½m E of Yarmouth. Turn past New Inn into Mill Rd. Please park before going through NT gates. Entrance is first on L. Less than 5 mins walk. Just over 1 acre on gravelly soil, exposed to Westerlies. Walled garden; croquet lawn with fine views over Newtown Creek and Solent. Meandering path through wild flower meadow leading to waterlily pond and semi-tropical planting. New borders, maturing shrub borders and exotic flowering shrubs and trees. Newly planted South garden. Home-made TEAS in aid of Shalfleet Church. Adm £2.50, chd free. Sun 14 Aug (2-5.30). Private visits welcome by appt. Tel 01983 531319

⑧ 4 Greenway, Binstead ♿⌂
(Mr & Mrs G Riddell) 2m W of Ryde. From the A3054 turn into Newnham Rd at the top of Binstead Hill. Take 1st L into Kings Rd, 1st R into Parkway, 1st R into The Mall and 1st L into Greenway. Award-winning small garden developed over 26yrs and still evolving. Huge variety of plants gives all-yr colour and interest. A riot of colour during summer. Incl pergolas, water features and several places to sit and enjoy the garden. Home-made TEAS in aid of local cancer charities. Adm £2, chd free. Sun 21 Aug (11-5). Private visits welcome by appt for groups of 10+, 1 June to 31 Aug. Tel 01983 565406

⑨ Hamstead Grange, Yarmouth 🚻⌂
(Mr & Mrs Tom Young) 3m E of Yarmouth. Entrance to 1½m private drive on A3054. 3 acres with rose garden, shrubs, lawns, trees and water garden. Superb views of Solent.
Evening Opening £5, wine, Sat 11 June (6-8)

⑩ Highwood, Cranmore ♿⌂
(Mr & Mrs Cooper) 2m E of Yarmouth on A3054. 2m from Yarmouth, turning on A3054, opp bus shelter, unmade rd. Garden for all seasons and plant enthusiasts. Pond, woodland area with hellebores, borders and island beds. Adm £2.50, chd free. Private visits welcome by appt for groups of 10+. Tel 01983 760550

⑪ Kings Manor, Freshwater 🚻♿⌂
(Mr & Mrs Jamie Sheldon) 1m NE of Yarmouth. E out of Yarmouth over R Yar bridge. Approx 1m turn L at top of Pixleys Hill. Entrance on L at top of next hill. 3-acre informal garden with shrubs and spring bulbs. Frontage onto marshes. Special features incl views of estuary and saltings, formal garden around lily pond. Maturing arboretum. TEAS. Adm £2.50, chd free (share to Fortune Centre of Riding Therapy). Easter Sun 27 Mar (2.30-5)

⑫ ♦ Mottistone Manor Garden, Mottistone 🚻⌂
(The National Trust) 8m SW Newport on B3399 between Brighstone & Brook. Medium-sized formal terraced garden, backing onto Mediaeval and Elizabethan manor house, set in wooded valley with fine views of English Channel. Light refreshments and TEAS. Adm £3, chd £1.50, family £7.50. 20 Mar to 30 Oct. **For NGS:** Thu 7 July (11-5.30). Guided walks at 11.30 & 2.30. Tel 01983 714302

⑬ Northcourt Gardens, Shorwell 🚻⌂
(Mrs C D Harrison, Mr & Mrs J Harrison) 4m SW of Newport. On entering Shorwell from Carisbrooke, entrance on R, immed after rustic footbridge. 15 acres incl bathhouse,

walled kitchen garden, stream. Terraced Mediterranean and sunken subtropical garden. Many shrubs and tender plants. Jacobean manor house (part open). Quattr-Archi string quartet will be playing in the garden. Accommodation. TEAS in aid of Brighstone Sea Scouts. Adm £2.50, chd 20p. Sun 1 May (2-5)

⑭ Nunwell House, Coach Lane, Brading ♿⌂
(Colonel & Mrs J A Aylmer) 3m S of Ryde. Signed off A3055 in Brading into Coach Lane. 5-acre, beautifully set formal and shrub gardens with exceptional views of Solent. 1-acre walled garden recently re-planned. House (not open) developed over 5 centuries, full of architectural interest. Coaches by appt only. Home-made TEAS in aid of Brading WI. Adm £2.50, chd free. Sun 5 June (2-5). Tel 01983 407240

⑮ Pitt House, Love Lane, Bembridge 🚻♿
(Mr L J Martin) Enter Bembridge village, pass museum & take 1st L into Love Lane. Continue down lane (5 min walk) as far as bend; Pitt House is on L. Enter tall wrought iron gates. By car enter Ducie Ave 1st L before museum. Pitt House at bottom on R. Parking in Ducie Ave. Approx 4 acres with varied aspects, sea views and points of interest. A number of sculptures dotted around garden; also Victorian greenhouse, mini waterfall and 4 ponds. Light refreshments and TEAS. Adm £2, chd 50p. Thurs 9 June; 7 July; 11 Aug (2-5)

⑯ Thorley Manor, Yarmouth ♿
(Mr & Mrs Anthony Blest) 1m E of Yarmouth. From Bouldnor take Wilmingham Lane. House ½m on L. 2 acres of restored informal gardens. Water garden. Ongoing project with much interest and mixed plantings. Garden divided by old walls. TEAS. Adm £2.50, chd free. Sun 19 June (2.30-5)

Evening Opening (See also garden description)

Hamstead Grange   11 June

---

ngs
gardens open for charity

More than £20 million has been donated to charity since the NGS began in 1927

Kent

County Organiser: Mrs Mervyn Streatfeild, Hoath House, Chiddingstone Hoath, Edenbridge, Kent TN8 7DB
Tel 01342 850362 email janestreatfeild@hoath-house.freeserve.co.uk

Assistant County Organisers: Mrs Edward Barham, Hole Park, Rolvenden, Cranbrook, Kent TN17 4JB
Tel 01580 241386 email clarebarham@holepark.com
Mrs Philip Boyce, 185 Borden Lane, Sittingbourne, Kent ME10 1DA
Tel 01795 472243 email philip.boyce1@btinternet.com

(Radio) Mrs Jeremy Gibbs, Edells Cottage, Mark Beech, Kent TN8 5PB Tel 01342 851063
Mrs Richard Latham, Stowting Hill House, Ashford, Kent TN25 6BE
Tel 01303 862881 email vjlatham@hotmail.com
Mrs Roddy Loder-Symonds, Denne Hill Farm, Womenswold, Canterbury, Kent CT4 6HD
Tel 01227 831203 email cloder_symonds@hotmail.com

(Press & Publicity Officer) Mrs Ingrid Morgan Hitchcock, 6 Brookhurst Gardens, Southborough, Tunbridge Wells, Kent
TN4 0NA Tel 01892 528341 email ingrid@morganhitchcock.co.uk
Miss Elspeth Napier, 53 High Street, East Malling, Kent ME19 6AJ
Tel 01732 522146 email elspeth.napier@virgin.net
Mrs Nicholas Ward, Hookwood House, Shipbourne, Kent TN11 9RJ
Tel 01732 810525 email felicity.l.b.ward@hookwood.demon.co.uk

County Treasurer: Mr Simon Toynbee, Old Tong Farm, Brenchley, Kent TN12 7HT
Tel 01892 723552 email toynbeea@aol.com

Maps: Numbers shown next to each garden entry refer to that garden's entry on the county map. This position is approximate; distance and directions from the nearest main town are generally shown in the garden text.
A precise location is available for those gardens featured on the NGS website by visiting www.ngs.org.uk.

Symbols: Information relating to symbols is given on page 21

DATES OF OPENING

Evening openings
See end of county listing

Private gardens open regularly for NGS
Kypp Cottage, Biddenden *(47)*
Old Buckhurst, Markbeech, nr Edenbridge *(68)*
Yew Tree Cottage, Penshurst *(119)*

Gardens open to the public
For details see garden description
Beech Court Gardens, Challock *(4)*
Belmont, Throwley, Faversham *(5)*
Broadview Gardens, Hadlow College, Hadlow *(12)*
Brogdale Horticultural Trust, Faversham *(13)*
Charts Edge, Westerham *(16)*
Chartwell, nr Westerham *(17)*
Cobham Hall, Cobham *(19)*
Doddington Place, nr Sittingbourne *(24)*
Edenbridge House, Edenbridge *(27)*
Emmetts Garden, Ide Hill *(28)*
Godinton House & Gardens, Ashford *(31)*
Goodnestone Park Gardens, Wingham *(33)*
Great Comp Garden, Platt *(35)*
Hever Castle & Gardens, nr Edenbridge *(39)*
Higham Park, Bridge *(40)*
Hole Park, Rolvenden, Cranbrook *(42)*
Iden Croft Herb Gardens, Staplehurst *(43)*
Ightham Mote, Ivy Hatch *(44)*
Knole, Sevenoaks *(45)*
Marle Place, Brenchley *(61)*
Mount Ephraim, Hernhill, Faversham *(64)*
Old Buckhurst, Markbeech, nr Edenbridge *(68)*

The Owl House, Lamberhurst *(75)*
Penshurst Place, Penshurst *(77)*
The Pines Garden, St Margaret's Bay *(78)*
Quex House Gardens, Birchington *(82)*
Riverhill House Gardens, Sevenoaks *(84)*
Scotney Castle, Lamberhurst *(90)*
Sissinghurst Garden, Sissinghurst *(92)*
Squerryes Court, Westerham *(101)*
The World Garden at Lullingstone Castle, Eynsford *(115)*
Yalding Organic Gardens, nr Maidstone *(118)*

By appointment only
For telephone number and other details see garden description. Private visits welcomed
April Cottage, Ospringe, Faversham *(2)*
Dolly's Garden, West Wickham *(25)*
Haydown, Great Buckland, Luddesdown *(38)*
Old Place Farm, High Halden *(70)*
Pedlinge Court, Saltwood *(76)*
South Hill Farm, Hastingleigh *(96)*
Southover, Hunton, Maidstone *(97)*
Troutbeck, Otford *(107)*

February 13 Sunday
190 Maidstone Road, Chatham *(60)*

February 24 Thursday
Broadview Gardens, Hadlow College, Hadlow *(12)*

March 3 Thursday
Yew Tree Cottage, Penshurst *(119)*

March 4 Friday
Yew Tree Cottage, Penshurst *(119)*

March 5 Saturday
Yew Tree Cottage, Penshurst *(119)*

March 6 Sunday
Great Comp Garden, Platt *(35)*

March 10 Thursday
Yew Tree Cottage, Penshurst *(119)*

March 11 Friday
Yew Tree Cottage, Penshurst *(119)*

March 12 Saturday
Sissinghurst Place, Sissinghurst *(93)*
Yew Tree Cottage, Penshurst *(119)*

March 13 Sunday
Copton Ash, Faversham *(20)*
Goodnestone Park Gardens, Wingham *(33)*
Great Comp Garden, Platt *(35)*
Sissinghurst Place, Sissinghurst *(93)*

March 17 Thursday
Yew Tree Cottage, Penshurst *(119)*

March 18 Friday
Yew Tree Cottage, Penshurst *(119)*

March 19 Saturday
Yew Tree Cottage, Penshurst *(119)*

March 20 Sunday
Godinton House & Gardens, Ashford *(31)*
Great Comp Garden, Platt *(35)*
The Owl House, Lamberhurst *(75)*
Stonewall Park, Chiddingstone Hoath *(102)*
Tram Hatch, Charing Heath *(106)*

March 24 Thursday
Yew Tree Cottage, Penshurst *(119)*

March 25 Friday (Easter)
Yew Tree Cottage, Penshurst *(119)*

March 26 Saturday (Easter)
Yew Tree Cottage, Penshurst *(119)*

March 27 Sunday (Easter)
Copton Ash, Faversham *(20)*
Great Comp Garden, Platt *(35)*
190 Maidstone Road, Chatham *(60)*
Mere House, Mereworth *(62)*
The Pines Garden, St Margaret's Bay *(78)*

March 28 Monday (Easter)
Copton Ash, Faversham *(20)*
Mere House, Mereworth *(62)*

March 31 Thursday
Yew Tree Cottage, Penshurst *(119)*

April 1 Friday
Yew Tree Cottage, Penshurst *(119)*

April 2 Saturday
Yew Tree Cottage, Penshurst *(119)*

April 3 Sunday
Cobham Hall, Cobham *(19)*
Godinton House & Gardens, Ashford *(31)*
Godmersham Park, Godmersham *(32)*
Higham Park, Bridge *(40)*
Lodge House, nr Ashford *(57)*
Spilsill Court, Staplehurst *(99)*

April 6 Wednesday
Lodge House, nr Ashford *(57)*

April 7 Thursday
Yew Tree Cottage, Penshurst *(119)*

April 8 Friday
Yew Tree Cottage, Penshurst *(119)*

April 9 Saturday
Sissinghurst Place, Sissinghurst *(93)*
Yew Tree Cottage, Penshurst *(119)*

April 10 Sunday
1 Brickwall Cottages, Frittenden *(11)*
Copton Ash, Faversham *(20)*
Hall Place, Leigh *(37)*
Little Sissinghurst, St Mary's Bay *(54)*
Sissinghurst Place, Sissinghurst *(93)*
Sotts Hole Cottage, Borough Green *(95)*

April 14 Thursday
Yew Tree Cottage, Penshurst *(119)*

April 15 Friday
Yew Tree Cottage, Penshurst *(119)*

April 16 Saturday
Yew Tree Cottage, Penshurst *(119)*

April 17 Sunday
Edenbridge House, Edenbridge *(27)*
Hole Park, Rolvenden, Cranbrook *(42)*
Longacre, Selling *(58)*
Marle Place, Brenchley *(61)*
Withersdane Hall, Wye *(113)*

April 18 Monday
Sissinghurst Garden, Sissinghurst *(92)*

April 21 Thursday
Riverhill House Gardens, Sevenoaks *(84)*
Yew Tree Cottage, Penshurst *(119)*

April 22 Friday
Yew Tree Cottage, Penshurst *(119)*

April 23 Saturday
Yew Tree Cottage, Penshurst *(119)*

April 24 Sunday
Bradbourne House and Gardens, East Malling *(9)*
Brogdale Horticultural Trust, Faversham *(13)*
Copton Ash, Faversham *(20)*

Mount Ephraim, Hernhill, Faversham *(64)*
Old Orchard, Loose, Maidstone *(69)*

April 28 Thursday
Yew Tree Cottage, Penshurst *(119)*

April 29 Friday
Yew Tree Cottage, Penshurst *(119)*

April 30 Saturday
Old Buckhurst, Markbeech, nr Edenbridge *(68)*
Yew Tree Cottage, Penshurst *(119)*

May 1 Sunday
Longacre, Selling *(58)*
Old Buckhurst, Markbeech, nr Edenbridge *(68)*
St Michael's Gardens, East Peckham *(88)*
Stonewall Park, Chiddingstone Hoath *(102)*

May 2 Monday (Bank Hol)
Copton Ash, Faversham *(20)*
Longacre, Selling *(58)*

May 4 Wednesday
Knole, Sevenoaks *(45)*
Old Buckhurst, Markbeech, nr Edenbridge *(68)*

May 5 Thursday
Yew Tree Cottage, Penshurst *(119)*

May 6 Friday
Yew Tree Cottage, Penshurst *(119)*

May 7 Saturday
Yew Tree Cottage, Penshurst *(119)*

May 8 Sunday
1 Brickwall Cottages, Frittenden *(11)*
Edenbridge House, Edenbridge *(27)*
Flint Cottage, Bishopsbourne *(30)*
Hole Park, Rolvenden, Cranbrook *(42)*
Ladham House, Goudhurst *(48)*
Luton House, Selling *(59)*
Old Buckhurst, Markbeech, nr Edenbridge *(68)*
Old Orchard, Loose, Maidstone *(69)*
Torry Hill, Frinsted *(105)*

May 11 Wednesday
Edenbridge House, Edenbridge *(27)*
The Spinney, Sevenoaks *(100)*

May 12 Thursday
Yew Tree Cottage, Penshurst *(119)*

May 13 Friday
Yew Tree Cottage, Penshurst *(119)*

May 14 Saturday
Emmetts Garden, Ide Hill *(28)*
Old Buckhurst, Markbeech, nr Edenbridge *(68)*
Scotney Castle, Lamberhurst *(90)*
Yew Tree Cottage, Penshurst *(119)*

May 15 Sunday
Battel Hall, Leeds, Maidstone *(3)*
Bilting House, nr Ashford *(6)*
Charts Edge, Westerham *(16)*
Flint Cottage, Bishopsbourne *(30)*
Longacre, Selling *(58)*
Marle Place, Brenchley *(61)*
Old Buckhurst, Markbeech, nr Edenbridge *(68)*
Puxted House, Brenchley *(81)*
Sandling Park, Hythe *(89)*
Sea Close, Hythe *(91)*
The Spinney, Sevenoaks *(100)*

May 18 Wednesday
Penshurst Place, Penshurst *(77)*
Rock Farm, Nettlestead *(85)*
Waystrode Manor, Cowden *(109)*

May 19 Thursday
Kypp Cottage, Biddenden *(47)*
Riverhill House Gardens, Sevenoaks *(84)*
Yew Tree Cottage, Penshurst *(119)*

May 20 Friday
Kypp Cottage, Biddenden *(47)*
Yew Tree Cottage, Penshurst *(119)*

May 21 Saturday
Burrswood, Groombridge *(14)*
Kypp Cottage, Biddenden *(47)*
Placketts Hole, Bicknor, nr Sittingbourne **(Evening)** *(79)*
Rock Farm, Nettlestead *(85)*
Yew Tree Cottage, Penshurst *(119)*

May 22 Sunday
Beech Court Gardens, Challock *(4)*
Hole Park, Rolvenden, Cranbrook *(42)*
Kypp Cottage, Biddenden *(47)*
Larch Cottage, Doddington *(49)*
Mounts Court Farmhouse, Acrise, nr Folkestone *(65)*
Old Orchard, Loose, Maidstone *(69)*
Rogers Rough, Kilndown *(86)*
St Michael's Gardens, East Peckham *(88)*
Waystrode Manor, Cowden *(109)*

May 26 Thursday
Yew Tree Cottage, Penshurst *(119)*

May 27 Friday
Iden Croft Herb Gardens, Staplehurst *(43)*
Kypp Cottage, Biddenden *(47)*
Yew Tree Cottage, Penshurst *(119)*

May 28 Saturday
Iden Croft Herb Gardens, Staplehurst *(43)*
Kypp Cottage, Biddenden *(47)*
Yew Tree Cottage, Penshurst *(119)*

May 29 Sunday
Crawden Bank, Hartley *(22)*
Fern Cottage, Swanley *(29)*
11 Grayshott Close, Sittingbourne *(34)*
Kypp Cottage, Biddenden *(47)*
Larch Cottage, Doddington *(49)*
Longacre, Selling *(58)*
190 Maidstone Road, Chatham *(60)*
Mill House, Hildenborough *(63)*
Olantigh, Wye *(67)*
Old Buckhurst, Markbeech, nr Edenbridge *(68)*
The Pines Garden, St Margaret's Bay *(78)*
Woodhay, Ightham Common *(114)*

May 30 Monday (Bank Hol)
Copton Ash, Faversham *(20)*
Kypp Cottage, Biddenden *(47)*
Longacre, Selling *(58)*

May 31 Tuesday
Kypp Cottage, Biddenden *(47)*

June 1 Wednesday
Kypp Cottage, Biddenden *(47)*
Old Buckhurst, Markbeech, nr Edenbridge *(68)*

June 2 Thursday
Yew Tree Cottage, Penshurst *(119)*

June 3 Friday
Yew Tree Cottage, Penshurst *(119)*

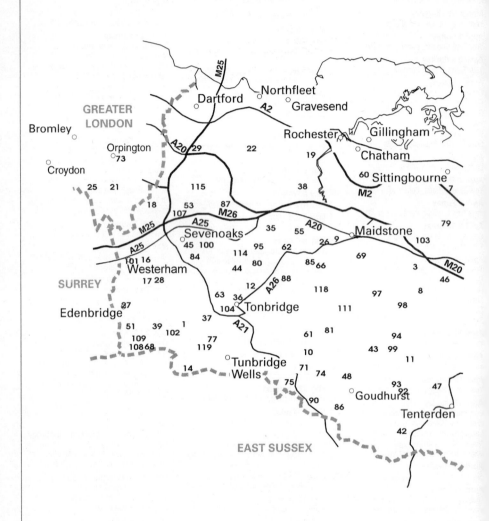

GREATER
LONDON

Bromley ○

Croydon ○

Orpington
○73

M25

Dartford ○   ○ Northfleet
                        ○ Gravesend
              A2

Rochester   Gillingham

         19   ○ Chatham

22   60 Sittingbourne ○

A20 29

25   21

          18

      115   38   M2   7

A20

         87
53   M26
107
      A25
M25   Sevenoaks   A20   Maidstone
A25   45 100   55   26 9   103
101 16   84   114   95   62   85 66   69   3
      Westerham   80   M20
SURREY 17 28   44   12 88   118   97   8   46
                 63 36 A26   98
Edenbridge 27   104 Tonbridge   111
        51 39   1   37 A21
        109 102   61 81   94
        108 68   77   43 99   11
              119   10
    14   Tunbridge   71 74 48
              Wells 75   93 92   47
                        90 86 Goudhurst ○   Tenterden
                                              42
              EAST SUSSEX

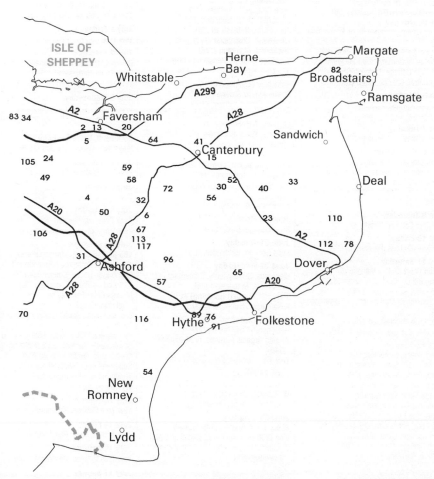

KENT

kms 0   10

miles 0   10

June 4 Saturday
Canterbury Cathedral Gardens *(15)*
Little Westwood Farm, Kingston *(56)*
Thornham Friars, Thurnham *(103)*
Yew Tree Cottage, Penshurst *(119)*

June 5 Sunday
Abbotsmerry Barn, Penshurst *(1)*
185 Borden Lane, Sittingbourne *(7)*
1 Brickwall Cottages, Frittenden *(11)*
Canterbury Cathedral Gardens *(15)*
Cottage Farm, Cudham *(21)*
Kypp Cottage, Biddenden *(47)*
Larch Cottage, Doddington *(49)*
Lindisfarne, Bridge, nr Canterbury *(52)*
Little Westwood Farm, Kingston *(56)*
Lodge House, nr Ashford *(57)*
Nettlestead Place, Nettlestead *(66)*
Olantigh, Wye *(67)*
Old Buckhurst, Markbeech, nr Edenbridge *(68)*
Quex House Gardens, Birchington *(82)*
St Michael's Gardens, East Peckham *(88)*
Sotts Hole Cottage, Borough Green *(95)*
Tram Hatch, Charing Heath *(106)*

June 6 Monday
Kypp Cottage, Biddenden *(47)*
Sissinghurst Garden, Sissinghurst *(92)*

June 7 Tuesday
Kypp Cottage, Biddenden *(47)*

June 8 Wednesday
Kypp Cottage, Biddenden *(47)*
Lodge House, nr Ashford *(57)*
Rock Farm, Nettlestead *(85)*
Upper Pryors, Cowden **(Day & Evening)** *(108)*

June 9 Thursday
Yew Tree Cottage, Penshurst *(119)*

June 10 Friday
Yew Tree Cottage, Penshurst *(119)*

June 11 Saturday
Boyton Court, Sutton Valence *(8)*
Denne Hill Gardens, Womenswold *(23)*
Kypp Cottage, Biddenden *(47)*
Old Buckhurst, Markbeech, nr Edenbridge *(68)*
Rock Farm, Nettlestead *(85)*
Yew Tree Cottage, Penshurst *(119)*

June 12 Sunday
Bilting House, nr Ashford *(6)*
Boyton Court, Sutton Valence *(8)*
Charts Edge, Westerham *(16)*
Copton Ash, Faversham *(20)*
Cottage Farm, Cudham *(21)*
Denne Hill Gardens, Womenswold *(23)*
Edenbridge House, Edenbridge *(27)*
Hole Park, Rolvenden, Cranbrook *(42)*
Kypp Cottage, Biddenden *(47)*
Larch Cottage, Doddington *(49)*
St Clere, Kemsing *(87)*
Slaney Cottage, Staplehurst *(94)*
Waystrode Manor, Cowden *(109)*
Windy Ridge, St Margarets-at-Cliffe *(112)*

June 14 Tuesday
Kypp Cottage, Biddenden *(47)*

June 15 Wednesday
Edenbridge House, Edenbridge **(Day & Evening)** *(27)*
Kypp Cottage, Biddenden *(47)*

Little Sissinghurst, St Mary's Bay **(Day & Evening)** *(54)*
Penshurst Place, Penshurst *(77)*
Rock Farm, Nettlestead *(85)*
Whitehurst, Chainhurst *(111)*
Wyckhurst, Aldington *(116)*

June 16 Thursday
Ightham Mote, Ivy Hatch *(44)*
Kypp Cottage, Biddenden *(47)*
Yew Tree Cottage, Penshurst *(119)*

June 17 Friday
Kypp Cottage, Biddenden *(47)*
Yew Tree Cottage, Penshurst *(119)*

June 18 Saturday
East Malling Gardens *(26)*
Kypp Cottage, Biddenden *(47)*
Orchard End, Horsmonden *(74)*
Rock Farm, Nettlestead *(85)*
Whitehurst, Chainhurst *(111)*
Wyckhurst, Aldington *(116)*
Yew Tree Cottage, Penshurst *(119)*

June 19 Sunday
Brenchley Gardens *(10)*
Chevening, nr Sevenoaks *(18)*
Cottage Farm, Cudham *(21)*
Doddington Place, nr Sittingbourne *(24)*
Leydens, Edenbridge *(51)*
Old Tong Farm, Brenchley *(71)*
Orchard End, Horsmonden *(74)*
Plaxtol Gardens *(80)*
Waystrode Manor, Cowden *(109)*
Whitehurst, Chainhurst *(111)*
The World Garden at Lullingstone Castle, Eynsford *(115)*
Wyckhurst, Aldington *(116)*

June 20 Monday
Kypp Cottage, Biddenden *(47)*

June 21 Tuesday
Kypp Cottage, Biddenden *(47)*

June 22 Wednesday
Highlands, St Stephen's, Canterbury *(41)*
Rock Farm, Nettlestead *(85)*
Torry Hill, Frinsted **(Evening)** *(105)*
Whitehurst, Chainhurst *(111)*

June 23 Thursday
Whitehurst, Chainhurst *(111)*
Yalding Organic Gardens, nr Maidstone *(118)*
Yew Tree Cottage, Penshurst *(119)*

June 24 Friday
Iden Croft Herb Gardens, Staplehurst *(43)*
Whitehurst, Chainhurst *(111)*
Yew Tree Cottage, Penshurst *(119)*

June 25 Saturday
Beech Court Gardens, Challock *(4)*
Iden Croft Herb Gardens, Staplehurst *(43)*
Placketts Hole, Bicknor, nr Sittingbourne **(Evening)** *(79)*
Rock Farm, Nettlestead *(85)*
Whitehurst, Chainhurst *(111)*
Yew Tree Cottage, Penshurst *(119)*

June 26 Sunday
Cottage Farm, Cudham *(21)*
Hole Park, Rolvenden, Cranbrook *(42)*
Kypp Cottage, Biddenden *(47)*
Laurenden Forstal, Challock *(50)*
Little Went, West Malling *(55)*

Old Buckhurst, Markbeech, nr Edenbridge *(68)*
The Orangery, Mystole *(72)*
Rogers Rough, Kilndown *(86)*
Sea Close, Hythe *(91)*
Whitehurst, Chainhurst *(111)*

June 27 Monday
Kypp Cottage, Biddenden *(47)*

June 28 Tuesday
Kypp Cottage, Biddenden *(47)*

June 29 Wednesday
Kypp Cottage, Biddenden *(47)*
Rock Farm, Nettlestead *(85)*

June 30 Thursday
Kypp Cottage, Biddenden *(47)*
Yew Tree Cottage, Penshurst *(119)*

July 1 Friday
Yew Tree Cottage, Penshurst *(119)*

July 2 Saturday
Belmont, Throwley, Faversham *(5)*
Rock Farm, Nettlestead *(85)*
Yew Tree Cottage, Penshurst *(119)*

July 6 Wednesday
Chartwell, nr Westerham *(17)*
Old Buckhurst, Markbeech, nr Edenbridge *(68)*
Rock Farm, Nettlestead *(85)*
Waystrode Manor, Cowden *(109)*

July 7 Thursday
Yew Tree Cottage, Penshurst *(119)*

July 8 Friday
Yew Tree Cottage, Penshurst *(119)*

July 9 Saturday
Rock Farm, Nettlestead *(85)*
Yew Tree Cottage, Penshurst *(119)*

July 10 Sunday
185 Borden Lane, Sittingbourne *(7)*
1 Brickwall Cottages, Frittenden *(11)*
Edenbridge House, Edenbridge *(27)*
115 Hadlow Road, Tonbridge *(36)*
Mounts Court Farmhouse, Acrise, nr Folkestone *(65)*
Old Buckhurst, Markbeech, nr Edenbridge *(68)*
Riddles Road Allotments, Sittingbourne *(83)*
St Michael's Gardens, East Peckham *(88)*
Sparks Hall, Sutton Valence *(98)*
Squerryes Court, Westerham *(101)*
Windy Ridge, St Margarets-at-Cliffe *(112)*
Wye Gardens *(117)*

July 14 Thursday
Yew Tree Cottage, Penshurst *(119)*

July 15 Friday
Yew Tree Cottage, Penshurst *(119)*

July 16 Saturday
Yew Tree Cottage, Penshurst *(119)*

July 17 Sunday
Charts Edge, Westerham *(16)*
Cobham Hall, Cobham *(19)*
Orchard Cottage, Bickley *(73)*

July 21 Thursday
Yew Tree Cottage, Penshurst *(119)*

July 22 Friday
Yew Tree Cottage, Penshurst *(119)*

July 23 Saturday
Kypp Cottage, Biddenden *(47)*
Yew Tree Cottage, Penshurst *(119)*
July 24 Sunday
Hall Place, Leigh *(37)*
Highlands, St Stephen's, Canterbury *(41)*
Kypp Cottage, Biddenden *(47)*
Larch Cottage, Doddington *(49)*
Tonbridge School, Tonbridge *(104)*
July 25 Monday
Kypp Cottage, Biddenden *(47)*
July 26 Tuesday
Kypp Cottage, Biddenden *(47)*
July 27 Wednesday
Kypp Cottage, Biddenden *(47)*
July 28 Thursday
Yew Tree Cottage, Penshurst *(119)*
July 29 Friday
Iden Croft Herb Gardens, Staplehurst *(43)*
Yew Tree Cottage, Penshurst *(119)*
July 30 Saturday
Iden Croft Herb Gardens, Staplehurst *(43)*
Kypp Cottage, Biddenden *(47)*
Yew Tree Cottage, Penshurst *(119)*
July 31 Sunday
115 Hadlow Road, Tonbridge *(36)*
Knowle Hill Farm, Ulcombe *(46)*
Kypp Cottage, Biddenden *(47)*
Larch Cottage, Doddington *(49)*
190 Maidstone Road, Chatham *(60)*
Old Buckhurst, Markbeech, nr Edenbridge *(68)*
The Orangery, Mystole *(72)*
Sotts Hole Cottage, Borough Green *(95)*
Spilsill Court, Staplehurst *(99)*
August 2 Tuesday
Kypp Cottage, Biddenden *(47)*
August 3 Wednesday
Kypp Cottage, Biddenden *(47)*
Old Buckhurst, Markbeech, nr Edenbridge *(68)*
Quex House Gardens, Birchington **(Evening)** *(82)*
August 4 Thursday
Knole, Sevenoaks *(45)*
Kypp Cottage, Biddenden *(47)*
Yew Tree Cottage, Penshurst *(119)*
August 5 Friday
Kypp Cottage, Biddenden *(47)*
Yew Tree Cottage, Penshurst *(119)*
August 6 Saturday
Kypp Cottage, Biddenden *(47)*
Old Buckhurst, Markbeech, nr Edenbridge *(68)*
Yew Tree Cottage, Penshurst *(119)*
August 7 Sunday
385 Borden Lane, Sittingbourne *(7)*
Doddington Place, nr Sittingbourne *(24)*
Kypp Cottage, Biddenden *(47)*
Leydens, Edenbridge *(51)*
Old Buckhurst, Markbeech, nr Edenbridge *(68)*
Sea Close, Hythe *(91)*
August 11 Thursday
Yew Tree Cottage, Penshurst *(119)*
August 12 Friday
Yew Tree Cottage, Penshurst *(119)*

August 13 Saturday
Yew Tree Cottage, Penshurst *(119)*
August 14 Sunday
Beech Court Gardens, Challock *(4)*
Mounts Court Farmhouse, Acrise, nr Folkestone *(65)*
Old Buckhurst, Markbeech, nr Edenbridge *(68)*
August 15 Monday
Sissinghurst Garden, Sissinghurst *(92)*
August 18 Thursday
Yalding Organic Gardens, nr Maidstone *(118)*
Yew Tree Cottage, Penshurst *(119)*
August 19 Friday
Yew Tree Cottage, Penshurst *(119)*
August 20 Saturday
Orchard End, Horsmonden *(74)*
Yew Tree Cottage, Penshurst *(119)*
August 21 Sunday
Laurenden Forstal, Challock *(50)*
Orchard End, Horsmonden *(74)*
West Studdal Farm, West Studdal *(110)*
August 25 Thursday
Yew Tree Cottage, Penshurst *(119)*
August 26 Friday
Yew Tree Cottage, Penshurst *(119)*
August 27 Saturday
Yew Tree Cottage, Penshurst *(119)*
August 28 Sunday
Doddington Place, nr Sittingbourne *(24)*
115 Hadlow Road, Tonbridge *(36)*
Longacre, Selling *(58)*
The Pines Garden, St Margaret's Bay *(78)*
Withersdane Hall, Wye *(113)*
August 29 Monday (Bank Hol)
Longacre, Selling *(58)*
September 1 Thursday
Yew Tree Cottage, Penshurst *(119)*
September 2 Friday
Yew Tree Cottage, Penshurst *(119)*
September 3 Saturday
Old Buckhurst, Markbeech, nr Edenbridge *(68)*
Yew Tree Cottage, Penshurst *(119)*
September 4 Sunday
Little Oast, Otford *(53)*
Old Buckhurst, Markbeech, nr Edenbridge *(68)*
Squerryes Court, Westerham *(101)*
September 7 Wednesday
Old Buckhurst, Markbeech, nr Edenbridge *(68)*
September 8 Thursday
Yew Tree Cottage, Penshurst *(119)*
September 9 Friday
Yew Tree Cottage, Penshurst *(119)*
September 10 Saturday
Old Buckhurst, Markbeech, nr Edenbridge *(68)*
Yew Tree Cottage, Penshurst *(119)*
September 11 Sunday
Broadview Gardens, Hadlow College, Hadlow *(12)*
Doddington Place, nr Sittingbourne *(24)*

Nettlestead Place, Nettlestead *(66)*
Sotts Hole Cottage, Borough Green *(95)*
September 14 Wednesday
Edenbridge House, Edenbridge *(27)*
Higham Park, Bridge *(40)*
September 15 Thursday
Yew Tree Cottage, Penshurst *(119)*
September 16 Friday
Yew Tree Cottage, Penshurst *(119)*
September 17 Saturday
Orchard End, Horsmonden *(74)*
Yew Tree Cottage, Penshurst *(119)*
September 18 Sunday
Copton Ash, Faversham *(20)*
Edenbridge House, Edenbridge *(27)*
Goodnestone Park Gardens, Wingham *(33)*
Orchard End, Horsmonden *(74)*
The Owl House, Lamberhurst *(75)*
Windy Ridge, St Margarets-at-Cliffe *(112)*
September 22 Thursday
Yew Tree Cottage, Penshurst *(119)*
September 23 Friday
Yew Tree Cottage, Penshurst *(119)*
September 24 Saturday
Yew Tree Cottage, Penshurst *(119)*
September 25 Sunday
Marle Place, Brenchley *(61)*
Mount Ephraim, Hernhill, Faversham *(64)*
September 29 Thursday
Yew Tree Cottage, Penshurst *(119)*
September 30 Friday
Yew Tree Cottage, Penshurst *(119)*
October 2 Sunday
Sea Close, Hythe *(91)*
October 10 Monday
Sissinghurst Garden, Sissinghurst *(92)*
October 16 Sunday
Hole Park, Rolvenden, Cranbrook *(42)*
October 23 Sunday
Hole Park, Rolvenden, Cranbrook *(42)*
October 30 Sunday
Beech Court Gardens, Challock *(4)*
Brogdale Horticultural Trust, Faversham *(13)*
November 6 Sunday
Great Comp Garden, Platt *(35)*

The Yellow Book is the UK's most popular garden visiting guide with a circulation of over 60,0000 copies

DESCRIPTIONS OF GARDENS

❶ Abbotsmerry Barn, Salmans Lane, Penshurst 🚻♿
(Margaret & Keith Wallis) *5m W of Tonbridge. Off B2176 in direction Leigh: 200yds N of Penshurst turn L, 1m down lane with speed ramps.* Garden developed over 20yrs on a 7½-acre undulating S-facing slope to take advantage of existing features and differing planting conditions. Herbaceous plants and roses are complemented by bulbs, shrubs and trees to provide a cheerful variety of flowers and foliage. Light refreshments and TEAS. *Adm £3, chd free (share to Demelza-James Children's Hospice at Home). Sun 5 June (11-5)*

❷ NEW April Cottage, Brogdale Road, Ospringe, Faversham
(Mr Peter Reid) *½m S of Faversham. M2 J6, L to Faversham, staying on A2, L into Brogdale Rd. 100yds S of Brogdale Horticultural Trust.* Small garden on acid soil, planted for yr-round interest, aiming to have *something* in flower every day. Many shrubs, climbers and plants, some of S American origin; rhododendrons and camellias etc, also many bulbs in season (tender ones in tubs), showing what can be done in limited space. *Adm £1.50. Private visits welcome by appt for singles, couples and small groups only, Mons May to Aug (not Bank Hols). Please phone Sat & Sun eves for appt. Tel 01795 533282*

Arden Lodge, Pastens Road, Limpsfield 🚻♿
See Surrey.

◆ Bateman's, Burwash 🚻♿
See Sussex.

❸ Battel Hall, Burberry Lane, Leeds, Maidstone 🚻♿
(Mr John D Money) *5m E of Maidstone. From A20 Hollingbourne roundabout take B2163 S (signed Leeds Castle). At top of hill take Burberry Lane, house 100yds on R.* Garden of approx 1 acre created since 1954 around medieval house (not open); very ancient wisteria, mixed planting of bulbs, shrubs, roses and herbaceous plants. Home-made TEAS. *Adm £2, chd £1. Sun 15 May (2-5.30)*

❹ ◆ Beech Court Gardens, Challock 🚻♿🚻
(Mr & Mrs Vyvyan Harmsworth) *5m N of Ashford. W of Xrds A251/A252, off the Lees.* Informal woodland garden surrounding medieval farmhouse (not open). Spring bulbs, rhododendrons, azaleas and viburnums give superb spring colour; climbing roses, summer borders and hydrangeas follow; fine collection of trees incl acers give autumn colour; plus extensive lawns, meandering paths and surprising vistas. Picnic area. Cream TEAS. *Adm £4, chd £1, concessions £3.50, groups of 12+ £3. Mar 19 to Oct 16, Mons to Thurs (10.30-5.30), Sats, Suns (12-6), closed Fris. For NGS: Sat 25 June. Suns 22 May; 14 Aug; 30 Oct. Tel 01233 740735* www.beechcourtgardens.co.uk

❺ ◆ Belmont, Belmont Park, Throwley, Faversham 🚻♿🚻
(Harris (Belmont) Charity) *4½m SW of Faversham. A251 Faversham-Ashford. At Badlesmere, brown tourist signs to Belmont.* House surrounded with large formal lawns dotted with fine specimen trees, woodland area, pinetum and small walled garden, the latter containing long borders, wisteria and large rose border. Large walled kitchen garden, recently restored (designed by Arabella Lennox Boyd), features mix of lawns, fruit, vegetables and flowers. Also formal beds, nuttery and wild grass. Featured in BBC 'Gardens Illustrated' 2004. Light refreshments and TEAS. *House & Garden adm £5.25, concessions £4.75, chd £2.50. Garden only £2.75, chd £1. Sats to Thurs, Apr to Sept (10-6). House Sats, Suns & Bank Hol Mons, Apr to Sept (2-5, last tour 4). For NGS: Sat 2 July (10-6). Tel 01795 890202* www.belmont-house.org

❻ Bilting House, nr Ashford 🚻♿
(Mr John Erle-Drax) *5m NE of Ashford. A28, 9m from Canterbury. Wye 1½m.* 6-acre garden with ha-ha set in beautiful part of Stour Valley. Wide variety of rhododendrons, azaleas and ornamental shrubs. Woodland walk with spring bulbs. Mature arboretum with new planting of specimen trees. Rose garden and herbaceous borders. Conservatory. Home-made TEAS. *Adm £2.50, chd £1. Suns 15 May; 12 June (2-6)*

❼ 185 Borden Lane, Sittingbourne 🚻♿🚻
(Mr & Mrs P A Boyce) *½m S of Sittingbourne. At A2/A249 junction turn E off roundabout towards Sittingbourne. After about 1m turn R into Borden Lane just after Coniston Hotel.* Formal garden at front incl herbs for medicinal, culinary, pot-pourri and dyeing use. To the rear, long, narrow informal garden divided into 4 areas with trees, shrubs and herbaceous borders; wildlife pond and mini oak barn/summerhouse; trained fruit trees and soft fruit cage, vegetable potager. Maintained by owners. Home-made TEAS. *Adm £2, chd free. Suns 5 June; 10 July; 7 Aug (2-5). Also open 10 July* **Riddles Road Allotments**. *Private visits welcome by appt. Tel 01795 472243*

❽ Boyton Court, Sutton Valence 🚻
(Richard & Patricia Stileman) *5m SE of Maidstone. ½m E of Sutton Valence, turn R at 1st Xrds on rd from Sutton Valence to E Sutton, Boyton Court 200yds on L.* 3-acre garden on S edge of greensand ridge affording spectacular views over the Weald. Garden falls in series of slopes and terraces through which water from a natural spring has been harnessed to create ponds and other water features. Continuing development of herbaceous planting, incl grasses, euphorbias and sedums, lavender bank and new areas for perennial geraniums. Featured in 'Wealden Times' 2003. Accommodation. Light refreshments and TEAS in aid of the Alex Fund, Romania. *Adm £3, chd £1, concessions £2. Sat, Sun 11, 12 June (2-6). Private visits welcome by appt. Tel 01622 844065* richstileman@aol.com

❾ Bradbourne House and Gardens, East Malling 🚻♿🚻
(East Malling Research) *4m NW of Maidstone. Entrance is E of New Rd, which runs from Larkfield on A20 S to E Malling.* The Hatton Fruit Garden consists of demonstration fruit gardens of particular interest to amateurs, in walled former kitchen garden and incl intensive forms of apples and pears. Members of staff will be available for questions. Science displays and children's quiz also provided. Light refreshments and TEAS. *Adm £3, chd under 16 free. Sun 24 Apr (2-5)*

❿ Brenchley Gardens
6m SE of Tonbridge. From A21, 1m S of Pembury, turn N on to B2160; turn R at Xrds in Matfield for Brenchley. Map given to all visitors. Home-made TEAS at Old Tong Farm. *Combined adm £3, chd free. Sun 19 June (2-6)*

Old Tong Farm 🚻🚻 (Simon Toynbee) (See separate entry).

Puxted House 🚻♿🚻 (Mr P J Oliver-Smith) (See separate entry).

⓫ 1 Brickwall Cottages, Frittenden 🚶♿
(Mrs Sue Martin) *6m NW of Tenterden. E of A229 between Cranbrook & Staplehurst & W of A274 between Biddenden & Headcorn. Park in village & walk along footpath opp school.* Small cottage garden in centre of village which incl borders full of unusual hardy perennials; lavender walk, pleached limes, potager, small gravel area, specialist nursery. The pond has been filled in and turned into a bog for moisture-loving plants. Shade areas with woodland plants. Home-made TEAS in aid of local charities. *Adm £2, chd free. Suns 10 Apr; 8 May; 5 June; 10 July (2-6). Private visits welcome by appt. Tel 01580 852425 suemartin@brickcot.fsnet. co.uk*

⓬ ◆ Broadview Gardens, Hadlow College, Hadlow 🚶♿✿ NCCPG
(Hadlow College) *4m NE of Tonbridge. On A26 9m SW of Maidstone.* 9 acres of ornamental planting in attractive landscape setting; 110yd double long border, island beds with mixed plantings, lake and water gardens; series of demonstration gardens incl Italian, oriental and cottage gardens. Light refreshments and TEAS. *Adm £2, chd free. Gardens open all yr 10-5, Sun 10-4.* **For NGS:** *Thur 24 Feb (10-5); Sun 11 Sept (10-4). Tel 01732 850551 www.hadlow.ac.uk*

⓭ ◆ Brogdale Horticultural Trust, Faversham 🚶✿♿
(Brogdale Horticultural Trust) *½m S of Faversham. Leave M2 at J6, turn L towards Faversham, follow brown tourist signs.* The National Fruit Collections. 60 acres of orchards with 4,000 old and new varieties of apples, pears, plums and cherries. Guided tours and expert advice. Light refreshments and TEAS. *Adm £4, chd £3, concessions £3.50. Daily all yr.* **For NGS:** *Suns 24 April; 30 Oct (10-4). Tel 01795 535286 www.brogdale.org*

⓮ Burrswood, Groombridge 🚶
(Burrswood Christian Hospital) *6m SW of Tunbridge Wells. From E Grinstead (10m) use A264, from Crowborough (5m) use B2118, then take B2110 to Groombridge village centre. Burrswood signed on village green.* 220 acres with outstanding views S and W. Formal Victorian and Edwardian terraced gardens, park with ponds and pools, woodland and farmland. Striking spring display of rhododendrons and azaleas. Decimus

Burton house (not open) is now a Christian hospital and place of healing. Italianate Church of Christ the Healer. Christian bookshop, gift shop, tea room for delicious lunches and teas - booking advisable. Light refreshments and TEAS. *Adm £3, chd free. Sat 21 May (10-4). Tel 01892 863673 www.burrswood.org.uk*

⓯ NEW Canterbury Cathedral Gardens
Canterbury Cathedral Precincts. Enter Precincts by main Christchurch gate. **No access for cars: please use park & ride and public car parks.** *Gardens will be signed within Precincts. Some wheelchair limitation.* Five gardens all set against the magnificent background of Canterbury Cathedral. Home-made TEAS and plant sale at No 29 in aid of overseas charity. *Precinct pass holders £3. Combined Cathedral and gardens ticket £7.50, concessions £6.50. Sat 4 (11-5.30), Sun 5 June (2-5.30) www.canterbury-cathedral.org*

NEW Archdeaconry 29 The Precincts 🚶✿ (The Archdeacon & Mrs Evans) ¾ acre of medieval walled garden with mixed planting of roses, shrubs, grasses and very old mulberry tree.

NEW The Deanery 🚶✿ (The Dean) Large garden of over 1 acre with small orchard and 'wild' area, lawns, herbaceous border and vegetable garden.

NEW 15 The Precincts 🚶✿ (Canon & Mrs R Marsh) Large walled garden bounded on one side by the City Wall. Large herbaceous bank. A little more formal, in keeping with the historical house.

NEW 19 The Precincts 🚶✿ (Canon C Edwards) Small enclosed garden with a view dominated by the Cathedral.

NEW 22 The Precincts 🚶✿ (Canon & Mrs E Condry) Front garden planted to attract birds and insects. Back garden a very small walled 'secret' garden.

⓰ ◆ Charts Edge, Westerham 🚶♿
(Mr & Mrs J Bigwood) *½m S of Westerham, 4m N of Edenbridge. On B2026 towards Chartwell.* 7-acre hillside garden being restored by present owners; large collection of rhododendrons, azaleas and magnolias; specimen trees and newly-planted mixed borders; many rare plants; majority of plants labelled; Victorian folly; walled fruit garden;

rock garden. New water gardens and cascade. Fine views over N Downs. Featured on ITV 2004. Home-made TEAS. *Adm £3, chd free. Weds & Fris 20 Apr to 16 Sept (2-4.30).* **For NGS:** *Suns 15 May; 12 June; 17 July (2-5). Tel 01732 504556 pignmix@aol.com*

⓱ ◆ Chartwell, nr Westerham 🚶
(The National Trust) *4m N of Edenbridge. 2m S of Westerham. Fork L off B2026 after 1½m.* 12-acre informal gardens on hillside with glorious views over Weald of Kent. Water garden and lakes together with red-brick wall built by Sir Winston Churchill, former owner of Chartwell. Avenue of golden roses given by Sir Winston's children on his golden wedding anniversary. Work began in 2004 to restore the kitchen garden to a representation of the place the Churchills knew. Garden partially accessible to wheelchairs. Light refreshments and TEAS. *House & garden adm £8. Garden only £4, chd £2. Weds to Suns & Bank Hol Mons end Mar to start Nov; Tues to Suns & Bank Hols July & Aug.* **For NGS:** *Wed 6 July (11-5, last entry 4.15). Tel 01732 868381 www.nationaltrust.org.uk*

⓲ Chevening, nr Sevenoaks 🚶♿
(The Board of Trustees of the Chevening Estate) *4m NW of Sevenoaks. Turn N off A25 at Sundridge T-lights on to B2211; at Chevening Xrds 1½m turn L.* 27 acres with lawns and woodland garden, lake, maze, formal rides, parterre. Home-made TEAS in aid of Church charities. *Adm £3, chd £1. Sun 19 June (2-5)*

⓳ ◆ Cobham Hall, Cobham 🚶♿
(Mr N G Powell) *5m W of Rochester. 8m E of M25 J2. Driveway entrance within 100yds of A2 exit signed Cobham, Shorne, Higham.* Beautiful Elizabethan mansion in 142 acres, landscaped by Humphry Repton at end C18. Herbaceous borders, formal parterres, C17 and C18 garden walls, yew hedges, lime avenue. Park with fine mature trees (cedars, oaks, ginkgos) and acres of naturalised daffodils, snowdrops and bluebells. Scheme to restore the grounds and garden buildings, incl Darnley Mausoleum, will start in 2005. Cream TEAS. *House & garden adm £7. Garden only £4.50, chd/concessions £3.50. Suns & Weds 20 Mar to 10 Apr, 6 July to 31 Aug.* **For NGS:** *Suns 3 Apr; 17 July (2-5, last tours 4). Tel 01474 823371 taylorb@cobhamhall.com*

NEW Columcille, 9 Norlands Crescent, Chislehurst 🚻🐾⊕
See London.

20 Copton Ash, 105 Ashford Road, Faversham 🚻🐾⊕
(Drs Tim & Gillian Ingram) *½m S of Faversham. On A251 Faversham to Ashford rd opp E-bound junction 6 with M2.* Garden grown out of a love and fascination with plants from an early age. Contains very wide collection incl many rarities and newly introduced species raised from wild seed. Interesting from snowdrops and hellebores of earliest spring to colours and fruits of autumn. Raised scree and peat beds. Specialist nursery. Home-made TEAS in aid of local charities. *Adm £2, chd free. Suns 13, 27 Mar; 10, 24 Apr; 12 June; 18 Sept. Bank Hol Mons 28 Mar; 2, 30 May (2-6). Private visits welcome by appt. Tel 01795 535919*

21 Cottage Farm, Cackets Lane, Cudham ⊕
(Phil & Karen Baxter) *5m NW of Sevenoaks, 4m SW of Orpington. Sign for Cudham from Green-Street-Green roundabout on A21. 3m into village, turn L past garage. 2nd block cottages on R. Entrance through working farmyard.* Cottage garden. No lawns! Intimate and individual style. Approx 1 acre. Self-sufficient vegetable and fruit gardens. Tropical garden. Greenhouses. Ponds. Pergolas. Created and maintained by owner. Accommodation. Cream TEAS in aid of Bromley Harris HospisCare. *Adm £3, chd £1. Suns 5, 12, 19, 26 June (1.30-5). Private visits welcome by appt, groups welcome. Tel 01959 532506*

22 Crawden Bank, Merton Avenue, Hartley 🐾⊕
(Jackie Adams) *4m SE of Dartford. From A2, at Longfield mini-roundabout, follow signs to Hartley into Ash Rd, after ½m Merton Ave is on L. From A20, at New Ash Green roundabout follow sign to Hartley, after 1½m Merton Ave on R. Limited parking in Merton Ave, please park in side rds.* ½-acre garden in which hardy perennials are used extensively. Low on grass, high on colour, texture, scent and contrast. TEAS. *Adm £2, chd 50p. Sun 29 May (2-5).* Also open **Fern Cottage, Swanley Village**

23 NEW Denne Hill Gardens, Womenswold
6m SE of Canterbury. Midway between Canterbury and Dover, NE of A2. Take B2046 signed Wingham at Barham crossover. After approx ¼m turn R at Armada Beacon. Two contrasting gardens at Denne Hill *(1st and 2nd entrances on R)*, linked by a parkland drive or walk, weather permitting. Home-made TEAS at Denne Hill Farm in aid of Friends of St Margaret's Church, Wymynswold. *Combined adm £3, chd free. Sat, Sun 11, 12 June (2-6)*

NEW Denne Hill Farm 🚻🐾⊕
(Mr & Mrs R Loder-Symonds) Victorian farmhouse garden set in ancient parkland with magnificent views and mature trees (yew tree mentioned in Domesday Book). Shrubs, herbaceous borders, roses, ha-ha wall. Recent additions incl wild flower meadow and pond. Coach parking available.

Westmore House (Mrs Jenny Cracknell) Plantsman's garden of approx 1 acre, lovingly created by the owners within an old chalkpit. Plantings attract a wide variety of wildlife.

24 ♦ Doddington Place, nr Sittingbourne 🚻⊕
(Mr & Mrs Richard Oldfield) *6m SE of Sittingbourne. From A20 turn N opp Lenham or from A2 turn S at Teynham or Ospringe (Faversham), all 4m.* 10-acre garden, landscaped with wide views; trees and yew hedges; woodland garden with azaleas and rhododendrons; Edwardian rock garden; formal garden with mixed borders. Gothic folly. Light refreshments and TEAS. *Adm £3.50, chd 75p. Suns & Bank Hol Mons Easter Day to end June. For NGS: Suns 19 June; 7, 28 Aug; 11 Sept (2-5). Tel 01795 886155 amicia@demoubray.plus.com*

25 Dolly's Garden, 43 Layhams Road, West Wickham 🚻
(Mary Robertson) *4m S of Bromley, off A232.* Semi-detached house recognisable by small sunken flower garden in the front. Opp Wickham Court Farm. Dolly Robertson created her garden over 60yrs ago and it has been organic ever since. She made raised vegetable beds which she gardened from her wheelchair until her death in 2004. Her daughter now manages the garden, 24ft X 70ft, with disabled visitors in mind. It is a loved garden. Refreshments on request. *Adm by donation. Private visits welcome by appt. Tel 020 8462 4196 mary.elaine@virgin.net*

26 NEW East Malling Gardens
4m NW of Maidstone. S of A20 at Larkfield. New Rd becomes High St beyond Xrds at King & Queen. Car park and 53 High St off High St. Disabled parking only at 24 New Rd. Home-made TEAS at 24 New Road. *Combined adm £4, chd free. Sat 18 June (2-5)*

NEW 53 High Street (Elspeth Napier) Approx 1000sq yd plot with mixed collection of shrubs, herbaceous and bulbs; more experimental than artistic. Fruit trees and small vegetable garden.

NEW 24 New Road 🚻🐾⊕ (Sally & David Simpson) ¾-acre plantsman's garden containing many interesting trees, shrubs, herbaceous perennials and climbers, incl magnificent *Vitis cognetiae* and white wisteria. Also incl a wildlife pond, greenhouse and small kitchen and herb gardens.

27 ♦ Edenbridge House, Edenbridge 🚻🚻
(Mrs M T Lloyd) *1½m N of Edenbridge. Nr Marlpit Hill, on B2026.* House part C16 (not open). 5-acre garden laid out in 1930s as a series of rooms, with herbaceous and mixed borders, old-fashioned and shrub roses, alpines, ornamental trees and shrubs, water and gravel gardens, orchard and wildlife pond, kitchen garden and greenhouses; many unusual plants. Featured in 'Gardening Which' 2003. Home-made TEAS on NGS days. *Adm £3, chd 25p. Tues & Thurs, Apr to Sept (2-5). For NGS: Suns 17 Apr; 8 May; 12 June; 10 July; 18 Sept (2-6). Weds 11 May; 15 June: 14 Sept (1-5). Day & Evening Opening £4, wine, Wed 15 June (6-9). Tel 01732 862122*

28 ♦ Emmetts Garden, Ide Hill 🚻🚻
(The National Trust) *5m SW of Sevenoaks. 1½m S of A25 on Sundridge-Ide Hill Rd. 1½m N of Ide Hill off B2042.* 5-acre hillside garden, with the highest tree top in Kent, noted for its fine collection of rare trees and flowering shrubs. The garden is particularly fine in spring, while a rose garden, rock garden and extensive planting of acers for autumn colour extend the interest throughout the season. Light refreshments and TEAS. *Adm £4, chd £1. Tues to Sun and Mar to end May; June Wed to Sun; July to end Oct Wed, Sat, Sun & Bank Hols. For NGS: Sat 14 May (11-5, last entry 4.15). Tel 01732 868381 www.nationaltrust.org.uk*

29 NEW Fern Cottage, Swanley Village Road, Swanley 🚻⊕
(John & Lynn Lucas) *From J3 M25 take A20 towards Farningham. 2nd L Button St to end, L into Swanley*

Village Rd. Garden opp Nursery. Small cottage garden that has crammed an acre into a ¼-acre plot. Many unusual plants and seats in hidden corners. Pond and inviting summerhouses are enhanced by the open aspect. PH 200yds. TEAS at **Crawden Bank**. *Adm £2, chd 50p (share to Ellenor Hospice at Home). Sun 29 May (2-5)*

㉚ Flint Cottage, Bishopsbourne ✿⊕
(Mr & Mrs P J Sinnock) 4m SE of Canterbury. Turn off A2 to Bridge, through village, turn W at church, follow garden signs. Small garden: large Scots pine underplanted with trees and shrubs to encourage birdlife. Main garden: 4 ponds and water features; bog areas; mixed borders; alpines in sink gardens; herb garden; vegetables in raised beds. Not suitable for small children. Home-made TEAS in aid of Breast Buddies & St Mary's Church. Adm £2, chd 50p. Suns 8, 15 May (2-6)

㉛ ◆ Godinton House & Gardens, Godinton Lane, Ashford ⬥✿⊕
(Godinton House Preservation Trust) 1½m W of Ashford. M20 J9 to Ashford. Take A20 towards Charing and Lenham, then follow brown tourist signs. Formal area designed c1900 by Reginald Blomfield. Famous for its vast yew hedge, cut to reflect the distinctive gables, topiary, formal and informal ponds. In spring the wild garden is a mass of daffodils with fritillaries and other spring flowers. Walled garden contains the Delphinium Society's border, a new greenhouse and cutting garden. The intimate Italian garden has Mediterranean-style planting. Newly designed and planted rose garden. Garden a wonderful setting for the Jacobean house. Home-made TEAS, Fri, Sat, Sun. House & garden adm £6. Garden only £3, chd free. Thurs to Mons, Mar to Oct; House Fris to Suns Mar to Oct. For NGS: Suns 20 Mar; 3 Apr (2-5.30). Tel 01233 620773 www.godinton-house-gardens.co.uk

㉜ Godmersham Park, Godmersham ⬥✿⊕
(Mr John B Sunley) 5m NE of Ashford. Off A28, midway between Canterbury & Ashford. Associations with Jane Austen. Early Georgian mansion (not open) in beautiful downland setting, 24 acres of formal and landscaped gardens, topiary, rose beds, herbaceous borders and superb daffodils in restored wilderness. Light refreshments and TEAS in aid of

Godmersham Church. Adm £3, chd free. Sun 3 Apr (11-5)

㉝ ◆ Goodnestone Park Gardens, Wingham ⬥✿⊕
(The Lady FitzWalter) 6m SE of Canterbury. Village lies S of B2046 from A2 to Wingham. Brown tourist signs off B2046. 10-12 acres; good trees; woodland garden, snowdrops, spring bulbs, walled garden with old-fashioned roses. Connections with Jane Austen who stayed here. 2 arboretums planted 1984 & 2001, gravel garden established 2003. Picnics allowed. Home-made TEAS. Adm £4, chd under 12 50p, concessions £3.50. 21 Mar to 30 Sept, Mons, Weds to Fris (11-5), Suns (12-5.30), closed Tues, Sats. For NGS: Suns 13 Mar; 18 Sept. Tel 01304 840107 www.goodnesteparkgardens.co.uk

㉞ 11 Grayshott Close, Sittingbourne ✿
(Mr & Mrs D Rawding) ¾m S of Sittingbourne. From Sittingbourne station on A2, ¼m E towards Faversham. Turn R at T-lights signed Tunstall. Straight over 2 T-lights, approx 100yds turn 1st L into Highsted Rd. 100yds 1st L into Grayshott Close. Front garden designed for mid to late season colour. Informal rear garden 60ft x 40ft with over 500 different plants incl clematis, geraniums, alliums and iris. Wildlife pond. Plenty of interest for the plant lover. Adm £2, chd free. Sun 29 May (10.30-5.30)

㉟ ◆ Great Comp Garden, Platt ⬥✿⊕
(Great Comp Charitable Trust) 7m E of Sevenoaks. A20 at Wrotham Heath, take Seven Mile Lane, B2016; at 1st Xrds turn R; garden on L ½m. Skilfully designed 7-acre garden of exceptional beauty. Spacious setting of well-maintained lawns and paths lead visitors through plantsman's collection of trees, shrubs, heathers and herbaceous plants. Good autumn colour. Early C17 house (not open). Magnolias, hellebores and snowdrops are great feature in spring. A great variety of perennials in summer incl salvias, dahlias and crocosmias. Light refreshments and TEAS. Adm £4, chd £1. Daily 1 Apr to 31 Oct. For NGS: Suns 6, 13, 20, 27 Mar; Sun 6 Nov (11-5.30). Tel 01732 886154 www.greatcomp.co.uk

㊱ 115 Hadlow Road, Tonbridge ✿
(Mr & Mrs Richard Esdale) Take A26 from N end of High St signed Maidstone, house 1m on L in service

rd. ⅓-acre unusual terraced garden with large collection of modern roses, island herbaceous border, many clematis, hardy fuchsias, heathers, grasses, hostas and ferns, shrub borders, alpines, annuals, kitchen garden and pond; well labelled. TEAS. Adm £2.50, chd free. Suns 10, 31 July; 28 Aug (2-6). Private visits welcome by appt, groups welcome. Tel 01732 353738

㊲ Hall Place, Leigh ⬥
(The Lady Hollenden) 4m W of Tonbridge. From A21 Sevenoaks-Tonbridge, B245 to Hildenborough, then R onto B2027 through Leigh & on R. Large outstanding garden with 11-acre lake, lakeside walk crossing over picturesque bridges. Many rare and interesting trees and shrubs. Home-made TEAS. Adm £4, chd £2. Suns 10 Apr; 24 July (2-6)

㊳ Haydown, Great Buckland, Luddesdown ✿⊕
(Dr & Mrs I D Edeleanu) 6m W of Rochester. 4m S of A2. Take turning for Cobham, at war memorial straight ahead down hill, under railway bridge to T-junction. Turn R, after 200yds take L fork, follow narrow lane for 1½m. Entrance on L after riding stables. N Downs 9-acre hillside garden incl woodland with indigenous and unusual trees and meadowland with many varieties of hardy orchids; orchard, ponds, vineyard (wine available) and other features. TEAS. Adm £3, chd free. Private visits welcome by appt Apr to July. Tel 01474 814329 ion-dan@edeleanu.com

㊴ ◆ Hever Castle & Gardens, nr Edenbridge ⬥⊕
(Broadland Properties Ltd) 3m SE of Edenbridge. Between Sevenoaks & East Grinstead off B2026. Signed from junctions 5 & 6 of M25, A21, A264. Romantic double moated castle, the childhood home of Anne Boleyn, in award-winning gardens. 110 metre-long herbaceous border planted in Edwardian style, colours from white through blues, pinks and hot colours. Formal Italian gardens with statuary, sculpture and fountains; large lake; 'splashing' water maze; rose garden, Tudor herb and knot garden, topiary, maze. Light refreshments and TEAS. Castle & Garden £8.80, chd (5-14) £4.80, OAP £7.40, family £22.40. Garden only £7, chd £4.60, OAP £6, family £18.60. Concessions for groups of 15+. Daily 1 Mar to 30 Nov, gardens 11-6, castle 12-6. Tel 01732 865224 www.hevercastle.co.uk

40 ◆ **Higham Park, Bridge** ♿※
(Mrs P Gibb) *3m SE of Canterbury.
Use A2 exit signed Bridge, Higham
Park at top of Bridge Hill. Amazing
restoration by lady owners. Palladian
mansion 1320. 24 acres. Carpets of
spring bulbs. Yew-hedged Italian
water garden, temple, fountains
(Harold Peto). Dry-stone walled rose
garden, ever-changing long borders,
trees, scented shrubs. Sweeping
lawns. Colour spring to autumn.
Featured on TV Richard & Judy,
local TV & radio and in 'Daily
Telegraph', 'Daily Mail',
'Independent' and other publications.
Light refreshments and TEAS. Adm
£4, chd £1, concessions £3.50. Easter
to end Sept, gardens 11-5, house
tours 12.30 & 2.30. June to Aug
daily, not Fri, Sat. Apr, May, Sept not
Fri, Sat, Mon (except Bank Hols).* **For
NGS:** *Sun 3 Apr; Wed 14 Sept.*
*Tel 01227 830830 www.higham-
park.co.uk*

41 **Highlands, Hackington Close,
St Stephen's, Canterbury** ♿※
(Dr & Mrs B T Grayson) *1m N of
Canterbury. At the foot of St
Stephen's Hill, 200yds N of
Archbishops School, on rd to Tyler
Hill & Chestfield. Car parking on St
Stephen's Hill Rd or Downs Rd, opp
Hackington Close.* 2-acre peaceful
garden, set in S-facing bowl, with
island beds of herbaceous perennials,
roses, azaleas, acers, hydrangeas,
hebes and other shrubs. Many conifer
and broad-leafed trees, incl
plantation of ornamental trees. Two
ponds, small alpine bed and hanging
gardens feature. TEAS. *Adm £2.50,
chd free. Wed 22 June; Sun 24 July
(11-5). Private visits welcome by
appt. Tel 01227 765066
terrygrayson@supanet.com*

42 ◆ **Hole Park, Rolvenden,
Cranbrook** ♿※※
(Mr & Mrs E G Barham) *4m SW of
Tenterden. On B2086.* 1st opened in
1927. 15-acre garden surrounded by
parkland with beautiful views, yew
hedges, large lawns and specimen
trees. Walled gardens, pools and
mixed borders combine with bulbs,
rhododendrons and azaleas. Massed
bluebells in woodland walk, standard
wisterias, orchids in flower meadow
and glorious autumn colours make
this a garden for all seasons. Home-
made TEAS Suns only. *Adm £3.50,
chd 50p. Suns Easter to 3 July incl &
Oct 16, 23. Weds & Thurs Easter to
end Oct.* **For NGS:** *Suns 17 Apr; 8, 22
May; 12, 26 June; 16, 23 Oct (2-6).
Tel 01580 241344 www.holepark.
com*

43 ◆ **Iden Croft Herb Gardens,
Frittenden Road, Staplehurst**
♿※ NCCPG
(Mr Philip Haynes) *9m S of
Maidstone. Brown tourism signs on
A229 just S of Staplehurst.* Created
over the past 32yrs. Threaded with
winding paths, which lead to Tudor
walled garden. Unique atmosphere,
with massed rosemary, wall plants
and herbaceous borders. Themed
gardens incl culinary, medicinal, pot-
pourri and sensory. National Plant
Collections of mentha, nepeta and
origanum and large collections of
lavenders and thyme. Light
refreshments and TEAS. *Adm £2, chd
50p, concessions £1.50. Mar to Oct:
Mon to Sat (9-5), Suns & Bank Hols
(11-5). Mon to Fri Oct to Feb (9-4).*
For NGS: *Fris, Sats 27, 28 May; 24, 25
June; 29, 30 July (9-5). Tel 01580
891432 www.herbs-uk.com*

44 ◆ **Ightham Mote, Ivy Hatch**
♿※※
(The National Trust) *6m E of
Sevenoaks. Off A25, 2½m S of
Ightham. Buses from rail stations
Sevenoaks or Borough Green to Ivy
Hatch, ½m walk to Ightham Mote.*
14-acre garden and moated medieval
manor c1330. Mixed borders with
many unusual plants; lawns;
courtyard; orchard of Kent apples;
water features incl small lake, leading
to woodland walk with trees,
rhododendrons and other shrubs.
Light refreshments and TEAS. *Adm
£7, chd £3.50, free to NT Members.
Daily except Tues & Sats, 18 Mar to
30 Oct.* **For NGS:** *Thur 16 June
(10-5.30, last adm 5). Tel 01732
810378 www.nationaltrust.org.uk*

45 ◆ **Knole, Sevenoaks** ♿※
(The Lord Sackville) *1m SE of
Sevenoaks. Station: Sevenoaks. Well
signed.* Pleasance, deer park,
landscape garden, herb garden. *Adm
£2, chd £1. Every Wed 23 Mar to 26
Oct.* **For NGS:** *Wed 4 May; Thur 4
Aug (11-4, last adm 3). Tel 01732
462100*

46 **Knowle Hill Farm, Ulcombe**
♿※※
(The Hon Andrew & Mrs Cairns) *7m
SE of Maidstone. From M20 J8
follow A20 towards Lenham for
approx 3m. Turn R to Ulcombe.
After 1½m, 1st L, ½m 1st R. Past
Pepper Box PH, 1m 1st L.* 1½-acre
garden created over last 18yrs on S-
facing slope of the Downs with
spectacular views. Mixed borders
contain Mediterranean and tender
plants, roses and grasses. Pool and rill
is enclosed within small walled
garden planted mainly with white

flowers. New easy-care (we hope)
planting around entrance. Home-
made TEAS in aid of All Saints
Church, Ulcombe. *Adm £3, chd free.
Sun 31 July (2-6). Private visits
welcome by appt. Tel 01622 850240*

47 **Kypp Cottage, Woolpack
Corner, Biddenden** ※
(Mrs Zena Grant) *5m N of
Tenterden. At Tenterden Rd A262
junction with Benenden Rd. Not for
the tidy minded!* ½-acre romantic
foliage enfolding garden where
shrubs, 200 different roses, mainly
scented, and 60 clematis ramble and
entwine. Thick tapestry of ground
cover, predominantly geraniums,
ferns and shade lovers in semi-
woodland. Summerhouse. Garden
created from builder's yard, planted
and maintained by owner. Home-
made TEAS. *Adm £2, chd 50p (share
to NSPCC). Thur to Sun 19 to 22, Fri
to Tues 27 to 31 May; many dates in
June (see diary section); Sat to Wed
23 to 27, Sat, Sun 30, 31 July; Tues
to Sun 2 to 7 Aug (weekdays
10.30-5.30, Suns 2-6). Private visits
welcome by appt for groups of 10+
on open days, eves by appt.
Tel 01580 291480*

48 **Ladham House, Goudhurst**
♿※
(Mr Guy Johnson) *8m E of
Tunbridge Wells. On NE of village,
off A262. Through village towards
Cranbrook, turn L at The Chequers
PH. 2nd R into Ladham Rd, main
gates approx 500yds on L.* 10 acres
with rolling lawns, fine specimen
trees, rhododendrons, camellias,
azaleas, shrubs and magnolias.
Arboretum. Spectacular twin mixed
borders; ha-ha; fountain and bog
gardens. Edwardian rockery reopened
but inaccessible to wheelchairs. Fine
view. Home-made TEAS. *Adm £3.50,
chd 50p. Sun 8 May (2-5)*

49 **Larch Cottage, Seed Road,
Doddington** ♿※※
(Mr & Mrs J Howell) *9m S of
Sittingbourne. From A2 nr Ospringe
to Newnham turn L by church, 2½m
S along Seed Rd. From A20 nr
Lenham proceed to Warren St. At
Harrow turn N, follow signs for
Newnham along Slade Rd, approx
1½m.* 3-acre garden on N Downs
developed and maintained by the
owners over the past 25yrs.
Contrasting areas incl knot garden,
woodland and rhododendrons,
colour-themed mixed borders, ponds
and secret garden. Limited wheelchair
access. WC. TEAS. *Adm £3, chd free.
Suns 22, 29 May; 5, 12 June; 24, 31
July (2-5). Private visits welcome by*

appt for groups, but access rd not suitable for coaches. Tel 01795 886259 johnhowell450@hotmail.com

50 Laurenden Forstal, Blind Lane, Challock &⊗
(Mrs M Cottrell) *6m N of Ashford. Close to junction of A251 & A252, access from both. All parking in field off village hall car park behind house.* 2-acre garden with woodland and rhododendrons, around part C14 house (not open). Rose walk and extensive yew hedging framing lawns and borders. Partly walled rose garden overlooking large wildlife pond; courtyard white garden. Featured in 'The English Garden' & 'Kent Life' 2003. Home-made TEAS in aid of St Cosmas & St Damian Church. *Adm £2, chd free. Suns 26 June; 21 Aug (2-6). Private visits welcome by appt. Tel 01233 740310*

51 Leydens, Edenbridge &⊗⊗
(Mr Roger Platts) *1m S of Edenbridge. On B2026 towards Hartfield (use Nursery entrance & car park).* Private garden of garden designer/nursery owner, designer of exhibit to celebrate 75yrs of NGS at Chelsea 2002 (Best in Show). Created during 1999/2000 and still under development. ½ acre surrounding house (not open) with small natural-style pond, beds planted with wide range of shrubs and perennials. Wild flower meadow. Plenty of planting ideas and good selection of unusual varieties. Adjacent nursery and display/propagation beds. Author of 'Traditional Gardens' pub. 2004. TEAS. *Adm £2.50, chd free. Suns 19 June; 7 Aug (12-5)*

52 NEW Lindisfarne, Bekesbourne Road, Bridge, nr Canterbury &⊗⊗
(Richard & Vicky Bradburn) *2m SE of Canterbury. From A2 southbound (and A2050, new Dover rd) take slip rd for Bridge. Turn R at T-junction and follow signs to car parking. From A2 northbound take exit for Bridge and follow signs through village. Parking in lay-by 2mins walk from garden.* ¾-acre wildlife garden. Herbaceous borders, large pond and bog gardens; chalk grass meadow with wild flowers. Many naturalised spring-flowering bulbs. Water feature and diversity of planting attracts wide variety of wildlife. Not suitable for children. TEAS in aid of Kent Wildlife Trust. *Adm £2. Sun 5 June (2-6). Private visits welcome by appt vickybradburn@macace.net*

53 Little Oast, High Street, Otford ⊗
(Mrs Pam Hadrill) *3m N of Sevenoaks. At W end of village, just past Horns PH, turn R into private drive. (Please park in public car park opp Bull PH or in Catholic church car park 80yds past Little Oast).* This tranquil and peaceful garden had taken over 50yrs to become what it is today, full of mature trees, plants, ferns grasses and shrubs, 3 summerhouses and a pond, with seats in secluded corners where you can enjoy your tea and cakes. Home-made TEAS. *Adm £2, chd free. Sun 4 Sept (2-5). Private visits welcome by appt for groups of 10+. Tel 01959 523637*

54 Little Sissinghurst, 121 Jefferstone Lane, St Mary's Bay ⊗
(Mr Ian Hamish MacKay) *6m SW of Hythe. From A259 coast rd, ½m N in Jefferstone Lane. 1m from Dymchurch. Car park in field 100yds R past garden.* Nostalgic 1960s seaside cottage garden, surrounding 1933 chalet bungalow, 40ft x 147ft and created over 36yrs by owner and his late mother, a trained gardener and artist. 3 archways, 2 small patios, 2 rockeries, small water feature, large herbaceous bed, 2 summerhouses. Shrubs and small trees give seclusion. Original oil paintings by owner's mother will be on display. Very limited access for wheelchairs. Featured in 'Period Living & Traditional Homes' 2004. *Adm £2, chd under 14 free. Sun 10 Apr (11-4). Day (11-4) & Evening Opening £1.50, Wed 15 June (6-7.30)*

55 Little Went, 106 High Street, West Malling &⊗⊗
(Anne Baring) *5m W of Maidstone. In middle of West Malling opp car park; entry through gates marked.* Long narrow secret garden, ponds, potager, aviary, conservatory. New gravel garden. Exhibition of paintings for sale. Home-made TEAS. *Adm £3, chd under 12 free (share to St Mary the Virgin, West Malling). Sun 26 June (11-5). Private visits welcome by appt. Tel 01732 843388*

56 Little Westwood Farm, Kingston &⊗
(Christopher & Frances Harrap) *7½m SE of Canterbury. On A2 4½m S of Canterbury turn off to Bishopsbourne. At church keep R & continue 3m following signs.* 1-acre garden surrounded by open farmland; wide variety of unusual trees, shrubs and perennials set in series of individual gardens; vegetables in raised beds; wildlife pond and bog garden. TEAS in aid of St Giles Church. *Adm £2.50, chd 50p. Sat, Sun 4, 5 June (2-6)*

57 Lodge House, Smeeth, nr Ashford &⊗
(Mr & Mrs J Talbot) *4½m SE of Ashford. From M20 J10 take A20 3m towards Sellindge. Turn L signed Smeeth. At Woolpack turn R. Continue for ½m. Opp Pound Lane turn R into drive.* Family home since 1450, and its oast house (neither open), look over the deer park (now sheep) of the former Scots Hall. Large, mature, informal cottage-style garden incl interesting old trees,

DANGER
GIANT VENUS
FLY-TRAP

massed daffodils, irises, delphiniums, herbaceous borders, pergola, ha-ha and ponds. Child-friendly. Country walks and several visit-worthy Norman churches nearby. Featured on ITV Britain's Best Back Gardens 2004. Home-made TEAS. *Adm £2.50, chd free (share to St Mary's, Brabourne). Suns, Weds 3, 6 Apr; 5, 8 June (12-6). Private visits welcome by appt for individuals & groups, one coach max. French & German spoken. Tel 01303 813184*

⑤⑧ Longacre, Selling ♿⊗☺
(Dr & Mrs G Thomas) *5m SE of Faversham. From A2 (M2) or A251 follow signs for Selling, passing White Lion on L. 2nd R & immed L, continue for ¼m. From A252 at Chilham, take turning signed Selling at Badgers Hill Garden Centre. L at 2nd Xrds, next R, L & then R.* Plantsman's garden with wide variety of interesting plants, gravel garden and raised vegetable beds. We aim to have colour and interest throughout spring and summer using bulbs, annuals and many containers with cannas, eucomis, *Arundo donax*, etc. New conservatory displays range of tender plants. Home-made TEAS in aid of local charities. *Adm £2, chd free. Suns, Mons 17 Apr; 1, 2, 15, 29, 30 May; 28, 29 Aug (2-5). Private visits welcome by appt for individuals & groups. Tel 01227 752254*

Lullingstone Castle, Eynsford
see **The World Garden**.

⑤⑨ Luton House, Selling ⊗
(Sir John & Lady Swire) *4m SE of Faversham. From A2 (M2) or A251 make for White Lion, entrance 30yds E on same side of rd.* 6 acres; C19 landscaped garden; ornamental ponds; trees underplanted with azaleas, camellias, woodland plants. Hellebores, spring bulbs, magnolias, cherries, daphnes, halesias, maples, Judas trees and cyclamen. *Adm £3. Sun 8 May (2-6)*

⑥⓪ 190 Maidstone Road, Chatham ⊗☺
(Dr M K Douglas) *1m S of Chatham. On A230.* Informal ¼-acre garden; herbaceous borders on either side of former tennis court; scree garden and pool; many snowdrops and other spring bulbs. Doll's house (¹⁄₁₂ scale model of house) may also be viewed. Home-made TEAS, not Feb 13. *Adm £1.50, chd free. Suns 13 Feb; 27 Mar; 29 May; 31 July (2-5). Private visits welcome by appt. Tel 01634 842216*

March Cottage, 58 Warren Road (old side), Chelsfield ☺
See London.

⑥① ◆ Marle Place, Brenchley ♿⊗☺
(Mr & Mrs Gerald Williams) *8m SE of Tonbridge. From A21 Kippings Cross roundabout take B2160 to Matfield, R to Brenchley, then follow brown tourist signs.* Victorian gazebo, plantsman's shrub borders, walled scented garden, Edwardian rockery, herbaceous borders, bog and kitchen gardens. Woodland walks, mosaic terrace, artists' studios, gallery. Autumn colour. Restored Victorian 40ft greenhouse with orchid collection. C17 listed house (not open). Collection of interesting chickens. Guided tours by appt, coaches by arrangement. Art exhibition. 'Kent Life' Gold prizewinner High Weald Gardening for Wildlife 2003. Light refreshments and TEAS, Cream TEAS NGS days. *Adm £4.50, chd £1, concessions £4. Fris to Mons 25 Mar to 30 Sept.* **For NGS:** *Suns 17 Apr; 15 May; 25 Sept (10-last adm 5). Tel 01892 722304*
www.marleplace.co.uk

⑥② Mere House, Mereworth ♿☺
(Mr & Mrs Andrew Wells) *7m E of Tonbridge. From A26 turn N on to B2016 & then into Mereworth village. 3½m S of M20/M26 interchange, take A20, then B2016 to Mereworth.* 6-acre garden with C18 lake; ornamental shrubs and trees with foliage contrast; lawns, daffodils; Kentish cobnut plat; woodland walk; major new tree planting. Home-made TEAS. *Adm £2.50, chd free. Sun, Mon 27, 28 Mar (2-5.30)*

⑥③ Mill House, Mill Lane, Hildenborough ♿⊗☺
(Dr & Mrs Brian Glaisher) *5m S of Sevenoaks. From B245 turn into Mill Lane at Mill garage.* 2½-acre garden laid out in 1906; herbaceous and mixed borders; secluded herb garden; old shrub roses and climbers; clematis and many fine trees. Golden garden, designed in 1999 by Judith Sharpe, Chelsea medallist. Formal garden with topiary; ruins of windmill with tree ferns and conservatory with exotics. *Adm £3, chd free. Sun 29 May (2-6)*

⑥④ ◆ Mount Ephraim, Hernhill, Faversham ♿☺
(Mrs M N Dawes, Mr & Mrs E S Dawes) *3m E of Faversham. From M2 & A299 take Hernhill turning opp Duke of Kent.* Herbaceous border; topiary; daffodils and

rhododendrons; rose terraces leading to small lake. Rock garden with pools; water garden; young arboretum; new grass maze. Rose garden with arches and pergola planted to celebrate the millennium. Magnificent trees. Superb views over fruit farms to Swale estuary. Home-made TEAS. *Adm £4, chd £1, groups £3.50. Weds, Thurs, Sats, Suns, Easter to end Sept (1-5); Bank Hol Mons (11-5).* **For NGS:** *Suns 24 Apr; 25 Sept. Tel 01227 751496*
www.mountephraimgardens.co.uk

⑥⑤ Mounts Court Farmhouse, Acrise, nr Folkestone ♿⊗☺
(Graham & Geraldine Fish) *6m NW of Folkestone. From A260 Folkestone-Canterbury rd, turn L at Swingfield (Densole) opp Black Horse Inn, 1½m towards Elham & Lyminge, on N side.* 1½ acres surrounded by open farmland; variety of trees, shrubs, grasses and herbaceous plants; pond and bog garden. 20,000 gallon rainwater reservoir waters garden and keeps pond topped up; compost heated to 170° for fast turnover. Home-made TEAS in aid of Abbeyfield, Lyminge. *Adm £2.50, chd free. Suns 22 May; 10 July; 14 Aug (2-5). Private visits welcome by appt, coaches permitted. Tel 01303 840598*
graham.s.fish@btinternet.com

⑥⑥ Nettlestead Place, Nettlestead ♿
(Mr & Mrs Roy Tucker) *6m W/SW of Maidstone. Turn S off A26 onto B2015 then 1m on L, next to Nettlestead Church.* C13 manor house (not open) in 7-acre plantsman's garden on different levels. Formal rose garden with shrub, species, floribunda, hybrid tea and climbing roses. Large herbaceous garden of island beds with rose and clematis walkway leading to garden of China roses. Fine collection of trees and shrubs; sunken pond garden, terraces, glen garden, acer lawn, and young pinetum. Light refreshments and TEAS. *Adm £4, chd free (share to St Mary's Church, Nettlestead). Suns 5 June; 11 Sept (2-5.30)*

⑥⑦ Olantigh, Wye ⊗
(Mr & Mrs J R H Loudon) *6m NE of Ashford. Turn off A28 to Wye. 1m from Wye on Olantigh rd towards Godmersham.* Edwardian garden in beautiful 20-acre setting; wide variety of trees; river garden; rockery; shrubbery; herbaceous border; extensive lawns; tree sculpture and woodland walks. Sorry, no teas, but please feel free to bring your own.

Adm £2.50, chd free. Suns 29 May, 5 June (2-5)

68 ◆ **Old Buckhurst, Markbeech, nr Edenbridge** 🅰🅱🅲

(Mr & Mrs J Gladstone) *4m SE of Edenbridge. B2026, at Queens Arms PH turn E to Markbeech. In approx 1½m, 1st house on R after leaving Markbeech.* 1-acre partly-walled cottage garden around C15 farmhouse (not open). Shrubs, clematis, climbing and shrub roses, anemones, astilbes, campanulas, eryngiums, day lilies, hardy geraniums, grasses, iris, jasmine, lilies, peonies, poppies, penstemons, wisteria for yr-round interest using structure, texture, scent and colour. WC. Group visits welcome by arrangement. Featured in 'Daily Telegraph' & on ITV 2004. *Adm £2.50, chd free. 1st & last Sats, every Wed May, June, July. For NGS: Sat 30 Apr; Wed 4, Sat, Suns 1, 8, 14, 15, 29 May; Wed 1, Sat, Suns 5, 11, 26 June; Wed 6, Suns 10, 31 July; Wed 3, Sat, Suns 6, 7, 14 Aug; Wed 7, Sats, Sun 3, 4, 10 Sept (11-5.30). Tel 01342 850825*

69 **Old Orchard, 56 Valley Drive, Loose, Maidstone** 🅰🅱🅲

(Mike & Hazel Brett) *2½m S of Maidstone. On A229, turn R towards Loose village, parking on hill; at top of hill take footpath to Valley Drive. Limited parking for disabled at house, in cul-de-sac.* Approx 1 acre, plant lovers' informal garden with rockeries, raised beds, scree and mixed island beds containing many unusual plants. Home-made TEAS in aid of Talking Newspapers Assoc UK. *Adm £2, chd £1. Suns 24 Apr; 8, 22 May (2-6). Private visits welcome by appt for individuals & groups. Tel 01622 746941*

70 **Old Place Farm, High Halden** 🅰🅱🅲

(Mr & Mrs Jeffrey Eker) *10m SW of Ashford. From A28, centre of village, take Woodchurch Rd (opp Chequers PH) for ½m.* 4-acre garden, mainly designed by Anthony du Gard Pasley, surrounding period farmhouse (not open) and buildings, with paved herb garden and parterres, small lake, ponds, lawns, mixed borders, cutting garden and potager, old shrub roses, foliage plants and specimen trees. All created since 1969. 2 bridges leading to woodland and fields. Featured in 'The English Garden' 2005. Home-made TEAS by prior arrangement. *Adm £3.50, chd £1. Private visits welcome by appt. Tel 01233 850202 Old Place Farm, High Halden, Ashford, Kent TN26 3JG*

71 **Old Tong Farm, Tong Road, Brenchley** 🅰🅱

(Simon Toynbee) *6m E of Tunbridge Wells. 1½m S of Brenchley village. From A21 going S, past B2160, turn L into Cryals Rd. After 2m R into Tong Rd, house is 600yds on L. Or exit Brenchley village on rd to Horsmonden. Turn R, Fairmans Rd leads to Tong Rd.* 4-acre terraced garden around pre-Tudor farmhouse (not open) with mixed borders, rose garden, nuttery, pond, meadow and small organic vegetable garden. Emphasis on tamed informality and non-regimented approach. Recently coppiced wood over stream provides interesting site of former iron workings. Parking in orchard 300yds S of property. Home-made TEAS. *Adm £3, chd free. Sun 19 June (2-6). Also open* **Puxted House**

72 **The Orangery, Mystole** 🅰🅱

(Rex Strickland & Anne Prasse) *5m SW of Canterbury. Turn off A28 through Shalmsford Street. After 1½m at Xrds turn R down hill. Keep straight on, ignoring rds on L (Pennypot Lane) & R. Ignore drive on L signed 'Mystole House only' & at sharp bend in 600yds turn L into private drive signed 'Mystole Farm'.* 1½-acre gardens around C18 orangery, now a house (not open). Front gardens, established well-stocked herbaceous border and large walled garden with a wide variety of shrubs and mixed borders. Splendid views from terraces over ha-ha and paddocks to the lovely Chartham Downs. Water features and very interesting collection of modern sculptures set in natural surroundings. *Adm £2.50, chd £1 (share to Project Peru). Suns 26 June; 31 July (11-5)*

73 **Orchard Cottage, 3 Woodlands Road, Bickley** 🅰🅱🅲

(Mrs J M Wall) *1½m E of Bromley. About 400yds from the A222. From Bickley Park Rd turn into Pines Rd, then 1st R into Woodlands Rd, No 3 is 1st house on L.* Attractive, colourful and varied ⅓-acre garden, compartmentalised and themed, with many interesting and unusual herbaceous plants and shrubs. Incl areas of scree beds, troughs and pots with alpines and other specialist plants. Home-made TEAS. *Adm £2, chd free (share to Diabetes UK). Sun 17 July (2-5)*

74 🆕 **Orchard End, Cock Lane, Spelmonden Road, Horsmonden** 🅱🅲

(Mr & Mrs Hugh Nye) *8m E of Tunbridge Wells. From A21 going S*

turn L at roundabout towards Horsmonden on B2162. After 2m turn R into Spelmonden Rd, ½m to top of hill, R into Cock Lane. Garden 50yds on R. Classically English garden on 1½-acre sloping site, landscaped 10yrs ago by owners' designer son. Divided into rooms with linking vistas. Incl hot borders, cottage and white gardens, exotics with pergola, raised summerhouse overlooking lawns and drive planting. Formal fish pond with bog garden. Ornamental vegetable and fruit areas. Wildlife orchard. 2 deep ponds, therefore unsuitable for children under 10. Home-made TEAS. *Adm £3, chd free. Sats, Suns 18, 19 June; 20, 21 Aug; 17, 18 Sept (11-6). Private visits welcome by appt. Tel 01892 723118*

75 ◆ **The Owl House, Mount Pleasant, Lamberhurst** 🅰

(The Iveagh Trust) *6m SE of Tunbridge Wells. 1m W of A21, signed from Lamberhurst.* 16½-acre romantic woodland garden surrounding C16 cottage (not open), created by the late Maureen, Marchioness of Dufferin and Ava over 45yrs and continued by her family. Spring bulbs, rhododendrons, camellias, unusual roses, water garden, herbaceous border and good autumn colour. Light refreshments and TEAS. *Adm £4, chd £1. Daily, not Christmas Day or New Yr's Day. For NGS: Suns 20 Mar; 18 Sept (11-6). Tel 01892 891290 www.owlhouse. com*

76 **Pedlinge Court, Saltwood** 🅱🅲

(Mr & Mrs J P Scrivens) *½m W of Hythe. Top of hill, on A261 from Hythe up hill signed M20 & Ashford opp sign 'Pedlinge'. From Newingreen 1m opp sign 'Hythe twinned with....'.* 1½-acre garden with a profusion of interesting plants around C14 farmhouse (not open), birthplace of the orchid foxglove 'Saltwood Summer'. Wide variety of cottage garden plants, ferns, old shrub roses, medicinal and culinary herbs with a backdrop of trees and shrubs incl topiary. *Adm £2.50, chd £1 (share to Cats Protection). Private visits welcome by appt May, June, July for small groups. Tel 01303 269959 susan@pedlinge-court.co.uk*

77 ◆ **Penshurst Place, Penshurst** 🅰🅱

(Viscount De L'Isle) *6m NW of Tunbridge Wells. SW of Tonbridge on B2176, signed from A26 N of Tunbridge Wells.* 10 acres of garden dating back to C14; garden divided into series of rooms by over a mile of clipped yew hedge; profusion of spring bulbs: herbaceous borders; formal rose garden; famous peony border. Toy museum. All-yr interest. Light refreshments and TEAS. *House & garden adm £7, chd £5, concessions £6.50. Garden only £5.50, chd £4.50, concessions £5. Apr to Oct.* **For NGS:** *Weds 18 May; 15 June (10.30-6, last entry 5). Tel 01892 870307 www.penshurstplace.com*

78 ♦ The Pines Garden, St Margaret's Bay ♿
(St Margaret's Bay Trust) *4½m NE of Dover. Approach village of St Margaret's-at-Cliffe via B2058 off A258 Dover/Deal rd. Continue through village centre & down Bay Hill. Signed just before beach.* Adjacent to cliff walks and beach, this mature garden offers a mixture of open undulating parkland, trees, shrubs and secluded areas. Lake, waterfall, grass labyrinth, roundhouse shelter, famous Oscar Nemon statue of Winston Churchill. Access for disabled, ample seating, picnics. Garden open all yr (10-5). Museum opening times only: Easter, Bank Hol Mons; end of May to Sept, Weds to Suns 12-5. Home-made TEAS on NGS days. *Adm £3, chd 50p, concessions £2.50, wheelchair users £1. Museum £1, chd free.* **For NGS:** *Suns 27 Mar; 29 May; 28 Aug. Tel 01304 852764 enquiries@baytrust.org.uk*

79 Placketts Hole, Bicknor, nr Sittingbourne ♿🌿⊙
(Mr & Mrs D P Wainman) *5m S of Sittingbourne. W of B2163. Signed from B2163 at top of Hollingbourne Hill, & from A249 at Stockbury Valley.* 3-acre garden in the North Downs Area of Outstanding Natural Beauty around charming old house, C16 with Georgian additions (not open). Interesting mix of shrubs, large lawns and borders, old-fashioned rose garden, walled herb garden, informal pond and bamboo features. **Evening Openings** *£3, wine, Sats 21 May; 25 June (5.30-8)*

80 Plaxtol Gardens
5m N of Tonbridge. 6m E of Sevenoaks. Turn E off A227 to Plaxtol village. Large car park at nursery next to Spoute Cottage. Tickets and maps available at both gardens. *Combined adm £3, chd free. Sun 19 June (2-6)*

Ducks Farm, Dux Lane 🌿⊙ (Mr & Mrs H Puleston Jones) *½m N of Plaxtol.* 2 acres surrounding medieval/Victorian farmhouse

(not open). Mixed herbaceous borders; walled garden; vegetable garden; herb garden; rose pergola. Lovely views over Bourne Valley.

Spoute Cottage, Long Mill Lane ♿🌿 (Mr & Mrs Donald Forbes) *At bottom of The Street in Plaxtol village, on L.* 1 acre of mixed borders of contrasting flower and foliage plants, especially for flower arranging; 5 separate garden rooms, small pond and stream. Japanese garden.

81 Puxted House, Brenchley Road, Brenchley ♿🌿⊙
(Mr P J Oliver-Smith) *6m SE of Tonbridge. From A21 1m S of Pembury turn N onto B2160, turn R at Xrds in Matfield signed Brenchley. ¾m from Xrds stop at 30 mph sign at village entrance.* 1½ acres, planted with scented and coloured foliage shrubs selected to ensure yr-long changing effects. Meandering gravel paths lead from the alpine garden via herbaceous borders and croquet lawn with its thyme terrace to formal rose garden and thereafter swing amongst oriental woodland plants and bamboos about a lily pond. Large glasshouse protects many Australasian shrubs and cacti. Cream TEAS. *Adm £2.50, chd free. Sun 15 May (2-6). Also opening with* **Brenchley Gardens** *Sun 19 June. Private visits welcome by appt. Tel 01892 722057 pjospux@aol.com*

82 ♦ Quex House Gardens, Birchington ♿🌿⊙
(The Powell-Cotton Museum Trust) *10m NE of Canterbury. On A28 take rd to Acol, just before Birchington Sq; park entrance is off Park Lane. Or take A253 Ramsgate rd & turn N for Acol. Look for signs to the Powell-Cotton Museum, Quex House & Gardens.* 15 acres of woodland and informal garden with fine specimen trees, naturalised spring bulbs; old wisteria walk, shrub borders, old figs and mulberries and long herbaceous border. Garden incl Victorian walled kitchen garden being extensively restored. Opportunity to visit Powell-Cotton Museum and House during visit. Light refreshments and TEAS. *House, garden & museum adm £5, chd/concessions £4. Garden only £1.50, chd/concessions £1. Tues, Weds, Thurs, Suns & Bank Hols.* **For NGS:** *Sun 5 June (11-5).* **Evening Opening,** *£1.50, chd £1, wine, Wed 3 Aug (6-9). Tel 01843 842168 powell-cotton.museum@virgin.net*

83 Riddles Road Allotments, Sittingbourne 🌿
(Sittingbourne Allotment and Gardeners' Society) *½m S of Sittingbourne. At A2/A249 junction turn E off roundabout towards Sittingbourne. After approx 1m turn R into Borden Lane, just after Coniston Hotel. Riddles Rd is 2nd L after approx ½m.* This is a standard allotment site: a number of plots will be demonstrated showing a variety of horticultural techniques for growing fruit and vegetables and some flowers. Featured in 'Daily Telegraph' 2004. *Adm £2, chd free, OAP £1.50. Sun 10 July (11-4). Also open* **185 Borden Lane**

84 ♦ Riverhill House Gardens, Sevenoaks 🌿⊙
(The Rogers Family) *2m S of Sevenoaks. On A225.* Mature hillside garden with extensive views; specimen trees, sheltered terraces with roses and rare shrubs; bluebell wood with rhododendrons and azaleas; picnics allowed. Unsuitable for wheelchairs but users may have free access to the tea terrace (on the level and with views across the garden). Personal welcome from members of the family. TEAS NGS days. *Adm £3, chd 50p. Suns & Bank Hol weekends, 25 Mar to 19 June.* **For NGS:** *Thurs 21 Apr; 19 May (11-5). Tel 01732 458802*

85 Rock Farm, Gibbs Hill, Nettlestead 🌿⊙
(Mrs S E Corfe) *6m W of Maidstone. Turn S off A26 onto B2015, then 1m S of Wateringbury turn R up Gibbs Hill.* 2-acre garden set around old Kentish farmhouse (not open) in beautiful setting; created with emphasis on all-yr interest and ease of maintenance. Plantsman's collection of shrubs, trees and perennials for alkaline soil; extensive herbaceous border, vegetable area, bog garden and plantings around two large natural ponds. *Adm £3, chd free, concessions £3 (share to St Mary's Church, Nettlestead). Wed, Sat 18, 21 May: Weds 8 June to 6 July incl. Sats 11 June to 9 July incl (11-5). Private visits welcome by appt. Tel 01622 812244 www.rockfarmhousebandb.co.uk*

86 Rogers Rough, Kilndown ♿🌿⊙
(Richard & Hilary Bird) *10m SE of Tonbridge. From A21 2m S of Lamberhurst turn E into Kilndown; take 1st R down Chick's Lane until rd divides.* Garden writer's 1½-acre garden, divided into many smaller gardens containing herbaceous

borders, rock gardens, shrubs, small wood and pond. Very wide range of plants, incl some unusual ones. Extensive views. TEAS in aid of local charities. *Adm £3, chd 50p. Suns 22 May; 26 June (11-5.30)*

87 St Clere, Kemsing

(Mr & Mrs Ronnie Norman) *6m NE of Sevenoaks. Take A25 from Sevenoaks toward Maidstone; 1m past Seal turn L signed Heaverham & Kemsing. In Heaverham take rd to R signed Wrotham & W Kingsdown; in 75yds straight ahead marked private rd; 1st L & follow rd to house.* 4-acre garden, full of interest. Formal terraces surrounding C17 mansion (not open), with beautiful views of the Kent countryside. Herbaceous and shrub borders, productive kitchen and herb gardens, lawns and rare trees. Home-made TEAS. *Adm £3, chd 50p. Sun 12 June (2-6)*

88 St Michael's Gardens, East Peckham

5m NE of Tonbridge, 5m SW of Maidstone. On A26 at Mereworth roundabout take S exit (A228) signed Paddock Wood, after 1½m turn L at top of rise (signed Roydon). Gardens ¼m up hill on L. From Paddock Wood follow A228. 1m after Wheelbarrow roundabout turn R into Roydon Hall Rd. Old Victorian vicarage and cottages. Home-made TEAS. *Combined adm £3, chd free. Suns 1, 22 May; 5 June; 10 July (2-5)*

St Michael's Cottage (Mr & Mrs Peter Fox) Garden designed so it cannot be seen all at once; formal garden, woodland and wildlife areas, pond, collection of ornamental grasses and herb garden. Traditional cottage garden with roses, collection of lavenders, pinks, hostas, heathers, alpines and over 30 different climbers. Featured in 'Amateur Gardening' 2003.

St Michael's House (Brig & Mrs W Magan) Grey stone old vicarage with yew topiary hedges surrounding flower beds planned in coordinated colours. Lovely display of tulips followed by splendid irises, then a mass of roses from red-hot to old soft colours. Wonderful views from the meadow. Featured in 'Homes & Gardens', '25 Beautiful Gardens' 2004.

89 Sandling Park, Hythe

(The Hardy Family) *1½m NW of Hythe. Entrance off A20 only. From M20 J11 turn E onto A20. Entrance ¼m.* 25-acre woodland garden with an extensive collection of trees and shrubs with rhododendrons, azaleas, magnolias and other interesting plants that also relish acid soil. TEAS. *Adm £3, chd 50p (share to Church of St Peter & St Paul, Saltwood). Sun 15 May (10-5)*

90 ◆ Scotney Castle, Lamberhurst

(Mrs Christopher Hussey, The National Trust) *6m SE of Tunbridge Wells. On A21 London-Hastings. Bus: (Mon to Sat) Tunbridge Wells-Wadhurst, alight Lamberhurst Green.* Picturesque landscape garden, created by the Hussey family in the 1840s surrounding moated C14 Castle. Old Castle open May to end Sept (same times as garden). Picnic area in car park. *Adm £4.80, chd £2.40 (share to Trinity Hospice). Weds to Suns.* **For NGS:** *Sat 14 May (11-6, last adm 5). Tel 01892 891081 www.nationaltrust.org.uk*

91 Sea Close, Cannongate Road, Hythe

(Major & Mrs R H Blizard) *½m from Hythe towards Folkestone (A259), on L. Signed.* All-yr-round plantsman's garden on 1¼ acre steep hillside overlooking the Channel. 27th yr of opening. Achieved since 1966 by a now 83yr-old and his wife, totally unaided from concept to present day. Wide variety of plants and shrubs, many unusual, planted for maximum effect, with changes since last yr. A wonderful garden, just as good in autumn. Cold refreshments. *Adm £2.50, chd free (share to Royal Signals Benevolent Fund). Suns 15 May; 26 June; 7 Aug (2-5); 2 Oct (2-4). Private visits welcome by appt. Tel 01303 266093*

92 ◆ Sissinghurst Garden, Sissinghurst

(The National Trust) *16m E of Tunbridge Wells. On A262 1m E of village. Bus: Arriva Maidstone-Hastings, alight Sissinghurst 1¼m. Direct bus Tues & Suns mid-May to Aug. Station: Staplehurst.* Garden created by the late V Sackville-West and Sir Harold Nicolson. Spring garden, herb garden, cottage garden, white garden, rose garden. Tudor building and tower, partly open to public. Moat. Exhibition on history of the garden and property. Light refreshments and TEAS. *Adm £7.50, chd £3.50, free to NT Members. 19 Mar to 30 Oct: Mons, Tues, Fris (11-6.30); Sats, Suns, Bank Hols (10-6.30).* **For NGS:** *Mons 18 Apr; 6 June; 15 Aug; 10 Oct . Tel 01580 710700 www.nationaltrust.org.uk*

93 Sissinghurst Place, Sissinghurst

(Mr & Mrs Simon macLachlan) *10m E of Tunbridge Wells. E of Sissinghurst village, ½m from Sissinghurst NT garden on A262.* Large old-fashioned garden with views, herbaceous beds and fine trees. Established yew hedges; lime walk; herbs and climbers in ruin of original house. Special spring openings for hellebores, daffodils and spring bulbs in woodland garden. *Adm £3, chd free (share to St George's Institute, Sissinghurst). Sats, Suns 12, 13 Mar; 9, 10 Apr (11-5). Private visits welcome by appt, made not more than 1 week in advance, June & July for groups of 4+. Tel 01580 712863*

94 Slaney Cottage, Headcorn Road, Staplehurst

(Roger & Trisha Fermor) *10m SE of Maidstone. About 1m to E of A229 (Maidstone-Hastings). Please park in adjoining farmyard; parking for disabled only on verge outside.* Garden writer's traditional country garden full of scents, surrounding a C18 cottage (not open). A riot of old roses, more than 70 varieties of hardy geraniums, clematis species, usual and unusual plants, wildlife pond and woodland. Gold medallist in Gardening for Wildlife 2004. Home-made TEAS. *Adm £2, chd 50p. Sun 12 June (2-6). Private visits welcome by appt. Tel 01580 893426*

95 Sotts Hole Cottage, Crouch Lane, Borough Green

(Mr & Mrs Jim Vinson) *7m E of Sevenoaks. Crouch Lane runs SE from A25 between Esso garage & Black Horse PH, garden at bottom of 2nd hill, approx ¾m.* 6 acres of landscaped cottage garden relying entirely on the threat of visitors to motivate the owners to maintain it. We look forward to seeing you. Home-made TEAS in aid of Heart of Kent Hospice. *Adm £2.50, chd free. Suns 10 Apr; 5 June; 31 July; 11 Sept (10-6)*

96 South Hill Farm, Hastingleigh

(Sir Charles Jessel) *4½m E of Ashford. Turn off A28 to Wye, go through village & ascend Wye Downs. In 2m turn R at Xrds marked Brabourne & South Hill, then 1st L. Or from Stone St (B2068) turn W opp Stelling Minnis, follow signs to Hastingleigh. Continue towards Wye & turn L at Xrds marked Brabourne & South Hill, then 1st L.* 2 acres high up on N Downs, C17/18 house (not open); old walls; ha-ha; formal water garden;

old and new roses; unusual shrubs, perennials and foliage plants. TEAS. *Adm £2.50, chd free. Private visits welcome by appt for groups of any size, June and July only. Coaches permitted. Tel 01233 750325*

97 Southover, Grove Lane, Hunton, Maidstone &⊕
(Mr & Mrs David Way) *6m S of Maidstone. Via B2163, turn S down Hunton Hill & West St. By school, R into Grove Lane, parking adjacent to garden or beyond, as indicated; in winter or spring seek prior advice.* 1½-acre enthusiasts' garden in delightful country setting. Continuously developed over 26yrs to accommodate ever-expanding plant collection. Many new and unusual perennials. Strong on internal and external vistas and wildlife habitats. Wide range of features ensure interest at all seasons. Extensive snowdrop and penstemon collections. *Adm £3, chd free. Private visits welcome by appt for groups of 15+, coaches permitted. Tel 01622 820876*

98 Sparks Hall, Forsham Lane, Sutton Valence &&⊕
(Charles Day & Virginia Routh) *6m SE of Maidstone. Take A274 towards Headcorn. At bottom of Sutton Valence hill turn R into Forsham Lane. Sparks Hall is ½m on L next to oast house.* 1½-acre garden created 10yrs ago. Features incl formal garden with water feature, rose garden, ha-ha, pond, herbaceous/mixed borders and collection of old-fashioned varieties of apple grown as 'step-over' trees. Home-made TEAS in aid of St Mary's Church, Sutton Valence. *Adm £3, chd free. Sun 10 July (2-6). Private visits welcome by appt. Tel 01622 843248 routh1804@aol.com*

99 Spilsill Court, Staplehurst &&⊗⊕
(Mrs C G Marshall) *8m S of Maidstone. Proceed to Staplehurst on A229 (Maidstone-Hastings). From S enter village, turn R immed after garage on R & just before 30mph sign, into Frittenden Rd; garden ½m on L. From N go through village to 40mph sign, immed turn L into Frittenden Rd.* Approx 4 acres of garden, orchard and paddock; series of gardens incl blue, white and silver; roses; lawns; shrubs, trees and ponds. Small private chapel. Jacob sheep and unusual poultry. Light refreshments and TEAS Apr, Cream TEAS July. *Adm £2, chd 50p. Suns 3 Apr; 31 July (11-5)*

100 The Spinney, 38 Wildernesse Mount, Sevenoaks &⊕
(Patricia McAlister) *1½m N of Sevenoaks. 3m from M25 J5, follow A25 in direction of Maidstone to Seal Hollow Rd. Turn R at T-lights; 400yds, turn R at Hillingdon Avenue & 1st L into Wildernesse Mount. Proceed to turning circle (¼m). No. 38 on L.* Garden set in ⅔ acre surrounding house (not open). Mainly spring garden - camellias, magnolias, rhododendrons, azaleas and pieris. Good collection of trees - rowans (hybrids), liriodendron (variegated), eucalyptus, cercidiphyllum, robinia, birch, amelanchier, various acers, pine, Atlantic cedar, various conifers. Interesting water feature. Lawns/garden on 3 levels incl terrace garden. TEAS. *Adm £3, chd free, concessions £2.50. Wed 11, Sun 15 May (11-5)*

101 ◆ Squerryes Court, Westerham &
(Mrs John Warde) *½m W of Westerham. Signed from A25.* 15 acres of well-documented historic garden, C18 landscape. Part of the formal garden has been restored by the family using C18 plan. Lake, spring bulbs, azaleas, herbaceous borders, C18 dovecote, cenotaph commemorating Gen Wolfe; woodland walks. Children's Garden Trail by Kent Gardens Trust. Featured on Meridian TV 2004. Light refreshments and TEAS. *House & garden adm £5.50, chd £3, concessions £5. Garden only £3.60, chd £2, concessions £3.30. Weds, Thurs, Suns & Bank Hol Mons, 3 Apr to 29 Sept.* **For NGS:** *Suns 10 July; 4 Sept (12-5.30). Tel 01959 562345 www.squerryes.co.uk*

102 Stonewall Park, Chiddingstone Hoath
(Mr & Mrs Valentine Fleming) *4m SE of Edenbridge. Via B2026. Halfway between Markbeech & Penshurst.* Large walled garden with herbaceous borders and vegetable garden backed by 100yr-old espalier pear trees. A sea of wild daffodils in March. 12 acres of woodland garden in romantic setting featuring species and hybrid rhododendrons, magnolias, azaleas, range of interesting trees and shrubs, wandering paths and lakes. Featured on Meridian ITV 2004. TEAS. *Adm £3, chd free. Suns 20 Mar; 1 May (1.30-5)*

103 Thornham Friars, Pilgrims Way, Thurnham &&⊗
(Mr Geoffrey Fletcher) *4m NE of Maidstone. From M20 or M2 take A249. Turn into Detling & 1m along Pilgrims Way to garden. From Bearsted take Thurnham Lane, 1¼m to Thurnham.* Tudor house (not open). 2-acre garden on chalk. 12-acre park and magnificent views. Many unusual shrubs; trees; lawns with special beds for ericaceous shrubs. Designed to be relatively labour-free. Home-made TEAS in aid of The Children's Society. *Adm £2.50, chd 50p. Sat 4 June (2-5.30)*

104 Tonbridge School, Tonbridge &
(The Governors) *At N end of Tonbridge High St. Parking signed off London Rd (B245 Tonbridge-Sevenoaks).* Behind the school lie 150 acres of sports grounds and gardens, with magnificent trees, incl the Headmaster's garden and Ferox Hall garden. St Augustine's Chapel (restored after fire in 1988) will be open. TEAS. *Adm £3, chd free. Sun 24 July (2-5.30)*

105 Torry Hill, Frinsted &&⊗⊕
(The Lord & Lady Kingsdown) *5m S of Sittingbourne. Situated in triangle formed by Frinsted, Milstead & Doddington. From M20 J8 take A20 (Lenham), roundabout by large hotel turn L for Hollingbourne & Frinsted (B2163). From M2 J5 take A249 towards Maidstone, then L through Bredgar/Milstead.* 8 acres; large lawns, specimen trees, flowering cherries, rhododendrons, azaleas and naturalised daffodils; walled gardens with lawns, shrubs, herbaceous borders, rose garden incl shrub roses, wild flower areas and vegetables. Extensive views to Medway and Thames estuaries. Home-made TEAS. *Adm £2.50, chd 50p (share to St Dunstan's Church, Frinsted). Sun 8 May (2-5).* **Evening Opening** *£2.50, wine, Wed 22 June (6.30-9). Private visits welcome by appt. Tel 01795 830258 lady.kingsdown@btinternet.com*

106 NEW Tram Hatch, Charing Heath &&⊗⊕
(Mrs P Scrivens) *10m NW of Ashford. A20 turn towards Charing railway station. Continue on Pluckley Rd over motorway, 1st R signed Barnfield to end. Turn L, follow lane past Barnfield, Tram Hatch on L.* C14 manor house with tithe barn (not open) set in 3 acres of formal garden with the Great River Stour edging its boundary. Vegetable and fruit garden, orchard, rose garden, bog garden and 2 large ponds, one with ornamental wildfowl. Large variety of plants and trees. Home-made TEAS in aid of RNLI. *Adm*

£2.50, chd £1. Suns 20 Mar; 5 June (2-5)

107 Troutbeck, Otford ⊛
(Dr & Mrs Huw Alban Davies) 3m N of Sevenoaks. At W end of village. 3-acre garden surrounded by branches of R Darent. Developed over 14yrs combining the informal landscape of the river, a central pond and small wild meadow with structural planting using box and yew. Knots and topiary shapes are displayed. Featured in 'The English Garden' 2003, 'Gardens Illustrated' 2004. Adm £2.50. Private visits welcome by appt. Tel 01959 525439

108 Upper Pryors, Cowden 🚾🐾
(Mr & Mrs S G Smith) 4½m SE of Edenbridge. From B2026 Edenbridge-Hartfield, turn R at Cowden Xrds & take 1st drive on R. 10 acres of country garden - woodland, water gardens, magnificent lawns and a profusion of herbaceous colour. TEAS. Adm £2.50, chd 50p. Day (1-6) & **Evening Opening** £3.50, wine, Wed 8 June (6-9)

109 Waystrode Manor, Spode Lane, Cowden 🚾🐾⊛
(Mrs Jill Wright) 4½m SE of Edenbridge. From B2026 Edenbridge-Hartfield, turn off at

Cowden Pound. House C15 (not open). 8 acres; sweeping lawns, borders, ponds, bulbs, shrub roses, clematis and many tender plants. Orangery. All trees and shrubs labelled. TEAS. Adm £3, chd 50p. Weds 18 May; 6 July. Suns 22 May; 12, 19 June (2-5.30). Private visits welcome by appt. Tel 01342 850695

110 West Studdal Farm, West Studdal 🚾⊛
(Mr & Mrs Peter Lumsden) 4m SW of Deal; 2½m W of Eastry. N of Dover halfway between Eastry & Whitfield. Take A256. Then rd signed to Studdal at roundabout. At top of hill turn R & entrance ¼m on L. Medium-sized garden around old farmhouse (not open) set by itself in small valley; herbaceous borders, roses and fine lawns protected by old walls and beech hedges. Home-made TEAS. Adm £2, chd 50p. Sun 21 Aug (2-6)

111 Whitehurst, Chainhurst 🚾🐾
(John & Lyn Mercy) 6m S of Maidstone, 3m N of Marden. From Marden station turn R into Pattenden Lane & under railway bridge; at T-junction turn L; at next fork bear R to Chainhurst, then 2nd turning on L. 1½ acres of trees, roses and water garden. Victorian spiral staircase leading to aerial walkway through

the tree tops and other quite original features. Exhibition of root dwellings and demonstration of work in conjunction with the South East Open Studios scheme. Home-made TEAS Suns only. Adm £2, chd £1. Sats, Suns 18, 19, 25, 26, Weds 15, 22, Thur 23, Fri 24 June (10-5)

112 Windy Ridge, Victory Road, St Margarets-at-Cliffe ⊛
(Mr & Mrs D Ryder) 4½m NE of Dover. From Duke of York roundabout on A2 N of Dover follow A258 signed Deal. Take 3rd rd on R (Station Rd), then 3rd rd on L (Collingwood Rd). Continue onto unmade track & follow signs (approx ½m). Telephone for map. Plantsman's garden on top of chalk hill, with extensive views over open country and sea. Island beds of shrubs and perennials (many rare). Large collection of penstemon and salvia. Wildlife pond. Gravel seating area and viewpoint. Additional ⅔-acre extension to garden under construction. Small specialist nursery. Featured in 'The Kent Gardener' 2003. Home-made TEAS. Adm £2, chd free. Suns 12 June; 10 July; 18 Sept (2-6). Private visits welcome by appt for groups. Tel 01304 853225 www.gardenplants-nursery.co.uk

⓲ Withersdane Hall, Wye ⚓⚘
(Imperial College Wye Campus) *3m NE of Ashford. A28 take fork signed Wye. Bus Ashford-Canterbury via Wye. Pass Imperial College Wye Campus & continue up Scotton St.* Well-labelled garden of educational and botanical interest, containing several small carefully designed gardens; flower and shrub borders; spring bulbs; recently renovated culinary herb garden and herbaceous borders. Rain-fed garden. TEAS. *Adm £2.50, chd 50p. Suns 17 Apr; 28 Aug (2-5)*

⓴ NEW Woodhay, Copt Hall Road, Ightham Common ⚘
(John & Rosemary Bickley) *3m E of Sevenoaks. From Borough Green W on A25 for 1½m, L into Common Rd. ¼m, park before Harrow PH. At Xrds R into Copt Hall Rd, 2nd house on L. From Seal on A25 for 1¾m. After Crown Point PH, R into Coach Rd and park in rd. Copt Hall Rd 1st L, walk down hill ¼m, garden on R.* 1¼-acre sloping informal country garden developed over 20yrs. Incorporating many varied herbaceous plants, shrubs and trees incl pond and small stream. Home-made TEAS. *Adm £2.50, chd free. Sun 29 May (12-5)*

⓯ ◆ The World Garden at Lullingstone Castle, Eynsford ⚓⚘
(Guy Hart Dyke) *1m from Eynsford. M25 J3, signs to Brands Hatch then Eynsford. In Eynsford turn R at church over ford bridge. Follow lane under viaduct, with Lullingstone Roman Villa on R, to private rd sign, follow signs for World Garden.* Interactive world map of plants laid out as a map of the world within a walled garden. The oceans are yew pathways as you follow the world in 1 acre. You can climb Everest, sip water from waterfalls, see Ayers Rock and walk alongside the Andes whilst reading intrepid tales of the plants of the past and present. This map will show how many plants are not actually native to Britain. *Adm £5.50, chd £2.50, concessions £5. Easter to end Oct, Fri & Sat 12-5; Sun 2-6, Wed & Thur booked*

parties. **For NGS:** *Sun 19 June (2-6). Tel 01322 860762 germinatable@supanet.com*

⓰ Wyckhurst, Mill Road, Aldington ⚓⚘⊕
(Mr & Mrs C Older) *4m SE of Ashford. Leave M20 at J10, on A20 travel 2m to Aldington turning; turn R at Xrds; proceed 1½m to Aldington village hall, at Walnut Tree take rd down Forge Hill signed to Dymchurch, after ¼m turn R into Mill Rd. C16 cottage (not open).* 1-acre cottage garden in romantic setting with unusual topiary; extensive views across Romney Marsh; continually developing garden. Home-made TEAS in aid of St Rumwold's Church, Bonnington. *Adm £3, chd free. Wed, Sat, Sun 15, 18, 19 June (11-dusk). Topiary courses by appt. Tel 01233 720395 judyoldertopiary@yahoo.co.uk*

⓱ Wye Gardens
3m NE of Ashford. From A28 take turning signed Wye. Bus: Ashford to Canterbury via Wye. Train: Wye station. 4 unusual gardens in historic village. Start at centre of village. Teas and plant sale at Church. TEAS & plant sale at Church in aid of JaJa's Home, Ugandan Children's Hospice. *Combined adm £3, chd free. Sun 10 July (2-6)*

3 Bramble Close, Bramble Lane ⚓⚘ (Dr M & Mrs D Copland) A very wild garden planted in 1989. Wild flower meadow, pond and ditches, mown paths, native copse and hedges buzzing with wildlife. A unique experience.

Cumberland Court, Church Street ⚓⚘ (Mr & Mrs F Huntington) An exciting courtyard garden created in 1999 from asphalt car park. Densely planted with wide range of unusual plants. Water feature and unique artefacts.

NEW Latin School Garden, High Street ⚘ (Imperial College Wye Campus) Enclosed garden in the midst of medieval buildings, incl many unusual and interesting plants.

Mistral, Oxenturn Road ⚓⚘ (Dr & Mrs G Chapman) Garden

developed, in part, on site of old hard tennis court. 450 species of botanical interest incl white and alpine gardens. All plants labelled. Accommodation.

⓲ ◆ Yalding Organic Gardens, nr Maidstone ⚓⚘⊕
(HDRA the Organic Organisation) *6m SW of Maidstone, ½m S of Yalding. On B2162. Yalding served by buses from Maidstone & Tonbridge, railway station 1½m.* 5 acres of stunning gardens tracing the history of gardening from medieval times to the present day. Children's garden. Home cooking a speciality. Light refreshments and TEAS. *Adm £3.50, chd free, concessions £3. Weds to Suns & Bank Hols May to Sept; weekends only Apr & Oct. For NGS: Thurs 23 June; 18 Aug (10-5). Tel 024 7630 8211 www.hdra.org.uk*

⓳ Yew Tree Cottage, Penshurst ⚘⊕
(Mrs Pam Tuppen) *4m SW of Tonbridge. From A26 Tonbridge to Tunbridge Wells rd, join B2176 Bidborough to Penshurst rd. 2m W of Bidborough, 1m before Penshurst.* Small hillside cottage garden with lots of seats and secret corners, full of unusual plants - hellebores, spring bulbs, old roses, perennials. Autumn colour; something to see in all seasons. Very restricted car parking, utterly unsuitable for coaches. Please phone if needing advice for directions. Please visit throughout long opening period to ease pressure on small garden. TEAS. *Adm £2, chd free. Thurs, Fris, Sats 3 Mar to 30 Sept (10-5). Tel 01892 870689*

Evening Opening (See also garden description)	
Placketts Hole	21 May
Upper Pryors	8 June
Edenbridge House	15 June
Little Sissinghurst	15 June
Torry Hill	22 June
Placketts Hole	25 June
Quex House Gardens	
	3 August

Lancashire, Merseyside & Greater Manchester

County Organisers: Mr & Mrs Ray Doldon, 2 Gorse Way, Formby, Merseyside L37 1PB Tel 01704 834253
(Press & Publicity Officer) Mr & Mrs Bill & Barbara Seddon, Woodside, Prince's Park, Shevington, Wigan, Lancashire WN6 8HY Tel 01257 255255
County Treasurer: Mr Ray Doldon, 2 Gorse Way, Formby, Merseyside L37 1PB Tel 01704 834253

Maps: Numbers shown next to each garden entry refer to that garden's entry on the county map. This position is approximate; distance and directions from the nearest main town are generally shown in the garden text. A precise location is available for those gardens featured on the NGS website by visiting www.ngs.org.uk.

Symbols: Information relating to symbols is given on page 21

DATES OF OPENING

Evening openings
See end of county listing

Private gardens open regularly for NGS
Willow House, Walton-le-Dale *(26)*

Gardens open to the public
For details see garden description

Cobble Hey Farm & Gardens, Claughton-on-Brock *(7)*
The Ridges, Cowling Road, Limbrick *(21)*

By appointment only
For telephone number and other details see garden description. Private visits welcomed

Cross Gaits Cottage, Blacko, Nelson *(9)*
3 Longfield Bungalow, Hindley Green, Wigan *(15)*
Woodside Garden, Shevington *(27)*

February 13 Sunday
Weeping Ash, Glazebury *(25)*
February 20 Sunday
Weeping Ash, Glazebury *(25)*
April 24 Sunday
Weeping Ash, Glazebury *(25)*
May 1 Sunday
The Ridges, Cowling Road, Limbrick *(21)*
May 7 Saturday
Big Jeff's Garden, Central Manchester *(2)*
May 14 Saturday
Brookfield, Flixton *(5)*
May 18 Wednesday
Brookfield, Flixton *(5)*

£1.84 million donated to national nursing, caring and gardening charities in 2004

May 21 Saturday
Big Jeff's Garden, Central Manchester *(2)*
May 25 Wednesday
Willow House, Walton-le-Dale *(26)*
May 29 Sunday
Clearbeck House, Higher Tatham *(6)*
Heywood Gardens, Brookhouse *(13)*
Perennial Paradise, Holmeswood *(20)*
June 1 Wednesday
Willow House, Walton-le-Dale *(26)*
June 4 Saturday
Big Jeff's Garden, Central Manchester *(2)*
Cobble Hey Farm & Gardens, Claughton-on-Brock *(7)*
Montford Cottage, Fence, nr Burnley *(17)*
June 5 Sunday
480 Aigburth Road, Liverpool *(1)*
Bretherton Gardens *(3)*
Montford Cottage, Fence, nr Burnley *(17)*
June 8 Wednesday
Willow House, Walton-le-Dale *(26)*
June 12 Sunday
Crab Tree Lane Gardens, Burscough *(8)*
June 15 Wednesday
Willow House, Walton-le-Dale *(26)*
June 18 Saturday
Big Jeff's Garden, Central Manchester *(2)*
June 19 Sunday
Crab Tree Lane Gardens, Burscough *(8)*
Heaselands, Entwistle *(11)*
June 22 Wednesday
Willow House, Walton-le-Dale *(26)*
June 26 Sunday
Clearbeck House, Higher Tatham *(6)*
Hesketh Bank Village Gardens *(12)*
Mill Barn, Samlesbury Bottoms *(16)*
June 29 Wednesday
Willow House, Walton-le-Dale *(26)*
July 2 Saturday
Huntingdon Hall, Dutton *(14)*
The Stones & Roses Garden, Heapey *(24)*
July 3 Sunday
Bretherton Gardens *(3)*
Clearbeck House, Higher Tatham *(6)*
Heywood Gardens, Brookhouse *(13)*
Huntingdon Hall, Dutton *(14)*
Mill Barn, Samlesbury Bottoms *(16)*
14 Saxon Road, Birkdale *(22)*
The Stones & Roses Garden, Heapey *(24)*

July 6 Wednesday
Brinscall Hall, Brinscall, nr Chorley *(4)*
Willow House, Walton-le-Dale *(26)*
July 9 Saturday
Southlands, Stretford *(23)*
July 10 Sunday
260 Orrell Road, Orrell *(19)*
Perennial Paradise, Holmeswood *(20)*
14 Saxon Road, Birkdale *(22)*
Southlands, Stretford *(23)*
July 13 Wednesday
Brookfield, Flixton *(5)*
Willow House, Walton-le-Dale *(26)*
July 15 Friday
The Old Zoo Garden, Brockhall Village *(18)*
July 16 Saturday
Brookfield, Flixton *(5)*
July 17 Sunday
Hawthornes Nursery Garden, Hesketh Bank *(10)*
Heaselands, Entwistle *(11)*
The Old Zoo Garden, Brockhall Village *(18)*
July 20 Wednesday
Willow House, Walton-le-Dale *(26)*
July 24 Sunday
Weeping Ash, Glazebury *(25)*
July 27 Wednesday
Willow House, Walton-le-Dale *(26)*
August 3 Wednesday
Willow House, Walton-le-Dale *(26)*
August 10 Wednesday
Willow House, Walton-le-Dale *(26)*
August 17 Wednesday
Willow House, Walton-le-Dale *(26)*
August 27 Saturday
Cobble Hey Farm & Gardens, Claughton-on-Brock *(7)*
August 28 Sunday
The Ridges, Cowling Road, Limbrick *(21)*
September 18 Sunday
Mill Barn, Samlesbury Bottoms *(16)*
September 25 Sunday
Mill Barn, Samlesbury Bottoms *(16)*
Weeping Ash, Glazebury *(25)*
October 2 Sunday
Mill Barn, Samlesbury Bottoms *(16)*

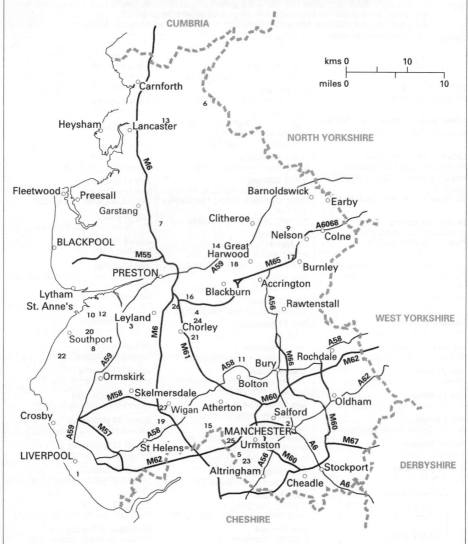

LANCASHIRE, MERSEYSIDE & GREATER MANCHESTER

CUMBRIA

kms 0   10

miles 0   10

Carnforth

6

Heysham   Lancaster   13

NORTH YORKSHIRE

M6

Fleetwood   Preesall

Garstang   7

Barnoldswick   Earby

Clitheroe

Nelson   9   A6068   Colne

BLACKPOOL   M55

14 Great Harwood

A59   18   M65   17   Burnley

PRESTON

Accrington

Lytham St. Anne's

16   Blackburn

26   Rawtenstall   A56

WEST YORKSHIRE

10 12   Leyland   4 24   Chorley

20   Southport   3   M6   21

22   8   A59   M61

A58   Rochdale   M62

Ormskirk

A58   11   Bury   M66   M62

Bolton

M58   Skelmersdale   M60   Oldham   A62

Crosby   27   Wigan   Atherton   Salford   M60

A59   M57   19   A58   15   MANCHESTER   2   A6   M67

LIVERPOOL   St Helens   25   Urmston

M62   5   23   A56   M60   Stockport   DERBYSHIRE

1   Altringham   Cheadle   A6

CHESHIRE

DESCRIPTIONS OF GARDENS

❶ 480 Aigburth Road, Liverpool ♿♨

(Mrs Bridget Spiegl) *4m S of Liverpool town centre. On main rd (A561) between city & Runcorn bridge. Just past Liverpool Cricket Club, on LH-side of rd going towards the city.* Plantswoman's small town garden. Mixed herbaceous and shrubs. Some interesting and unusual plants. Spring bulbs, particularly good display of crocus species mid-February. *Adm £1.50, chd free. Sun 5 June (2-5). Private visits welcome by appt. Tel 0151 427 2344*

❷ Big Jeff's Garden, Atherton Street, Central Manchester ♿❀

(Granada Television) *From Deansgate turn down Quay St, at Granada TV office block turn L and walk straight ahead to security lodge. The garden is opp.* An interesting garden covering approx ½ acre, built for television programmes; many interesting plants and shrubs; water features. A special Japanese entrance and small Chinese garden with rock feature. TEAS. *Adm £2, chd £1. Sats 7, 21 May; 4, 18 June (10.30-4)*

❸ Bretherton Gardens
8m SW of Preston. Between Southport & Preston, on A59, take B5248 towards Chorley for 1m. Gardens off North Rd (B5247) & South Rd (B5248). Maps available at each garden. Home-made TEAS at Church Hall in aid of local Church. *Combined adm £2.50, chd free. Suns 5 June; 3 July (12-5)*

NEW Glynwood House, Eyes Lane ♿❀ (Terry & Sue Riding) A developing garden surrounded by open aspects and mature woodland. Approx ¾-acre incorporating shrubs and herbaceous borders. Large architecturally designed pergola with raised borders and water feature; woodland walk and wildlife pond.

Hazel Cottage, 6 South View, Bamfords Fold (off South Rd) ♿❀ (John & Kris Jolley) Victorian cottager's plot of ⅓ acre divided into rooms to filter the wind and disguise the long, narrow shape. Emphasis on foliage and form with many seed-raised perennials. Mixed borders, kitchen garden, ponds, orchard. *Private visits welcome by appt. Tel 01772 600896*

Hazelwood, North Road ♿❀♨ (Jacqueline Iddon & Thompson Dagnall) 1½-acre garden and

hardy plant nursery. Originally orchard, now has gravel garden with silver and variegated foliage plants, shrubs, herbaceous borders and large stream-fed pond with woodland walk and sculpture. Featured in 'Lancashire Life' & 'Gardens Illustrated' 2004. *Private visits welcome by appt May to Sept, coaches permitted, also groups of 20+. Tel 01772 601433 www.jacquelineiddonhardy plants.co.uk*

Magnolia Cottage, South Road ♿❀ (Michael & Mikki Boston) Small shady garden architecturally designed creating 3 rooms each with their own individual features; shade-loving plants mostly green and white giving the garden an air of peace and tranquility. *Private visits welcome by appt. Tel 01772 600895*

❹ Brinscall Hall, Brinscall, nr Chorley ❀
(Dr & Mrs I M Cairncross) *2m N of Chorley. M61 exit 8. Take A647 towards Blackburn for ½m; Turn R to Brinscall, then R at village school, R at Cricketer's Arms.* C19 Victorian country house (not open) and garden in 4-acre estate. Garden presently being redeveloped in 2 acres adjacent to house. Mixed herbaceous borders, rockeries, lawns, 2 ponds and pergola. Parterre garden developing in place of sunken tennis courts; woodland walk to orchard; undulating paths and steps. Home-made TEAS in aid of St James Independent Primary School, Stockport. *Adm £2, chd free. Wed 6 July (1-4)*

❺ **NEW** Brookfield, 11 Irlam Road, Flixton ❀♨
(Bob & Beryl Wheeler) *2½m SW of Urmston. From J10 on M60 go S through 2 roundabouts to T-lights, turn R into Moorside Rd. At next roundabout take 2nd rd signed Lymm, after next T-lights take 5th rd on R Irlam Rd.* ⅓-acre town garden on triangular plot divided into sections with several pathways. Herbaceous beds and borders with mature trees and shrubs planned for yr-round effect; rockery, pond and water feature; shade areas; patio with troughs and containers. Greenhouse. Home-made TEAS & Plant sales in aid of St Ann's Church, Manchester. *Adm £2, chd free. Sats, Weds 14, 18 May; 13, 16 July (2-5)*

❻ Clearbeck House, Higher Tatham ♿♨
(Peter & Bronwen Osborne) *13m NE of Lancaster. Signed from Wray (M6 junction 34, A683, B6480) & Low Bentham.* This creative garden extends beyond traditional terraced borders through vistas and secret ways. Many charming surprises incl follies (walk-through pyramid, temple and turf maze), sculptures, fountains, streams, ponds and 2-acre wildlife lake, attracting many species of birds and insects. Planting incl herbaceous borders, bog plants, bamboos and grasses. Garden Hopping BBC 2003, featured in 'Gardens Illustrated' 2004. Light refreshments and TEAS in aid of Church of the Good Shepherd Tatham Fells & Save the Children Fund. *Adm £2, chd free. Suns 29 May; 26 June; 3 July (11-5). Private visits welcome by appt. Tel 01524 261029 clearbeck@waitrose.com*

❼ ◆ Cobble Hey Farm & Gardens, Claughton-on-Brock ❀♨
(Mr & Mrs D Miller) *4m S of Garstang. Leave M6 at junction 32 or 33. Take brown sign from A6 nr Bilsborough. Claughton is 2m E, up Butt Hill Lane, 2nd farm rd on L.* 2-acre hillside garden on working farm. Mature beds of hardy herbaceous perennials; over 200 species of phlox; primulas and hellebores; natural streams with stone banks; fruit garden. Woodland and colour themed garden, prairie and potterage under development. Lapwing walk and farm animals to view. Tourism award - Design & Innovation, Featured in 'Gardens Illustrated, 'Gardening Which' & 'Gardens of England NW' 2004. *Adm £2.50, chd £1. Open every Sat & Sun Easter to end Sept.* **For NGS:** *Sats 4 June; 27 Aug (10.30-4.30). Tel 01995 602643 www.cobblehey.co.uk*

❽ Crab Tree Lane Gardens, Burscough
3m NE of Ormskirk. Follow A59 Preston - Liverpool rd to Burscough. From N before 1st bridge turn R into Redcat Lane - Brown sign Martin Mere. From S pass through village over 2nd bridge, then L into Redcat Lane, after ¾m turn L into Crabtree Lane. Gardens by level Xing. TEAS at 79 Crabtree Lane. *Combined adm £2.50, chd free (share to Burscough Methodist Church). Suns 12, 19 June (1-5.30)*

79 Crabtree Lane ♿❀ (Sandra & Peter Curl) ½ acre comprising different areas. Patio with hostas and grasses; herbaceous area surrounded by beech hedge, island beds with conifers and shrubs. Rose garden and 2 ponds; pergola for relaxing surrounded by young clematis and wisteria. *Private visits welcome by appt. Tel 01704 893713*

81 Crabtree Lane 🚻♿🧺 (Prue & Barry Cooper) Small plantswomans' enclosed garden, 6ft old brick wall, pond and water features. Old-fashioned rockery; vine-covered pergola, trompe l'oeil. Beds comprising shrubs but mostly herbaceous plants. Arches with clematis and climbing roses.

❾ Cross Gaits Cottage, Blacko, Nelson 🚻♿🧺
(Mr & Mrs S J Gude) *5m N of Burnley. Take M65 exit junction 13. Follow Barrowford signs then Barnoldswick signs. Garden 1½m on Barnoldswick Rd opp Cross Gaits Inn.* ⅔-acre walled cottage garden, shrub and herbaceous borders; 2 ornamental ponds. 700ft above sea level; fine view of Pennines. TEAS. *Adm £2, chd free. Private visits welcome by appt June, July & Aug, groups of 4+. Tel 01282 617163 gudegarden@onetel.com*

❿ Hawthornes Nursery Garden, Marsh Road, Hesketh Bank 🚻🧺
(Mr & Mrs R Hodson) *10m SW of Preston. From Preston take A59 towards Liverpool. Turn R at T-lights for Tarleton. Through Tarleton Village into Hesketh Bank. Large car park at Station Rd/Shore Rd. WC.* 1 acre plant lovers garden. Intensively planted perennial borders and island beds with 150 shrub roses, many species roses, over 200 clematis with collections of viticella and herbaceous varieties, many rare. Large wildlife pond area. Adjoining nursery. Home-made TEAS. *Adm £2, chd free. Sun 17 July (12-5). Also open with Hesketh Bank Village Gardens Sun 26 Jun. Private visits welcome by appt, groups of 10+, coaches permitted. Tel 01772 812379 www.hawthornes-nursery.co.uk*

⓫ Heaselands, Overshores Road, Entwistle ♿🧺
(Mr & Mrs T D Bullough) *5m N of Bolton. Follow A666, then take B6391 (midway between Bolton & Darwen).Turn L at Batridge Rd. Strictly no access or parking on Overshores Rd. Please park either at Entwistle Reservoir car parks or Greens Arms Rd and enjoy the lovely 5min walk across the dam of the reservoir.* ½-acre garden with beautiful open moorland views.

Densely planted, scented country garden with pond, water features; gravel gardens, arbours, pergolas and summerhouse; many rare and unusual perennials, 100+ clematis etc. Featured in 'Lancashire Life' 2004. Cream TEAS in aid of local charites. *Adm £2.50. Suns 19 June; 17 July (11-5). Private visits welcome by appt, groups of 10+, between 12 Jun & 18 July. Day or Evening. Tel 078660 69789/fax 01204 853536*

⓬ Hesketh Bank Village Gardens *10m SW of Preston. From Preston take A59 towards Liverpool, then turn R at Tarleton in village. Straight through Tarleton to Hesketh Bank. Free vintage bus between gardens. Maps available at each garden.* Home-made TEAS at 31 Becconsall Lane & 11 Douglas Ave in aid of Tarleton Ladies Luncheon Club, Charity of the Year. *Combined adm £3, chd free. Sun 26 June (11-5)*

31 Becconsall Lane 🚻♿🧺 (Mr & Mrs J Baxter) Cottage style garden with pond, white and green beds and semi-woodland walk. Organic garden. New hot bed. *Private visits welcome by appt. Tel 01772 813018*

74 Chapel Road (Mr & Mrs T Iddon) Compact colourful garden. Wide variety of plants. Pond, arbour and gazebo. *Private visits welcome by appt. Tel 01772 813172*

11 Douglas Avenue 🚻♿🧺 (Mr & Mrs J Cook) Large established garden with lawns, mature trees, mixed herbaceous borders and naturalised areas, with pond. *Private visits welcome by appt. Tel 01772 813727*

Hawthornes Nursery Garden, Marsh Road 🚻🧺 (Mr & Mrs R Hodson) (See separate entry).

155 Station Road 🚻♿ (Mr & Mrs G Hale) Large garden with lawns; cottage style herbaceous borders. Summer house and pond.

Wedgwood, Shore Road 🚻♿🧺 (Mr & Mrs D Watson) An old garden which is being developed into diverse planting areas. These incl gravel, woodland, herbaceous, formal pond, lawns, large glasshouse, orchard with meadow and colour-themed parterre, rainbow-garden.

⓭ NEW Heywood Gardens, Heywood House, Brookhouse ♿🧺
(Mike & Lorraine Cave) *4m E of Lancaster. From J34 M6, follow*

A683 to Caton/Kirkby Lonsdale at mini island turn R to Brookhouse. At Black Bull PH turn R, garden ¾m on LH-side. Secluded 2-acre garden with many unusual trees and shrubs, sweeping lawns with beautiful herbaceous borders leading to large natural wildlife pond, gravel garden, pergolas with an abundance of roses and climbers, folly, woodland garden with natural stream. An alternative view can be enjoyed from the garden railway. Steam Garden Railway available for rides (small charge). Home-made TEAS. *Adm £2.50, chd free. Suns 29 May; 3 July (11-5). Private visits welcome by appt June & July. Tel 01524 770977*

⓮ Huntingdon Hall, Huntingdon Hall Lane, Dutton 🚻♿🧺
(Mr & Mrs J E Ashcroft) *6m NE of Preston. Leave M6 J31. Take A59 towards Clitheroe, turn L at 1st T-lights to Ribchester along B6245. After bridge over R Ribble take next R up Gallows Lane. T-junction turn L. Next R into Huntingdon Hall Lane.* C17 house (not open) situated in glorious countryside. An interesting garden, large herbaceous borders, woodland walk, terraced pond garden, many unusual plants. Home-made TEAS. *Adm £2.50, chd free. Sat, Sun 2, 3 July (11-5)*

⓯ 3 Longfield Bungalow, Leigh Road, Hindley Green, Wigan 🧺
(Rod & Marion Raines) *5m E of Wigan. From N leave M61 at junction 5 then R onto A58 L onto B5235 R onto A577 after 1m L onto A578. Garden 400yds on L. From S M6, junction 22 follow signs for Leigh R onto A580, L onto A579, L onto A572, R onto A578 for approx 2½m opp P.P.G. Works entrance.* 1 acre. Mixed borders, scree beds, woodland area, Japanese garden, climbers, rockeries, hostas and ferns. Rose garden. Mediterranean garden, deck, pond and bog garden. TEAS in aid of Local Methodist Church. *Adm £2, chd free. Private visits welcome by appt May, June & July. Tel 01942 259834*

⓰ Mill Barn, Goose Foot Close, Samlesbury Bottoms 🚻♿
(Dr C J Mortimer) *6m E of Preston. From M6 J31 2½m on A59/A677 B/burn. Turn S. Nabs Head Lane, then Goose Foot Lane.* 1½-acre tranquil, terraced garden along the banks of the R Darwen, constantly evolving. Varied artistic planting incl some uncommon herbaceous perennials. Adjacent the recently developed Primrose Bank follows the contours of the hillside. Cream TEAS.

Adm £2, chd free. Suns 26 June; 3 July (1-5); 18, 25 Sept; 2 Oct (2-5). Private visits welcome by appt Jun, July & Sept, groups of 10+. Tel 01254 853300 chris@millbarn.globalnet.co.uk

❼ Montford Cottage, Cuckstool Lane, Fence, nr Burnley &⊛
(Craig Bullock & Tony Morris) *4m N of Burnley. From J13 M65 , take A6068 (signs for Fence) & in 2m turn L onto B6248 (signs for Brierfield). Proceed down hill for ½m (past Forest PH). Entrance to garden on L, with limited car park further down hill. Gardens within a garden within an acre. Wide variety of plants and architectural features - a one off garden with atmosphere, of particular interest for the plantsman, artist and flower arranger.. Visit the website. Cream TEAS. Adm £2.50, chd 50p. Sat, Sun 4, 5 June (2-6) www.montford.p3online.net*

❽ NEW **The Old Zoo Garden, Cherry Drive, Brockhall Village** &
(Gerald & Linda Hitman) *5m N Blackburn. Leave M6 J31, take A59 Clitheroe approx 10m. Follow signs for Old Langho & Brockhall Village just prior to Blackburn roundabout (junction A666) follow signs to The Old Zoo. Partial access to wheelchairs & prams. 15 acres. The Old Zoo garden is constructed with pleasure in mind; it encloses figurative sculpture, 16 varieties of Lancashire apples, water courses, unusual planting and very unusual earth workings. The size and speed with which The Old Zoo has been constructed has made it one of the North's premier gardens, with its acclaim growing by the week. Featured in 'The Garden Design Journal' & 'Lancashire Life' 2004. Light refreshments and TEAS in aid of Crossroads (Ribble Valley Branch). Adm £4, chd £1.50. Fri, Sun 15, 17 July (2-6)*

❾ 260 Orrell Road, Orrell &⊗⊛
(David & Anne Reece) *3m W of Wigan. Exit 26 from M6. Take local rd to Skelmersdale/Orrell. (A577), straight through T-lights at Orrell, garden is 800yds on R. 1 acre of lawns, colourful mixed herbaceous borders and island beds divided off into secluded areas and set amidst an array of native and unusual shrubs. Flower arranger's garden with wildlife pond, white garden, and range of cottage garden plants. Light refreshments and TEAS. Adm £2.50, chd free (share to Derian House Childrens Hospice). Sun 10 July (1-5)*

❿ Perennial Paradise, Boundary House Farm, Holmeswood &⊗⊛
(Graham & Linda Birchall) *10m NW of Ormskirk. From A59 at Rufford take B5246 W 3m to Boundary House Farm signed. Large cottage garden featuring island and herbaceous borders well-stocked and incl many unusual perennials. Ponds; scree; dell; ha-ha, and old Lancashire pit, situated within picturesque enviromentally friendly scenery. Adjacent nursery. Featured in 'Lancashire Life' 2003. Cream TEAS. Adm £2, chd free. Suns 29 May; 10 July (1-5)*

❷❶ ◆ The Ridges, Weavers Brow, Cowling Road, Limbrick &⊛
(Mr & Mrs J M Barlow) *2m SE of Chorley. J27 M6 or J8 M61 approaching Chorley on A6, follow signs for town centre, then signs for Cowling & Rivington. From A6 S turn R at 1st roundabout, R at Morrison Supermarket. Up Brooke St, take Cowling Brow, approx ¼m garden on RH-side. 2½ acres. Incl old walled kitchen garden, cottage style; herbaceous borders; new natural garden with stream, ponds. Laburnum arch leads to large formal lawn, surrounded by natural woodland. Shrub borders and trees with contrasting foliage. New walled area planted with scented roses and herbs. Paved area with dovecote. Accommodation. Light refreshments and TEAS. Adm £2, chd 50p. Suns, Mons 2, 29, 30 May; 29 Aug (11-5); Weds in June, July (11-7). For NGS: Suns 1 May; 28 Aug (11-5). Tel 01257 279981 www.bedbreakfast-gardenvisits.com*

❷❷ 14 Saxon Road, Birkdale &⊗⊛
(Margaret & Geoff Fletcher) *1m S of Southport. Off A565 Southport to Liverpool rd. 4th rd on L after roundabout opp St James Church. ¼-acre walled garden containing long border, informal beds, raised areas, winding gravel and bark paths. Greenhouse, conservatory gazebo, 2 ponds, 2 water features; fruit and vegetable beds. Mature trees and shrubs, climbing roses, clematis and many hardy plants. Featured in 'Lancashire Life' 2004. Home-made TEAS. Adm £2, chd free (share to Cancer Research UK). Suns 3, 10 July (10.30-4.30) . Private visits welcome by appt. Tel 01704 567742*

❷❸ Southlands, 12 Sandy Lane, Stretford ⊗⊛
(Maureen Sawyer) *3m S of Manchester. Sandy Lane (B5213) is situated off A5181 (A56) ¼m from M60 junction 7. ¼-acre suburban garden created by Maureen Sawyer and artist, Duncan Watmough. The long, narrow site has been divided into distinct areas incl; Mediterranean garden containing architectural plants and exotics; woodland; kitchen and ornamental gardens with herbaceous borders and gravel walk; two ponds; water feature; large greenhouse with specimen plants and vines. Live Jazz twice daily (weather permitting). Featured in 'Lancashire Life' 2003, 'Amateur Gardening' & Gardens of England's NW 2004; ITV 'Britains Best Back Gardens 2005. Light refreshments and TEAS. Plant sales in aid of Christie Hospital, Manchester. Adm £2, chd 50p. Sat, Sun 9, 10 July (1-6). Private visits welcome by appt June, July & Aug. Tel 0161 283 9425 southlands12@hotmail.com*

❷❹ The Stones & Roses Garden, White Coppice Farm, Heapey &⊗⊛
(Raymond & Linda Smith) *3m NE of Chorley. Junction 8 M61. A674 to Blackburn. 3rd R to Heapey & White Coppice. ¾-acre garden newly built with much stonework where the cows used to live. Sunken garden with 400 roses, 2 fountains, cascade, waterfall, stone bridge over stream; blossom, herbaceous, birch tree, herb and rockery gardens. Pool where the farm effluent tank used to be. Hobbit's garden shed. Set in lovely hamlet on edge of the moors. TEAS in aid of Hillside Methodist Church. Adm £2.50, chd free. Sat, Sun 2, 3 July (2-5) . Private visits welcome by appt. Tel 01257 277633 stonesandroses@btinternet.com*

❷❺ Weeping Ash, Bents Garden Centre, Warrington Road, Glazebury &⊗
(John Bent) *15m W of Manchester. ¼m S A580 (East Lancs Rd Greyhound roundabout, Leigh) on A574 Glazebury/Leigh Boundary. 2-acre garden of all-yr interest. Broad sweep of lawn with mixed borders of shrubs and herbaceous perennials leads to secret areas where pools, rose beds and island beds create scenes of clarity and perfection. Hot Mediterranean planting leads to further extensive lawn and impressive herbaceous border. Featured in 'Gardening Which' 2004. Light refreshments and TEAS from Bents Garden Centre. Adm £3, chd free. Suns 13, 20 Feb; 24 Apr; 24 July; 25 Sept (11-4.30). Private visits welcome by appt, groups of 10+. Tel 01942 266303/266300 www.bents.co.uk*

㉖ Willow House, 106 Higher Walton Road, Walton-le-Dale 🚹🚫🏡

(Mrs Sue Coupe) *3m SW of Preston. Exit 29 M6. M65 exit 1, M61 exit Bamber Bridge/Chorley. Bungalow on A675 (nr to Inside Out Restaurant).* Approx ⅓ acre, overlooking fields to ancient woodland. Herbaceous borders, small box parterre. Pond with koi; rockery and summerhouse. Grasses and alpine troughs. Thyme path. Many unusual ideas. French Garden Bric a Brac for Sale. Prize winner Lancashire Life Garden Competition 2004. Cream TEAS in aid of Preston Renal Unit. *Adm £2, chd 50p. Weds, 25 May to 17 Aug (2-5). Private visits welcome by appt May to July, small groups, coaches permitted. Tel 01772 257042 francescoupe@hotmail.com*

㉗ Woodside Garden, Princes Park, Shevington 🚫🏡

(Barbara & Bill Seddon) *4m W of Wigan. M6 exit 26/27, B5206, follow to Shevington. Princes Park is a small side rd off Gathurst Lane. ⅔-acre undulating garden with gravel beds, rockeries and water features, linked by excellent lawns providing backdrop for early bulbs, camelias, magnolias, azaleas and rhododendrons followed by specimen hydrangeas and large herbaceous border. Prize winner 'Lancashire Life' 2003. Adm £2, chd 50p. Private visits welcome by appt, groups of 2 to maximum 40, refreshments & parking by arrangement. Tel 01257 255255 www.woodsidegarden.net*

ngs gardens open for charity

The National Trust Careership Scheme

In 2004, five more gardeners commenced a three-year National Trust vocational training programme in historic gardening with a bursary from The National Gardens Scheme. Fifteen trainees at different Trust gardens throughout England and Wales receive support from the NGS. The trainees range from school leavers to those looking to change their careers. The National Trust's scheme, known as Careership, combines day-to-day practical experience under the guidance of a head gardener with periods of residential training and study at Reaseheath College, Cheshire.

Applications for places are available from March 2005, and the three year course commences in early September 2005.

For more information on Careerships, contact:

HR Service Centre – Careership Scheme,
The National Trust, Rowan, Kembrey Park, Swindon, Wiltshire SN2 8YL
or visit the National Trust Website **www.nationaltrust.org.uk**

"We don't get much trouble from the neighbours now!"

Leicestershire & Rutland

County Organisers:
(Leicestershire)   Mr John Oakland, Long Close, Woodhouse Eaves, Loughborough LE12 8RZ
Tel/Fax 01509 890376 or 01509 890616 (Business Hours)
(Rutland)   Mrs Jennifer Wood, Townsend House, Morcott Road, Wing, Nr Oakham, Rutland LE15 8SA
Tel 01572 737465
Assistant County Organiser: Mrs Rose Dejardin, 5 Top Street, Wing, Nr Oakham LE15 8SE Tel 01572 737557
(Press & Publicity Officer) Rutland   Mr Michael Peck, Parsons Orchard, Post Office Lane, Lyndon, Nr Oakham LE15 8TX
Tel 01572 737248
County Treasurers:
(Leicestershire)   Mr John Oakland, Long Close, Woodhouse Eaves, Loughborough LE12 8RZ
Tel/Fax 01509 890376 or 01509 890616 (Business Hours)
(Rutland)   Mr David Wood, Townsend House, Morcott Road, Wing, nr Oakham, Rutland LE15 8SA
Tel 01572 737465

Maps: Numbers shown next to each garden entry refer to that garden's entry on the county map. This position is approximate; distance and directions from the nearest main town are generally shown in the garden text.
A precise location is available for those gardens featured on the NGS website by visiting www.ngs.org.uk.
Symbols: Information relating to symbols is given on page 21

DATES OF OPENING

Evening openings
See end of county listing

Private gardens open regularly for NGS
Long Close, Main St, Woodhouse Eaves
(16)
Stoke Albany House, Stoke Albany *(22)*
Orchards, Walton Gardens *(24)*

Gardens open to the public
For details see garden description
Barnsdale Gardens, Exton, nr Oakham *(3)*
1700 Melton Road, Rearsby *(18)*
Whatton Gardens, nr Loughborough *(27)*

By appointment only
*For telephone number and other details see garden description.
Private visits welcomed*
Pine House, Gaddesby *(19)*

February 20 Sunday
Burbage Gardens *(7)*
February 27 Sunday
Wartnaby Gardens, Wartnaby, Nr Melton
Mowbray *(26)*
March 6 Sunday
1700 Melton Road, Rearsby *(18)*
March 13 Sunday
The Homestead, Normanton-by-Bottesford
(15)
March 20 Sunday
Buckminster Park, Buckminster, nr
Grantham *(6)*
April 3 Sunday
Long Close, Main St, Woodhouse Eaves
(16)
April 17 Sunday
Barnsdale Gardens, Exton, nr Oakham *(3)*

April 24 Sunday
Wartnaby Gardens, Wartnaby, Nr Melton
Mowbray *(26)*
May 2 Monday (Bank Hol)
Burbage Gardens *(7)*
May 4 Wednesday
Stoke Albany House, Stoke Albany *(22)*
May 8 Sunday
The Homestead, Normanton-by-Bottesford
(15)
Warren Hills Cottage, Coalville *(25)*
May 11 Wednesday
Stoke Albany House, Stoke Albany *(22)*
May 15 Sunday
Ashwell Gardens *(2)*
Whatton Gardens, nr Loughborough *(27)*
May 18 Wednesday
Gilmorton Gardens, Nr Lutterworth
(Evening) *(10)*
Stoke Albany House, Stoke Albany *(22)*
May 21 Saturday
Holly Hayes, Birstall *(14)*
May 22 Sunday
Gilmorton Gardens, Nr Lutterworth *(10)*
Holly Hayes, Birstall *(14)*

May 25 Wednesday
Stoke Albany House, Stoke Albany *(22)*
May 29 Sunday
Hambleton Gardens *(11)*
Long Close, Main St, Woodhouse Eaves
(16)
June 1 Wednesday
Stoke Albany House, Stoke Albany *(22)*
June 5 Sunday
The Dairy, Coleorton *(9)*
Prebendal House, Empingham *(20)*
Walton Gardens *(24)*
Warren Hills Cottage, Coalville *(25)*
June 8 Wednesday
Stoke Albany House, Stoke Albany *(22)*
Walton Gardens *(24)*
June 11 Saturday
Brook House, Welham *(4)*
June 12 Sunday
Brook House, Welham *(4)*
Burbage Gardens *(7)*
Ridlington Gardens *(21)*
Whatton Gardens, nr Loughborough *(27)*

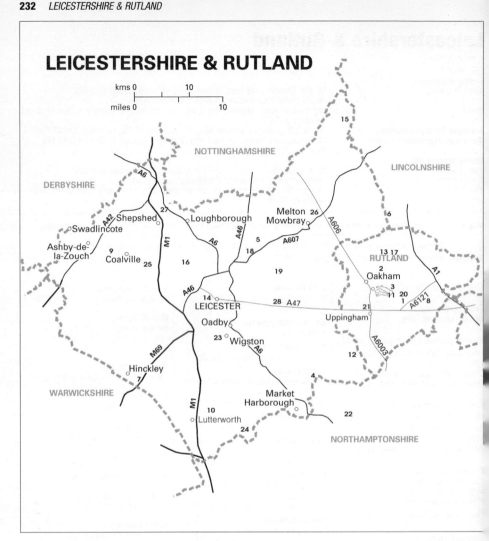

June 15 Wednesday
Stoke Albany House, Stoke Albany *(22)*

June 19 Sunday
Brooksby Melton College, Brooksby, nr Melton Mowbray *(5)*
Buckminster Park, Buckminster, nr Grantham *(6)*
High Holme, Hallaton *(12)*
Wartnaby Gardens, Wartnaby, Nr Melton Mowbray *(26)*

June 22 Wednesday
The Court House, Geeston, Ketton **(Evening)** *(8)*
Stoke Albany House, Stoke Albany *(22)*

June 26 Sunday
The White House Farm, Ingarsby *(28)*

June 29 Wednesday
Stoke Albany House, Stoke Albany *(22)*

July 6 Wednesday
Stoke Albany House, Stoke Albany *(22)*

July 10 Sunday
Acre End, North Luffenham *(1)*

July 13 Wednesday
Stoke Albany House, Stoke Albany *(22)*

July 17 Sunday
Market Overton Gardens *(17)*
Warren Hills Cottage, Coalville *(25)*

July 20 Wednesday
Stoke Albany House, Stoke Albany *(22)*

July 24 Sunday
University of Leicester 'Harold Martin' Botanic Garden, Oadby *(23)*

July 27 Wednesday
Stoke Albany House, Stoke Albany *(22)*

August 21 Sunday
Warren Hills Cottage, Coalville *(25)*

September 11 Sunday
The White House Farm, Ingarsby *(28)*

September 18 Sunday
Hill House, Market Overton *(13)*

October 2 Sunday
1700 Melton Road, Rearsby *(18)*

October 23 Sunday
Barnsdale Gardens, Exton, nr Oakham *(3)*

DESCRIPTIONS OF GARDENS

❶ Acre End, The Jetties, North Luffenham &🚫🅿
(Mr & Mrs J R Bolton) *7m SE of Oakham. Via Manton & Edith Weston, 7m SW of Stamford via Ketton. 2m off A47 through Morcott village.* 1-acre garden, imaginatively designed and intensively planted, incl knot garden, oriental courtyard garden, mixed borders, circular lawn with island beds, herb and wild flower garden. Working fruit and vegetable garden, long herbaceous border and woodland garden. Many unusual trees, shrubs, herbaceous perennials and tender exotics in containers. All organically managed to encourage wildlife. Studio Art Exhibition (share to NGS). Challenging Quiz. Featured in 'Leicestershire & Rutland Life' 2004. Light refreshments and TEAS in aid of North Luffenham Church. *Adm £2, chd free. Sun 10 July (11-5). Private visits welcome by appt, groups welcome. Tel 01780 720906*

❷ Ashwell Gardens 🚫
3m N of Oakham. Via B668 towards Cottesmore, turn L for Ashwell. Lunches & TEAS at Ashwell House. *Combined adm £2.50, chd free (share to St Mary's Church, Ashwell). Sun 15 May (11.45-6)*

Ashwell House &🅿 (Mr & Mrs S D Pettifer) 1½-acre walled vicarage garden, 1812. Against background of ancient trees; front lawns are bordered by interesting shrubs and plants with classical summer pavilion. The formal swimming pool garden leads to traditional planting of vegetables and fruit.

The Old Hall (Mrs N L McRoberts) Medium-sized garden, mixed borders, good variety of shrubs, climbers and herbaceous plants. Good trees and view of church.

❸ ◆ Barnsdale Gardens, Exton, nr Oakham &🚫🅿
Nick & Sue Hamilton) *3m E of Oakham. Turn off A606 at Barnsdale Lodge Hotel then 1m on L.* 8 acres of individual gardens used by the late Geoff Hamilton for BBC TV Gardeners World'. Wide variety of ideas and garden designs for all-yr interest. Chelsea 2003 & Gardeners' World Live 2004 medal winners. Light refreshments and TEAS. *Adm £5, chd free. Open daily Mar to May, Sept, Oct (9-5); June to Aug (9-7); Nov to Feb (10-4) last entry 2hrs prior to closing. Closed 23 to 25 Dec. For NGS: Suns 17 Apr; 23 Oct (9-5).*

Tel 01572 813200
www.barnsdalegardens.co.uk

◆ Belvoir Castle, Grantham 🚫
See Lincolnshire.

[NEW] Bishops Cottage, 89 Main Street, Kinoulton &🚫🅿
See Nottinghamshire.

❹ [NEW] Brook House, Cranoe Road, Welham &🚫🅿
(Nick & Janet Meek) *6m NE of Market Harborough. Halfway between the villages of Welham & Cranoe. From Market Harborough to Thorpe Langton, Welham then Cranoe. From Leicester A6 to Kibworth, then Turlangton, Cranoe then Welham. From Uppingham to Stockerton, Hallaton then Cranoe and Welham.* ⅔-acre informal cottage garden surrounded by fields with wonderful views. Extensive and interesting herbaceous borders, planted brook, sheltered kitchen garden with raised beds, greenhouse and cold frames. Plant store. Home-made TEAS in aid of St Andrews Church, Welham. *Adm £2, chd free. Sat, Sun 11, 12 June (2-5)*

❺ Brooksby Melton College, Brooksby, nr Melton Mowbray 🅿
(Chief Executive) *6m SW of Melton Mowbray. From A607 (9m from Leicester or 6m from Melton Mowbray) turn at Brooksby; entrance 100yds. Bus: Leicester-Melton Mowbray; alight Brooksby turn, 100yds.* Extensive lawns, lake, stream, specimen trees, shrub borders, herbaceous beds, 2 national plant collections, rose garden, topiary, wild flower meadows, rock gardens, pergola. Church built 1220. Cream TEAS. *Adm £2, chd free. Sun 19 June (12-4)*

❻ Buckminster Park, Buckminster, nr Grantham &🚫🅿
(Sir Lyonel Tollemache) *8m SW of Grantham. Buckminster Park, Buckminster Village. 10m E of Melton Mowbray on B676.* Terraced garden with mixed island beds. Woodland walk, walled and scented garden, children's maze. TEAS in aid of Buckminster and Sewstern PCC. *Adm £2.50, chd free. Suns 20 Mar; 19 June (2-5)*

❼ Burbage Gardens
1m S of Hinckley. From M69 junction 1, take B4109 signed Hinckley. A pleasant West Leicestershire village. Home-made TEAS at 6 Denis Rd (Feb & May

only) in aid of Air Ambulance. *Combined adm £1.50, chd free (Feb & May); £.2.50, chd free (June). Sun 20 Feb; Mon 2 May (1-5); Sun 12 June (1-6)*

6 Denis Road 🚫🅿 (Mr & Mrs D A Dawkins) *Sketchley Manor Estate. Signed Hinckley then 1st L after 2nd roundabout.* Small garden designed to appear much larger with wide range of plants incl hardy geraniums, ferns, hostas, foliage plants, species clematis, hellebores and spring bulbs. Alpines in sinks. Collection of snowdrops.

7 Hall Road &🚫🅿 (Mr & Mrs D R Baker) *Sketchley Manor Estate. Signed Hinckley at 2nd roundabout L then R to Sketchley Lane. 1st R; 1st R; 1st L Hall Rd.* Medium-sized garden; mixed borders; foliage plants; good mixture of shrubs. Collection of hellebores and spring bulbs, collection of snowdrops. Hostas, hardy geraniums and unusual perennials; pond, good design ideas. *Private visits welcome by appt. Tel 01455 635616*

[NEW] 13 Hall Road &🚫🅿 (Mr & Mrs G A & A T Kierton) *Sketchley Manor Estate, signed Hinckley at 2nd roundabout turn L then R to Sketchley Lane then 1st R, 1st R again then 1st L into Hall Rd.* Decorative medium-sized flower garden, incoporating pool and waterfall, herbaceous borders, central lawn, scree garden, 2 patios, pergola, summer house. greenhouse and small fountain. Winner Regional WI Medium Sized Garden Competition 2003. *Not open Sun 20 Feb, Mon 2 May*

12 Johns Close &🚫 (Bob & Cynthia Roberts) *Signed Hinckley, 2nd island 1st exit then 1st R 4 times.* Medium-sized garden with mixed herbaceous borders having a wide variety of plants and shrubs around shaped lawn with island bed. Vegetable garden with raised beds. *Not open Sun 20 Feb; Mon 2 May*

❽ The Court House, Geeston, Ketton &🅿
(Bas & Jane Clarke) *3m W of Stamford. On the A43 in middle of Collyweston take rd to Ketton (1½m).* Turn into Geeston Rd the Court House 200yds on R. 2½-acre garden incl formal garden (designed by Bunny Guinness), walled vegetable garden, immaculate lawns, wild flower meadow, woodland and river.

TEAS. *Adm £1.50, chd free.* **Evening Opening**, *Wed 22 June (5-9)*

❾ The Dairy, Moor Lane, Coleorton 🅰️🐕♿
(Mr & Mrs J B Moseley) *4m E of Ashby De La Zouch. Off A512 200yds W of Peggs Green roundabout.* Approx ½-acre of mature trees, shrubs and herbaceous borders containing many unusual and architectural plants. Herb garden, fragrant roses, pergola, Japanese garden and newly created dry area with grasses and agaves. The separate 'rooms' of the garden create surprises around every corner. Featured on BBC 1 East Midlands Today 2004. Home-made TEAS. *Adm £2, chd free. Sun 5 June (1.30-5). Private visits welcome by appt groups of 10+, coaches permitted. Tel 01530 834539*

❿ Gilmorton Gardens, Nr Lutterworth
12m S of Leicester. 4m from junction 20 of M1. Proceed through Lutterworth town centre. Turn R at police station. Follow signs to Gilmorton. From Leicester follow A426 towards Lutterworth. At Dunton Bassett turn L signposted to Gilmorton. Also A50 Leicester/Northampton Rd via Bruntingthorpe signposted Gilmorton. Very old village with interesting Victorian Church which will be open. Excellent Kempe stained glass windows. Home-made TEAS (Wed), Light Refreshments & TEAS (Sun) at & in aid of Gilmorton Village Hall. *Combined adm £3, chd free. Sun 22 May (11-5).* **Day & Evening Opening** *Wed 18 May (2-8)*

'Al Manzel', Main Street (Mr David & Janet Grundy) *Nr Crown PH end of Main St opp Porlock Drive.* Average-size plant lovers' garden constructed from an old walled farmyard, with many interesting plants, structures and features. Ponds and running water, rockery, gravel garden, greenhouse, formal garden. Extensive use of small trees, clematis and plants in pots. Featured in '25 Beautiful Gardens' 2004. *Private visits welcome by appt. Tel 01455 556586*

Moatfield, Church Lane 🅰️🐕 (Mr & Mrs R P Morgan) Country garden started in 1995 in old farmyard close to the church with mixed beds, arbour and pergola with roses, various climbers. Tree collection with daffodils, large natural pond and old moat in adjoining field. *Private visits welcome by appt March, June & late Oct. Tel 01455 552282*

Tudor Cottage, Main Street (Mr & Mrs D Dolby) *Nr Crown PH opp 'Al Manzel'.* Well constructed ½-acre garden around a C17 cottage (not open). Water features in enclosed garden. Large well planted borders, parterre, topiary, and quirky features. 'A true artist's garden'.

Ulverscroft Close, Ashby Road 🐕♿ (Mr & Mrs M J Maddock) ½-acre garden of great atmosphere. Growing amongst shrubs, trees, perennials and grasses are 120 clematis. Features incl pond, bog garden, pergola, short ave of mop head robinias, parterre. Newly laid formal kitchen garden. *Private visits welcome by appt. Tel 01455 553226 michael.maddock@care4free. net.uk*

⓫ Hambleton Gardens
3½m E of Oakham. Follow sign to Hambleton. Home-made TEAS at and in aid of village hall. *Combined adm £2.50, chd free. Sun 29 May (10-5)*

Chestnuts 🅰️♿ (Mr & Mrs A Tibbert) *Turn R at church. 70yds down hill. Turn L at village hall on to a track 3rd on R. Only gravel drive.* Sloping S-facing garden of approx 1½ acres overlooking Rutland Water. Various borders of shrubs and perennials lead down to rose arbour and then to natural pond hidden by willow trees at the bottom of garden.

Stone Cottage, Ketton Road, Hambleton ♿ (Jenny & Malcolm Bonser) *Keep L at Church House, opp Hambleton Hall.* Approx 1-acre garden with interesting plants; shrubs, roses, herb garden and water features. Orchard

underplanted with bulbs and shrubs. Orangery, views of Rutland Water.

⓬ High Holme, 43 High Street, Hallaton 🐕♿ (Matthew & Nicky Lyttelton) *5m SW of Uppingham. Signs off A47-A6 to Hallaton. In village follow yellow signs to garden at end of High St.* 1-acre garden which has been developed from an offset paddock, previously a gravel pit. Designed to exploit the change in levels in a dynamic way using stone and water. Teas, plant stall and baskets in nearby cottage garden at 4 High St. *Adm £1.50, chd free. Sun 19 June (2-6)*

⓭ Hill House, 18 Teigh Road, Market Overton 🅰️♿
(Brian & Judith Taylor) *6m N of Oakham. Beyond Cottesmore, 5m from A1 via Thistleton, 10m E from Melton Mowbray via Wymondham.* ½-acre plant enthusiasts' garden consisting mainly of mixed beds designed for seasonal interest. The emphasis is on architectural plants and unusual hardy and tender perennials. Featured in '25 Beautiful Gardens' 2004. Home-made TEAS. *Adm £2, chd free. Sun 18 Sept (11-5). Also opening with Market Overton Gardens Sun 17 July. Private visits welcome by appt mid June - end Sept, groups of 10+, coaches permitted. Tel 01572 767337*

⓮ Holly Hayes, 216 Birstall Road, Birstall 🅰️
(Mrs Edith A Murphy) *3m N of Leicester. Adjoining Ecology Centre. Take Birstall Rd from Redhill island. Near village hall.* 4-acre garden with rhododendrons, azaleas, fine old trees incl redwoods, wisteria, pergola, flower borders and pond. TEAS. *Adm £1.20, chd free. Sat, Sun 21,22 May (2-6)*

NEW **Holywell Hall, Holywell** 🅰️
See Lincolnshire.

NEW **Homefield House, West Thorpe, Willoughby on the Wolds** 🅰️🐕♿
See Nottinghamshire.

⓯ The Homestead, Normanton-by-Bottesford ♿ NCCPG
(Mr & Mrs J E Palmer) *8m W of Grantham. On A52. In Bottesford turn N, signposted Normanton; last house on R before disused airfield.* ¾-acre informal plant lover's garden. Vegetable garden, small orchard,

woodland area, many hellebores and single peonies. Collections of hostas and sempervivums. National Collection of heliotropes. Home-made TEAS. *Adm £1.25, chd free. Suns 13 Mar; 8 May (2-6). Private visits welcome by appt. Tel 01949 842745*

⓰ Long Close, Main St, Woodhouse Eaves ⬤
(John Oakland & Pene Johnson) *4m S of Loughborough. Nr M1 junction 23. From A6, W in Quorn.* 5-acres spring bulbs, rhododendrons, azaleas, camellias, magnolias, many rare shrubs, mature trees, lily ponds; terraced lawns, herbaceous borders, potager in walled kitchen garden, penstemon collection, wild flower meadow walk. Winter, spring, summer and autumn colour, a garden for all seasons. Featured in 'Daily Telegraph' best gardens to visit & voted one of Top 30 NGS gardens by 'Gardening Which' readers 2003. Home-made TEAS. *Adm £3, chd 50p. Suns 3 Apr Specialist Plant Fair (2-5.30); 29 May (2-6), tickets from garden. Daily Tues to Sats & Bank Hol Mons Mar to July & Autumn (9.30-5.30). Tickets Pene Crafts Gift Shop opp. Tea/coffee facilities. Group visits also welcome, catering by arrangment. Tel 01509 890616 or 890376 www.longclose.org.uk*

⓱ Market Overton Gardens
6m N of Oakham. Beyond Cottesmore; 5m from the A1 via Thistleton; 10m E from Melton Mowbray via Wymondham. Two plantsmen's gardens comprising mixed borders, roses, specimen trees, shrubs and water features. Home-made TEAS. *Combined adm £3, chd free. Sun 17 July (11-5)*

Hill House, 18 Teigh Road ⬤⬤
(Brian & Judith Taylor) (See separate entry).

Old Hall, Main Street ⬤⬤ (Mr & Mrs T Hart) S-facing 3-acre garden, lawns on 2 levels. Herbaceous borders, climbing roses; pond; unusual trees and bulbs, lovely views.

⓲ ◆ 1700 Melton Road, Rearsby
⬤⬤⬤ NCCPG
Mrs Hazel Kaye) *6m NE of Leicester. On A607.* A garden for all seasons opening in early March and October to tempt the hardiest of garden visitors. 1½ acres with extensive borders, shade beds, pergola and water feature with wide range of interesting hardy plants, National Collection of Tradescantia andersoniana. TEAS. *Adm £2, chd free. Tues to Sat and Bank Hols*

(10-5) Suns (10-12) Mar - Oct; Nov - Feb by appt . For NGS: Suns 6 Mar; 2 Oct (2-5). Tel 01664 424578 hazelkaye.kgn@nascr.net

The Old Rectory, Clifton Campville
⬤⬤⬤
See Staffordshire & part of West Midlands.

⓳ Pine House, Gaddesby ⬤⬤
(Mr & Mrs T Milward) *8m NE of Leicester. From A607, Rearsby Rd at Rearsby turn off for Gaddesby.* 2-acre garden with fine mature trees, woodland walk, and water garden. Herb and potager garden and wisteria archway to Victorian vinery. Pleached lime trees, mixed borders with rare and unusual plants and rock garden; new gravel garden and terracotta pot garden. Interesting topiary hedges and box trees. Home-made TEAS in aid of local charities. *Adm £3. Private visits welcome by appt, coaches permitted and groups of 10 +. Tel 01664 840213*

⓴ Prebendal House, Empingham
⬤⬤
(Mr & Mrs J Partridge) *5m E of Oakham. 5m W of Stamford. On A606.* House (not open) built in 1688; summer palace for the Bishop of Lincoln. 4-acre garden incl herbaceous borders, water garden, topiary and kitchen garden. Home-made TEAS. *Adm £2.50, chd free. Sun 5 June (2-5)*

㉑ Ridlington Gardens
2½m N of Uppingham. Turn off A47 to Ayston from Uppington roundabout. Village map available to all visitors. Home-made TEAS at village hall, Main Street in aid of St Mary Magdalene & St Andrew Church, Ridlington. *Combined adm £3, chd free. Sun 12 June (2-5)*

[NEW] **The Elms** ⬤⬤ (Mrs Jean Boyes) Colourful shrub garden sweeping down towards the Chater Valley.

[NEW] **Jotry Cottage** (Mr & Mrs J Mason) Architectural yet softly planted cottage garden incorporating an upward gradient.

[NEW] **9 Main Street** (Mr & Mrs Ian MacDonald) Typical cottage garden, with a variety of scented plants, mainly roses, pinks and lavender, overlooking valley.

Ridlington House ⬤ (Mr & Mrs Moubray) 1½ acres; roses; herbaceous border; flowering shrubs; vegetables; orchard.

Stone Cottage (Mr & Mrs Gavin Simpson) ½-acre informal cottage

garden; wide views across Chater Valley.

㉒ Stoke Albany House, Stoke Albany ⬤⬤
(Mr & Mrs A M Vinton) *4m E of Market Harborough. Via A427 to Corby; turn to Stoke Albany; R at the White Horse (B669); garden ½m on L.* 4-acre country-house garden; fine trees and shrubs with wide herbaceous borders and sweeping striped lawn. Good display of bulbs in spring, roses June and July. Walled grey garden; nepeta walk arched with roses, parterre with box and roses. Mediterranean garden. Heated greenhouse, potager with topiary, water feature garden and sculptures. *Adm £2.50, chd free (share to Marie Curie). Every Wed, 4 May to 27 July (2-4.30). Private visits welcome by appt May to July, Mon to Thurs only. Tel 01858 535227*

㉓ University of Leicester 'Harold Martin' Botanic Garden, 'The Knoll', Glebe Road, Oadby
⬤⬤⬤ NCCPG
(University of Leicester) *1½m SE of Leicester. On outskirts of city opp race course.* 16-acre garden incl grounds of Beaumont Hall, The Knoll, Southmeade and Hastings House. Wide variety of ornamental features and glasshouses laid out for educational purposes incl National Collections of aubrieta, Lawson cypress, hardy fuchsia and skimmia. TEAS. *Adm £2, chd free. Sun 24 July (11-4)*

㉔ Walton Gardens
4m NE of Lutterworth. M1 exit 20 and, via Lutterworth follow signs for Kimcote and Walton, or from Leicester take A5199. After Shearsby turn R signposted Bruntingthorpe. Follow signs. Small village in South Leicestershire. Village maps given to all visitors. Home-made TEAS at Orchards. *Combined adm £2.50, chd free. Sun, Wed 5, 8 June (11-5)*

The Meadows, Mowsley Lane ⬤⬤ (Mr & Mrs Falkner) Plantsmans garden, with emphasis on wildlife friendly flowers. Interesting water features. New developments for 2005.

Orchards, Hall Lane, Walton Gardens ⬤⬤ (Mr & Mrs G Cousins) 1¼-acre green garden with colour from flowers not foliage. Exceptionally interesting design. Views of the countryside. Featured on TV & in Hortus on Orchards by Graham Cousins. *Sat, Sun, Mon, Tues 21, 22, 30 31 May; Sats, Suns 25, 26 June;*

23, 24 July. Private visits welcome by appt May to July. Tel 01455 556958 orchards@cousins88.fsnet.co.uk

Sandyland, Hall Lane 🏵️🏵️
(Martin & Linda Goddard) ⅓-acre country garden. Rockery based on old gravel workings, herbaceous borders, lily pool, kitchen garden, with attractive rural views.

㉕ Warren Hills Cottage, Warren Hills Road, Coalville 🏵️🏵️🏵️ NCCPG
(Mr Graham Waters) *5m NW of Leicester. Approx 4m NW of M1 junction 22 on B587 Copt Oak to Whitwick Rd, near schools.* Restful, secluded yet changing 2-acre garden for plantaholics, incl a display area for the National Collection of Astrantias. Cottage gardens, streams and pond, raised beds and alpine area creating yr-round colour and interest. Adjacent small nursery with hardy and unusual perennials for sale. Specialist plant fair Sun 17 July, also qualified garden expert for advice. Gold Medal winners Shrewsbury Flower Show & Tatton Park 2004. Cream TEAS. *Adm £2, chd 50p. Suns 8 May; 5 June; 17 July; 21 Aug (12-5). Private visits welcome by appt. Tel 01530 812350 warrenhills@tinyworld.co.uk*

㉖ Wartnaby Gardens, Wartnaby, Nr Melton Mowbray 🏵️🏵️
(Lord & Lady King) *4m NW of Melton Mowbray. From A606 turn W in Ab Kettleby, from A46 at Six Hills Hotel turn E on A676.* Large garden. Shrubs, herbaceous borders, rose garden with a good collection of old-fashioned roses and others; Formal vegetable garden, series of ponds, spring garden and woodland walks. Specialist plant sale 19 June, over 20 stalls. Featured in 'House & Garden' & 'Leicestershire Life' 2004. TEAS. *Adm £2.50, chd free (share to Wartnaby Church). Suns 27 Feb (display of spring bulbs (11-3); 24 Apr; 19 June (11-4). Private visits welcome by appt. Tel 01664 822493*

7a Weskers Close, Clipston 🏵️🏵️
See Northamptonshire.

㉗ ◆ Whatton Gardens, nr Loughborough 🏵️
(Lord & Lady Crawshaw) *4m NE of Loughborough. On A6 between Hathern & Kegworth; 2½m SE of junction 24 on M1.* The garden dates back to 1802 and comprises, 15 acres; shrub and herbaceous borders, lawns, rose and wild gardens, pools; arboretum and mature trees; spring bulbs. A peaceful setting in which to relax and roam. Home-made TEAS (NGS days only). *Adm £2.50, chd*

free. Mons to Fris 1 Mar to 31 Oct (11-4). **For NGS:** *Suns 15 May; 12 June (2-6). Tel 01509 842225*

㉘ NEW The White House Farm, Billesdon Road, Ingarsby 🏵️🏵️
(Pam & Richard Smith) *7m E of Leicester. Take A47 from Leicester through Houghton-on-the-Hill towards Uppingham. 1m after Houghton, turn L (signed Tilton). After 1m turn L (signed Ingarsby), garden is 1m further on.* Large country garden incl courtyard, cottage garden, terrace and lawn to ha-ha; pergola garden with roses, clematis, honeysuckle, vines and mixed borders; box parterres, fruit orchard with espaliers, cascade of informal rill and pools. Woodland walk, wild garden, reed bed, pond and lake. Started 5yrs ago, further development planned. Plant Sales in aid of local charity. Light refreshments and TEAS in aid of SSAFA. *Adm £3, chd free. Suns 26 June; 11 Sept (11-5). Private visits welcome by appt. Tel 0116 259 5448*

Evening Opening (See also garden description)

Gilmorton Gardens	18 May
The Court House	22 June

---

ngs gardens open for charity

Your garden in the Yellow Book?

The NGS is always interested to hear of gardens with potential, large or small, that might open in the future.

For more information about opening your garden, please contact the County Organiser in your area, preferably at the time of year that you would like your garden to open.

---

ngs gardens open for charity

Specialist Plant Sales in Leicestershire

Long Close Gardens	Sunday April 3
Wartnaby Gardens	Sunday June 19
Warren Hills Cottage	Sunday July 17

See garden entries for details

Lincolnshire

County Organiser:	Mrs Patrick Dean, The Orchards, Old Somerby, Grantham, Lincolnshire NG33 4AG
	Tel 01476 565456
Assistant County Organisers:	Lady Bruce-Gardyne, The Old Rectory, Aswardby, Spilsby, Lincolnshire PE23 4JS
	Tel 01790 752652
	Lady Cholmeley, The Dower House, Easton, Grantham, Lincolnshire NG33 5AP
	Tel 01476 530235
	Mrs Lucy Dawes, The Grange, Bulby, Bourne, Lincolnshire PE10 0RU Tel 01778 591220
	Mrs Sally Grant, Holly House, Fishtoft Drove, Boston, Lincolnshire PE22 7ES
	Tel 01205 750486
(Press & Publicity Officer)	Mrs Erica McGarrigle, Corner House Farm, Little Humby, Grantham, Lincolnshire NG33 4HW
	Mrs Margaret Sandberg, Croft House, Ulceby, Lincolnshire DN39 6SW Tel 01469 588330
County Treasurer:	Mr Peter Sandberg, Croft House, Ulceby, Lincolnshire DN39 6SW Tel 01469 588330

Maps: Numbers shown next to each garden entry refer to that garden's entry on the county map. This position is approximate; distance and directions from the nearest main town are generally shown in the garden text.
A precise location is available for those gardens featured on the NGS website by visiting www.ngs.org.uk.

Symbols: Information relating to symbols is given on page 21

DATES OF OPENING

Evening openings
See end of county listing

Gardens open to the public
For details see garden description

Belton House, Grantham *(2)*
Belvoir Castle, Grantham *(3)*
Easton Walled Gardens, Grantham *(9)*
Grimsthorpe Castle, Bourne *(13)*
Gunby Hall, Spilsby *(15)*
Hall Farm, Harpswell *(16)*
73 Saxilby Road, Sturton by Stow *(28)*

By appointment only
*For telephone number and other
details see garden description.
Private visits welcomed*

Croft House, Ulceby, nr Brigg *(8)*

February 12 Saturday
Little Ponton Hall, Grantham *(21)*

February 13 Sunday
Little Ponton Hall, Grantham *(21)*

February 19 Saturday
21 Chapel Street, Hacconby, Bourne *(6)*

February 20 Sunday
21 Chapel Street, Hacconby, Bourne *(6)*

March 3 Thursday
21 Chapel Street, Hacconby, Bourne *(6)*

March 28 Monday (Easter)
21 Chapel Street, Hacconby, Bourne *(6)*

April 10 Sunday
Sutton St Edmund Village Gardens *(32)*

April 17 Sunday
Grimsthorpe Castle, Bourne *(13)*
The Old Rectory, East Keal *(24)*

April 30 Saturday
Belton House, Grantham *(2)*

May 1 Sunday
2 School House, Stixwould *(29)*

May 5 Thursday
21 Chapel Street, Hacconby, Bourne *(6)*

May 7 Saturday
Goltho House, Goltho *(11)*

May 12 Thursday
The Old Rectory, East Keal *(24)*

May 14 Saturday
Woodlands, Fotherby, Louth *(36)*

May 15 Sunday
Woodlands, Fotherby, Louth *(36)*

May 22 Sunday
Grantham House, Grantham *(12)*
Martin Gardens *(22)*

June 1 Wednesday
Belvoir Castle, Grantham *(3)*

June 2 Thursday
Belvoir Castle, Grantham *(3)*
21 Chapel Street, Hacconby, Bourne
(Evening) *(6)*

June 4 Saturday
Belvoir Castle, Grantham *(3)*

June 5 Sunday
Belvoir Castle, Grantham *(3)*
Fishtoft Drove Gardens, Frithville, Boston
(10)
Kexby House, Gainsborough *(19)*
Les Allées, Caythorpe *(20)*
15 Vicarage Gardens, Scunthorpe *(34)*

June 7 Tuesday
Belvoir Castle, Grantham *(3)*

June 8 Wednesday
Belvoir Castle, Grantham *(3)*
Easton Walled Gardens, Grantham *(9)*

June 9 Thursday
Belvoir Castle, Grantham *(3)*

June 10 Friday
Holywell Hall, Holywell *(18)*

June 11 Saturday
Belvoir Castle, Grantham *(3)*
The Grove, Faldingworth *(14)*

June 12 Sunday
Belvoir Castle, Grantham *(3)*
The Grove, Faldingworth *(14)*
Little Ponton Hall, Grantham **(Evening)** *(21)*
The Old Rectory, East Keal *(24)*
The Old Vicarage, Holbeach Hurn *(25)*
Old White House, Holbeach Hurn *(26)*
Sutton-on-Sea Gardens *(31)*

June 14 Tuesday
Belvoir Castle, Grantham *(3)*

June 15 Wednesday
Belvoir Castle, Grantham *(3)*
Woodlands, Fotherby, Louth **(Evening)** *(36)*

June 16 Thursday
Belvoir Castle, Grantham *(3)*
Grimsthorpe Castle, Bourne *(13)*

June 18 Saturday
Belvoir Castle, Grantham *(3)*

June 19 Sunday
Belvoir Castle, Grantham *(3)*
Sutton St Edmund Village Gardens *(32)*

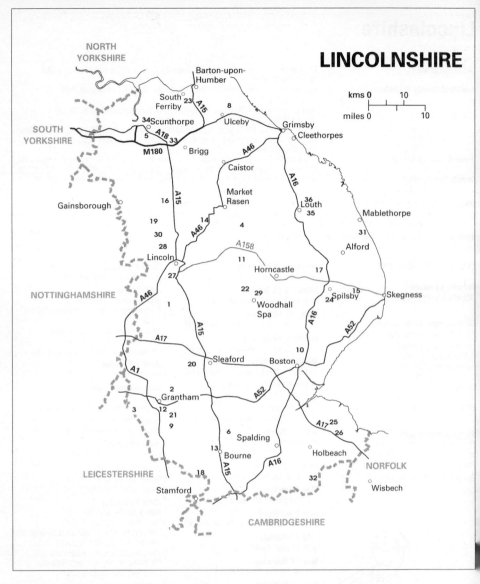

LINCOLNSHIRE

NORTH YORKSHIRE

SOUTH YORKSHIRE

NOTTINGHAMSHIRE

LEICESTERSHIRE

NORFOLK

CAMBRIDGESHIRE

Barton-upon-Humber

South Ferriby 23

Scunthorpe 34

Ulceby 8

Grimsby

Cleethorpes

Brigg

Caistor

Market Rasen

Louth 36 35

Mablethorpe

Gainsborough

16

19

30

28

Lincoln

14

11

Horncastle 17

31

Alford

27

22 29

Woodhall Spa

1

Spilsby 15 24

Skegness

A17

20

Sleaford

Boston

10

A1

2

Grantham

3

12

21

9

6

Spalding

13

Bourne

Holbeach

25

26

18

Stamford

32

Wisbech

kms 0 — 10

miles 0 — 10

August 4 Thursday
21 Chapel Street, Hacconby, Bourne *(6)*
August 6 Saturday
Woodlands, Fotherby, Louth *(36)*
August 7 Sunday
56 Burringham Road, Ashby, Scunthorpe *(5)*
Harrington Hall, Spilsby *(17)*
Woodlands, Fotherby, Louth *(36)*
August 13 Saturday
70 North Street, Winterton *(23)*
August 14 Sunday
70 North Street, Winterton *(23)*
68 Watts Lane, Louth *(35)*
September 1 Thursday
21 Chapel Street, Hacconby, Bourne *(6)*
September 3 Saturday
Belton House, Grantham *(2)*
September 4 Sunday
Hall Farm, Harpswell *(16)*
September 11 Sunday
Aubourn Hall, Aubourn *(1)*
October 2 Sunday
21 Chapel Street, Hacconby, Bourne *(6)*
October 9 Sunday
73 Saxilby Road, Sturton by Stow *(28)*
2 School Lane, Stow *(30)*
2006
February 18 Saturday
21 Chapel Street, Hacconby, Bourne *(6)*
February 19 Sunday
21 Chapel Street, Hacconby, Bourne *(6)*

DESCRIPTIONS OF GARDENS

❶ Aubourn Hall, Aubourn ⓢ☉
(Lady Nevile) *7m SW of Lincoln. Signed off A607 at Harmston & off A46 at Thorpe. Approx 5 acres.* Lawns, mature trees, shrubs, roses, mixed borders, new wild garden and topiary, ponds. C11 church adjoining. TEAS in aid of St Peter's Church Repairs. *Adm £2.50. Sun 11 Sept (2-5)*

❷ ◆ Belton House, Grantham ⓢ☉
(The National Trust) *3m NE of Grantham. On A607 Grantham to Lincoln rd. Easily reached & signed from A1 (Grantham N junction). 32 acres incl formal Italian and Dutch gardens. Orangery by Sir Jeffrey Wyatville. Cream TEAS. House and garden adm £6.50, chd £3.40. Weds to Suns, incl Bank Hol Mons, 23 Mar to 30 Oct (11-5.30). For NGS: Sats 30 Apr; 2 July; 3 Sept (11-5.30). Tel 01476 566116 belton@nationaltrust.org.uk*

❸ ◆ Belvoir Castle, Grantham ☉
The Duke & Duchess of Rutland) *)m from Grantham. Follow brown heritage signs for Belvoir Castle on*

A52, A1, A607. *English Heritage Grade 2 garden. Secluded in steep woodland ½m from castle. A haven of tranquillity created around original moss house. Magical hillside setting in natural amphitheatre with fresh water springs. Many mature specimen trees and shrubs ensure all-yr colour. Rhododendrons, azaleas, naturalised daffodils, primroses and bluebells. Tallest bird cherry (90ft) and yew tree (93ft) in British Isles. Flat shoes essential. Rose garden with sculpture exhibition. Light refreshments and TEAS. House and Garden adm £10, OAP £9. Garden only adm £5, chd free. Daily (except Mons & Fris) . For NGS: Tues, Weds, Thurs, Sats, Suns, 1 June to 30 June (11-5). Tel 01476 871003 - Nicola Wheeler www.belvoircastle.com*

❹ NEW Bleasby House Farm, Legsby ⓢ☉
(Janet & John Dring) *4m SE of Market Rasen. From Market Rasen take the B1202 through Linwood, take next L signed Legsby & Bleasby. Garden 1m on L.* 1-acre country garden with lawns and herbaceous borders. Discover the willow dome through the pergola, past the ornamental pond and statuesque clipped yews. The formal garden with roses and box edging leads to the woodland fringe and herb wheel in the gravel garden. Accommodation. TEAS. *Adm £2, chd free. Sun 26 June (2-6)*

❺ 56 Burringham Road, Ashby, Scunthorpe ☉
(Mr & Mrs Foster) *½m S of Scunthorpe. Approaching Scunthorpe A159 from S turn L on B1450 (Burringham Rd). Garden 200yds on L. Park in Monks Rd.* ⅓-acre plant collectors' garden full of unusual treasures. Large fish pond surrounded by raised beds, large rockery and waterfall. Vegetable garden with trained fruit trees and cutting flowers. Long herbaceous borders, wildlife pond with marginal planting and bog garden. Further raised beds with dwarf conifers and summer display areas of cactus and succulents. Recent introduction of South African rarities, restios and leucodendron/protea species; also several types of musa species. Featured in 'Lincolnshire Pride' 2004. Light refreshments and TEAS in aid of Lindsey Lodge Hospice, Scunthorpe. *Adm £1.50, chd 50p. Suns 10 July; 7 Aug (10-5). Private visits welcome by appt June, July, Aug. Tel 01724 334480 kevin.2.foster@bt.com*

❻ 21 Chapel Street, Hacconby, Bourne ⓢ☉
(Cliff & Joan Curtis) *3m N of Bourne. A15, turn E at Xrds into Hacconby.* Cottage garden overflowing with plants for yr-round interest; special interest alpines, bulbs, herbaceous. Early opening for hellebores and snowdrop collection. Asters for late opening. TEAS in aid of Marie Curie Cancer Care. *Adm £1.50, chd free. Sat, Sun 19, 20 Feb; Thur, Mon 3, 28 Mar; Thurs 5 May; 4 Aug; 1 Sept ; Sun 2 Oct (11-5). Thurs (2-6); Evening Opening £1.50, Thur 2 June (5-9). Sat, Sun 18, 19 Feb 2006. Private visits welcome by appt anytime, coaches permitted. Tel 01778 570314*

❼ NEW Church Farmhouse, Church End, North Somercotes ☉
(Julian & Helen Drewett) *10m E of Louth. Situated ½m W of main village. Turn into South Rd from A1031 at Axe & Cleaver PH. After ½m turn L into Church End signed 'Church'. House opp St Mary's Church.* Parking in nearby field & lane. C18 cottage and outbuildings provide the backdrop to a developing cottage garden approx ⅓-acre. Colourful borders, picket fencing, ornamental kitchen garden and large pond with native marginal planting; also rare breeds of poultry. Textile artist's studio open for framed work and cards. Home-made TEAS. *Adm £2, chd free. Sat, Sun 2, 3 July (2-6)*

❽ Croft House, Pitmoor Lane, Ulceby, nr Brigg ⓢ☉
(Mr & Mrs Peter Sandberg) *9m NE of Brigg. At War Memorial from E turn L, from W turn R into Front St & then into Pitmoor Lane.* 2-acre garden set within formal design filled with informal planting. Many old favourites alongside sought-after varieties. Mixed and herbaceous borders, bulbs, gravel bed, Victorian vinery. Wide grassy spaces, mature trees and cottagey planting give a relaxed and peaceful atmosphere to the garden. Light refreshments and TEAS. *Adm £2, chd under 12 free. Private visits welcome by appt, coaches permitted. Tel 01469 588330 peterhsandberg@hotmail. com*

❾ ◆ Easton Walled Gardens, Grantham ⓢ☉
(Sir Fred & Lady Cholmeley) *7m S of Grantham. 1m off A1 N of Colsterworth roundabout. Follow village signposts via B6403.* 12 acres of forgotten gardens undergoing extensive renovation. Set in parkland

with dramatic views over gardens. C16 garden with Victorian embellishments. Italianate terraces; canal; yew tunnel; ancient walled garden; snowdrops and cut flower garden. Featured in 'The Independent' & 'Gardens Illustrated' 2004. Light refreshments and TEAS. *Adm £3.50, chd free.* **For NGS:** *Wed 8 June (11-4). Tel 01476 530063 www.eastonwalledgardens.co.uk*

⑩ Fishtoft Drove Gardens, Frithville, Boston
3m N of Boston, 1m S of Frithville. Unclassified rd. On W side of the West Fen Drain. TEAS at Holly House in aid of Pilgrim Heart & Lung Fund. *Combined adm £2.50, chd free. Sun 5 June (12-5.30)*

Barley End Cottage 🌿 (Andy & Yvonne Mathieson) *100yds W of Holly House.* ⅓-acre traditional cottage garden, very informal. Relaxed mixture of borders, shrubs, vegetables, natural areas, with some quirky features.

Holly House 🅰🌿🅗 (Sally & David Grant) Approx 1-acre informal gardens with mixed borders, scree beds, old sinks with alpines and steps leading down to large pond with cascade and stream. Softly curving beds are full of unusual and interesting herbaceous plants. Small woodland area. '25 Beautiful Gardens' feature 2003.

Pottery Cottage 🌿 (Carol & Mike Day) Small garden approx ⅓-acre in cottage garden style. Small pond; covered arches with roses and clematis; gravelled area with water feature, full of unusual and interesting herbaceous plants. Recently constructed formal pond. Featured in 'Great Container Ideas' 2004.

Sycamore Cottage (Roy & Jane Lovett) Approx 1-acre with mature trees, recently developed; mixed borders. Woodland area, formal kitchen garden and ponds.

⑪ Goltho House, Goltho 🅰🌿🅗
(Mr & Mrs S Hollingworth) *10m E of Lincoln. On A158, 1m before Wragby. Garden on LH-side (not in Goltho Village).* 4½-acre garden started in 1998 but looking established with long grass walk flanked by abundantly planted herbaceous borders forming a focal point. Paths and walkway span out to other features incl nut walk, prairie border, wild flower meadow, rose garden and large pond area. TEAS.

Adm £2. Sat 7 May; Sun 26 June (1-5)

⑫ Grantham House, Castlegate, Grantham 🅰🌿
(Major General Sir Brian Wyldbore Smith) *Entrance in Castlegate opp St Wolfram's Church.* 3-acre garden created by the late Lady Wyldbore Smith with many specimen trees brought from her former home in Sussex. Several sections of individual style. Lawns, a woodland walk, rockery and greenhouse, orchard with recently planted riverbanks, walled garden, Lady Molly's garden, vegetable and herb gardens. TEAS in aid of Red Cross. *Adm £2, chd £1, or donation. Sun 22 May (2-5)*

⑬ ◆ Grimsthorpe Castle, Bourne 🅰🅗
(Grimsthorpe & Drummond Castle Trust) *3m NW of Bourne. 8m E of A1 on A151 from Colsterworth junction.* 15 acres of formal and woodland gardens incl bulbs and wild flowers. Formal gardens encompass fine topiary, roses, herbaceous borders and unusual ornamental kitchen garden. Light refreshments and TEAS. *Castle & garden adm £7, chd £3.50, concessions £6. Garden only adm £3, chd £2, concessions £2.50. Suns, Thurs & Bank Hols Apr, May & Sept; Suns to Thurs June, July, Aug.* **For NGS:** *Sun 17 Apr; Thur 16 June (12-6). Tel 01778 591205 ray@grimsthorpe.co.uk*

⑭ NEW The Grove, Stocks Lane, Faldingworth 🌿
(Mr & Mrs T Howard) *4m SW of Market Rasen. On A46 between Market Rasen & Lincoln. Take Spridlington rd, Stocks Lane is approx 100 metres on R. No parking in Stocks Lane, park at village hall.* ⅓-acre garden, informal borders of trees, shrubs and perennials with waterfall, stream and 2 wildlife ponds. Approx 200 roses with clematis and honeysuckle on trellis, ropes, rails and in borders. Kitchen garden. Light refreshments and TEAS at village hall. *Adm £1.50, chd free. Sat, Sun 11, 12 June (11-4)*

⑮ ◆ Gunby Hall, Spilsby 🅰🅗
(Mr & Mrs J Wrisdale, The National Trust) *2½m NW of Burgh-le-Marsh. 7m NW of Skegness. On A158. Signed off Gunby roundabout.* 7 acres of formal and walled gardens; old roses, herbaceous borders; herb garden; kitchen garden with fruit trees and vegetables. Tennyson's 'Haunt of Ancient Peace'. House built by Sir William Massingberd 1700.

Home-made TEAS (NGS days). *Adm £2.50, chd £1. House & Gardens Weds, garden only Thurs April to end Sept.* **For NGS:** *Sun 17 July (2-6). Tel 07790 810039 www.gunbyhall.ic24.net*

⑯ ◆ Hall Farm, Harpswell 🅰🌿🅗
(Pam & Mark Tatam) *7m E of Gainsborough. On A631. 1½m W of Caenby Corner.* 1½-acre garden with mixed borders of trees, shrubs, old roses and unusual perennials. Sunken garden, pond, courtyard garden, walled gravel garden and orchard. Short walk to old moat and woodland. Free seed collecting in garden Sept 4. Light refreshments and TEAS (NGS day). *Adm £2.50, chd 50p. Open daily throughout summer, phone in winter.* **For NGS:** *Sun 4 Sept (10-5.30). Tel 01427 668412 www.hall-farm.co.uk*

⑰ Harrington Hall, Spilsby 🌿🅗
(Mr & Mrs David Price) *6m NW of Spilsby. Turn off A158 (Lincoln-Skegness) at Hagworthingham, 2m from Harrington.* Approx 6-acre Tudor and C18 walled gardens, incl 3 walled gardens; herbaceous borders, croquet lawn leading to viewing terrace, Tennyson's High Hall Garden in 'Maud'. Organic kitchen garden, shrub borders, roses and wilflife pond. Partly suitable for wheelchairs. Home-made TEAS in aid of South Ormsby Group of Parishes. *Adm £2, chd free. Sun 7 Aug (2-5). Private visits welcome by appt. Tel 01790 753764*

Holmes Villa, Holmes Lane, Walkeringham, nr Gainsborough 🅰🌿🅗
See Nottinghamshire.

⑱ NEW Holywell Hall, Holywell 🅰
(Mr & Mrs R Gillespie) *8m N of Stamford. From A1 signed Clipsham. Through Clipsham then turn R to Holywell. Entrance to Hall 2m on L.* The gardens at Holywell are among the most handsome and historically interesting in S Lincolnshire. Nestled in a vale they are laid out on a broad S-facing slope overlooking C18 lake. Numerous water features, walled vegetable garden, stunning herbaceous borders, chapel, fishing temple and orangery. TEAS. *Adm £2, chd 50p. Fri 10 June (2-6)*

⑲ Kexby House, Gainsborough 🅰🅗
(Herbert & Jenny Whitton) *12m NNW of Lincoln. 6m E of Gainsborough. On B1241, outskirts*

of Kexby village. Approx 4 acres of gardens which have evolved over last 100yrs. Long herbaceous borders, unusual plants, wildlife pond and bog garden, scree gardens and new all-white border. Home-made TEAS. *Adm £3, chd free. Sun 5 June (11-5). Private visits welcome by appt, groups up to 35. Tel 01427 788338*

⑳ Les Allées, 12 Frieston Road, Caythorpe 🚾🌱
(Alan & Marylyn Mason) *8m N of Grantham. From Grantham A607 towards Lincoln. L turn to Caythorpe village, immed L again into Frieston Rd. No 12 300yds ahead.* A plantsman's garden created by Alan Mason, TV gardener and garden designer. Ornamental potager, woodland walk, specimen trees and shrubs, Italian avenue of cypresses. Pond; large mixed borders; tree house; subtropical border. A garden of different styles and atmospheres which link seamlessly. Avenues and allées lead round the garden. TEAS. *Adm £3, chd free, concessions £2.50. Sun 5 June (2-6)*

㉑ Little Ponton Hall, Grantham 🚾🌱
(Mr & Mrs Alastair McCorquodale) *2m S of Grantham. ½m E of A1 at S end of Grantham bypass.* 3 to 4-acre garden. Spacious lawns with cedar tree over 200yrs old. Many varieties of old shrub roses and clematis; borders and young trees. Stream with spring garden; bulbs and river walk with massed snowdrops and aconites. Newly designed walled kitchen garden and listed dovecote. Victorian greenhouses with many plants from exotic locations. Featured in 'Independent on Sunday' 2004. Light refreshments and TEAS in aid of Little Ponton Church. *Adm £3, chd 50p. Sat, Sun 12, 13 Feb (11-4). Evening Opening £3, Sun 12 June (5-8)*

㉒ Martin Gardens
15m SE of Lincoln. On B1191. 4m W of Woodhall Spa. Both gardens on main rd. Parking on roadside. Home-made TEAS at Holmdale House. *Combined adm £2, chd 50p (share to THRIVE). Sun 22 May (11-5)*

49 High Street 🚾🌱 (Helen & Laurie Whittle) ⅓-acre plot organically transformed over 6yrs to be wildlife friendly and enviromentally low impact with long flowering season of nectar and berry-rich species. 2 ponds, mixed native hedging, species-rich grassland and dry garden. Herbaceous perennials, cottage border and drought-tolerant species. All plants for sale are peat free.

Holmdale House 🚾🌱 (Ian Warden & Stewart Mackenzie) ½-acre plantsman's garden started March 2000, surrounding Victorian farmhouse and barns (not open). Informal mixed borders planted to reflect owners' interest in unusual hardy plants, especially good foliage and variegated leaf forms. Collection of hostas, large pond and developing courtyard gardens and nursery. *Private visits welcome by appt . Garden groups especially welcome. Tel 01526 378838 www.holmdalehouse.co.uk*

㉓ 70 North Street, Winterton 🚾🌱
(Peter & Gail Phillips) *6m N of Scunthorpe. From Barton on Humber head W on A1077. After approx 7m turn L into Winterton at Winterton/Winteringham Xrds (B1207). House approx ½m on L.* ¼-acre plantaholic's garden with colour from April to September. Feature fish pond and two wildlife ponds (frogs and newts). Wild flower area, alpine bed, Japanese-style garden, tropical

area and mini orchard. Beds of unusual perennials, old favourites and cottage garden plants. Adjacent nursery. Cream TEAS. *Adm £1.50. Sat, Sun 13, 14 Aug (12-6) . Private visits welcome by appt, also schools & clubs May to Aug. Tel 01724 733695 www.bgplantnursery.co.uk*

㉔ The Old Rectory, East Keal 🌱🌼
(Mrs Ruth Ward) *2m SW of Spilsby. On A16. Turn into Church Lane by PO.* Beautifully situated, with fine views, rambling cottage garden on different levels falling naturally into separate areas, with changing effects and atmosphere. Steps, paths and vistas to lead you on, with seats well placed for appreciating special views and plant combinations or just relax, and enjoy the peace. TEAS. *Adm £2, chd free. Suns, Thur 17 Apr; 12 May; 12 June (2-5). Private visits welcome by appt. Tel 01790 752477*

㉕ The Old Vicarage, Low Road, Holbeach Hurn 🌱🌼
(Mrs Liz Dixon-Spain) *2m NE of Holbeach. Turn off A17 N to Holbeach Hurn, past post box in middle of village, 1st turn R into Low Rd. Old Vicarage on R approx 400yds.* 2 acres of gardens with mature trees, old grass tennis court and croquet lawns surrounded by borders of shrubs, roses, herbaceous; informal areas incl pond and bog garden, wild flowers and bulbs, shrub roses and herb garden in old paddock area. Environmentally maintained. Light refreshments and TEAS in aid of St Matthew Housing Trust. *Combined with* **Old White House** *adm £3, chd free. Sun 12 June (11-5). Private visits welcome by appt. Tel 01406 424148 lizds@ukonline. co.uk*

Your garden in the Yellow Book?

The NGS is always interested to hear of gardens with potential, large or small, that might open in the future.

For more information about opening your garden, please contact the County Organiser in your area, preferably at the time of year that you would like your garden to open.

㉖ Old White House, Holbeach Hurn &⚙

(Mr & Mrs A Worth) *2m N of Holbeach. Turn off A17 N to Holbeach Hurn, follow signs to village, go straight through, turn R after Rose & Crown at Baileys Lane.* 1½ acres of mature garden, featuring herbaceous borders, roses, patterned garden, herb garden and wild garden with small pond. Walled kitchen garden. Light refreshments and TEAS in aid of St Matthew Housing Trust. *Combined with* **The Old Vicarage** *adm £3, chd free. Sun 12 June (12-5.30)*

Park Farm, Normanton &
See Nottinghamshire.

㉗ 4 Ringwood Close, Birchwood &⚙☺

(Margaret & John Brown) *1½m SW of Lincoln. From A46 bypass take Skellingthorpe Rd (signed Birchwood) for ¼m; turn R at T-lights BP garage, 1st R then R again. Parking at Green Barrel PH.* ⅓-acre garden, bordered by mature woodland and created over 30yrs by enthusiastic plant collectors. Gravel bed with ornamental grasses, herbaceous borders featuring some rare and unusual plants. Blue fenced contemplative garden with blue/yellow planting scheme. 'Millennium bandstand' with wisteria and clematis; courtyard with ferns and hostas; vegetables in raised beds. Featured in 'Gardens Monthly' 2003. TEAS. *Adm £2, chd free. Sun 26 June (11-5). Private visits welcome by appt, for groups of 10+. Tel 01522 683960 browngarden@aol.com*

㉘ ◆ 73 Saxilby Road, Sturton by Stow &⚙☺

(Charles & Tricia Elliott) *9m NW of Lincoln. On B1241. Halfway between Lincoln & Gainsborough.* ¼-acre garden and hardy plant nursery in open aspect. Extensively cultivated in a cottage garden style. Beds and borders contain wide range of perennial plants, grasses and shrubs, many unusual, to give all-yr interest and colour. Featured in 'Garden News' 2004. Home-made TEAS. *Adm £1.50, chd 50p. Garden & nursery Fri to Mon Mar to mid Oct (10-5), NGS collection box.* **For NGS:** *Sun 26 June (1-5). Combined with* **2 School Lane**, *adm £2.50, Sun 9 Oct (11-5). Tel 01427 788517*

㉙ 2 School House, Stixwould ⚙☺

(Andrew & Sheila Sankey) *1½m N of Woodhall Spa.* ¼-acre garden, redesigned in Oct 1994 by owners in cottage garden style, to incl front

garden with unusual perennials and shrubs, herb garden, and small turf maze. Featured in 'Garden Answers' book entitled 'Britain's Inspirational Gardens' 2004. TEAS. *Adm £1, chd free. Suns 1 May; 10 July (2-6). Private visits welcome by appt. Tel 01526 352453*

㉚ 2 School Lane, Stow &⚙☺

(Alec Wyllie) *10m NW of Lincoln. On B1241. E along Ingham Lane - 1st L. No parking in lane. Please park in village.* ½-acre on edge of village. Hedged fountain garden with mixed borders and small hot front garden. Curved herbaceous walk leading to short woodland path and lawn. Various small trees and shrubs. Continual redevelopment. Lunches and TEAS in aid of St Mary's Church, Stow. *Adm £2.50, chd 50p, combined with* **73 Saxilby Road**. *Sun 9 Oct (11-5). Private visits welcome by appt. Tel 01427 788860 alexander@alecwyllie.fsworld.co.uk*

㉛ Sutton-on-Sea Gardens

16m N of Skegness. From Alford into Sutton-on-Sea on A1111. Home-made TEAS at The Cottage in aid of MCR. *Combined adm £2, chd £1.50. Sun 12 June (11-4)*

The Cottage, 46 High Street &⚙☺ (R C Lightsey & C N Edwards) *Into High St. Garden on L past Steve Woods garage.* Secluded garden of approx ¼ acre with mature trees and shrubs, herbaceous beds, pond and formal front garden with many quirky features and recycling ideas. Decking and patio. First Prize Cup Best Small Garden in Village 2004. Featured in 'Gardening Which' 2005. *Private visits welcome by appt. Tel 01507 443205*

Marigold Cottage, Hotchin Road &☺ (Betty & Stephanie Lee) *From High St facing sea, turn R at Corner House Café, along Furlong's Rd past playing fields, round bend, into Hotchin Rd. Garden 2nd on L.* ½-acre seaside garden containing a large variety of hardy perennials. Paths, pergolas, arches and secret trails make the garden magical. Features incl Japanese bed, slate dry water feature, planting schemes to excite the palette and newly extended Oriental courtyard. First Prize Cup Best Large Garden in Village 2004. Featured in 'Gardening Which' 2005. *Private visits welcome by appt. Tel 01507 442151 marigold@dircon.co.uk*

㉜ Sutton St Edmund Village Gardens

16m NE of Spalding. 18m from Peterborough, 8m from Wisbech. Cream TEAS at Holly Tree Farm in aid of Cystic Fibrosis. *Combined adm £2, chd 50p. Suns 10 Apr (2-5); 19 June (2-6)*

Guanock House, Guanock Gate &⚙☺ (Arne Maynard & William Collinson) *In village, facing S turn L & next L onto Guanock Gate, house ½m.* Formal style English garden, created by garden designer owner over the last 10yrs. Herbaceous garden, rose garden, topiary and knot garden, pleached lime walk, kitchen garden and orchard.

Holly Tree Farm, Hallgate &⚙☺ (Mr & Mrs C Pate) *In village facing S take R into Chapel Gate. Next L onto Hallgate, farm 1st on R.* 1-acre family garden, island beds of perennials and white beds, vegetables, fruit, scree, all in cottage garden style; pasture for cows and free range poultry. New spinney with native wild flowers. *Private visits welcome by appt, Apr to 31 Aug Weds & Thurs, Teas available for group booking (10-4). Tel 01945 700773*

㉝ 5 Valewood, Bottesford &⚙

(Mr & Mrs T Ashton) *2m S of Scunthorpe. 2nd turning off Holme Lane nr St Peter's Church, 1st turning.* A garden full of colour March to October. Soft curving beds in lawn area with ponds, tubs and hanging baskets. Winding paths to cottage garden area, full of old and new favourites. A garden of different styles with lots of seating areas to enjoy the atmosphere. Partly suitable for wheelchairs. Light refreshments and TEAS in aid of Wish Upon a Star. *Adm £2, chd £1. Sun 3 July (1-6)*

㉞ 15 Vicarage Gardens, Scunthorpe ⚙☺

(Chris & Jill Dyson) *In centre of Scunthorpe, off Oswald Rd & adjacent to museum. Parking in rd & museum car park.* Plantsman's garden of ⅓ acre with many interesting features in this surprising location. Gravel garden, scented garden; pergola walk, mixed borders, woodland garden with wildlife pond and stream, courtyard garden with formal pond. TEAS in aid of Frodingham Parish Church. *Adm £2, chd free. Sun 5 June (2-5). Private visits welcome by appt. Tel 01724 846566*

35 68 Watts Lane, Louth 🚪♿
(Mrs J Grasham) ½m S of Louth
town centre. Watts Lane off B1200
Louth to Mablethorpe rd. Turn by
Browns Rover Garage and Londis
shop. Sun only, extra parking at rear
of Browns, 300yds from garden.
Blank canvas of ⅔ acre developed
over 10yrs. Generous curving
borders, raised bed. Hundreds of
plants, shrubs and trees, traditional
to tropical, jostle for space providing
long season of interest. 2 ponds of
different styles, water features,
secluded seating areas and
summerhouse. A surprise garden on
entering from street. Ample
conservatory space for shelter. Plus
new area of work in progress.
Opened 2004 and ongoing 2005.
Home-made TEAS. Adm £1.50, chd

free (share to Louth and District
Hospice). Wed 13 July; Sun 14 Aug
(1-6). Private visits welcome by appt
13 July to 11 Sept, coaches permitted.
Tel 01507 601004/07977 318145

**36 Woodlands, Peppin Lane,
Fotherby, Louth** 🚪♿
(Ann & Bob Armstrong) 2m N of
Louth. On A16. Leave bypass (A16)
signposted Fotherby. Woodlands is
situated nr far end of Peppin Lane, a
no through rd, running E from village
centre. No parking at garden, only
limited parking beyond disused
railway line. Plenty of space halfway
down lane opp allotments. Mature
woodland garden being further
developed by the present owners.
Packed with rare and unusual
perennials, shrubs, ferns and

climbers. Meandering paths lead to
surprises around every corner. In
contrast, the planting nearer the
house takes advantage of the more
open aspect but is equally interesting.
Award winning professional artist's
studio/gallery open to visitors. Home-
made TEAS in aid of St Mary's
Church, Fotherby. Adm £2. Sats,
Suns 14, 15 May; 6, 7 Aug (11-5);
Evening Opening £2, wine, Wed 15
June (6-9). Private visits welcome by
appt. Tel 01507 603586

Evening Opening (See also garden description)	
21 Chapel Street	2 June
Little Ponton Hall	12 June
Woodlands	15 June

ngs
gardens open for charity

Every time you visit a garden which opens for the NGS you are helping to raise money for

- Macmillan Cancer Relief
- Marie Curie Cancer Care
- Help the Hospices
- Crossroads – Caring for Carers
- The Queen's Nursing Institute
- The Nurses Welfare Service
- The Royal Gardeners' Orphan Fund
- NGS Gardeners' Bursaries – The National Trust Careership Scheme
- Perennial – Gardeners' Royal Benevolent Society
- County Nursing Associations
- Additional charities nominated by owners

London (Greater London Area)

County Organisers:	Mrs Penny Snell, Moleshill House, The Fairmile, Cobham, Surrey KT11 1BG Tel 01932 864532 email pennysnellflower@aol.com
Assistant County Organisers:	
NW London	Ms Susan Bennett & Mr Earl Hyde, 5 St Regis Close, Alexandra Park Road, Muswell Hill, London N10 2DE Tel 020 8883 8540
(E London)	Ms Paula Caiger, 21 Brunswick Street, Walthamstow Village, London E17 9NB Tel 020 8923 4238 email paulacaiger@hotmail.com
(SW London)	Miss Joey Clover, 13 Fullerton Road, London SW18 1BU Tel 020 8870 8740 email joeyclover@dsl.pipex.com
(Hampstead)	Mrs Ruth Gorb, 17 Redington Road, London NW3 7QX Tel 020 7435 0680
(SE & Outer London)	Mrs Winkle Haworth, 38 Killieser Avenue, London SW2 4NT Tel 020 8671 4196 email winklehaworth@hotmail.com
(Tours)	Mrs Julia Hickman, Little Lodge, Watts Road, Thames Ditton, Surrey KT7 0BX Tel 020 8339 0931 email garden.information@virgin.net Mr Peter Hickman, Little Lodge, Watts Road, Thames Ditton, Surrey KT7 0BX Tel 020 8339 0931 email garden.information@virgin.net
(Islington)	Mrs Anna McKane, 36 Thornhill Square, London N1 1BE Tel 020 7609 7811 email a.r.mckane@city.ac.uk
(SE London)	Mrs Pat Rae, The Coach House, 3 The Hermitage, Forest Hill, London SE23 3QD Tel 020 8699 6326 email pat@rae2061.freeserve.co.uk
(W London)	Mrs Jenny Raworth, 7 St George's Road, St Margaret's, Twickenham, Middlesex TW1 1QS Tel 020 8892 3713 email jenny@jraworth.freeserve.co.uk
(Barnes, Putney, Chiswick & Holland Park)	Mrs Lesley West, 11 Woodlands Road, Barnes, London SW13 0JZ Tel 020 8876 4155
(Highgate, St John's Wood & W London)	Mrs Sue Whittington, Southwood Lodge, Kingsley Place, London N6 5EA Tel 020 8348 2785
County Treasurer:	Mr Maurice Snell, Moleshill House, The Fairmile, Cobham, Surrey KT11 1BG Tel 01932 864532

Maps: Owing to the large number of gardens, London maps are no longer practicable. Please refer to your A-Z or visit the Garden Finder at www.ngs.org.uk for a location map.

Symbols: Information relating to symbols is given on page 21

DATES OF OPENING

Evening openings
See end of county listing

Gardens open to the public
For details see garden description

Chelsea Physic Garden, SW3 *(28)*
Fenton House, Hampstead Grove, NW3 *(50)*
Ham House, Richmond *(60)*
Museum of Garden History, SE1 *(99)*
Myddelton House Gardens, Enfield *(100)*
Natural History Museum Wildlife Garden, SW7 *(101)*
Roots and Shoots, SE11 *(126)*
The Gardens of Westminster Abbey, SW1 *(157)*

By appointment only
For telephone number and other details see garden description. Private visits welcomed

21 Brunswick Street, Walthamstow, E17 *(16)*

February 27 Sunday
Myddelton House Gardens, Enfield *(100)*

March 12 Saturday
The Elms, Kingston-on-Thames *(47)*
Kew Gardens Group *(83)*

March 13 Sunday
The Elms, Kingston-on-Thames *(47)*
Kew Gardens Group *(83)*
167 Rosendale Road, SE21 *(127)*

April 3 Sunday
Chelsea Physic Garden, SW3 *(28)*
7 The Grove, N6 *(59)*

April 10 Sunday
Natural History Museum Wildlife Garden, SW7 *(101)*

April 16 Saturday
The Elms, Kingston-on-Thames *(47)*
Trinity Hospice, SW4 *(145)*

April 17 Sunday
5 Burbage Road, SE24 *(19)*
The Elms, Kingston-on-Thames *(47)*
Trinity Hospice, SW4 *(145)*

April 23 Saturday
The Holme, NW1 *(73)*
Lambeth Palace, SE1 *(87)*
The Gardens of Westminster Abbey, SW1 *(157)*

April 24 Sunday
Edwardes Square, W8 *(46)*
The Holme, NW1 *(73)*
Malvern Terrace Gardens, N1 *(91)*
209 Massingberd Way, SW17 *(94)*
Myddelton House Gardens, Enfield *(100)*
64 Thornhill Road, E10 *(144)*
7 Upper Phillimore Gardens, W8 *(148)*
47 Winn Road, Lee, SE12 *(161)*

May 1 Sunday
10 Chiltern Road, Eastcote *(29)*
Chiswick Mall, W4 *(30)*
51 Cholmeley Crescent, N6 *(31)*
5 St Regis Close, N10 *(134)*
Southside House, Wimbledon Common, SW19 *(138)*

May 8 Sunday
Elmsdale Road Gardens, E17 *(48)*
Grims Dyke Hotel, Harrow Weald *(58)*
2 Millfield Place, N6 *(96)*
94 Oakwood Road, NW11 *(106)*
The Orchard, W4 *(107)*
116 Peckham Park Road, SE15 *(113)*
1 Rosslyn Hill, NW3 *(128)*
Southside House, Wimbledon Common, SW19 *(138)*
The Watergardens, Kingston-on-Thames *(153)*
42 West Park Road, Kew *(154)*

May 14 Saturday
The Elms, Kingston-on-Thames *(47)*
Highwood Ash, Mill Hill, NW7 *(66)*
116 Peckham Park Road, SE15 *(113)*

May 15 Sunday
The Elms, Kingston-on-Thames *(47)*
29 Gilston Road, SW10 *(56)*
Highwood Ash, Mill Hill, NW7 *(66)*
17a Navarino Road, E8 *(102)*
263 Nether Street, N3 *(103)*
Southwood Lodge, N6 *(139)*
131 Upland Road, SE22 *(147)*

May 18 Wednesday
Whitton CRC, Whitton *(158)*
May 19 Thursday
12 Lansdowne Road, W11 *(88)*
May 21 Saturday
Lambeth Palace, SE1 *(87)*
Museum of Garden History, SE1 *(99)*
Tudor Road Gardens, Hampton **(Evening)**
(146)
May 22 Sunday
15a Buckland Crescent, NW3 *(18)*
Eccleston Square, SW1 *(45)*
14 Frank Dixon Way, SE21 *(54)*
Kew Green Gardens *(84)*
15 Norcott Road, N16 *(105)*
1 Pond Street, NW3 *(119)*
Tudor Road Gardens, Hampton *(146)*
May 24 Tuesday
The Gardens of Westminster Abbey, SW1
(Evening) *(157)*
May 28 Saturday
Lambeth Community Care Centre, SE11
(86)
Regents College's Botany Garden, Inner
Circle, Regents Park, NW1 *(124)*
Tewkesbury Lodge Garden Group, SE23
(Evening) *(143)*
May 29 Sunday
Chiswick Mall, W4 *(30)*
5 Garden Close, SW15 *(55)*
48 Hampstead Way, NW11 *(62)*
38 Killieser Avenue, SW2 *(85)*
Lambeth Community Care Centre, SE11
(86)
Myddelton House Gardens, Enfield *(100)*
263 Nether Street, N3 *(103)*
Tewkesbury Lodge Garden Group, SE23
(143)
64 Thornhill Road, E10 *(144)*
June 1 Wednesday
The Hurlingham Club, SW6 *(79)*
11 Spencer Road, SW18 **(Evening)** *(140)*
June 5 Sunday
37 Alwyne Road, N1 *(4)*
97 Arthur Road, SW19 *(6)*
Barnes Gardens, SW13 *(9)*
35 Camberwell Grove, SE5 *(22)*
Choumert Square, SE15 *(32)*
26 Claygate Road, W13 *(34)*
26 College Gardens, Chingford, E4 *(36)*
142 Court Lane, Dulwich, SE21 *(38)*
De Beauvoir Gardens, N1 *(39)*
66A East Dulwich Road, SE22 *(44)*
Fishponds House, Surbiton *(52)*
116 Hamilton Terrace, NW8 *(61)*
Highgate Village, N6 *(65)*
1A Hungerford Road, N7 *(77)*
62 Hungerford Road, N7 *(78)*
Little Lodge, Thames Ditton *(89)*
3 The Park, N6 *(111)*
174 Peckham Rye, SE22 *(114)*
Pembridge Cottage, Twickenham *(115)*
2a Penn Road, N7 *(117)*
167 Rosendale Road, SE21 *(127)*
7 St George's Road, St Margaret's,
Twickenham *(130)*
South End Road, NW3 *(136)*
2 Western Lane, SW12 *(156)*
12 Woodfield Avenue, SW16 *(164)*

June 8 Wednesday
Little Lodge, Thames Ditton **(Day &**
Evening) *(89)*
18 Sibella Road, SW4 **(Evening)** *(135)*
June 9 Thursday
Fenton House, Hampstead Grove, NW3
(Evening) *(50)*
June 10 Friday
26 Claygate Road, W13 **(Evening)** *(34)*
28 Granville Park, SE13 **(Evening)** *(57)*
The Pagoda, SE3 **(Evening)** *(110)*
June 11 Saturday
Holly Cottage, Hampton *(72)*
116 Peckham Park Road, SE15 **(Evening)**
(113)
Roots and Shoots, SE11 *(126)*
Trinity Hospice, SW4 *(145)*
June 12 Sunday
Albion Square Gardens, E8 *(3)*
33 Balmuir Gardens, Putney, SW15 *(8)*
64 Blenheim Gardens, NW2 *(12)*
Boscastle Road & Grove Terrace Mews,
NW5 *(13)*
46 Church Crescent, N10 *(33)*
15 Dukes Avenue, N10 *(41)*
Dulwich Gardens, SE21 *(42)*
Ealing Gardens, W5 *(43)*
Holly Cottage, Hampton *(72)*
10 Hoveden Road, NW2 **(Evening)** *(76)*
Islington Gardens, N1 *(80)*
12 Jeymer Avenue, Willesden Green, NW2
(82)
March Cottage, Chelsfield *(93)*
Pembridge Cottage, Twickenham *(115)*
Penge Gardens, SE20 *(116)*
101 Pitt Crescent, SW19 *(118)*
112 Rectory Road, N16 *(120)*
Roots and Shoots, SE11 *(126)*
19 St Gabriel's Road, NW2 *(129)*
4 Stradbroke Grove, Buckhurst Hill *(142)*
64 Thornhill Road, E10 *(144)*
Trinity Hospice, SW4 *(145)*
1 Vineyard Hill Road, Wimbledon, SW19
(149)
6 Westbury Lane, Buckhurst Hill *(155)*
54 Wildwood Road, NW11 *(159)*
June 14 Tuesday
Charterhouse, EC1 **(Evening)** *(27)*
June 15 Wednesday
5 Burbage Road, SE24 **(Evening)** *(19)*
239a Hook Road, Chessington **(Evening)**
(74)
June 19 Sunday
42 Breakspear Road South, Ickenham *(14)*
7 The Butts, Brentford *(20)*
Columcille, Chislehurst *(37)*
36 Downs Hill, Beckenham *(40)*
14 Farm Avenue, NW2 *(49)*
34 Heath Drive, NW3 *(64)*
Ormeley Lodge, Richmond *(108)*
39 Redington Road, NW3 *(122)*
7 St George's Road, St Margaret's,
Twickenham *(130)*
June 22 Wednesday
60 Castelnau, SW13 **(Evening)** *(25)*
2 Millfield Place, N6 **(Evening)** *(96)*
June 24 Friday
James Allen's Girls' School Botany
Gardens, SE22 **(Evening)** *(81)*

June 26 Sunday
80 Bromfelde Road, SW4 *(15)*
Canonbury Gardens, N1 *(24)*
10 Chiltern Road, Eastcote *(29)*
Hill Farm, Ruislip *(67)*
5 Hillcrest Avenue, NW11 *(68)*
19 Montana Road, SW17 *(97)*
64 Redington Road, NW3 *(123)*
5 St Regis Close, N10 *(134)*
47 Winn Road, Lee, SE12 *(161)*
66 Woodbourne Avenue, SW16 *(163)*
June 29 Wednesday
Hill Farm, Ruislip **(Evening)** *(67)*
5 Hillcrest Avenue, NW11 **(Evening)** *(68)*
July 3 Sunday
24 Hills Road, Buckhurst Hill *(70)*
Natural History Museum Wildlife Garden,
SW7 *(101)*
July 6 Wednesday
Ham House, Richmond **(Evening)** *(60)*
116 Hamilton Terrace, NW8 **(Evening)** *(61)*
Roots and Shoots, SE11 **(Evening)** *(126)*
July 7 Thursday
24 Hills Road, Buckhurst Hill **(Evening)**
(70)
July 9 Saturday
27 Wood Vale, N10 *(162)*
July 10 Sunday
12 Aberdare Gardens, NW6 *(1)*
7 Byng Road, High Barnet *(21)*
83 Camberwell Grove, SE5 *(23)*
54 Ferndown, Northwood Hills *(51)*
Lyndhurst Square Gardens, SE15 *(90)*
1 Maple Close, SW4 *(92)*
59 Murray Road, Wimbledon Village, SW19
(98)
13 Redbridge Lane West, E11 *(121)*
South London Botanical Institute, SE24
(137)
28 Stanley Road, Northwood *(141)*
2 Western Lane, SW12 *(156)*
27 Wood Vale, N10 *(162)*
July 14 Thursday
10A The Pavement, West Norwood, SE27
(Evening) *(112)*
July 16 Saturday
26 Hillcroft Crescent, Wembley Park *(69)*
July 17 Sunday
Badgers Retreat, New Malden *(7)*
52A Berrylands Road, Surbiton *(10)*
58 Blakes Lane, New Malden *(11)*
71 Central Hill, SE19 *(26)*
26 Hillcroft Crescent, Wembley Park *(69)*
Holly Cottage, Hampton *(72)*
17a Navarino Road, E8 *(102)*
5 New Road, Crouch End, N8 *(104)*
57 St Quintin Avenue, W10 *(133)*
July 20 Wednesday
Badgers Retreat, New Malden **(Evening)**
(7)
Roots and Shoots, SE11 **(Evening)** *(126)*
July 23 Saturday
Lambeth Palace, SE1 *(87)*
July 24 Sunday
60 Brunswick Street, E17 *(17)*
13 College Cross, N1 *(35)*
66A East Dulwich Road, SE22 *(44)*
73 Forest Drive East, E11 *(53)*

157 Hampstead Way, NW11 *(63)*
3 Hillside Gardens, Walthamstow, E17 *(71)*
47 Maynard Road, Walthamstow, E17 *(95)*
10A The Pavement, West Norwood, SE27 *(112)*
5 St Regis Close, N10 *(134)*
11 Warwick Road, Walthamstow, E17 *(151)*
24 Warwick Road, Walthamstow, E17 *(152)*
86 Willifield Way, NW11 *(160)*

July 30 Saturday
St Michael's Convent, Richmond *(132)*

July 31 Sunday
29 Addison Avenue, W11 *(2)*
60 Castelnau, SW13 *(25)*
31 Roedean Crescent, SW15 *(125)*
57 St Quintin Avenue, W10 *(133)*
11 Warwick Road, Walthamstow, E17 *(151)*
24 Warwick Road, Walthamstow, E17 *(152)*

August 7 Sunday
66A East Dulwich Road, SE22 **(Evening)** *(44)*
2 Western Lane, SW12 *(156)*

August 11 Thursday
28 Stanley Road, Northwood **(Evening)** *(141)*

August 14 Sunday
1A Hungerford Road, N7 *(77)*

August 21 Sunday
5 New Road, Crouch End, N8 *(104)*
20A St John's Grove, N19 *(131)*

August 28 Sunday
12 Jeymer Avenue, Willesden Green, NW2 **(Evening)** *(82)*
19 Montana Road, SW17 *(97)*

September 1 Thursday
63B Overhill Road, East Dulwich, SE22 **(Evening)** *(109)*

September 3 Saturday
Trinity Hospice, SW4 *(145)*

September 4 Sunday
1 Arlingford Road, SW2 *(5)*
54 Ferndown, Northwood Hills *(51)*
Trinity Hospice, SW4 *(145)*

September 10 Saturday
The Holme, NW1 *(73)*

September 11 Sunday
The Holme, NW1 *(73)*

September 18 Sunday
Hornbeams, Stanmore *(75)*

September 27 Tuesday
Waltham Forest Register Office, E17 *(150)*

October 16 Sunday
The Watergardens, Kingston-on-Thames *(153)*

2006

February 26 Sunday
Myddelton House Gardens, Enfield *(100)*

DESCRIPTIONS OF GARDENS

❶ 12 Aberdare Gardens, NW6 ⌖⊕
(Mrs O Bishop) *Located ½m from the West Hampstead, Finchley Rd, Swiss Cottage & Hampstead tube stations. Buses on West End Lane: 139, 328, C11; on Finchley Rd: 13, 82, 113, 187, 268, 777.* Intimate, densely planted 40ft x 100ft garden with a strong sense of design that evolves as conditions change. Emphasis on leaf texture and pattern but generally muted, complementary flower colours. Laid out to be seen from the house but concealed elements reveal themselves during a walk around the garden. Designed for all-yr interest. Some unusual plants and a pot patio. TEAS. *Adm £2.50, chd free. Sun 10 July (2.30-6)*

❷ 29 Addison Avenue, W11 ⌖
(Mr & Mrs D B Nicholson) *No entry for cars from Holland Park Avenue, approach via Norland Square & Queensdale Rd. Tube: Holland Park. Bus 94, 148.* A garden designed to be at its peak in July and August. Unusual wall shrubs, itea, schizophragma, clerodendrum, surround beds of colourful perennials, phlox, monarda, agastache, eupatorium. A pear tree dominates the central lawn and a giant *Euonymus japonicus*, 150yrs old, amazes all who see it. Featured on BBC2 Gardeners' World 2004. *Adm £2, chd free. Sun 31 July (2-6)*

❸ Albion Square Gardens, E8
2m N of Liverpool St station (mainline & tube). 1m S of Dalston/Kingsland station (mainline). Buses: 22, 67, 149, 243, alight Downham Rd. By car approach from Queenbridge Rd northbound turning L into Albion Drive leading to Albion Square. Enjoy sumptuous teas in leafy formal garden oasis of Albion Square and collect walking maps for gardens. Home-made TEAS at Albion Square central gardens. *Combined adm £7, chd £2. Sun 12 June (2-5.30)*

4 Albion Square ⌖ (Kate Turner) An established garden full of exotic evergreens. Gradually evolving under the current owners to include flowers and children's area.

12 Albion Square (Michael & Sarah Parry) Surprisingly spacious garden with a Victorian Gothic church backdrop. Trees and shrubs allow unfolding areas of interest incl established borders, sunny herb garden and willow arbour.

24 Albion Square ⌖⊕ (David French) 80ft town garden designed to unfold as a series of views and focal points divided by a yew hedge. Emphasis on foliage plants rather than flowers. Secluded seating areas, fountain. Through shared Gothic summerhouse to No 25. *(share to St Josephs Hospice)*

25 Albion Square ⌖⊕ (Sandy MacLennan) 80ft informal walled garden on two levels with pond featuring ornamental shrubs and trees creating interest in foliage, form and colour.

252 Haggerston Road ⌖⊕ (Ms Heather Wilson) 60ft long, mid-terrace shady town garden. Informal, densely planted design with emphasis on unusual perennials and shrubs, incl peat bed, herbs, ferns, dry shade area, herbaceous border and (friendly) beehive (share to UNIPAL).

24 Middleton Road ♿⌖⊕ (Donald & Ann Jameson) A 90ft walled garden, mainly lawn but surrounded by beds with mixed planting, some unusual; fruit trees incl medlar and mulberry. Huge actinidia, spreading over the back of the house and garage, produces crop of kiwi fruits from Christmas to Easter. *Private visits welcome by appt. Tel 020 7241 3696 annjam@globalnet.co.uk*

54 Middleton Road (Kate & Charlie Hoult) Secluded S-facing town garden combining sunlit borders and shade with an elegant symmetrical design. Emphasis on form and foliage.

❹ 37 Alwyne Road, N1 ♿⌖⊕
(Mr & Mrs J Lambert) *Buses: 38, 56, 73, 341 on Essex Rd; 4, 19, 30, 43 on Upper St, alight at the Town Hall; 271 on Canonbury Rd, A1. Tube: Highbury & Islington on the Victoria Line.* The New River curves around the garden, the trees and sky are big, you could be in the country. Clipped box, holly and yew keep things in order, a line-up of pots reclaim space for strong colours. Hidden formal garden; old-fashioned roses along the river. Shelter if it rains. Astrantia for sale. Wheelchairs possible only with own assistant for 3 entrance steps. TEAS. *Adm £2, chd £1 (share to Rose Bowl Youth Club). Sun 5 June (2-6)*

❺ 1 Arlingford Road, SW2 ⌖⊕
(Jane Millar) *Close to Effra Road & Tulse Hill. Buses: 2, 3, 37, 196. 8 mins walk from Brixton Tube.* Artist's garden created with Chelsea medal winner Jane Brockbank. 18ft x

30ft walled garden at rear of house. 2 wide borders exuberantly planted with seasonal colour schemes, culminating in autumn. Interesting climbers, wall shrubs, multi-stemmed birch and area for shade-loving plants. Home-made TEAS. *Adm £1.50, chd 50p. Sun 4 Sept (2-6). Private visits welcome by appt. Tel 020 8674 7624*

❻ 97 Arthur Road, SW19 🚻♿
(Tony & Bella Covill) *Wimbledon Park tube station then 200yds up hill on R.* Long garden views over Wimbledon Park, developed over 14yrs. Interesting mix of herbaceous shrubs giving yr-round colour. Lawns, secret areas, small pond and a rose arch leading to a small box garden with mulberry tree. *Adm £2, chd free. Sun 5 June (2-6)*

❼ NEW Badgers Retreat, 39 Motspur Park, New Malden ♿🚻
(Peter Barham & Jenny McCarter) *3m N Kingston town centre. Buses: 213 from Kingston or Sutton; 265 Putney to New Malden; K5 from Kingston; K9 Epsom to New Malden. 7-10 mins walk Motspur Park railway station. By car: A3 to New Malden roundabout, L to Worcester Park, 3rd turning on L.* Garden with Japanese exotic theme with waterfall, fish and wildlife ponds. Tree ferns and fernery, banana palms, agave, acers, bamboos, grasses and many more. Decking with pots, exotic plants and summer house, all in 90ft x 40ft. Home-made TEAS Sun only. *Adm £2.50, chd 50p (share to Kingston Hospital Cancer Unit Appeal). Sun 17 July (1-6);* **Evening Opening** *£3.50, wine, Wed 20 July (6.30-9). Private visits welcome by appt. Tel 020 8949 3733*

❽ 33 Balmuir Gardens, Putney, SW15 🚻♿
(Mrs Gay Wilson) *5 mins walk from Putney mainline station. Off the Upper Richmond Rd on corner with Howards Lane. Buses: 337, 74, 14.* Designer's garden completely re-landscaped in spring 1998. Secluded tiny mixed borders backed by stained beams. Slate and pebble mosaics, formal pond with waterfall through moose antlers and a still water lily pond. Plenty of planting for shade. Passionate plantswoman who tries out different colour combinations. All crammed into 80ft x 38ft at widest, only 16ft at narrowest. Featured in '25 Beautiful Gardens' 2003. *Adm £2.50, chd 50p, concessions £2 (share to Robert Owen Communities). Sun 12 June (2-6)*

❾ Barnes Gardens, SW13
TEAS at 8 Queen's Ride & 6 Cumberland Road. *Adm £2, chd 50p, OAP £1 each garden. Sun 5 June (2-6)*

NEW 6 Cumberland Road, SW13
🚻♿ (Fred & Pat Tuckman) *Buses: 33, 72, 209, 283, 419 to Red Lion PH, Barnes. Walk to Ferry Rd and follow to path on L after Westmoreland Rd. In this cul-de-sac continue, taking 1st rd on L (Cumberland Rd). No 6 at far end.* Developed over the years as an informal country garden. Successive swathes of colour from a combination of trees, shrubs and plants, marking the different seasons. Sunny patio, 'secret' garden surrounded by scented shrubs, wild patch, herb corner, small pond and some fruit. TEAS.

NEW 16 Cumberland Road, SW13
🚻♿ (Mrs Linda Thomas) *Buses: 33, 72, 209, 283, 419 to Red Lion Pub, Barnes. Walk to Ferry Rd and follow to path on L after Westmoreland Rd. In this cul-de-sac continue, taking 1st rd on L (Cumberland Rd).* A wonderfully exuberant garden with a profusion of colours that would grace an artist's palette! Arranged on 2 levels, there are endless layers. Dazzling, vigorous flowers, shrubs, roses and 10ft tall delphiniums, as well as vegetables, pond and baskets in interesting combinations. It all unites to create a volume of colour that is breathtaking.

32 Dryburgh Road, SW15 (Hugh & Viv Thompson) *Dryburgh Rd sandwiched between Lower & Upper Richmond Rd. Nearest BR Putney or Barnes. Equidistant from Putney Bridge or East Putney underground. 5 mins walk from No 22 bus terminal at Putney Common. Garden at Queen's Ride 3 mins walk away.* Layered city garden in suburban setting filled with exotic foliage, incl several different bamboos, quirky sculptures and gargoyles. Remember - small is beautiful! *(Share to Cancer Resource Centre).*

8 Queen's Ride, SW13 🚻♿ (H H Sir Frank & Lady White) *Mainline: Barnes, R down Rocks Lane, then L Queen's Ride. Bus: 22 to Putney Hospital.* Large garden on a tree-lined corner site facing Barnes Common. Croquet lawn surrounded by a variety of mixed borders. Rose beds and History of the Rose Garden. Garden quiz.

12 Westmoreland Road, SW13 🚻
(Mrs Norman Moore) *Buses: 33, 72, 209, 283, 419 to the Red Lion from Hammersmith.* Raised stone terrace planted with choisya, wisteria, jasmine and decorative herbs. Two lower lawns, densely planted borders and pretty gazebo with solanum, golden hop, roses and clematis. Circular lawn with pool and fountain, hydrangeas, ferns and hostas *(share to International Myeloma Foundation).*

❿ 52A Berrylands Road, Surbiton ♿🚻
(Dr Tim & Mrs Julia Leunig) *A3 to Tolworth; A240 (dir Kingston) for approx 1m, then R into Berrylands Rd (after Fire Station). 52A is on R after Xrds.* Jason Payne designed and planted T-shaped garden. Planted 2002 and already mature enough to open. Lawn and patio surrounded by cannas, lavender, cistus, albizia, tetrapanex, abutilon, roses and ginger. Natural wooded area under copper beech arranged around pond, stream and waterfall with eucalyptus, bamboo, tree fern, gunnera etc. Home-made TEAS. *Adm £2, chd free. Sun 17 July (2-5.30)*

⓫ 58 Blakes Lane, New Malden 🚻♿
(Ann & Tony Rutherford) *3m Kingston town centre. Bus: 265 from Putney to New Malden, 213 Sutton to Kingston. Motspur Park main line station 7-10 mins walk. By car, A3 to New Malden roundabout, 1st L towards Worcester Park.* A modern garden with stylish hard landscaping. Stocked with shrubs, perennials and summer bedding. Baskets and tubs, pond and fountain. Lots of seating areas. Prize winner in Kingston in Bloom Competition 2004. Light Refreshments and TEAS. *Adm £2, chd 50p (share to Princess Alice Hospice). Sun 17 July (1-6). Private visits welcome by appt. Tel 0208 942 2423*

⓬ 64 Blenheim Gardens, NW2 🚻
(Claudia Kerner) *5 mins walk from Willesden Green tube. Buses: 260, 266 to corner of Walm Lane & Anson Rd.* Mixed shrubs, roses, climbers and perennials informally planted to give a lush and dense effect. Garden is organically maintained. Pergola area with wildlife pond. Small, shady hideaway. Courtyard with small pond, statue and containers. *Adm £1.50, chd 50p. Sun 12 June (2.30-6)*

⓭ Boscastle Road & Grove Terrace Mews, NW5
Boscastle Rd is nr Highgate Rd at SE corner of Parliament Hill Fields. Grove Terrace Mews can be reached in a lane between 21 & 22 Grove Terrace or through 17 Boscastle Rd. Tube: Kentish Town or Tufnell Park; or Gospel Oak station, North London Line. Buses C2, C11, 214 alight at Grove Terrace. Home-made TEAS outside Grove Terrace Mews. Combined adm £4, chd free. Sun 12 June (2-6)
17 Boscastle Road ⌘⊙ (Tim & Caroline Gladstone) Gently stepped garden based on a design of curved and circular stonework against background of mature trees.

Grove Terrace Mews ⌘⊙ (Debbie & Tim James) Country garden oasis set within the walls of an old orchard. Mixed borders, pond and courtyard, as well as fruit trees, create a tranquil atmosphere.

⓮ NEW 42 Breakspear Road South, Ickenham ⌘
(Keith & Judith Simpson) *1m N of Ickenham. From A40 at Swakeleys Roundabout, take B467 to Ickenham. Straight across 1st roundabout, L at next mini roundabout, 1st R into service rd. Nearest tube: Ickenham, Metropolitan line.* Plantsman's delight. Medium-sized garden with hosta walk leading to terrace with many pots containing unusual grasses and tropical plants. Steps leading down to large themed borders containing a varied range of perennials, architectural plants, shrubs and trees. TEAS. *Adm £2.50, chd free (share to Arthritis Research Campaign). Sun 19 June (11-5). Private visits welcome by appt. Tel 01895 631996*

⓯ 80 Bromfelde Road, SW4 ⌘⊙
(Susan Collier) *Buses & Northern Line tube to Clapham North. 2nd turning on R off Gauden Rd.* Low maintenance front garden has progressed and self-seeded. The back garden, 65ft x 30ft, includes much replanting with new glade area, the focus on colour and light. Winding path amongst abundant perennials and bamboos through gravel planting to urban water feature, paved outdoor 'dining room' and studio garden - a family space. Featured in 'Secret Gardens of London', 2004. Home-made TEAS. *Adm £2, chd free (share to The Son-Rise Programme). Sun 26 June (2-6). Private visits welcome by appt for groups of 4+,*

May, June and end August. Tel 020 7720 4080

⓰ 21 Brunswick Street, Walthamstow, E17 ⌘⊙
(Paula Caiger) *10 mins walk from Walthamstow (mainline/tube) towards Walthamstow Village or bus W12 to Addison Rd. 1st turning off Addison Rd into Comely Bank.* Densely planted Victorian terrace garden with over 150 varieties of plants for shade and full sun, in a 33ft x 16ft space. Traditional herbaceous plants combine with the unusual to create modern Mediterranean setting. Featured in 'Garden Answers' 2003, C4's Urban Gardener and Carlton TV Garden Makers 2004. *Adm £3, chd £1. Private visits welcome by appt June to Sept. Tel 020 8923 4238 paulacaiger@hotmail.com*

⓱ NEW 60 Brunswick Street, E17 ⌘⊙
(Henry Burgess) *10 mins Walthamstow Central mainline/tube towards Walthamstow village.* Young but quickly maturing garden. Winding path leads through imposing planting, past raised beds, finishing under a secluded pergola. Young vine, fig and vegetable bed. Lots to see in an untypical London terrace garden. Home-made TEAS. *Adm £1.50, chd 50p. Sun 24 July (11-5). Also open 3 Hillside Gardens, 73 Forest Drive East, 47 Maynard Road, 11 & 24 Warwick Road. Private visits welcome by appt spring and summer only. Tel 020 8520 7377*

⓲ 15a Buckland Crescent, NW3 ⌘⌘⊙
(Lady Barbirolli) *Tube: Swiss Cottage. Buses: 46, 113 (6 mins) or 268 (request stop nearby). ½-acre; interesting collection of shrubs and plants, incl a small bamboo bed, in well-designed garden. Adm £2, chd free. Sun 22 May (2.30-5.30)*

⓳ 5 Burbage Road, SE24 ⌘⊙
(Crawford & Rosemary Lindsay) *Nr junction with Half Moon Lane. Herne Hill mainline station, 5 mins walk. Buses: 2, 3, 37, 40, 68, 196.* Garden of member of The Society of Botanical Artists. 150ft x 40ft with large and varied range of plants. Herb garden, herbaceous borders for sun and shade, climbing plants, pots, terraces, lawns. Subject of many articles in the gardening & national press. TEAS. *Adm £2, chd free. Sun 17 Apr (2-5);* **Evening Opening** *£3, wine, Wed 15 June (6-8.30). Private visits welcome by appt, coaches permitted. Tel 020 7274 5610*

⓴ 7 The Butts, Brentford ⌘⌘⊙
(Mrs Susan Sharkey) *2m S of Ealing. Turning off Half Acre, buses: E2 & E8. Short walk from Brentford High St, buses 267 & 235. Parking free after 6.30.* Garden designer's walled garden, 90ft x 45ft. Divided into three rooms, the first a terrace next to house with raised beds and water feature. A pergola divides this from cloud-pruned box-edged lawn with deep borders. Pleached hedge and arch lead to secret garden with a circular terrace and pond with further water feature. Planting biased towards foliage featuring leaf shape, texture and colour for max impact and yr-round interest. Featured in 'English Garden' 2004. TEAS. *Adm £3, chd £1.50. Sun 19 June (1-6). Private visits welcome by appt, groups of 10+. Tel 020 8560 6961 susansharkey@onetel.com*

㉑ 7 Byng Road, High Barnet ⌘⊙
(Mr & Mrs Julian Bishop) Plantaholic heaven, packed with unusual flowers, incl many salvias, echiums and digitalis. Organic garden divided into different sections - bright 'hot' coloured area and more subdued planting through an arch. Experimental Piet Oudolf-inspired front garden with knautias, alliums, lavender and contrasting yellows. Many pots full of pampered treasures. Home-made TEAS. *Adm £2, chd free (share to Barnet Hospital Special Care Baby Unit). Sun 10 July (2-5). Private visits welcome by appt. Tel 020 8440 2042*

㉒ 35 Camberwell Grove, SE5 ⌘
(Lynette Hemmant & Juri Gabriel) *From Camberwell Green go down Camberwell Church St. Turn R into Camberwell Grove. No 35 is on the L. 120ft x 20ft London garden, backing onto St Giles Church.* Typical cottage garden, a lot of colour, pots overflowing. Artist's studio a feature. Featured in '25 Beautiful Gardens', 2003, 'The Garden Shed' (USA) 2003, 'Evening Standard' and 'Mail on Sunday', 2004. *Adm £2, chd 50p (share to The St Giles Trust, Camberwell). Sun 5 June (2-7). Private visits welcome by appt late May/June for groups of 20+. Tel 020 7703 6186 jurigabriel@compuserve.com*

㉓ 83 Camberwell Grove, SE5 ⌘⊙
(John Hall & Robert Hirschhorn) *5 mins from Denmark Hill mainline station. Buses: 12, 36, 68, 148, 171, 176, 185, 436. Entrance through modern garden room at rear. Narrow 75ft x 18ft beautifully designed plant-*

lovers' garden. Abundant unusual planting within a formal structure of box hedging. Gravel and York stone paths and seating areas. Not suitable for prams. Featured in 'Evening Standard' Home & Property supplement 2004. TEAS. *Adm £2. Sun 10 July (2-6)*

24 Canonbury Gardens, N1
Tube: Highbury and Islington. Buses: 277 along St Paul's Rd, 38, 56, 73 & 341 along Essex Rd to Canonbury Rd stop or 4, 19, 30 & 43 along Upper St to town hall stop. Visitors can walk to each garden via the Georgian splendour of Canonbury Square. Light refreshments and TEAS at 78 Canonbury Road & 5 Northampton Park. *Combined adm £5 or £2 each garden, chd £2.50 or £1 each garden. Sun 26 June (2-6)*

78 Canonbury Road ⊛ (Sue Tahran) A small town garden on a busy street, surprisingly quiet and tranquil. Bricked and paved with raised beds crowded with a great variety of plants, many unusual or rare. Planting with an eye for subtle colour, contrasting shapes and textures.

5 Northampton Park ⬧⊛ (Anne Brogan & Andrew Bernhardt) *Off St Pauls Rd (northern side). Tube: Highbury & Islington. Buses: 73, 30, 38, 277. Mainline station Canonbury (North London line).* L-shaped, S-facing, walled garden. Different areas are constantly evolving, divided by yew and lavender hedging and black bamboo. Planting leans toward foliage and leaf shade with Mediterranean influence. Light refreshments and TEAS. *Private visits welcome by appt. Tel 020 7503 4735 abernhardt@blueyonder.co.uk*

60 St Paul's Road ⊛ (John & Pat Wardroper) *Buses: 30, 277 stop outside.* 70ft x 20ft walled garden with fountains, designed to form 3 separate rooms: tree-shaded York stone patio with ferns, lawn with shrub border and arch leading to sunny sitting area planted for scent. *Private visits welcome by appt pwardroper@blueyonder.co.uk*

25 60 Castelnau, SW13 ⬧⊛⊛
(David & Margaret Minch) *Buses: 33, 72, 209 & 283 to or from Hammersmith. Alight at Washington Rd stop.* The walls around this densely-planted London garden shelter many unusual and tender plants. In addition shrubs and

perennials, especially salvias, penstemons, cannas and oleanders, provide extended seasonal colour. Herb garden and conservatory. Home-made TEAS Sun only. *Adm £2, chd 50p. Sun 31 July (2-6);* **Evening Opening** *£3, wine, Wed 22 June (5-8), (share to West London Action for Children)*

26 71 Central Hill, SE19
(Sue Williams) *Midway between Harold Road and Rockmount Road on Central Hill is narrow, unmade road. Proceed to bottom of this and garden is through cast iron gates. No parking in lane.* Hidden away at end of unmade track lies this ½-acre 'secret garden'. Formerly a Victorian nursery, the garden is now an eclectic mix of large traditional herbaceous beds and structural Mediterranean planting. Wildlife pond, formal pond and numerous objects of C19 architectural salvage provide further interest. Home-made TEAS. *Adm £2.50, chd £1. Sun 17 July (2-4)*

27 Charterhouse, Charterhouse Square, EC1 ⬧⊛
Buses: 4, 55. Nearest tube station Barbican. Turn L out of station L into Carthusian St & into square. Entrance through car park. Parking free after 6.30pm. Enclosed courtyard gardens within the grounds of the historic Charterhouse, which dates back to 1347, featuring herbaceous borders, roses, ancient mulberry trees and small pond in both formal and informal settings. Various garden herbs found here are still used in the kitchen today. Buildings not open. **Evening Opening** *£4, wine, Tue 14 June (6-9)*

28 ◆ Chelsea Physic Garden, 66 Royal Hospital Road, SW3 ⬧⊛⊛
(Chelsea Physic Garden self funding charity) *Bus: 239. Station: Sloane Square (10 mins). Parking Battersea Park (charged). Entrance in Swan Walk (except wheelchairs).* 2nd oldest Botanic Garden in UK; 3¾ acres; medicinal and herb garden, perfumery border; family order beds; historical walk, glasshouses. Recently restored cool fernery and Robert Fortune's tank pond. Home-made TEAS Apr to Oct when open to public. *Adm £5, chd £3. Suns 6, 13 Feb (11-3); Suns (2-6) & Weds (12-5)*

3 Apr to 30 Oct. **For NGS:** *Sun 3 Apr (2-6). Tel 020 7352 5646 ext 2 www.chelseaphysicgarden.co.uk*

Chevening, nr Sevenoaks ⬧⊛
See Kent.

29 10 Chiltern Road, Eastcote ⊛⊛
(Mrs G & Mr D Cresswell) *2m E of Ruislip. Off Cheney St & Barnhill/Francis Rd which link Cuckoo Hill/Eastcote High Rd (B466) with Bridle Rd/Eastcote Rd. Please park in Francis Rd.* Plantswoman's garden approx ½ acre on clay soil with mature trees incl variegated Liriodendron (tulip tree) and gleditsia 'Sunburst'. Mixture of shrubs, climbers and perennials. Some unusual plants for sale propagated from the garden. Home-made TEAS. *Adm £1.50, chd free. Suns 1 May; 26 June (2-5)*

30 Chiswick Mall, W4
Tube station: Stamford Brook (District Line). Buses: 27, 267, 391 & 190 to Young's Corner from Hammersmith through St Peter's Sq under A4 to river. By car A4 westbound turn off at Eyot Gdns S, then R into Chiswick Mall. Riverside community near Chiswick Eyot. Home-made TEAS at 16 Eyot Gardens. *Individual adm charge (see each garden for open days). Suns 1, 29 May (2-6)*

Eyot Cottage (Mrs Peter Trumper) Two interconnecting gardens, both with beautiful river frontage. One an old walled garden recently replanted with many unusual white plants and shrubs. Other an upper terrace garden laid out by owners with imaginative use of old stones and pavers. *Adm £1, chd 50p. Not open Sun 1 May*

16 Eyot Gardens, W6 ⊛ (Ms Dianne Farris) Small town garden. Front garden planted to complement Victorian house. Back shows what can be done with a small space, by using the walls for yr-round interest. Terrace, fountain and garden art. *Adm £1, chd free, OAP 50p. Suns 1, 29 May*

Lingard House ⊕ (Rachel Austin) Walled garden divided into brick courtyard and terrace with huge acacia tree; formal lawn with miniature pond and water-spout and unusual herbaceous planting. Wire-work pergola reveals wild garden with ancient apple trees, climbing roses and beehive. *Adm £1, chd free. Not open Sun 1 May. Private visits welcome by appt end of May to end of June. Tel 020 8747 1943*

Swan House &✗ (Mr & Mrs George Nissen) Informal walled garden. Herbaceous border, fruit trees, small vegetable garden. Tiny greenhouse. Small wild flower area. 2 ponds and a rill. *Adm £1 (share to West London Action for Children). Not open Sun 1 May*

Walpole House ✗ (Mrs Patricia Benson) Plantsman's garden; species and tree peonies; water garden; spring flowers. CI6-CI8 house (not open), once home of Barbara Villiers, Duchess of Cleveland. *Adm £2, chd 50p, OAP 50p. Not open Sun 29 May*

㉛ 51 Cholmeley Crescent, N6 ✗⊕
(Ernst & Janet Sondheimer) *Highgate. Between Highgate Hill & Archway Rd, off Cholmeley Park. Nearest tube Highgate.* Approx ⅓-acre garden with many alpines in screes, peat beds, tufa, troughs and greenhouse; shrubs, rhododendrons, camellias, magnolias, pieris, ceanothus etc. Clematis, bog plants, roses, primulas, tree ferns. Water features. Featured on Swedish TV 2003. TEAS. *Adm £2, chd £1. Sun 1 May (2-6). Private visits welcome by appt. Tel 020 8340 6607 ernst@sondheimer.fsnet.co.uk*

㉜ Choumert Square, SE15 &✗⊕
(The Residents) *Via wrought iron gates off Choumert Grove. Peckham Rye mainline station is visible from the gates, & buses galore (12, 36, 37, 171, 312, 78, 63, 345) less than 10 mins walk. Free car park 2 mins.* About 46 mini gardens with maxi-planting in a Shangri-la situation that the media has described as a 'Floral Canyon', which leads to small communal 'secret garden'. Open day has village fête atmosphere with many stalls and delicious refreshments. Featured in BBC 'Good Homes' 2003. Prizewinner Communal Gardens Camberwell 2004. Light refreshments and TEAS. *Adm £2.50, chd 50p, concessions £1.50 (share to St Christopher's Hospice, SE26). Sun 5 June (2-6)*

㉝ NEW 46 Church Crescent, N10 ✗
(Fenella Crichton) *Tube: Highgate, turn R and walk 10 mins down Muswell Hill Rd, turn R. Bus: 43 or 134, which stops at bottom of rd.* Beautiful trees of Parkland Walk (access available) provide spectacular backdrop to 100ft terraced garden. 1st level: Relatively formal beds planted for diversity of texture and shape; 2nd with pond and pots incl some unusual small trees; 3rd wilder and more woodland with bamboo, birch and ferns. Lots of climbing roses, grasses and perennials. Steps are steep and this garden is not recommended for the very young or infirm. TEAS. *Adm £2, chd free. Sun 12 June (2-5)*

㉞ 26 Claygate Road, W13 ✗
(Irena Sawyer & John Bishop) *Easy walk from Northfields tube station (Piccadilly Line). Situated between Northfield Ave & Boston Manor Rd. 5 mins drive from J2 M4.* Colourful front garden leading to imaginative, small (33ft x 21ft) back garden which maximises space in artistic and imaginative ways. The garden is a haven of tranquillity in the heart of suburbia. Abundance of climbing roses interplanted with clematis. Fruit trees, herbs, profusion of beautiful pots, window boxes, hanging baskets and herbaceous borders. Home-made TEAS served in enchanting next door garden. *Adm £1.50, chd free. Sun 5 June (2-6); Evening Opening £3.50, wine, Fri 10 June (7-9)*

㉟ 13 College Cross, N1 ✗
(Diana & Stephen Yakeley) *Nearest tube station Highbury & Islington.* Black slate and glass balustrade provide contemporary design interest in this peaceful green oasis. Paved areas for dining surrounded by architectural plants chosen for form and texture are enlivened by white flowers incl several different types of lily. *Adm £2, chd free. Sun 24 July (2-6). Private visits welcome by appt dy@yakeley.com*

㊱ NEW 26 College Gardens, Chingford, E4
(Lynnette Parvez) *2m from Walthamstow. 15 mins walk from Chingford mainline station. 97 bus from Walthamstow Central tube station. Alight at College Gardens then short walk down hill.* Large suburban garden, approx ⅔ acre. Sun terrace leads to established borders and variety of climbing roses. Beyond this, wildlife pond and lawn, small woodland walk with spring plants and orchard. A further garden area was recently uncovered and will be

restored and planted over time. TEAS. *Adm £2, chd free. Sun 5 June (2-5)*

㊲ NEW Columcille, 9 Norlands Crescent, Chislehurst &✗⊕
(Nancy & Jim Pratt) *Off A222 turn into Cricket Ground Rd, then 1st R into Norlands Cres. 4m from Chislehurst Station. Bus: 162 or 269, Bank House stop.* Small garden featuring many recycled materials. Colourful display of roses, lupins, peonies and delphiniums. Japanese sanctuary, influenced by Zen tradition, incl water feature and shed transformed into a tea house. Prizewinner for Most Inspired Themed Garden in Bromley in Bloom Competition 2004. Home-made TEAS. *Adm £2, chd free (share to Harris Hospiscare). Sun 19 June (2-5). Private visits welcome by appt May - Sept. Tel 020 8467 9383*

Cottage Farm, Cackets Lane, Cudham ⊕
See Kent.

㊳ 142 Court Lane, Dulwich, SE21 &✗⊕
(Jeremy & Jackie Prescott) *Nr Court Lane entrance to Dulwich Park, ½m from Dulwich Village (N Dulwich train station/P34 bus); also 40, 176, 185 buses. ½-acre garden at former home of Anne Shelton (the "Forces' Favourite"), backing on to trees and rhododendrons of Dulwich Park.* Urban garden planted from 1994 featuring rose garden, mixed border with roses, central lawn with fruit trees, vegetable bed, all on a circular theme. Light refreshments and TEAS. *Adm £2, chd free (share to St Christopher's Hospice, Sydenham). Sun 5 June (2-6)*

㊳ De Beauvoir Gardens, N1 *Tubes: Victoria Line to Highbury & Islington then 30 or 277 buses from St Paul's Rd; Angel tube then 38 or 73 bus, alight at stop after Essex Rd station. Entrance for cars via Southgate Rd - park in Northchurch Rd or via Kingsland & Downham Rd.* 2 mature gardens in leafy enclave of period houses. Cream TEAS at Brewster House. Combined adm £3 or £2 each garden, chd £1 or 50p each garden. *Sun 5 June (2-6)*

Brewster House, 82a Mortimer Road &✗⊕ (Mrs Elizabeth Haines) The spacious garden is an oasis of fertility and calm, designed around a sunny snowman-shaped lawn. Sunken patio, small pond and wide selection of trees, shrubs and plants. *(Share to Motor Neurone Disease Assoc).* Cream TEAS.

NEW **21 Northchurch Terrace** 🚫
(Ms Nancy Korman) Walled
town garden (30ft x 75ft) with
formal feel. Deep herbaceous
borders, pond, fruit trees,
pergola, patio pots and herb
beds. Entrance from 4 steps.
*Private visits welcome by appt in
June. Tel 0207 249 4919*

**Dolly's Garden, 43 Layhams Road,
West Wickham** 🚫
See Kent.

40 36 Downs Hill, Beckenham
(Marc & Janet Berlin) *3m W of
Bromley. 2 mins from Ravensbourne
mainline station nr top of Foxgrove
Rd.* Long ⅔-acre E-facing garden
sloping steeply away from house.
Ponds, water courses and sheltered
patio area with many tender unusual
plants and hundreds of pots. Wooded
area, dense planting of trees, shrubs
and flowers. New raised beds, paths
and patio areas. Art exhibition and
music. Featured on BBC Gardeners'
World 2004. Home-made TEAS.
*Adm £2 (share to NSPCC). Sun 19
June (2-5). Private visits welcome by
appt. Tel 020 8650 9377*

41 NEW 15 Dukes Avenue, N10
🚫
(Vivienne Parry) *Short walk from
main Muswell Hill roundabout.
Buses: 43, 134, alight Muswell Hill
Broadway or 7 from Finsbury Park.
Tube: Highgate, then bus 43 or 134.*
Mediterranean-style gravel front
garden in silver, lilacs, pinks and
blues. Small lawned back garden with
wide variety of plants. Colour in both
areas provided by constantly
changing containers and pots. TEAS.
Adm £2, chd free. Sun 12 June (2-5)

42 Dulwich Gardens, SE21
*Mainline: London Bridge to W
Dulwich & from Victoria to W
Dulwich then 10-15 mins walk.
Tube: Brixton then P4 bus passes
both gardens. Street parking.* 2
Georgian houses with large gardens,
2 mins walk from Dulwich Picture
Gallery & Dulwich Park. Home-
made TEAS 103 Dulwich Village.
*Combined adm £4, chd free (share to
Macmillan Cancer Relief - local
branch). Sun 12 June (2-5)*

103 Dulwich Village 🚫 (Mr &
Mrs N Annesley) About ½-acre
'country garden in London'. Long
herbaceous border, spacious
lawn, ornamental pond, roses
and many and varied other
plants, plus fruit and vegetable
garden.

105 Dulwich Village 🚫 (Mr &
Mrs A Rutherford) About ½-acre,
mostly herbaceous with lawns
and lots of old-fashioned roses.
Shrubbery, ornamental pond,
water garden. Very pretty garden
with many unusual plants.

43 Ealing Gardens, W5
*From London on Westway: at
Hanger Lane gyratory system keep
going W but keep at ground level. Do
not use underpass, 1st L into
Lynwood Rd; Birkdale Rd. From
Birkdale Rd, R into Mount Ave, R
into Brentham Way.* TEAS at 9
Birkdale Rd. *Combined adm £2, chd
50p. Sun 12 June (2-5)*

9 Birkdale Road 🚫 (Stella &
Redmond Smith) About ½-acre.
Rose garden leading to park-like
area. Widening to incl pond with
decorative anti-heron feature, and
a variety of trees and bamboos.
Also a new rose - 'Little Wren',
raised in the garden.

**Winscombe Lodge, 1 Brentham
Way** 🚫 (Mr & Mrs M
Chapman) Stepped access into
secluded walled garden with old
'alpine stream', waterfall and
pond. Some formal and informal
plantings - many rocks.

**44 66A East Dulwich Road, East
Dulwich, SE22** 🚫
(Kevin Wilson) *Basement flat
overlooking Goose Green, opp
Dulwich Swimming Baths. Walking
distance from mainline East Dulwich
station. Buses: 185, 176, 37.* Secret
tranquil 100ft garden with decking,
architectural planting, gravel and
ponds, plunge pool, swing raised
viewing platforms. Just taken over ⅓
of next door garden and have
veranda, 4 person swing and
vegetable garden. Featured on ITV's
Britain's Best Back Garden 2004.
TEAS. *Adm £2, chd £1 (share to The
Globe Centre). Suns 5 June; 24 July
(12-6);* **Evening Opening** *£3.50, wine,
Sun 7 Aug (8-11). Private visits
welcome by appt for parties of 10+.
Tel 020 8693 3458
Kevin@edulwich66.fsnt.co.uk*

45 Eccleston Square, SW1
🚫 **NCCPG**
(Roger Phillips & the Residents) *Off
Belgrave Rd nr Victoria station,
parking allowed on Suns.* 3-acre
square planned by Cubitt in 1828.
The Garden Committee has worked
over the last 21yrs to see what can be
created despite the inner city
problems of drought, dust, fumes,
shade and developers. The garden is
sub-divided into mini-gardens incl
camelia, iris, rose, fern and container
garden. National Collection of

ceanothus incl more than 70 species
and cultivars is held in the Square.
Home-made TEAS. *Adm £3, chd
£1.50. Sun 22 May (2-5)*

46 Edwardes Square, W8 🚫
(Edwardes Square Garden
Committee) *Tube stations Kensington
High St & Earls Court. Buses: 9, 10,
27, 28, 31, 49 & 74 - bus stop,
Odeon Cinema. Entrance in South
Edwardes Square.* One of London's
prettiest secluded garden squares. 3½
acres laid out differently from other
squares, with serpentine paths by
Agostino Agliothe, Italian artist and
decorator who lived at no. 15 from
1814-1820, and a beautiful Grecian
temple which is traditionally the
home of the gardener. Good displays
of bulbs and blossom. *Adm £3, chd
free. Sun 24 Apr (2-5)*

**47 The Elms, 13 Wolverton
Avenue, Kingston-on-Thames**
🚫
(Prof & Mrs R Rawlings) *1m E of
Kingston. On A308. Kingston
Hospital & Norbiton mainline
station 100yds. Enter via garage in
Manorgate Rd at foot of Kingston
Hill.* Some parking restrictions -
Saturdays. 55ft x 25ft garden owned
by 'plantaholic'! Trees, shrubs,
climbers, herbaceous and ground
cover plants, some rare. Pool, fruit
trees and soft fruits. Roof garden not
open on NGS days. Home-made
TEAS. *Adm £1.50, chd 50p (share to
Terrence Higgins Trust). Sats, Suns
12 , 13 Mar; 16 , 17 Apr; 14 , 15
May (2.30-4.30) . Private visits
welcome by appt for groups of 10+.
Tel 07885 045685*

48 Elmsdale Road Gardens, E17
*Walthamstow Central tube (Victoria
Line) & mainline station (from
Liverpool St). 10 mins walk via High
Street & Erskine Rd. Buses incl 2, 20,
34, 48, 58, 69, 212, 215, 251, 257,
275, 505, 551, W11, W15 to
Walthamstow Central & 123 along
Forest Rd. Parking permits not
required on Suns although spaces
likely to be very limited. Free car
park in Palmerston Rd.* Three
gardens are open for full viewing
with an additional two gardens
providing home-made teas and a
well-stocked plant stall. Home-made
TEAS at 17 & 38 Elmsdale Rd.
*Combined adm £3, chd free. Sun 8
May (2-6)*

17 Elmsdale Road 🚫 (Cristina
Franchi & Peter Argall) Organic
family garden using borrowed
landscape, internal vistas and
lush plantings to suggest a much
larger garden. Planting
emphasises foliage and texture

with seasonal highlights. Wildlife pond; fruit tree tunnel; hidden sunny terrace.

20 Elmsdale Road (Melanie Watson) A long narrow low maintenance garden with water features, patio and mix of favourite and slug-proof plants. Shrubs, roses, bamboos, herbs and bulbs. *Solanum Jasminoides Album* flowers almost yr-round over an arbour.

55 Elmsdale Road (Jean Duggleby) Unusual rear porch on stilts with climbers and raised brick beds. Ivy covered archways lead to a small lawn. Mixed plantings, pond, waterfall and bridge.

㊾ 14 Farm Avenue, NW2

(Mrs Christine Winterburgh) *Buses: 13, 82, 113, 245, 260, 328, 460. Off Cricklewood Lane near Hendon Way (A41). Train: Cricklewood (Thameslink).* Informal garden planned for yr-round interest. Packed borders of herbaceous perennials and shrubs. Tall pear tree with Rambling Rector rose. Recently redesigned terrace with pots. Seasonally changing front garden with lavender hedge. Home-made TEAS (delicious cakes!). *Adm £2, chd free. Sun 19 June (2-6)*

㊿ ◆ Fenton House, Hampstead Grove, NW3

(The National Trust) *300yds from Hampstead tube. Entrances: top of Holly Hill & Hampstead Grove.* Timeless 1½-acre walled garden, laid out on three levels, containing imaginative plantings concealed by yew hedges. The herbaceous borders give yr-round interest while the brick-paved sunken rose garden, replanted 2000-2001, provides a sheltered hollow of scent and colour. The formal lawn area contrasts with the rustic charm of the kitchen garden and orchard. Vine house built in 1998. **For NGS: Evening Opening** *£3.50, chd £1.50, wine, Thur 9 June (6.30-8.30)*

NEW Fern Cottage, Swanley Village Road, Swanley

See Kent.

(51) NEW 54 Ferndown, Northwood Hills

(David & Ros Bryson) *Tube: Northwood (Metropolitan line) 5 mins walk. R out of station, R down Briarwood Drive then 1st R.* Unusual collection of exotics, cacti and Australasian plants. Palm trees, tree ferns and bananas set in an original design. Elevated deck overlooks the garden underplanted with rare ferns and aroids beside a trickling brook. TEAS. *Adm £2.50, chd free. Suns 10 July; 4 Sept (11.30-5.30). Private visits welcome by appt. Tel 020 8866 3792 david@bryson77.freeserve.co.uk*

(52) NEW Fishponds House, 219 Ewell Road, Surbiton

(Robert & Belinda Eyre-Brook) *1m from Tolworth junction on A3 towards Kingston on A240. House in middle of The Fishponds, a public park bordered by Ewell Rd, Browns Rd, King Charles Rd & Hollyfield Rd. Park in neighbouring rds. (Disabled drivers access from Ewell Rd).* A large part formal, part terrace garden with adjoining woodland overlooking a small lake. Partly redesigned by Andy Sturgeon and filled with structural plants and grasses. Visitors could visit the park for a picnic before garden opening. TEAS. *Adm £2, chd free. Sun 5 June (2-6)*

(53) 73 Forest Drive East, E11

(Alec Wyllie) *Leytonstone. Into Whipps Cross Rd, then SW into James Lane. 1st L into Clare Rd, 1st R into Forest Drive E. By bus to Whipps Cross Hospital or tube to Leytonstone & bus to James Lane.* 20ft x 65ft country garden in miniature, but with full-sized plants. Small lawn with mixed borders leading to shrub and woodland area. Two fountains and various unusual plants. Conservatory. Also 20ft square front garden informally planted around formal paths and centrepiece. TEAS. *Adm £1.50, chd 50p (share to The Margaret Centre, Whipps Cross Hospital). Sun 24 July (11-5). Also open* **60 Brunswick Street, 3 Hillside Gardens, 47 Maynard Rd, 11 & 24 Warwick Road**

(54) 14 Frank Dixon Way, SE21

(Frank & Angie Dunn) *From Dulwich Village pass Dulwich Gallery on R and Frank Dixon Way (a private rd) is 500metres on L.* Large family garden surrounded by mature trees, low maintenance shrub borders and annual plantings. Lawns and a spectacular rowan. Sit-on railway around the garden for children's rides. Home-made TEAS. *Adm £2, chd free. Sun 22 May (12-5)*

(55) 5 Garden Close, SW15

(Vivien Fowler & Tom Jestico) *½m E of Roehampton. Off Portsmouth Rd, 7-10 mins walk from the Green Man public house, via Wildcroft Rd Putney Hill.* ¼-acre walled garden which serves as backdrop to architect's all-glass house. Oriental inspiration with black bamboos, and swathes of box, hebe, lavender and rhododendrons. Ponds and timber decks surround house. *Adm £2, chd free. Sun 29 May (12-5)*

(56) 29 Gilston Road, SW10

(Margaret & James Macnair) *Gilston Rd leads N from Fulham Rd to the Boltons.* Long walled town garden. Many spring bulbs and spring flowering shrubs, clematis and camellias. Interesting use of levels, arches and trellis to create different spaces. *Adm £1.50, chd free. Sun 15 May (2-5.30). Private visits welcome by appt. Tel 020 7352 7735*

(57) 28 Granville Park, SE13

(Joanna Herald) *Parking available on street, Suns & eves. 10 mins walk up hill (N) towards Blackheath from Lewisham mainline & DLR stations.* Garden designer's family garden in three sections. Pool garden, mixed herbaceous and shrub planting with bulbs around circular lawns, gravel garden and sunken terrace with pots. 100ft x 35ft. **Evening Opening** *£3.50, wine, chd £1, Fri 10 June (5-8). Also open* **The Pagoda**

(58) Grims Dyke Hotel, Old Redding, Harrow Weald

2m N of Harrow. Old Redding is off A409 Brookshill High Rd at junction with Common Rd & Clamp Hill. Grade II listed garden. 48 acres. Rhododendrons, azaleas and giant redwoods. Restored sunken rose garden. Bluebell orchard, lost valley garden and woodland walks. Restored fruit wall. Restoration of lake now in progress. Newly restored Victorian vegetable garden. Former home of Sir William Gilbert. Light refreshments and TEAS. *Adm £1, chd 50p. Sun 8 May (11-5). Private visits welcome by appt. Tel 020 8954 4227*

(59) 7 The Grove, Highgate Village, N6

(Mr Thomas Lyttelton) *The Grove is between Highgate West Hill & Hampstead Lane. Tube stations: Archway or Highgate (Northern Line, Barnet trains). Buses: 210, 271, 143 to Highgate Village from Archway, 214 from Camden Town.* ½ acre designed for max all-yr interest with its variety of conifers and other trees, ground cover, water garden, vistas, 19 paths, surprises. Home-made TEAS. *Adm £2, chd £1, concessions £1 (share to North London Hospice). Sun 3 Apr (2-5.30). Also opening with* **Highgate Village** *Sun 5 June. Private visits welcome by appt. Tel 020 8340 7205/0771 363 8161*

60 ◆ Ham House, Richmond 🔗🅿♿

(The National Trust) *Mid-way between Richmond & Kingston. W of A307 on Surrey bank of R Thames. Signposted with National Trust signs.* The beautiful C17 gardens incl much photographed Cherry Garden, featuring lavender parterres flanked by hornbeam arbours; S terrace with clipped yew cones, hibiscus and pomegranate trees; eight grass plats; maze-like wilderness; C17 orangery with working kitchen garden and licensed café; and terrace with reputedly the oldest Christ's thorn bush in the country. Meet the gardeners for a tour of the organic kitchen garden. Light refreshments and TEAS. *House and Garden Adm £7.50, chd £3.75, Garden only £3.50, chd £1.75. Garden all yr Sat to Wed (closed 25, 26 Dec; 1 Jan) (11-6) or dusk if earlier. House & garden Sat to Wed 19 Mar to 30 Oct (1-5 last entry 4.30).* **For NGS: Evening Opening** *£3.50, Wed 6 July (6.30-8.30). Tel 020 8940 1950, Christine Guthrie*

61 116 Hamilton Terrace, NW8 ♿

(Mr & Mrs I B Kathuria) *Tube: 5 mins walk from Maida Vale, 10 mins walk from St John's Wood. Buses: 16 & 98 from Marble Arch to Cricklewood.* Lush front garden full of dramatic foliage with a water feature and tree ferns. Large back garden of different levels with Yorkshire stone paving, many large terracotta pots and containers, water feature and lawn. Wide variety of perennials and flowering shrubs, many unusual and subtropical plants, succulents, acers, ferns, hebes, climbers, roses, fuchsias and prizewinning hostas. Packed with colour and rich foliage of varied texture. 1st Prize All London Gardens Championship 2003/4, featured on ITV Britain's Best Back Gardens 2004. Home-made TEAS. *Adm £2, chd 50p (share to St Mark's Church Appeal). Sun 5 June (2-6);* **Evening Opening** *£3, wine, Wed 6 July (5-9). Private visits welcome by appt. Tel 020 7625 6909*

62 48 Hampstead Way, NW11 ♿🅿

(Prue & Mervyn Unger) *Temple Fortune end of Hampstead Way, just before the junction with Willifield Way. Buses: 82, 102, 460 to Temple Fortune. Tube: Golders Green.* Small, densely planted garden designed to provide yr-round interest and support a variety of wildlife. Informal cottage-style front garden and semi-formal back garden with box-edged beds and York stone paths, designed to complement Arts & Crafts house (not open). Planting includes clematis (more than 30 varieties), ceanothus, wallflowers, tulips, hellebores, roses and hardy geraniums. Winner of 2004 Hampstead Garden Suburb "Prettiest Garden in the Suburb" competition. *Adm £1.50, chd free. Sun 29 May (2-6)*

63 157 Hampstead Way, NW11 🅿

(Mr & Mrs R Kemp) *Tube: Golders Green, then H2 bus to Hampstead Way.* Charming, 100ft split-level SW-facing cottage garden containing a wealth of informally planted hardy perennials and succulents, against a backdrop of interesting shrubs. *Adm £1.50, chd 50p. Sun 24 July (2-5)*

64 NEW 34 Heath Drive, NW3 🅿

(Mr & Mrs Reizenstein) *Corner of Bracknell Gardens, off Finchley Rd. Tube: 10 mins walk from Finchley Rd/ W Hampstead/ Hampstead. Buses: 13, 113, 82 Nbound.* Gardens on all sides of house include hot terrace with large-scale planting leading to cool sunken garden with pool and maples. Gravel path through double herbaceous borders leads to secluded seat in beech hedge and to casual terraces and family lawn with pergola, swing and wooded banks. Home-made TEAS. *Adm £2, chd 50p. Sun 19 June (2.30-5.30)*

65 Highgate Village, N6

The Grove is between Highgate West Hill & Hampstead Lane. Tube stations: Archway or Highgate (Northern Line, Barnet trains). Buses: 210, 214, 271, 211 to Highgate Village. The Grove is a famous Georgian terrace with breathtaking views over London. Home-made TEAS at 7 The Grove. *Combined adm £3.50, chd £1.50, concessions £1.50 (share to North London Hospice). Sun 5 June (2-5.30)*

4 The Grove ♿🅿 (Mr Cob Stenham) Two-tiered with formal upper garden; view across Heath; orchard in lower garden.

7 The Grove 🔗🅿 (Mr Thomas Lyttelton) (See separate entry).

66 Highwood Ash, Highwood Hill, Mill Hill, NW7 🔗🅿

(Mr & Mrs R Gluckstein) *From London via A41 (Watford Way) to Mill Hill Circus; turn R up Lawrence St; at top bear L up Highwood Hill; house at top on R. Tube stations: Totteridge & Whetstone or Edgware (Northern Line), Stanmore (Jubilee Line), Arnos Grove (Piccadilly Line). Bus: 251 to door.* 3¼ acre incl rose garden, shrub and herbaceous borders, rhododendrons, azaleas, lake with waterfall, terrace with raised herb garden, a mixture of formal and informal. Home-made TEAS. *Adm £2.50, chd 50p. Sat, Sun 14, 15 May (2-6)*

67 Hill Farm, Orchard Close, Ruislip 🔗♿🅿

(Jacqueline Alderton & John Ormshaw) *½m W of Ruislip. Turn into Sharps Lane off A4180 in Ruislip (Bury St). Carry on into Hill Lane, 2nd turning on R Orchard Close, park in Hill Lane if possible. Tube: Metropolitan/Piccadilly Line ½m. Central Line to W Ruislip, ½m to Ruislip.* Grade II listed medieval/Georgian timber framed farmhouse (not open) and barns. ⅔-acre garden of mixed formal/informal, herbaceous and annual plants, borders. A plethora of pots, containers and hanging baskets. Kitchen and herb gardens. Wooded area with natural pond; mature specimen trees. Old well with working pump and many interesting garden and agricultural antiques. Hardy perennial plants for sale. Home-made TEAS. *Adm £2.50, chd free (share to St Martins Church, Ruislip). Sun 26 June (12-6);* **Evening Opening** *£3.50, wine, Wed 29 June (6.30-9)*

68 5 Hillcrest Avenue, NW11 🅿🅿

(Mrs R M Rees) *Hillcrest Ave is off Bridge Lane. Buses: 82, 102, 460 to Temple Fortune. Nearest tube: Golders Green or Finchley Central. Walk down Bridge Lane.* Small labour-saving colourful garden with many interesting features; rockery, fish pond, conservatory, tree ferns, secluded patio. Prize-winning Mediterranean front garden and traditional back garden. Hampstead Horticultural Society prize-winning front garden, 2003. Home-made TEAS. *Adm £2, chd 50p, concessions £1 (share to Alzheimers Society, Barnet). Sun 26 June (2-6);* **Evening Opening** *£3, wine, Wed 29 June (6-9). Private visits welcome by appt. Tel 020 8455 0419 Ruthmrees@aol.com*

69 26 Hillcroft Crescent, Wembley Park 🔗♿🅿

(Gary & Suha Holmyard) *1½m from Wembley station. From A406 turn into Harrow Rd, approx 1½m to clock tower turn R into Wembley Hill Rd. At fork opp Wembley Conference Centre take L fork, Hillcroft Crescent is 2nd on R. Wembley Park underground approx 7 mins walk.* Small cottage front garden with fuchsias, wisterias, palm, canna and arum lilies. Rear garden designed around the original trees, approx 70ft x 80ft with greenhouse and water well. Planting incl fig, grape, vegetables, apple, pear and passion fruit. 10 different logged flower beds each holding its own particular interest, incl roses, rhododendron, hosta, jasmine, unusual evergreens, magnolia, several varieties of clematis and various potted plants. Home-made TEAS. *Adm £1.50, chd free. Sat, Sun 16, 17 July (11-5). Private visits welcome by appt. Tel 07773 691370*

⑦⓪ 24 Hills Road, Buckhurst Hill ⊗

(Sue Hargreaves) *Situated between Epping and Woodford. 5m from junction 26 on M25. Mainline: Chingford or Buckhurst Hill. Hills Rd is off A104, Epping New Rd.* Herbalist's organic garden designed by artist. Narrow Victorian garden featuring elements of potager using traditional and contemporary materials and planting. Many unusual features and details. 5 distinctive areas linked together; shady sunken terrace, herb garden, raised sleeper herbaceous beds, vegetable and trained fruit trees. *Adm £1, chd 50p (share to Studio Upstairs). Sun 3 July (2-6).* **Evening Opening** *£2.50, wine, Thur 7 July (7-9.30)*

⑦① 3 Hillside Gardens, Walthamstow, E17 ⊗⊙

(Gaynor Boudidit) *From Wood St mainline station, along Fyfield Rd; Hillside Gardens 4th turning on R. Bus 230 from Walthamstow Central to Bisterne Ave along Fyfield Rd into Hillside Gardens.* An oasis of colour and greenery. Moroccan-style courtyard and pond leads to borders of mixed perennials and shrubs with a central cottage garden style bed. Path leads to an informal patio area with many colourful pots and planting. Entrance via garage in Winsbeach. Home-made TEAS. *Adm £1.50, chd 50p, concessions £1. Sun 24 July (11-5). Also open* **60 Brunswick Street, 73 Forest Drive East, 47 Maynard Rd, 11 & 24 Warwick Road**

⑦② Holly Cottage, 40 Station Road, Hampton ⊗⊙

(Ms M Cartwright) *3m W of Kingston. Buses: 267 & 68 to Hampton Church. From river end 5 mins walk. Buses: 111 & 216 pass the house. Alight police station 100yds. Hampton mainline station 5 mins.* Long front garden planted for winter and spring interest leads on to

enchanting paved cottage garden (30ft x 25ft). Densely planted, it contains many hardy geraniums. Pergola, planted in shades of blue and white, links the two gardens. Ferns, pool, home grown mistletoe on old apple tree. Featured in 'Amateur Gardening' 2003. Home-made TEAS. *Adm £1.50, chd 50p. Sat, Sun 11, 12 June; Sun 17 July (2-5)*

⑦③ The Holme, NW1 ⊗⊙

(Lessee of The Crown Commission) *Inner Circle, Regents Park. Opp Open Air Theatre. Nearest tube: Regents Park or Baker St.* 4-acre garden filled with interesting and unusual plants. Sweeping lakeside lawns intersected by islands of herbaceous beds. Extensive rock garden with waterfall, stream and pool. Formal flower garden with unusual annual and half hardy plants, sunken lawn, fountain pool and arbour. *Adm £3, chd £1. Sat, Sun 23, 24 Apr; 10, 11 Sept (2.30-5.30)*

⑦④ 239a Hook Road, Chessington ⊗⊙

(Mr & Mrs D St Romaine) *4m S of Kingston. A3 from London, turn L at Hook underpass onto A243 Hook Rd. Garden is approx 300yds on L. Parking opp in park. Buses: 71, K4 465 from Kingston & Surbiton to North Star PH.* Garden photographer's garden. ¾-acre garden divided into two. Flower garden contains a good mix of herbaceous plants, shrubs, climbers and topiary. Also gravel garden, rose tunnel and pond. Potager, divided by paths into small beds, has many vegetables, soft fruit, fruit trees and herbs all planted with flowers. Accommodation. **Evening Opening** *£3, wine, Wed 15 June (6-9). Private visits welcome by appt groups welcome. Tel 020 8397 3761 www.gardenphotolibrary.com*

⑦⑤ Hornbeams, Priory Drive, Stanmore ⊗⊙

(Dr & Mrs R B Stalbow) *5m SE of Watford. Nearest tube Stanmore. Priory Drive private rd off Stanmore Hill (A4140 Stanmore-Bushey Heath Rd).* ½-acre garden designed by owner showing how to hide unsightly fences and use 'borrowed landscape' to create a feeling of space. Autumn-flowering cyclamen and sheets of Schizostylus coccinia and Clematis viticella for brilliant colour. Daphnes a speciality. Woodland walk, water features, fruit cage and conservatory with grapevine. New potager this yr. Home-made TEAS. *Adm £2.50, chd free (share to Jerusalem Botanical Garden). Sun 18 Sept (2.30-6). Private visits welcome by appt.*

Tel 020 8954 2218 barichard@btopenworld.com

⑦⑥ 10 Hoveden Road, NW2 ⊗

(Ian Brownhill & Michael Hirschl) *Tube: Kilburn or Willesden Green. Buses: 16, 32, 189, 226, 245, 260, 266 & 316 to Cricklewood Broadway, then consult A-Z.* 70ft x 25ft urban garden. Stylish deck with pergola and fish pond leads into attractive circular paved area surrounded by box hedging and deeply planted borders. Shade area at the end of the garden features gazebo. No access for pushchairs. Featured in range of publications incl 'BBC Gardeners' World' magazine 2003. **Evening Opening** *£3, wine, Sun 12 June (4-7)*

⑦⑦ 1A Hungerford Road, N7 ⊗⊙

(David Matzdorf) *6 mins walk from Caledonian Rd tube. Buses: 29 & 253 to Hillmarton Rd stop in Camden Rd. 17, 91 & 259 to last stop in Hillmarton Rd. 10 to York Way at Market Rd & 274 to junction of Market Rd & Caledonian Rd.* Unique eco-house with walled, lush front garden planted in modern-exotic style. Floriferous 'green roof' resembling scree slope. Front garden densely planted with palms, acacia, ginger lilies, brugmansias, bananas, euphorbias, cistus and spiky plants incl agave and aloe. The 'green roof' is planted with alpines, sedums, mesembryanthemums, bulbs, grasses and aromatic herbs - access only to part of roof for safety reasons (can be seen from below). Size of garden and roof is 50ft x 18ft in each case. Featured in 'Gardenlife' magazine 2004 & Garden Makers, sky TV 2004. *Adm £1.50, chd 50p (share to Terrence Higgins Trust). Suns 5 June; 14 Aug (2-6)*

⑦⑧ 62 Hungerford Road, N7 ⊗

(John Gilbert & Lynne Berry) *Nearest tube stn: Caledonian Rd, Piccadilly line.* Mature town garden at the rear of Victorian terrace house which has been designed to maximise space for planting and create several different sitting areas, views and moods. Arranged in a series of paved 'rooms' each 'over-stuffed' with a good range of shrubs and perennials. *Adm £2, chd £1 (share to Child Poverty Action Group). Sun 5 June (2-6)*

⑦⑨ The Hurlingham Club, Ranelagh Gardens, SW6 ⊗⊙

Main gate at E-end of Ranelagh Gardens. Nearest tube: Putney Bridge (110yds). 40-acre 'country-house' garden with lawns mainly laid to bowls, croquet and tennis, surrounded by shrubberies, herbaceous borders and formal bedding. Several mature trees of interest. 2-acre lake with water fowl. River walk. Light refreshments and TEAS. *Adm £5, chd £2. Wed 1 June (Guided Tours of 2hrs at 11 & 2). Private visits welcome by appt for groups of 10+ on other days. Tel 020 7471 8208 robert.morgan@hurlinghamclub. org.uk*

80 Islington Gardens, N1
Tube: Kings Cross. Buses: 17, 91, 259 to Caledonian Rd. Contrasting gardens in Barnsbury Conservation Area. Home-made TEAS at 4 Mountfort Crescent and 36 Thornhill Square. *Combined adm £4.50 or £2 per garden, chd £2 or £1 per garden, £1.50 for Barnsbury Wood. Sun 12 June (2-6)*

NEW Barnsbury Wood 🚻
(Islington Council) Off Crescent Street, N of Thornhill Square. Colourful borders lead to Islington's hidden secret. It is a place of peace and relaxation, the borough's only site of mature woodland and one of London's smallest nature reserves.

4 Mountfort Crescent 🚻🌀 *(Mary Elford & Richard Arnold) Off Barnsbury Square (unmade rd).* Evergreen and architectural plants give yr-round interest in family town garden 92ft x 41ft. Hybrid musk and English roses, box edging and cistus. Phormiums and euphorbias provide mixture of yellows and greens opp terrace. Good ground cover planting.

36 Thornhill Square 🌀⊕ *(Anna & Christopher McKane)* 120ft long informal garden in one of London's largest landscaped squares. Clematis, old roses and herbaceous perennials in curved borders giving a country garden atmosphere. Many unusual plants propagated for sale.

81 James Allen's Girls' School Botany Gardens, 144 East Dulwich Grove, SE22 🚻🌀⊕
Nearest station N Dulwich. Bus 37 stops outside school. Historic botany garden dating from 1896. Wildlife ponds, woodland area, order beds, country lane, bordered by hedgerow and ditch. Many varieties of wild flower. Light refreshments and TEAS. **Evening Opening** *£2, Fri 24 June (5-7)*

82 12 Jeymer Avenue, Willesden Green, NW2
(Adrianne Uziell-Hamilton) 6/7 mins walk from Willesden Green tube

station (Jubilee line). Parking in road. Occupying a corner site, this interesting garden, designed by Michael Chittenden, is divided into distinct areas. Lawn with borders and a water feature, patio with wirework planters, pots, reflective Japanese garden with gravel and grasses. Home-made TEAS. *Adm £2.50 (share to St Luke's Hospice, Harrow). Sun 12 June (12-5);* **Evening Opening** *£3, wine, Sun 28 Aug (7.30-9.30)*

83 Kew Gardens Group
2m N of Richmond. Nearest station Kew Gardens. Both gardens within 5 mins walk from station. Buses: 391 to Kew Gardens station, 65 to Kew Gardens, Victoria Gate. TEAS at 7 Maze Road. *Adm £1.50 each garden, chd free. Sat, Sun 12, 13 Mar (2-5)*

38 Leyborne Park 🌀⊕ *(Ann & Alan Sandall)* 120ft long mature garden; lawn with mixed borders; patio; interesting collection of pots and containers. All shades of hellebores, many raised from seed; primulas, unusual spring flowers.

7 Maze Road 🌀⊕ *(Celia Fisher)* Cottage garden divided into 4 triangular beds packed with spring flowers incl irises, hellebores, daffodils, primulas, fruit blossom and euphorbia collection. The owner is an art historian who writes and lectures on plants in art.

84 Kew Green Gardens
NW side of Kew Green. Tube: Kew Gardens. Nearest main line station Kew Bridge. Buses: 65, 391. Entrance via towpath. Three long gardens behind adjacent C18 houses on the Green; close to Royal Botanic Gardens. *Combined adm £4.50, chd free. Sun 22 May (2-6)*

69 Kew Green *(Mr & Mrs John Godfrey)* Mature English garden, profusely planted. Formal garden and terrace nr house; woodland and informal garden, meadow planting. Interesting shrubs and plants.

71 Kew Green *(Mr & Mrs Jan Pethick)* Large and informal London garden, laid out around tall, old trees; traditional border, irises and shaded borders within woodland. Well-established shrubs in rather crowded planting.

73 Kew Green *(Donald & Libby Insall)* The garden wanders from the main lawn and border by house, through woodland and surprises by arriving at a modern

planting of espaliered miniature fruit trees.

85 38 Killieser Avenue, SW2 🌀⊕
(Mrs Winkle Haworth) 5 mins walk from Streatham Hill mainline station. Buses: 159, 137, 133 to Telford Avenue. Killieser Ave 2nd turning L off Telford Ave. Exuberantly planted, romantic, 90ft x 28ft garden. Contains many unusual perennial plants, roses and viticella clematis. Classical rose arch, obelisk, Gothic arbour and water features. Top terrace with rose-filled parterre and lavender border. Accommodation. Featured in 'Evening Standard' 2003 & 'Woman & Home' 2004. Best Town Garden award 'English Garden' magazine, 2003. London Garden Society Silver Medal 2004. Home-made TEAS. *Adm £2, chd 50p. Sun 29 May (2-5.30). Private visits welcome by appt. Tel 020 8671 4196 winklehaworth@hotmail.com*

86 Lambeth Community Care Centre, Monkton Street, SE11 🚻🌀⊕
(Lambeth Community Care Centre) Tube or buses to Elephant & Castle, cut behind Leisure Centre to Brook Drive. Turn into Sullivan Rd, passage to Monkton St. Buses: 3, 109, 159 or drive (ample parking) to Kennington Rd; at Ship PH turn into Bishop's Terrace, 1st R to Monkton St. ⅓-acre garden. Mixed shrubs, trees, small rose garden, herbs, interesting walkways and mixed borders. Extensive plant sale. London Hospital Gardens Gold Cup Winner 2003. Home-made TEAS. *Adm £1.50, chd 50p, concessions 50p. Sat, Sun 28, 29 May (2-5)*

87 Lambeth Palace, SE1 🚻🌀⊕
(The Church of England (by kind permission of His Grace the Archbishop of Canterbury)) Waterloo mainline & tube; Westminster, Lambeth & Vauxhall tubes all about 10 mins walk. Buses: 3, C10, 76, 77, 77a, 344 go nr garden. Entry to garden on Lambeth Palace Rd (not at gatehouse). Lambeth Palace garden is one of the oldest and largest private gardens in London. Site occupied by Archbishops of Canterbury since end C12. Formal courtyards with historic white fig (originally planted 1555). Parkland style garden with mature trees, woodland and native planting, pond, hornbeam allée. Also formal rose terrace, new summer gravel border, herb garden and beehives. Home-made TEAS. *Adm £3, chd £1, concessions £2 (share to Lambeth Palace Garden). Sats 23 Apr; 21 May; 23 July (2-5.30)*

88 12 Lansdowne Road, W11 ♿
(The Lady Amabel Lindsay) *Turn N off Holland Park Ave nr Holland Park station; or W off Ladbroke Grove ½-way along. Buses: 12, 88, GL 711, 715. Bus stop & tube station: Holland Park, 4 mins.* Medium-sized fairly wild garden; borders, climbing roses, shrubs; mulberry tree 200yrs old. *Adm £2, chd £1. Thur 19 May (2-6)*

89 Little Lodge, Thames Ditton ♿⚀
(Mr & Mrs P Hickman) *2m SW of Kingston. Mainline station Thames Ditton 5 mins. A3 from London; after Hook underpass turn L to Esher; at Scilly Isles turn R towards Kingston; after 2nd railway bridge turn L to Thames Ditton village; house opp library after Giggs Hill Green.* Partly walled informal flower garden filled with shrubs and herbaceous plants that create an atmosphere of peace. Small secret garden; terracotta pots; stone troughs and sinks; roses; clematis; topiary; very productive parterre vegetable garden. Home-made TEAS. *Adm £2.50, chd free (share to Cancer Research UK). Sun 5 June (11.30-5.30); Wed 8 June (2.30-6) £2.50 &Evening Opening (6-8.30) £3.50, wine. Private visits welcome by appt. Tel 0208 339 0931 peter.hickman@virgin.net*

90 Lyndhurst Square Gardens, SE15
5mins walk NW from Peckham Rye station. Reduced service on Sunday. Bus: 36 from Oval tube or 171 from Waterloo. Park in nearby streets. Light refreshments and TEAS at 1 Lyndhurst Square. *Combined adm £3, chd £1, concessions £2. Sun 10 July (2-5)*

1 Lyndhurst Square ♿
(Josephine Pickett-Baker) 80ft x 40ft walled garden. Formal layout with lawn, flower beds, mosaic, gravel and flagstones. Sunken terrace with herb garden in retaining wall. Plants in terracotta containers. Evergreen, slightly tropical looking structure to planting, with perennials planted through and around. More foliage than flowers. Many unusual plants. Sitting areas in sun or shade.

3 Lyndhurst Square ♿⚀ (Mr Stephen Haines) Sophisticated cottage garden approx 80ft × 50ft. Old roses, herbaceous borders, many climbers on house and in garden, sunken garden with fountain and container

planting, surrounded by mature trees.

91 Malvern Terrace Gardens, N1 ♿
Approach from S via Pentonville Rd into Penton St, then into Barnsbury Rd. From N via Thornhill Rd opp Albion public house. Tube: Angel, Highbury & Islington. Buses: 19, 30 to Upper St, Town Hall. Group of unique 1830s London terrace houses built on the site of Thomas Oldfield's dairy and cricket field. Cottage-style gardens in cobbled cul-de-sac. Music and plant stall. Home-made TEAS. *Combined adm £2.50, chd free. Sun 24 Apr (2-5.30)*

92 1 Maple Close, SW4
(Brian Hannath) *Turn into Clarence Avenue from Kings Avenue. Maple Close 1st on L.* A 'dell' garden inspired by Arthur Rackham. Green oasis of ferns, ivy, hostas and fish pond. Rustic vine-covered arch leads to formal garden with box hedging containing flower beds, gazebo and lion head wall fountain. The very small plot is inspirational for anyone with a tiny town garden. Featured in 'Gardening Australia' and RHS 'The Garden' 2004. London Gardens Society Silver Medal 2004. *Adm £2. Sun 10 July (2-6)*

93 March Cottage, 58 Warren Road (old side), Chelsfield ♿
(Mrs Margaret Coppard & Richard Coppard) *9m SE of Bromley. From Orpington town centre, travel S along Sevenoaks Rd towards Green St Green. Approx 1m. Old Warren Rd is on L immed after pedestrian Xing. From Chelsfield mainline station, approx ½m W down Warren Rd. From M25, J4 take A224.* Small, Mediterranean inspired garden with many interesting features incl drought tolerant trees and shrubs designed around central water feature. Informal woodland retreat to front. Home-made TEAS. *Adm £2, chd free. Sun 12 June (11-5). Private visits welcome by appt. Tel 01689 854094*

94 NEW 209 Massingberd Way, SW17 ⚀
(Elizabeth & Patrick Palmer-Cafferkey) *Rd only on recent maps. Tube: Tooting Bec, then buses 249, 319 to Doctor Johnson Ave. Broad brick path diagonally to Church Lane, then 100yds to L. Car park by bus stop, alternatively Birchwood Rd.* 21ft x 25ft garden of brand new house. Planned by owner 2yrs ago around mature listed crab apple. Entirely blue and white for a sense of distance and space. All plants acquired cheaply and small (and

already jostling for room!) incl rarities eg from Australia/NZ. Size of garden may limit numbers. Home-made TEAS. *Adm £1.50, chd 50p (share to Sightsavers). Sun 24 Apr (2-6)*

95 47 Maynard Road, Walthamstow, E17 ⚀♿
(Don Mapp) *10 mins walk from Walthamstow (mainline/tube) towards Walthamstow Village or bus W12 to Addison Rd. Turn R, Beulah Rd or Beulah Path.* Plant collector's paradise. An eclectic mix of unusual and exotic plants in a 40ft x 16ft space. Entered via an eye catching and densely planted front garden. Incl exhibition of watercolours and Pergamano depicting botanical and landscape scenes by local artist Hazel Pettifer. *Adm £1.50, chd 50p. Sun 24 July (12-5). Also open* **60 Brunswick St, 73 Forest Drive East, 3 Hillside Gardens, 11 & 24 Warwick Road**

96 2 Millfield Place, N6 ♿⚀
Off Highgate West Hill, E side of Hampstead Heath. Buses: C2, C11 or 214 to Parliament Hill Fields. 1½-acre spring and summer garden with camellias, rhododendrons, many flowering shrubs and unusual plants. Spring bulbs; herbaceous borders; small orchard; spacious lawns. Home-made TEAS (Sun only). *Adm £2, chd 50p, family £5. Sun 8 May (2-6);* **Evening Opening** *£3, wine, Wed 22 June (5.30-9)*

97 19 Montana Road, SW17 ⚀♿
(Nigel Buckie) *Nearest tube Tooting Bec.* Architect's evolving exotic garden. Palms, bananas, ferns, agaves, cacti and exotic colour from gingers, cannas and eucomis. There are two seating areas, one with rill water feature, the other among herbs and kitchen garden. Home-made TEAS. *Adm £1.50. Suns 26 June; 28 Aug (1-5.30)*

98 NEW 59 Murray Road, Wimbledon Village, SW19 ♿⚀
(Lili Lion) *Tube & Main Line:Wimbledon, then 200 bus to 2nd stop on Ridgway. Murray Rd is between the Common & Ridgway. Alternatively, 93 bus to Wimbledon High St.* Small exotic garden with pergola designed by Myles Challis. Gravel and lawn. Many unusual and tender plants incl trachycarpus, musa and *Catalpa bignonioides* and many clematis. TEAS. *Adm £2.50. Sun 10 July (2.30-5.30)*

99 ◆ Museum of Garden History, Lambeth Palace Road, SE1

Bus: 507 Red Arrow from Victoria or Waterloo mainline & tube stations (C10 only on Sundays); alight Lambeth Palace. Nearest tube: Lambeth N, Vauxhall, Waterloo. Historic tools, information displays, changing exhibitions, shop and café housed in former church of St-Mary-at-Lambeth. Reproduction C17 knot garden with period plants, topiary and box hedging. Light refreshments and TEAS. *Adm £3, chd free, concessions £2.50 (share to Museum of Garden History). Daily Feb to mid Dec.* **For NGS:** *Sat 21 May (10.30-5). Tel 020 7401 8865 www.museumgardenhistory.org.uk*

100 ◆ Myddelton House Gardens, Bulls Cross, Enfield (NCCPG)

(Lee Valley Regional Park Authority) *2m N of Enfield. Junction 25 (A10) off M25 S towards Enfield. 1st set T-lights R into Bullsmoor Lane, L at end along Bulls Cross.* 4 acres of gardens created by E A Bowles. Gardens feature diverse and unusual plants incl National Collection of award winning bearded irises. Large pond with terrace, conservatory and interesting historical artefacts. A garden for all seasons. Home-made TEAS on NGS days. *Adm £2.40, chd £1.80, concessions £1.80. Mon to Fri, Apr to Sept (10-4.30), Oct to Mar (10-3); Suns Easter to end Oct (12-4).* **For NGS:** *Suns 27 Feb (10-3); 24 Apr; 29 May (10-4.30); 26 Feb 2006 (10-3). Tel 01992 202200 www.leevalleypark.com*

101 ◆ Natural History Museum Wildlife Garden, Cromwell Road, SW7

S Kensington. 5 mins walk from S Kensington tube station. Garden designed and created in 1995 to show range of typical habitats found in lowland Britain, incl deciduous woodland, meadow, chalk downland, fen and heathland. Areas linked by meandering paths and three ponds provide a central focus. Despite its central London location the garden has already attracted an impressive and varied amount of wildlife, which is being monitored by Museum staff and volunteers. Meet the Scientists and learn about some of the garden's wildlife. Brighter Kensington & Chelsea Scheme award, 1st prize in Wildlife Garden category 2004. London in Bloom, Winner of the Wild Flower & Environment Trophy 2004. TEAS. *Adm £2, chd free.* **For NGS:** *Suns 10 Apr; 3 July (2-5). Tel 020 7942 5889*

102 17a Navarino Road, E8

(Mr John Tordoff) *Situated between Dalston & Hackney. Connects Graham Rd with Richmond Rd. Buses: 38, 277, 30 or 242 to Graham Rd stop.* Garden as Theatre - Italian or Japanese, the choice is yours. Stage-set of mirrored arches and half concealed vistas, the splash of fountain and stream, offer the visitor a garden whose prime ingredients are mystery and surprise. Featured in 'The London Magazine' 2003. Light refreshments and TEAS. *Adm £2.50, chd £1, concessions £1.50. Suns 15 May; 17 July (12-6)*

103 263 Nether Street, N3

(Judy & Malcolm Wiseman) *Turn L from W Finchley tube. House is on the L, 2mins along the rd. Parking in roads off Nether St. House is directly facing Penstemon Close.* Sculptor's garden that develops and matures through periods of neglect interspersed with energetic bouts of artistic and horticultural activity. Owner's fascination for body parts has increasingly been complemented by experimentation with other works incl a cast concrete table, stone sofa and innovative vertical planting frames. Mud baths, squirting statues and chandeliers, all presented against a lush, vibrant green (though deliberately non-floriferous!) backdrop. Featured on Channel 4 My Eden, 2003/4. *Adm £2, chd free. Suns 15, 29 May (2-6)*

104 NEW 5 New Road, Crouch End, N8

(The Misses S & M West) *Bus: W7 Muswell Hill to Finsbury Park or W5. Alight Wolsey Rd. New Rd is cul-de-sac. Some parking rear of Health Centre, better parking Middle Lane or Park Rd.* Traditional country garden 60ft x 24ft in heart of Crouch End, evolved over 50yrs. Small prizewinning front garden adjoins colourful conservatory leading to back garden planted for yr-round interest. Many unusual and

borderline tender plants - abutillons, streptocarpus, achimenes, crinum. Fruit trees, ornamental shrubs and trees, small pond, lawn and productive greenhouse create a delightful experience of cherished nostalgia. *Adm £1.50, chd 50p. Suns 17 July; 21 Aug (2-6). Private visits welcome by appt. Tel 020 8340 8149*

105 15 Norcott Road, N16

(Mr & Mrs J Welch) *Buses: 73, 149, 76, 67, 243. Clapton & Rectory Rd mainline stations.* Largish (for Hackney) walled back garden developed by present owners over 25yrs, with pond, long-established fruit trees, abundantly planted with a great variety of herbaceous plants, especially perennial geraniums and campanulas, day lilies, flag and other irises. Home-made TEAS. *Adm £1.50, chd 50p (share to SENSE). Sun 22 May (2-6)*

106 NEW 94 Oakwood Road, NW11

(Michael Franklin) *Hampstead Garden Suburb. Nearest Tube: Golders Green. Bus: H2 to Northway.* Large garden divided into 2 rooms by box hedging and an arch. Lawns, woodland with apple and pear blossom, old wisteria, tree paeonies, beds filled with colour and foliage. *Adm £1.50, chd free. Sun 8 May (2-5.30)*

107 The Orchard, 40a Hazledene Road, W4

(Vivien Cantor) *10 mins walk from Chiswick mainline & Gunnersbury tube. Close to junction of A4 & Sutton Court Rd, off Fauconberg Rd.* Informal, romantic ¼-acre garden with mature flowering trees, shrubs and imaginative planting in flowing herbaceous borders. Climbers, water features and new fern planting in this ever evolving garden. Home-made TEAS. *Adm £2.50, chd 50p. Sun 8 May (2-6)*

"... but I distinctly remember asking for <u>Morris</u> dancers!"

Orchard Cottage, 3 Woodlands Road, Bickley ♿✄✉
See Kent.

108 Ormeley Lodge, Ham Gate Avenue, Richmond ✄
(Lady Annabel Goldsmith) *2m S of Richmond. From Richmond Park, exit at Ham Gate into Ham Gate Ave. 1st house on R. From Richmond A307, 1½m past New Inn on R, 1st turning on L. House is last on L. Bus: 65. Large walled garden in delightful rural setting on Ham Common. Wide herbaceous borders and box hedges. Walk through to orchard with wild flowers. Vegetable garden, knot garden, aviary. Trellised tennis court with roses and climbers. TEAS. Adm £2.50, chd 75p. Sun 19 June (3-6)*

109 63B Overhill Road, East Dulwich, SE22 ✉
(Robin Beresford) *Edge of Forest Hill and East Dulwich. Buses: London Road 185, 176, 312. Plantsman's wildlife garden with naturalised pond. Collections of plants from all over the world, incl acacias, banana trees, abutilons, tree ferns, palms, cannas, hostas and many unusual exotics both planted and in pots. Bonsai trees and carniverous plants. Yr-round interest incl winter. Sloping SE facing. Not suitable for pushchairs. **Evening Opening** £2.50, wine, Thur 1 Sept (5-8). Private visits welcome by appt, individuals or groups of up to 6. Tel 020 8516 1900*

110 The Pagoda, Pagoda Gardens, SE3 ✄
(Caroline & Philip Cooper) *Blackheath. Mainline Lewisham, mainline/DLR 10 mins walk. ½-acre historic garden of historic house, Jekyll-Jungle. Variety of gardens - terraced formal with 60' rill; informal water garden with stream; lush subtropical planting; white garden, orientally inspired pergola and details. **Evening Opening** £3.50 (share to Cystic Fibrosis Trust), wine, Fri 10 June (6-9). Also open **28 Granville Park***

111 3 The Park, N6 ✄✉
(Mr & Mrs G Schrager) *3 mins from Highgate tube, up Southwood Lane. The Park is 1st on R. Buses: 43, 134, 143, 263. Large garden with pond and frogs, fruit trees and eclectic planting. Interesting plants for sale. Home-made TEAS. Adm £2, chd £1 (share to St Mary's Hospital Kidney Patient Assoc). Sun 5 June (2-6)*

112 10A The Pavement, Chapel Road, West Norwood, SE27 ✉
(Mr Brendan Byrne) *Located off Ladas Rd down alleyway, L as you approach from Chapel Rd. Buses: 268 & 432 to Knights Hill alight at Norwood bus garage. Mainline: W Norwood, no trains from London Bridge on Suns. Smallest garden in London. A hidden oasis behind houses and shops. Country type of garden, with cottage garden planting, mostly in containers. Shrubs, herbaceous, bedding, rare plants and herbs continually changing. Special interest to gardeners with small spaces. Featured in Garden Makers, Carlton and sky TV, 2004. Adm £1.50, chd free (share to Horses & Ponies Protection Assoc). Sun 24 July (10-12 & 2-6); **Evening Opening** £3, wine, Thur 14 July (6-8). Private visits welcome by appt June, July only. Tel 020 8761 5651 brendan.byrne@tiscali.co.uk*

113 NEW 116 Peckham Park Road, SE15
(Jilly Sharpe) *Peckham Park Rd is B216 running between Old Kent Rd and Peckham Hill St. Tube: Elephant & Castle then 63 bus. Alight at Bird in Bush Rd. 1 acre. Gravel garden with drought-tolerant plants. Eclectic mix of unusual plants. Evolving garden with some wild areas. Hot and dry area and woodland garden. Specialist nursery with collection of mightily unusual plants for sale. 'Daily Telegraph' & 'The London Gardener' features 2004. Light refreshments and TEAS. Adm £2, chd free. Sun 8, Sat 14 May (11-6); **Evening Opening** £3.50, wine, Sat 11 June (6-8). Private visits welcome by appt. Tel 07900 823374 jillysharpe@hotmail.com*

114 174 Peckham Rye, SE22 ♿✄✉
(Mr & Mrs Ian Bland) *Overlooks Peckham Rye Common from Dulwich side. Reached by alley to side of house. 100ft x 30ft rear garden originally designed (and frequently changed) by Judith Sharpe. Easy-care and child-friendly while displaying a wide variety of contrasting foliage and yr-round interest. Best in early June when pink and blue flowers predominate, especially in new woodland border. TEAS. Adm £2, chd free (share to St Christopher's Hospice). Sun 5 June (2.30-5.30)*

115 Pembridge Cottage, 10 Strawberry Hill Road, Twickenham ✄
(Ian & Lydia Sidaway) *1m from Twickenham town centre. Close to*

Strawberry Hill mainline station. 140ft x 20ft constantly evolving artist's garden with studio building. Divided into several brick, gravel and wooden seating areas. Strong evergreen shrub structure providing yr-round interest. Many thin Italian cypress, maples, trimmed and shaped box, lonicera, lavender, santolina, laurels and viburnum. Euphorbias, bamboo, herbs, ferns and gunnera. A packed garden influenced by Mediterranean, Japanese and northern European styles. Light refreshments and TEAS. Adm £2, chd free. Suns 5, 12 June (12-6). Private visits welcome by appt. Tel 020 8287 8993

116 Penge Gardens, SE20
1m from Beckenham or Crystal Palace. 5 mins walk from Kent House mainline station. Buses: 227, 176, 194, 312 & 358. 3 gardens all within easy walking distance, nr junction A213 & A234. Home-made TEAS at 26 Kenilworth Rd & 26 Stodart Rd. Combined adm £3 (share to St Christopher's Hospice). Sun 12 June (2-5)

9 Howard Road ✄✉ (Marc Carlton & Nigel Lees) *40ft x 120ft suburban garden. Organic and wildlife friendly, designed to incorporate many native species, but without sacrificing aesthetic standards. Wetland areas, nectar border and newly-built wild bee house. Information sheets available about many aspects of gardening for wildlife. Private visits welcome by appt April to July only. Tel 020 8659 5674 www.foxleas.com*

26 Kenilworth Road ♿✄✉ (Mhairi & Simon Clutson) *5 mins walk from Kent House mainline station. Buses: 227, 176, 194, 312, & 358. Small contemporary garden on 2 levels, designed in 1995 to be easily maintained and have a strong Mediterranean theme. Circular paved and gravelled area planted with many rare Mediterranean native shrubs, perennials and bulbs. Euphorbias and cistus surround olive tree and mosaic water feature. Featured in 'Real Homes' magazine 2004. Private visits welcome by appt May & June only. Tel 020 8402 9035 www.grozone.co.uk*

26 Stodart Road, Anerley ✄ (Les Miller & Elizabeth Queen) *Small sloping town garden on different levels. Mature shrubs and trees provide green oasis. Rose arches, clematis, honeysuckle and tiny pond. Shady area with ferns,* hellebores and symphytum. A cottage garden in an urban environment.

⑪⑦ 2a Penn Road, N7 ♿☺
(Mr & Mrs P Garvey) *Tube: Caledonian Rd. Turn L out of station and continue N up Caledonian Rd for approx 700yds. Penn Rd is on LH-side. Busus: 17, 91, 259 along Caledonian Rd; 29, 253 to nearby Nags Head.* 100ft × 30ft walled garden; long, shady, side entrance border; small seaside-themed front garden. Huge variety of plants in well stocked borders. Over 60 containers. Greenhouse and small vegetable plot. Mature trees create secluded feel close to busy urban thoroughfares. TEAS. *Adm £1.50, chd free. Sun 5 June (2-6)*

◆ **Penshurst Place, Penshurst** ♿☺
See Kent.

⑪⑧ NEW 101 Pitt Crescent, SW19
(Karen Grosch) *Tube: Wimbledon Park 10 mins walk. Bus: 156 along Durnsford Rd. Limited parking in Pitt Crescent.* Small garden of 100ft x 25ft, cleverly planted on different levels with ornamental trees. Soft colours of grey, green and variegated plants. Pebbled patio leads up to vine-covered pergola and an arbour of apple and pear trees leads onto raised vegetable beds and soft fruit, edged with roses and clematis. *Adm £1.50, chd free. Sun 12 June (2-6)*

⑪⑨ 1 Pond Street, NW3 ☺
(Mrs Barbara Frost) *Tube: Belsize Park, turn R on exit. Buses: C11, 24, 46, 168 & 268.* Large L-shaped garden, overflowing with spring colour, divided into three, reached via a sheltered courtyard with colourful containers, herb troughs and water feature. Circular lawn bordered by an old stone path. Subtle use of colour in the beds with many unusual shrubs and perennials, tulips, roses, clematis and other climbers. TEAS. *Adm £2, chd 50p. Sun 22 May (2-6)*

⑫⓪ 112 Rectory Road, N16 ☺☺
(Mr & Mrs S Donnellan) *Stoke Newington. Buses: 67, 73, 76, 106, 149, 243, 276, 349, 393, 476. Mainline station Stoke Newington.* Romantic town garden, 23ft x 55ft, abundantly planted from scratch in 2003. Terrace with lots of pots, deep curved borders, raised beds with herbs and scented plants, gravelled area, pergola. Lots of clematis, roses, hardy geraniums, scented pelargoniums, jasmine, vine. Home-made TEAS. *Adm £2, chd 50p. Sun 12 June (2-6). Private visits welcome by appt groups of 10+. Tel 020 7502*

6048 www.thedonnellans.pwp.blueyonder. co.uk/NGS.htm

⑫① NEW 13 Redbridge Lane West, E11 ☺☺
(Kathy Taylor) *2 mins drive from Redbridge roundabout at N Circular/A12/M11 junction (off M11 link road towards Leytonstone). Tube: 5 mins walk from Wanstead (Central Line).* Designed by Chelsea medal winner, 14metres x 6.5metres, 2-roomed garden created 3 yrs ago, gardened without chemicals. S-facing end comprises decking, gravel, formal wildlife pond with bog area and mixed planting for a sunny aspect. The N-facing end has raised beds with plants for sun and semi-shade. Art installation in the garden shed and garden photography exhibition. Home-made TEAS. *Adm £1.50, chd free (share to Soil Association). Sun 10 July (2-5)*

⑫② 39 Redington Road, NW3
(Freda Uziyel) *Buses: 82, 13 to Finchley Rd. 10 mins walk Hampstead tube station. From Hampstead tube station, cross Hampstead High St; turn L into Heath St, R into Church Row, R into Frognal. 1st L Redington Rd.* Italianesque garden, full of terraces, antiquities and containers. Water features and dense planting with emphasis on colour harmony and balance; contemporary sculptures by Thomas Schütte and Anthony Gormley. Light refreshments. *Adm £2.50, chd 50p. Sun 19 June (2-6). Private visits welcome by appt May & June only. Tel 020 7435 5278*

⑫③ NEW 64 Redington Road, NW3 ☺
(Mr & Mrs C Kaplanis) *Tube: Hampstead (1 km). Bus: 46 (Hampstead High St) or 82 & 13 to Heath Drive.* Large, elegant, terraced garden. Balustraded upper terrace with formal pool has steps down to lawn, thickly planted beds, interesting sculptures, a small grove of birch trees and a little Oriental garden for contemplation with pool. *Adm £2, chd 50p. Sun 26 June (2.30-5.30)*

⑫④ Regents College's Botany Garden, Inner Circle, Regents Park, NW1 ☺
Located at the junction of York Bridge & the Inner Circle. Baker St tube is 5 mins walk. Buses: 13, 18, 27, 30, 74, 82, 113, 139, 159, 274. Enter main gate or garden gate adjacent to footbridge at Clarence Gate. Described as a Secret Garden, this former Botanic Garden has been sympathetically developed so as to

retain its intrinsic charm and relaxed, naturalistic atmosphere. Garden areas flow together and host a diverse selection of plants. TEAS. *Adm £1.50, chd £1, concessions £1. Sat 28 May (12-5). Private visits welcome by appt. Tel 020 7487 7494*

⑫⑤ 31 Roedean Crescent, SW15 ♿☺☺
(Francine Watson Coleman) *Roedean Crescent lies just outside Roehampton Gate of Richmond Park.* Spacious organic garden with strong formal design with interesting and beautiful vegetables, fruit and herbs planted throughout. Wide borders contain an imaginative mix of choice shrubs, perennials and attractive edible plants with shady and hot paths offering different environments and views. Dedicated kitchen garden with raised beds, heritage vegetables, compost, nursery and organic plant food production. Pots of lemons, limes, figs, olives and grapes add a touch of the exotic. Featured in 'The New Kitchen Garden' 2003 & 'The Kitchen Garden' magazine 2005. *Adm £2, chd £1.00 (share to HDRA). Sun 31 July (2-6)*

⑫⑥ ◆ Roots and Shoots, Walnut Tree Walk, SE11 ♿☺☺
(Trustees of Roots and Shoots) *Tube: Lambeth North. Buses: 159, 59, 3. Just off Kennington Rd, 5 mins from Imperial War Museum. No car parking on site. Pedestrian entrance through small open space on Fitzalan St, SE11.* ½-acre wildlife garden with large summer meadow, beehives, observation beehive, old roses, echiums, 2 large ponds. Wildlife displays, nest box cameras, activities for children and adults. Hot borders, Mediterranean mound. Run by innovative charity providing training, garden advice and plant sales. Fine walnut tree and *Acacia dealbata*. Our new Eco Learning Centre will open June 2005. Featured in 'Independent on Sunday' and 'Sunday Times', 2004. Light refreshments and TEAS only on NGS days, garden open days and National Apple Day 23 Oct. *Adm £1.50, chd 50p. Nursery open Mon to Fri May to end of June (9-4) Sats (10-2). Garden open Mon to Fri (9.30-5.30) tel first.* **For NGS:** *Sat, Sun 11, 12 June (11-4).* **Evening Opening** *£2.50, wine, Weds 6, 20 July (6.30-8.30). Tel Linda Phillips 020 7587 1131 www.roots-and-shoots.org*

⑫⑦ 167 Rosendale Road, West Dulwich, SE21 ☺☺
(Mr & Mrs A Pizzoferro) *House at junction of Rosendale Rd & Lovelace*

Rd. Station Tulse Hill, West Dulwich. Back garden 100ft long with stream (which runs naturally in winter), running through small woodland area. Bog garden and wildlife pond are bordered by timber deck. Central shingle and cobble circle is surrounded by generous mixed borders. Collections of hostas, acers and pittosporums in pots live in alleyway. Front garden has a hotter colour theme with range of euphorbias. Featured in 'Groei & Bloei' Dutch garden magazine 2004. Home-made TEAS. Adm £2, chd 50p (share to London Children's Flower Society). Suns 13 Mar (1-4); 5 June (2-6). Private visits welcome by appt. Tel 020 8766 7846

⑫⑧ 1 Rosslyn Hill, NW3 ⌖⌘
(Jill Norman) On corner of Rosslyn Hill & Belsize Lane. Tube: Belsize Park. Buses: C11, 168 & 268 stop almost outside. 46 & 24 nearby. Garden on three sides of 1870's house (not open) with mature trees, herbaceous and mixed borders, rockery, pool with fountain, herb garden, spring bulbs, camellias and early clematis. Adm £1.50, chd 50p. Sun 8 May (2-5)

⑫⑨ 19 St Gabriel's Road, NW2 ⌖⌘
(Jane & Geoffrey Smith) Tube: Willesden Green. Buses: 260, 266 & 460 to Willesden Green station, 98 to Willesden Lane, 16, 32, 189, 245 & 316 to Cricklewood Broadway. Garden approx 35ft x 95ft, dominated by large aspen tree; terrace with display of a variety of pelargoniums in containers; formal beds with informal planting incl unusual plants, grasses and ferns; beyond, a woodland bank being developed as a spring garden. Adm £2, chd free. Sun 12 June (2.30-6)

⑬⓪ 7 St George's Road, St Margaret's, Twickenham ⌖⌘
(Mr & Mrs R Raworth) 1½m SW of Richmond. Off A316 between Twickenham Bridge & St Margaret's roundabout. ½-acre maturing town garden. Divided into rooms. Unusual shrubs, clematis and old English roses. Large conservatory with rare plants and climbers. Pond and bog garden; pergola; sunken garden; knot garden. Home-made TEAS. Adm £2.50, chd 50p. Suns 5, 19 June (2-6). Private visits welcome by appt, groups of 10+. Tel 020 8892 3713 jenny@jraworth.freeserve.co.uk

⑬① 20A St John's Grove, N19 ⌖⌘
(Tania Stokes) Tube: Archway. Buses: 41, 43, 134, 210 & 271, stop

at Archway. 3 mins walk. A green oasis designed to soothe the mind and nourish the soul. Shady garden with small pond and pet hens. Some steps with handrail. TEAS. Adm £1.50, chd 50p, OAP 50p (share to International Animal Rescue). Sun 21 Aug (2-6)

⑬② St Michael's Convent, 56 Ham Common, Richmond ⌖⌘
(Community of the Sisters of the Church) 2m S of Richmond. From Richmond or Kingston, A307, turn onto the common at the Xrds nr the New Inn, 100yds on the R adjacent to Martingales Close. Mainline trains to Richmond (also District Line tube) to Kingston, then bus 65 from either to Ham Common. 4-acre organic garden comprises walled vegetable garden, orchards, vine house, ancient mulberry tree, extensive borders, meditation and Bible gardens. Adm £2.50, chd 50p. Sat 30 July (11-4)

⑬③ 57 St Quintin Avenue, W10 ⌖⌘
(Mr H Groffman) 1m from Ladbroke Grove or White City tube. From Ladbroke Grove station, buses 7 or 70 to North Pole Rd. From White City, bus 220 to North Pole Rd. 30ft x 40ft walled garden; wide selection of plant material. Patio; unusual shrubs for foliage effects; dual environment adjacent water features; hanging baskets; special features and focal points. Special floral display to commemorate 60th anniversary of VE day, incorporating visitor-chosen colour theme. New for 2005 - raffle with prizes. Featured on BBC2 Gardeners' World and in 'Garden News', 2004. TEAS. Adm £2.50, chd £1, £2 each for parties of 10+. Suns 17, 31 July (2-7). Private visits welcome by appt for groups of 10+ throughout July, evenings & weekends only. Tel 020 8969 8292

⑬④ 5 St Regis Close, Alexandra Park Road, N10 ⌖⌘⌘
(Ms S Bennett & Mr E Hyde) 2nd L in Alexandra Park Rd from Colney Hatch Lane. Tube stations: Bounds Green or E Finchley then bus 102 or 299. Alight at St Andrew's Church on Windermere Rd. Bus: 43 or 134 to Alexandra Park Rd. Unique artists' garden renowned for colourful architectural features created on site incl 'Baroque' temple, pagodas, turquoise raku-tiled mirrored oriental enclosure concealing plant nursery. Evolving combination of humour and trompe l'oeil - Maureen Lipman's favourite garden. Carp ponds, waterfalls, lawns, abundant borders and imaginative container planting create an inspirational restoring

experience. Featured in 'House Beautiful' 2003, ITV Britain's Best Back Gardens and Carlton Garden Makers, 2004. Home-made TEAS. Adm £2, chd 50p. Suns 1 May; 26 June; 24 July (2-7). Private visits welcome by appt. Tel 020 8883 8540

⑬⑤ NEW 18 Sibella Road, SW4 ⌖
(Judith & Michael Strong) From Clapham High Rd, take Gauden Rd. 2nd R into Bromfelde Rd, Sibella Rd is on L. From Wandsworth Rd, take Albion Ave and continue over Larkhall Rise into Sibella Rd. Tube: Clapham North less than 10 mins walk. Small walled garden with formal framework softened by expressionist colour-themed planting. Small ophiopogon-lined path leads from Mediterranean-inspired patio to tiny octagonal lawn. Terrace framed with lavender, dicentras, ferns and hostas and some more unusual woodland plants. An old bramley, white lilac, weeping pear and cloud-pruned ceanothus add height and are festooned with roses and clematis (over 20 varieties). **Evening Opening** £3, wine, Wed 8 June (6-8.30)

⑬⑥ South End Road, NW3
Hampstead tube station, walk down Hampstead High St, L into Downshire Hill, South End Rd gardens facing Freemason's Arms PH. Part of historic Hampstead opposite the Heath. Home-made TEAS at 101 South End Rd. Combined adm £3.50, chd £1. Sun 5 June (2-6)

95 South End Road ⌖ (Ms Deborah Moggach) Profusely planted cottage front garden. Back garden with ponds and hens.

97 South End Road ⌖⌘ (Dr Edward Brett) Small cottage garden. Small Italianate back garden.

101 South End Road ⌖ (Mr & Mrs Paul Lindsay) Long cottage borders lead to house. Back garden is romantic, arbours and pergolas covered in roses and clematis, ponds and fountains.

⑬⑦ South London Botanical Institute, 323 Norwood Road, SE24 ⌖⌘
Main line: Tulse Hill. Buses: 68, 196, 322 & 468 stop at junction of Norwood Rd & Romola Rd. London's smallest botanic garden, formally laid out with many paved paths. Densely planted with over 500 labelled species and many rare and interesting plants of worldwide origin incl medicinal, carnivorous, British

plants and ferns. Home-made TEAS. *Adm £1.50, chd free (share to South London Botanical Institute). Sun 10 July (2-5)*

⓲ Southside House, 3-4 Woodhayes Road, Wimbledon Common, SW19 🥀
(Pennington Mellor Munthe Charity Trust) *1m W of Wimbledon Village. House at the junction of Cannizaro, Southside and Woodhayes Rds.* Romantic country garden extending to almost 2 acres. Mature trees and hedges and a long informal canal form the structure of this unique and amusing garden. 2 grottos, 2 temples, pet cemetery, young orchard and wildflower meadow. Many of the smaller plantings are being gradually renovated. Lovely swathes of bluebells, small fernery and black and white garden. House open for guided tours Sats, Suns, Weds, Easter Sat to 2 Oct. **For NGS:** *Adm £2.50 garden only, chd £1. Suns 1, 8 May (11-5). TEAS. Private visits welcome by appt. Tel 0208 946 7643 www.southsidehouse.com*

⓳ Southwood Lodge, 33 Kingsley Place, N6 🥀
(Mr & Mrs C Whittington) *Off Southwood Lane. Buses: 210, 271, 143, 214. Tube: Highgate.* Romantic, hidden garden laid out last century on steeply sloping site, now densely planted with wide variety of shrubs, bulbs, roses and perennials. Pond, waterfall, frogs. Many unusual plants are grown and propagated for sale. Home-made TEAS. *Adm £2, chd 50p. Sun 15 May (2-5.30). Private visits welcome by appt. Tel 020 8348 2785*

⓴ 11 Spencer Road, SW18 🥀
(Mr & Mrs A Goff) *From Clapham Junction mainline station go up St John's Hill towards Wandsworth. Spencer Rd is at the top of the hill on L.* Walled garden cleverly designed to disguise length. Features incl 2 decks, one with vine-covered pergola, and a formal box-edged bed of yew, holly and hebe. Lawn surrounded by beds densely planted with unusual shrubs and perennials - many kinds of euphorbia, alliums, hellebores, some exotics and a variety of climbers. Featured in 'Evening Standard' 2004. **Evening Opening** *£3, wine, Wed 1 June (6-8)*

㉑ 28 Stanley Road, Northwood 🥀
(Mr Warren Reeves) *2m N of Ruislip. From A40 to Ruislip, then along Eastcote Rd through to Northwood Hills. Off roundabout into Northwood Way, R into Stanley Rd.*

4 mins walk from Northwood Hills tube. Plenty of parking space. Front gravel garden with unusual plants and features. Back garden has terrace with groups of small and large pots and steps leading to plantsman's garden. 18ft pergola with many rare climbers, water features, raised beds, natural bog area and small pond. Large plant sale 10 July, many unusual plants. Featured in '25 Beautiful Gardens' 2004. Home-made TEAS. *Adm £2.50, chd free (share to The Lions Club, Poole). Sun 10 July (11-5);* **Evening Opening** *£3, wine, Thur 11 Aug (7-9.30). Private visits welcome by appt. Tel 07970 500047 warrenreeves1@csi.com*

㉒ NEW 4 Stradbroke Grove, Buckhurst Hill 🥀
(Mr & Mrs Brighten) *Between Epping & Woodford, 5m from J 26 on M25. Turn R at tube station Buckhurst Hill (Central Line), cross road to Stradbroke Grove.* Secluded garden, designed to enhance its sloping aspect. Steps wind downwards to thickly planted pergola, leading to rose-screened vegetable and fruit garden. Central gravelled area with an unusual mix of grasses, shells, pots and succulents. Home-made TEAS. *Adm £1.50, chd 50p. Sun 12 June (11-5). Also open* **6 Westbury Lane, Buckhurst Hill**. *Private visits welcome by appt June only. Tel 020 8505 2716 carol@cbrighten.fsnet.co.uk*

㉓ Tewkesbury Lodge Garden Group, SE23
10 mins from Forest Hill Station. Off South Circular (A205) behind Horniman Museum & Gardens. Nearest mainline station Forest Hill or buses 176, 185, 312, P4 (10 mins walk). A group of gardens on the hill above Forest Hill, spectacular views both N and S. Home-made TEAS at 53 Ringmore Rise. *Combined adm £4, chd free (share to Marsha Phoenix Trust & St Christopher's Hospice). Sun 29 May (2-6);* **Evening Opening** *£4, wine, Sat 28 May (6-9)*

The Coach House, 3 The Hermitage 🥀
(Pat Rae) Sculptor's mature courtyard garden. Crammed full of unusual plants and sculptures. Water-features, vegetables and decorative plants in containers large and small changing with the seasons. Roof garden also in containers.

27 Horniman Drive 🥀 (Rose Agnew) Small, low maintenance, N-facing front garden with shrubs creating tapestry of green. Evolving back garden with emphasis on colour harmony using perennials, roses and

shrubs. Vegetable areas, greenhouse, views over S London and N Downs.

53 Ringmore Rise 🥀 (Valerie Ward) Corner plot with spectacular views over London. Front garden inspired by Beth Chatto's dry garden, with stunning borders in soft mauves, yellows and white. Rear garden on three levels. Themed beds, some shaded, others sunny. Large pond; patio with pergola. *(share to St Christopher's Hospice)*

19 Westwood Park 🥀 (Mark & Sabine North) W-sloping family garden dominated by old oak tree. Large vegetable and fruit garden, perennials, climbers, pots and small ponds for abundant wildlife.

㉔ 64 Thornhill Road, E10 🥀
(Mr P Minter & Mr M Weldon) *Off Oliver Rd, nr Leyton Orient football ground. Leyton tube 10 mins walk.* Town garden 165ft x 30ft, strongly architectural design. Densely planted mixed borders, framed by mature trees, soften the garden's formality. Packed with interest, many unusual plants and large flowering shrubs. The romantic character early in the season, camelias and spring bulbs, gives way to billowing roses and aquilegias. Home-made TEAS. *Adm £3. Suns 24 Apr; 29 May; 12 June (2-6.30). Private visits welcome by appt 15 Apr to 15 June only. Tel 020 8558 5895*

㉕ Trinity Hospice, SW4 🥀
Tube: Clapham Common. Buses: 37, 137, 35 stop outside. 2-acre park-like garden restored by Lanning Roper's friends as a memorial to him and designed by John Medhurst. Ricky's sculpture a feature. Home-made TEAS. *Adm £1, chd free. Sats, Suns 16, 17 Apr; 11, 12 June; 3, 4 Sept (2-5)*

㉖ Tudor Road Gardens, Hampton
3m W of Kingston. Bus: R70 from Twickenham & Richmond to Tudor Ave Hampton/Buses 111, 216 to Hampton main line station. Tudor Rd 7 mins walk. Three neighbouring gardens in leafy W London suburb. Home-made TEAS. *Combined adm £4, chd 50p (share to The Shooting Star Trust - Hampton). Sun 22 May (2-6);* **Evening Opening** *£4.50, wine, Sat 21 May (6-8)*

45 Tudor Road 🥀 (Rita & Colin Armfield) A surprising W-facing garden (140ft x 25ft). Raised terrace with seating and many planted pots, citrus, fig, palms etc. Spring shrubs and trees divide this interesting garden into rooms. York stone path gently curves past small bog garden, pond and waterfall, greenhouse and herbaceous planting through to bamboos, ferns and raised woodland area. Many tasteful features throughout the garden.

[NEW] 84 Tudor Road ♿🌿 (Ian & Lynda Clark) Tranquil, urban garden of 130ft, offering privacy and greenery. Stocked with mature shrubs and trees including well-established Japanese maple tree. Water feature flows over smooth pebbles and slate and a pergola offers a secluded and shaded seating area.

[NEW] 88 Tudor Road ♿🌿 (Alexandra & Barrington Skinner) Long, narrow, 130ft garden for gentle enjoyment at rear of Edwardian semi-detached house (not open). Featuring rose arbour, weeping cherry tree, pond and small vegetable plot of easily-grown produce. Natural areas with logs and nettles for insects and wild life.

147 131 Upland Road, SE22 ♿🌿 (Glenys Payne & Peggy Harvey) *Buses: P13, 63, 12.* Unusual, oriental-style, small rear garden, designed for effect and low maintenance. Tranquil ponds and waterfall linked by graceful acers in lush evergreen setting dominated by an outstanding black bamboo. Winding path of paddle stones passes 2 'dinosaur eggs' under a gleditsia 'umbrella' tree. Side garden with tall bamboo. Entry through enclosed, informal front garden with climbers over wrought iron gate and fence. *Adm £1, chd 50p. Sun 15 May (2-5)*

148 7 Upper Phillimore Gardens, W8 🌿 (Mr & Mrs B Ritchie) *From Kensington High St take either Phillimore Gdns or Campden Hill Rd; entrance Duchess of Bedford Walk.* 100ft x 35ft garden; rockery, sunken garden; Italian wall fountain, ground cover planting, pergola. TEAS. *Adm £1.50, chd 50p. Sun 24 Apr (2-6)*

149 [NEW] 1 Vineyard Hill Road, Wimbledon, SW19 ♿ (Rodney & Penny Short) *Tube: Wimbledon Park. 5 mins walk. Bus: 156 to Durnsford Rd. No. 1 is close to junction with Leopold Rd.* Classic summer borders with English roses, clematis, lupins, peonies and a wide variety of hardy geraniums. Walk through rose-covered arch to fruit trees supporting enormous Kiftsgate rose and the vegetable plot, all protected by original 1899 120ft long

brick wall. TEAS. *Adm £2, chd free. Sun 12 June (2-6)*

150 Waltham Forest Register Office, 106 Grove Road, E17 ♿🌿♻ (Garden Curator: Teresa Farnham) *Situated on corner of Grove Rd & Fraser Rd. Bus to Lea Bridge Rd, Bakers Arms & 5 mins walk up Fraser Rd.* Front and rear gardens of former Victorian vicarage in Walthamstow. Despite adverse conditions, a garden has been created using cuttings as well as plants from seed to survive drought and shallow soil. Walkway, planted with roses and passion flowers, leads to honeysuckle and clematis arbour. Mixed borders and recently planted oak. Cuttings when available for visitors. Light refreshments and TEAS. *Adm £1, chd free. Tue 27 Sept (11-4). Private visits welcome by appt. Tel 020 8530 6729 farnham2001@aol.com*

151 [NEW] 11 Warwick Road, Walthamstow, E17 🌿♻ (June & Ernie Norkett) *(See 24 Warwick Rd for directions).* Medium-sized cottage style garden with perennials, shrubs and roses. Lawn with path that winds it's way to an arched garden area. Large pond. Home-made TEAS. *Combined Adm £3, chd 50p with **24 Warwick Rd**. Suns 24 , 31 July (10-5)*

152 [NEW] 24 Warwick Road, Walthamstow, E17 🌿♻ (John & Barbara Allsop) *Bus: W11 from Walthamstow Central to Highham Hill Library. N along Countess Rd, up Priors Croft. 1st R; W15 from Walthamstow Central to Highham Hill Rd, junction Claremont Rd. Down Claremont Rd, 3rd L; 158 from Blackhorse Rd Station to Billet Rd junction Highham Hill Rd, 1st L, Carlton Rd, Proceed to end and bear R.* Small garden divided into rooms. Archways lead to areas displaying over 300 varieties of fuchsias set amongst trees, shrubs and perennial plants. Featured in 'Garden News' magazine 2004. *Combined Adm £3, chd 50p with **11 Warwick Rd**. Suns 24 , 31 July (10-5)*

153 The Watergardens, Warren Road, Kingston-on-Thames ♿🌿 (The Residents' Association) *1m E of Kingston. From Kingston take the A308 (Kingston Hill) towards London; after about ½m turn R into Warren Rd.* Japanese landscaped garden originally part of Coombe Wood Nursery, approx 9 acres with

water cascade features. *Adm £3, chd £1. Suns 8 May; 16 Oct (2-4.30)*

154 42 West Park Road, Kew 🌿 (Mr Michael Anderson) *3 mins walk from Kew Gardens tube station.* Low maintenance 40ft x 25ft tranquil S-facing walled garden in the heart of Kew village. Key design elements incl decking bisected with small water canal and reflecting pool, pebble garden and small sandstone terrace. Focus on natural materials and a diversity of plant forms and textures to create an evolving garden throughout the seasons. Featured in 'BBC Gardeners World' magazine 2004. *Adm £1.50, chd 50p. Sun 8 May (2-6)*

155 [NEW] 6 Westbury Lane, Buckhurst Hill ♻ (Mr & Mrs Schweizer) *2m Loughton, 5m Epping, 2m Woodford. Between Woodford Green & Loughton. 5mins walk from Buckhurst Hill Station (Central Line). Turn R and up Palmerston Rd, take L-hand fork at Baptist Chapel. By car, turn off A104 down Queen's Rd (just past Bald Faced Stag carvery). Westbury Lane is 1st L down hill; No 6 is at bottom opp Baptist Chapel.* N-facing front garden thickly planted with shrubs, roses, hellebores and other perennials. At rear, cottage-type garden with lawn, winding paths and herbaceous borders, old fruit trees, rambling and climbing roses. Lots of perennials incl hardy geraniums and day lilies. Gravel bed with sun-loving plants. Small pond. Plant-lover's garden. *Adm £1.50, chd 50p. Sun 12 June (11-5). Also open **4 Stradbroke Grove, Buckhurst Hill***

156 2 Western Lane, SW12 🌿 (Mrs Anne Birnhak) *Clapham South or Balham tube stations, Wandsworth Common mainline station. Please park in Nightingale Lane.* Enchanting patio garden (25sq yds) crammed with 2000 different plants. Walkways offer views of the spectacular clematis collection (250 varieties). Stunning wooden pergola, thundering waterfall, metal parasols and containers stacked in tiers. Anne's insatiable appetite for collecting rare plants gives visitors the opportunity to enjoy a constantly changing show. No access for prams or bicycles. Featured in '25 Beautiful Gardens' and on C4 TV Urban Gardens in 2003, 'Gardeners' World' 2004. *Adm £2, chd £2. Suns 5 June; 10 July; 7 Aug (3-5). Private visits welcome by appt annebirnhak@castlebalham.fsnet. co.uk*

157 ◆ The Gardens of Westminster Abbey, SW1 🚼⊗⊕
(The Dean & Chapter of Westminster) *Tubes: St James' Park & Westminster. Buses: 11, 24, 88 & 211. Approach gardens via cloister from Dean's Yard.* Oldest garden in UK under constant cultivation for more than 900yrs. 3 gardens to visit - College Garden, Little Cloister Garden and St Catherine's Garden. 4-acre site. 2 fountains, one old and one new. Knot garden; medicinal herbs; bulbs and spring flowers; notable fig tree. Light refreshments and TEAS. *Adm £2, chd free, concessions £1.50 (share to Westminster Abbey). Tues to Thurs, Apr to Sept (10-6), Oct to Mar (10-4).* **For NGS:** *Sat 23 Apr (2-5);* **Evening Opening** *£3.50, wine, Tue 24 May (6-8). Tel Jan Pancheri 020 7654 4946 gardeners@westminster-abbey.org*

158 Whitton CRC, 1 Britannia Lane, off Constance Road, Whitton 🚼⊗⊕
(London Borough of Richmond) *3m W of Richmond. Mainline station: Whitton; bus H22 alight at Whitton station. No parking in Britannia Lane. Free parking in Constance Rd & surrounding streets.* Narrow 180ft organic garden maintained by staff and people with learning disabilities whose day centre occupies the remainder of the site. The cottage-style planting has produced a mass of colour and scent with a lavender and fuchsia bed, mixed borders, butterfly garden, wildlife pond and a raised bed of shrubs and roses. Winner 'Best Enviromental Garden 2004' Richmond in Bloom competition. Light Refreshments and TEAS. *Adm £1.50, chd free. Wed 18 May (11-3)*

159 54 Wildwood Road, NW11 ⊗
(Tony Stone) *Golders Green tube; bus H2 stops at corner of Wildwood Rd and Neville Drive.* Country-style garden, a little wild. Created by owner and his late wife, Barbara. Contemporary sculpture in tune with setting. Oak trees, honeysuckle and roses, an arbour, wild flowers and fruit trees. TEAS. *Adm £2, chd 50p. Sun 12 June (2.30-5.30)*

160 86 Willifield Way, NW11 ⊗
(Diane Berger) *Tube: Golders Green, then H2 bus to Willifield Way.*

Award-winning cottage garden with lots of interest and variety. Terrace pond area; pergola with roses & clematis; deck; hot border; herbaceous bed; lots of interesting perennials, trees & shrubs. A plantsman's delight. Home-made TEAS. *Adm £1.50, chd 50p. Sun 24 July (2-5)*

161 47 Winn Road, Lee, SE12 🚼⊕
(Mr & Mrs G Smith) *8m SE Central London. 15 mins walk from Lee or Grove Park station from Charing Cross. By car A20 Sidcup bypass or A205 South Circular.* ½-acre plantsman's mature garden maintained by owners. Mixed borders, alpine beds, fruits and vegetables, three greenhouses with displays of pelargoniums, fuchsias, begonias, cacti and succulents. Home-made TEAS. *Adm £2, chd free (share to The Fifth Trust). Suns 24 Apr; 26 June (2-5)*

162 27 Wood Vale, N10 ⊗⊕
(Mr & Mrs A W Dallman) *Muswell Hill 1m. A1 to Woodman public house; signed Muswell Hill. From Highgate tube, take Muswell Hill Rd, sharp R into Wood Lane leading to Wood Vale.* ¾-acre garden, 300ft long, abounding with surprises. Herbaceous borders, shrubbery, pond and a new feature every year. Once inside you would think you were in the countryside. Seating for over 90 people, with shady areas and delicious home-made teas. Every effort is made to make our visitors welcome. Home-made TEAS. *Adm £2, chd 50p (share to Hornsey Royal British Legion, Sun). Sat, Sun 9, 10 July (1.30-6)*

163 66 Woodbourne Avenue, SW16 🚼⊕
(Brian Palmer & Keith Simmonds) *Enter from Garrads Rd by Tooting Bec Common (by car only).* Garden designer's garden constantly evolving. Cottage-style front garden 40ft x 60ft containing roses, irises and herbaceous plants together with a subtropical twist with proteas from South Africa. Rear garden approx 40ft x 80ft with recently added features, shrubs, trees, gazebo and pool, creating a tranquil oasis in an urban setting. 10th yr of opening in 2005 and record attendance in 2004.

Home-made TEAS. *Adm £2, chd 50p. Sun 26 June (1.30-6)*

164 12 Woodfield Avenue, SW16 🚼⊗⊕
(Dorothy Perotti) *Streatham Hill mainline station 5 mins walk.* 80ft x 60ft densely planted garden with good variety of shrubs, herbaceous plants, good leaf colour and all-yr interest. Sheltered by climbing plants and mature trees. Pots and sink gardens on terrace. Home-made TEAS. *Adm £1.50, chd 50p. Sun 5 June (2-6)*

◆ The World Garden at Lullingstone Castle, Eynsford 🚼⊗⊕
See Kent.

Evening Opening (See also garden description)

Tudor Road Gardens	21 May
The Gardens of Westminster Abbey	24 May
Tewkesbury Lodge Garden Group	28 May
11 Spencer Road	1 June
Little Lodge	8 June
18 Sibella Road	8 June
Fenton House, Hampstead Grove	9 June
26 Claygate Road	10 June
28 Granville Park	10 June
The Pagoda	10 June
116 Peckham Park Road	11 June
10 Hoveden Road	12 June
Charterhouse	14 June
5 Burbage Road	15 June
239a Hook Road	15 June
60 Castelnau	22 June
2 Millfield Place	22 June
James Allen's Girls' School Botany Gardens	24 June
Hill Farm	29 June
5 Hillcrest Avenue	29 June
Ham House	6 July
116 Hamilton Terrace	6 July
Roots and Shoots	6 July
24 Hills Road	7 July
10A The Pavement	14 July
Badgers Retreat	20 July
Roots and Shoots	20 July
66A East Dulwich Road	7 August
28 Stanley Road	11 August
12 Jeymer Avenue	28 August
63B Overhill Road	1 September

ngs gardens open for charity

Chelsea Week Garden Tours

An opportunity to visit an exclusive selection of private gardens, all opening for charity.

Prices quoted are per person, per full day tour including visits, transport, lunch, wine & VAT.

❀ **Monday 23rd May, South East London Gardens - £68**
Visit South East London Gardens including a unique nursery in Peckham. Meet at the Museum of Garden History, picnic lunch in one of the gardens. Return to Museum of Garden History.

❀ **Tuesday 24th May, Petersham & Kew Gardens - £68**
Includes a visit and lunch at the innovative and exciting new nursery at Petersham. Meet and return to Old Deer Park car park, Richmond

❀ **Wednesday 25th May, Oxfordshire Gardens - £68**
Visit exceptional gardens in Oxfordshire, not normally open. Lunch locally. Meet at and return to Hillingdon tube.

❀ **Thursday 26th May, South West London Gardens - £68**
Visit a diverse group of gardens on the outskirts of London, including the newly restored vegetable garden at Ham House. Picnic lunch in one of the gardens. Meet at and return to Museum of Garden History.

❀ **Friday 27th May, North London Gardens - £68**
Includes two neighbouring gardens not normally open. Picnic lunch in one of the gardens. Meet at and return to Golders Green station.

❀ **Saturday 28th May, Sussex Gardens - £68**
Four very different gardens in Sussex and a picnic lunch in one of them. Meet at and return to Surbiton station.

For more details or to book a tour please contact the NGS representative, Peter Hickman, Tel: 020 8339 0931, e-mail: garden.information@virgin.net or write, stating the date and tour required and enclosing a sterling cheque made payable to NGS Enterprises Ltd., to The National Gardens Scheme, c/o Peter Hickman, Little Lodge, Watts Road, Thames Ditton, Surrey KT7 0BX. A refund will only be made if the place can be resold. A friend may come in your place.

Norfolk

County Organisers: Mrs Anthea Foster, Lexham Hall, King's Lynn, Norfolk PE32 2QJ Tel 01328 701341
Mrs Tessa McCosh, Baconsthorpe Old Rectory, Holt, Norfolk NR25 6LU Tel 01263 577611
Assistant County Organisers: Mrs Fiona Black, The Old Rectory, Ridlington, North Walsham NR28 9NZ
Tel 01692 650247 blacks7@email.com
Mrs Isabel Cator, Reedside, Farm Lane, Ranworth, Norwich NR13 6HY Tel 01603 270748
Mrs Holly Rawkins, Kempstone Lodge, Litcham, King's Lynn, Norfolk PE32 2LG
Tel 01328 701557
County Treasurer: Mr Neil Foster, Lexham Hall, King's Lynn, Norfolk PE32 2QJ Tel 01328 701288

Maps: Numbers shown next to each garden entry refer to that garden's entry on the county map. This position is approximate; distance and directions from the nearest main town are generally shown in the garden text.
A precise location is available for those gardens featured on the NGS website by visiting www.ngs.org.uk.
Symbols: Information relating to symbols is given on page 21

DATES OF OPENING

Evening openings
See end of county listing

Private gardens open regularly for NGS
Desert World, Santon Downham (14)
The Old Cottage, Colby Corner, nr Aylsham (36)

Gardens open to the public
For details see garden description
Alby Crafts Gardens, Erpingham (1)
Blickling Hall, Aylsham (7)
Bradenham Hall, Bradenham (9)
East Ruston Old Vicarage, East Ruston (16)
Elsing Hall, Dereham (17)
The Exotic Garden, Thorpe, Norwich (18)
Felbrigg Hall, Cromer (19)
Houghton Hall Walled Garden, Houghton (27)
Hoveton Hall Gardens, nr Wroxham (28)
Mannington Hall, nr Saxthorpe/Corpusty (34)
Oxburgh Hall Garden, Oxburgh (39)
The Plantation Garden, Norwich (40)
Priory Maze Gardens, Beeston Regis, Sheringham (42)
Raveningham Hall, Raveningham (43)
Sandringham Gardens, Sandringham (45)
Severals Grange, Hoecroft Plants, Wood Norton (46)
Sheringham Park, Upper Sheringham (47)
Stody Lodge, Melton Constable (48)

By appointment only
For telephone number and other details see garden description.
Private visits welcomed
Hawthorn House, Hindringham (23)
Hill Cottage, Edingthorpe (25)

February 6 Sunday
Bagthorpe Hall, Bagthorpe (3)
Lexham Hall, nr Litcham (33)

April 3 Sunday
Gayton Hall, King's Lynn (21)

Mannington Hall, nr Saxthorpe/Corpusty (34)
The Plantation Garden, Norwich (40)

April 10 Sunday
Desert World, Santon Downham (14)

April 17 Sunday
Wretham Lodge, East Wretham (57)

April 23 Saturday
East Ruston Old Vicarage, East Ruston (16)

April 24 Sunday
Alby Crafts Gardens, Erpingham (1)
Bradenham Hall, Bradenham (9)
Stow Hall, Stow Bardolph (49)

May 1 Sunday
Bolwick Hall, Marsham (8)
Clermont House, Little Cressingham (11)
Lake House, Brundall (32)
The Old House, Ranworth (37)
Stody Lodge, Melton Constable (48)

May 2 Monday (Bank Hol)
Lake House, Brundall (32)
Witton Hall, nr North Walsham (54)

May 7 Saturday
Priory Maze Gardens, Beeston Regis, Sheringham (42)

May 8 Sunday
Croft House, Dersingham (13)
Plovers Hill, Strumpshaw (41)
Stody Lodge, Melton Constable (48)

May 15 Sunday
The Cottage, Edingthorpe Green (12)
Lexham Hall, nr Litcham (33)
Maple Cottage, Aylsham (35)
10 St Michael's Close (44)
Stody Lodge, Melton Constable (48)

May 22 Sunday
How Hill Farm, Ludham (30)
Lexham Hall, nr Litcham (33)
The Old Rectory, Kirby Bedon (38)
Sheringham Park, Upper Sheringham (47)
Stody Lodge, Melton Constable (48)

May 29 Sunday
Clermont House, Little Cressingham (11)
Stody Lodge, Melton Constable (48)
Stow Hall, Stow Bardolph (49)
Woodwynd, Dersingham (56)

May 30 Monday (Bank Hol)
Chestnut Farm, West Beckham (10)
Stody Lodge, Melton Constable (48)

June 5 Sunday
Bishop's House, Norwich (6)
Sheringham Park, Upper Sheringham (47)
Sundown, Roydon, Diss (50)
The Wicken, Castle Acre, nr King's Lynn (52)

June 11 Saturday
The Dutch House, Ludham (15)

June 12 Sunday
Raveningham Hall, Raveningham (43)

June 17 Friday
Hoveton Hall Gardens, nr Wroxham (28)

June 19 Sunday
Elsing Hall, Dereham (17)
Oxburgh Hall Garden, Oxburgh (39)
Stow Hall, Stow Bardolph (49)
Withern, West Runton (53)

June 25 Saturday
Priory Maze Gardens, Beeston Regis, Sheringham **(Evening)** (42)

June 26 Sunday
Baconsthorpe Old Rectory, Holt (2)
Felbrigg Hall, Cromer (19)
Gayton Hall, King's Lynn (21)
Intwood Hall, nr Cringleford (31)

July 3 Sunday
Desert World, Santon Downham (14)
High House Gardens, Shipdham (24)
Hoveton House, nr Wroxham (29)

July 5 Tuesday
Houghton Hall Walled Garden, Houghton (27)

July 10 Sunday
Blickling Hall, Aylsham (7)

July 17 Sunday
Beck House, Colby, nr Aylsham (4)
The Garden in an Orchard, Bergh Apton (20)
The Old Cottage, Colby Corner, nr Aylsham (36)
Oxburgh Hall Garden, Oxburgh (39)
West Lodge, Aylsham (51)
Woodwynd, Dersingham (56)

NORFOLK

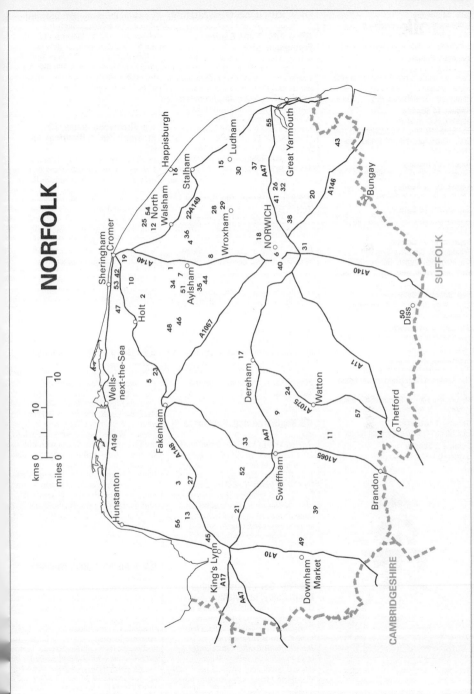

kms 0 — 10 — 10

miles 0 — 10

Hunstanton

A149

Wells-next-the-Sea

Sheringham
Cromer

Holt

Fakenham

A148

Dereham

A47

Swaffham

A1065

King's Lynn
A17

A47

Downham Market

A10

Brandon

Thetford

A11

Watton
A1075

A1067

Aylsham

A140

NORWICH

Wroxham

A149
North Walsham

Stalham

Ludham

Happisburgh

Great Yarmouth
A47
A146

Bungay

Diss

SUFFOLK

CAMBRIDGESHIRE

1 2 3 4 5 6 7 8 9 10 11 12 13 14 15 16 17 18 19 20 21 22 23 24 25 26 27 28 29 30 31 32 33 34 35 36 37 38 39 40 41 42 43 44 45 46 47 48 49 50 51 52 53 54 55 56 57

July 24 Sunday
Bradenham Hall, Bradenham *(9)*
Plovers Hill, Strumpshaw *(41)*
Sundown, Roydon, Diss *(50)*

August 7 Sunday
Birchwood House, Hindringham *(5)*
Clermont House, Little Cressingham *(11)*
Hollycroft, Blofield Heath *(26)*
Plovers Hill, Strumpshaw *(41)*

August 14 Sunday
Blickling Hall, Aylsham *(7)*
The Exotic Garden, Thorpe, Norwich *(18)*
Severals Grange, Hoecroft Plants, Wood Norton *(46)*

August 21 Sunday
Hoveton Hall Gardens, nr Wroxham *(28)*

September 4 Sunday
The Grange, North Walsham *(22)*

September 10 Saturday
Woodlands Farm, Stokesby, Gt Yarmouth *(55)*

September 11 Sunday
Felbrigg Hall, Cromer *(19)*
The Plantation Garden, Norwich *(40)*
Woodlands Farm, Stokesby, Gt Yarmouth *(55)*

September 17 Saturday
Priory Maze Gardens, Beeston Regis, Sheringham *(42)*

September 24 Saturday
The Garden in an Orchard, Bergh Apton *(20)*

September 25 Sunday
Bradenham Hall, Bradenham *(9)*
The Garden in an Orchard, Bergh Apton *(20)*
Mannington Hall, nr Saxthorpe/Corpusty *(34)*

October 1 Saturday
East Ruston Old Vicarage, East Ruston *(16)*

October 2 Sunday
Gayton Hall, King's Lynn *(21)*

"You can come down now Henry, they've all gone!"

DESCRIPTIONS OF GARDENS

❶ ◆ Alby Crafts Gardens, Erpingham &⌂
(Mr & Mrs John Alston) *4m N of Aylsham. On A140. Park in Alby Crafts car park.* 4-acre garden with 4 ponds and small wood. Primroses, hellebores, spring bulbs, primulas, many unusual shrubs and trees, 8 large mixed beds and borders. Fritillary and wild orchid meadow. Home-made TEAS. *Adm £2.50, chd free. Tues to Suns & Bank Hols (10-5) .* **For NGS:** *Sun 24 Apr (11-5). Tel 01263 761226*

❷ Baconsthorpe Old Rectory, Holt &⌂⌂
(Mr & Mrs David McCosh) *3m SE of Holt. Follow sign to Baconsthorpe from Holt bypass for 3m. Rectory is beside church at far end of village.* Well-established herbaceous borders, interesting shrubs and kitchen garden within framework of old box hedges and walls. Large conservatory and sunken garden. Views of church past mulberry tree and thatched summerhouse. Huge copper beech and ilex dominate S lawn. Decorative outbuildings and yards. Visiting nurseries. Home-made TEAS in aid of St Mary's Church, Baconsthorpe. *Adm £3, chd free. Sun 26 June (2-6). Private visits welcome by appt. Tel 01263 577611*

❸ Bagthorpe Hall, Bagthorpe ⌂⌂
(Mr & Mrs D Morton) *3½m N of East Rudham, off A148. At King's Lynn take A148 to Fakenham. At East Rudham (approx 12m) turn L by Cat & Fiddle PH. 3½m into hamlet of Bagthorpe. Farm buildings on L, wood on R, white gates set back at top.* Many varieties of snowdrops, carpeting woodland walks. Snowdrop walk. Home-made TEAS. *Adm £2, chd free. Sun 6 Feb (11-5)*

❹ NEW Beck House, Bridge Road, Colby, nr Aylsham &⌂⌂
(Hazel & Tony Blackburn) *14m N of Norwich. Take B1145 from N Walsham to Aylsham, after 3½m turn R into Bridge Rd opp Banningham Bridge Old Garage, next to school (Colby).* 1-acre, packed borders of unusual perennials, shrubs and trees, large natural pond and paths through wild areas with lovely views across the river. S-facing front garden with drought loving plants; sit and enjoy the tranquil

views on the many seats provided. Parents be aware dangers for children, pond and river unfenced. TEAS in aid of Greenfingers Garden Club. *Adm £1.50, chd free. Sun 17 July (11-5). Alos open* **The Old Cottage***. Private visits welcome by appt. Tel 01263 733167*

❺ Birchwood House, 13 Moorgate Road, Hindringham ⌂⌂
(Stella & Peter Challen) *18m SW of Cromer. Between Fakenham & Holt off A148. Take Hindringham Rd at Crawfish PH. Continue 2m to village, past church, 2nd R.* Small intensive inspirational plantsman's garden approx ¼-acre. An interesting collection incl agapanthus, agave, canna, corkscrew baytrees, hosta, sempervivum, eryngium, grasses. Dahlia, hydrangea and gazebo. Mature speciman of coral tree: Erythrina crista-galli. Proceeds of plant sale to St Martins Church, Hindringham. *Adm £2, chd free. Sun 7 Aug (2-6)*

❻ Bishop's House, Bishopgate, Norwich &⌂⌂
(The Bishop of Norwich) *City centre. Entrance opp Law Courts on Bishopgate on N side of Cathedral (not through The Close). Through Archway on R. Public car parking nearby. No parking at Bishop's House.* Walled garden dating back to the C12. Extensive lawns with old specimen trees and interesting shrubs. Spectacular herbaceous borders flanked by ancient yew hedges. Rose gardens, new meadow labyrinth and long shade border with hostas and Himalayan poppies. Home-made TEAS in aid of local charity. *Adm £3, chd free. Sun 5 June (2-5)*

❼ ◆ Blickling Hall, Aylsham &⌂⌂
(The National Trust) *15m N of Norwich. 1½ miles NW of Aylsham on N side of B1354.* Large garden, orangery, crescent lake, azaleas, rhododendrons, herbaceous borders. Historic Jacobean house. Wheelchairs and batricars available. Cream TEAS on NGS days. *House and garden adm £7.30, garden only £4.20, chd £2.10. Weds to Suns 19 Mar to 30 Oct (10.15-5.15). Also limited winter opening.* **For NGS:** *Suns 10 July; 14 Aug (10.15-5.15). Tel 01263 738030 www.nationaltrust.org.uk/blickling*

8 Bolwick Hall, Marsham 🏵️⊕
(Mr & Mrs G C Fisher) *½m S of
Aylsham. On A140 towards
Aylsham, take 1st R past Plough PH
at Marsham, then next R onto private
rd to front of Hall.* Landscaped
gardens and park, attributed to
Humphry Repton, surrounding late
Georgian hall (not open) and stable
block. Collection of mature trees,
woodland walks around stream and
mill pond, as well as more recently
planted borders and working
vegetable garden. Home-made TEAS
in aid of All Saints, Marsham. *Adm
£2.50, chd free. Sun 1 May (2-5).
Private visits welcome by appt.
Tel 01263 732131
gandcfisher@supanet.com*

**9 ◆ Bradenham Hall,
Bradenham** 🅱️🏵️⊕
(Chris & Panda Allhusen) *6m E of
Swaffham. 5m W of East Dereham
off A47. Turn S signed Wendling &
Longham. 1m turn S signed
Bradenham, 2m.* Massed daffodils,
arboretum of over 800 species, all
labelled. Rose garden, herbaceous
and mixed borders, wall shrubs and
roses, fruit and vegetable garden,
glasshouses. Home-made TEAS. *Adm
£4, chd free (House not open). 2nd &
4th Suns Apr to Sept.* **For NGS:** *Suns
24 Apr; 24 July; 25 Sept (2-5.30).
Tel 01362 687243/687279
www.bradenhamhall.co.uk*

**10 Chestnut Farm, West
Beckham** 🅱️🏵️⊕
(Mr & Mrs John McNeil Wilson)
*½m S of Sheringham. Mid-way
between Holt & Cromer. 1m S off
the A148 at the Sheringham Park
entrance. Sign post indicates 'By Rd
to W Beckham'.* Chestnut Farm
located behind the village sign. 3-acre
garden developed over the last 40yrs
by a keen gardener and plant
enthusiast, with an emphasis on
shrub borders and ground-cover
plants. There are two herbaceous
borders, small paddock with pond
and specimen trees, wildlife area
planted to encourage birds and
butterflies. Woodland garden with
hellebores, spring flowering bulbs.
fountain garden and iris border with
alliums. Plants for sale, visiting
nurseries. Featured in 'House and
Garden', 2004. Light refreshments
and TEAS. *Adm £2.50, chd free
(share to St Helen & All Saints
Church, West Beckham). Mon 30
May (11-5)*

**11 Clermont House, Little
Cressingham** 🅱️⊕
(Mr & Mrs John Davies) *6m SW of
Dereham. From Watton take the
B1108 towards Lt Cressingham.
Turn L off the B1108 at Lt
Cressingham. Entrance is ½m on L.*
Established since 1984, approx 13
acres lawns, woodland garden,
arboretum, formal walled garden and
lake. Several woodland walks with
developing arboretum, flowering
shrubs, daffodils, narcissus and
spring-flowering bulbs. Many species
of *Acer, Aesculus, Betula, Malus,
Sorbus, Quercus, Crataegus* and
other specimens. Turf labyrinth built
in 2003 - Chartres inspired. Home-
made TEAS in aid of The Friends of
St Andrew's Church, Lt Cressingham.
*Adm £3, chd under 15 free. Suns 1,
29 May; 7 Aug (2-5)*

**12 The Cottage, Hennesseys
Loke, Edingthorpe Green** 🅱️🏵️⊕
(Tim & Mary Richardson) *2½m NE
of North Walsham. Off B1150
halfway between Bacton and North
Walsham, turn L at village sign then
sharp L and follow rd for 200yds. At
L bend turn R onto dirt rd and car
park. ½-acre* garden with 4 ponds,
bog areas, densely planted with reeds,
bamboos and gunneras. Roses,
clematis and shrubs all jostle for
space giving the garden a lush and
relaxed atmosphere. A haven for
wildlife and all creatures are
respected. No chemicals for over
30yrs within the garden. 3
summerhouses provide tranquil and
restive settings. Partially suitable for
wheelchairs. Light refreshments and
TEAS in aid of Hawk & Owl Trust.
*Adm £2.50, chd free. Sun 15 May
(11-5)*

**13 [NEW] Croft House, 111 Manor
Road, Dersingham** 🏵️
(Walter & Jane Blaney) *8m NE of
King's Lynn. Take A149 N from
King's Lynn then B1440 into
Dersingham. At T-lights turn R into
Chapel Rd. In ½m bear R into
Manor Rd.* Croft House opp church
car park. Park in adjacent rds. New
garden being created with formal and
informal planting for yr-round
interest from a 2-acre neglected
spinney. Jungle effect planting
surrounds wildlife ponds with many
unusual shrubs. Winding woodland
paths connect wild and cultivated
areas. Formal areas comprise lawns,
small aboretum, orchard, kitchen
garden and paved patios with water
features. TEAS. *Adm £2.50, chd free
(share to Tapping House Hospice).
Sun 8 May (2-5)*

**14 Desert World, Santon
Downham** 🏵️⊕
(Mr & Mrs Barry Gayton) *4m N of
Thetford. On B1107 Brandon 2m.*
1¼ acres landscaped plantsman's
garden. Radio Norfolk's gardener,
specialising in tropical plants, alpines,
herbaceous and spring bulbs,
bamboos with summer lilies, incl
sempervivums. Glasshouses
containing 12,500 cacti and
succulents. Desert garden. 40
varieties passion flowers. Views from
roof garden. Viewing of glasshouses
by appt only. Featured in Britain's
Inspirational Gardens book 2004, &
Radio 2004/05. Light refreshments
and TEAS. *Adm £2.50, chd free.
Daily, not Fri (dawn til dusk). Suns
10 Apr; 3 July (1-5). Private visits
welcome by appt,cacti flowering in
glasshouses May to Aug. Tel 01842
765861*

15 The Dutch House, Ludham
🅱️🏵️
(Mrs Peter Seymour) *5m W of
Wroxham. B1062 Wroxham to
Ludham 7m. Turn R by Ludham
village church into Staithe Rd.*
Gardens ¼m from village. Long,
narrow garden of approx 2½ acres
leading through marsh and wood to
Womack Water. Designed and
planted originally by the painter
Edward Seago and recently replanted
by the present owner. Home-made
TEAS. *Adm £3, chd free. Sat 11 June
(2-5). Private visits welcome by appt,
June, July only, coaches permitted.
Tel 01692 678225*

**16 ◆ East Ruston Old Vicarage,
East Ruston** 🅱️🏵️⊕
(Alan Gray & Graham Robeson) *3m
N of Stalham. Turn off A149 onto
B1159 signed Bacton, Harrisburgh.
After 2m turn R 200yds N of East
Ruston Church (ignore sign to East
Ruston).* 20-acre exotic coastal
garden incl traditional borders, exotic
garden, desert wash, sunk garden,
topiary, water features, walled and
Mediterranean gardens. Many rare
and unusual plants, stunning plant
combinations, wild flower meadows,
old-fashioned cornfield, vegetable
and cutting gardens. Featured in
'Independent' , rated garden in top 50
in Europe 2003. TEAS. *Adm £4, chd
£1. Weds, Fris, Sats, Suns & Bank
Hol Mons 25 Mar to 29 Oct.* **For
NGS:** *Sats 23 Apr; 1 Oct (2-5.30).
Tel 01692 650432 www.e-
rustonoldvicaragegardens.co.uk*

⑰ ◆ Elsing Hall, Dereham 🚷🐕
(David & Shirley Cargill) *5m E of Dereham. Off A47 signed N Tuddenham then signed Elsing Hall.* Medieval house (not open) surrounded by moat. Over 200 varieties of old-fashioned roses. Wild flower lawn, walled kitchen garden with roses, fruit trees and clematis. Many water plants by moat and fish stew. Rare and interesting trees in arboretum. Formal garden with clipped box, lavender, sage, santolina and thyme. Suitable for wheelchairs in places. Featured in 'The Telegraph', 'EDP' & various magazines 2004. Home-made TEAS. *Adm £3.50, chd free. Suns June to Sept.* **For NGS:** *Sun 19 June (2-6). Tel 01362 637224*

Ely Gardens II
See Cambridgeshire.

⑱ ◆ The Exotic Garden, 6 Cotman Road, Thorpe, Norwich 🐕
(Mr Will Giles) *Off A47. New entrance & car park via side entrance of Alan Boswell Insurance 126 Thorpe Rd next to DEFRA. Approx ½m from Thorpe railway station.* Exotic city garden covering approx 1 acre on a S-facing hillside including new ½-acre garden. In high summer the garden is a riot of colour among towering architectural plants such as cannas, bananas, aroids, palms etc giving the garden a truly subtropical feel, especially with its use of houseplants as bedding. Will Giles is a BBC Radio Norfolk's gardener and author of The New Exotic Garden. Home-made TEAS. *Adm £3.50, chd free. Suns 19 June to 9 Oct; Bank Hol Mon 29 Aug.* **For NGS:** *Sun 14 Aug (1.30-5.30). Tel 01603 623167 www.exoticgarden.com*

⑲ ◆ Felbrigg Hall, Cromer 🚷🐕 NCCPG
(The National Trust) *2½m SW of Cromer. S of A148; main entrance from B1436.* Large pleasure gardens; mainly lawns and shrubs; orangery with camellias; large walled garden restored and restocked as fruit, vegetable, herb and flower garden; vine house; dovecote; dahlias; National Collection of *Colchicum*; wooded parks. 1 electric and 2 manual wheelchairs available. Light refreshments and TEAS. *House and Garden adm £6.60, Garden only adm £2.70. Sats to Weds Mar to Oct.* **For**

NGS: *Suns 26 June; 11 Sept (11-5). Tel 01263 837444 tina.hammond@nationaltrust.org.uk*

⑳ The Garden in an Orchard, Mill Road, Bergh Apton 🚷🐕
(Mr & Mrs R W Boardman) *6m SE of Norwich. Off A146 at Hellington Corner signed to Bergh Apton. Down Mill Rd 300yds.* 3½-acre garden created by the owners set in old orchard. Many rare plants set out in an informal pattern of wandering paths. ½ acre of wild flower meadows, many bamboos, species roses and Michaelmas daisies. 9 species of eucalyptus. A plantsman's garden. Home-made TEAS. *Adm £2, chd free. Sun 17 July; Sat, Sun 24, 25 Sept (11-5). Private visits welcome by appt. Tel 01508 480322*

㉑ Gayton Hall, King's Lynn 🚷🐕
(The Earl & Countess of Romney) *6m E of King's Lynn. On B1145; R on B1153. R down Back St 1st entrance on L.* 20-acre water garden, with over 2m of paths. Lawns, woodland, lakes, streams and bridges. Many unusual trees and shrubs. Spring bulbs and autumn colour. Traditional and waterside borders. Primulas, astilbes, hostas, lysichitums, gunneras and many more. Home-made TEAS. *Adm £3, chd free (share to Local Charities). Suns 3 Apr; 26 June; 2 Oct (2-6). Private visits welcome by appt. Tel 01553 636259 ciciromney@tiscali.co.uk*

㉒ [NEW] The Grange, Tungate, North Walsham 🚷
(Mrs Betty Rossi) *1m W of North Walsham. Leaving North Walsham on A149 Cromer Rd turn L into Greens Rd. Straight over staggered junction (Aylsham Rd). The Grange is situated 300yds on LH-side just past Rossis Leisure Centre.* An exposed location around 10yr old house (not open) surrounded by open fields and big Norfolk skies. Originally part of a field this profesionally designed 2 acre garden is being developed in a traditional style incl topiary, courtyard garden and several different areas of large mixed borders incorporating an increasingly wide range of plants and shrubs. Home-made TEAS. *Adm £2.50, chd free. Sun 4 Sept (11-5)*

㉓ Hawthorn House, Hindringham 🚷🐕
(Bryony Jacklin) *18m SW of Cromer. Between Fakenham and Holt, off*

A148. Take Hindringham Rd at Crawfish PH. Continue 2m to village, past church, 2nd R. Large 3-acre garden featuring herbaceous borders, island beds, pond and bog, gravel and herb gardens, willow work, traditional kitchen garden, orchard, butterfly garden and wild beds. TEAS. *Adm £2, chd free. Private visits welcome by appt, incl coaches May to Aug. Tel 01328 878441 bryony@argonet.co.uk*

㉔ High House Gardens, Blackmoor Row, Shipdham 🚷🐕
(Mr & Mrs F Nickerson) *6m W of Dereham. Take the airfield or Cranworth Rd off A1075 in Shipdham. Blackmoor Row is signed.* Large country garden with colour-themed herbaceous borders with extensive range of perennials. Box-edged rose and shrub borders. Woodland garden, pond and bog area. Small orchard, fruit and vegetable garden. Glasshouse with interesting plants. Home-made TEAS. *Adm £2.50, chd free. Sun 3 July (12-5.30)*

㉕ Hill Cottage, School Road, Edingthorpe 🚷🐕
(Shirley Gilbert) *3m NE of North Walsham. Off B1150 half way between North Walsham and Bacton leave main rd at Edingthorpe Green and continue straight towards Paston for ¾m. Cottage on L at top of hill. Parking in adjacent field.* Cottage garden, approx ¼ acre, surrounding former farm worker's cottage. Densely planted with both traditional and unusual varieties of drought-resistant climbers, shrubs, perennials and annuals. Organic vegetables and fruit, herb collection. A real butterfly and wildlife paradise. Adjacent small nursery, member of Norfolk Cottage Garden Society. Featured in 'The English Garden' 2003 & EDP Norfolk Magazine 2004. *Adm £2.50 chd free. Private visits welcome by appt, incl garden groups & coaches permitted. Tel 01692 403519 shirley.gilbert@dial.pipex.com*

㉖ Hollycroft, 51 Blofield Corner Road, Blofield Heath 🐕
(Emma & Seb Duncan) *5m E of Norwich. A47, follow signs to Blofield Heath. L turn onto Blofield Corner Rd. Hollycroft ½m on LH-side. Parking at R C Snelling Ltd (follow signs) with kind permission of Mr Roy Snelling.* Cottage gardening with a twist! ½-acre garden

surrounding a C17 thatched cottage (not open). Areas of interest incl exotic borders, collection of succulents, long interest herbaceous borders and potager. Regional winner ITV Britains Best Back Gardens 2004. Home-made TEAS in aid of Woodbastwick WI & Aid for Animals. *Adm £2.50, chd free. Sun 7 Aug (11-5). Private visits welcome by appt. Tel 01603 712430 www.enchantingplants.co.uk*

㉗ ◆ Houghton Hall Walled Garden, Houghton &⚘☺
(The Marquess of Cholmondeley) *11m W of Fakenham. Signposted from A148 approx half way between King's Lynn and Fakenham.* Since 1991 the 5-acre garden has been completely renovated. Yew hedges divide the whole area into 20 garden rooms. These incl a 120yd long herbaceous border, a rose parterre and kitchen garden with 77 apple varieties. Vehicles available for visitors with reduced mobility. Light refreshments and TEAS June 5 July. *House and Garden adm £7, Garden only adm £4.50, chd £2. Weds, Thurs, Suns & Bank Hol Mons 27 Mar to 29 Sept.* **For NGS:** *Tue 5 July (11-5.30). Tel 01485 529219 www.houghtonhall.com*

㉘ ◆ Hoveton Hall Gardens, nr Wroxham &⚘☺
(Mr & Mrs Andrew Buxton) *8m N of Norwich. 1m N of Wroxham Bridge. Off A1151 Stalham Rd - follow brown tourist signs.* Early C19 house (not open). 15-acre gardens and grounds featuring daffodils, azaleas, rhododendrons and hydrangeas in woodland. Mature, walled herbaceous garden. Water plants, lakeside walk and walled kitchen garden. Light refreshments and TEAS. *Adm £4, chd £1.50, concessions, wheelchairs & helpers £2. Easter Sun to 4 Sept; Suns, Weds, Thurs, Fris May, June & Bank Hols Mons.* **For NGS:** *Fri 17 June; Sun 21 Aug (10.30-5). Tel 01603 782798*

㉙ Hoveton House, nr Wroxham &⚘
(Sir John & Lady Blofeld) *9m N of Norwich. ½m Wroxham on B1062 Horning-Potter Heigham Rd. Entry to drive from Wroxham clearly marked on LH-bend beyond church (200yds). From Potter Heigham & Horning, poster boards on R of rd. Car park.* Old-fashioned walled garden; magnificent herbaceous and other borders full of unusual plants and bulbs; rock garden. Rhododendron grove 100yrs old and towering 30ft. Kitchen garden. Park, lawns and walks with magnificent view. William and Mary House (not open). Home-made TEAS in aid of St John's Church, Hoveton. *Adm £3, chd free. Sun 3 July (2-5.30)*

㉚ How Hill Farm, Ludham &☺
(Mr P D S Boardman) *2m W of Ludham.* On A1062; then follow signs to How Hill. Farm garden S of How Hill. 3 very pretty gardens started in 1968. Approx 10 acres with conservation area, water and 3 ponds, 2-acre Broad (dug as conservation project), water lilies and view over the R Ant to fine old mill. Paths through rare conifers. Unusual and rare rhododendrons with massed azaleas, ornamental trees, shrubs and some herbaceous plants. Collections of English holly, *Ilex aquifolium* (over 100 varieties), and 65 different bamboos. TEAS. *Adm £2.50, chd free. Sun 22 May (2-5)*

㉛ Intwood Hall, nr Cringleford &⚘☺
(The Lord & Lady Darling) *3½m SW of Norwich. From Norwich via A11 to Cringleford, fork L (avoid dual carriageway), over Cringleford bridge, L turn, over Xrds, level Xing, bypass, after ½m on R thatched lodge.* Victorian house (not open) in 5 acres of gardens surrounded by parkland with lovely trees, incl 2 cedars of Lebanon. Tudor walled water garden with gazebo, walled Victorian rose garden; herbaceous borders leading to woodland walks, one to Saxon Church. Walled kitchen garden with greenhouses. Newly-created lake in former orchard. Home-made TEAS. *Adm £3. Sun 26 June (2-5). Private visits welcome by appt. Tel 01603 454554 jdarling@intwood.org.uk*

㉜ Lake House, Postwick Lane, Brundall ☺
(Mr & Mrs Garry Muter) *5m E of Norwich.* On A47; take Brundall

turn at roundabout. Turn R into Postwick Lane at T-junction. 2 acres of water gardens set among magnificent trees in steep cleft in river escarpment. Informal flower beds with interesting plants; naturalist's paradise; unsuitable for young children or the infirm. Stout shoes advisable. Beautiful lake - shore restoration. Featured on ITV Britain's Best Back Gardens & Glorious Gardens 2004. Home-made TEAS in aid of Wateraid. *Adm £3, chd free. Sun, Mon 1, 2 May (11-5). Private visits welcome by appt for groups of 10+. Tel 01603 712933*

㉝ Lexham Hall, nr Litcham &⚘☺
(Mr & Mrs Neil Foster) *2m W of Litcham. 6m N of Swaffham off B1145.* Fine C17/18 Hall (not open). Parkland with lake and river walks. Formal garden with terraces, yew hedges, roses and mixed borders. Traditional kitchen garden with crinkle crankle wall. 3-acre woodland garden with azaleas, rhododendrons, spring bulbs, incl snowdrops and rare trees. Dogs on leads welcome Feb only. Home-made TEAS in aid of All Saints Church, Litcham, (Feb), St Andrews, E Lexham (15 May), Tapping House Hospice (22 May). *Adm £3, chd free. Suns 6 Feb (11-4); 15, 22 May (2-6). Private visits welcome by appt for groups of 20+, May to July, coaches permitted. Tel 01328 701288 lexhamestate@farming.me.uk*

㉞ ◆ Mannington Hall, nr Saxthorpe/Corpusty &⚘☺
(The Lord & Lady Walpole) *18m NW of Norwich. 2m N of Saxthorpe via B1149 towards Holt. At Saxthorpe/Corpusty follow sign posts to Mannington.* 20 acres feature shrubs, lake, trees and roses. History of the Rose display and period gardens. Sensory garden. Extensive countryside walks and trails. Moated manor house and Saxon church with C19 follies. Wild flowers. Light refreshments and TEAS. *House and Garden adm £6 (ground floor only), Garden only adm £4, chd free, concessions £3. Suns May to Sept (12-5), Weds, Thurs, Fris June to Aug (11-5).* **For NGS:** *Suns 3 Apr; 25 Sept (12-5). Tel 01263 584175 www.manningtongardens.co.uk*

㉟ Maple Cottage, 86 Hungate Street, Aylsham ⚘
(Chris & Sue Ellis) *N from Norwich on A140. Roundabout S of Aylsham, turn L, then 1st R into Hungate St,*

approx 300yds on L. Small town garden densely planted with perennials, bulbs small specimen trees and rhododendrons; raised beds, sunken pond and pebble areas. Many pots of hostas; greenhouses and vegetable area. *Adm £2, chd free (share to Hungate Street Surgery). Sun 15 May (10-4).* Also open **10 St Michael's Close**

㊱ The Old Cottage, Colby Corner, nr Aylsham ⬤⬤⬤
(Judith & Stuart Clarke) *14m N of Norwich. Take B1145 from N Walsham to Aylsham. After 3½m turn R opp Banningham Bridge Inn Garage onto Bridge Rd. Pass Colby school on R & continue straight, following Colby Corner sign. Garden on the L, parking by the poly tunnel.* This 2-acre garden can provide inspiration for all gardeners. Helpful, practical advice available about the garden and its planting, across a range of soil conditions. Easy access to all areas. New for 2005 is the enlarged exotic area, raised vegetable beds. Plants and organic produce for sale. Light refreshments and TEAS (Sun), TEAS (Weds). *Adm £3, chd free. Weds, 6 Apr to 28 Sept (2-7); Sun 17 July (11-5). Also open* **Beck House** *17 July. Private visits welcome by appt. Tel 01263 734574*

㊲ The Old House, Ranworth ⬤⬤
(Mr Francis & The Hon Mrs Cator) *9m NE of Norwich. Nr S Walsham, below historic Ranworth church.* Attractive linked and walled gardens alongside beautiful, peaceful Ranworth inner broad. Bulbs, shrubs, potager and mown rides through arboretum where dogs may be walked on leads. Pond with many species of ducks and geese. ½m of woodland walk. TEAS. *Adm £3, chd free (share to Norfolk & Norwich Assoc for the Blind). Sun 1 May (2-5)*

㊳ The Old Rectory, Kirby Bedon ⬤⬤
(Mr & Mrs Peter de Bunsen) *3m SE of Norwich. From southern bypass take A146 exit. Filter L at T-lights signed Kirby Bedon. 2m turn L to Wood End, entrance 50yds on L. Parking in church car park.* Early C18 house (not open) surrounded by 1½-acre garden designed by present owners and designer Tessa Hobbs. Formal front with topiary and hedges on stilts. Old walls and mature trees divide lawns from sunken fountain garden. Old roses and mixed planting, . Featured in 'The English

Garden' 2004. TEAS in aid of St Andrews Church, Kirby Bedon. *Adm £2.50, chd free. Sun 22 May (2-6). Private visits welcome by appt. Tel 01508 491648*

㊴ ◆ Oxburgh Hall Garden, Oxburgh ⬤⬤
(The National Trust) *7m SW of Swaffham. At Oxburgh on Stoke Ferry rd.* Hall and moat surrounded by lawns, fine trees, colourful borders; charming parterre garden of French design. Orchard and vegetable garden. Light refreshments and TEAS. *Adm £3, chd £1.50.* **For NGS:** *Suns 19 June; 17 July (11-5)*

㊵ ◆ The Plantation Garden, 4 Earlham Road, Norwich ⬤⬤⬤
(Plantation Garden Preservation Trust) *Nr St John's R C Cathedral.* 3-acre Victorian town garden created 1856-97 in former medieval chalk quarry. Undergoing restoration by volunteers. Remarkable architectural features incl 60ft Italianate terrace, unique 30ft Gothic fountain, restored rustic bridge and summerhouse. Surrounded by mature trees. Beautifully tranquil atmosphere. Home-made TEAS Suns mid Apr to end Sept. *Adm £2.50, chd free. Daily (9-6 or dusk if earlier).* **For NGS:** *Suns 3 Apr; 11 Sept (2-5). Tel 01603 452176 www.plantationgarden. co.uk*

㊶ Plovers Hill, Strumpshaw ⬤⬤
(Mr & Mrs J E Saunt) *9m E of Norwich. Off A47 at Brundall continuing through to Strumpshaw village. Turn R 300yds past PO, then R at T-junction. Plovers Hill is 1st on R up the hill.* Well-established 1-acre garden divided into several narrow 'rooms'. Main lawn garden flanked by wide borders leads through high yew hedge arch to more borders featuring, inter alia, mature mulberry, sedums, hemerocallis and hostas; spring bulbs in May. To rear, top fruit and soft fruit orchard and vegetable garden. Modern minimalist orangery. Home-made TEAS in aid of How Hill Educational Trust. *Adm £2.50, chd free, concessions £2. Suns 8 May; 24 July; 7 Aug (11-5). Private visits welcome by appt. Tel 01603 714587 jamessaunt@hotmail.com*

㊷ [NEW] ◆ Priory Maze Gardens, Beeston Regis, Sheringham
(Mike & Liz Tacchi) *1m E of Sheringham. Roundabout on the*

A149 Cromer Rd. Unique garden experience with woodlands, meadow and stream gardens in an incredibly tranquil atmosphere. The garden features Norfolk's only traditional hedge maze and new romantic garden. The Scandinavian Log tearooms offer a wide range of refreshments and the plant centre offers both the usual and unusual. Featured in EDP 2003, 'Daily Telegraph' (one of 3 gardens to visit in Norfolk) 2004. Light refreshments and TEAS. *Adm £4, chd £2.50, concessions £3.50. Daily 25 Mar to 30 Sept.* **For NGS:** *Sats 7 May; 17 Sept (10-5).* **Evening Opening** *£4, wine, Sat 25 June (6-9). Tel 01263 822986 www.priorymazegardens.com*

㊸ ◆ Raveningham Hall, Raveningham ⬤⬤
(Sir Nicholas Bacon) *14m SE of Norwich. 4m from Beccles off B1136.* Traditional country house garden with an interesting collection of herbaceous plants and shrubs. Restored Victorian conservatory and walled kitchen garden. Newly planted arboretum, lake and herb garden. Contemporary sculpture. Home-made TEAS. *House and Garden adm £6, Garden only adm £2.50, chd free concessions £2. All Bank Hol Suns & Mons & 12, 13 June.* **For NGS:** *Sun 12 June (2-5). Tel 01508 548152 www.raveningham.com*

㊹ 10 St Michael's Close ⬤⬤⬤
(Mr M I Davies) *8m S of Cromer, 12m N of Norwich. Aylsham NW on B1354 towards Blickling Hall; 500yds from market place, turn R, Rawlinsons Lane, then R again. Park in St Michael's Infants School, in Rawlinsons Lane.* Front gravelled area with mixed shrub and herbaceous border; small rockery. Back garden with large variety of shrubs, herbaceous plants, bulbs, small lawn, roses, azaleas. Pond, aviary and guinea pigs. Cream TEAS in aid of WSPA. *Adm £1.50. Sun 15 May (11-6). Also open* **Maple Cottage** *Private visits welcome by appt. Tel 01263 732174*

㊺ ◆ Sandringham Gardens, Sandringham ⬤⬤⬤
(Her Majesty The Queen) *6m NW of King's Lynn. By gracious permission the House, Museum & Grounds at Sandringham will be open.* 60 acres of formal gardens, woodland and lakes, with rare plants and trees. Donations are given from the Estate to various charities. Light

refreshments and TEAS Visitor Centre Tearoom. *Adm House and Grounds £7.50, OAP/students £6, chd £4.50 (5-15), Family £19.50 (2 adults, 3 chd). Grounds only £5, concessions £4, chd £3. House, museum & gardens open Sat 26 Mar to 23 July, reopening Sun 31 July to 30 Oct (10.30-5). Tel 01553 612907 Public Enterprises Manager www.sandringhamestate.co.uk*

46 ◆ **Severals Grange, Hoecroft Plants, Wood Norton** 🏠🌳
Jane Lister) *8m S of Holt, 6m E of Fakenham. 2m N of Guist on LH-side of B1110. Guist is situated 5m NE of Fakenham on A1067 Norwich rd.* This 13yr old garden has evolved from a bare field and is a perfect example of how colour, shape and form can be created by the use of foliage plants, large shrubs and small alpines. Movement and lightness is achieved by interspersing these plants with a wide range of ornamental grasses. Featured in 'Saturday Telegraph' Nursery of the Week 2003. *Home-made TEAS. Adm £1.50, chd free. Thur to Suns Apr to Oct (10-4).* **For NGS:** *Sun 14 Aug (11-5). Tel 01362 684206 www.hoecroft.co.uk*

47 ◆ **Sheringham Park, Upper Sheringham** 🏠🌳
The National Trust) *2m SW of Sheringham. Access for cars off A148 Cromer to Holt Rd, 5m W of Cromer, 6m E of Holt, signs in Sheringham town.* 50 acres of species rhododendron, azalea and magnolia. Also numerous specimen trees incl handkerchief tree. Viewing towers, waymarked walks, sea and parkland views. Special walkway and WCs for disabled. Electric wheelchairs available. *Light refreshments and EAS. Adm Car parking £3. Daily Dawn til Dusk).* **For NGS:** *Suns 22 May; 5 June (Dawn til Dusk). Tel 01263 823778*

48 ◆ **Stody Lodge, Melton Constable** 🏠🌳
Mr & Mrs Ian MacNicol) *16m NW of Norwich, 3m S of Holt. Off 1354. Signed from Melton Constable on Holt Rd.* 15 acres of spectacular gardens having one of the largest concentration of rhododendrons and azaleas in Anglia and incl a Japanese water garden and formal garden with stunning walks and vistas. *Home-made TEAS. Adm £4, chd under 12 free. Donation to NGS.* **For NGS:** *Suns May to 29 May; Mon 30 May*

(2-5). Tel 01263 860572 (9-12 noon) www.stodyestate.co.uk

49 **Stow Hall, Stow Bardolph** 🏠🌳
(Lady Rose Hare) *2m N of Downham Market. Off A10.* Large garden with mature trees, small secluded areas with alpines, bulbs, irises and roses. High walls and cloisters planted with scented and tender climbers. Victorian kitchen garden containing a mix of old fruit trees, apples, pears, quince, medlar and mulberry and recently planted old Norfolk varieties of apples. *Home-made TEAS in aid of local charities. Adm £3, chd free. Suns 24 Apr; 29 May; 19 June (2-5). Private visits welcome by appt. Tel 01366 383194*

50 [NEW] **Sundown, Hall Lane, Roydon, Diss**
(Elizabeth Bloom) *2m W of Diss. From Diss take A1066 Thetford Rd, ½m after Roydon White Hart PH, turn R into Hall Lane. Sundown ¼m on L. From Thetford - on A1066, approx 1m after Blooms of Bressingham, turn L into Hall lane.* 1-acre plantsman's garden established over 35yrs. Densely planted with wide variety of unusual perennials, shrubs and trees for colour and foliage yr-round. Woodland walk featuring rhododendrons and other woodland favourites; formal pond and patio area. *TEAS. Adm £2.50, chd free. Suns 5 June; 24 July (11-5). Private visits welcome by appt. Tel 01379 642074 liza.bloom@virgin.net*

51 ◆ **West Lodge, Aylsham** 🏠
(Mr & Mrs Jonathan Hirst) *¼m NW of Aylsham. Off B1354 Blickling Rd out of Aylsham, turn R down Rawlinsons Lane, garden on L.* 9-acre garden with lawns, splendid mature trees, rose garden, well stocked herbaceous borders, ornamental pond, magnificent C19 walled kitchen garden (maintained as such). Georgian House (not open) and outbuildings incl a well-stocked toolshed (open) and greenhouses. *TEAS in aid of Aylsham Caring Trust. Adm £3, chd free. Sun 17 July (2-5)*

52 **The Wicken, Castle Acre, nr King's Lynn** 🏠🌳
(Lady Keith of Castleacre) *2m N of Castle Acre. On Gt Massingham Rd, (Peddars Way) at Xrds signed on R*

to The Wicken. Woodland garden with spring flowering bulbs, azaleas, camellias, rhododendrons, leading to quiet garden. Walled garden with glasshouses, gazebo, herbaceous borders surrounding 4 different beds centred on silver weeping pears. Planted courtyard, herb border, fine views from large lawns. Formal pool garden with blue and white planting. *Cream TEAS. Adm £3, chd free (share to The Friends of Castleacre Church). Sun 5 June (2-5)*

53 **Withern, Sandy Lane, West Runton** 🏠🌳
(Margaret & Clive Mitchell) *3m W of Cromer. From the A148 Cromer/Holt rd on entering Aylmerton from Cromer turn R at Roman Camp Inn into Sandy Lane. Continue to junction, turn L, garden faces you.* A plantaholic's woodland garden of over 1 acre with winding paths through spring bulbs, ferns, hellebores, rhododendrons, herbaceous border, collection of hydrangeas and fuchsias, grasses, hostas and much more. Fruit trees, vegetables, greenhouse, bottle bank and glass sculpture. *Light refreshments and TEAS served in garden next door, (welcome to browse) in aid of Aylmerton Church & Sheringham Flower Club. Adm £2, chd free. Sun 19 June (11-5). Private visits welcome by appt. Tel 01263 837397*

54 **Witton Hall, nr North Walsham** 🌳
(Sally Owles) *3½m NW of North Walsham. Off (B1150) to Bacton Rd, by-way to Edingthorpe, then, take R fork to Bacton Woods picnic area, driveway 200yds on L.* A natural woodland garden. Walk past the handkerchief tree and wander through carpets of English bluebells, rhododendrons and azaleas. Stunning views over farmland to the sea. Featured in EDP 'Norfolk' magazine 2003. *Light refreshments and TEAS in aid of St Margaret's Church, Witton. Adm £2.50, chd free. Mon 2 May (11-5)*

55 [NEW] **Woodlands Farm, Stokesby, Gt Yarmouth** 🏠🌳
(Vivienne Fabb) *2m E of Acle. From Norwich A47 to Acle, A1064 to Caister, 1st R after bridge over river, into Filby Rd just past Bungalow Stores, 1st L after the end of 30mph limit. From Gt Yarmouth A1064 via Caister, L to Stokesby & Runham then as above.* Mature garden which has been redesigned to enhance the

existing planting and borders with emphasis on herbaceous plants, trees and shrubs. Vegetable garden and woodland walk. Cream TEAS in aid of St Andrews Church, Stokesby. *Adm £2.50, chd free. Sat, Sun 10, 11 Sept (11-5)*

56 Woodwynd, 6 Dodds Hill Road, Dersingham &⌀⌂
(Mr & Mrs D H Dingle) *8m NE of King's Lynn. ¾m N of Sandringham House. Take B1440 from Sandringham & continue into Dersingham. Turn R into Dodds Hill Rd just past the Feathers Hotel. Garden approx 1½ acres comprising low maintenance dry garden, lawns,*

island beds and borders containig mixed plantings of perennials, grasses, shrubs and trees. Steep S-facing slope to dell garden of gunnera manicata, tree ferns and many shade tolerant plants, bounded by spring fed brook all encased in Sandringham's royal woodland. TEAS in aid of Tapping House Hospice. *Adm £2.50, chd £1. Suns 29 May; 17 July (12-5). Private visits welcome by appt. Tel 01485 541218*

57 Wretham Lodge, East Wretham &⌀⌂
(Mr Gordon Alexander) *6m NE of Thetford. A11 E from Thetford, L up A1075, L by village sign, R at Xrds*

then bear L. In spring masses of species tulips, hellebores, fritillaries, daffodils and narcissi; bluebell walk. In June hundreds of old roses. Walled garden, with fruit and interesting vegetable plots. Mixed borders and fine old trees. Double herbaceous borders. Wild flower meadows. TEAS. *Adm £2.50, chd free. Sun 17 Apr (11-5)*

Evening Opening (See also garden description)

Priory Maze Gardens 25 June

gardens open
for charity

Every time you visit a garden which opens for the NGS you are helping to raise money for

- **Macmillan Cancer Relief**
- **Marie Curie Cancer Care**
- **Help the Hospices**
- **Crossroads – Caring for Carers**
- **The Queen's Nursing Institute**
- **The Nurses Welfare Service**
- **The Royal Gardeners' Orphan Fund**
- **NGS Gardeners' Bursaries – The National Trust Careership Scheme**
- **Perennial – Gardeners' Royal Benevolent Society**
- **County Nursing Associations**
- **Additional charities nominated by owners**

Marie Curie Cancer Care

Research has shown that 75% of people seriously ill with cancer would like to be cared for at home. Every year, Marie Curie Nurses make that wish possible for thousands of cancer patients in cities, towns and villages across the UK. Marie Curie Nurses provide expert hands-on care, as well as comfort and emotional support to the family.

"The Marie Curie Nurses made a huge difference to both mum's quality of life and ours. Without them we wouldn't have been able to care for mum at home." AS East Yorkshire

Thanks to supporters such as The National Gardens Scheme, our care is always free of charge.

Find out more at **www.mariecurie.org.uk**

Charity Reg. No. 207994

New gardens for 2005

Every year hundreds of gardens open for the NGS for the very first time....

2005 is no exception with over 450 garden owners deciding to open their garden gates to the public to raise money for the NGS beneficiary charities. Enjoy here a sneak preview of what's new over the garden hedge for 2005.

1. Whibble Hill House, Devon
   (Philip Smith)
2. Woolstone Mill House, Oxon
   (Rosalind Simon)

3. Felindre Mill, Powys
   (Elizabeth Spear)

4. 5 Clyne Valley Cottages,
   Glamorgan
   (Carrie Thomas)

5. Touchwood, 4 Clyne Valley
   Cottages, Glamorgan
   (NCCPG aquilegia vulgaris)
   (Carrie Thomas)

6. Farleigh House, Hants
   (John Glover)

10. The Cors, Carmarthenshire
    (Charles Hawes)

11. Hannams Hall, Essex
    (Marcus Harper)

12. Mapsland, Carmarthenshire
    (Charles Hawes)

13. Ty Capel Ffrwd, Gwynedd
    Ty Ficerdy a Capel Gardens, Gwynedd
    (Mary Bolt)

14. Ger-y-Llan, Gwynedd
    Ty Ficerdy a Capel Gardens, Gwynedd
    (Carys Lewis)

15. 16 Lilac Crescent, Northumberland
    Lilac Crescent Gardens
    (Susie White)

16. Rhos y Gilwern Mansion, Pembrokeshire
    (Charles Hawes)

Monty Don

Garden Writer and
Television Presenter

Photograph: Ari Ashley

Sharing with others

There is a special pleasure in sharing the intimate, personal qualities of your own back garden with fellow gardeners. After all, gardening is both the most private and most generous of pastimes. The National Gardens Scheme taps into this in a unique way. Each one of the thousands of gardens that take part are someone's private, personal garden. Each one has a story to tell that can enlarge and enrich our own experience and improve our own gardens.

As well as this, The National Gardens Scheme raises important money for charity. So when you buy the Yellow Book and visit their gardens you will not only play an important contribution in supporting their beneficiary charities but also share privileged access to the best private gardens in England & Wales.

Photograph: (Ian Gowland)

Photograph: Ari Ashley

ngs gardens open for charity

Garden themes

Featured here are gardens with unusual and interesting themes, along with allotments and vegetable plots, many of which were new only last year to the Yellow Book.

1. Maze, Painswick, Rococo Garden, Glos. (Charles Hawes)
2. Sculpture, Hamblyn's Coombe, Devon (Jason Ingram)
3. Containers, Caereuni, Denbighshire & Colwyn (Eric Crichton)
4. Roof garden, RISC, Berks (Peter Savage)

5. The Yew Walk, Cefntilla, Gwent
   (Charles Hawes)

6. Question Mark Wall, Scypen,
   Devon (Charles Hawes)

7. Japanese Bridge, The Mill House,
   Ceredigion (Charles Hawes)

8. Topiary, Mapperton Gardens,
   Dorset (Jason Ingram)

9. Japanese Gardens, Dorset
   (Jason Ingram)

10 Seaside, Hortus, Devon
   (Nicola Stocken Tomkins)

11. Firs, Whiteknights, Berkshire
   (Peter Savage)

12. Heather Garden, The Bannut, Herefordshire
   (Charles Hawes)

Allotments & vegetables

1. Clinton Lodge, Sussex
   (Nicola Stocken Tomkins)
2. Cotherstone Village Gardens, Durham
   (Shanah Smailes)
3. Moorlands Allotments, Warwickshire

4. Riddles Road produce,
   (Philip Boyce)

5. Riddles Road Allotments, Kent
   (Philip Boyce)

6. Walled kitchen garden,
   Melplash Court, Dorset
   (Charles Hawes)

7. Veddw House, Gwent
   (Charles Hawes)

8. Hannams Hall, Essex
   (Marcus Harper)

Northamptonshire

County Organiser:	Mrs Annabel Smyth-Osbourne, Versions Farm, Brackley, Northamptonshire NN13 5JY Tel 01280 702412
Assistant County Organisers:	Mr David Abbott, Wroxton Lodge, Church Hill, Finedon, Northamptonshire NN9 5NR Tel 01933 680363
	Mrs Ruth Dashwood, Farthinghoe Lodge, Brackley, Northants NN13 5NX Tel 01295 710377
	Mr Derek Welman, 4 Elmington Cottages, Elmington, Oundle, Northamptonshire PE8 5JZ Tel 01832 226373
County Treasurer:	Mr Michael Heaton, Mulberry Cottage, 6 Yew Tree Lane, Spratton, Northamptonshire NN6 8HL Tel 01604 846032

Maps: Numbers shown next to each garden entry refer to that garden's entry on the county map. This position is approximate; distance and directions from the nearest main town are generally shown in the garden text. A precise location is available for those gardens featured on the NGS website by visiting www.ngs.org.uk.

Symbols: Information relating to symbols is given on page 21

DATES OF OPENING

Evening openings
See end of county listing

Private gardens open regularly for NGS
54a Banbury Road, Brackley *(2)*

Gardens open to the public
For details see garden description
Canons Ashby House, Daventry *(5)*
Castle Ashby House, nr Northampton *(6)*
Coton Lodge, Guilsborough *(9)*
Coton Manor Garden, Guilsborough *(10)*
Cottesbrooke Hall Gardens, nr Creaton *(11)*
Deene Park, nr Corby *(13)*
Holdenby House Gardens, Northampton *(28)*
Kelmarsh Hall, Northampton *(29)*
The Menagerie, Horton *(35)*
The Old Rectory, Sudborough *(39)*
Woodchippings, Juniper Hill *(53)*

By appointment only
For telephone number and other details see garden description. Private visits welcomed
Hill Grounds, Evenley *(27)*

February 13 Sunday
Beech House, Burton Latimer *(3)*
February 27 Sunday
Dolphins, Great Harrowden *(14)*
March 13 Sunday
The Old Rectory, Sudborough *(39)*
March 27 Sunday (Easter)
Evenley Wood Garden, Brackley *(15)*
March 28 Monday (Easter)
Evenley Wood Garden, Brackley *(15)*
Great Addington Manor *(20)*
April 10 Sunday
Charlton Gardens, nr Banbury *(8)*
Flore Spring Gardens *(18)*
April 17 Sunday
Maidwell Hall, Maidwell *(34)*

April 24 Sunday
Kelmarsh Hall, Northampton *(29)*
May 1 Sunday
Evenley Wood Garden, Brackley *(15)*
Great Brington Gardens *(21)*
May 2 Monday (Bank Hol)
Evenley Wood Garden, Brackley *(15)*
May 15 Sunday
Guilsborough and Hollowell Gardens *(23)*
Middleton Gardens, Market Harborough *(36)*
May 18 Wednesday
54a Banbury Road, Brackley *(2)*
May 22 Sunday
Badby and Newnham Gardens *(1)*
Deene Park, nr Corby *(13)*
The Old Glebe, Brackley *(38)*
Turweston Mill, Turweston *(48)*
Versions Farm, Turweston *(49)*
May 25 Wednesday
54a Banbury Road, Brackley *(2)*
May 29 Sunday
Evenley Wood Garden, Brackley *(15)*
Lois Weedon House, Weedon Lois *(32)*
Old Barn, Weedon Lois *(37)*
7a Weskers Close, Clipston *(51)*
May 30 Monday (Bank Hol)
Evenley Wood Garden, Brackley *(15)*
7a Weskers Close, Clipston *(51)*
June 1 Wednesday
54a Banbury Road, Brackley *(2)*
Woodchippings, Juniper Hill *(53)*
June 5 Sunday
Canons Ashby House, Daventry *(5)*
Dolphins, Great Harrowden *(14)*
Great Harrowden Lodge, Great Harrowden *(22)*
The Old Rectory, Sudborough *(39)*
Park House, Norton *(40)*
Preston Capes Gardens *(42)*
June 8 Wednesday
Woodchippings, Juniper Hill *(53)*
June 11 Saturday
Titchmarsh House, Titchmarsh *(46)*

June 12 Sunday
Kilsby Gardens, nr Rugby *(30)*
The Menagerie, Horton *(35)*
Spratton Gardens *(43)*
Sulgrave Gardens, nr Banbury *(44)*
Top Lodge, Glendon *(47)*
June 15 Wednesday
54a Banbury Road, Brackley *(2)*
Woodchippings, Juniper Hill *(53)*
June 18 Saturday
Cottesbrooke Hall Gardens, nr Creaton *(11)*
Flore Gardens, nr Northampton *(17)*
June 19 Sunday
Cedar Farm, Desborough *(7)*
Courteenhall, Northampton *(12)*
Finedon Gardens *(16)*
Flore Gardens, nr Northampton *(17)*
Long Buckby Gardens *(33)*

"Is that a helter-skelter tree, Mum?"

NORTHAMPTONSHIRE

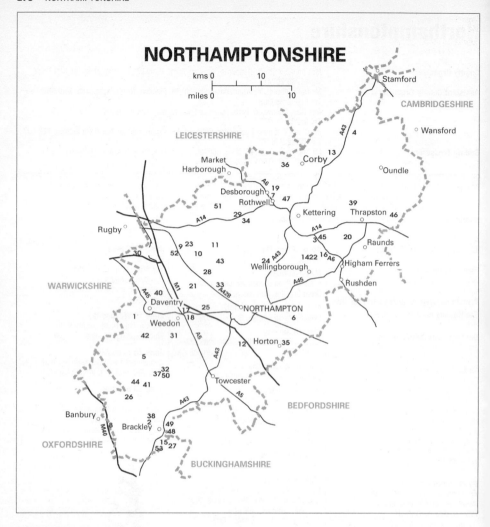

June 22 Wednesday
54a Banbury Road, Brackley *(2)*
Woodchippings, Juniper Hill *(53)*

June 23 Thursday
Finedon Gardens **(Evening)** *(16)*

June 26 Sunday
Harpole Gardens, Northampton *(25)*
Kelmarsh Hall, Northampton *(29)*
Litchborough Gardens, nr Towcester *(31)*

June 29 Wednesday
54a Banbury Road, Brackley *(2)*
Woodchippings, Juniper Hill *(53)*

June 30 Thursday
Finedon Gardens **(Evening)** *(16)*

July 3 Sunday
Hannington Gardens, nr Kettering *(24)*
The Hill, Thorpe Mandeville *(26)*

Weedon Lois Gardens *(50)*
West Haddon Gardens *(52)*

July 6 Wednesday
54a Banbury Road, Brackley *(2)*
Woodchippings, Juniper Hill *(53)*

July 9 Saturday
Terracend, Burton Latimer *(45)*

July 10 Sunday
Bulwick Gardens, nr Corby *(4)*
Castle Ashby House, nr Northampton *(6)*

July 13 Wednesday
54a Banbury Road, Brackley *(2)*
Woodchippings, Juniper Hill *(53)*

July 16 Saturday
Terracend, Burton Latimer *(45)*

July 17 Sunday
Peters Farm, Helmdon *(41)*

July 20 Wednesday
54a Banbury Road, Brackley *(2)*
Woodchippings, Juniper Hill *(53)*

July 23 Saturday
Terracend, Burton Latimer *(45)*

July 27 Wednesday
54a Banbury Road, Brackley *(2)*
Woodchippings, Juniper Hill *(53)*

July 31 Sunday
Coton Lodge, Guilsborough *(9)*
Froggery Cottage, Desborough *(19)*

August 3 Wednesday
54a Banbury Road, Brackley *(2)*

August 7 Sunday
Cottesbrooke Hall Gardens, nr Creaton *(11)*

August 10 Wednesday
54a Banbury Road, Brackley *(2)*

August 17 Wednesday
54a Banbury Road, Brackley *(2)*
August 24 Wednesday
54a Banbury Road, Brackley *(2)*
August 31 Wednesday
54a Banbury Road, Brackley *(2)*
September 3 Saturday
Canons Ashby House, Daventry *(5)*
September 4 Sunday
Deene Park, nr Corby *(13)*
September 11 Sunday
Coton Manor Garden, Guilsborough *(10)*
Holdenby House Gardens, Northampton *(28)*
2006
February 26 Sunday
Dolphins, Great Harrowden *(14)*

DESCRIPTIONS OF GARDENS

❶ Badby and Newnham Gardens
3m S of Daventry on E side of A361.
Home-made TEAS at St Marys
Church, Badby in aid of their Death
Watch Beetle Fund. *Combined adm
£3. Sun 22 May (2-6)*

Church Hill, Badby (Dr & Mrs C
M Cripps) Medium-sized country
garden with internal yew and
beech hedges enclosing mixed
borders. Some interesting plants,
clipped yews, shady border,
pond, vegetable garden and
conservatory.

The Cross, Manor Lane, Newnham
❀ (M Dawkins) A cottage
garden incl wall plants,
perennials, a few unusual plants
and pond.

Hilltop, Church Street, Newnham
❀ (David & Mercy Messenger)
Spread over 3 acres. Cottage-style
with mature trees and shrubs to
focus and separate areas. Lovely
views, dense planting, spring
bulbs. Largely organic due to our
own compost. Garden room,
nursery and vegetable beds.

The Old House, Badby (Dr & Mrs
M MacGregor) A medium-sized
enclosed garden with fine views
over Badby woods. Secluded
courtyard; mostly stone-raised
beds, densely planted with many
traditional herbaceous plants and
roses.

❷ 54a Banbury Road, Brackley
❀❀
(Mrs Jean Goodall) *S from Town
Hall turn R into Old Banbury Rd.* 1-
acre SW-facing garden. Part-terraced
with views over lake and fields
beyond. Themed gardens incl bog,
rose, prairie, gravel, oriental , peony
and day lily. Home-made TEAS. *Adm
£2. Weds 18, 25 May, 1 June, 15*

*June through to 31 Aug (2-5). Private
visits welcome by appt incl coaches.
Tel 01280 705745*

**❸ NEW Beech House, 73 Church
Street, Burton Latimer** ❀❀
(Mr & Mrs Nicholas Loake) *4m S of
Kettering. From High St turn into
Church St by War Memorial, Beech
House is on the L 100yds past the
church.* Semi-formal garden with
winter/spring interest. Clipped box
and yew hedging frame borders
containing over 150 cultivars of
snowdrops plus hellebores etc.
Home-made TEAS in aid of Burton
Latimer Parish Church. *Adm £2.50,
chd free. Sun 13 Feb (11.30-4).
Private visits welcome by appt.
Tel 01536 723593 gloake@hotmail.
com*

❹ Bulwick Gardens, nr Corby
10m SW of Stamford. ½m off A43.
Unspoilt Northamptonshire stone
conservation village. Interesting C14
church and public house with
restaurant. Home-made TEAS at
Bulwick Hall. *Combined adm £2, chd
free (share to Multiple Sclerosis
Research). Sun 10 July (2-5)*

Bulwick Hall ❀ (Mr & Mrs G T
G Conant) Formal terraced 8-
acre walled garden leading to
river and island. Double
herbaceous borders; holly walk
ending at attractive C17 wrought
iron gates (house not open). C19
orangery and C17 arcade; large
kitchen garden; fine mature trees;
peacocks. Motorised transport
around the garden available for
disabled or elderly persons.

19 Church Lane (David Haines)
Small cottage garden with fruit
trees and vegetables, courtyard
and water features.

**Hollyberry Barn, Blatherwycke
Road** ❀ (Colin McAlpine)
Cottage garden with curved
herbaceous borders; arches;
raised vegetable bed;
greenhouses; cold frames;
gravelled area with alpine plants
and pots.

The Shambles, 12 Main Street
(Roger Glithero) Herbaceous
plants, many containers,
vegetable garden with fruit and
original village well; lawns,
hedges and stone walls.

**❺ ◆ Canons Ashby House,
Daventry** ❀❀❀
(The National Trust) *12m NE of
Banbury, 9m S of Daventry. On
unclassified rd between B4525 and
A5. Follow NT tourist signs locally.*

Formal gardens of London and Wise
style enclosed by walls. Gate piers
from 1710; fine topiary; axial
arrangement of paths and terraces;
wild flowers, old varieties of fruit
trees, herb border, newly planted
gardens. Home of the Dryden family
since C16, Manor House 1550. Light
refreshments and TEAS. *House and
Garden Adm £5.80, Garden only
Adm £2. Sats to Weds, (11-5.30), 22
Mar-2 Nov.* **For NGS:** *Sun 5 June; Sat
3 Sept (11-5.30). Tel 01327 861344*

**❻ ◆ Castle Ashby House, nr
Northampton** ❀❀
(Earl Compton) *6m E of
Northampton. 1½m N of A428; turn
off between Denton & Yardley
Hastings.* View to parkland incl
avenue planted at suggestion of
William III in 1695; lakes etc by
Capability Brown; Italian gardens
with orangery; extensive lawns and
trees. Elizabethan house (not open).
Home-made TEAS from 2.30. *Adm
£2.80, chd £1.90, concessions £1.90.*
For NGS: *Sun 10 July (10-5.30).
Tel 01604 696187
petercox@castleashby.co.uk*

❼ Cedar Farm, Desborough
❀❀❀
(Mr & Mrs R Tuffen) *6m N of
Kettering, 5m S of Market
Harborough. Directions signed from
A6.* 2-acre garden with a further 8
acres. Secret garden with roses and
clematis. Orchard with many
interesting trees and shrubs. Borders
colour planted, wildlife ponds and
walks. Home-made TEAS in aid of St
Giles Church. *Adm £2.50, chd free.
Sun 19 June (2-6). Private visits
welcome by appt. Tel 01536 763992
thetuffenfamily@aol.com*

❽ Charlton Gardens, nr Banbury
*7m SE of Banbury. 5m W of
Brackley. From B4100 turn off N at
Aynho; or from A422 turn off S at
Farthinghoe.* Home-made TEAS at
The Cottage. *Combined adm £3, chd
free. Sun 10 Apr (2-6)*

The Cottage ❀ (Lady Juliet
Townsend) Flowering shrubs,
spring bulbs, roses, lawns,
woodland walk, stream and
lakes. House in village street.

Holly House ❀ (The Hon
Nicholas Berry) Walled garden
with beautiful views. C18 house,
not open.

❾ ◆ Coton Lodge, Guilsborough
❀❀❀
(Peter Hicks & Joanne de Nobriga)
10m NW of Northampton, 10m E of

Rugby. 2m W of Guilsborough on West Haddon Rd on L signed Coton Lodge. Follow drive for ¾ mile to end, crossing two cattle grids. Mature 2-acre garden with panoramic views over beautiful unspoilt countryside. Intimate enclosed areas are complemented by an informal woodland stream and pond giving interest throughout the seasons. Massed tulips and wisteria in spring, rose covered arches and scents in summer and hot exotic planting for autumn. Home-made TEAS. *Adm £3. Every Thurs in May & June, last full weekend in each month Apr-Aug incl Bank Hols.* **For NGS:** *Sun 31 July (12-5). Tel 01604 740215*

⑩ ◆ Coton Manor Garden, Guilsborough ♿⚘🕭
(Mr & Mrs Ian Pasley-Tyler) 10m N of Northampton. 11m SE of Rugby. Nr Ravensthorpe Reservoir. From A428 & A5199 (formerly A50) follow Tourist signs. 10-acre garden set in peaceful countryside with old yew and holly hedges, extensive herbaceous borders containing many unusual plants, rose, water, herb and woodland gardens, famous bluebell wood, wildflower meadow. Adjacent specialist nursery with over 1000 plant varieties propagated from the garden. BBC 2 - Flying Gardener May 2003. Light refreshments and TEAS. *Adm £4.50, chd £2, concessions £4. Tues to Sats, Easter to end Sept, Suns in April & May.* **For NGS:** *Sun 11 Sept (12-5.30). Tel 01604 740219 www.cotonmanor.co.uk*

⑪ ◆ Cottesbrooke Hall Gardens, nr Creaton ♿⚘🕭
(Mr & Mrs A R Macdonald-Buchanan) 10m N of Northampton. Signposted from J1 on A14. Notable gardens of great variety incl fine old cedars and specimen trees, herbaceous borders, water and wild gardens. Unusual plants - home grown. Home-made TEAS. *Adm £4, chd £2 (5-14 yrs). Weds & Thurs, May, June; Thurs, July to Sept; Bank Hol Mons May-Sept (2-5.30).* **For NGS:** *Sat 18 June; Sun 7 Aug (2-5). Tel 01604 505808 www.cottesbrookehall.co.uk*

⑫ Courteenhall, Northampton ♿⚘
(Charles & Joan Wake) At J15 of M1 take A508 S signed Milton Keynes. Exactly 1m turn L immediately before pillar box. Follow signs down drive. Fine arboretum, formal gardens with extensive lawns and good herbaceous beds. Interesting

walled garden. Georgian House (not open) by Samuel Saxon with traditional Repton Park. Home-made TEAS. *Adm £3, chd free. Sun 19 June (2-5)*

Cublington Gardens
See Buckinghamshire.

⑬ ◆ Deene Park, nr Corby ♿⚘
(Mr E Brudenell & The Hon Mrs Brudenell) 5m N of Corby. On A43 Stamford-Kettering Rd. Large garden; long mixed borders, old-fashioned roses, rare mature trees, shrubs, natural garden, large lake and waterside walks. Parterre designed by David Hicks echoing the C16 decoration on the porch stonework. Interesting Church and Brudenell Chapel with fine tombs and brasses. TEAS NGS days only. *Adm £3.50, chd £1.50 (10-14). Suns, Jun-Aug 2-5.30.* **For NGS:** *Suns 22 May; 4 Sept (2-5.30). Tel 01780 450278 www.deenepark.com*

⑭ Dolphins, Great Harrowden ♿⚘🕭
(Mr & Mrs R C Handley) 2m N of Wellingborough. 5m S of Kettering on A509. 2-acre country garden surrounding old stone house (not open). Many old roses grown among interesting trees, shrubs and wide range of hardy perennials. Irises a special favourite. Early opening for snowdrops and hellebores. Cream TEAS and Light refreshments in aid of Great Harrowden Church (Feb) and ARC (June). *Adm £2, chd free. Suns 27 Feb (10-4); 5 June (2-6); 26 Feb 2006. Open with* **Great Harrowden Lodge** *5th June*

⑮ Evenley Wood Garden, Brackley ♿
(R T Whiteley) ¾m S of Brackley. A43, turn L to Evenley straight through village towards Mixbury, 1st turning L. Woodland garden spread over a 60-acre mature wood. Acid and alkaline soil. Magnolias, rhododendrons, azaleas, malus, quercus, acers, euonymus collection and many other species. Large collection of bulbous plants. Home-made TEAS in aid of Mixbury Church. *Adm £3, chd £1. Sun, Mon 27, 28 Mar; 1, 2, 29, 30 May (2-6). Private visits welcome by appt. Tel 01280 703329 timwhiteley@totalise.co.uk*

⑯ Finedon Gardens
2m NE of Wellingborough. On the A510, 6m SE Kettering on the A6.

Home-made TEAS at 67-69 High St in aid of Finedon Church Flower Festival Fund. *Combined adm £1.50, chd free. Sun 19 June (2-6).* **Evening Opening** *£2, wine, Thur 23, 30 June (5-9)*

NEW **Sandown, 20 Burton Road** ♿⚘🕭 *(Graham & Kath Smith)* Garden set in ½-acre surrounded by trees. Lawns with feature shrubs and perennials. Herbaceous borders, tubs and containers. *Not open 23,30 Jun*

1 Grove Way ♿⚘🕭 *(Mr & Mrs P J Sibley)* Small plantsman's garden with columnar fruit trees, rare perennials and a collection of bedding perlagoniums. *Not open 23,30 Jun. Private visits welcome by appt June, July. Tel 01933 680704*

67-69 High Street ♿⚘🕭 *(Mr & Mrs S Hendry)* Constantly evolving, ⅓-acre rear garden of C17 cottage (not open). Mixed borders, obelisks and containers, kitchen garden and herb bed. *Private visits welcome by appt, June & July. Tel 01933 680414*

7 Walkers Way ⚘🕭 *(Mr & Mrs D Humphrey)* Small recently-established garden with gravel areas, containers and pond. *Not open 23,30 Jun*

⑰ Flore Gardens, nr Northampton
7m W of Northampton. 5m E of Daventry. On A45. Established Village Flower Festival. Maps provided. Home-made TEAS at Flore House & Chapel, Lunches at Chapel. *Combined adm £3, chd free (share to All Saints and U.R. Churches). Sat, Sun 18 19 June (11-6)*

24 Bliss Lane ⚘ *(John & Sally Miller)* Small cottage garden filled with flowers, fruit, herbs and vegetables. Summer House and newly developed greenhouse area.

Bliss Lane Nursery *(Geoff & Chris Littlewood)* Informal garden and nursery opening out to a larger garden with views overlooking the Nene Valley. For summer 2005, 'Jacob's Ladder', 3rd prizewinner in BBC Gardener of the Year 2004 created by Johnnie Amos assisted by Chris Littlewood, will be replicated within the grounds of Bliss Lane Nursery.

The Croft, King's Lane *(John & Dorothy Boast)* Medium-sized cottage garden planted with a formal layout, interesting perennials, both mature and recently planted, deciduous trees and shrubs.

NEW **The Garden House** 🚹🖉 (Edward & Penny Aubrey-Fletcher) Former walled kitchen garden replanted when the new house was built in the 90's. Approx ½-acre of formal design with informal planting.

The Manor House 🖉 (Richard & Wendy Amos) 1-acre garden with mature trees, newly planted avenue of 120 hornbeam, yew house. Pond with newts, walled kitchen garden.

The Old Bakery, Sutton Street 🖉 (Johnnie Amos & Karl Jones) Four-yr-old garden arranged over different levels. Divided into smaller 'rooms' with terraces and a small lawn. Many unusual plants for full sun and shade. Formal and informal planting. A C19 pergola with 'Empresses of India' theme. Small vegetable garden. BBC Gardener of the Year 2004 - Johnnie Amos 3rd prizewinner; garden being re-created for summer 2005 at Bliss Lane Nursery.

NEW **Stone Cottage** 🖉 (John & Pat Davis) Medium-sized informal cottage garden with pond, patios, fruit and vegetables.

6 Thornton Close (Mr & Mrs D L Lobb) Medium-sized garden with a good variety of plants and bulbs, two small ponds.

⊕ Flore Spring Gardens
7m W of Northampton. 5m E of Daventry on A45. Map provided. TEAS at URC Chapel School Room in aid of Flore Flower Festival. *Combined adm £2.50, chd free. Sun 10 Apr (2-6)*

Bliss Lane Nursery (Chris & Geoff Littlewood) Spring colours consisting of acer phoenix, hellebores, anemones and bluebells, with drifts of daffodils and tulips in the borders. *Private visits welcome by appt May-Sept, groups. Tel 01327 340918*

NEW **Butlins Farm** (John & Delia Askew) Former farmyard which was developed as a garden in 2001. Mixed herbaceous planting along stream and pond. Shrub planted bank to the N, lawns and pergola.

NEW **Flore Fields** 🖉 (Catherine Morton) Large informal garden with wide herbaceous border and drifts of daffodils in the adjoining field.

NEW **3 Meadow Farm Close** (Eric & Jackie Ingram) Newly

developed woodland garden with spring planting around the house.

NEW **Stone Cottage** 🖉 (John & Pat Davis) Medium-sized informal cottage garden with pond, patios, fruit and vegetables.

6 Thornton Close (Derek & Penny Lobb) Medium-sized garden with good variety of plants and bulbs, two small ponds.

⊕ Froggery Cottage, 85 Breakleys Road, Desborough 🚹🖉 **NCCPG**
(Mr John Lee) *6m N of Kettering. 5m S of Market Harborough. Signed off A6 & A14.* ¾-acre plantsman's garden full of rare and unusual plants. National Collection of 425 varieties of penstemons incl dwarfs and species. Artefacts on display incl old ploughs and garden implements. As seen on BBC Gardener's World September 2004. Lunches and TEAS in aid of Marlow House Day Centre and Desborough Town Welfare Committee. *Adm £2, chd free. Sun 31 July (11.30-6)*

⊕ Great Addington Manor
(Mr & Mrs G E Groome) *4m W Thrapston. A510 exit off A14 signed Finedon & Wellingborough. Turn 2nd L to the Addingtons.* 4½-acre manor gardens with lawns, mature trees, mulberry, yew hedges, pond and spinney. Spring daffodils. Home-made TEAS. *Adm £2.50, chd 5+ 50p. Mon 28 Mar (2-5)*

⊕ Great Brington Gardens
7m NW of Northampton. Off A428 Rugby Rd. 1st L turn past main gates of Althorp. Tickets (maps and programmes provided) at church, reading room & free car park. Gardens signed in village. Lunches and TEAS at Reading Room and Church in aid of Parish Church. *Combined adm £2.50, chd free. Sun 1 May (11-5)*

Beard's Cottage 🖗 (Captain L G Bellamy) ½-acre of lawns, shrubs and herbaceous borders. Large orchard with maturing bluebells and primroses in three small copses. *Private visits welcome by appt. Tel 01604 770257 bill.bellamy@talk21.com*

8 Bedford Cottages (Mr & Mrs Bob Billingsby) Long N-facing garden with outstanding views. Designed, created and maintained by the owners. Many shrubs and herbaceous plants for all year interest.

10 Bedford Cottages (Sue Paice & Phil Richardson) Wildlife garden designed to encourage wild flowers, butterflies, birds, bats, other mammals and insects. Ponds, feeding stations, hedgerows, nestboxes and small meadow form part of this totally organic garden.

Brington Lodge 🚹🖗 (Mr & Mrs P J Cooch) Old garden on edge of village, approx ¾ acre, partially walled with a number of spring flowering trees and shrubs.

30 Great Brington 🚹 (Mr & Mrs John Kimbell) Interesting small garden attached to old stone cottage (not open), well-stocked with shrubs, climbers and perennials. Small pond with bog area; secret garden.

New Cross 🚹🖉 (Mr R J Kimbell) ½-acre old country garden surrounding a mellow Northamptonshire stone house (not open). Mature trees and shrubs with many spring bulbs.

The Old Rectory 🚹 (Mr & Mrs R Thomas) 3-acre garden with mature trees, yew hedging, formal rose garden, vegetable garden, flower borders and ⅓ acre orchard.

Ridgway House 🚹🖉 (Mr & Mrs R Steedman) 1½ acres with lawns, herbaceous borders and many spring-flowering shrubs and bulbs.

Rose Cottage 🚹 (Mr David Green & Mrs Elaine MacKenzie) Estate cottage garden, designed, built and planted by owner. Variety of fan fruit trees, rockery and brick terrace with pagoda with natural freshwater pond. Deep pond - supervised children welcome.

The Stables 🚹 (Mr & Mrs A George) Small cottage garden containing shrubs, herbaceous plants and climbers. Compact and unusual shape with water feature and summer house.

⊕ Great Harrowden Lodge, The Slips, Great Harrowden 🚹🖉
(Mrs J & Mr R M Green) *2m N of Wellingborough. 5m S of Kettering on A509. Situated ¾m from Great Harrowden Church on lane to Finedon.* 1¼-acre garden on a dry exposed site. Wide variety of herbaceous plants in long borders and island beds. Herb garden. *Adm £2, chd free. Combined with Dolphins Sun 5 June (2-6)*

❷❸ Guilsborough and Hollowell Gardens
10m NW of Northampton. 10m E of Rugby. Between A5199 - A428. Parking for Guilsborough Gardens in field at Guilsborough House. Maps provided. Light refreshments and TEAS, soup & sandwiches at 4 Acres, coffee at church, in aid of Church, teas at Dripwell & Hollowell Village Hall in aid of Hall. *Combined adm £3.50, chd free. Sun 15 May (11-5)*

Dripwell House, Guilsborough 🖫🌼🏠 (Mr J W Langfield & Dr C Moss) *Behind Ward Arms car park (in High St.).* 3-acre mature garden. Many fine trees and shrubs on partly terraced slope. Rock garden; herbaceous borders; herb, wild flower and vegetable gardens; soft fruit and apple orchard. Unusual shrubs, rhododendrons and azaleas in woodland garden. *Private visits welcome by appt. Tel 01604 740755/740140 cattimoss@aol. com*

Four Acres, The Green, Guilsborough 🖫 (Mark & Gay Webster) *From village green, past primary school and village hall under archway and follow gravel drive.* Incorporating 2 smaller gardens: **Little Four Acres** (Mark & Judithe Revitt-Smith) and **Walter's Yard** (Frances & Richard Scammell). 3 inter-connected gardens approx 3 acres in exposed position with beautiful views. Mature mixed shrub and herbaceous borders; pergolas with climbing and rambler roses; patio gardens with many planted containers; potager and wildlife pond in meadow - developed autumn 2001. Incls garden to newly-built house (not open), started from scratch summer 2001.

Gower House, Guilsborough 🖫🌼🏠 (Peter & Ann Moss) *Behind Ward Arms car park (in High St).* Small garden evolving since 1991 on part of Dripwell vegetable garden. Plantsman's garden with herbaceous alpine, climbing plants and shrubs. *Private visits welcome by appt. Tel 01604 740755*

Guilsborough House, Guilsborough 🖫 (Mr & Mrs John McCall) *Southern extreme of Guilsborough on Hollowell Rd.* Country garden; terraces; lawns and hedges; mature trees. Plenty of room and shade for picnic in field.

Nortoft Grange, Guilsborough 🖫🏠 (Sir John & Lady Lowther)

On Naseby/Welford rd out of village. Our herbaceous borders are full of interest and colour. Walk through our wild flower meadow down to the pond and feed the fish. Bring a picnic and enjoy our lovely garden.

The Old House, Guilsborough 🖫 (Richard & Libby Seaton Evans) *Entrance by bus shelter in village centre.* Approx 1 acre of lawns, herbaceous borders, roses, shrubs and walled kitchen garden. Additional woodland with wild flowers; paddocks and a wonderful view now enhanced by llamas.

Rosemount, Church Hill, Hollowell 🖫🌼🏠 (Mr & Mrs J Leatherland) *In village, behind bus shelter towards Church, entrance 100yds on R.* ½-acre plantsman's garden. Unusual plants and shrubs; alpine garden; fish pond; small collections of clematis; camellias and abutilons. *Private visits welcome by appt groups of 10+. Tel 01604 740354*

❷❹ Hannington Gardens, nr Kettering
5m S of Kettering. On A43 Hannington is signposted at Xrds adjacent to garage and Henrys restaurant. A small village combining traditional stone dwellings with the modern. Particularly interesting and historical church. TEAS at Village Hall in aid of Hannington Parish Church. *Combined adm £2.50, chd free. Sun 3 July (11-5)*

Brookmead, 6 Orchard Close 🖫🌼🏠 (Mr & Mrs A Shardlow) *Orchard Close is 1st R turn on entering village.* Recently established medium-sized garden featuring lawns, shrubs and herbaceous borders. Climbers, seating areas and small water feature. Open countryside views.

The Hamptons, Main Street 🌼 (Mr & Mrs T Civil) Small to medium mature walled garden featuring a pergola and trelliswork.

NEW **Karmira, Bridle Road** (Mr & Mrs P Gyselynck) *On entering village from A43 Bridle Rd is 1st L.* Medium-sized garden of lawns, shrubs and herbaceous borders. Mature trees, patio and seating areas. Pot plants, pergola walk, dovecote and fish pond.

The Old House 🖫🌼 (Mr & Mrs J Rogers) *Centre of village, opp church.* Established, medium-sized, enclosed garden, consisting

of lawns, shrub and herbaceous borders, mature and specimen trees, fruit trees and rose garden. Many other interesting features incl obsolete stone well and patio sitting area.

❷❺ Harpole Gardens, Northampton
4m W Northampton. On A45 towards Weedon. Turn R at The Turnpike Hotel into Harpole. Village maps given to all visitors. Home-made TEAS at The Close from 2pm. *Combined adm £2.50, chd free. Sun 26 June (12-6)*

The Close 🖫🌼 (Michael Orton-Jones) Old-fashioned English country garden with large lawns, herbaceous borders and mature trees. Stone house, not open.

The Cottage (Mr & Mrs J Roan) Informal cottage garden transformed from a rubbish tip.

Darnley, 47b High Street 🌼 (Mr & Mrs Peter Rixon) Enclosed ⅛-acre garden consisting of cottage borders, rockery, pond, rose and herb areas; Japanese-style feature and large collection of cacti and succulents.

74 Larkhall Lane 🏠 (Mr & Mrs J Leahy) Medium-sized informal garden with a wide variety of plants, shrubs, some mature trees, climbers, alpines and pond.

17 Manor Close (Mr & Mrs I Wilkinson) Small, well stocked plantaholics' garden with lawns, gravel areas, pond and mixed borders. Featured in 'The Garden' 2003.

19 Manor Close 🌼 (Mr & Mrs E Kemshed) 40yds × 10yds flower arranger's garden on an estate, cultivated by present owners since 1975. Award for NGS Openings - 20 years 2004.

Millers (Mr & Mrs M Still) Old stone farmhouse (not open) with approx 1 acre of lawns and mixed borders, mainly shrubs; some mature trees; good views overlooking the farm and strawberry field.

Thorpe House (Mr & Mrs R Fountain) Secluded largely walled garden, extending to approx ½ acre. Sunken area with pond and ceramic features. Lawns and herbaceous borders with some unusual plants and shrubs.

㉖ NEW **The Hill, Thorpe Mandeville** ⬤🅮
(Mrs Annis Garfield) *Banbury 6m. Brackley 8m. Between Thorpe Mandeville and Wardington, signed from B4525.* The Hill (house not open) was built in 1897 for Hope-Brooke, the White Rajah of Sarawak. The pre-1914 gardens have been restored into a pocket park incorporating an old quarry and water features. There are extensive woodland walks for the more energetic. Home-made TEAS in aid of the Village Church. *Adm £3, chd £2. Sun 3 July (2.30-6)*

㉗ **Hill Grounds, Evenley** 🅮
(Mr & Mrs C F Cropley) *1m S of Brackley. On A43. Turn L into Evenley.* Plantsman's garden of 2 acres, surrounded by C19 200yd yew hedge. Planted for yr-round interest. Bulbs, terrace, rose pergola, double herbaceous borders. Many rare and less hardy plants grown. Millennium 'arborette'. *Adm £3. Private visits welcome by appt. Tel 01280 703224 bob@cropley.freeserve.co.uk*

㉘ ◆ **Holdenby House Gardens, Northampton** ⬤🅮
(Mr & Mrs James Lowther) *6m NW of Northampton. Signposted from A5199 & A428.* Just 2m across the fields from Althorp, this impressive house (not open) and garden were built from the Elizabethan remains of the largest house in England. Miniature Elizabethan garden by Rosemary Verey. Fragrant border replanted by Rupert Golby. Silver border and kitchen garden. Falconry centre boasts over 50 birds embracing many species of falcons, hawks, buzzards, kites, owls and eagles. Flying displays. *Adm £4.50 gardens & falconry, chd £3, concessions £4. Suns, Easter to Sept 1-5.* **For NGS:** *Sun 11 Sept. Tel 01604 770074 www.holdenby.com*

㉙ ◆ **Kelmarsh Hall, Northampton** ⬤🅮
(The Kelmarsh Trust) *5m S of Market Harborough. On A508 to Northampton. ½m N of junction with A14. Entrance at Xrds in Kelmarsh Village.* 1730 Palladian house by James Gibbs. C18 landscape with lake and woods. C20 garden by Nancy Lancaster. Spring bulbs, rose gardens, scented garden, herbaceous borders planted by Norah Lindsay, woodland walks and cut flower borders. TEAS. *House & Garden adm £4.50, chd £2.50, concessions £4, Garden only £3.50, chd £2, concessions £3. House & garden*

Suns, Bank Hol Mons, 27 Mar- 4 Sept. Gardens only Tues to Thurs 29 Mar- 29 Sept (2.30-5). **For NGS:** *Suns 24 Apr; 26 June. Tel 01604 686543 www.kelmarsh.com*

㉚ **Kilsby Gardens, nr Rugby**
5m SE of Rugby. On A428 turn R on B4038 through village. 6m N of Daventry on A361. Embroidery Exhibition in Kilsby Room. TEAS at and in aid of Kilsby Village Hall. *Combined adm £3. Sun 12 June (2-6)*
NEW **The Elms** 🅮 (Mrs D Jackson) New owners opening the redesigned garden. Courtyard area, pond, lawns, flowering shrubs and vegetable garden with fruit trees.
NEW **19 Fishers Close** ⬤🅮 (Mr & Mrs A Haycock) Small plot with shrubs, containers, herbaceous and annual borders.
NEW **15 Main Road** ⬤🅮 (Mr & Mrs R Dobson) A developing garden with formal and informal areas and a vegetable garden.
NEW **2 Postle Close** 🅮 (Cordelia White) Small garden, pond, plants in various containers and shrubs.
Pytchley House, 14 Main Road ⬤🅮🅘 (Mr & Mrs T F Clay) Garden downsized to ½-acre re-developed in 2004. Two ponds, one a C19 domed reservoir discovered while creating a new herbaceous bed. Linked lawns with island beds. Small vegetable garden, fruit trees and soft fruit.
Rainbow's End, 7 Middle Street ⬤🅮 (Mr & Mrs J Madigan) Ever-changing garden with mirror features, large pond and pergolas.
NEW **Tudor Cottage** (Mr & Mrs A. J Shuter) Small decorative garden designed to be family friendly and for oudoor living.
NEW **White House** ⬤🅮 (John & Lesley Loader) ½-acre walled garden with heather bed. Perennial border, pond, stream and vegetable garden with raised beds.

㉛ **Litchborough Gardens, nr Towcester**
10m SW of Northampton. Please use car park nr village green. Village maps provided. TEAS at the Village Hall. *Combined adm £3, chd free (accompanied) (share to Litchborough Baptist Church). Sun 26 June (2-6)*

Bruyere Court ⬤🅮 (Mr R M Billington) 3 acres of landscaped garden. Lawns, 2 ornamental lakes with rock streams and fountain, oriental-style garden, shrubs, rhododendrons, azaleas and herbaceous borders, old-fashioned roses, ornamental trees and conifers.
The Hall ⬤🅮 (Mr & Mrs A R Heygate) Large garden with open views of parkland, laid to lawns and borders with clipped hedges. Extensive woodland garden has large numbers of specimen trees and shrubs. Walks wind through this area and around the lakes.
4 Kiln Lane ⬤🅮 (Mr & Mrs Morling) 300yr-old cottage (not open) with modern cottage garden. Developed over 6yrs following levelling, terracing and hard landscaping incl the construction of 2 ponds, retaining existing trees and shrubs.
The Old School, Northampton Road ⬤ (Simon & Christine Burd) Gravel garden developed from original school playgrounds surrounding old village school. Includes courtyard, prairie style beds, mediterranean areas, mature trees and wild flower bank.
Orchard House, Banbury Road 🅮🅘 (Mr & Mrs B Smith) Landscape architects' country garden surrounding listed building (not open) designed for low maintenance. Orchard, pools, conservatory and working pump. *Private visits welcome by appt. Tel 01327 830144*
Tivy Farm (Mr & Mrs Pulford) Lawn sloping down to large wildlife pond surrounded by beautiful trees. Patio with lovely pots and containers.
51 Towcester Road (Mr Norman Drinkwater) Small council house garden featuring lawns, shrubs, rockery and productive vegetable garden.

㉜ **Lois Weedon House, Weedon Lois** ⬤
(Sir John & Lady Greenaway) *7m W of Towcester. On the eastern edge of village. Last entrance on R going E towards Wappenham.* Large garden with terraces and fine views; lawns; pergola; water garden; mature yew hedges; pond. Home-made TEAS in aid of Lois Weedon & Weston Playgroup. *Adm Combined £2.50, chd free. Sun 29 May (2-6). Combined with* **The Old Barn**

③ Long Buckby Gardens
8m NW of Northampton. 4 gardens in Long Buckby village midway between the A428 and A5. WC and parking facilities at village square. Gardens close to square. Mill House at junction of A428 and Ravensthorpe Rd. TEAS at The Old Fountain in aid of Long Buckby & District Gardening Club. *Combined adm £3, chd free. Sun 19 June (1-6) www.longbuckby.net*

45 Brington Road &🗑️⊕ (Derick & Sandra Cooper) ½-acre organic village garden designed to create haven of peace and harmony, home to unusual wildlife. Features incl rose walk, 4 varied water features, Victorian-style greenhouse and summerhouse surrounded by box-edged raised vegetable plots. All constructed from reclaimed materials. Featured on SKY Garden of All Seasons, 2003. *Private visits welcome by appt. Tel 01327 843762*

7 High Stack &🗑️ (Tiny & Sheila) 60ft x 90ft cottage garden on 2 levels, established over 5 yrs. Mixed borders, vegetable and fruit; pond, patio and seating area. Gravelled front garden with perennial planting.

Mill House, East Haddon & (Ken and Gill Pawson) Site of East Haddon windmill. Over 1 acre on Northamptonshire sand, developed over 11 yrs. Large vegetable plot, orchard, pond, pergola and shady areas. Plant combinations and layout are echoes of Home Farm by Dan Pearson. *Private visits welcome by appt 12-18 Jun only. Tel 01604 770103*

The Old Fountain, 25 High Street &⊕ (Annie & David Croston) Long and narrow ½-acre partially walled garden. Interesting and unusual perennials with herbaceous borders in series of colour themes set amongst mature trees. Vegetable area and greenhouses. Formal pond, terrace and wide range of container grown specimens. Plant enthusiasts' garden. Accommodation. *Private visits welcome by appt. Tel 01327 842345 fountainplants&@tiscali.co.uk*

Torestin, 10 Lime Avenue ⊕ (June Ford) ½-acre mature garden divided into 3 separate areas incorporating water features, rockeries and pergolas. Interesting perennials, clematis and roses.

NEW Loughton Village Gardens
See Buckinghamshire.

③ Maidwell Hall, Maidwell &🗑️
(Maidwell Hall School) *A508 N from Northampton, 6m S of Market Harborough, entrance via main drive off A508 on S edge of village.* 45 acres of lawns, playing fields, woodland, daffodils, spring bulbs, mature rose garden, lake and arboretum. *Adm £3, chd £3. Sun 17 Apr (2-5)*

③ ♦ The Menagerie, Horton &🗑️⊕
(Mr A Myers) *6m S of Northampton. 1m S of Horton. On B526, turn E at lay-by, across field.* Newly developed gardens set around C18 folly, with 2 delightful thatched arbours. Recently completed large formal walled garden with fountain, used for vegetables, fruits and cutting flowers. Recently extended exotic bog garden and native wetland area. Also rose garden, shrubberies, herbaceous borders and wild flower areas. Home-made TEAS. *Adm £3.50, chd £1.50, concessions £2.50. Mons, Thurs, 1 May to 30 Sept (2-5); last Sun in month (2-6).* **For NGS:** *Sun 12 June (2-5). Tel 01604 870957*

Middleton Cheney Gardens, nr Banbury
See Oxfordshire.

③ Middleton Gardens, Market Harborough
On B607 Corby to Market Harborough rd. TEAS at Cannam House. *Combined adm £3, chd free. Sun 15 May (2-6)*

Cannam House (Mr & Mrs R Pollard) ¾-acre walled garden with formal herb garden and colour-themed borders.

Clairmont (Mr & Mrs N J Henson) ½-acre garden on a steep slope with magnificent views over Welland Valley. Island beds with many unusual shrubs and plants, partially re-landscaped to provide a large patio area.

Fosse Way House, School Lane, Cottingham 🗑️⊕ (Mr & Mr R H Newman) Hillside garden of hidden corners. Herbaceous borders intermix with fruit (some less usual) and vegetable areas. Vines and vistas.

③ Old Barn, Weedon Lois 🗑️⊕
(Mr & Mrs John Gregory) *7m N of Brackley. In the centre of the village of Weedon Lois adjacent to the*

parish church. Plantsman's garden designed by the owners. Extensive collection of hardy plants incl campanulas, euphorbias, geraniums and violas. Plants grown in the garden for sale. *Adm Combined £2.50, chd free. Sun 29 May (2-6). Combined with* **Lois Weedon House.** *Private visits welcome by appt June & July. Tel 01327 860577*

③ The Old Glebe, Brackley
(Richard Watson) *1½m N from Brackley town centre. On the Radstone rd.* 6-acre formal garden with large landscaped pond and cascade. A number of unusual stone follies are dispersed around a large landscape. Home-made TEAS at Versions Farm in aid of Whitfield Church. *Combined adm £3, chd free. Sun 22 May (2-5.30). Combined with* **Versions Farm & Turweston Mill**

③ ♦ The Old Rectory, Sudborough &🗑️
(Mr & Mrs A Huntington) *8m NE of Kettering. Exit 12 off A14. Village just off A6116 between Thrapston & Brigstock.* Classic 3-acre country garden with extensive borders of unusual plants, roses, shrubs, trees, pond and stream surrounding Georgian Rectory (not open). In spring the woodland walk, bulbs and hellebore collection plus tulips are a speciality. Potager designed in 1985 by Rosemary Verey, the owners are now assisted by Chelsea Gold Medalist Rupert Golby. TEAS. *Adm £3.50, chd free. Tues Apr to Sept; Sats Apr to June; Easter and Spring BH weekends (10-4) Share to All Saint's Church.* **For NGS:** *Suns 13 Mar; 5 June (2-6). Tel 01832 733247 info@oldrectorygardens.co.uk*

④ Park House, Norton &🗑️⊕
(Mr & Mrs J H Wareing Russell) *3½m N of Weedon. (A5) 2nd Norton/Daventry turn on L off A5. Entrance L before village.* Approx 5 acres. Lawns leading down to lakes. Large variety of trees and shrubs, herbaceous borders, heather beds, azaleas, roses and ¼m lakeside walk. Home-made TEAS. *Adm £3, chd free. Sun 5 June (2-5). Private visits welcome by appt. Tel 01327 702455*

④ Peters Farm, Helmdon &⊕
(Sue Wallace) *4m S of Brackley. 8m E of Banbury. Follow B4525 W from A43, turn R to Helmdon (N). Bear L at war memorial to Sulgrave (W). 1m out of village.* 5-acre plot in middle of countryside where wildlife meets formal garden. Complete mix from

trees and shrubs to perennials and annuals, from meadow grasses and pond to clipped hedges and geometrical beds. Farm Museum also open. Home-made TEAS in aid of Helmdon Church. *Adm £3. Sun 17 July (2-6)*

♦ **Pettifers, Lower Wardington** ⑤⑧
See Oxfordshire.

㊷ Preston Capes Gardens
6m SW of Daventry. 13m NE of Banbury. 3m N of Canon's Ashby. Between A361 & A5. Unspoilt rural village. Local sandstone houses & cottages and Norman Church. In the Northamptonshire Uplands. Village maps for all visitors. Light lunches and Home-made TEAS at Old West Farm, Little Preston in aid of St Peter & St Paul Church. *Combined adm £3, chd 50p. Sun 5 June (12-5)*

City Cottage ⑤⑧⊕ (Mr & Mrs Gavin Cowen) Mature garden in the middle of an attractive village. Walled herbaceous border, rose beds, flowering shrubs and wisteria.

Forge Cottage, Old Forge Lane (Beverley Bayne & Andrew Korbus) N-facing garden, themed borders with emphasis on fragrant plants. In 2005 a garage and garden room are being built and ⅓will be in the process of redevelopment.

NEW Langdale House (Michael & Penny Eves) 1-acre (approx) country garden with far reaching views. Borders and island beds with both sun and shade loving plants, many chosen primarily for foliage.

NEW North Farm ⑤⑧⊕ (Mr & Mrs Tim Coleridge) Rural farmhouse garden maintained by owners. Outstanding view towards Fawsley and High Wood. 2mins walk from Old West Farm.

Old West Farm, Little Preston ⑤⑧⊕ (Mr & Mrs Gerard Hoare) ¾m E of Preston Capes. Rural 2-acre garden. Borders of interesting and unusual plants, roses and shrubs. Woodland area underplanted with shrubs. Exposed site with shelter planting, maintained by the owners without help, so designed for easy care. Changes are being made for 2005.

West Orchard Farm House ⑤⑧⊕ (Mr & Mrs Nick Price) 1-acre informal garden with outstanding views. Renovated completely by

Caroline Price and replanted with shrubs and herbaceous plants.

㊸ Spratton Gardens
6½m NNW of Northampton. Off A5199. Turn E to Brixworth. Car park & gardens signed in village. TEAS at, and in aid of, St Andrew's Church. *Combined adm £3, chd free. Sun 12 June (1.30-5.30)*

NEW 5 Brixworth Road ⑤⊕ (Andy & Shelly Wykes) Garden developed from a field over 15 yrs. 300ft long, split into rooms, mixed planting and ponds.

9 Glebelands ⑤ (Mr & Mrs R Smith) Small garden recently extended to incl wildlife pond, herbaceous borders and fruit trees.

Homeleigh Cottage 4 Brixworth Road (Mr & Mrs T Evans) Small split-level old-fashioned cottage garden; herbaceous and mixed borders and archway with lower courtyard garden.

Mulberry Cottage, 6 Yew Tree Lane ⑤⊕ (Mr & Mrs M Heaton) ½-acre part cottage-style. Feature mulberry tree; lawns; herbaceous, rose and shrub borders; shady planting and water features.

The Stables ⑤ (Mr & Mrs A Woods) ¾-acre garden planted for all-yr colour with shrubs, herbaceous borders, rockery, scree planting, ponds and pergola.

㊹ Sulgrave Gardens, nr Banbury
8m NE of Banbury. Just off B4525 Banbury to Northampton rd, 7m from J11 off M40. Small historic village with lovely stone houses, C14 church and C16 manor house, home of George Washington's ancestors. Home-made TEAS at The Cottage. *Combined adm £3, chd free, concessions free. Sun 12 June (2-6)*

Church Cottage, Church Street (Hywel & Ingram Lloyd) ½-acre garden with shrubs, trees, rambling roses and pond. Mixed planting for colour, form and scent throughout the yr. Good range of shade tolerant plants; developing wild area. Fine view.

Ferns, Helmdon Road ⑤⑧⊕ (George & Julia Metcalfe) Approx ⅜-acre providing conditions for a wide range of plants, incl 'Mediterranean' gravel garden; mixed borders in sun and shade; fern collection; damp area and small alpine house.

Mill Hollow Barn (David Thompson) 3-acre garden with different levels and aspects, being developed for all-yr interest and to house a wide range of plants. Currently incls water gardens, shrubberies, herbaceous borders and gravel garden.

The Old Stocks ⑤ (Mr & Mrs Robin Prior) Imaginatively planted garden of ⅓-acre surrounding stone house (not open) with S-facing terrace. Wide range of interesting, unusual and colourful perennials in a peaceful setting encouraging a diversity of birds.

Sulgrave Manor Herb Garden ⑤⊕ (The Herb Society at Sulgrave Manor) New garden created during 2002/2003 within the gardens of Sulgrave Manor. Features the herbs taken across to America by the Pilgrim Fathers, and additional themed herb beds. *Private visits welcome by appt. Tel 01295 760205*

The Thatched House (Professor & Mrs C Ward) Informal 1-acre garden. Restoration work in progress; vine, roses, topiary, small orchard with old varieties of fruit, dovecote and good views. Quiz for children.

NEW Threeways ⑤ (Dr & Mrs D Lewis) Old cottage garden on two levels enclosed by stone walls & restored over the past seven years. Mainly herbaceous planting with various fruit trees and container grown vegetables.

㊺ Terracend, 58 Station Road, Burton Latimer ⊕
(Bill & Daphne Frum) *3m S of Kettering. Approached from A14, A509 & A6. Parking by kind permission of Sunseeker Windows 72-84 Station Rd.* Town garden 100ft long with areas of special interest, wealth of containers with hostas, lilies, fuchsias and clematis - over 75 varieties in different situations. Many ferns, vegetables and fruit in raised beds. Light refreshments and TEAS. *Adm £1.50, chd free. Sats, 9 July to 23 July (1-5). Private visits welcome by appt Jun & Jul only, max 18 per group. Tel 01536 722455*

㊻ Titchmarsh House, Chapel Street, Titchmarsh
(Sir Ewan & Lady Harper) *2m N of Thrapston. 6m S of Oundle. On A605, Titchmarsh signed as turning to E.* 4-acres extended and laid out since 1972; cherries, magnolias, herbaceous, irises; shrub roses,

clematis, range of unusual shrubs, walled borders and ornamental vegetable garden. Light refreshments at lunchtime and TEAS, both available at the village fete. *Adm £2, chd free. Sat 11 June (12-5). Private visits welcome by appt April, May and June only. Tel 01832 732439*

㊼ Top Lodge, Glendon &⊗⊕ (Glenn & Anne Burley) *3m NW of Kettering. Take A6003 to Corby, off roundabout W of Kettering turn L onto Glendon Rd, signed Rothwell, Desborough, Rushton. Approx 2m L into Violet Lane.* 1½-acre garden surrounding main house (not open), set in countryside. Many structural features, enhanced by large collection of climbers, herbaceous plants and shrubs separating defined areas, incl water garden with pond, stream, waterfalls and woodland area. Mediterranean and secluded garden. Cream TEAS in aid of Rushton Parish Church. *Adm £2.50, chd free. Sun 12 June (2-5.30). Private visits welcome by appt May, June, July. Tel 01536 511784*

㊽ Turweston Mill, Turweston & (Mr & Mrs Harry Leventis) *2m N of Brackley. A43 from M40 J10. On Brackley bypass turn R on A422 towards Buckingham, ½m turn L signed Turweston.* 5 acres. Mill stream, sunken formal water garden and wildlife ponds with waterfall. Lawns and herbaceous borders. Cream TEAS at Versions Farm in aid of Whitfield Church. *Adm Combined £3, chd free. Sun 22 May (2-5.30). Combined with* **Versions Farm and Old Glebe**

㊾ Versions Farm, Turweston &⊗⊕ (Mrs E T Smyth-Osbourne) *2m N of Brackley. R turn to Turweston.* 3-acre plantsman's garden; wide-range of unusual plants, shrubs and trees. Old stone walls; terraces; old-fashioned rose garden; pond. Conservatory. Cream TEAS in aid of Whitfield Church. *Adm Combined £3, chd free. Sun 22 May (2-5.30). Combined with* **Old Glebe & Turweston Mill**

Walton Gardens
See Leicestershire & Rutland.

㊿ Weedon Lois Gardens *7m N of Brackley. 8m W of Towcester. In centre of village, close to Parish Church.* Home-made TEAS at Old Barn. *Combined adm £3, chd free. Sun 3 July (2-6)*

Home Close ⊗ (Clyde Burbidge) 2-acre garden estabished over last 6 yrs. Informal cottage garden surrounding stone barn conversion, meadow, ponds and small spinney, vegetable garden, new herbaceous borders. 'Four Shires' Magazine 2004.

Old Barn (Mr & Mrs John Gregory) (see separate entry).

Stable Cottage &⊗ (Lynn Medlicott) Pretty courtyard garden with informal planting of trees, herbaceous plants and vegetables. Botanical illustrations and paintings for sale in the studio. 'Four Shires' Magazine 2004.

51 7a Weskers Close, Clipston &⊗ (Mr & Mrs K Rutland) *4m S of Market Harborough. 3m from A14, junction 2. Signed from A14, A508. Car parking in village hall car park.* ¾-acre informal garden in lovely village setting with rural views. Wide variety of perennial herbaceous plants and large number of mature trees and shrubs. ½-acre meadow being developed to encourage wild flowers, butterflies and insects. Natural ponds. Home-made TEAS. *Adm £2, chd free. Sun, Mon 29, 30 May (2-6). Private visits welcome by appt 19 Mar-10 Apr, May & Jun, groups accepted. Tel 01858 525305 carolyn7a@aol.com*

52 West Haddon Gardens *10m NW of Northampton. On the A428 between Rugby & Northampton; lies 4m E of M1 J18.* Cream TEAS at West Cottage, 10% to Human Communication International. *Combined adm £3, chd free. Sun 3 July (2-6)*

Clover Cottage ⊗ (Helen & Stephen Chown) Walled cottage garden with terraces, cobbles, gravel, pots and decking. Very sunny sheltered space with a lovely lemon tree.

Lime House ⊗ (Lesley & David Roberts) ½-acre walled garden

with rockeries, herbaceous borders, walk-through shrubbery, rose beds; croquet lawn. Summerhouse and patio with greenhouse.

Townley Barn &⊗ (Kate & Richard Tilt) 1-acre organic garden with wild flower meadow, kitchen garden, stream, waterfall, pond, shrubs, flowers and peaceful inner courtyard. Beautiful views over meadow.

NEW **Weslyan Cottage** (Arnie & Gillean Stensones) Small walled garden with walkways and paved sitting areas. Colourful borders, pond and summer house.

West Cottage & (Geoff & Rosemary Sage) 1-acre of mixed borders and lawns; informal ponds; lawn tennis court; kitchen garden and greenhouses. Many containers and baskets; herb garden.

Witchend & (John & Pat Baldwin) A recently extended and developed garden with numerous containers and perennials. A garden with more in it than first meets the eye.

53 ◆ Woodchippings, Juniper Hill ⊗⊕ (Richard Bashford & Valerie Bexley) *3m S of Brackley. Off A43. 3m N J10 M40, S of Croughton roundabout take L turn, ½m to Juniper Hill.* ⅓-acre plantsman's garden surrounding stone cottage. Densely and abundantly planted for colour and scent. Cool charm with hellebores and woodland garden in spring, vibrant perennials in the hot borders, summer and autumn. Small nursery. Not suitable for pushchairs. Featured in 'The Countryman' 2003, 'Daily Telegraph' 2004. TEAS in aid of Juniper Hill Playing Field Assoc. *Adm £2, chd free. Weds 2 Mar to 31 Aug (2.30-6).* **For NGS:** *Weds, 1 June to 27 July (2.30-6). Tel 01869 810170*

Evening Opening (See also garden description)	
Finedon Gardens	23 June
Finedon Gardens	30 June

Northumberland & Tyne and Wear

County Organiser:	Dr Julie Livsey, Brandlehow, Brigwood, Hexham, Northumberland NE47 6EX Tel 01434 688611 email julielivsey@hotmail.com
Assistant County Organiser:	Mrs Patricia Fleming, Wooperton Hall, Alnwick, Northumberland NE66 4XS Tel 01668 217009
Press Officer:	Mrs Susie White, Chesters Walled Garden, Chollerford, Hexham, Northumberland NE46 4BQ Tel 01434 681483
County Treasurer:	Mrs D Kinniment, Sike View, Kirkwhelpington, Northumberland NE19 2SA Tel 01830 540393

Maps: Numbers shown next to each garden entry refer to that garden's entry on the county map. This position is approximate; distance and directions from the nearest main town are generally shown in the garden text.
A precise location is available for those gardens featured on the NGS website by visiting www.ngs.org.uk.

Symbols: Information relating to symbols is given on page 21

DATES OF OPENING

Evening openings
See end of county listing

Private gardens open regularly for NGS
Dilston Physic Garden & Northumberland
  Medicinal Plants, nr Corbridge *(7)*

Gardens open to the public
For details see garden description

Bide-a-Wee Cottage, Stanton, Morpeth *(2)*
Bradley Nursery & Gardens, Wylam *(3)*
Chesters Walled Garden, Chollerford *(5)*
Cragside, Rothbury *(6)*
Herterton House, Hartington *(12)*
Wallington, Cambo *(19)*

By appointment only
*For telephone number and other
details see garden description.
Private visits welcomed*

Ingram Cottage, West Woodburn *(13)*

April 23 Saturday
Bide-a-Wee Cottage, Stanton, Morpeth *(2)*

May 4 Wednesday
Dilston Physic Garden & Northumberland
  Medicinal Plants, nr Corbridge *(7)*

May 8 Sunday
Chesters Walled Garden, Chollerford *(5)*
Wallington, Cambo *(19)*

May 11 Wednesday
Dilston Physic Garden & Northumberland
  Medicinal Plants, nr Corbridge *(7)*

May 18 Wednesday
Dilston Physic Garden & Northumberland
  Medicinal Plants, nr Corbridge *(7)*
Loughbrow House, Hexham *(17)*

May 22 Sunday
Lilburn Tower, Alnwick *(16)*

May 25 Wednesday
Dilston Physic Garden & Northumberland
  Medicinal Plants, nr Corbridge *(7)*

June 1 Wednesday
Dilston Physic Garden & Northumberland
  Medicinal Plants, nr Corbridge *(7)*

June 5 Sunday
Garden Cottage, Bolam *(8)*

June 8 Wednesday
Dilston Physic Garden & Northumberland
  Medicinal Plants, nr Corbridge *(7)*

June 12 Sunday
Greystones, Allendale *(10)*
Lilac Crescent Gardens, Burnopfield *(15)*

June 15 Wednesday
Dilston Physic Garden & Northumberland
  Medicinal Plants, nr Corbridge *(7)*

June 16 Thursday
Herterton House, Hartington *(12)*

June 19 Sunday
9 Grenville Court, Darras Hall *(9)*
Mindrum, nr Cornhill on Tweed & Yetholm
  (18)

June 22 Wednesday
Dilston Physic Garden & Northumberland
  Medicinal Plants, nr Corbridge *(7)*
Loughbrow House, Hexham *(17)*

June 26 Sunday
Berryburn, Ancroft *(1)*
16 Lilac Crescent, Burnopfield **(Evening)**
  (14)

June 29 Wednesday
Dilston Physic Garden & Northumberland
  Medicinal Plants, nr Corbridge *(7)*

July 6 Wednesday
Dilston Physic Garden & Northumberland
  Medicinal Plants, nr Corbridge *(7)*

July 10 Sunday
Cragside, Rothbury *(6)*
Hamilton Terrace, West Boldon *(11)*

July 13 Wednesday
Dilston Physic Garden & Northumberland
  Medicinal Plants, nr Corbridge *(7)*

July 14 Thursday
Herterton House, Hartington *(12)*

July 20 Wednesday
Dilston Physic Garden & Northumberland
  Medicinal Plants, nr Corbridge *(7)*
Loughbrow House, Hexham *(17)*

July 27 Wednesday
Dilston Physic Garden & Northumberland
  Medicinal Plants, nr Corbridge *(7)*

July 31 Sunday
16 Lilac Crescent, Burnopfield **(Evening)**
  (14)

August 3 Wednesday
Dilston Physic Garden & Northumberland
  Medicinal Plants, nr Corbridge *(7)*

August 4 Thursday
Herterton House, Hartington *(12)*

August 7 Sunday
Wallington, Cambo *(19)*

August 10 Wednesday
Dilston Physic Garden & Northumberland
  Medicinal Plants, nr Corbridge *(7)*

August 17 Wednesday
Dilston Physic Garden & Northumberland
  Medicinal Plants, nr Corbridge *(7)*

August 24 Wednesday
Dilston Physic Garden & Northumberland
  Medicinal Plants, nr Corbridge *(7)*

August 27 Saturday
Bide-a-Wee Cottage, Stanton, Morpeth *(2)*

August 28 Sunday
Castle Morpeth Gardens, Morpeth *(4)*

August 31 Wednesday
Dilston Physic Garden & Northumberland
  Medicinal Plants, nr Corbridge *(7)*

September 7 Wednesday
Dilston Physic Garden & Northumberland
  Medicinal Plants, nr Corbridge *(7)*

September 14 Wednesday
Dilston Physic Garden & Northumberland
  Medicinal Plants, nr Corbridge *(7)*

September 21 Wednesday
Dilston Physic Garden & Northumberland
  Medicinal Plants, nr Corbridge *(7)*

September 28 Wednesday
Dilston Physic Garden & Northumberland
  Medicinal Plants, nr Corbridge *(7)*
16 Lilac Crescent, Burnopfield **(Evening)**
  (14)

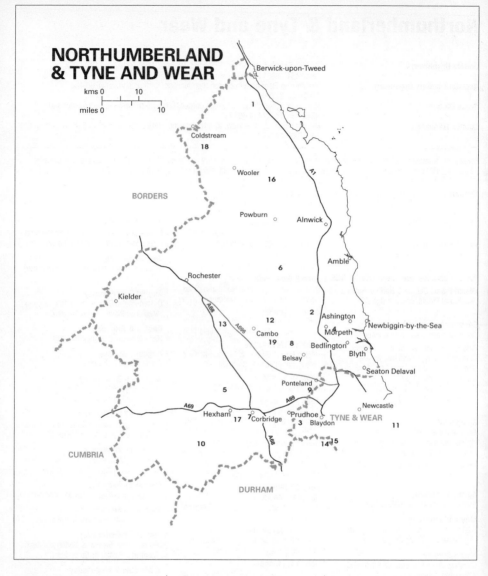

NORTHUMBERLAND & TYNE AND WEAR

kms 0 — 10
miles 0 — 10

Berwick-upon-Tweed
1
Coldstream
18
Wooler
16
BORDERS
Powburn
Alnwick
Amble
6
Rochester
Kielder
2
Ashington
Newbiggin-by-the-Sea
13
12
Cambo
Morpeth
19
8
Bedlington
Belsay
Blyth
5
Ponteland
Seaton Delaval
9
Newcastle
A69
Hexham
17
7
Corbridge
Prudhoe
3
Blaydon
TYNE & WEAR
11
10
14
5
CUMBRIA
DURHAM

DESCRIPTIONS OF GARDENS

❶ Berryburn, Ancroft ♿🏵
(Mr & Mrs W J Rogers-Coltman) *6m
S of Berwick-upon-Tweed. Turn off
A1 to Ancroft Mill. 2nd turning on R
after 1m.* Garden developed from
wilderness since 1981. The Berry
Burn winds through 6 acres of lawns,
mixed borders and woodland walks
with a varied collection of coniferous
trees. TEAS. *Adm £2.50, chd under
16 free (share to Ancroft Village
Hall). Sun 26 June (2-6). Private*

visits welcome by appt. Tel 01289
387332

**❷ ◆ Bide-a-Wee Cottage,
Stanton, Morpeth** 🚫🏵NCCPG
(Mr M Robson) *7m NNW of
Morpeth. Turn L off A192 out of
Morpeth at Fairmoor. Stanton is 6m
along this rd.* A unique secret garden
created over the last 26yrs out of a
small sandstone quarry, it features
rock and water. Unusual perennials
are woven within a matrix of ferns,
trees and shrubs. The garden contains

the National Collection of centaurea,
and many other plants seldom seen.
Featured in RHS 'The Garden' 2004.
*Adm £2.50, chd under 12 free. Open
Weds & Sats May to end Aug.* **For
NGS:** *Sats 23 Apr (1.30-4.30); 27 Aug
(1.30-5). Tel 01670 772262*
www.bideawee.co.uk

**❸ ◆ Bradley Nursery & Gardens,
Sled Lane, Wylam** ♿🏵
(Chris Potter) *3m W of Blaydon.
Follow signs from A695, or 1m S of
Wylam station.* 2-acre Victorian

walled garden with replanted herbaceous borders, shrubbery and herb beds. Magnificent restored conservatory now houses a café specialising in home baking. Permanent garden sculpture exhibition with some work for sale. Light refreshments and TEAS. *Donation to NGS. Daily Mar to Oct (9-5). Tel 01661 852176*

4 NEW **Castle Morpeth Gardens, Morpeth**
TEAS in Carlisle Park potting shed. *Combined adm to both gardens £2, chd free, concessions 50p. Sun 28 Aug (1-4). Tel 01670 500781 anthonyspiers@castlemorpeth.gov.uk*

NEW **William Turner Garden, Carlisle Park** (Castle Morpeth Borough Council) *Off Castle Square. Parking outside Waterford Arms Hotel or over Telford Bridge at mini-roundabout, 2nd exit to next roundabout. Library car park on R.* Garden celebrates the life and times of William Turner, C16 herbalist, doctor, physician, MP and traveller.

NEW **The Chelsea Garden, Low Stanners** (Castle Morpeth Borough Council, in conjunction with The Northumberland County Blind Association) *1m from Carlisle Park, in grounds of County Blind Assoc. Pass Library, turn R and park beyond the Centre.* Garden was a Show Garden at Chelsea in 2004, winning a Bronze Medal.

5 ♦ **Chesters Walled Garden, Chollerford** 🅱🌶🄿 NCCPG
(Mrs S White) *6m N of Hexham. Off the B6318. ½m W of Chollerford.* 2-acre walled garden containing very extensive collection of herbs. Thyme bank, home to the National Collection of thyme, also National Collection of marjoram. Roman garden; Elizabethan-style knot garden, gold and silver garden and collection of dye plants. Herbaceous borders contain many unusual plants and old-fashioned roses. Relaxed style of gardening. *Adm £2.50, chd 10-16 £2, under 10 free. Daily Easter to end Oct. For NGS: Sun 8 May (10-5). Tel 01434 681483 www.chesterswalledgarden.co.uk*

6 ♦ **Cragside, Rothbury** 🌶🄿
(The National Trust) *13m SW of Alnwick. (B6341); 15m NW of Morpeth (A697).* Formal garden in the 'High Victorian' style created by the 1st Lord Armstrong. Fully restored orchard house, carpet bedding, dahlia walk and fernery. 3½

acres of rock garden. Extensive grounds of over 1000 acres famous for rhododendrons and beautiful lakes. Light refreshments and TEAS. *House and garden adm £8.50, chd (5-17) £4. Garden only £5.70, chd £2.60. For NGS: Sun 10 July (10.30-7, last adm 5). Tel 01669 621267 www.nationaltrust.org.uk*

7 **Dilston Physic Garden & Northumberland Medicinal Plants, nr Corbridge** 🌶
(Professors Elaine & Robert Perry) *1m W of Corbridge. On A695 between Corbridge & Hexham, turn off along lane with Dilston Mill B&B sign. Special arrangements for parking.* Garden above the beautiful Devil's Water, with over 500 different medicinal plants and herbs clearly labelled with their traditional uses. Bamboo walk, Japanese torii gate, sage garden, poison garden and chamomile lawn. Featured in 'Living North' 2003. *Adm £2.50, chd free. Every Wed 4 May to 28 Sept, weather permitting (10-12). Private visits welcome by appt, for groups. Tel Johanna Sheehan 01434 606159 dilstonphysicgarden.com*

12 & 13 Durham Road, Middle Herrington, Sunderland 🅱🌶🄿
See Durham.

8 **Garden Cottage, Bolam** 🅱🌶🄿
(Mr & Mrs J A Russell) *8m N of Ponteland. Turn R off A696 at Belsay for Bolam Lake. Take next 2 R turns. Field parking near Bolam Church.* Colourful and creative garden (over 1 acre) in lovely setting with good structure and imaginative planting. Artistic use of colour, texture, sculpture and water features. Interesting gravel areas inspired by dry river beds. Meadow garden, with stunning views to Simonside. Always something new. TEAS in aid of Macmillan Cancer Relief Northumberland Appeal. *Adm £2.50, chd free. Sun 5 June (2-5). Private visits welcome by appt. Tel 01661 881660 russell@bolamhall.demon.co.uk*

9 **9 Grenville Court, Darras Hall** 🅱🌶🄿 NCCPG
(Mr & Mrs J C Scott) *2m SW of Ponteland. A696, turn L after crossing river travelling N (signed Darras Hall). At the end of Darras Rd turn R (Western Way) 2nd turning on L. ½ acre of mixed borders; a number of small gardens within the garden. Special interest in hardy geraniums (over 100) and hostas. National Collection of*

Brunnera macrophylla. Home-made TEAS. *Adm £2, chd free. Sun 19 June (2-5.30). Private visits welcome by appt. Tel 01661 825002 e@johncassscott.fslife.co.uk*

10 **Greystones, The Dene, Allendale** 🌶
(Paul Procter) *On N edge of Allendale, turn opp Deneholm Centre, 400yds on R. Disabled parking in drive, otherwise walk from Allendale village (10 mins).* Ann Procter's garden is a 1½-acre S-facing garden with panoramic views. Just 6yrs old, already looking mature. Formed by a series of terraces graded from formal nr house, through species-rich meadows down to pretty woodland stream. Well-planted borders, rock garden and natural ponds, with diverse wildlife. Bird hide in wood. Very limited disabled access. Home-made TEAS in aid of Compassion in World Farming. *Adm £2.50, chd free. Sun 12 June (2-5)*

11 **Hamilton Terrace, West Boldon** 🅱🌶🄿
(Sue Jackson) *8m SE of Newcastle. On A184. Turn at Bank Top Garage, West Boldon, into Hylton Lane, then 1st L into Dipe Lane (following signs for Boldon Golf Club). Lane 2nd L 50yds.* Award-winning hidden cottage garden transformed 10yrs ago from a derelict lane. Much enjoyed by residents for peaceful relaxation and social gatherings, it comprises a collection of shrubs, perennials and annuals in beds and containers. Constantly evolving, a tranquil space providing a true place to escape. Award winner Northumbria in Bloom, featured on Tyne Tees Tonight 2003 and in RHS 'The Garden' & regional press 2004. Home-made TEAS and plant sales in aid of St Benedict's Hospice, Sunderland. *Adm £2, chd free. Sun 10 July (12-5)*

12 ♦ **Herterton House, Hartington** 🌶♦
(Mr Frank Lawley) *12m W of Morpeth. 23m NW of Newcastle. 2m N of Cambo on the B6342 signed to Hartington.* 1 acre of formal garden in stone walls around C16 farmhouse (not open). Incl small topiary garden, physic garden, flower garden, fancy garden, gazebo and nursery garden. Featured in 'Telegraph', 'The English Garden' & RHS 'The Garden' 2003. *Adm £2.80, chd (5-15) £1. Mons, Weds, Fris, Sats & Suns Apr to Sept. For NGS: Thurs 16 June; 14 July; 4 Aug (1.30-5.30). Tel 01670 774278*

⓭ Ingram Cottage, West Woodburn 🏵⊕
(Mrs Mary Virden) *18m N of Corbridge. From A68. In the village turn E behind the Bay Horse Inn for ½m along no through rd.* 1-acre organic garden with panoramic views; divided into an informal, closely-planted ornamental garden with emphasis on form and texture as well as colour; wide range of perennials, some unusual. Vegetable and fruit garden, wildlife priority garden. Two ponds; poultry. Featured in RHS 'The Garden' 2004. Home-made TEAS. *Adm £2, chd free. Private visits welcome by appt, mid-June to Aug. Tel 01434 270334*

⓮ NEW 16 Lilac Crescent, Burnopfield
(John R Grundy) *6m W of Gateshead. From A1 N follow signs for Gibside, along A694 up Busty Bank to war memorial, turn R into Front St (B6310). From A1 S follow A692 signed Consett, R after Pack Horse PH into Front St. Parking at Masonic Hall, Burnopfield CIU Club and behind Methodist Church, all on B6310. Walk up Lilac Crescent, 2nd L opp CIU Club.* Gravel path winds through this plantsman's garden; interesting herbaceous planting, grasses, specimen trees and clematis varieties. Wooden bridge over informal wildlife pond housing all three species of British newts. **Evening Openings** *£1, Suns 26 June; 31 July; Wed 28 Sept (7-9)*

⓯ NEW Lilac Crescent Gardens, Burnopfield 🏵⊕
6m W of Gateshead. From A1 N follow signs for Gibside, along A694 up Busty Bank to war memorial, turn R into Front St (B6310). From A1 S follow A692 signed Consett, R after Pack Horse PH into Front St. Parking at Masonic Hall, Burnopfield

CIU Club and behind Methodist Church, all on B6310. Walk up Lilac Crescent, 2nd L opp CIU Club. Three contrasting small urban gardens, each offering a very different atmosphere. Light refreshments and TEAS at 19 Lilac Crescent. *Combined adm £2.50, chd 50p (share to Emmanuel House, Lobley Hill). Sun 12 June (11-5)*

NEW 15 Lilac Crescent (Judith Cloe) Flower and vegetable garden. Full of nooks and crannies - a delight for children who love hidden corners. Colourful container planting.

NEW 16 Lilac Crescent (John R Grundy) (See separate entry).

NEW 19 Lilac Crescent (Jim Jackson & Steve Paske) A developing garden with wooden summerhouse. Lawned and paved areas where teas are served.

⓰ Lilburn Tower, Alnwick 🏵⊕
(Mr & Mrs D Davidson) *3m S of Wooler. On A697.* 10 acres of walled and formal gardens incl conservatory and large glasshouse. Approx 30 acres of woodland with walks and pond garden. Rhododendrons and azaleas. Also ruins of Pele Tower, and C12 church. Home-made TEAS. *Adm £2.50, chd free. Sun 22 May (2-6). Private visits welcome by appt. Tel 01668 217291*

⓱ Loughbrow House, Hexham 🏵⊕
(Mrs K A Clark) *1m S of Hexham. Take B6303 from Hexham, signed Blanchland, after ¼m take RH-fork. After a further ¼m you come to another fork, lodge gates are in intersection. Garden ½m up the drive.* Woodland garden with rhododendrons and azaleas. Bog garden with pond. Old-fashioned roses and a long bed of hybrid teas; 3

herbaceous borders; large area of lawns. Extensive kitchen garden and paved courtyard. *Adm £2, chd free. Weds 18 May; 22 June; 20 July (12.30-3). Private visits welcome by appt. Tel 01434 603351*

⓲ Mindrum, nr Cornhill on Tweed & Yetholm 🏵⊕
(Hon P J & Mrs Fairfax) *6m SW of Coldstream, 9m NW of Wooler. 4m N of Yetholm. 5m from Cornhill on Tweed on B6352.* Old-fashioned roses; rock and water garden; shrub borders. Wonderful views along Bowmont Valley. Approx 3 acres. Home-made TEAS. *Adm £2.50, chd free. Sun 19 June (2-6). Private visits welcome by appt. Tel 01890 850246*

⓳ ◆ Wallington, Cambo 🏵⊕ NCCPG
(The National Trust) *12m W of Morpeth. From N B6343; from S via A696 from Newcastle, 6m W of Belsay, B6342 to Cambo.* Walled terraced garden with fine herbaceous and mixed borders; Edwardian conservatory; 100 acres woodland and lakes. National Collection of sambucus. House dates from 1688 but altered, interior greatly changed c1740; exceptional rococo plasterwork by Francini brothers. Light refreshments and TEAS. *House and garden adm £7.30, chd £3.65. Garden only £5.20, chd £2.60. Garden open all yr.* **For NGS:** *Suns 8 May; 7 Aug (10-7). Tel 01670 774389 john.ellis@nationaltrust.org.uk*

Evening Opening (See also garden description)	
16 Lilac Crescent	26 June
	31 July
	28 September

"We don't get much trouble from the neighbours now!"

Nottinghamshire

County Organisers:	Mr & Mrs Martin Brown, Gardeners' Cottage, Rectory Lane, Kirkby in Ashfield, Nottingham NG17 8PZ Tel 01623 489489
Assistant County Organisers:	Mr Bernard Theobald, 37 Loughborough Road, Ruddington, Nottingham NG11 6LL Tel 0115 984 1152
	Mrs Mary Hepburn, 6 Miller Hives Close, Cotgrave, Nottingham NG12 3QY Tel 0115 989 9012
County Treasurer:	Mrs Pat Webb, 25 Greenbank Drive, Sutton in Ashfield, Nottingham NG17 2DY Tel 01623 556447

Maps: Numbers shown next to each garden entry refer to that garden's entry on the county map. This position is approximate; distance and directions from the nearest main town are generally shown in the garden text. A precise location is available for those gardens featured on the NGS website by visiting www.ngs.org.uk.

Symbols: Information relating to symbols is given on page 21

DATES OF OPENING

Evening openings
See end of county listing

Gardens open to the public
For details see garden description
Clumber Park Kitchen Garden, Worksop *(12)*
Felley Priory, Underwood *(19)*
Hodsock Priory Gardens, Blyth *(23)*
Holme Pierrepont Hall, Holme Pierrepont, Nottingham *(24)*
Norwell Nurseries, Norwell *(33)*

March 27 Sunday (Easter)
Woodpecker Cottage, Girton *(51)*
March 30 Wednesday
Woodpecker Cottage, Girton *(51)*
April 10 Sunday
Felley Priory, Underwood *(19)*
April 17 Sunday
The Beeches, Milton, Tuxford *(6)*
April 19 Tuesday
Holme Pierrepont Hall, Holme Pierrepont, Nottingham *(24)*
April 24 Sunday
Gardeners' Cottage, Kirkby in Ashfield *(20)*
May 1 Sunday
Ashdene, Halam *(3)*
Darby House, Nottingham *(15)*
Living Rooms, Nuthall *(29)*
May 2 Monday (Bank Hol)
Gorene, Beauvale Estate, Newthorpe *(22)*
Mill Hill House, East Stoke *(30)*
May 8 Sunday
61 Lambley Lane, Burton Joyce *(28)*
Squirrel Lodge, Retford *(46)*
14 Temple Drive, Nuthall *(47)*
May 15 Sunday
Ashdene, Halam *(3)*
The Beeches, Milton, Tuxford *(6)*
Brackenhurst, Mansfield *(9)*
7 Collygate, Swingate, Kimberley *(13)*
May 19 Thursday
Brackenhurst, Mansfield *(9)*

May 22 Sunday
Bishops Manor, Southwell *(8)*
Brook Cottage, Caythorpe *(10)*
Norwell Nurseries, Norwell *(33)*
The Old Vicarage, Halam Village *(35)*
May 29 Sunday
Homefield House, West Thorpe, Willoughby on the Wolds *(27)*
Papplewick Hall, Papplewick *(38)*
University of Nottingham Gardens, Nottingham *(48)*
May 30 Monday (Bank Hol)
Holmes Villa, Walkeringham, nr Gainsborough *(25)*
Mill Hill House, East Stoke *(30)*
June 5 Sunday
Ashdene, Halam *(3)*
Newbray House, Granby *(31)*
The Old Vicarage, Halam Village *(35)*
June 10 Friday
Roselea, Coddington **(Evening)** *(44)*
June 12 Sunday
Askham Gardens, Markham Moor *(4)*
17 Dovedale Road, West Bridgford *(16)*
12 Dunster Road, West Bridgford, Nottingham *(18)*
Home Farm Cottage, Oxton *(26)*
Oakwood Cottage, Oxton *(34)*
June 15 Wednesday
Bishops Cottage, Kinoulton **(Evening)** *(7)*
Gorene, Beauvale Estate, Newthorpe *(22)*
June 17 Friday
Baxter Farm, Willoughby on the Wolds **(Evening)** *(5)*
June 19 Sunday
4 Ash Grove, Keyworth *(1)*
29 Ash Grove, Keyworth *(2)*
Bishops Cottage, Kinoulton *(7)*
9 Winster Avenue, Carlton *(50)*
June 21 Tuesday
Holme Pierrepont Hall, Holme Pierrepont, Nottingham *(24)*
June 23 Thursday
9 Winster Avenue, Carlton **(Evening)** *(50)*
June 24 Friday
Park Farm, Normanton **(Day & Evening)** *(39)*

June 25 Saturday
Orchard House, Mansfield *(36)*
Park Farm, Normanton **(Day & Evening)** *(39)*
June 26 Sunday
Norwell Gardens *(32)*
Orchard House, Mansfield *(36)*
Redlands, Hucknall *(42)*
Rose Cottage, Underwood *(43)*
June 29 Wednesday
Norwell Gardens **(Evening)** *(32)*
July 3 Sunday
Cottage Farm, Keyworth *(14)*
Woodpecker Cottage, Girton *(51)*
July 6 Wednesday
Woodpecker Cottage, Girton *(51)*
July 10 Sunday
Camellias, Southwell *(11)*
16 Glensford Gardens, Nottingham *(21)*
Park Farm, Southwell *(40)*
July 13 Wednesday
Camellias, Southwell **(Evening)** *(11)*
Home Farm Cottage, Oxton **(Evening)** *(26)*
Oakwood Cottage, Oxton **(Evening)** *(34)*
July 14 Thursday
Park Farm, Southwell **(Evening)** *(40)*
July 17 Sunday
7 Collygate, Swingate, Kimberley *(13)*
Dumbleside, Burton Joyce *(17)*
32 Victoria Street, Hucknall *(49)*
July 20 Wednesday
9 Winster Avenue, Carlton **(Evening)** *(50)*
July 23 Saturday
Clumber Park Kitchen Garden, Worksop *(12)*
July 24 Sunday
Gorene, Beauvale Estate, Newthorpe *(22)*
Roselea, Coddington *(44)*
125 Shelford Road, Radcliffe on Trent *(45)*
July 31 Sunday
Rose Cottage, Underwood *(43)*
14 Temple Drive, Nuthall *(47)*
9 Winster Avenue, Carlton *(50)*
August 7 Sunday
28 Prestwood Drive, Aspley *(41)*
Squirrel Lodge, Retford *(46)*

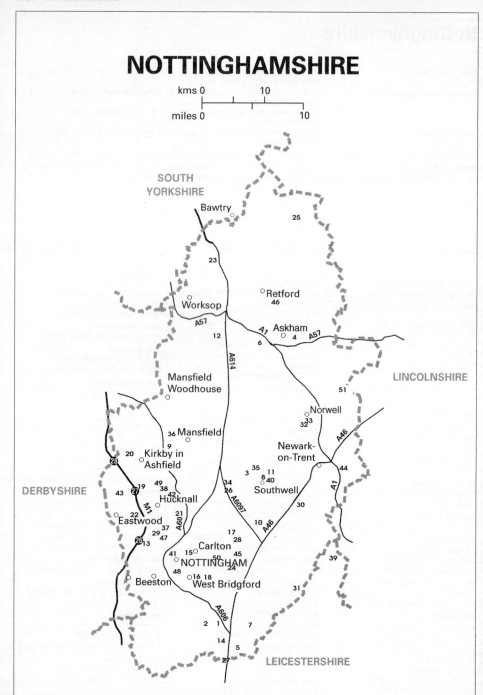

NOTTINGHAMSHIRE

kms 0   10

miles 0   10

SOUTH
YORKSHIRE

Bawtry

25

23

°Retford
46

Worksop

A57

12   A1 °Askham
6   4   A57

A614

LINCOLNSHIRE

Mansfield
Woodhouse
°

51

°Norwell
32 33

36 °Mansfield
9   °

Newark-
on-Trent

20 °Kirkby in   A46
Ashfield

28   3 35 11
34   8 40
26   Southwell

DERBYSHIRE   49
19 38 42
43 27 °Hucknall   A1 44

M1   A6097   30

22 21
29 37 47
°Eastwood   10 A46
26 13   17   28

41 15°   Carlton
50   45
48 °NOTTINGHAM
24   39

°Beeston °16 18
West Bridgford   31

A606

2 1   7

14   5
27   LEICESTERSHIRE

ugust 14 Sunday
ardeners' Cottage, Kirkby in Ashfield *(20)*
ıe Old Vicarage, Halam Village **(Evening)**
35)

ugust 21 Sunday
ɔse Cottage, Underwood *(43)*
ıiversity of Nottingham Gardens,
ɹottingham *(48)*

eptember 4 Sunday
ɔse Cottage, Underwood *(43)*

eptember 11 Sunday
) The Paddocks, Nuthall *(37)*

eptember 14 Wednesday
) The Paddocks, Nuthall **(Evening)** *(37)*

eptember 18 Sunday
ıe Old Vicarage, Halam Village *(35)*

'ESCRIPTIONS OF GARDENS

❶ NEW 4 Ash Grove, Keyworth
⅂]
.inda & Paul Truman) *8m SE of
'ottingham. Turn off A606 Melton
d signposted Plumtree/Keyworth.
'hrough Plumtree under railway
'idge. Turn L at Keep L sign onto
icker Hill, R onto Wolds Drive,
ıd L past shops onto Beech Ave.
ıd R into Ash Grove. Garden
ımed on R.* This extraordinary
iniature garden has taken 10 yrs to
eate, and has undoubtedly taken its
fluence from the land of the rising
ın. To describe it is to do it an
justice! It is a testimony to skill,
ɪrseverance, and dedication, and
ɔove all it is a garden crying out to
e shared. *Adm combined with* **29
sh Grove** *£3, chd free. Sun 19 June
-5.30)*

❷ 29 Ash Grove, Keyworth ⊗⊛
ːynn & Gary Longworth) *8m SE of
'ottingham. Turn off A606 Melton
d. Signposted Plumtree/Keyworth.
'rive through Plumtree under
ːilway bridge. Turn L at Keep L sign
ɪto Nicker Hill, R onto Wolds Dr,
ıd L past shops onto Beech Ave.
ıd R on Beech Ave into Ash Grove.
) is at far end of cul-de-sac.*
ɪedium-sized, gardeners' garden.
ːrge pond, variety of maples both
ɪanted and potted. Various shrubs,
ɪrbaceous perennials, climbers and
ımboos; numerous hanging baskets
ıd pots; raised peat bed; mixed
ɪrders; pergola with roses, clematis,
ɔneysuckles. Huge variety of plants,
ɔme exotic, some unusual, to
terest all tastes. Plant sales. Home-
ade TEAS in aid of James Ward,
ɪty Hospital. *Adm Combined with* **4
shgrove** *£3, chd free. Sun 19 June
-5.30)*

❸ Ashdene, Radley Road, Halam
⅃⅁⊛
(David & Glenys Herbert) *2m W of
Southwell. From B6386 in Halam
village 300yds from church.*
Developed from orchard over 22yrs.
Many mature trees incl 2 magnificent
walnuts (200yrs), paulownia (50yrs)
and mulberry. Japanese style garden
with living architectural features incl
mature spiral yew. Formal species
rose, scented rose and woodland
gardens. Many clematis, hebes.
Home-made TEAS in aid of Halam
Church. *Adm £2, chd free. Suns 1, 15
May; 5 June (1-5.30). Private visits
welcome by appt. Tel 01636 812335
david@herbert.newsurf.net*

**❹ Askham Gardens, Markham
Moor**
*10m E of Worksop. On A638, in
Rockley village turn E to Askham.* A
variety of pleasant English village
gardens. Home-made TEAS at Thorn
Lea Cottage in aid of Askham
Church. *Combined adm £2.50, chd
free. Sun 12 June (2-6)*

Dovecote Cottage (Mr & Mrs D J
Slack) A traditional English
cottage garden incl roses on the
wall.

Nursery House (Mr & Mrs D
Bird) A secluded and very private
garden, with every plant
meticulously labelled.

NEW Thorn Lea Cottage (Mr &
Mrs M Hunter-Wyatt) Small
English cottage garden near to
the church, complete with
chickens.

Villosa (Mr T Townrow) A
plantsman's paradise with a
sequence of different beds leading
to a small arboretum.

**❺ Baxter Farm, Willoughby on
the Wolds** ⅃⅁⊛
(Dr & Mrs Peter Tatham) *10m S of
Nottingham. 12m N of Leicester.
About ½m off A46 at the E end of
Main St.* Old farmhouse and barns.
1-acre garden planted last 20yrs.
Conservatory, old cattle drinking
pond now planted, herbaceous
borders, informal plantings of old
roses, irises, hardy geraniums and
many climbers. Pergola, beech and
yew hedged walks. Kitchen garden.
Evening Opening *£2, wine, Fri 17 June
(6-9). Private visits welcome by appt.
Tel 01509 880975 tatham@onetel.
com*

**❻ The Beeches, The Avenue,
Milton, Tuxford** ⅃⅁⊗⊛
(Margaret & Jim Swindin) *12m N of
Newark. Exit A1 at Markham Moor
roundabout, take Walesby sign into*

village (1m). 1-acre garden with 2-
acre old hay meadow (access around
perimeter). Mature trees, shrubs,
wide variety herbaceous plants, some
unusual climbers, wild flower area
and wildlife ponds, small woodland
with bulbs and shade loving plants.
Vegetables in raised beds and tunnel.
Top and soft fruit. Organic
cultivation. Newcastle Mausoleum
open with guide. Home-made TEAS.
*Adm £2 (share to Brooke Hospital).
Suns 17 Apr; 15 May (2-5.30).
Private visits welcome by appt Mar,
Apr, May & June (teas provided).
Coaches permitted. Tel 01777
870828*

**❼ NEW Bishops Cottage, 89
Main Street, Kinoulton** ⅃⊗⊛
(Ann & Steve Hammond) *8m SE of
West Bridgford. Kinoulton is off A46
just N of intersection with A606. Into
village, pass school & village hall.
Garden on R after bend on Main St.*
This mature, large cottage garden,
with roses round the door (and
everywhere else!) and mixed
herbaceous beds is the essence of
dreams, and the colourful frothiness
belies a careful management. It is
indeed a place where you could
believe that 'time might stand still'.
*Adm £2.50, chd free. Sun 19 June
(1.30-6).* **Evening Opening** *£2.50, Wed
15 June (7-9)*

**❽ Bishops Manor, Bishops
Drive, Southwell** ⅃⅁⊗
(The Rt Reverend George Cassidy,
Bishop of Southwell) *Centre of
Southwell, end of Bishops Dr on S
side of Minster.* House built into part
of old medieval palace of the
Archbishops of York. Ruins form
delightful enclosed garden, lawns, 4
seasons tree garden in unusual
setting. Herb knot garden and other
features under development. Teas in
Minster Refectory until 4pm (not for
NGS). *Adm £2.50, chd free. Sun 22
May (12-5)*

**❾ Brackenhurst, Derby Road,
Mansfield** ⅃⅁⊗⊛
(Pat & Peter Musgrove) *1m S of
Mansfield. Approaching Mansfield on
the A60 from Nottingham, Derby Rd
is L at the West Notts College T-
lights. Brackenhurst is on corner at
next lights.* When you walk through
the gate, you might think you had
travelled halfway round the world!
This Mansfield garden was designed
with oriental features and planting
long before it was fashionable. Its
maturity, flowers, foliage and maples,
together with its design, are
inspirational. Featured in
'Nottinghamshire Today' 2004.

Home-made TEAS in aid of Mansfield Flower Arranging Society (NAFAS). *Adm £2.50, chd free. Sun 15 May (2-6), Thur 19 May (2-7). Private visits welcome by appt. Tel 01623 625531*

⑩ Brook Cottage, 12 Main Street, Caythorpe &⊗☺
(Jenny Wheelhouse) *9m NE of Nottingham. A612 from Nottingham to Lowdham, follow signs to Caythorpe. 1¼m from railway crossing, Brook Cottage is on RH-side of Main St before the pottery & Black Horse PH.* Second yr of opening but a different season and still the beck at the bottom of the garden has ducks and moorhens! This cottage garden by an experienced plantswoman is full of colour, foliage and flair, and will appeal to and inspire most who dream of peace and tranquillity. Home-made TEAS. *Adm £2, chd free. Sun 22 May (2-5)*

⑪ NEW Camellias, 2 Farthingate, Southwell &⊗☺
(Alan & Shirley Curtis) *600yds from Southwell Minster at junction of Church St (A612) & Farthingate.* This front garden is merely a taste of what's to come. The back garden and 'inner sanctum' are breathtaking. This garden could restock a garden centre with clematis, and is that of a plant collector who has never been restrained! The grass and lawns are getting smaller all the time as the borders expand. Car parking and refreshments at 'Hearty Goodfellow' opp. *Adm £2, chd free (share to Notts & Lincs Air Ambulance). Sun 10 July (2-6).* **Evening Opening** *£3, wine, Wed 13 July (6-8.30)*

⑫ ◆ Clumber Park Kitchen Garden, Worksop &☺
(The National Trust) *4m S of Worksop. From the Clumber Xrds in centre of Park, turn S towards the main facilities. Take 2nd turning L, opp wooden bus shelter, then 2nd turning on R to kitchen garden.* Over recent years the Duke of Newcastle's famous walled kitchen garden and extensive glasshouses have been considerably restored and are now well worth visiting, even though restoration will not be complete for some years. The NGS open day coincides with a 'tasting day' where some of the garden's unusual produce is skilfully worked into old recipes by the resident chef. First come, first served. Taste Test Days 14 May, 25 June, 23 Jul, 27 Aug, 17 Sept, 15 Oct, 19 Nov (2-5). Light Refreshments and TEAS in restaurant. *Adm £4 per vehicle.*

Kitchen Garden, adult £1, chd free. Fri 25 Mar to Sun 30 Oct, Mons to Fris (10-5) Sats, Suns & Bank Hols (10-6). **For NGS:** *Sat 23 July (10-6). NT members free. Tel 01909 476592 Neil Porteous neil.porteous@nationaltrust.org.uk*

⑬ NEW 7 Collygate, Swingate, Kimberley &⊗☺
(Doreen Fahey & John Arkinstall) *6m W of Nottingham. From M1 J26 take A610 towards Nottingham. L at next island on B600 into Kimberley. At Sainsbury's mini island take L. L at top. Park on this rd in 500yds. Collygate on R.* This delightful garden has been created by serious plant addicts and is tucked away at the end of a short narrow lane in Swingate. It greets you with an impact of unexpected colour and delights you with the variety and sensitivity of the planting. A peaceful backwater in an urban setting. No parking in Collygate. Home-made TEAS. *Adm £2, chd free (share to Breast Cancer). Suns 15 May; 17 July (2-6)*

⑭ Cottage Farm, Widmerpool Lane, Keyworth &⊗☺
(Malcolm Plant & Brenda Smith) *8m SE of Nottingham. From A606, take sign to Plumtree/Keyworth. In Keyworth, L fork along Nicker Hill, R along Willow Brook, next L towards Widmerpool. 1st house on R among trees.* Peaceful cottage garden and extensive grounds, in all 12 acres comprising informal planting of herbaceous borders, old apple orchard, wildlife pond, mature woodland and meadow. Take a wild flower walk, stroll under lofty elms, spy varied birdlife. Young children's garden games. Light refreshments and TEAS. *Adm £2.50, chd free. Sun 3 July (11-5). Private visits welcome by appt for groups of 10 or more. Tel 0115 937 2022 malcolm@plantm36.fsnet.co.uk*

⑮ Darby House, 10 The Grove, Southey Street, Nottingham ☺
(Jed Brignal) *¾m NE of city centre take A610, turn R into Forest Rd, first L into Southey St.* Unusual city garden designed and developed by artist owner is a tranquil oasis in unlikely location. Victorian walled garden with ponds, waterfall, gazebos and a fairy-tale shady area surrounded by mature trees. House (1849) and garden provide temporary home and sanctuary for actors, writers, dancers and other creative visitors. Rare plant nurseries & deli stall (not NGS). Featured in 'Gardens Monthly' 2003. TEAS. *Adm £2, chd*

free. Sun 1 May (2-5). Private visits welcome by appt. Tel 0115 970 4977

⑯ NEW 17 Dovedale Road, West Bridgford ⊗
(Mr & Mrs Backhouse) *2m S of Nottingham. From Trent Bridge follow A606 Melton Rd. Approx 1½m turn L into Dovedale Rd.* Attractively designed medium-sized flower garden with varied, maturing planting schemes. Kitchen garden with interesting collection of soft and tree fruit. Home-made TEAS in aid of Save the Children. *Adm combined with **12 Dunster Road** £2.50, chd 30p. Sun 12 June (2-5)*

⑰ Dumbleside, 17 Bridle Road, Burton Joyce &☺
(Mr & Mrs P Bates) *5m NE of Nottingham. In Burton Joyce turn off A612, Nottingham to Southwell Rd into Lambley Lane. Bridle Rd is an impassable looking rd to the R off Lambley Lane. Car parking easiest BEYOND garden.* 2 acres of varied habitat. Natural spring and stream planted with primulas, fritillaries and fine specimen shrubs. Bulbs and flowers in meadow grass and shaded woodland paths. Opening in July this yr when 60yd mixed herbaceous border should be at its best. There is no seaon when there is not something to see. *Adm £2. Sun 17 July (2-6). Private visits welcome by appt, groups welcome. Tel 0115 931 3725*

⑱ 12 Dunster Road, West Bridgford, Nottingham ⊗☺
(Madelaine & Michael Jones) *2m S of Nottingham. From Trent Bridge follow A606 Melton Rd. Approx 1m turn L into Burleigh Rd, take 4th R into Dunster Rd.* 90ft × 30ft plantsman's garden designed and developed by owners to create distinct areas, each giving a different feel. Terrace with many tender perennials in pots leading to lawn and summerhouse. Beds with many shrubs and herbaceous plants grown for foliage, colour and scent. Small pond and bog garden. Archway lead up to shady woodland area. TEAS at 17 Dovedale Road. *Adm combined with **17 Dovedale Road** £2.50, chd 30p (share to Alzheimer's Society). Sun 12 June (2-5)*

⑲ ◆ Felley Priory, Underwood &⊗☺
(The Hon Mrs Chaworth Musters) *8m SW of Mansfield. Off A608 ½m W M1 J27.* Garden for all seasons with yew hedges and topiary, snowdrops, hellebores, orchard of daffodils, herbaceous borders and

old-fashioned rose garden. There are pergolas, a medieval garden, a small arboretum and borders filled with unusual trees, shrubs, plants and bulbs. The grass-edged pond is planted with primulas, bamboo, iris, roses and eucomis. Featured in 'Nottinghamshire Today' 2004. *Adm £2.50, chd free. Sun 6 Feb (11-4); Tues, Weds & Fris (9-12.30) all yr; every 2nd & 4th Wed Mar to Oct (9-4); every 3rd Sun Mar to Oct (11-4).* **For NGS:** *Sun 10 Apr (11-4). Light refreshments & TEAS by Marie Curie Cancer Care. Tel 01773 810230 for further information*

㉑ Gardeners' Cottage, Rectory Lane, Kirkby in Ashfield 🚻✗♿
(Martin & Chris Brown) *1m W of Kirkby. From the A38, take the B6018 towards Kirkby in Ashfield. Straight across mini island. Rectory Lane (no parking) is at the side of St Wilfrid's Church, on Church St.* This 1½-acre maturing plant enthusiasts' garden is beginning to blossom in very sense of the word. Its steeply sloping site owes much of its appeal to the borrowed landscape of surrounding meadow, and the many paths that interweave its packed and varied borders. Featured in 'Nottinghamshire Today' 2004 and on BBC TV 2004. Home-made TEAS. *Adm £2. Suns 24 Apr; 14 Aug (1-5). Private visits welcome by appt. Tel 01623 489489*

㉒ 16 Glensford Gardens, Nottingham ✗♿
(Don & Vicky Butt) *5m N of Nottingham city centre. From N or city, approach on A611 (Nottingham-Hucknall). Opposite Bulwell golf course turn into Hestwood Park Dr West at T-lights. 1st L Brownlow Dr. Glensford Gardens is 4th R. Park on Brownlow Dr please.* Described by Tommy Walsh of 'Ground Force' as 'paradise'. This immaculate garden is packed full both front and back and needs to be seen to be believed. Massive water feature, containers, annuals, perennials, even tropicals. Featured on BBC TV 2003 and in 'Nottinghamshire Today' 2004. TEAS. *Adm £2, chd £1.50. Sun 10 July (11-5). Private visits welcome by appt, minimum of 5 visitors please. Tel 0115 976 4633 vbuttdon@hotmail.com*

㉓ Gorene, 20 Kirby Road, Beauvale Estate, Newthorpe ✗
(Gordon & Irene Middleton) *5m NE of Nottingham. From M1 J26 take A610 (Eastwood & Kimberley bypass) exit Langley Mill (not Eastwood). At island turn R to Eastwood to 1st set of T-lights. Keep L down Mansfield Rd, turn R at bollards (Greenhills Rd).Turn R at the 7th rd - Kirby Rd.* Over 600 plants, shrubs and trees fill this average-sized, prizewinning garden. Included are perennials, palms, ferns and bamboo. Also three water features, lawn areas, exotic aviary and 'secret' garden. An all-yr garden, one not to be missed. Featured on BBC TV 2003. TEAS. *Adm £2, acc chd free. Mon 2 May (1-5); Wed 15 June (2-5); Sun 24 July (1-5). Private visits welcome by appt. Tel 01773 788407*

◆ Hall Farm, Harpswell 🚻✗♿
See Lincolnshire.

㉓ ◆ Hodsock Priory Gardens, Blyth ♿✗🚻
(Sir Andrew & Lady Buchanan) *4m S of Bawtry. 4m N of Worksop off B6045, Blyth-Worksop rd approx 2m from A1. Well signed.* 5-acre private garden on historic Domesday site. Sensational winter garden and snowdrop wood. Many fragrant winter flowering shrubs, trees, hellebores and bulbs. Light refreshments and TEAS. *Adm £4, chd £1 (6-16yrs). Daily Sat 29 Jan to Sun 6 Mar (10-4). Tel 01909 591204 www.snowdrops.co.uk*

㉔ ◆ Holme Pierrepont Hall, Holme Pierrepont, Nottingham ♿
(Mr & Mrs Robin Brackenbury) *5m E of Nottingham. From Nottingham A52 E-bound. Follow signs for National Watersports Centre. Continue 1m past main entrance. House on LH-side next to church. Park outside church.* Courtyard garden with box parterre, flower borders and climbing roses laid out in 1875 - restored by current owners. East garden laid out approx 35yrs ago, featuring flowering shrubs, roses, unusual trees, yew walk, meadow and spring walk with many spring bulbs incl rare native *Tulipa sylvestris*. House open for additional £2. TEAS. *Adm £2.50, chd £1.50. Mons, Tues, Weds 1 Feb to 23 Mar (2-5).* **For NGS:** *Tues 19 Apr; 21 June (2-5). Tel 0115 933 2371 www.holmepierreponthall.com*

㉕ Holmes Villa, Holmes Lane, Walkeringham, nr Gainsborough ♿✗🚻
(Peter & Sheila Clark) *4m NW of Gainsborough. A620 from Retford or A631 from Bawtry/Gainsborough & A161 to Walkeringham then towards Misterton. Follow yellow signs for last mile.* 1¾-acre plantsman's interesting and inspirational garden; surprises around every corner with places to sit and ponder; gazebos; arbours; ponds; hosta garden; unusual perennials and shrubs for flower arranging. Plant stalls, home-made preserves, pickles (not for NGS). Home-made TEAS in aid of Walkeringham Senior Citizens' Christmas Party. *Adm £1.50, chd free. Mon 30 May (1-5). Private visits welcome by appt, coaches permitted. Tel 01427 890233/07801 625870 clarkshaulage@aol.com*

㉖ NEW Home Farm Cottage, Blind Lane, Oxton ✗♿
(Pauline & Brian Hansler) *4m SW of Southwell. From B6386 turn into Oxton village (Blind Lane). Home Farm Cottage is on L opp Green Dragon PH, immed before T-junction.* A small cottage garden where the impact is sensational. The planting is apparently haphazard but this garden will delight and satisfy, and perhaps give rise to a small feeling of envy within the visitor. Home-made TEAS in aid of British Epilepsy Association 12 June. *Adm £2.50, chd free. Combined with* **Oakwood Cottage.** *Sun 12 June (2-5).* **Evening Opening** *Wed 13 July (6-9). Private visits welcome by appt June & July only. Tel 0115 965 5860*

㉗ NEW Homefield House, West Thorpe, Willoughby on the Wolds ♿✗🚻
(Mr & Mrs John Peck) *12m S of Nottingham. Turn off A46 and follow signs into Willoughby. West Thorpe is at bottom end of Main St. Take direction to Wysall. Homefield House is last house on R.* The landscaping and planting are the outstanding features of this garden, and peace and tranquillity have been achieved in the sweep of lawns down to a natural, well-positioned pond. There are hidden corners of well-stocked and diverse planting to create interest and surprise and a superb glasshouse filled with tender gems. TEAS. *Adm £2.50, chd free. Sun 29 May (2-5.30)*

Kexby House, Gainsborough ♿✗
See Lincolnshire.

㉘ 61 Lambley Lane, Burton Joyce ✗
(Mr & Mrs R B Powell) *6m N of Nottingham. In Burton Joyce turn off A612 Nottingham to Southwell Rd into Lambley Lane. Approx ¾-acre of spring flowering shrubs, plants and bulbs. Mixed borders, greenhouse and terrace, cacti, vegetable garden. Adm £2, chd free. Sun 8 May (2-6)*

㉙ Living Rooms, 2 Coronation Road, Nuthall &
(Neil & Jo Gribby) *5m NW of Nottingham. From M1 J26 take A610 towards Nottingham. At roundabout take 1st exit B600 towards Kimberley.Take 2nd R and then 1st L into Coronation Rd.* A recently designed and planted small garden in the 'living room' style. Neat and compact with themed areas centred on a naturalised fish pond. This is the small garden to which so many of us can relate. Nottingham area winner ITV's 'Britain's Best Back Garden' 2004, screened Spring 2005. Cream TEAS in aid of RSPB. *Adm £2, chd free. Sun 1 May (11-5). Private visits welcome by appt. Tel 0115 919 0332*

㉚ Mill Hill House, Elston Lane, East Stoke ⊛ NCCPG
(Mr & Mrs R J Gregory) *5m S of Newark. Elston Lane. On A46 turn to Elston. Garden ½m on R. Entrance via car park (signed).* ½-acre country garden close to site of Battle of East Stoke (1487). Closely planted with many unusual hardy/half hardy plants providing yr-round interest and tranquil atmosphere. This established and mature garden is now enjoying some new planting that is revitalising its old-fashioned charm. National Collection of berberis. *Adm £2, chd free. Mons 2, 30 May (11-5). Private visits welcome by appt, individual or groups May to Sept (excl Aug). Coaches permitted. Tel 01636 525460 millhill@talk21. com*

㉛ Newbray House, Church Street, Granby & ⊛ ⊛
(Mrs Shirley Oxby & Stan Taylor) *14m E of Nottingham. 2m off A52 signposted Granby.* 2 acres of gardens, paddock and orchard. Gardens extensively developed over last 6yrs, incl large herbaceous beds, rose pergola; herb and woodland areas. Gravel garden with long season of interest. Ponds with limestone rockery. Several arbours. Fruit and vegetable garden. A wide variety of interesting and unusual plants. Home-made TEAS in aid of Hope & Homes for Children. *Adm £2.50. Sun 5 June (2-6). Private visits welcome*

by appt. Tel 01949 859090 shirley.oxby@btinternet.com

㉜ Norwell Gardens
6m N of Newark. Off A1 at Cromwell turning. Beautiful medieval church, also open, with flower arrangements and an exhibition showing something of its history. TEAS at village hall in aid of Windmills Playgroup (Sun only). *Combined adm £2.50, chd free. Sun 26 June (2-5.30).* **Evening Opening** *£3, wine, Wed 29 June (6.30-9)*

Black Horse Farm & ⊛ (Mr & Mrs Craig Bown) An exciting developing garden. Mixed borders leading to woodland walk/orchard, moat, young native trees and shrubs, avenue of lime trees, vegetable plot, soft fruit and cutting garden. Landscaping and beds close to buildings, incl camomile lawn and pond/water feature. Lake walk.

Northfield Farm & ⊛ (Mr & Mrs D Adamson) *½m from village hall down Ossington Rd.* Well laid out country and family garden with large vegetable plot, herbaceous border, herb garden and water feature.

Norwell Nurseries & ⊛ ⊛ (Andrew & Helen Ward) (See separate entry). *Private visits welcome by appt, coaches & groups in June & July. Tel 01636 636337*

㉝ ◆ Norwell Nurseries, Woodhouse Road, Norwell & ⊛ ⊛
(Andrew & Helen Ward) *6m N of Newark. Turn off A1 at Cromwell turning.* A treasure trove of over 2000 different, beautiful, rare and unusual plants set out in ¾-acre plantsman's garden incl woodland with orchids and meconopsis, specimen grasses. Large alpine and scree area, bell garden with penstemons and dierama, and patio plants. Extensive herbaceous borders, hot beds and sumptuous colour-themed beds. TEAS in aid of village hall charity (Sun 22 May). *Adm £2, chd free. Open 1 Mar to 20 Oct (except Tues & Sats) (10-5). Closed Aug. For NGS: Sun 22 May (2-5.30). Also opening with* **Norwell Gardens**

Sun 26 June (2-5.30); Wed 29 June (6.30-9). Tel 01636 636337

㉞ NEW Oakwood Cottage, Forest Road, Oxton ⊛ ⊛
(Tracey & Paul Akehurst) *4m SW of Southwell. From B6386 turn into Oxton village (Blind Lane). At T-junction turn R onto Forest Rd. Oakwood Cottage is immed on RH-side up a gravel drive (no parking).* Tucked behind a public house in the middle of the village is an unlikely place to find a little garden that demands sharing. The apparent simplicity is the work of a trained eye. A gem in an unlikely spot. Home-made TEAS in aid of DEBRA (Dystrophic Epidermolysis Bullosa Research Assoc) 12 June. *Adm £2.50, chd free. Combined with* **Home Farm Cottage.** *Sun 12 June (2-5).* **Evening Opening** *Wed 13 July (6-9). Private visits welcome by appt June & July only. Tel 0115 965 2114 tracey.akehurst@virgin.net*

㉟ The Old Vicarage, Halam Hill, Halam Village
(Mrs Beverley Perks) *1m W of Southwell. On approach to Halam village down hill on LH-side.* This 2-acre, rapidly maturing, colourful garden, has much to inspire the visitor and excite the plant hunter. Its wooded and sloping aspect, and use of texture and design, all contribute towards its peaceful country garden atmosphere. Home-made TEAS in aid of St Michael's Church, Halam, & Burns Unit, City Hospital. *Adm £2.50, chd free. Suns 22 May; 5 June 18 Sept (1-5).* **Evening Opening** *£3.50 wine, Sun 14 Aug (5-8)*

㊱ Orchard House, High Oakham Road, Mansfield ⊛ ⊛
(Mr & Mrs Michael Bull) *S side of Mansfield. High Oakham Rd joins the A60-Nottingham Rd at junction with Forest Rd and Waverley Rd, leading to Atkin Lane at the western end.* This garden is one of Mansfield's treasures in a quiet and secluded area. A flower arranger's garden featuring foliage, mixed borders and water. Mature trees help to make it a peaceful and tranquil oasis on the edge of this busy town. Approx ¾ acre. Home-made TEAS. *Adm £2, chd free. Sat 25, Sun 26 June (2-6)*

㊲ 20 The Paddocks, Nuthall & ⊛ ⊛
(Mr & Mrs Bowness-Saunders) *5m NW of Nottingham. From M1 J26, A610 towards Nottingham. At 1st roundabout take B600 towards Kimberley. Paddocks is 2nd rd on L*

after Three Ponds PH. Parking in cul-de-sac restricted, please park on main rd or on L as you enter The Paddocks. Fun garden shared with children and dogs which unlike oil and water do mix in this unusual combination of interesting gardens. Many inspirational ideas incl beach, well, living willow structures, ponds, mature trees, herbaceous borders and vegetables. Mainly organic encouraging a variety of wildlife. A gardener's playground not to be missed. TEAS in aid of Nuthall Methodist Church. *Adm £2, chd free. Sun 11 Sept (2-5).* **Evening Opening** *with illuminations £2.50, wine, Wed 14 Sept (6-9)*

❸❽ Papplewick Hall, Papplewick 🔗🐕❀

(Dr & Mrs R B Godwin-Austen) *7m N of Nottingham. N end of Papplewick village on B683, off the A60. Parking at Hall.* This mature 8-acre established garden, mostly shaded woodland, abounds with hostas, ferns, rhododendrons and spring bulbs. A programme of re-planting ornamental trees and shrubs is being carried out. *Adm £2.50, chd £1. Sun 29 May (2-5)*

❸❾ Park Farm, Normanton 🔗

(Mr & Mrs John Rose) *5m WNW of Grantham. Halfway on lane between Long Bennington & Bottesford, 1m from Normanton village. 5 mins from Long Bennington A1 turn off, & 10 mins from A52, Bottesford.* Created from a flat field site this 5-acre garden incl lakes, formal and informal ponds, scree garden, formal colour garden and Japanese tea house; thatched summerhouse; woodland garden and new lakeside evolving thatched summerhouse. Designer planted with painting in mind. Come and see before the wildlife takes over. Featured in Water Garden' magazine, 2003. Home-made TEAS. *Adm £3, chd free.* **Day and Evening Opening** *£3, Fri 24, Sat 25 June (11-8). Private visits welcome by appt for private club visits only. Tel 01949 842303*

❹❶ Park Farm, Crink Lane, Southwell 🔗🐕❀

(Dr & Mrs Ian Johnston) *1m SE of Southwell. On A612 out of Southwell towards Newark take rd to Fiskerton and 200yds approx up hill turn R into Crink Lane.* This extensive garden commands impressive views of Southwell Minster and the superb surrounding countryside. It has been carefully developed by enthusiasts into a peaceful, private and tranquil garden of 3 acres, which reflects the

owners' passion for a very wide variety of plants, trees and shrubs of both colour and foliage. No coaches. TEAS. *Adm £2.50, chd free (share to Campaign to Protect Rural England - Notts branch). Sun 10 July (2-6).* **Evening Opening** *£3.50, wine, Thur 14 July (5.30-8.30)*

❹❶ 28 Prestwood Drive, Aspley 🔗🐕❀

(Mary Humphreys) *1m W of Nottingham. W of Nottingham along Aspley Lane to T-lights junction with Robins Wood Rd. Turn L into Robins Wood Rd, Prestwood Dr 1st L.* Small plantaholic's garden (50ft x 50ft) incl pergolas, obelisks, gazebo, unusual climbers and plants. Aimed at yr-round interest and showing possibilities of small garden. Becoming known for the unusual size/height of plants. Tranquil atmosphere. Several rare plants and native plants to encourage wildlife. Featuring in ITV's 'Britain's Best Back Gardens' 2005. TEAS. *Adm £2, chd free. Sun 7 Aug (2-5). Private visits welcome by appt, groups of 10 or more. Tel 0115 919 5921*

❹❷ Redlands, 136 Papplewick Lane, Hucknall 🐕❀

(Mr & Mrs J Smith) *5m N of Nottingham. From Nottingham on A611, turn R at Byron cinema. Turn L at 3rd mini island. Garden approx 400yds on R.* ¾-acre, long, plantsman's garden. Herbaceous borders with an abundance of species and varieties. Many ornamental trees and shrubs. Two ponds, incl wildlife pond. Patio areas with baskets and containers displaying a wide variety of interesting and unusual plants. An established garden with many interesting features. To appear in Summer edition of '25 Beautiful Gardens 2005'. Light refreshments and TEAS. *Adm £2, chd free (share to Neuro Degenerative Support Group at QMC). Sun 26 June (11-5). Private visits welcome by appt for garden clubs & groups. Tel 0115 963 1936 j_js@lineone.net*

❹❸ Rose Cottage, 82 Main Road, Underwood 🔗🐕❀

(Mrs Marie Lowe) *10m N of Nottingham. 1½m from J27 M1. Take B608 towards Heanor. Join B600, after about 200yds turn R into Main Rd by large sign for Hole in the Wall Inn.* Flower arranger's cottage garden with ponds; shrubs; small secret garden. Rear garden of approx 1000 sq yds with surprise features, partly developed from a field over last few yrs. Goats and other animals. Featured in 'Garden News' 2003.

Home-made TEAS. *Adm £1.50, chd free. Suns 26 June; 31 July; 21 Aug; 4 Sept (2-6). Private visits welcome by appt. Tel 01773 719556*

❹❹ Roselea, Newark Road, Coddington 🐕❀

(Bruce & Marian Richmond) *1½m E of Newark. Leave A1 signed Coddington, 100yds from junction S; 300yds from junction N.* Gardeners' medium-sized garden closely planted with all seasons in mind. Many clematis, climbers, alpines and some unusual plants adorn this interesting garden. Still developing as the gardeners mature along with the garden. Home-made TEAS in aid of Parkinson's Support Group, Newark. *Adm £1.75, chd free. Sun 24 July (11-5).* **Evening Opening** *Fri 10 June (5-9). Private visits welcome by appt. Tel 01636 676737 richmonds@roselea47.fsnet.co.uk*

2 School Lane, Stow 🔗🐕❀
See Lincolnshire.

❹❺ 125 Shelford Road, Radcliffe on Trent ❀

(John & Elaine Walker) *4m E of Nottingham. From A52 follow signs to Radcliffe. In village centre take turning for Shelford (by Co-op). Approx ¾m on LH-side.* ½-acre designed for overall effect of colour, texture and movement, incorporating many unusual varieties especially hardy perennials and grasses. Front garden is formal in layout with packed, overflowing borders incl hot and cool colour-themed beds. Back is based on flowing curves with informal planting and incl gazebo, pond, bog garden and numerous unusual features. TEAS. *Adm £2, chd free. Sun 24 July (2-5). Private visits welcome by appt for groups of 10 or more. Tel 0115 911 9867*

---

ngs gardens open for charity

Your garden in the Yellow Book?

The NGS is always interested to hear of gardens with potential, large or small, that might open in the future.

For more information about opening your garden, please contact the County Organiser in your area, preferably at the time of year that you would like your garden to open.

46 **NEW** **Squirrel Lodge, 2 Goosemoor Lane, Retford** ⊛
(Peter & Joan Whitehead) *1m S of Retford. Travelling N from A1 on A638, 3m to outskirts of Retford. Travelling out of Retford on A638, last R turn before railway bridge.* L-shaped, mature woodland plot, set in ⅓ of an acre. Horsechestnuts, limes, four separate gardens, shy gnomes! Rockeries, features, colourful borders, frog pond (no need for chemicals) free flowing lawns, courtyard, decks, verandah, kitchen garden. A country feel within walking distance of town. Light refreshments and TEAS. *Adm £2, chd 50p. Suns 8 May; 7 Aug (2-6)*

47 **14 Temple Drive, Nuthall** ৬⊛ ৫⊛
(Mr & Mrs T Leafe) *4m NW of Nottingham. From M1 leave at J26, A610 towards Nottingham. Circle 1st roundabout in A6002 then Nottm Rd lane, leave on minor rd. From Nottingham take A610, turning off at Broxtowe Inn, Cinderhill. Parking restricted, use Nottingham Rd.* ⅓-acre gardeners' mature garden with unusual plants. Winding grass paths separate closely planted, colourful herbaceous and shrub borders. Specimen trees give height and arbours are covered with climbers. Troughs and urns, climbing and shrub roses, fern border and collections of hardy geraniums and clematis. Productive fruit and vegetable garden. TEAS in aid of Cats Protection. *Adm £2, chd free. Suns 8 May; 31 July (2-5). Private visits welcome by appt. Tel 0115 927 1118*

48 **University of Nottingham Gardens, University Park, Nottingham** ৬
(Ian Cooke) *1½m W of Nottingham. From J25 M1 take A52 to Nottingham. The University is 3m from city centre & is well signed from all routes. Gardens tour starts at the Millennium Garden, which is on University Park and well signed within campus. No buses on Suns.* University Park has many beautiful gardens incl the award-winning Millennium Garden with its dazzling flower garden, timed fountains and turf maze. The Jekyll Garden looks lovely in June and Highfields Walled Garden is aglow with exotic plantings in Aug. 300 acres of beautiful landscape. Green Flag Award Winner 2004. TEAS. *Adm £2.50, chd free. Suns 29 May; 21 Aug (2-5)*

49 **32 Victoria Street, Hucknall** ৫⊛
(Miss Perri Morton) *½m N of Hucknall. From Hucknall town centre, take rd towards Mansfield. Victoria St is on R off Annesley Rd, just before National School (on L).* An inspiring small garden with enough plants to fill a large one. All-yr colour and abundant artwork, even visited by the Japanese. A remarkable and amazingly intense garden with ideas for everyone. Featured in 'Amateur Gardening' 2003. *Adm £2. Sun 17 July (12-5). Private visits welcome by appt June & July only. Tel 07939 938837 p.morton@ntlworld.com*

50 **9 Winster Avenue, Carlton** ৫⊛
(Mr & Mrs J Thorp) *4m N of Nottingham. Follow the Carlton Rd into Carlton. Turn L at Tesco past police station. Over the mini island pass the cemetery up Cavendish Rd. R into Cromford Rd. 1st L into Winster Ave.* Front garden with abundance of roses. Rear garden has a very showy collection of standard fuchsias and hanging baskets, mixed flower beds with hostas, perennials and penstemon, giving a colourful presentation. Enjoy a view over Carlton. Children's quiz. Featured on ITV 'Britain's Best Back Gardens' 2005. Home-made TEAS, fresh strawberry scones. *Adm £1.50, chd free. Suns 19 June; 31 July (11-5).* **Evening Opening** *£2.50, wine, Thur 23 June; Wed 20 July (6-9). Private visits welcome by appt. Tel 0115 911 5734*

51 **Woodpecker Cottage, Girton** ৬৫⊛
(Mr & Mrs Roy Hill) *8m N of Newark. W off A1133. 1st cottage on R in village.* Traditional English cottage garden, a feature of which is its informality and diverse nature. Contains wide range of shrubs, herbaceous plants, annual flowers and herbs. Vegetables and fruit are mixed together combining the useful and beautiful. Home-made TEAS in aid of St Cecilia's Church, Girton. *Adm £2, chd free. Sun 27, Wed 30 Mar; Sun 3, Wed 6 July (2-5)*

Evening Opening (See also garden description)	
Roselea	10 June
Bishops Cottage	15 June
Baxter Farm	17 June
9 Winster Avenue	23 June
Park Farm	24 June
Park Farm	25 June
Norwell Gardens	29 June
Camellias	13 July
Home Farm Cottage	13 July
Oakwood Cottage	13 July
Park Farm	14 July
9 Winster Avenue	20 July
The Old Vicarage	14 August
20 The Paddocks	14 September

"Kenneth is a bit of a perfectionist when it comes to lawncare!"

Oxfordshire

County Organisers:	Mr John Ainley, South Newington House, South Newington, Nr Banbury, Oxfordshire OX15 4JW Tel 01295 721207 Fax 01295 722165 email rojoainley@btinternet.com Mrs Angela Baker, Hartford Greys, Sandy Lane, Boars Hill, Oxford OX1 5HN Tel/Fax 01865 739360
Assistant County Organisers:	
(N Oxon: Banbury & Chipping Norton areas)	Mrs Roberta Ainley, South Newington House, South Newington, Nr Banbury, Oxfordshire OX15 4JW Tel 01295 721207 Mrs Lynn Baldwin, 2 Queen Street, Middleton Cheney, Banbury, Oxon OX17 2NP Tel 01295 711205
(W Oxon: Burford, Charlbury, Kidlington & Salford)	Mr & Mrs Michael Drew, Middle Farm, Hailey, Witney, Oxon OX29 9UB Tel 01993 702624
(NW Oxon)	Mrs Priscilla Frost, 27 Ditchley Road, Charlbury, Chipping Norton OX7 3QS Tel 01608 810578
(S Oxon: Blewbury, Didcot, Goring, Henley & Wallingford areas)	Mrs Diana Gordon, Bishop Oak, Jarn Way, Old Boars Hill, Oxford OX1 5JF Tel 01865 735107
(E Oxon: Bicester, Headington, Iffley, Steeple Aston & Thame areas)	Mr & Mrs Jack Lankester, 19 Cumnor Hill, Oxford OX2 9EY Tel 01865 864771
(Editor & Advertising Manager)	Mrs Catherine Pinney, Pond House, Pyrton, Watlington, Oxon OX9 5AP Tel 01491 61238
(Vale of White Horse & SW Oxon: Abingdon, Bampton, Faringdon & Wantage areas)	Mrs Victoria Whitworth, Abbey Farm, Goosey, Faringdon, Oxfordshire SN7 8PA Tel 01367 710252
County Treasurer:	Dr David White, Placketts, High Street, Adderbury, Banbury OX17 3LS Tel 01295 812679 email david.white@doctors.org.uk

Maps: Numbers shown next to each garden entry refer to that garden's entry on the county map. This position is approximate; distance and directions from the nearest main town are generally shown in the garden text.
A precise location is available for those gardens featured on the NGS website by visiting www.ngs.org.uk.

Symbols: Information relating to symbols is given on page 21

DATES OF OPENING

Evening openings
See end of county listing

Private gardens open regularly for NGS
Old Church House, Wantage *(58)*

Gardens open to the public
For details see garden description
Blenheim Palace, Woodstock *(8)*
Brook Cottage, Alkerton *(11)*
Broughton Castle, nr Banbury *(12)*
Chastleton House *(18)*
Greys Court, Rotherfield Greys *(32)*
Kingston Bagpuize House, nr Abingdon *(45)*
Magdalen College, Oxford *(48)*
Nettifers, Lower Wardington *(62)*
University of Oxford Botanic Garden, Oxford *(79)*
Waterperry Gardens, Wheatley *(81)*

ngs gardens open for charity

£1.84 million donated to national nursing, caring and gardening charities in 2004

By appointment only
For telephone number and other details see garden description.
Private visits welcomed
The Arches, Tadmarton *(3)*
Clematis Corner, Shillingford *(21)*
The Filberts, North Moreton *(28)*
Fiveways Cottage, Shutford *(29)*
Home Close, Garsington *(40)*
Home Farm, Balscote *(41)*
The Mill House, Sutton Courtenay *(55)*
9 Rawlinson Road, Oxford *(64)*
Tadmarton Manor, Tadmarton *(77)*
Wheelwright House, Long Compton *(84)*

February 20 Sunday
Waterperry Gardens, Wheatley *(81)*

March 20 Sunday
Wadham College, Oxford *(80)*

March 28 Monday (Easter)
Kencot Gardens, nr Lechlade *(43)*

March 29 Tuesday
Handywater Farm, Sibford Gower *(34)*

April 3 Sunday
Buckland, nr Faringdon *(15)*
Epwell Mill, nr Banbury *(26)*
Kingston Bagpuize House, nr Abingdon *(45)*
Magdalen College, Oxford *(48)*
Merton College Fellows' Garden, Oxford *(53)*
Shotover House, Wheatley *(68)*

April 5 Tuesday
Handywater Farm, Sibford Gower *(34)*
Stansfield, Stanford-in-the-Vale *(74)*

April 10 Sunday
Ashbrook House, Blewbury *(4)*
The Old Rectory, Coleshill *(60)*
Trinity College, Oxford *(78)*

April 12 Tuesday
Handywater Farm, Sibford Gower *(34)*

April 16 Saturday
The Queen's College, Oxford *(63)*

April 17 Sunday
Lime Close, Drayton *(47)*

April 19 Tuesday
Handywater Farm, Sibford Gower *(34)*

April 24 Sunday
Waterperry Gardens, Wheatley *(81)*
Wick Hall & Nurseries, Radley *(86)*

April 26 Tuesday
Handywater Farm, Sibford Gower *(34)*

May 1 Sunday
Adderbury Gardens *(1)*
Friars Court, Clanfield *(30)*
The Manor House, Bletchingdon *(50)*

May 2 Monday (Bank Hol)
Garsington Manor, nr Oxford *(31)*

May 3 Tuesday
Handywater Farm, Sibford Gower *(34)*
Stansfield, Stanford-in-the-Vale *(74)*

May 8 Sunday
Broughton Grange, Broughton *(13)*
Holywell Manor, Oxford *(39)*
Monks Head, Bletchingdon *(56)*

May 10 Tuesday
Handywater Farm, Sibford Gower *(34)*

OXFORDSHIRE

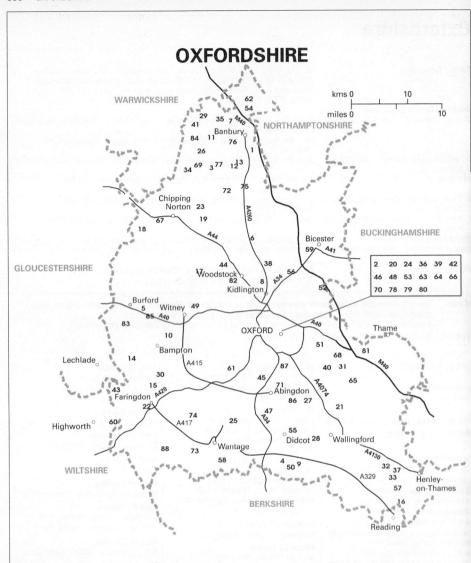

kms 0   10

miles 0   10

WARWICKSHIRE

NORTHAMPTONSHIRE

Banbury

Chipping Norton

GLOUCESTERSHIRE

Bicester

BUCKINGHAMSHIRE

2	20	24	36	39	42
46	48	53	63	64	66
70	78	79	80		

Woodstock

Kidlington

Burford

Witney

OXFORD

Thame

Bampton

Lechlade

Faringdon

Abingdon

Highworth

Wantage

Didcot

Wallingford

WILTSHIRE

Henley-on-Thames

BERKSHIRE

Reading

June 2 Thursday
Monks Head, Bletchingdon **(Day & Evening)** *(56)*
University of Oxford Botanic Garden, Oxford **(Evening)** *(79)*

June 4 Saturday
Hill Court, Tackley *(38)*
Maryland, Fencott, nr Islip *(52)*

June 5 Sunday
All Saints Convent & St Johns Home, East Oxford *(2)*
Hill Court, Tackley *(38)*
Iffley Gardens, Iffley Village *(42)*
Lime Close, Drayton *(47)*
Maryland, Fencott, nr Islip *(52)*
Steeple Aston Gardens *(75)*

June 7 Tuesday
Handywater Farm, Sibford Gower *(34)*
Stansfield, Stanford-in-the-Vale *(74)*

June 8 Wednesday
South Newington House, South Newington *(72)*

June 12 Sunday
Brize Norton Gardens *(10)*
Broughton Poggs & Filkins Gardens *(14)*
Clock House, Coleshill **(Day & Evening)** *(22)*
Lady Margaret Hall, Norham Gardens, Oxford *(46)*
Manor Farm, Old Minster Lovell *(49)*
Salford Gardens, nr Chipping Norton *(67)*

June 14 Tuesday
Handywater Farm, Sibford Gower *(34)*

June 18 Saturday
Hanwell Gardens *(35)*

June 19 Sunday
Asthall Manor, Asthall, nr Burford *(5)*
Blewbury Gardens *(9)*
Charlbury Gardens *(17)*
Coltscombe, Swerford *(23)*
Hanwell Gardens *(35)*
Kiddington Hall, Kiddington, nr Woodstock *(44)*
The Manor House, Wheatley *(51)*
Middleton Cheney Gardens, nr Banbury *(54)*
The Old Manor House, Chesterton *(59)*
Osse Field, Appleton *(61)*
Rofford Manor, Little Milton *(65)*
Sibford Gower Gardens *(69)*

June 21 Tuesday
Hearns House, Gallows Tree Common **(Evening)** *(37)*

June 22 Wednesday
Clock House, Coleshill **(Day & Evening)** *(22)*

June 26 Sunday
Adderbury Gardens *(1)*
Blenheim Palace, Woodstock *(8)*
Broughton Grange, Broughton *(13)*
The Manor House, Blewbury *(50)*
St Hilda's College, Oxford *(66)*

July 2 Saturday
Pettifers, Lower Wardington *(62)*

July 3 Sunday
Somerville College, Oxford *(70)*

July 5 Tuesday
Stansfield, Stanford-in-the-Vale *(74)*

July 7 Thursday
Monks Head, Bletchingdon **(Day & Evening)** *(56)*

July 10 Sunday
Chastleton Gardens *(18)*
25 Newfield Road, Sonning Common *(57)*

July 17 Sunday
Chalkhouse Green Farm, nr Kidmore End *(16)*
Headington Gardens, Oxford *(36)*
Wadham College, Oxford *(80)*
Wayside, Kidlington *(82)*
Whitehill Farm, nr Burford *(85)*

July 24 Sunday
Kingston Bagpuize House, nr Abingdon *(45)*

July 30 Saturday
Christ Church Masters' Garden, Oxford *(20)*
Corpus Christi College, Oxford *(24)*
Greystone, Kingwood *(33)*

July 31 Sunday
Beech Court, Horley *(7)*
Broughton Castle, nr Banbury *(12)*
Greystone, Kingwood *(33)*
191 South Avenue, Abingdon *(71)*
Trinity College, Oxford *(78)*

August 2 Tuesday
Stansfield, Stanford-in-the-Vale *(74)*

August 7 Sunday
Headington Gardens, Oxford *(36)*
Merton College Fellows' Garden, Oxford *(53)*
Shotover House, Wheatley *(68)*
191 South Avenue, Abingdon *(71)*

August 14 Sunday
The Cottage, East Hanney *(25)*

August 28 Sunday
Hearns House, Gallows Tree Common *(37)*

August 29 Monday (Bank Hol)
Hearns House, Gallows Tree Common *(37)*

September 4 Sunday
Ashbrook House, Blewbury *(4)*
Chivel Farm, Heythrop *(19)*
Woolstone Mill House, nr Faringdon *(88)*

September 6 Tuesday
Stansfield, Stanford-in-the-Vale *(74)*

September 11 Sunday
Broughton Grange, Broughton *(13)*
Clock House, Coleshill *(22)*
Epwell Mill, nr Banbury *(26)*
Kingston Bagpuize House, nr Abingdon *(45)*
The Old Rectory, Coleshill *(60)*
Rofford Manor, Little Milton *(65)*

September 24 Saturday
Pettifers, Lower Wardington *(62)*

September 25 Sunday
Garsington Manor, nr Oxford *(31)*
Waterperry Gardens, Wheatley *(81)*

October 2 Sunday
Clock House, Coleshill *(22)*

DESCRIPTIONS OF GARDENS

❶ Adderbury Gardens
3m S of Banbury. J10 M40, onto A422 signposted Banbury, then A4260 to Adderbury. Attractive Hornton stone village with a fine church. TEAS at The Institute, on the green. *Combined adm £3, chd free (share to Katharine House Hospice). Suns 1 May; 26 June (2-6)*

Berry Hill House, Berry Hill Road ⓖⓐ🅡 (Mr & Mrs J P Pollard) *Off A4260 signed Milton, Bloxham, W Adderbury.* 2 acres; mature trees; lawns; shrubbery; mixed herbaceous and shrub borders. Kitchen garden. *Not open Sun 26 June*

Crosshill House, Manor Road ⓖ (Mr & Mrs Gurth Hoyer Millar) Georgian house (not open) surrounded by 4-acre classic Victorian walled gardens. *Not open Sun 26 June*

Fairfield, Cross Hill Road 🅐 (Mr & Mrs M Adams) 'Exquisite' was a remark overheard last yr; this tiny garden is a tapestry of beautiful plants and a patchwork of colour, interwoven with a selection of unusual and interesting clematis. *Not open Sun 1 May. Private visits welcome by appt. Tel 01295 810109*

Home Farm House, Manor Road ⓖ (Mr & Mrs J V Harper) 2 acres; lawns, mature trees and shrubs, newly landscaped paddock, carp pond. *Not open Sun 1 May*

Placketts, High Street 🅐 (Dr D White) *Nr Church.* Queen Anne cottage (not open); 0.2-acre walled garden, sheltered gravel courtyard. Main garden exposed and sunny with views. Many tulips, euphorbias, primulas, anemones. Numerous clematis, roses and lilies. Open both dates.

❷ NEW All Saints Convent & St Johns Home, St Mary's Road, East Oxford ⓖⓐ🅡 (Society of All Saints Sisters of the Poor) *1m E of Oxford. Bus 1 or 5 from Queen St along Cowley Rd. Alight at Manzil Way, cross Cowley Rd, 1st turn R into Leopold St, then 1st L into St Mary's Rd and 1st gateway on L.* Approx 2-acre garden with lawns, mature trees, shrubberies, mixed herbaceous and shrub borders. Vegetable garden; secluded quiet garden and wild flower meadow. Comper Chapel open. *Adm £2, accompanied chd free, concessions £1.50 (share to St Johns Home). Sun 5 June (2-5)*

❸ The Arches, 16 Swalcliffe Road, Tadmarton 👤♿🐕
(Mr & Mrs J Bolland) *5m SW of Banbury. On B4035.* ⅓-acre garden designed and created by present owners since 1983. Formal front garden with heather and ornamental grass beds. Series of garden rooms at rear in various themes. Garden for sitting in. *Adm £1, chd free. Private visits welcome by appt Apr to Sept, weekdays only. Tel 01295 788264*

❹ Ashbrook House, Blewbury 👤🐕
(Mr & Mrs S A Barrett) *4m SE of Didcot. Turn off A417 in Blewbury into Westbrook St. 1st house on R.* 3½-acre chalk garden with small lake, stream, spring bulbs and herbaceous borders. New glasshouse and bog garden. No plant stall for Sept opening. TEAS. *Adm £2.50, chd free. Suns 10 Apr; 4 Sept (2-6)*

❺ Asthall Manor, Asthall, nr Burford
(Rosanna Taylor) *3m E of Burford. At roundabout between Witney & Burford on A40, take turning to Minster Lovell. Turn immed L (signed to Asthall). At bottom of hill, follow avenue of trees and look for car park signs.* 6 acres of garden surround this C17 manor (not open) once home to the Mitford family and overlooking the R Windrush. Sloping parterres and formal lawns with sculptural yew; lake and woodland; orchard and wild flowers; grass mound with spiral path; stone tubs overgrown with roses and borders spilling over gravel paths. *Adm £4, chd free. Sun 19 June (2-6)*

54a Banbury Road, Brackley 🐕🐾
See Northamptonshire.

❻ Barton Abbey, Steeple Barton 👤🐕
(Mr & Mrs P Fleming) *8m E of Chipping Norton. On B4030, ½m from junction of A4260 & B4030.* 15-acre garden with views from house (not open) across sweeping lawns and picturesque lake. Walled garden with colourful herbaceous borders, separated by established yew hedges and espalier fruit, contrasts with more informal woodland garden paths with vistas of specimen trees and meadows. Working glasshouses and fine display of fruit and vegetables. Home-made TEAS in aid of St Mary's Church, Steeple Barton. *Adm £3, chd free. Sun 29 May (2-5)*

❼ Beech Court, Horley 👤♿🐕
(Mr & Mrs V Hillman) *2½m NW of Banbury. From Warwick Rd,*

Stratford Rd into Horley take rd to church. Signposted from there. About ¾ acre; lawns, mixed flower borders, herbaceous borders, rose bed. Lots of pots and baskets incl many fuchsias; goldfish ponds. Interesting walkways, well stocked vegetable garden; all within a walled area. Small new garden water feature. Home-made TEAS. *Adm £1.50, chd free. Sun 31 July (2-6)*

❽ ◆ Blenheim Palace, Woodstock 👤🐕
(His Grace the Duke of Marlborough) *8m N of Oxford. Bus: 20 Oxford-Chipping Norton, alight Woodstock.* Blenheim Gardens, originally laid out by Henry Wise, include the formal Water Terraces and Italian Garden by Achille Duchêne, Rose Garden, Arboretum, and Cascade. The Secret Garden, opened in 2004, offers a stunning garden paradise for all seasons. Blenheim Lake, created by 'Capability' Brown and spanned by Vanburgh's Grand Bridge, is the focal point of over 2,000 acres of landscaped parkland. The Pleasure Gardens complex includes the Herb and Lavender Garden and Butterfly House. Other activities incl Marlborough Maze, putting greens, adventure play area, giant chess and draughts. Light refreshments and TEAS. *Adm call info line on 08700 60 20 80 or visit www.blenheimpalace.com. 12 Feb to 11 Dec (closed Mons & Tues from 31 Oct to 6 Dec incl) (10.30-5.30) Last adm 4.45.* **For NGS:** *Sun 26 June (10.30-5.30)*

❾ Blewbury Gardens
4m SE of Didcot. On A417. Follow yellow signs for car parks. 7 gardens in a charming downland village. Featured on 'Gardeners' World', 2003. Cream TEAS at and in aid of St Michael's Church. *Combined adm £4, chd free. Sun 19 June (1-6)*

Carpenters ♿ (Nick & Melanie Longhurst) Garden surrounds C16 thatched cottage (not open) with mature trees and evolving, mixed planting at the back and remodelled front, designer Robin Williams, 1996.

Chapmans ♿ (Jenny Craig) ⅔-acre garden with listed house (not open) and stream. Informal cottage beds with established and new herbaceous planting featuring some unusual plants. Small wild flower meadow.

Farnley Tyas 👤♿ (Clare Bassett & Fod Barnes) Colourful cottage garden designed by local artist with focus on colour harmonies

in a series of herbaceous borders. Interesting selection of unusual plants, mingled with some old favourites.

Green Bushes 🐕🐾 (Phil & Rhon Rogers) A garden for plant lovers created around a C16 cottage (not open). Large range of plants grown in a variety of settings; colour-themed borders, ponds and poolside planting, alpine troughs, ferns, pleached limes and roses.

Hall Barn 👤♿ (Malcolm & Deirdre Cochrane) Garden and paddocks extend to 4 acres with traditional herbaceous borders and a kitchen garden. Special features include a quality croquet lawn, C16 dovecote, a thatched cob wall and clear chalk streams.

New Inn Cottage 🐕 (Mrs L Fergusson) Small garden redesigned in 2002 addressing the problem of a steep narrow garden. Features a shady courtyard with interesting pond leading up through a series of terraces planted with climbers tumbling down the walls.

Stocks 👤♿ (Richard & Norma Bird) Around this early cruck-constructed thatched cottage (not open), a densely planted collection of lime-tolerant herbaceous perennials offers tiers of colour throughout the year.

❿ Brize Norton Gardens
3m SW of Witney. Brize Norton village, S of A40, or on Burford Rd. . Church open with Flower Festival. Home-made TEAS at Elder Bank Hall & Lingermans in aid of WI. Ice cream at Ramshead Cottage & by bicycle seller. *Combined adm £3.50. Sun 12 June (1-6)*

Barnstable House (Mr & Mrs P Butcher) Delightful small garden; wishing well.

17 Chichester Place (Mr & Mrs D Howard) Medium-sized garden designed with a family in mind. Garden contains a decking area with built-in barbecue, paved areas, a water feature with rockery and shrub borders. Conservatory.

Church Farm House 🐕 (Philip & Mary Holmes) A garden designed with seating areas at different levels and viewpoints and incl herb garden, rockery, water features, mixed borders, pergola, gazebo, greenhouse and pool enclosure with bougainvillea and oleanders.

Gaylyn (Mr & Mrs Wallace) ⅓ of an acre, with mature trees, roses and mixed herbaceous borders.

Lingermans (Mrs E Dobson) *Approx 2m from village.* 1 acre. Sunken garden with pergola, centred border with old-fashioned roses, wildlife area with frog pond, secret garden and mini meadow. Teas also available here. *Private visits welcome by appt in writing, Lingermans, Burford Rd, Brize Norton OX18 3NZ*

Mijeshe (Mr & Mrs M Harper) Enclosed garden with mixed herbaceous borders and duck pond. Gardens to front and rear with many mature flowering beds.

4 Moat Close (Mr & Mrs J Moss) Enclosed garden in quiet close laid to grass with mixed trees, shrubs, borders and patio plants, also two ponds.

Painswick House (Mr & Mrs T Gush) Approx ¾-acre mature garden; old apple trees; herb garden; vegetable garden.

Ramshead Cottage (Ann Elsmore) Small new secret garden. Ice creams available here.

Rosedale (Mr & Mrs S Finlayson) Approx ⅓-acre of mature garden with herbaceous borders, fruit trees and wildlife pond.

School Garden, Station Road [&] (Brize Norton Primary School) Flowers; vegetables; beautiful pond area; chickens and willow dome. All created and maintained with the help of the school children.

Stone Cottage, Station Road (Mr & Mrs K Humphris) Small enclosed garden with lawns, herbaceous borders, shrubs and patio.

⓫ ◆ Brook Cottage, Alkerton [※] (Mrs David Hodges) *6m NW of Banbury. ½m off A422. Follow signs in village.* 4-acre hillside garden formed since 1964. Wide variety of trees, shrubs and perennials in areas of differing character. Water gardens; gravel garden; colour coordinated borders. Over 200 shrub and climbing roses. Many clematis; interesting throughout season. Cream TEAS Bank Hol Mons; DIY tea, coffee, biscuits daily; light refreshments & teas for groups by appt. *Adm £4, chd free, concessions £3. 28 Mar to 31 Oct, every Mon to Fri incl Bank Hols (9-6). Tel 01295 70303 or 670590*

⓬ ◆ Broughton Castle, nr Banbury [& ※ ※]
(The Lord Saye & Sele) *2½m SW of Banbury. On Shipston-on-Stour rd (B4035).* 1 acre; shrubs, herbaceous borders, walled garden, roses, climbers seen against background of C14-C16 castle surrounded by moat in open parkland. House also open, extra charge. TEAS. *House and garden adm £6, chd £2.50, garden only adm £2.50, chd £1. Weds & Suns 1 May to 15 Sept; also Thurs in July & Aug (2-5). For NGS: Sun 31 July (2-5). Tel 01295 276070*

⓭ Broughton Grange, Wykham Lane, Broughton [& ※ ※]
¼m out of village. From Banbury take the B4035 to village of Broughton. At the Seye & Sele Arms (public house) turn L up Wykham Lane (one way). Follow rd out of village along lane for ¼m. Entrance on R. An impressive 25 acres of gardens and light woodland in an attractive Oxfordshire setting. The centrepiece is a large terraced walled garden created by Tom Stuart-Smith in 2001. Vision has been used to blend the gardens into the countryside. Good early displays of bulbs followed by outstanding herbaceous planting in summer. Formal and informal areas combine to make this a special site incl newly laid arboretum with many ongoing projects. Featured in 'Homes & Gardens' 2003, 'Architectural Digest', 2003, 'Gardens Illustrated' 2004. Light refreshments and TEAS. *Adm £4, chd £2. Suns 8 May; 26 June; 11 Sept (10-5)*

⓮ Broughton Poggs & Filkins Gardens
3m E of Lechlade. 7m SW of Burford. Two beautiful Cotswold stone villages. Village maps will be provided. Light refreshments and TEAS at village hall in aid of church. *Combined adm £3. Sun 12 June (2-5.30)*

Broughton Hall, Broughton Poggs [& ※] (Karen & Ian Jobling) Formal walled garden, together with less formal grounds.

Broughton Poggs Mill [※] (Charles & Avril Payne) *On B4477 as it crosses Broadwell Brook, between Filkins & Broughton Poggs.* Contemporary garden, with newly-formed linked 'rooms' in a traditional Cotswold watermill setting, combining local materials with modern planting. Mill workings also open.

Corner Cottage, Broughton Poggs (D & E Stephenson) Flowers, shrubs, fish pond.

Filkins Farmhouse, Filkins [&] (Chris & Barbara Bristow) Traditional walled farmhouse garden. Lawns, borders, rose trellis, orchard.

Goodfellows, Filkins (Mr C Morley) Mixture of formal Cotswold stone terraces by stream and informal planting, bog garden.

Little Peacocks, Filkins (Colvin & Moggridge) Garden made by Brenda Colvin 1956 onwards. *Private visits welcome by appt. Tel 01367 860225*

NEW **The Paddocks, Cross Tree Lane, Filkins** [&] (Pat & Mike Clark) *A few yds down small lane leading from the Cross Tree behind the Cotswold Woollen Weaving Mill at northern end of village.* Informal garden divided by low stone walls into several areas:- meadow garden with duckpond, soft fruits and vegetable garden, rose garden with summerhouse, small fruit-tree lined croquet lawn in former open air theatre. House (not open) is a former stone-built smallholding and barn, c1700 with approx ⅓ of an acre of garden.

NEW **Pip Cottage, Filkins** [& ※] (G B Woodin) Village house garden - formal in front; lawn, hedges and a view at the back. Steps at rear; no ramp.

Sunnyside, Broughton Poggs [& ※] (Peter & Jenny Huggett) Small English garden planted with a traditional flow.

⓯ Buckland, nr Faringdon [※]
(Mrs Richard Wellesley) *3m NE of Faringdon. Signposted to Buckland off A420, Lane between two churches.* Beautiful lakeside walk; fine trees; daffodils; shrubs. Norman church adjoins garden. Home-made TEAS. *Adm £3, chd free (share to Richard Wellesley Memorial Transport Fund). Sun 3 Apr (2-7). Private visits welcome by appt. Tel 01367 870235*

⓰ Chalkhouse Green Farm, nr Kidmore End [& ※]
(Mr & Mrs J Hall) *2m N of Reading, 5m SW of Henley-on-Thames. Situated between A4074 & B481. From Kidmore End take Chalkhouse Green Rd. Follow yellow signs.* 1-acre garden and open traditional farmstead. Herbaceous borders, herb garden, shrubs, old-fashioned roses, trees incl medlar, quince and

mulberries. Rare breed farm animals incl an ancient breed of British White cattle, sheep, Suffolk punch horse, donkeys, Berkshire pigs, piglets, goats, chickens, ducks and turkeys. Vintage farm machinery displays. Farm trail and donkey rides, vintage tractor trailer rides. Swimming in covered pool, plant stall. Dogs on leads only. Cream TEAS in aid of Soundabout, Music for the Disabled. *Adm £2.50, chd under 16 free, wheelchairs & carers free. Sun 17 July (2-6). Private visits welcome by appt. Tel 01189 723631*

⓱ Charlbury Gardens

6m SE of Chipping Norton. Large Cotswold village on B4022 Witney-Enstone rd. TEAS at & in aid of St Mary's Church, Charlbury. *Combined adm £3, chd free. Sun 19 June (2-6)*

Heathfield, Browns Lane &⬤ (Helen & Trevor Jones) *In Browns Lane between Spendlove car park & The Bull. ½-acre* walled garden. Mixed borders, with a variety of interesting plants, have been created over the last six years, by the owners, around newly designed landscape features and existing trees. *Private visits welcome by appt. Tel 01608 810644 trevor.jones@ophiopogon.com*

11 Lees Heights &⬤⬤ (Peter Bridgman) *Turn R off Sturt Rd or take the Slade, turn L at top.* Small garden on clay limestone crammed with plants incl trees, shrubs, herbaceous, ferns, grasses and annuals: some unusual. Many containers; small bonsai collection; wildlife pond; small glasshouse; plant raising area. Owner Kew trained with a lifetime's interest in plants and gardens. *Private visits welcome by appt, individuals or small groups. Tel 01608 810184*

NEW Lydbrook ⬤ (Aija & Christopher Hastings) *Turn R off The Slade by primary school.* A typical long 1930's garden that has been divided into a number of rooms incl patios, lawns and a vegetable patch. Planting includes some exotic species such as tree ferns, bananas and bamboos.

The Priory &⬤⬤ (Dr D El Kabir & Colleagues) *Adjacent to church.* Formal terraced topiary gardens with Italianate features; foliage colour schemes, parterres, specimen trees and shrubs, water features, sculptures and 3-acre arboretum.

⓲ Chastleton Gardens

4m NW of Chipping Norton. 3m SE of Moreton-in-Marsh on A44. Cream TEAS at Chastleton Glebe in aid of village church 10 July. *Combined adm £4. Sun 10 July (2-6)*

Chastleton Glebe (Prue Leith) 5 acres, old trees, terraces (one all red); small lake, island; Chinese-style bridge, pagoda; formal vegetable garden; views; rose tunnel.

◆ **Chastleton House** (The National Trust) *From A436 off A44. Car park 270yds from garden.* 3-acre garden with a typical Elizabethan/Jacobean layout, ring of fascinating topiary at its heart. At Chastleton House (not open) the rules of modern croquet were codified in 1866. Croquet lawn survives.

NEW 1 Glebe Cottage ⬤ (Mr & Mrs Ray Pearse) Plantsman's garden comprising intensely planted island beds, herbaceous borders, alpine garden, pond, many clematis, baskets and pots.

⓳ Chivel Farm, Heythrop &⬤

(Mr & Mrs J D Sword) *4m E of Chipping Norton. Off A361 or A44.* Medium-sized country garden, with extensive views, designed for continuous interest. Colour-schemed borders with many unusual trees, shrubs and herbaceous plants. Small formal white garden. Conservatory. TEAS in aid of Bloxham WI. *Adm £2.50, chd free. Sun 4 Sept (2-6). Private visits welcome by appt. Tel 01608 683227 rosalind.sword@virgin.net*

⓴ Christ Church Masters' Garden, Oxford ⬤

Entrance on Christ Church Meadow, through War Memorial garden on St Aldate's. Created in 1926; has unusual decorative plants within herbaceous borders and new shrub border featuring autumn colour and berries. A walk through the newly designed and replanted Pocock's Garden, past Pocock's Plane, an oriental plane planted in 1636, leads to the Cathedral Garden. *Adm £3.50, chd 50p. Sat 30 July (2-5). Combined with* **Corpus Christi**

㉑ Clematis Corner, 15 Plough Close, Shillingford &⬤ NCCPG

(Mike & Dorothy Brown) *4m NW of Wallingford. At Shillingford roundabout (on A4074), take A329 towards Warborough & Thame. Clematis Corner is 200yds from roundabout, 1st on L inside Plough*

Close, just around sharp L bend. A series of small gardens, within a ¼-acre plot, featuring all types of clematis. A National Collection of herbaceous clematis is grown informally amongst a good selection of other garden plants. Many clematis are also grown in containers for educational purposes and display effect. *Adm £2.50, chd 50p, groups of 10 or more adults £2. Private visits welcome by appt 1 May to 31 July (1-50 persons, coaches permitted). Tel 01865 858721 clematiscorner@supanet.com*

◆ **Cliveden, Taplow** &⬤
See Buckinghamshire.

㉒ Clock House, Coleshill

(Denny Wickham & Peter Fox) *3½m SW of Faringdon. On B4019.* Rambling garden on hilltop overlooking NT parkland and Vale of the White Horse. On the site of Coleshill House, burnt down in 1952, the floor plan has been laid out as a garden with lavender and box 'walls' and gravel 'rooms' full of self-sown butterfly-attracting flowers. Exuberant, not too tidy, garden with unusual plants; walled garden; greenhouse; vegetables. Featured in 'The Times' & 'Oxfordshire Life' 2004. Home-made TEAS. *Adm £2. Suns 22 May; 11 Sept; 2 Oct (2-6). Day & Evening Opening £2, Sun 12, Wed 22 June (2-8). Private visits welcome by appt. Tel 01793 762476*

㉓ NEW Coltscombe, Swerford ⬤

(M J Osborne & N Wellard) *4m E of Chipping Norton. Off A361 to Banbury, turn L off rd to Swerford. Look for sign on this rd which will indicate parking for garden.* Developing garden consisting of: walled garden, parterre, woodland border, meadow, girdle walk through new plantation with views. Home-made TEAS. *Adm £3, chd free. Sun 19 June (11-6)*

㉔ Corpus Christi College, Oxford &⬤⬤

(Mr C Holmes, Domestic Bursar) *Entrance from Merton St.* Several small gardens and courtyards overlooking Christ Church meadow. Fellows' private garden not normally open to the public. *Adm £2, combined adm £3.50, chd 50p. Sat 30 July (2-5). Combined with* **Christ Church**

㉕ NEW The Cottage, Main Street East Hanney ⬤⬤

(Gill Spencer & David Parry) *4m NE of Wantage. Turn into E Hanney off A338 opp restaurant & fork L. 25yd past Black Horse PH on R.* Small ⅓ of an acre S-facing garden attached to C17 thatched cottage (not open). Developed over last 10yrs by a 'plantaholic' and her willing helper, both with busy lives. Herbaceous borders, trees and shrubs enclosing different areas for yr-round interest. Cordon fruit trees, vegetable patch and newly planted terrace. Limited local parking. Village hall car park approx ¼m. Home-made TEAS in aid of The October Club, Wantage (Alzheimer's & Dementia Day Centre). *Adm £2, chd free. Sun 14 Aug (2-5)*

㉖ Epwell Mill, nr Banbury &⊕
(Mrs William Graham & Mrs David Long) *7m W of Banbury. Between Shutford & Epwell.* Medium-sized garden interestingly landscaped in open country, based around former watermill; terraced pools; bulbs; azaleas; autumn colour. White double border. New allium bed. Home-made TEAS in aid of St Anne's, Epwell. *Adm £2, chd free. Suns 3 Apr; 15 May; 11 Sept (2-6)*

㉗ Evelegh's, High Street, Long Wittenham &⊠⊕
(Dr & Mrs C S Ogg) *3m NE of Didcot. Take A415 from Abingdon to Clifton Hampden, turn R at T-lights. Cross river to Long Wittenham. Drive into village - Evelegh's is next to the Plough on RH-side.* ¾-acre garden leading through areas of different characters to River Thames. Well stocked with many unusual shrubs, bulbs and perennials, incl collections of old bush roses, delphiniums, tree and herbaceous peonies, irises and clematis. Flower festival in church. Art exhibition. Plant sale in aid of Long Wittenham Church. Home-made TEAS by WI in village hall. *Adm £2.50, chd under 16 free. Sun 29 May (2-6)*

Evenley Wood Garden, Brackley &
See Northamptonshire.

㉘ The Filberts, North Moreton &⊠⊕
(Mr & Mrs S Prescott) *3m SE of Didcot. Off A4130 (Didcot-Wallingford rd).* 1-acre garden featuring island beds planted for shade, architectural foliage and drought tolerance. Colourful mixed borders with many unusual plants, over 120 varieties of clematis and more than 50 of penstemon; stream and bog garden; lily and fish ponds; vegetable garden; sweet peas; rose beds in parterre form and an orchard.

TEAS & plants in aid of North Moreton Church & Thames Valley and Chilterns Air Ambulance Trust. *Adm £2.50, chd free. Private visits welcome by appt 1 May to 31 Aug. Tel 01235 815353*

㉙ Fiveways Cottage, Tadmarton Road, Shutford &⊕
(Dr & Mrs M R Aldous) *5m W of Banbury. Between A422 to Shutford & B4035 to Shipston, on the Tadmarton Rd.* Just over ½ acre, started 1986. Essentially cottage garden style, with shrubs, roses, small woodland areas, herbaceous beds, borders and ponds. Many clematis varieties grown. *Adm £2, chd free. Private visits welcome by appt June, July & August. Tel 01295 780624*

㉚ Friars Court, Clanfield &⊠
(Mr J H Willmer) *5m N of Faringdon. On A4095 Faringdon to Witney. ½m S of Clanfield.* C16 part-moated farmhouse (not open). Approx 4 acres of informal grounds; moat ponds with examples of woven willow work; woodland and nature trail to lake area. Wind and solar demonstration area, display rooms and shop. TEAS. *Adm £3, chd under 12 free. Sun 1 May (2-5). Private visits welcome by appt, groups of 12 to 50. Tel 01367 810206 www.friarscourt.co.uk*

㉛ Garsington Manor, nr Oxford &⊕
(Mr & Mrs L V Ingrams) *3m SE of Oxford. N of B480.* C17 house of architectural interest (not open). Monastic fish ponds, water garden, dovecote c1700; flower parterre and Italian garden laid out by Philip and Lady Ottoline Morrell; fine trees and yew hedges. Home-made TEAS in aid of local churches. *Adm £3, chd free. Mon 2 May; Sun 25 Sept (2-5)*

㉜ ◆ Greys Court, Rotherfield Greys &⊠⊕
(The National Trust) *3m W of Henley-on-Thames. Signposted from Nettlebed taking B481. Direct route from Henley-on-Thames town centre (unsigned for NT). Follow signs to Badgemore Golf Club towards Rotherfield Greys, about 3m out of Henley.* 8 acres amongst which are the ruined walls and buildings of original fortified manor. Rose, cherry, wisteria and white gardens; lawns; kitchen garden; ice house; Archbishop's maze. Tudor house open with C18 alterations on site of original C13 house fortified by Lord Grey in C14. Donkey wheel and tower. A band plays during the afternoon. Home-made TEAS. *House*

& garden adm £4, chd £2. **For NGS:** *Sat 14 May (2-6). Tel 01491 628529 Abi Barclay-Watt*

㉝ NEW Greystone, Colmore Lane, Kingwood
(Duncan & Carol Heather) *5m W of Henley. Kingwood Common is between Sonning Common & Stoke Row village. Follow Stoke Row Road until you find the Unicorn PH. Turn into the PH as if going to car park. You are in Colmore Lane & Greystone is 1m down lane on RH-side. Parking is 100yds past house on LH-side (one-way system).* Top international garden designer Duncan Heather and his wife Carol are opening their modern 2-acre woodland garden. Mediterranean courtyard, French potager, American-style prairie planting and woodland garden. Featured in 'Garden Design Journal' 2005. TEAS. *Adm £4. Sat 30, Sun 31 July (10.30-5)*

Hambleden Gardens
See Buckinghamshire.

㉞ Handywater Farm, Sibford Gower ⊠⊕
(Mr & Mrs W B Colquhoun) *7m W of Banbury. S of B4035 in Pound Lane towards village.* Hillside garden created by the owners since 1980 in lovely pastoral surroundings in open rolling countryside. Extensive mixed planting around westerly sloping lawns, pond and stream. A peaceful setting for reflection with plenty of seating areas. Light refreshments and TEAS. *Adm £2, chd free. Tues, 29 Mar to 31 May; Tues, 7, 14 June (11-6). Also opening with Sibford Gower Gardens Sun 19 June*

㉟ Hanwell Gardens
2m NW of Banbury. Village access from A423 & B4100, then yellow signs. Small, charming Horton stone village with notable C12 church. Home-made TEAS at New Cottage in aid of Dogs for the Disabled. *Combined adm £2, chd free. Sat 18, Sun 19 June (1-6)*

New Cottage, Main Street ⊠⊕
(Albert & Pat King) Small village garden, mixed planting, many shrubs, roses and old-fashioned plants.

Stonebrook, Main Street &⊠
(Colin & Shiela Palmer) Cottage-type garden, front and rear, with herbaceous borders specialising in hybrid aquilegias, delphiniums and clematis. Plant stall in aid of British Legion.

Vale Cottage &⊠ (Dennis & Shiela Reader) Courtyard garden leading to lawns, borders. Water features.

㊱ Headington Gardens, Oxford
2m E from centre of Oxford. Off London Rd, ¾m inside ring rd. Combined adm £2.50, chd free. Suns 15 May; 17 July; 7 Aug (2-6)

The Coach House, The Croft, Old Headington 🅰 (Mr & Mrs David Rowe) *After T-lights in centre of Headington, 2nd turn on R. Approx ¼ acre behind high stone walls, 2 gardens surrounded by trees: the larger, lawn with mature hedges behind which is tiny woodland garden; the smaller, a courtyard with a gravel garden interconnecting ponds on several levels. Not open Suns 15 May; 7 Aug*

2 Fortnam Close 🄗 (Mr & Mrs D Holt) *Off Headley Way, follow signs to John Radcliffe Hospital. ¼-acre garden on 3 levels, trees, shrubs, heathers, azaleas and large wisteria. Roses, bearded iris and other herbaceous plants in planned layout which incl pond and pergola.*

Greenways, 40 Osler Road 🄐🄗 (Mr & Mrs N Coote) *After T-lights in centre of Headington, 2nd turn on R. Spacious 29yr-old town garden ⅔ acre with mature specimens of exotics. Passion for design and planting, use of decorative pots, mosaic paths, whitewashed walls, shutters: Mediterranean fantasy in a cold climate. Selected to participate in Modern Gardens Open Day (RHS Bicentenary). Private visits welcome by appt, preferably groups. Tel 01865 767680 (after dark) nicholas@coote100. freeserve.co.uk*

Stoke Cottage, Stoke Place 🄐 (Steve & Jane Cowls) *Off St Andrew's Rd. Mature trees and old stone walls provide a framework for a linked series of paths and flower beds containing many contrasting shrubs and plants which give an atmosphere of seclusion. Not open Suns 17 July; 7 Aug*

㊲ Hearns House, Gallows Tree Common 🄐🄗
(Mr & Mrs John Pumfrey) *5m N of Reading, 5m W of Henley. From A4074 turn E at The Fox, Cane End. 2-acre garden in woodland setting provides design and planting ideas for small as well as larger gardens. Good foliage and single colour areas with paved courtyards, water features and shady walks. Wide variety of hardy*

plants incl many new varieties, chosen and propagated for yr-round interest. Jazz evening Tues 21 June, with picnic tables bookable. TEAS in aid of Oxfam. *Adm £2.50, chd free. Sat 14, Sun 15 May; Sun 28, Mon 29 Aug (10-12 & 2-5).* **Evening Opening** *£6, wine, Tue 21 June (6.30-9.30). Private visits welcome by appt, not suitable for coaches. Tel 01189 722848*

NEW The Hill, Thorpe Mandeville 🄐🄗
See Northamptonshire.

㊳ Hill Court, Tackley 🄐🄗🄗
(Mr & Mrs Andrew C Peake) *9m N of Oxford. Turn off A4260 at Sturdy's Castle. Walled garden of 2 acres with yew cones at top of terrace as a design feature by Russell Page in the 1960s. Terraces incl silver, pink and blue plantings, white garden, herbaceous borders, shrubberies, orangery. Many rare and unusual plants. Entry incl History Trail with unique geometric fish ponds (1620), C17 stables, pigeon house, C18 lakes, ice house (not suitable for wheelchairs). Music in gardens (Sun only). Home-made TEAS in aid of village charities. Adm £2, chd free. Sat 4, Sun 5 June (2-6). Private visits welcome by appt for groups during daytime, fee payable. Tel 01869 331218*

㊴ Holywell Manor, Oxford 🄐🄗🄗
(Balliol College Graduate Centre) *In town centre. Corner of Manor Rd & St Cross Rd. Garden of approx 1 acre, not normally open to the public. Imaginatively laid out 50yrs ago around horse chestnut to give formal and informal areas. Mature gingko avenue, spinney with spring flowers and bulbs. Home-made TEAS. Adm £2. Sun 8 May (2-5)*

㊵ Home Close, Southend, Garsington 🄗🄗
(Miss M Waud & Dr P Giangrande) *3m SE of Oxford. Southend. N of B480. 2-acre garden with listed house (not open) and granary. Trees, shrubs and perennials planted for all-yr interest. Terraces, walls and hedges divide the garden into ten distinct areas. Adm £2, chd free. Private visits welcome by appt 1 Apr to 30 Sep. Tel 01865 361394*

㊶ Home Farm, Balscote 🄐🄗
(Mr & Mrs Godfrey Royle) *5m W of Banbury. ½m off A422. C17 house and barn (not open), with attractive views from ½-acre plant lover's peaceful garden giving yr-round*

interest with unusual plants, coloured foliage, flowering shrubs, bulbs and perennials. All created and designed in an informal way by the gardening owners in last 20 yrs. TEAS. *Adm £3. Private visits welcome by appt 1 April to 1 Sept. Tel 01295 738194*

㊷ Iffley Gardens, Iffley Village
2m S of Oxford. Within Oxford's ring rd, off A4158 from Magdalen Bridge to Littlemore roundabout. Map provided at each garden. Secluded old village with renowned Norman church, featured on cover of Pevsner's Oxon guide. Short footpath from Mill Lane leads to scenic Iffley Lock and Sandford to Oxford towpath. TEAS at church hall. *Combined adm £3, chd free, concessions £2. Sun 5 June (2-6)*

NEW 6 Abberbury Avenue
(Philippa Scoones) Established 1-acre family garden with mature borders, shrubs, terrace, water garden, raised vegetable beds and wild flower area. Many features of the original 1930s layout remain. Unusual and interesting plants throughout.

15 Abberbury Road 🄗 (Allen & Boglarka Hill) Variety of beds planted over the last 10yrs in different styles featuring many shrubs, climbers, and perennials.

NEW Cherry Orchard, 26 Abberbury Road (Mr & Mrs Anthony Reid) ½-acre traditional English family garden incl orchard, rose garden, borders and secret garden.

65 Church Way 🄐🄗 (Mrs J Woodfill) Small cottage garden planted with shrubs, perennials and herbs, many of them grown for their historical associations.

122 Church Way 🄐🄗 (Sir John & Lady Elliott) Small secluded cottage style garden with trees, shrubs, roses and herbaceous plants behind listed house (not open) with view of church tower.

The Thatched Cottage, 2 Mill Lane 🄗 (Mr & Mrs Bones) *Mill Lane.* Delightful ¾-acre garden tucked behind C17 village house (not open). Range of specimen trees and plants in terracing; water features, formal gardens and water meadow with Thames frontage. *Private visits welcome by appt. Tel 01865 711453 chrisbones@yahoo.co.uk*

㊸ Kencot Gardens, nr Lechlade
5m NE of Lechlade. E of A361 between Burford & Lechlade. Charming Cotswold village with interesting Norman church. TEAS in

village hall in aid of village hall fabric fund. *Combined adm £3, chd free. Mon 28 Mar (2-6)*

The Allotments Four plots containing vegetables, fruit and flowers. Featured in 'Sunday Times' 2004.

De Rougemont ♿ (Mr & Mrs D Portergill) ½-acre garden with very varied planting: over 350 named plants; beds for perennials, conifers, fuchsias, herbs and roses; spring bulbs; vegetables and fruit trees; soft fruit cage; greenhouse with vine; well.

The Gardens ♿ (Lt Colonel & Mrs John Barstow) ¼-acre garden featuring shrubs, spring bulbs, dahlias, roses, herbaceous, rock plants, old apple trees and well.

Ivy Nook (Mr & Mrs W Gasson) Cottage garden; rockeries, lawns, mixed borders.

Kencot House ♿⚘ (Mr & Mrs Andrew Patrick) 2-acre garden with lawns, trees, borders; quantities of daffodils and other spring bulbs; roses and over 50 different clematis; notable ginkgo tree. Interesting carved C13 archway.

Manor Farm ♿⚘☺ (Mr & Mrs J R Fyson) 2-acre garden with lawns and herbaceous borders; naturalised spring bulbs, incl long-established fritillaries; clipped yew, pleached lime walk, pergola with rambling and Gallica roses. Mature orchards. C17 listed farmhouse, not open.

Pinnocks (Mr & Mrs J Coxeter) Informal garden with mixed herbaceous and shrub borders.

44 **Kiddington Hall, Kiddington, ar Woodstock** ♿⚘☺
The Hon Maurice & Mrs Robson) *m NW of Woodstock. From A44)xford-Stratford, R at Xrds in Kiddington & down hill; entrance on .. Large grounds with lake, parkland lesigned by 'Capability' Brown, erraced rose garden, parterre and >rangery beside house designed by Sir *Charles Barry (not open); C12 *hurch, C16 dovecote, large walled :itchen garden. Rose tunnel, erbaceous borders. Victorian rock arden, riverside walk. Home-made EAS in aid of The Wootton ilympton & Kiddington PCC. *Adm 2.50. Sun 19 June (2-6)*

45 ♦ **Kingston Bagpuize House, r Abingdon** ♿⚘☺
Mrs Francis Grant) *5m W of Ibingdon. In Kingston Bagpuize just*

off A415, ¼m S of A415/A420. Notable collection of unusual trees, shrubs, perennials and bulbs, incl snowdrops, providing yr-round interest and colour. Home-made TEAS. *House and garden adm adult £4.50, concessions £4, chd £2.50, garden only adm £2.50, chd free, concessions £2. 5, 6, 19, 20 Feb; 13, 27, 28 Mar; 3, 16, 17 Apr; 1, 2, 15, 29, 30 May; 12, 26 June; 3, 16, 17, 24 July; 6, 7, 28, 29 Aug; 10, 11, 25 Sept; 9 Oct.* **For NGS:** *Suns 3 Apr; 24 July; 11 Sept (2-5.30).* Tel 01865 820259 Virginia Grant *www.kingstonbagpuizehouse.org.uk*

46 **Lady Margaret Hall, Norham Gardens, Oxford** ⚘☺
(Principal & Fellows of Lady Margaret Hall) *1m N of Carfax. From Banbury Rd, R at T-lights into Norham Gdns.* 8 acres of formal and informal gardens; mixed herbaceous and shrub borders; specimen trees and grasses a specialty; walk by R Cherwell. Home-made TEAS. *Adm £1.50, chd free. Sun 12 June (2-5)*

47 **Lime Close, 35 Henleys Lane, Drayton** ♿☺
(M C de Laubarede) *2m S of Abingdon. Henleys Lane is off main rd through Drayton.* 3-acre mature plantsman's garden with rare trees, shrubs, perennials and bulbs. Mixed borders, raised beds, pergola, unusual topiary and shade borders. Herb garden designed by Rosemary Verey. Listed C16 house (not open). New cottage garden focusing on colour combinations. Plants for sale from Phoenix Perennial Plants. TEAS. *Adm £3, chd under 12 free. Suns 17 Apr; 5 June (2-5.30). Private visits welcome by appt in writing for groups 10+. 35 Henleys Lane, Drayton, Abingdon,*

Oxon OX14 4HU mail@mclgardendesign.com

48 ♦ **Magdalen College, Oxford** ♿⚘
(Magdalen College) *Entrance in High St.* 60 acres incl deer park, college lawns, numerous trees 150-200yrs old, notable herbaceous and shrub plantings; Magdalen meadow, where purple and white snake's-head fritillaries can be found, is surrounded by Addison's Walk, a tree-lined circuit by the R Cherwell developed since the late C18. An ancient herd of 60 deer is located in the grounds. *Adm £3, chd £2, concessions £2. Oct to Mar (1-dusk), Apr to June (1-6), July to Sept (12-6) Every day except 24 Dec to 3 Jan inc. Occasional other closures.* **For NGS:** *Sun 3 Apr (1-6).* Tel 01865 276000 *www.magd.ox.ac.uk*

49 **Manor Farm, Old Minster Lovell** ♿☺
(Lady Parker) *1 ½m W of Witney. Off B4047 rd between Witney/Burford. Follow sign opp White Hart down to R Windrush, 100yds over bridge turn R at Old Swan & up village street. Manor Farm is last house on R before continuing to Crawley. Parking: enter at end of 1st field towards Crawley if approaching from village. Drive back across field to enter close to garden. No parking in village.* 6-acre garden of C15 farmhouse (not open) adjoining Minster Lovell Hall ruin. Old shrub and climbing roses, fish ponds, herbaceous and lawns. Old barns within garden area. Grasses area. TEAS in aid of WI. *Adm £2.50, chd under 12 free. Sun 12 June (2-5)*

50 The Manor House, Blewbury ♿※🅟
(Alice Coptcoat) *4m SE of Didcot. Turn off A417 in Blewbury into Westbrook St, after 1/3m bear R at sign to village hall (car parking in village hall car park). Continue into Berry Lane & house is 20yds on L.* Part C17 Manor House (not open) with moat set in a garden of about 10 acres. Features incl a parterre; flower garden, herbaceous and mixed borders; pergola; decorative vegetable and herb garden; stream planting and woodland area; lake and newly laid out sunken gravel garden surrounded by hornbeam allées. Home-made TEAS. *Adm £4, chd (5-16) £2 (share to The Malcolm Coptcoat Memorial Trust). Suns 1 May; 26 June (2-6). Private visits welcome by appt for groups of 20 or more. The Manor House, Blewbury, Oxon OX11 9QJ alice@coptcoat.co.uk*

51 The Manor House, Wheatley ♿※
(Mr & Mrs Edward Hess) *5m E of Oxford. Off A40.* 1½-acre garden of Elizabethan manor house (not open). Formal box walk; herb garden, cottage garden with rose arches and a shrubbery with old roses. A romantic oasis in this busy village. Cream TEAS in aid of Wheatley Windmill Restoration Society. *Adm £2, chd free. Sun 19 June (2-6)*

52 Maryland, Black Bull Lane, Fencott, nr Islip ♿※🅟
(Mac & Pat Warner) *4m from Islip. 10m NE of Oxford M40 J9 A34 turn to Islip. Turn L to Charlton on Otmoor (4m) to Fencott, turn L into Black Bull Lane.* 2½-acre garden, flowing stream, ponds and grasses in gravel walk, rose garden, kite garden, yew walk. Herbaceous and mixed borders arranged in separate areas. Deep water in ponds. 'Oxford Times' Garden of the Year 2004, overall 1st Prize Winner. Light refreshments and TEAS. *Adm £2.50, chd free (share to Nat Assoc of Colitis & Crohn Disease). Sat 4, Sun 5 June (2-6)*

53 Merton College Fellows' Garden, Oxford ♿※
(Warden & Fellows) *Merton St, parallel to High St.* Ancient mulberry said to have associations with James I; specimen trees incl Sorbus and Malus vars; long mixed border; recently established herbaceous bed; view of Christ Church meadow. *Adm £2, chd free. Suns 3 Apr; 7 Aug (2-5)*

54 Middleton Cheney Gardens, nr Banbury
3m E of Banbury. From M40 junction 11 follow A422, signposted Middleton Cheney. Map available at all gardens. Large village with a diversity of gardens and William Morris church. Home-made TEAS at Peartree House. *Combined adm £3, chd free. Sun 19 June (2-6)*

Brasenose Cottage, 47 High Street ♿※🅟 (Gerald & Betty Chandler) Cottage flower garden. Very peaceful and relaxing.

15 Church Lane ♿🅟 (Dr Jill Meara) *Entrance in narrow lane to L of church spire.* A series of open spaces incl cottage garden, vegetable patch, orchard area and field ending in a stream.

38 Midway ※🅟 (Margaret & David Finch) *Take High St. First R into Bull Baulk. L into Midway.* Small front garden. Back garden with mixed borders and shrubs. Water feature with pond and waterfall and other interesting features.

Peartree House ♿※ (Roger & Barbara Charlesworth) *Glovers Lane is 200yds N of All Saints Church.* Approx ½-acre cottage garden with extensive water feature.

2 Queen Street ※ (Lynn Baldwin) *At roundabout take 1st exit. Queen St is 1st L after 30 mph sign.* Small front and back garden. Informal and densely planted.

NEW 14 Queen Street ※ (Brian & Kathy Goodey) Mature cottage garden that has evolved through family use. Rooms in a rectangle where there is always room for an extra plant.

55 The Mill House, Sutton Courtenay ♿※🅟
(Mrs Jane Stevens) *2m S of Abingdon.* Approx 8½ acres; R Thames runs through garden on several islands now planted with wild flowers. Ruin of an old paper mill and millpond, rose garden and herbaceous border. *Adm £5, chd free. Private visits welcome by appt May, June, mid July, for groups of 10+. Tel 01235 848219*

56 Monks Head, Weston Road, Bletchingdon ※🅟
(Sue Bedwell) *Approx 4m N of Kidlington. From A34 take B4027 to Bletchingdon, turn R at X-rds into Weston Rd.* Plantaholics' garden for all-yr interest. Bulb frame and alpine area, greenhouse. Home-made TEAS at and in aid of St Giles Church,

Bletchingdon (Sun 8 May), Home Farm Trust (weekdays). *Adm £2, £1.50 for groups of over 10 adults. Sun 8 May (2-6);* **Day & Evening Opening** *£2, Thurs 12 May (2-7); 2 June; 7 July (2-8). Private visits welcome by appt. Tel 01869 350155*

57 25 Newfield Road, Sonning Common ♿※
(Joyce & David Brewer) *5m N of Reading. On B481 Nettlebed Rd, on leaving village turn L past Catholic Church, Shiplake Bottom then immed L into Newfield Rd. Free parking behind village hall in Wood Lane, then garden 5 mins walk N.* Interesting garden of ¼ acre developed over 40 yrs. Over 250 varieties of clematis; unusual shrubs, spring bulbs, annuals and containers; mature trees and vegetable plot. Fish pond, waterfall, bantams and miniature ducks. TEAS. *Adm £2, chd free (share to Against Breast Cancer). Sun 10 July (2-6). Private visits welcome by appt. Tel 0118 9723611*

58 Old Church House, Wantage ♿
(Dr & Mrs Dick Squires) *Situated next to Parish Church nr Wantage market square.* Unusual town garden running down to the Letcombe Brook. Much interest with different levels, follies, water, mature trees and many special plants. Light refreshments and TEAS at Vale & Downland Museum. *Adm £1.50. Daily Apr to Sept. Private visits welcome by appt. Tel 01235 762785*

59 The Old Manor House, Manor Farm Lane, Chesterton ♿※🅟
(Mr & Mrs G A Strivens) *2m SW of Bicester. From M40 J9 take A41 direction Bicester. In 1½m turn to Chesterton. At Red Cow public house turn R. In 100yds turn R by church into Manor Farm Lane (no parking, cul-de-sac). Cars can be left in village. Disabled parking in church car park.* 2½-acre dry stone walled garden. Extensive herbaceous and mixed borders. Rose and herb gardens. Double lime avenue planted 1986 enclosed by shrub borders. Large lawned area planted 1988 with oak and hornbeam circles and specimen trees. Mill pond and stream. Listed Norman undercroft dated 1140 with small explanatory exhibition, listed C17 house (not open) incorporating remains of medieval manor house. Home-made TEAS in aid of Chesterton Parish Church. *Adm £2.50, chd free. Sun 19 June (2-6)*

⑥⓪ The Old Rectory, Coleshill 🚻
(Sir George & Lady Martin) *3m SW
of Faringdon. Coleshill (NT village) is
on B4019.* Medium-sized garden;
lawns and informal shrub beds; wide
variety shrubs, incl old-fashioned
roses, 50yr-old standard wisteria.
Distant views of Berkshire and
Wiltshire Downs. House (not open)
dates from late C14. Home-made
TEAS. *Adm £1, chd free. Suns 10
Apr (2-6); 11 Sept (2-5)*

**The Old Rectory Farnborough, Nr
Wantage** 🕸️🏠
See Berkshire.

**◆ Old Thatch, Coldmoorholme
Lane, Well End** 🚻🕸️🏠
See Buckinghamshire.

⑥① Osse Field, Appleton 🚻🏠
(Mrs J Blackwell) *6m W of Oxford.
½m N of A420.* 7 acres of mature
and newly planned garden. Superb
borders. Walled and white gardens
recently designed by Martin Lane
Fox. Rose garden. Meadow walk to
water garden. Large ornamental
kitchen garden. Home-made TEAS.
Adm £3. Sun 19 June (2-6)

⑥② ◆ Pettifers, Lower Wardington
🚻🕸️
(Mr J & the Hon Mrs Price) *5m NE
of Banbury. On A361 Daventry road
from M40 junction 11. Opp church.*
C17 village house (not open). 15 yr-
old 1½-acre plantsman's garden
frames an exceptional view of sheep
pastures and wooded hills. It is an all-
yr garden with unusual perennials
and grasses. It features a beautiful
autumn border. Featured in 'Country
Life' 2003 & 'Gardens Illustrated'
2004. Home-made TEAS. *Adm £4,
chd free. 1st Wed of every month
Mar to Oct (10-4).* **For NGS:** *Sats 2
July (3.30-6.30); 24 Sept (2-5).*
Tel 01295 750232

**⑥③ The Queen's College, High
Street, Oxford** 🕸️
(The Queen's College) *Between
Carfax and Magdalen Bridge.* Front
and back quadrangles are formally
arranged. To the left are the Provost's
and the Fellows' Gardens. The
former, situated beside the Library,
has many interesting plants. The
latter, renovated a few years ago, is
developing into an interesting garden.
The Nuns' Garden has also been
replanted following restoration of the
intervening walls. *Adm £2.50, chd
free. Sat 16 Apr (2-5)*

⑥④ 9 Rawlinson Road, Oxford
🚻🕸️
(Rani Lall) *¾m N of Oxford Centre.
Rawlinson Rd runs between Banbury
& Woodstock Rds midway between
Oxford City Centre & Summertown
shops.* Small town garden with
structured disarray of roses. Terrace
of stone inlaid with brick and
enclosed by Chinese fretwork
balustrade, chunky brick and oak
pergola covered with roses, wisteria
and clematis; potted topiary. Until
autumn, garden delightfully replete
with aconites, lobelias, phloxes,
daisies and meandering clematis.
*Adm £1, chd 50p. Private visits
welcome by appt. Tel 01865 559614*

⑥⑤ Rofford Manor, Little Milton
🚻🕸️🏠
(Mr & Mrs J L Mogford) *10m SE of
Oxford. 1m from Little Milton on
Chalgrove Rd. Signposted Rofford
only.* 2 acres, within old walls laid
out since 1985. Vegetable, herb, rose
and swimming pool gardens; box
garden with raised pool. Yew hedges
and pleached limes; twin herbaceous
borders flanking croquet lawn;
curved ha-ha with views over two
recently constructed lakes. Featured
in 'Gardening Which', 2004. Home-
made TEAS in aid of St James'
Church, Little Milton. *Adm £3, chd
free. Suns 19 June; 11 Sept (2-6).
Private visits welcome by appt 13-18
June & 5-10 Sept. Head Gardener,
Rofford Manor, Little Milton, Oxon
OX44 7QQ*

**⑥⑥ St Hilda's College, Cowley
Place, Oxford** 🚻🕸️
(St Hilda's College) *½m E of
Oxford/Carfax centre. Approx
15mins walk E of city centre. Cross
Magdalen Bridge & turn R at
roundabout into Cowley Place.*
College lodge at end on R, or park in
public car park at St Clements.
Approx 5 acres laid to lawns with
mature trees and flower beds with
flood plain meadow containing
interesting wild flowers; walk by
River Cherwell. *Adm £2, chd under
12 free. Sun 26 June (2-5)*

**⑥⑦ Salford Gardens, nr Chipping
Norton**
*2m W of Chipping Norton. Off A44
Oxford-Worcester rd.* Small village
on the edge of the Cotswolds, with an
attractive church. Home-made TEAS
in garage at Old Rectory. *Combined
adm £3, chd free (share to W I). Sun
12 June (2-6)*

> **Manor Farm** 🚻🕸️ (Mrs P G
> Caldin) Small mature well-
> stocked garden.

Old Rectory 🚻🕸️🏠 (Mr & Mrs
N M Chambers) 1½ acres mainly
enclosed by walls. Yr-round
interest, with some unusual
plants in mixed borders, many
old roses, small orchard and
vegetable garden.

Salford Mill, Worcester Road 🚻🕸️
(Mr & Mrs C Teall) *From
Chipping Norton take A44 for
1½m. Note blue swinging sign by
bridge parapet on R, at lowest
point of road, BEFORE Salford
village. Approx 100yd driveway.*
1½-acre rambling wildlife
paradise! Bog garden, cottage
garden, rose and herb garden,
orchard. Jungly and fun.

Willow Tree Cottage 🚻🕸️🏠 (Mr
& Mrs J Shapley) Small walled
twin gardens with shrub and
herbaceous borders, many
clematis; one garden created from
old farmyard with large alpine
garden.

⑥⑧ Shotover House, Wheatley
🚻🏠
(Lt Col Sir John Miller) *6m E of
Oxford. On A40. Bus: Oxford to
Thame or Oxford to High Wycombe
to London; alight Islip turn.* Large
unaltered C18 landscape garden and
park with lakes, ornamental temples,
lawns and specimen trees; daffodils
and other bulbs in spring, shady
walks in summer. Also small
collections of rare cattle, sheep and
birds. Home-made TEAS. *Adm
£2.50, chd free. Suns 3 Apr; 7 Aug
(2-6)*

⑥⑨ Sibford Gower Gardens
*7m W of Banbury. Nr the
Warwickshire border, S of B4035, in
Pound Lane and in centre of village
nr Wykham Arms public house.*
Superlative views and numerous
intriguing tucked-away lanes are
features of this village. Home-made
TEAS at Handywater Farm.
*Combined adm £3, chd free (share to
Sibford Gower Primary School PTA).
Sun 19 June (2-6)*

> **Buttslade House, Temple Mill Road**
> 🏠 (Mr & Mrs Charles Smith) 5-
> yr-old garden designed by current
> owner. Areas of formal and
> informal planting. ⅓ of an acre
> packed with plants. Roses a
> speciality.

> **NEW** **Gowers Close** 🕸️ (Judith
> Hitching & John Marshall)
> Garden writer's cottage garden,
> tucked behind a wisteria clad
> thatched house (not open). Box
> parterre, herb garden, clipped
> yew hedges, rose smothered

pergola and bosky borders in purples and pinks.

Handywater Farm 🏡⊕ (Mr & Mrs W B Colquhoun) (See separate entry).

The Manor House, Temple Mill Road (Mr & Mrs Martyn Booth) Combination of well established garden and charming extensive patio area provides romantic setting for rambling thatched Manor House, not open.

⑦⓪ Somerville College, Woodstock Road, Oxford 🏡⊕
Enter from the Woodstock Rd, S of the Radcliffe Infirmary. Approx 2 acres, robust college garden planted for yr-round interest. Formal bedding, colour-themed and old-fashioned mixed herbaceous borders. TEAS. *Adm £2 (share to Friends of Oxford University Botanic Garden). Sun 3 July (2-6)*

⑦① NEW 191 South Avenue, Abingdon 🏡
(Susan Hammersley) *On outskirts of N Abingdon follow signs from Oxford Rd (A4183).* Long narrow back garden designed to create an illusion of width. Divided into three areas - formal patio and pond; perennial borders with interesting and unusual plants, mirror feature and gravel planting; potager. Home-made TEAS in aid of Girl Guides Jubilee House rebuilding fund. *Adm £1.50, chd free. Suns 31 July; 7 Aug (2-6)*

⑦② South Newington House, South Newington 🏡⊕
(Mr & Mrs John Ainley) *6m SW of Banbury. South Newington is between Banbury and Chipping Norton, on A361; take lane signed The Barfords, 200yds on L.* C17 yeomans hall house (not open) set in 5 acres paddocks and garden. A charming garden, created for yr-round interest. Tumbling rambling roses, softly coloured herbaceous borders. Ponds, organic fruit and vegetables. Accommodation. Home-made TEAS. *Adm £2.50, chd free. Weds 18, 25 May; 1, 8 June (2-5). Private visits welcome by appt. Tel 01295 721207 rojoainley@btinternet.com*

⑦③ Sparsholt Manor, nr Wantage 🏡⊕
(Sir Adrian & Lady Judith Swire) *3½m W of Wantage. Off B4507 Ashbury Rd.* Lakes and wildfowl; wilderness and summer borders. Wheelchair access by house and immediate surroundings. Home-made

TEAS in aid of Sparsholt Church. *Adm £2, chd free. Mon 30 May (2-6)*

⑦④ Stansfield, 49 High Street, Stanford-in-the-Vale 🏡🏡⊕
(Mr & Mrs David Keeble) *3½m SE of Faringdon. Park in street.* 1¼-acre plantsman's garden on alkaline soil, evolved since 1979. Great variety of plants, many uncommon, shown in appropriate scree, trough, damp, shade or woodland situations. Yr-round interest. TEAS. *Adm £1.50, chd free. Tues 5 Apr; 3 May; 7 June; 5 July; 2 Aug; 6 Sept (10-4). Private visits welcome by appt, incl evenings, also clubs & societies. Tel 01367 710340*

⑦⑤ Steeple Aston Gardens
14m N of Oxford, 9m S of Banbury. ½m off A4260. Beautiful stone village bordering Cherwell valley; interesting church and winding lanes with a variety of charming stone houses and cottages. Map available at all gardens. Home-made TEAS at, and in aid of, village hall. *Combined adm £4, chd free, concessions £3. Sun 5 June (1-6)*

Acacia Cottage (Jane & David Stewart) Approx ½-acre garden within high stone walls, developed since 1998. Herbaceous border, newly paved area around an Edwardian summerhouse and old stone barns. Box edged parterre with white planting in a courtyard setting.

The Court House 🏡 (Margaret & Roger Mason) House (not open) and garden designed and built together in the mid 1980s on a ½-acre plot. Now mature and pleasantly overgrown. Fine summerhouse, pond and intimate courtyard garden. Mostly shrubs and herbaceous plants with many bulbs in pots and naturalised.

Grangelea, Grange Park 🏡 (Julia & Ted Whybrew) ½-acre cottage garden in the stable block of an old manor house (not open). Vegetables, fruit cage and trees, cutting beds, grass, hedges, an interesting statue and a few surprises.

Kralingen 🏡 (Mr & Mrs Roderick Nicholson) 2-acre informal garden created gradually over many yrs by present owners without professional help. Over 200 varieties of interesting trees and shrubs and mixed borders lead down to the tranquil woodland/water/bog garden. Wheelchairs are welcome, but garden is steep.

The Longbyre 🏡 (Mr Vaughan Billings) Hornton stone house (not open) in ¼ acre. Garden constructed out of old orchard. Water feature, mixed perennials, shrubs, tubs on different levels.

Payne's Hill House ⊕ (Tim & Caroline Edwards) Old-established walled garden with some new planting schemes opens out to views across the middle of the village. 1½ acres, incl vegetables and fruit.

Primrose Cottage (Richard & Daphne Preston) Former walled kitchen garden, until the early 1950s, of about 1-acre. For the following 45 yrs it became a commercial vegetable garden. Now a garden in three parts, comprising lawns, herbaceous borders, glasshouses, large vegetable plot, ponds and much more.

Wickhams, Paines Hill 🏡🏡 (Caroline Owen-Lloyd) *Entrance via Payne's Hill House garden only.* A partially terraced cottage garden with mature fruit trees and herbaceous borders. The garden also features vegetable and cut flower patches.

⑦⑥ Stonehaven, Wroxton 🏡⊕
(Mr & Mrs Robert Fox) *3m W of Banbury. On A422 Stratford Rd. Horley Path, opp White Horse public house on main rd.* Just under ¼ acre; level; divided into separate areas to give interest and surprise. Shrubs and perennial flowers; roses and a few annuals. Home-made TEAS at church fête until 4pm. *Adm £1, chd free. Mon 30 May (12-5)*

⑦⑦ Tadmarton Manor, Tadmarton 🏡⊕
(Mr & Mrs R K Asser) *5m SW of Banbury. On B4035.* Old-established 2½-acre garden; beautiful views of unspoilt countryside; fine trees, great variety of perennial plants and shrubs; tunnel arbour; C15 barn and C18 dovecote. Agapanthus bed (Aug); bank of autumn cyclamen; stilted hornbeam hedge. *Adm £2.50. Private visits welcome by appt. Tel 01295 780212*

⑦⑧ Trinity College, Oxford 🏡🏡⊕
(Dr C R Prior, Garden Master) *Central Oxford. Entrance in Broad St.* Historic main College Gardens with specimen trees incl aged forked catalpa, spring bulbs, fine long herbaceous border and handsome garden quad originally designed by Wren. President's Garden surrounded by high old stone walls, mixed

borders of herbaceous, shrubs and statuary. Fellows' Garden: small walled terrace, herbaceous borders; water feature formed by Jacobean stone heraldic beasts. New award-winning lavender garden and walk-through rose arbour. Home-made TEAS in aid of Abingdon Child Contact Centre. *Adm £1.50, chd under 16 free, OAPs & students £1. Suns 10 Apr; 31 July (2-5)*

79 ◆ University of Oxford Botanic Garden, Rose Lane, Oxford ⅏☒☺NCCPG
(University of Oxford) *Situated at E end of High Street in central Oxford, on the banks of the R Cherwell by Magdalen Bridge & opp Magdalen College Tower. The Botanic Garden contains more species of plants per acre than anywhere else on earth. These plants are grown in 9 glasshouses, water and rock gardens, 2 large herbaceous borders, walled garden and every available space. In total there are 6,700 different plants to see. National Collection of Euphorbia.* **For NGS: Evening Opening** *£2.50, Thur 2 June (5-8). Tel 01865 286690 Louise Allen www.botanic-garden.ox.ac.uk*

◆ Upton House, nr Banbury ☒☺NCCPG
See Warwickshire & part of West Midlands.

80 Wadham College, Oxford ⅏☒
Parks Road. 5 acres, best known for trees, spring bulbs and mixed borders. In Fellows' main garden, fine ginkgo and Magnolia acuminata; in Back Quadrangle very large Tilia tomentosa 'Petiolaris'; in Mallam Court white scented garden est 1994; in Warden's garden an ancient tulip tree; in Fellows' private garden, Civil War embankment with period fruit tree cultivars, recently established shrubbery with unusual trees and ground cover amongst older

plantings. *Adm £2, chd free (share to Sobell House Hospice). Suns 20 Mar; 17 July (2-5)*

Warmington Village Gardens
See Warwickshire & part of West Midlands.

81 ◆ Waterperry Gardens, Wheatley ⅏☒☺NCCPG
(Mrs P Maxwell, Secretary) 9m E of Oxford. M40 J8 from London (turn off Oxford-Wheatley, first L to Wheatley, follow brown rose symbol). J8a from Birmingham (turn R Oxford-Wheatley over A40, first R Wheatley, follow brown rose symbol. We are 2½ m N of Wheatley. 8-acre garden featuring rock and alpine gardens, waterlily canal, formal and rose gardens, shrub and herbaceous borders incl our famous 200ft long border. Riverside walks and meadow pastures, nursery beds and trained fruit orchards. Other facilities incl plant centre, craft gallery, museum and Saxon church. National Collection of Saxifraga. Light refreshments and TEAS in Peartree Teashop. Adm Nov-Mar £2, Apr-Oct £4, chd Nov-Mar £2, Apr-Oct £2.50, concessions Nov-Mar £2, Apr-Oct £3.50. Open all year except Christmas week. **For NGS:** *Suns 20 Feb; 24 Apr; 25 Sept (Nov-Mar 9-5; Apr-Oct 9-5.30). Tel 01844 339254 www.waterperrygardens.co.uk*

82 Wayside, 82 Banbury Road, Kidlington ☒☺
(Margaret & Alistair Urquhart) 5m N of Oxford. On the RH-side of A4260 travelling N through Kidlington. ¾-acre garden with wide variety of plants and mature trees; hardy geraniums, fuchsias, clematis and bulbs. Conservatory and greenhouse with tender plants; pergola leading to woodland garden; rhododendrons, tree ferns and extensive collection of hardy ferns. TEAS in aid of EDS Support Group.

Adm £1.50, chd free. Suns 29 May; 17 July (2-6). Private visits welcome by appt May to July only. Tel 01865 460180

83 Westwell Manor, nr Burford ☒☺
(Mr & Mrs T H Gibson) 2m SW of Burford. From A40 Burford-Cheltenham, turn L ½m after Burford roundabout on narrow rd signposted Westwell. Unspoilt hamlet with delightful church. 6 acres surrounding old Cotswold manor house (not open), knot garden, potager, shrub roses, herbaceous borders, topiary, earth works, moonlight garden, rills and water garden. Adm £4, chd under 12 free (share to St Mary's Church, Westwell). Sun 22 May (2-6.30)

84 Wheelwright House, Long Compton ⅏☺
(Richard & Suzanne Shacklock) 4m N of Chipping Norton. Approach village on A3400. House is on Little Compton Rd, at S end of village, 200yds from A3400. 1-acre traditional English garden surrounding an old Cotswold stone house (not open). The centrepiece is a natural stream running through the garden with waterfalls, stepping stones and bridges, lined with moisture-loving plants. Also a formal lily pool, herbaceous borders, rose pergola, topiary features, shade gardens and Mediterranean planting in a sheltered sunny area. A plantswoman's garden with hundreds of spring bulbs and unusual plants. Featured as one of '101 Top Water Gardens' in 'Essential Water Gardens', 2003. Adm £2.50, chd free. Private visits welcome by appt. Tel 01608 684478 rbandsj.shacklock@virgin.net

Whichford & Ascott Gardens
See Warwickshire & part of West Midlands.

85 Whitehill Farm, nr Burford 🛇✻
(Mr & Mrs Paul Youngson) *1m E of Burford. From A40 take turn signposted Widford. Follow signs to Whitehill Farm Nursery.* 2 acres of hillside gardens and woodland with spectacular views overlooking Burford and Windrush valley. Informal plantsman's garden being continuously developed in various areas. Herbaceous and shrub borders, pond and bog area, old-fashioned roses, ground cover, ornamental grasses, bamboos and hardy geraniums. TEAS in aid of Burford WI. *Adm £2.50. Sun 17 July (2-6)*

Whitewalls, Quarry Wood Road, Marlow ♿✻
See Buckinghamshire.

86 Wick Hall & Nurseries, Audlett Drive, Radley ♿✻✻
(Mr & Mrs P Drysdale) *2m NE of Abingdon. Between Abingdon & Radley on Audlett Drive.* Approx 10 acres lawns and wild garden; topiary;

pond garden; rockeries; walled garden enclosing knot garden; young arboretum. Early C18 house (not open), barn and greenhouses, large display of old horticultural and agricultural tools. Cream TEAS in aid of Radley WI. *Adm £2, chd 50p. Sun 24 Apr (2-5)*

87 Wood Croft, Boars Hill ✻
(Ms Sara Dickson, Master's secretary) *2m S of Oxford. From ring rd follow signs to Wootton & Boars Hill. From junction at top Hinksey Hill, house 1st on L.* 1½ acres designed and planted by the late Prof G E Blackman FRS. Rhododendrons, camellias, azaleas, many varieties primula in woodland and surrounding natural pond; fine trees. TEAS. *Adm £2, chd free. Sat 14 May (2-5)*

88 NEW Woolstone Mill House, Woolstone, nr Faringdon ♿✻✻
(Mr & Mrs Anthony Spink) *7m W of Wantage. 7m S of Faringdon. Woolstone is a small village off*

B4507 below Uffington White Horse Hill. 1½-acre garden in pretty hidden village. Stream runs through garden. Large mixed herbaceous and shrub circular border bounded by yew hedges. Topiary. Medlars and old-fashioned roses. C18 mill house and barn, not open. Featured in 'Sunday Telegraph Magazine' 2003. Home-made TEAS in aid of All Saints Church, Woolstone. *Adm £3, chd free. Sun 4 Sept (2-6.30)*

Evening Opening (See also garden description)

Monks Head	12 May
Monks Head	2 June
University of Oxford Botanic Garden	2 June
Clock House	12 June
Hearns House	21 June
Clock House	22 June
Monks Head	7 July

ngs gardens open for charity

Every time you visit a garden which opens for the NGS you are helping to raise money for:

- Macmillan Cancer Relief
- Marie Curie Cancer Care
- Help the Hospices
- Crossroads – Caring for Carers
- The Queen's Nursing Institute
- The Nurses Welfare Service
- The Royal Gardeners' Orphan Fund
- NGS Gardeners' Bursaries – The National Trust Careership Scheme
- Perennial – Gardeners' Royal Benevolent Society
- County Nursing Associations

Additional charities nominated by owners

Waterperry Gardens

The Gardener's Paradise...

Visit Waterperry and discover more than just one of Oxfordshire's most beautiful gardens. At Waterperry we cultivate around 700 cultivars of herbaceous plants for our plant centre, many of which can be seen in the nursery beds and famous herbaceous border.

Friendly and knowledgeable staff are always on hand to offer advice and assistance to both the novice and experienced gardener alike.

Beautiful Gardens & Walks
Plant Centre & Shop
Ceramics, Jewellery & Fine Art Gallery
Country Life and Farming Museum
Delicious Home Baked Cakes & Teas

SEE OUR 2005 EVENTS CALENDAR

OPEN EVERY DAY
Including BANK HOLIDAYS
SIMPLY FOLLOW THE BROWN TOURIST SIGNS

Waterperry Gardens, Waterperry, Nr. Wheatley, Oxford OX33 1JZ
Telephone: 01844 339226
www.waterperrygardens.co.uk

ngs
gardens open for charity

Your garden in the Yellow Book?

The NGS is always interested to hear of gardens with potential, large or small, that might open in the future.

For more information about opening your garden, please contact the County Organiser in your area, preferably at the time of year that you would like your garden to open.

Powys
See separate Welsh section on page 474

Shropshire

County Organiser:	Mrs Sarah Stafford, The Old Rectory, Fitz, Shrewsbury, Shropshire SY4 3AS Tel 01743 850555
Assistant County Organiser:	Mrs Ann Cooke, Harnage Farm, Cound, Shropshire SY5 6EJ Tel 01952 510388
(Press & Publicity Officer)	Mr J Goodall, Rectory Cottage, Chetton, Bridgnorth, Shropshire WV16 6UF Tel 01746 789221
County Treasurer:	Mrs Ann Trevor-Jones, Preen Manor, Church Preen , Church Stretton, Shropshire SY6 7LQ Tel 01694 771207

Maps: Numbers shown next to each garden entry refer to that garden's entry on the county map. This position is approximate; distance and directions from the nearest main town are generally shown in the garden text.
A precise location is available for those gardens featured on the NGS website by visiting www.ngs.org.uk.

Symbols: Information relating to symbols is given on page 21

DATES OF OPENING

Evening openings
See end of county listing

Gardens open to the public
For details see garden description
Angel Gardens, Ludlow *(2)*
Attingham Park, Shrewsbury *(3)*
David Austin Roses, Albrighton *(10)*
Dudmaston, Quatt *(12)*
Hodnet Hall Gardens, nr Market Drayton *(19)*
Jessamine Cottage, Kenley *(21)*
Weston Park, Shifnal *(43)*
Wollerton Old Hall, Wollerton *(45)*

By appointment only
For telephone number and other details see garden description. Private visits welcomed
Diamond Cottage, Buttington, nr Welshpool *(11)*
Limeburners, Ironbridge *(22)*

February 26 Saturday
Attingham Park, Shrewsbury *(3)*
March 29 Tuesday
Radnor Cottage, Clun *(34)*
April 17 Sunday
Moortown, nr Wellington *(28)*
April 24 Sunday
Brownhill House, Ruyton XI Towns *(5)*

May 1 Sunday
Holly Grove, Church Pulverbatch *(20)*
Preen Manor, Church Preen *(33)*
May 2 Monday (Bank Hol)
Millichope Park, Munslow *(27)*
Oteley, Ellesmere *(32)*
May 4 Wednesday
Little Heldre, Buttington *(23)*
May 6 Friday
Wollerton Old Hall, Wollerton *(45)*
May 8 Sunday
Gate Cottage, Cockshutt *(14)*
May 9 Monday
Mawley Hall, Cleobury Mortimer *(26)*
May 10 Tuesday
Brownhill House, Ruyton XI Towns *(5)*
May 15 Sunday
Lower Hall, Worfield *(24)*
Stanley Hall, Bridgnorth *(38)*
May 18 Wednesday
Little Heldre, Buttington *(23)*
May 22 Sunday
Adcote School, Little Ness *(1)*
The Citadel, Weston-under-Redcastle *(7)*
Hatton Grange, Shifnal *(17)*
Highfield House, Whitchurch *(18)*
The Watermill, Maesbrook, nr Oswestry *(42)*
May 24 Tuesday
Brownhill House, Ruyton XI Towns *(5)*
May 27 Friday
Wollerton Old Hall, Wollerton *(45)*
May 29 Sunday
Chyknell, Bridgnorth *(6)*
The Old Vicarage, Clun *(31)*
Ruthall Manor, Ditton Priors *(35)*
Swallow Hayes, Albrighton *(39)*
Walcot Hall, Lydbury North *(41)*
May 30 Monday (Bank Hol)
Brownhill House, Ruyton XI Towns
(Evening) *(5)*
Oteley, Ellesmere *(32)*
Walcot Hall, Lydbury North *(41)*
May 31 Tuesday
Radnor Cottage, Clun *(34)*
June 1 Wednesday
Little Heldre, Buttington *(23)*

June 2 Thursday
Preen Manor, Church Preen *(33)*
June 4 Saturday
The Old Rectory, Fitz *(30)*
June 5 Sunday
The Bayliffe's House, Benthall, Broseley *(4)*
June 6 Monday
Mawley Hall, Cleobury Mortimer *(26)*
June 7 Tuesday
Brownhill House, Ruyton XI Towns *(5)*
June 12 Sunday
Adcote School, Little Ness *(1)*
Gate Cottage, Cockshutt *(14)*
Harnage Farm, Cound *(16)*
Morville Hall Gardens, nr Bridgnorth *(29)*
The Shear, Nash, nr Ludlow *(37)*
June 15 Wednesday
Little Heldre, Buttington *(23)*
June 17 Friday
Cruckfield House, Ford *(9)*
June 18 Saturday
Whittington Village Gardens, nr Oswestry *(44)*
June 19 Sunday
Marehay Farm, Gatten, Pontesbury *(25)*
Whittington Village Gardens, nr Oswestry *(44)*
June 21 Tuesday
Brownhill House, Ruyton XI Towns *(5)*
June 23 Thursday
Preen Manor, Church Preen *(33)*
June 25 Saturday
1 Cross Villas, Ruyton XI Towns *(8)*
June 26 Sunday
1 Cross Villas, Ruyton XI Towns *(8)*
David Austin Roses, Albrighton *(10)*
June 29 Wednesday
Little Heldre, Buttington *(23)*
July 4 Monday
Mawley Hall, Cleobury Mortimer *(26)*
July 5 Tuesday
Brownhill House, Ruyton XI Towns *(5)*
July 6 Wednesday
Little Heldre, Buttington *(23)*
Weston Park, Shifnal *(43)*

SHROPSHIRE

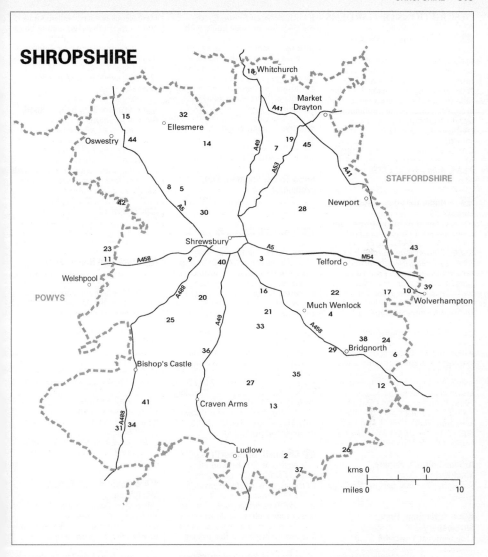

July 10 Sunday
Field House, Clee St Margaret *(13)*
Greythorpe, Gobowen *(15)*

July 14 Thursday
Preen Manor, Church Preen *(33)*

July 17 Sunday
Jessamine Cottage, Kenley *(21)*

July 19 Tuesday
Brownhill House, Ruyton XI Towns *(5)*
Radnor Cottage, Clun *(34)*

July 20 Wednesday
Little Heldre, Buttington *(23)*
Scotsmansfield, Burway Road, Church
  Stretton *(36)*

July 23 Saturday
Dudmaston, Quatt *(12)*

July 24 Sunday
Valducci Flower & Vegetable Gardens,
  Meole Brace *(40)*

July 28 Thursday
Preen Manor, Church Preen *(33)*

August 6 Saturday
1 Cross Villas, Ruyton XI Towns *(8)*
Hodnet Hall Gardens, nr Market Drayton
  (19)

August 7 Sunday
1 Cross Villas, Ruyton XI Towns *(8)*

August 13 Saturday
Hodnet Hall Gardens, nr Market Drayton
  (19)

August 28 Sunday
Jessamine Cottage, Kenley *(21)*

September 4 Sunday
Brownhill House, Ruyton XI Towns *(5)*

October 2 Sunday
Preen Manor, Church Preen *(33)*

October 23 Sunday
Millichope Park, Munslow *(27)*

DESCRIPTIONS OF GARDENS

❶ Adcote School, Little Ness
&.🗷😊
(Adcote School Educational Trust
Ltd) *8m NW of Shrewsbury. Via A5,
turn off NE follow signs to Little
Ness.* 26 acres; fine trees incl beeches,
tulip trees, oaks (American and
evergreen), atlas cedars, wellingtonia
etc. Rhododendrons, azaleas;
landscaped garden. House (part
shown) designed by Norman Shaw
RA; Grade I listed building; William
Morris wallpapers; de Morgan tiles.
TEAS. *Adm £3, chd £1. Suns 22
May; 12 June (2-5)*

❷ ◆ Angel Gardens, Angel Lane, Ludlow 🗷
(Dr K C Elliott & Ms J Roberts) *5m
E of Ludlow. Take A4117 rd off
Ludlow bypass (A49) signposted
Kidderminster. Remain on this rd for
3½m, look out for easily-missed L
turn into Angel Lane. Proceed up
Angel Lane for ½m.* Angel Gardens
on L. 3-acre garden around stone
cottage (not open) at 1000ft. Cottage
enclosed by stone wall and ha-ha
with decking, exotic plants, fernery,
water feature and multi-level
rockeries. Japanese gate leads to lake,
willow pattern bridge and pavilion
tearooms. Gazebo with panoramic
views. Hidden pool with Chinese
swing. No smoking. Accommodation.
Featured in 'Shropshire Magazine'
2004. Light refreshments and TEAS.
*Adm £2.50, chd £1 5-16 yrs. Weds,
Sats, Suns, Bank Hols, 1 May to 30
Sept (2-5). Tel 01584 890381 Dr K
C Elliot & Ms J Roberts*

Arbour Cottage, Napley, Mucklestone 🗷&.🗷😊
See Staffordshire & part of West
Midlands.

❸ ◆ Attingham Park, Shrewsbury 🗷&😊
(The National Trust) *4m SE of
Shrewsbury. From M54 follow A5 to
Shrewsbury then B4380 to Atcham.*
Attingham Park (House not open) is
a landscape park designed by
Humphry Repton. There are
attractive walks through the grounds
and along the river which is lined
with swathes of daffodils in March.
There are also extensive walks
through the woodland and deer park.
Light refreshments and TEAS. *Adm
£3, chd £1.50.* **For NGS:** *Sat 26 Feb
(11-5). Tel 01743 708162*

❹ The Bayliffe's House, 60 Spout Lane, Benthall, Broseley 🗷😊
(Jennie & Derek Osborn) *5m SW of
Telford centre. Signed from B4373 &*

*B4375. Between Ironbridge &
Broseley.* Tudor stone house with
yew hedges in 3-acre woodland
clearing; ⅔-acre plantsman's garden,
designed for colour-themed rooms,
exuberant planting, foliage and yr-
round interest; extending into lower
½-acre wild and species rose garden;
Woodland Trust walks adjacent.
Home-made TEAS. *Adm £3, chd
£1.50. Sun 5 June (2-5). Private visits
welcome by appt, groups of 10 or
more. Inaccessible for coaches.
Tel 01952 883135
derek_osborn1@btinternet.com*

Birch Trees, Copmere End, Eccleshall 🗷&.🗷😊
See Staffordshire & part of West
Midlands.

❺ Brownhill House, Ruyton XI Towns 🗷😊
(Roger & Yoland Brown) *10m NW
of Shrewsbury. On B4397. Park at
Bridge Inn.* Unusual and distinctive
hillside garden (over 600 steps)
bordering R Perry. Great variety of
plants and styles from laburnum walk
and formal terraces to woodland
paths, plus large kitchen garden. 200
varieties of plants for sale, proceeds
to NGS. Accommodation. Featured
in 'Gardens Monthly' 2003, 'The
Shire Journal' 2004. Home-made
TEAS. *Adm £2.50, chd free. Sun 24
Apr; Tues 10, 24 May; 7, 21 June; 5,
19 July; Sun 4 Sept (1.30-5).* **Evening
Opening** *£2.50, Mon 30 May
(6.30-8.30). Private visits welcome by
appt May to Aug. Tel 01939 261121
www.eleventowns.co.uk*

❻ Chyknell, Bridgnorth 🗷&.🗷😊
(Mr & Mrs W S R Kenyon-Slaney)
*5m E of Bridgnorth. Between
Claverley & Worfield. Signed off
A454 Wolverhampton to Bridgnorth
& A458 Stourbridge to Bridgnorth.* 5
acres of magnolias, rhododendrons,
azaleas, roses and herbaceous plants;
interesting shrubs and fine trees in
tranquil park setting. Formal
structure of hedged compartments
designed by Russell Page in 1951.
Hungry light soil susceptible to
drought. TEAS. *Adm £2.50, chd 50p.
Sun 29 May (2-6)*

❼ The Citadel, Weston-under-Redcastle 🗷
(Mr Beverley & Mrs Sylvia Griffiths)
*12m N of Shrewsbury. On A49. At
Xrds turn R for Hawkstone Park,
through village of Weston-under-
Redcastle, ¼m on R beyond village.*
Imposing castellated house (not open)
stands in 4 acres. Mature garden,
with fine trees, rhododendrons,
azaleas, acers and heathers.

Herbaceous borders; walled potager
and Victorian thatched summerhouse
provide added interest. Paths
meander around and over sandstone
outcrop at centre. Home-made TEAS.
*Adm £3, chd free. Sun 22 May
(2-5.30) www.thecitadelweston.
co.uk*

❽ 1 Cross Villas, School Road, Ruyton XI Towns 🗷😊
(Amy Heath & Adrian Thorn) *10m
NW of Shrewsbury. On B4397.
Parking at The Talbot Inn.*
Plantswoman's cottage garden
brimming with scented roses, clematis
and herbaceous perennials. *Adm £2.
Sats, Suns 25, 26 June; 6, 7 Aug
(2.30-6)* **Evening Opening by
appointment** *£2, wine, (6.30-8).
Private visits welcome by appt May,
June, July, Aug. Tel 01939 261052
amelia.heath@btopenworld.com*

❾ Cruckfield House, Ford 🗷😊
(Mr & Mrs G M Cobley) *5m W of
Shrewsbury. A458, turn L towards
Shoothill.* 4-acre romantic S-facing
garden, formally designed, informally
and intensively planted with
substantial variety of unusual
herbaceous plants. Nick's garden,
with many species trees and shrubs,
surrounds a large pond with bog and
moisture-loving plants. Ornamental
kitchen garden with pretty
outbuildings. Rose and peony walk.
New courtyard fountain garden and
an extensive shrubbery. Organically
managed for a number of years.
Home-made TEAS. *Adm £4, chd £1.
Fri 17 June (2-6). Private visits
welcome by appt June & July only,
groups of 25 or more. Tel 01743
850222*

❿ ◆ David Austin Roses, Albrighton 🗷&.
(Mr & Mrs David Austin) *8m NW of
Wolverhampton. Bowling Green
Lane, 4m from Shifnal (A464) L into
Bowling Green Lane; or junction 3,
M54 to Albrighton, follow , brown
signs.* Breeders of the famous English
roses. 900 varieties old roses, shrub,
species and climbing roses. Semi-wild
private garden, trees and water
garden with many plants. Sculpture
by Pat Austin. Dogs on leads. Light
refreshments and TEAS. *Adm £3, chd
free, OAP £1.50.* **For NGS:** *Sun 26
June (10-6)*

⓫ Diamond Cottage, Buttington, nr Welshpool 🗷😊
(Mr & Mrs D T Dorril) *5m N of
Welshpool. 17m W of Shrewsbury.
From Welshpool take A458
Shrewsbury rd for 3m, turn R into
Heldre Lane. From Shrewsbury turn*

L past Little Chef at Trewern into Sale Lane, follow lanes going uphill for 1½m. 1¾-acre plantaholic's garden on steep, N-facing slope at 700ft. Wooded dingle, stream, mixed island beds, pools and vegetable garden. Extensive views to Berwyn Mountains. Adm £2.50, chd free. Private visits welcome by appt Apr to Sept. Tel 01938 570570

⓬ ◆ Dudmaston, Quatt ☷☙
(The National Trust) *4m SE of Bridgnorth. On A442. Bus stop at gates ½m.* 8 acres with fine trees, shrubs; lovely views over Dudmaston Pool and surrounding country. Dingle walk. Home-made TEAS. *Adm £3.20, chd £1.40.* **For NGS:** *Sat 23 July (12noon-6). Tel 01746 780866 Sue Pope*

Edgewood House, Greensforge Lane, Stourton ☷☙
See Staffordshire & part of West Midlands.

⓭ Field House, Clee St Margaret ☷☙☷
(Dr & Mrs John Bell) *8m NE of Ludlow. Turning to Stoke St Milborough & Clee St Margaret, 5m from Ludlow, 10m from Bridgnorth along B4364. Through Stoke St Milborough to Clee St Margaret. Ignore R turn to Clee Village. Field House on L.* 1-acre garden created since 1982 for yr-round interest. Mixed borders; rose walk; pool garden; herbaceous borders; spring bulbs and autumn colours. TEAS in aid of Clee St Margaret Village Hall. *Adm £3, chd 50p. Sun 10 July (2-6)*

Field House Farm, Pipe Gate ☷
See Staffordshire & part of West Midlands.

⓮ Gate Cottage, Cockshutt ☷
(G W Nicholson & Kevin Gunnell) *10m N of Shrewsbury. On A528. At village of Cockshutt take rd signposted English Frankton. Garden 1m on R. Parking in adjacent field.* Garden at present about 2 acres. Informal mixed plantings of trees, shrubs, herbaceous plants of interest to flower arrangers and plantsmen. Pool, rock garden and informal pools. Large collection of hostas; old orchard with roses. Constant alterations being made to incl items of unusual growth or colour. TEAS in aid of WI. *Adm £2.50, chd 50p. Suns 8 May; 12 June (1-5). Private visits welcome by appt. Tel 01939 270606*

⓯ Greythorpe, By Pass Road, Gobowen ☷☙☷
(George & Helen Griffiths) *3m NE of Oswestry. From roundabout in Gobowen, take Whittington rd, Greythorpe is about 150yds from the roundabout on LH-side.* ¾-acre cottage style garden with large colourful mixed herbaceous and shrub borders. Wildlife pond; large lawns; productive vegetable and soft fruit garden; well-used greenhouse. Fruit trees and rough area for chickens and ducks. TEAS in aid of Hope House Hospice. *Adm £3, chd 50p. Sun 10 July (2-6)*

Hales Hall ☙☷
See Staffordshire & part of West Midlands.

⓰ Harnage Farm, Cound ☷☙☷
(Mr & Mrs Ken Cooke) *8m SE of Shrewsbury. On A458. Turn to Cound 1m S of Cross Houses. Harnage Farm 1m, bearing L past church.* ½-acre farmhouse garden; stocked with herbaceous plants, shrubs and climbers. Extensive views over beautiful Severn Valley. 15 min walk through fields to conservation wood and Ian's wildlife pool. TEAS. *Adm £3 (share to The Lingen Davies Cancer Centre Appeal). Sun 12 June (12-5)*

⓱ Hatton Grange, Shifnal ☷☷
(Rupert Kenyon-Slaney Esq) *5m SE of Telford. 2m S of Shifnal. Lodge gate entrance on A464. 1m up drive.* 25 acres surrounding striking Georgian house (not open) with many fine old trees in tranquil parkland setting. Attractive walks through formal gardens and along series of pools in the dingle: with azaleas, rhododendrons, roses, wild flowers, herbaceous borders and shrubbery. Home-made TEAS. *Adm £3, chd free (share to BACUP). Sun 22 May (2-6). Private visits welcome by appt June & July, for groups of 12 or more. Tel 01952 460338*

Heath House, Offley Brook, nr Eccleshall ☙☷
See Staffordshire & part of West Midlands.

⓲ Highfield House, Tarporley Road, Whitchurch ☷☙☷
(Margaret O'Neill) *19m N of Shrewsbury. 20m S of Chester. Take Hill Valley exit from Whitchurch bypass towards the town. Highfield House is approx ½m on L. Large monkey puzzle tree at gates. Parking on Haroldgate opp.* Developing garden of Victorian house. Approx 1 acre, mix of formal and informal.

Herbaceous borders; sloping lawn and terraces; kitchen garden. Also 3-acre paddock with copse of young native trees and large wildlife pond. Variety of farm animals! Bring wellies for walk to pond - umbrellas provided. Light refreshments and TEAS in aid of Bradbury Day Centre, Whitchurch. *Adm £3, chd £1. Sun 22 May (11.30-5.30)*

⓳ ◆ Hodnet Hall Gardens, nr Market Drayton ☷☷
(Mr & The Hon Mrs Heber-Percy) *5½m SW of Market Drayton. 12m NE Shrewsbury. At junction of A53 & A442.* 60-acre landscaped garden with series of lakes and pools; magnificent forest trees, great variety of flowers, shrubs providing colour throughout season. Unique collection of big-game trophies in C17 tearooms. Kitchen garden. Light refreshments and TEAS. *Adm £3.75, chd £1.75, OAP £3.25. Tues to Suns, Bank Hol Mons, Apr to Sept.* **For NGS:** *Sats 6, 13 Aug (12-5). Tel 01638 685786 Mrs Marlene Revie www.hodnethallgardens.co.uk*

⓴ Holly Grove, Church Pulverbatch ☷☙☷
(Mr & Mrs P C Unsworth) *6m S of Shrewsbury. Midway between Stapleton & Church Pulverbatch. From A49 follow signs to Stapleton & Pulverbatch.* 3-acre garden set in S Shropshire countryside. Yew and beech hedges enclosing 'rooms', box parterres, pleached limes, vegetable garden, rose and herbaceous borders containing many rare plants. New arboretum, lake and wild flower meadows. Opportunity to see rare White Park cattle and Soay sheep. Home-made TEAS. *Adm £3, chd free. Sun 1 May (2-6). Private visits welcome by appt. Tel 01743 718221*

㉑ ◆ Jessamine Cottage, Kenley ☷☙
(Lee & Pamela Wheeler) *6m W of Much Wenlock. Signposted from B4371 Much Wenlock to Church Stretton rd and from A458 Shrewsbury to Much Wenlock rd.* 3-acre garden, newly developed since 2000. Mature wildlife pond; large wild flower meadow; mixed island beds; lime avenue; large kitchen garden; new parterre; stream and woodland. One of 250 'Modern Gardens' opened nationally, 2004. Home-made TEAS. *Adm £3, chd £1. Weds to Suns & Bank Hols, 30 May to 4 Sept.* **For NGS:** *Suns 17 July; 28 Aug (2-6). Tel 01694 771279 Pam Wheeler pamandlee@pamandlee.fsnet.co.uk*

㉒ Limeburners, Ironbridge
🚻🐕🏠

(Mr & Mrs J E Derry) *3m S of Telford. Lincoln Hill. On outskirts of Ironbridge. From traffic island in Ironbridge take Church Hill & proceed up hill for ½m, garden on L 300yds below Lincoln Grange.* Garden formerly site of a rubbish tip, developed by owners as a nature garden to attract wildlife. Many unusual shrubs giving yr-round interest; water feature and pool. *Adm £2.50. Private visits welcome by appt Apr to Sept. Tel 01952 433715*

㉓ Little Heldre, Buttington
(Peter & Gillian Stedman) *12m W of Shrewsbury. Off A458. From Welshpool take A458 Shrewsbury rd for 3m, turn R into Heldre Lane. From Shrewsbury turn L past Little Chef at Trewern into Sale Lane, follow signs.* 1¾-acre garden on steep N-facing slope. Terracing; lawns; shrubs; herbaceous borders; pond; gunnera; wooded dingle circular walk. Moon gate giving extensive views to Berwyn Mountains. TEAS. *Adm £2, chd free. Weds 4, 18 May; 1, 15, 29 June; 6, 20 July (2-6)*

㉔ Lower Hall, Worfield 🚻
(Mr & Mrs C F Dumbell) *3½m E of Bridgnorth. ½m N of A454 in village centre.* 4 acres on R Worfe. Garden developed by present owners. Courtyard with fountain, walled garden with old-fashioned roses, clematis and mixed borders. Water garden with pool, primula island and rock garden. Woodland garden with rare trees incl magnolias, paper bark and Japanese maples. Home-made TEAS in aid of Worfield WI. *Adm £3.50, chd free. Sun 15 May (2-6). Private visits welcome by appt . Individuals, groups of 15 to 40. Catering (lunch or supper) available. Tel 01746 716607 dumbell@waitrose.com*

㉕ NEW Marehay Farm, Gatten, Pontesbury 🚻🐕
(Carol & Stuart Buxton) *Marehay Farm is 1½m from 'The Bridges' which lies 10m SW of Shrewsbury on the Longden road, a minor rd towards Bishops Castle (7m) where it is intersected by the very minor rd from Church Stretton over The Burway.* Marehay Garden was established 14 yrs ago on a heavy acidic boulder clay soil. It has evolved with an emphasis on perennial plants, shrubs and trees that will survive 40ins annual rainfall, winter waterlogging and 1100ft above sea level. 1½-acre woodland and water garden. Signposting will be prominently displayed. Semifinalist Percy Thrower's Competition (Shropshire Star) 2003. Home-made TEAS in aid of Chernobyl Children Lifeline. *Adm £3, chd free. Sun 19 June (11-6)*

㉖ Mawley Hall, Cleobury Mortimer 🚻🏠
(Mr & Mrs R A Galliers-Pratt) *11m E of Ludlow. 2m E of Cleobury Mortimer. On A4117 Bewdley-Ludlow rd. Bus: X92, alight at gate.* Natural garden in beautiful country with magnificent views; designed for wandering amongst roses, herbs, flowering shrubs and fine old trees. TEAS. *Adm £3, chd £1.50, OAP £1.50. Mons 9 May; 6 June; 4 July (2.30-5.30)*

㉗ Millichope Park, Munslow
(Mr & Mrs L Bury) *8m NE of Craven Arms. From Ludlow (11m) turn L off B4368, ¾m out of Munslow.* 13-acre garden with lakes, woodland walks, fine specimen trees, wild flowers and herbaceous borders. TEAS Mon 2 May only. *Adm £3, chd 50p (share to Munslow Church). Mon 2 May; Sun 23 Oct (2-6). Private visits welcome by appt. Tel 01584 841234 sarah@burys. freeserve.co.uk*

㉘ Moortown, nr Wellington 🐕🏠
(Mr David Bromley) *8m N of Telford. 5m N of Wellington. Take B5062 signed Moortown 1m between High Ercall & Crudgington.* Approx 1-acre plantsman's garden. Here may be found the old-fashioned, the unusual and even the oddities of plant life, in mixed borders of 'controlled' confusion. Collections of antique daffodils and *anemone nemorosas*. *Adm £4, chd £1. Sun 17 Apr (2-5.30)*

㉙ Morville Hall Gardens, nr Bridgnorth
3m NW of Bridgnorth. On A458 at junction with B4368. A varied and interesting group of gardens that surround a beautiful Grade 1 listed mansion (not open). Home-made TEAS at Morville Hall. *Combined adm £4, chd £1 (share to Morville Church). Sun 12 June (2- last entry 5)*

The Cottage (Mr & Mrs Begg) Pretty walled garden with good climbers.

The Dower House 🚻🏠 (Dr Katherine Swift) 1½-acre sequence of gardens in various historical styles designed to tell the history of British gardening from Medieval times to the present, incl turf maze, cloister garden, Elizabethan knot garden, Edwardian fruit and vegetable garden, C18 canal garden, wild garden. Regularly featured in the owner's weekly Times column.

Morville Hall (Dr & Mrs J C Douglas & The National Trust) 4-acre garden in fine setting, incl box parterre, mature shrub borders, pond garden, medieval stewpond and a small award-winning vineyard.

Poplar Cottage Farm (Elizabeth & Barry Bacon) ¾m NW of Morville on A458. ½-acre flower arranger's garden; yr-round interest, many unusual plants. *Private visits welcome by appt. Tel 01746 714368 elizabeth.bacon@virgin.net*

South Pavilion (Mr & Mrs B Jenkinson) Walled courtyard garden with a collection of hebes and cistus.

1 The Gatehouse (Mr & Mrs Rowe) Large colourful cottage garden with herbaceous, formal and woodland areas.

㉚ The Old Rectory, Fitz 🐕🏠
(Mrs J H M Stafford) *6m NW of Shrewsbury. A5; turn off at Montford Bridge, follow signs; from B5067 turn off at Leaton, follow signs.* 1¼-acre botanist's garden; shrubs, trees; water garden with emphasis on height and shade. Very attractive to wildlife especially vermin. Home-made TEAS. *Adm £3. Sat 4 June (12-5)*

㉛ NEW The Old Vicarage, Vicarage Road, Clun 🐕🏠
(Mr & Mrs Peter Upton) *16m NW of Ludlow. From Ludlow take A49 N to Craven Arms. At 1st roundabout, turn L under railway bridge on B4368, 9m to Clun. L beyond The Sun PH, cross bridge and go straight ahead to church. Turn L by lych gate into Vicarage Rd, garden on R (car park just beyond garden).* A garden since 1680s extending to 2 acres. Lower lawn has wall border and oval garden around a Gothic fountain and cloisters which lead into the Lion Court. Upper garden has plat with clipped yews and double border leading to beech rotunda and woodland walk. Archway leading to wisteria allée, fruit and herb gardens. Home-made TEAS. *Adm £2.50, chd 50p (share to Link Romania). Sun 29 May (2-6)*

㉜ Oteley, Ellesmere 🚻🏠
(Mr & Mrs R K Mainwaring) *1m SE of Ellesmere. Entrance out of Ellesmere past Mere, opp Convent nr*

to *A528/495 junction*. 10 acres running down to Mere, incl walled kitchen garden; architectural features; many interesting trees, rhododendrons and azaleas; views across Mere to Ellesmere Church. Featured in 'Telegraph' 2003. Home-made TEAS in aid of St Michael & All Angels, Welshampton Open to All appeal (2 May), NSPCC (30 May). *Adm £2.50, chd 50p. Mons 2, 30 May (2-6). Private visits welcome by appt, coaches permitted. Tel 01691 622514*

33 Preen Manor, Church Preen &⊗
(Mrs Ann Trevor-Jones) *6m W of Much Wenlock. Signposted from B4371 rd.* 6-acre garden on site of Cluniac monastery and Norman Shaw mansion. Kitchen, chess, water and wild gardens. Fine trees in park; woodland walks. Not suitable for wheelchairs on open days. Sundays, stall for church. Harvest Thanksgiving Sun 2 Oct (4.30). Church in garden. Home-made TEAS. *Adm £3.50, chd 50p. Suns 1 May; 2 Oct; (2-5), Thurs 2, 23 June; 14, 28 July; (2-6). Private visits welcome by appt, coaches, May, June & July, groups of 10 or more. Tel 01694 771207*

34 Radnor Cottage, Clun ⊗&⊗
(Pam & David Pittwood) *7m W of Craven Arms. 1m E of Clun on B4368.* 2 acres on S-facing slope, overlooking Clun Valley. Wide variety of garden habitats all densely planted. Incl sunny terracing with paving and dry-stone walling; alpine troughs; cottage garden borders; damp shade for white flowers and gold foliage; pond, stream and bog garden; orchard; rough grass with naturalised bulbs and wild flowers. Plant sales - share to Clun Surgery. Home-made TEAS. *Adm £2.50, chd 50p. Tues 29 Mar; 31 May; 19 July (2-6). Private visits welcome by appt Apr to July. Tel 01588 640451*

35 Ruthall Manor, Ditton Priors &⊗
(Mr & Mrs G T Clarke) *7m SW of Bridgnorth. Ruthall Rd signed nr garage.* 1-acre garden with ha-ha and old horse pond planted with water and bog plants. Rare specimen trees. Designed for easy maintenance with lots of ground cover and unusual plants. New gravel art garden. Teas available in village. *Adm £2.50, chd free. Sun 29 May (2-6). Private visits welcome by appt. Tel 01746 712608*

36 Scotsmansfield, Burway Road, Church Stretton
Close to Town Centre. 7 min walk NW from Church Stretton car park, up the Burway. Limited parking in Burway Rd. Arts and Crafts house with architect-designed garden set amongst Longmynd Hills. Home-made TEAS in courtyard in aid of Multiple Sclerosis Society. *Combined adm £2.50, chd free. Wed 20 July (2-6)*

No 2 Scotsmansfield, Burway Road ⊗⊛
(Barry & Chris Peer) Central part of this Edwardian garden laid out in 1908. Paved terraces, herbaceous borders, terrace walk. Tennis lawn bounded by yew hedges, leading to orchard/woodland garden. Terraced site with unavoidable steps.

No 3 Scotsmansfield, Burway Road ⊗⊛
(Mavis & Ian Anderson) Western part of Scotsmansfield's Edwardian garden. Rock garden, formal rose garden, paved terraces and steps; lower lawn enclosed by yew hedges; vegetable garden. Sloping site, many steps.

37 The Shear, Nash, nr Ludlow &⊛
(Mr & Mrs R M Knowles) *6m E of Ludlow. 3m N of Tenbury Wells. Off B4214, Tenbury Wells-Clee Hill Rd. Follow sign to The Shear at the Nash turning.* 1½-acres around C15 farmhouse, with glorious views. Shade, herbaceous and mixed borders. Extensive variety of trees, shrubs, climbers, clematis, hardy and tender perennials. Rose walk; sunken garden; lawns; rockery; greenhouse; dovecote. Home-made TEAS in aid of St John the Baptist Church, Nash. *Adm £2.50. Sun 12 June (2-6)*

Smithy Cottage, Mucklestone ⊗⊛
See Staffordshire & part of West Midlands.

38 Stanley Hall, Bridgnorth &
(Mr & Mrs M J Thompson) *½m N of Bridgnorth. Leave Bridgnorth by N gate; B4373; turn R at Stanley Lane.* Drive ½m with rhododendrons, azaleas, fine trees and chain of pools.

Cream TEAS in aid of Astley Abbotts Church. *Adm £2.50, chd 50p. Sun 15 May (2-6.30)*

39 Swallow Hayes, Rectory Road, Albrighton &⊛ NCCPG
(Mrs P Edwards) *7m NW of Wolverhampton. M54 exit 3. Rectory Rd to R, 1m towards Wolverhampton off A41 just past Wyevale Garden Centre.* 2 acres planted since 1968 with emphasis on all-yr interest and ease of maintenance. National Collection of *Hamamelis* and Russell lupins. Nearly 3000 different plants, most labelled. Children's trail; hardy geranium trials. Featured in RHS 'Garden' magazine, 2003, 'Garden Answers', 'Horticulture' (USA), 'Gardeners' World' & on BBC Gardeners World, 2004. Light refreshments and TEAS. *Adm £3, chd 10p. Sun 29 May (2-6). Private visits welcome by appt, entry £3.50 incl tea & biscuits, for groups. Tel 01902 372624 patedwards70@hotmail.com*

Tushingham Hall, Whitchurch &
See Cheshire & Wirral.

40 Valducci Flower & Vegetable Gardens, Vicarage Road Site, Meole Brace &⊗&
(Luigi Valducci) *Meole Brace Garden & Allotment Club. 2m W of Shrewsbury town centre. On A5 exit at Dobbies roundabout, direction Shrewsbury. At next (Meole Brace) roundabout (T-lights), take 2nd exit & continue for 200 yds. Turn into 1st rd on L, follow signs.* 1200 sq yds of gardens and allotments containing 4 greenhouses, orchard and site of Valducci National Collection of Brugmansias (Angel's Trumpets) with over 63 varieties. An Italian style of gardening focusing on vegetables and flowers with a European feel. Light refreshments and TEAS. *Adm £3, chd free. Sun 24 July (12-5). Private visits welcome by appt. Tel 01743 354764 (day), 01743 872030 (eve) valbros@btconnect.com*

41 Walcot Hall, Lydbury North 👤🅶

(The Hon Mrs E C Parish) *4m SE of Bishop's Castle. B4385 Craven Arms to Bishop's Castle, turn L by Powis Arms, in Lydbury North.* Arboretum planted by Lord Clive of India's son. Cascades of rhododendrons, azaleas amongst specimen trees and pools. Fine views of Sir William Chambers' Clock Towers, with lake and hills beyond. Walled kitchen garden; dovecote; meat safe; ice house and mile-long lakes. Outstanding ballroom where excellent teas are served. Home-made TEAS. *Adm £3.50, concessions £2.50. Sun, Mon 29, 30 May (1.30-5.30)*

42 The Watermill, Maesbrook, nr Oswestry 👤🅶🅶

(Frances & John Dexter) *5m S of Oswestry. From Black Horse public house at Maesbrook on B4398 (between Llanymynech & Knockin) take rd signposted 'Melverley'. Continue for approx 1m. Turn R onto Farm Lane and continue to end for parking.* The converted, non-working water mill is situated at the confluence of the Rivers Vyrnwy and Morda. There is a formal courtyard area and a riverside garden in adjoining field, both recently developed. The planting has been selected to cope with extreme conditions incl extensive flooding.

Home-made TEAS in aid of Maesbrook Village Hall. *Adm £3, chd 50p. Sun 22 May (2-5.30)*

43 ◆ Weston Park, Shifnal 🅶

(The Weston Park Foundation) *6m E of Telford. Situated on A5 at Weston-under-Lizard. J12 M6 & J3 M54.* Capability Brown landscaped gardens and parkland. Formal gardens restored to original C19 design, rose garden and long border together with colourful adjacent Broderie garden. Light refreshments and TEAS. *House and Garden Adm £6.50, chd £4.50, OAPs £5.50 , Garden only Adm £3.50, chd £2.50, OAPs £3. Easter to 4 Sept, weekends. Daily throughout most of July & Aug, please ring to confirm opening.* **For NGS:** *Wed 6 July (gardens (11-7), last adm 5; house (1-5), last adm 4.30). Tel 01952 852100 www.weston-park.com*

44 Whittington Village Gardens, nr Oswestry 👤🅶

2½m NE of Oswestry. Daisy Lane & Top St, Whittington. Turn off B5009 150yds NW of church into Top St. Car parking at Whittington Castle (charge) & Top St. 20th yr of opening for NGS. A diversity of 7 adjacent gardens ranging from small cottage to 1 acre. Unusual tree species, small parterres, old-fashioned roses and herbaceous borders. Fruits and vegetables - some old varieties,

hardy orchids, shade plants, water features. Patios and recreational family areas; ornamental grasses; bog and water plants; woodland walk; corn meadow; wild flower meadows. Best Small Garden Winner in 2004 Shropshire Star Competition (Pear Tree Cottage). Home-made TEAS in aid of village charities. *Adm £3, chd free. Sat, Sun 18, 19 June (1-5.30)*

45 ◆ Wollerton Old Hall, Wollerton 👤🅶🅶

(Mr & Mrs J D Jenkins) *4m SW of Market Drayton. Nr Market Drayton on A53 between Hodnet & A53-A41 junction. Follow brown signs.* 4-acre garden created around C16 house (not open). The formal structure creates a variety of gardens each with its own colour theme and character. The planting is mainly of perennials, the large range of which results in significant collections of salvias, clematis, crocosmias and geraniums. Light refreshments and TEAS. *Adm £4, chd £1. Fris (incl Good Fri), Suns, Bank Hol Mons, Easter to end Sept.* **For NGS:** *Fris 6, 27 May (12-5). Tel 01630 685760 J D Jenkins www.wollertonoldhallgarden.com*

Evening Opening (See also garden description)	
Brownhill House	30 May

---

ngs
gardens open for charity

The Yellow Book 2006

£7.99 *including UK p&p*

Available through **www.ngs.org.uk** or by enquiry to the NGS.

T +44 (0)1483 211535 **F** +44 (0)1483 211537 **E**mail ngs@ngs.org.uk

Cheques should be in £ sterling, made payable to The National Gardens Scheme and sent to:

The National Gardens Scheme, Hatchlands Park, East Clandon, Guildford, Surrey GU4 7RT

The book will be posted on publication (Feb/Mar 2006)

Somerset

County Organiser: Miss Patricia Davies-Gilbert, Coombe Quarry, West Monkton, Taunton, Somerset TA2 8RE
Tel 01823 412187 email patricia@pdg98.fsnet.co.uk
Assistant County Organisers: Mr Brian Bradley, Little Yarford Farmhouse, Kingston St Mary, Taunton, Somerset
TA2 8AN Tel 01823 451350
Mrs Dilly Bradley, Little Yarford Farmhouse, Kingston St Mary, Taunton, Somerset
TA2 8AN Tel 01823 451350
Miss Glenda Bryan, Blagdon House Lodge, Blagdon, North Somerset BS40 7TD
Tel 01761 462121
Mrs Lella Fountaine, 116 Wellsway, Bath BA2 4SD Tel 01225 334821
Ms Lucy Hetherington, Badgers Acre, Stone Allerton, Axbridge, Somerset BS26 2NW
Tel 01934 713159
Mrs Betty Hudspith, Rookwood, West Street, Hinton St George, Somerset TA17 8SA
Tel 01460 73450
Press & Publicity Officer: Mr Alan Hughes, Dodhill Firs, Nailsbourne, Taunton, Somerset TA2 8AT
Tel 01823 451633 email dodhill@hotmail.com
Mrs Alison Kelly, Candleford, Fernhill, East Stour, Nr Gillingham, Dorset SP8 5ND
Tel 01747 838133
Mrs Diana Sprent, Watermeadows, Clapton, Crewkerne, Somerset TA18 8PU
Tel 01460 74421
Mrs Beryl Stunt, The Close, Church Street, Blagdon, Somerset BS40 7SJ
Tel 01761 462349
County Treasurer: Mr John Spurrier, Tudor Cottage, 19 Comeytrowe Lane, Taunton, Somerset TA1 5PA
Tel 01823 333827

Maps: Numbers shown next to each garden entry refer to that garden's entry on the county map. This position is approximate; distance and directions from the nearest main town are generally shown in the garden text.
A precise location is available for those gardens featured on the NGS website by visiting www.ngs.org.uk.
Symbols: Information relating to symbols is given on page 21

DATES OF OPENING

Evening openings
See end of county listing

Private gardens open regularly for NGS
Little Garth, Dowlish Wake (54)

Gardens open to the public
For details see garden description

Barrington Court, Ilminster (5)
Cothay Manor, Greenham (20)
Crowe Hall, Widcombe (22)
Dunster Castle, Dunster (23)
East Lambrook Manor Gardens, East
Lambrook (24)
Elworthy Cottage, Elworthy (25)
Gants Mill & Garden, Bruton (29)
Gaulden Manor, Tolland (30)
Greencombe, Porlock (33)
Hadspen Garden, Castle Cary (34)
Hestercombe Gardens, Cheddon Fitzpaine
(41)
Kingsdon, Somerton (50)
Lower Severalls, Crewkerne (56)
Milton Lodge, Wells (61)
Montacute House, Montacute (62)
Prior Park Landscape Garden, Bath (71)
The Time-Trail of Roses, Wells (79)
Tintinhull, nr Yeovil (80)

By appointment only
For telephone number and other
details see garden description.
Private visits welcomed
Acers, West Chinnock (2)
Bourne House, Burrington (10)
Henley Mill, Wookey (40)
King Ina's Palace, South Petherton (49)
Sunnyside, Yarley (76)
Walnut Farm, Yarley (83)

February 13 Sunday
The Time-Trail of Roses, Wells (79)
March 8 Tuesday
Hestercombe Gardens, Cheddon Fitzpaine (41)
March 13 Sunday
Langford Court, Langford (53)
The Time-Trail of Roses, Wells (79)
March 19 Saturday
Uplands, Minehead (81)
March 20 Sunday
Fairfield, nr Stogursey (26)
Uplands, Minehead (81)
March 23 Wednesday
Somerfoss, Oakhill (73)
March 26 Saturday (Easter)
Elworthy Cottage, Elworthy (25)
March 28 Monday (Easter)
Elworthy Cottage, Elworthy (25)
April 2 Saturday
Stowleys, Porlock (75)

April 3 Sunday
Coley Court, Coley & Widcombe Lodge,
East Harptree (18)
Glencot House, Wookey Hole (31)
April 10 Sunday
Crowe Hall, Widcombe (22)
Elworthy Cottage, Elworthy (25)
Kingsdon, Somerton (50)
The Time-Trail of Roses, Wells (79)
Wayford Manor, Crewkerne (85)
April 17 Sunday
Montys Court, Norton Fitzwarren (63)
April 19 Tuesday
Bath Priory Hotel, Bath (9)
April 20 Wednesday
Somerfoss, Oakhill (73)
April 23 Saturday
Uplands, Minehead (81)
April 24 Sunday
Barrington Court, Ilminster (5)
Hadspen Garden, Castle Cary (34)
Hangeridge Farm, Wrangway (35)
Hartford Lodge, Brompton Regis (38)
Kingsdon, Somerton (50)
Somerfoss, Oakhill (73)
Uplands, Minehead (81)
May 1 Sunday
Holt Farm, Blagdon (46)
Lower Severalls, Crewkerne (56)
Thurloxton Gardens (78)
Wayford Manor, Crewkerne (85)

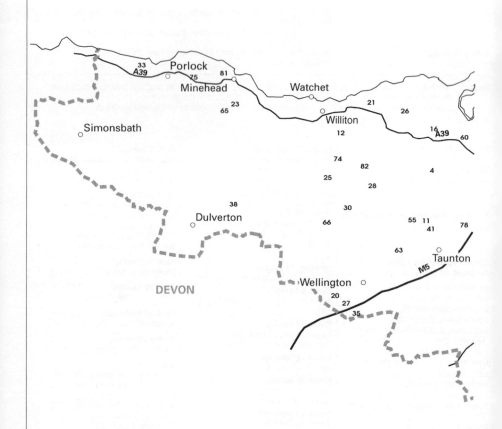

SOMERSET

kms 0   10

miles 0   10

33
A39

Porlock

75

81

Minehead

Watchet

23

21

65

26

Williton

12

16
A39

60

Simonsbath

74

82

4

25

28

38

30

Dulverton

66

55 11

41

78

63

Taunton

DEVON

Wellington

M5

20

27

35

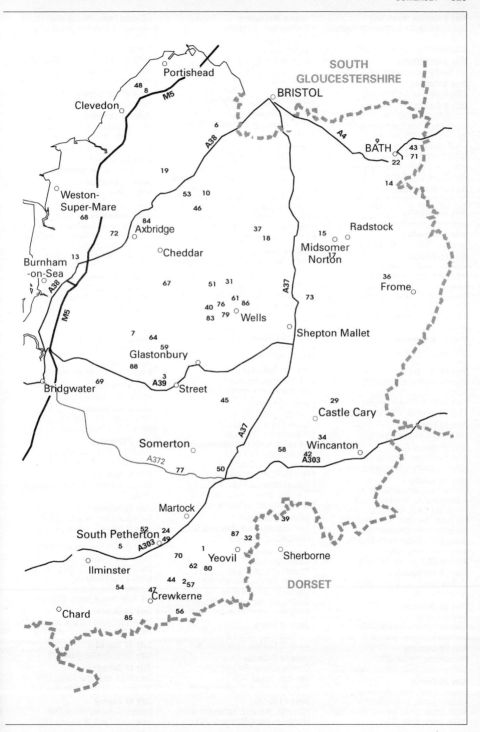

SOUTH GLOUCESTERSHIRE

Portishead

48 8
M5

Clevedon

BRISTOL

6
A38

A4

9
BATH
22
43
71

19

14

Weston-Super-Mare
68

53 10
46

84
Axbridge

72

37
18

Radstock

15

Midsomer Norton
17

36
Frome

Cheddar

13

Burnham -on-Sea

A38

67

51 31

A37

73

M5

40 76 61 86
83 79 Wells

7 64

59
Glastonbury

88

Shepton Mallet

3
A39
Street

69

Bridgwater

45

29
Castle Cary

Somerton

A37

34
Wincanton
42
A303

58

A372

77

50

Martock

39

52 24
South Petherton 49
5
A303

87 32

70
62 80
Yeovil
1

Sherborne

Ilminster

DORSET

54

44 2 57

47
Crewkerne

Chard

85

56

May 2 Monday (Bank Hol)
Cannington Centre Gardens, Cannington *(16)*
Wayford Manor, Crewkerne *(85)*

May 4 Wednesday
Rackley House, Compton Bishop *(72)*

May 5 Thursday
Little Garth, Dowlish Wake *(54)*

May 8 Sunday
Barton Farm, Catcott *(7)*
Court House, East Quantoxhead *(21)*
Hewletts Mill, Galhampton *(42)*
Lower Severalls, Crewkerne *(56)*
Old Orchard, Catcott *(64)*
The Time-Trail of Roses, Wells *(79)*
Zool House, Catcott *(88)*

May 11 Wednesday
Rackley House, Compton Bishop *(72)*

May 12 Thursday
Little Garth, Dowlish Wake *(54)*

May 14 Saturday
Hooper's Holding, Hinton St George *(47)*

May 15 Sunday
Flaxpool House, Crowcombe *(28)*
Hooper's Holding, Hinton St George *(47)*
Kites Croft, Westbury-sub-Mendip *(51)*
Lower Severalls, Crewkerne *(56)*
Milton Lodge, Wells *(61)*
Woodside, East Stoke, Stoke-sub-Hamdon *(87)*

May 18 Wednesday
Kites Croft, Westbury-sub-Mendip *(51)*
Rackley House, Compton Bishop *(72)*

May 19 Thursday
Elworthy Cottage, Elworthy *(25)*
Jasmine Cottage, Clevedon *(48)*
Little Garth, Dowlish Wake *(54)*
Vellacott, Lawford, Crowcombe *(82)*

May 20 Friday
Hapsford House, Great Elm *(36)*

May 21 Saturday
Elworthy Cottage, Elworthy *(25)*
Vellacott, Lawford, Crowcombe *(82)*

May 22 Sunday
Barrow Court, Barrow Gurney *(6)*
4 Brendon View, Crowcombe *(12)*
Hangeridge Farm, Wrangway *(35)*
Hill Lodge, Northend, Batheaston *(43)*
Lower Severalls, Crewkerne *(56)*
Manor Farm, Middle Chinnock *(57)*
Watcombe, Winscombe *(84)*
Wayford Manor, Crewkerne *(85)*

May 25 Wednesday
Rackley House, Compton Bishop *(72)*
Somerfoss, Oakhill *(73)*

May 26 Thursday
Barum, Clevedon *(8)*
Jasmine Cottage, Clevedon *(48)*
Little Garth, Dowlish Wake *(54)*

May 28 Saturday
Greencombe, Porlock *(33)*
Maple House, South Barrow, Yeovil *(58)*

May 29 Sunday
Harptree Court, East Harptree *(37)*
Lower Severalls, Crewkerne *(56)*
Maple House, South Barrow, Yeovil *(58)*
Milton Lodge, Wells *(61)*

June 1 Wednesday
Wellfield Barn, Wells *(86)*

June 2 Thursday
Barum, Clevedon *(8)*
Elworthy Cottage, Elworthy *(25)*
Hartford Lodge, Brompton Regis *(38)*
Jasmine Cottage, Clevedon *(48)*
Little Garth, Dowlish Wake *(54)*
Overbrook Cottage, nr Wedmore *(67)*

June 4 Saturday
Hinton St George Gardens, nr Crewkerne *(44)*

June 5 Sunday
Barton Farm, Catcott *(7)*
4 Brendon View, Crowcombe *(12)*
Hinton St George Gardens, nr Crewkerne *(44)*
The Hollies, Barton St David *(45)*
Holt Farm, Blagdon *(46)*
Lower Severalls, Crewkerne *(56)*
Old Orchard, Catcott *(64)*
Zool House, Catcott *(88)*

June 7 Tuesday
Hestercombe Gardens, Cheddon Fitzpaine *(41)*

June 8 Wednesday
Gaulden Manor, Tolland *(30)*

June 9 Thursday
Barum, Clevedon *(8)*
Gaulden Manor, Tolland *(30)*
Jasmine Cottage, Clevedon *(48)*
Little Garth, Dowlish Wake *(54)*
Overbrook Cottage, nr Wedmore *(67)*

June 11 Saturday
190 Goldcroft, Yeovil *(32)*
Rackley House, Compton Bishop *(72)*

June 12 Sunday
Ashcott Gardens *(3)*
Crowe Hall, Widcombe *(22)*
190 Goldcroft, Yeovil *(32)*
Hill Lodge, Northend, Batheaston *(43)*
Milton Lodge, Wells *(61)*
Penwood Farm, Chedzoy *(69)*
Prior Park Landscape Garden, Bath *(71)*
Rackley House, Compton Bishop *(72)*
The Time-Trail of Roses, Wells *(79)*
Wayford Manor, Crewkerne *(85)*

June 13 Monday
190 Goldcroft, Yeovil **(Evening)** *(32)*
Penwood Farm, Chedzoy *(69)*

June 16 Thursday
Barum, Clevedon *(8)*
Elworthy Cottage, Elworthy *(25)*
Jasmine Cottage, Clevedon *(48)*
Little Garth, Dowlish Wake *(54)*
Overbrook Cottage, nr Wedmore *(67)*
Vellacott, Lawford, Crowcombe *(82)*

June 17 Friday
Hapsford House, Great Elm *(36)*
Vellacott, Lawford, Crowcombe *(82)*

June 18 Saturday
Elworthy Cottage, Elworthy *(25)*
Stowleys, Porlock *(75)*
Vellacott, Lawford, Crowcombe *(82)*

June 19 Sunday
Hill Lodge, Northend, Batheaston *(43)*
Montacute House, Montacute *(62)*

Penwood Farm, Chedzoy *(69)*
Popinjays & Little Norton Mill, Little Norton *(70)*
Stogumber Gardens *(74)*
Vellacott, Lawford, Crowcombe *(82)*

June 20 Monday
Penwood Farm, Chedzoy *(69)*

June 22 Wednesday
Somerfoss, Oakhill *(73)*

June 23 Thursday
Jasmine Cottage, Clevedon *(48)*
Little Garth, Dowlish Wake *(54)*
Overbrook Cottage, nr Wedmore *(67)*

June 24 Friday
Somerfoss, Oakhill **(Evening)** *(73)*

June 25 Saturday
Greencombe, Porlock *(33)*
Heaven's Door, Rimpton *(39)*

June 26 Sunday
Brewery House, Southstoke, Bath *(14)*
1 Lambrook Gate, West Lambrook *(52)*
Olive Cottage, Langley Marsh, Wiveliscombe *(66)*
Somerfoss, Oakhill *(73)*

June 30 Thursday
Jasmine Cottage, Clevedon *(48)*
Little Garth, Dowlish Wake *(54)*

July 3 Sunday
Abbey Farm, Montacute *(1)*
Barford Park, Spaxton *(4)*
Fernhill, nr Wellington *(27)*
Tintinhull, nr Yeovil *(80)*

July 4 Monday
Abbey Farm, Montacute *(1)*

July 5 Tuesday
Abbey Farm, Montacute *(1)*

July 6 Wednesday
Abbey Farm, Montacute *(1)*
Fernhill, nr Wellington *(27)*

July 7 Thursday
Elworthy Cottage, Elworthy *(25)*
Little Garth, Dowlish Wake *(54)*

July 9 Saturday
Boweys and Rose Cottage, Kingston-St-Mary *(11)*

July 10 Sunday
Barrington Court, Ilminster *(5)*
Boweys and Rose Cottage, Kingston-St-Mary *(11)*
Brent Knoll Gardens, Highbridge *(13)*
Congresbury Gardens *(19)*
The Hollies, Barton St David *(45)*
Milton Lodge, Wells *(61)*
3 Palmer's Way, Hutton *(68)*
The Time-Trail of Roses, Wells *(79)*

July 11 Monday
Boweys and Rose Cottage, Kingston-St-Mary *(11)*

July 14 Thursday
Little Garth, Dowlish Wake *(54)*

July 16 Saturday
The Chalet, Midsomer Norton *(17)*
Old Rectory, Wootton Courtenay *(65)*

July 17 Sunday
Byways, Midsomer Norton *(15)*
Hangeridge Farm, Wrangway *(35)*

1 Lambrook Gate, West Lambrook *(52)*
The Mill, Cannington *(60)*
Old Rectory, Wootton Courtenay *(65)*
Sutton Hosey Manor, Long Sutton *(77)*

July 18 Monday
1 Lambrook Gate, West Lambrook *(52)*
The Mill, Cannington *(60)*

July 21 Thursday
Little Garth, Dowlish Wake *(54)*

July 24 Sunday
Hartford Lodge, Brompton Regis *(38)*
Meare Gardens, Meare *(59)*

July 28 Thursday
Little Garth, Dowlish Wake *(54)*

July 31 Sunday
Cothay Manor, Greenham *(20)*
Hangeridge Farm, Wrangway *(35)*

August 4 Thursday
Dunster Castle, Dunster *(23)*
Little Garth, Dowlish Wake *(54)*

August 7 Sunday
Fernhill, nr Wellington *(27)*

August 10 Wednesday
Fernhill, nr Wellington *(27)*

August 11 Thursday
Little Garth, Dowlish Wake *(54)*
Little Yarford Farmhouse, Kingston St Mary **(Evening)** *(55)*

August 12 Friday
Little Yarford Farmhouse, Kingston St Mary *(55)*

August 13 Saturday
Little Yarford Farmhouse, Kingston St Mary *(55)*

August 14 Sunday
1 Lambrook Gate, West Lambrook *(52)*
Little Yarford Farmhouse, Kingston St Mary *(55)*
The Time-Trail of Roses, Wells *(79)*

August 18 Thursday
Bath Priory Hotel, Bath *(9)*
Little Garth, Dowlish Wake *(54)*

August 21 Sunday
4 Brendon View, Crowcombe *(12)*
Olive Cottage, Langley Marsh, Wiveliscombe *(66)*

August 24 Wednesday
Somerfoss, Oakhill *(73)*

August 25 Thursday
Little Garth, Dowlish Wake *(54)*

August 27 Saturday
Gants Mill & Garden, Bruton *(29)*

August 28 Sunday
Elworthy Cottage, Elworthy *(25)*
Kites Croft, Westbury-sub-Mendip *(51)*
1 Lambrook Gate, West Lambrook *(52)*

August 31 Wednesday
Kites Croft, Westbury-sub-Mendip *(51)*

September 1 Thursday
Little Garth, Dowlish Wake *(54)*

September 4 Sunday
Hartford Lodge, Brompton Regis *(38)*
Somerfoss, Oakhill *(73)*

September 8 Thursday
Elworthy Cottage, Elworthy *(25)*

Little Garth, Dowlish Wake *(54)*
Vellacott, Lawford, Crowcombe *(82)*

September 10 Saturday
Vellacott, Lawford, Crowcombe *(82)*

September 11 Sunday
Hill Lodge, Northend, Batheaston *(43)*
The Time-Trail of Roses, Wells *(79)*

September 15 Thursday
Little Garth, Dowlish Wake *(54)*

October 1 Saturday
Elworthy Cottage, Elworthy *(25)*
Vellacott, Lawford, Crowcombe *(82)*

October 2 Sunday
Elworthy Cottage, Elworthy *(25)*
Vellacott, Lawford, Crowcombe *(82)*

October 6 Thursday
Elworthy Cottage, Elworthy *(25)*

October 9 Sunday
Holt Farm, Blagdon *(46)*
The Time-Trail of Roses, Wells *(79)*

2006

February 12 Sunday
The Time-Trail of Roses, Wells *(79)*

DESCRIPTIONS OF GARDENS

❶ Abbey Farm, Montacute
&⊗⊛
(Mr & Mrs G Jenkins) *4m from
Yeovil. Follow A3088, take slip rd to
Montacute, turn L at T-junction into
village. Turn R between Church &
King's Arms (no through rd). 2½
acres of mainly walled gardens on
sloping site, provide the setting for
Cluniac medieval Priory gatehouse.
Interesting plants incl roses, shrubs,
clematis. Herbaceous borders, white
garden, gravel garden. Small
arboretum. Pond for wildlife - frogs,
newts, dragonflies. Fine mulberry,
walnut and monkey puzzle trees.
Home-made TEAS Sun only, in aid of
All Saints Primary School. Adm
£3.50, chd free. Sun 3 July (11-5),
Mon, Tue, Wed 4, 5, 6 July (2-5).
Private visits welcome by appt.
Tel 01935 823572 gnjrj@dial.pipex.
com*

❷ NEW Acers, West Chinnock &
(Mr & Mrs J Burton) *3m NE of
Crewkerne. From A303 take
Crewkerne rd A356. After 1½m take
L turn to The Chinnocks. From A30
at Crewkerne take A356. After 2½m
take R turn to The Chinnocks. Acers
opp village PH. ½-acre garden with
variety of named, interesting, and
some unusual, trees and shrubs, incl
maples, cornus and ericaceous
examples. Adm donation of at least
£2.50. Private visits welcome by appt
daily Apr to Oct, 10-4. Tel 01935
881708*

Apple Acre, Star, Winscombe
&⊗⊛
See Bristol & South Gloucestershire.

❸ NEW Ashcott Gardens
*On A39, 3m W of Street. From A39,
turn opp Ashcott Inn into Middle St.
At T-junction turn R to car parking
at village hall and nearby field.*
Home-made TEAS at village hall in
aid of Water Aid. *Combined adm
£3.50, chd free. Sun 12 June (2-5.30)*

**NEW Manor House, 11 Middle
Street** &⊗ (Peter & Daphne
Willis) ¼-acre garden with mixed
herbaceous planting, small pond
and bog gardens with some hardy
exotics. Water feature and new
gravel garden planted with
alpines and grasses. Pergola
dividing ornamental garden from
vegetables grown in raised beds.

NEW Millgreen, 3 Station Road ⊗
(Ruth & Gus Wans) 1 acre
reclaimed from a field in the last
13yrs. Predominance of shrub
borders, incl perennial planting
and rose beds. Large areas of
grass, small pond. Productive
vegetable garden in raised beds
and large polytunnel. Varied
selection of trees.

**NEW The Normans, 22 Middle
Street** &⊗⊛ (Mary & David
Adkins) ½-acre garden developed
over the past 4yrs. Herbaceous
border, pond, small shady area,
vegetables, wild area newly
planted with trees and shrubs.

NEW 25A Ridgeway &⊗ (Mr &
Mrs Dommett) Small, low-
maintenance garden, mostly
shrubs.

NEW Tremerryn, Middle Street
&⊗ (Mr & Mrs Hemmings)
Small but colourful garden.

NEW West House, 27 Ridgeway
&⊗ (Margaret & Alan Donson)
Trees, shrubs and flowers
established over the yrs on a
hilltop site.

❹ Barford Park, Spaxton &⊛
(Mr & Mrs Michael Stancomb) *4½m
W of Bridgwater. Midway between
Enmore & Spaxton.* 10 acres incl
woodland walk. Formal garden, wild
garden and water garden,
surrounding a Queen Anne house
(not open) with park and ha-ha. *Adm
£3, chd free. Sun 3 July (2-5.30)*

❺ ◆ Barrington Court, Ilminster
&⊗⊛
(The National Trust) *5m NE of
Ilminster. In Barrington village on
B3168.* Well known garden
constructed in 1920 by Col Arthur
Lyle from derelict farmland (the C19

cattle stalls still exist). Gertrude Jekyll suggested planting schemes for the layout. Paved paths with walled rose and iris, white and lily gardens, large kitchen garden. Light refreshments and TEAS. *Adm £6, chd £3, family £14.50. Early Mar & Oct Thur to Sun 11-4.30. 21 Mar to 2 Oct daily (not Weds) 11-5.30.* **For NGS:** *Suns 24 Apr; 10 July (11-5.30, last adm 5). Tel 01460 242614 barringtoncourt@nationaltrust.org.uk*

6 **Barrow Court, Barrow Court Lane, Barrow Gurney** ⊕
(Mrs Jo Collins, Organiser) *16m NE of Weston-super-Mare & 8m SW of Bristol. On A370. Turn off onto A3130 to Barrow Gurney. Turn immed R into Barrow Court Lane. ½m up lane turn R into Barrow Court.* Early C20 listed Italianate garden, designed by Inigo Thomas. Formal areas are set on 3 levels and incl parterres, fish pond, balustrades and gazebos. Also a small arboretum and wild spinney. Home-made TEAS. *Adm £2, chd 50p. Sun 22 May (2-6)*

7 **Barton Farm, 18 Manor Road, Catcott** ⓖ⊘⊕
(Mr & Mrs P H S Mackay) *8m NE of Bridgwater. Off A39 between Bridgwater and Street to Catcott. Continue straight to Xrds. At King William PH straight downhill to T-junction. Turn L, passing Barton Farm on R. No parking at house. Please follow signs to school car park. 1st entry and maps for other gardens at Barton Farm.* Developed in an abandoned farmyard; plant lovers' naturalistic mixed planting of perennials, native flora, grasses, shrubs, trees, roses and climbers in large beds and borders surrounding C17 stone house (not open) and range of farm buildings. Wildlife pond, bog, herb and kitchen gardens. Sitting areas with seasonally planted containers. Home-made TEAS in aid of CAFOD. *Combined adm with* **Old Orchard** *&* **Zool House** *£5, chd 50p. Suns 8 May; 5 June (2-6)*

8 **Barum, 50 Edward Road, Clevedon** ⊘⊕
(Marian & Roger Peacock) *12m W of Bristol. M5 J20, follow signs to pier, continue N, past Walton Park Hotel, turn R at St Mary's Church. Up Channel Rd, over Xrds, turn L into Edward Rd at top.* An informal ½-acre plantsman's garden, reclaimed by the owners since 1991 from years of neglect. Now crammed with many shrubs and perennials from around the world, incl tender and exotic species using the clement coastal climate and well-drained soil. The

vegetable patch uses a no-tread bedding system growing several tender crops. Prizewinner BBC Points West Real Gardens competition 2004. *Adm £2, chd free. Thurs 26 May; 2, 9, 16 June (2-5). Private visits welcome by appt. Tel 01275 341584 www.50-barum. freeserve.co.uk*

9 **Bath Priory Hotel, Weston Road, Bath** ⓖ⊘⊕
(Jane Moore, Head Gardener) *Close to centre of Bath. From Bath centre take Upper Bristol Rd, turn R at end of Victoria Park & L into Weston Rd.* 3-acre walled garden. Main garden has croquet lawn, herbaceous borders and dell with snowdrops and spring bulbs. Adjoining garden has summer meadow and woodland borders with specimen trees. Formal pool surrounded by roses leads to stone gazebo overlooking the vegetable garden which supplies the restaurant. Winner Bath in Bloom 2004; top 20 hotels with gardens chosen by RAC. Home-made TEAS. *Adm £2.50, chd £1.50. Tue 19 Apr; Thur 18 Aug (2-5)*

10 **Bourne House, Bourne Lane, Burrington** ⓖ⊘⊕
(Mr & Mrs C Thomas) *12m S of Bristol. N of Burrington. Turn off A38 signed Blagdon-Burrington; 2nd turning L.* 5 acres, 2 paddocks. Stream with waterfalls and lily pond; pergola; mature trees and shrubs. Mixed borders; large area hardy cyclamen and rose bed. Spring bulbs. TEAS by arrangement. *Adm £2.50. Private visits welcome by appt for max 24, no coaches. Tel 01761 462494*

11 **Boweys and Rose Cottage, Church Lane, Kingston-St-Mary** ⓖ⊘⊕
(Mr N Palfrey, Mrs G Campbell, Mrs J M Palfrey & Miss D Palfrey) *2½m N of Taunton. Close to church in village. No parking at house, please use church car park. Disabled parking at Boweys.* Two interconnecting gardens. Mature cottage-style and garden in-the-making. Interesting stone walling and buildings, stone summerhouses, gazebo and pergola, stone steps and cobbles. Small pond and rill. Topiary, shrubs and climbers. Home-made TEAS in aid of St Mary's Church & Children's Hospice of the South West. *Adm £3, chd over 10 50p. Sat, Sun, Mon 9, 10, 11 July (2-6). Private visits welcome by appt. Tel 01823 451441/451868 www.country-matters.co.uk*

12 **4 Brendon View, Crowcombe** ⊘⊕
(Chris Hayes) *9m NW of Taunton. Off A358 signed Crowcombe. Garden opp turning for Hagleys Green.* Modest-sized, plantsman's garden, S-facing with views of the Quantock Hills. Subtropical planting, mixed herbaceous borders. Vegetables. Over 400 species of cacti in 2 greenhouses, many in flower in May & June. Cream teas available locally. *Adm £2, chd free. Suns 22 May; 5 June; 21 Aug (2-5.30)*

13 **Brent Knoll Gardens, Highbridge**
2m N of Highbridge. Off A38 & M5 J22. Beautiful Church. The Knoll is an iron-age hill fort, National Trust. Home-made TEAS at Copse Hall in aid of Parish Hall. *Combined adm £4.50, chd free. Sun 10 July (2-6)*

Copse Hall ⓖ⊕ (Mrs S Boss & Mr A J Hill) Several acres incl terraced gardens, crinkle crankle kitchen garden wall, ponds, shrubs, beech wood and Soay sheep. Some wheelchair access. *Private visits welcome by appt. Tel 01278 760301 suebo55@hotmail.com*

NEW **Laburnum Cottage** ⓖ⊘⊕ (Catherine Weber) ½-acre garden under development. Collection of over 400 hemerocallis (day lilies), some for sale. Registered hemerocallis display garden. *Private visits welcome by appt. Tel 01278 760594*

NEW **Liscombe** ⓖ⊘ (George Brown) Colourful annual garden, mainly fuchsias (double variety).

14 **Brewery House, Southstoke, Bath** ⊕
(John & Ursula Brooke) *2½m from Bath. Take A367 Radstock Rd out of Bath. At top of dual carriageway turn L onto B3110. Straight on at double roundabout. Take next R into Southstoke.* Established garden on 2 levels with fine views to the S. Herbaceous perennials, grasses, bamboos, euphorbias, hydrangeas, clematis. All organic. Upper garden surrounded by 10ft stone wall. Trees incl walnut, davidia, medlar, apple, mulberry etc. Large pool/water garden. A number of unusual plants. Limited wheelchair access. Cream TEAS in aid of Southstoke Village Hall. *Adm £2, chd 50p. Sun 26 June (2-6)*

15 **Byways, 4 Silver Street, Midsomer Norton** ⊘⊕
(Betty & Jim Pratten) *In centre of Midsomer Norton, next to Lloyds*

Bank (no parking). Ample parking in nearby public car park, South Rd, approx 200yds from Byways. ½-acre cottage garden providing oasis from traffic and close proximity of town. Mixed borders and pergolas, giving yr-round interest and colour to encourage wildlife where possible. Home-made TEAS in aid of Children of Chernobyl Fund. Adm £1.50, chd free. Sun 17 July (2-5.30)

⑯ Cannington Centre Gardens, Cannington &✗⌖
3m NW of Bridgwater. On A39 Bridgwater-Minehead rd. Old College; Benedictine Priory 1138; fine Elizabethan W front; 7 old sandstone walled gardens. Wide collection plants incl wisteria; organic kitchen garden; walk down well. Developing landscape features. Cream TEAS in aid of Students' Study Tour. Adm £3, chd £1. Mon 2 May (2-5)

⑰ NEW The Chalet, 52 Charlton Road, Midsomer Norton &✗⌖
(Sheila & Chris Jones) ½m from centre of Midsomer Norton. Just off A367. Past the White Post Inn towards Radstock, turn L immed after next mini roundabout into Charlton Rd. No parking at house, park at Centurion Hotel in Charlton Lane. Covering 1 acre, garden contains lots of interest with plenty of lawns, mixed borders, vegetable garden and 80yr-old rotating cedar shingle summerhouse. Topiary is slowly becoming a feature. A quiet, relaxing garden next to a busy rd, it is shared by Orchard Lodge (52a), the next generation of the family. Home-made TEAS in aid of N Somerset Jumbulance Group. Adm £1.50, chd free. Sat 16 July (2-6)

⑱ Coley Court, Coley & Widcombe Lodge, East Harptree
8m N of Wells. Home-made TEAS at Widcombe Lodge in aid of St Margaret's Church, Hinton Blewett. Combined adm £3, chd free. Sun 3 Apr (2-5)

Coley Court ✗⌖ (Mrs M J Hill) From A39 at Chewton Mendip take B3114 for 2m. Well before E Harptree turn R at sign Coley and Hinton Blewett. Early Jacobean house (not open). 1-acre garden, stone walls, spring bulbs; 1-acre old mixed orchard.

Widcombe Lodge ✗ (Mr & Mrs P M Walker) From W Harptree take B3114 (Chewton Mendip rd), turn L at E Harptree Xrds for about 1m. Garden on R. Old walled garden, mature shrubs and massed bulbs.

⑲ Congresbury Gardens
8m N of Weston-super-Mare. 13m S of Bristol on A370. At T-lights on A370 in Congresbury head E signed Churchill - Cheddar. Approx 500yds turn R into Silver St (please park in st). 3 Silver Mead is 1½m from Middlecombe Nursery, parking on site. TEAS at Meadowcroft. Combined adm £3, chd free. Sun 10 July (10.30-5)

Fernbank, High Street &✗⌖ (S & J Thyer) 100yds along High St from Ship & Castle. Informal ⅓ acre, narrow paths. Jungle-like conservatory. Hundreds of potted plants. 2 ponds, arbour, well pump, kitchen garden, raised beds. Cedar greenhouse. Picturesque potting shed and free range rare bantams. Quiz for small children.

Meadowcroft, 3 Silver Mead &✗⌖ (Terry & Geraldine Holden) ⅓ acre of shrub borders and trees developed over the past 18yrs from farmland. Two 'hot' Mediterranean-type patios, water features, wisteria-covered pergola. Many pots, lavender walk. Organic vegetable plot. New meadow area. Winner BBC Points West Real Gardens competition (Avon area) 2003.

Middlecombe Nursery & (Nigel J North) On the edge of Congresbury, on the Bristol side, turn to Wrington along the Wrington rd off the A370 Weston to Bristol rd. Garden 200yds on L. Series of gardens covering 1 acre, many different styles and features. Excellent shrub borders. Patio gardens, pond and water features, lawns, deck areas etc.

⑳ ◆ Cothay Manor, Greenham &✗⌖
(Mr & Mrs Alastair Robb) 5m SW of Wellington. At M5 J26 or 27 take direction Exeter or Wellington respectively. Approx 4m take direction Greenham. After 1m follow tourist signs. In lane keep always L. Car park 1m. Romantic, magical garden, plantsman's paradise, yew walk, courtyards, garden rooms, large garden, river. Medieval house open to groups. Featured in 'The English Garden' & BBC 'Homes & Antiques' 2004. Cream TEAS. Adm £4, chd £2. Weds, Thurs, Suns & Bank Hols, 1 May to 29 Sept incl. For NGS: Sun 31 July (2-6). Tel 01823 672283 cothay@realemail.co.uk

㉑ Court House, East Quantoxhead &⌖
(Sir Walter & Lady Luttrell) 12m W of Bridgwater. Off A39; house at end of village past duck pond. Lovely 5-acre garden; trees, shrubs, many rare and tender; herbaceous and 3-acre woodland garden. Views to sea and Quantocks. Home-made TEAS in village hall. Adm £4, chd free. Sun 8 May (2-5)

㉒ ◆ Crowe Hall, Widcombe &
(Mr John Barratt) 1m SE of Bath. L up Widcombe Hill, off A36, leaving White Hart on R. Large varied garden; fine trees, lawns, spring bulbs, series of enclosed gardens cascading down steep hillside. Italianate terracing and Gothic Victorian grotto contrast with park-like upper garden. Dramatic setting, with spectacular views of Bath. Views of the Teazle Garden created in 2003. Very restricted parking, limited parking for disabled. TEAS. Adm £3, chd £1. For NGS: Suns 10 Apr; 12 June (2-6). Tel 01225 310322

㉓ ◆ Dunster Castle, Dunster &✗ NCCPG
(Mr M Marshall, The National Trust) 3m SE of Minehead. NT car park approached direct from A39. Terraces of subtropical plants, shrubs and camellias surrounding the fortified home of the Luttrell family for 600yrs; fine views. National Collection of Arbutus (strawberry tree). Self-drive battery-operated car available. Grounds only £3.90, chd £1.70, family £9.50. For NGS: Thur 4 Aug (10-4.30). Tel 01643 821314 graham.crane@nationaltrust.org.uk

㉔ ◆ East Lambrook Manor Gardens, East Lambrook ✗⌖ NCCPG
(Robert & Marianne Williams) 2m N of South Petherton. Off A303 at South Petherton. Follow brown flower signs. One of England's best loved privately owned gardens created by the late Margery Fish and made famous through her many books and lectures. Intriguing cottage-style garden with important collection of plants, many of which she saved from virtual extinction. Ongoing restoration programme which will help improve many historically important areas. Restored display of the National Collection of geraniums. Featured in 'The English Garden' 2004. Light refreshments and TEAS. Adm £3.95, chd free, concessions £3.50. Daily 1 Feb to 31 Oct (10-5). Tel 01460 240328 www.eastlambrook.com

㉕ ◆ Elworthy Cottage, Elworthy ⌗⊕

(Mike & Jenny Spiller) *12m NW of Taunton. On B3188.* 1-acre plantsman's garden. Colour-themed island beds with many unusual bulbs, herbaceous plants and shrubs to provide yr-round interest. Planted to encourage wildlife; wild flower areas. Decorative vegetable garden. Living willow fence. Featured in 'Amateur Gardening' 2004. TEAS. *Adm £2, chd free. Adjacent nursery & garden open Thurs, Fris & Sats mid Mar to end May; Thurs June to Oct (10-4).* **For NGS:** *Sat, Mon 26, 28 Mar; Sun 10 Apr; Thur, Sat 19, 21 May; Thurs 2, 16, Sat 18 June; Thur 7 July; Sun 28 Aug; Thur 8 Sept; Sat, Sun 1, 2, Thur 6 Oct. Sats & Thurs (10-4), Suns & Mons (1.30-5). Opening with* **Vellacott** *19, 21 May; 16, 18 June; 8 Sept; 1, 2 Oct. Tel 01984 656427 www.elworthy-cottage.co.uk*

㉖ Fairfield, nr Stogursey ⌗⊕⌗

(Lady Gass) *7m E of Williton. 11m NW of Bridgwater. From A39 Bridgwater to Minehead rd turn N; garden 1½m W of Stogursey.* Woodland garden with bulbs, shrubs and fine trees; paved maze. Views of Quantocks. No coaches. TEAS. *Adm £3, chd free (share to Stogursey Church). Sun 20 Mar (2-5.30)*

㉗ Fernhill, nr Wellington ⌗⊕

(Peter & Audrey Bowler) *1m W of Wellington. On A38, White Ball Hill. Past Beam Bridge Hotel stay on A38 at top of hill, follow signs on L into garden & car park.* Mature wooded

garden in approx 2 acres with rose, herbaceous, shrub and mixed borders, all unique in colour and content. Interesting octagonal pergola; alpine and bog garden with waterfalls and pools leading to shady arbour. Fine views over ha-ha to Blackdowns and Mendips. TEAS. *Adm £2.50, chd free. Suns, Weds 3, 6 July; 7, 10 Aug (2-5.30). Private visits welcome by appt for groups of 10+. Tel 01823 672423 mysite.wanadoo.members. co.uk/psbhome*

㉘ Flaxpool House, Crowcombe ⌗

(Lady Clark) *8m SE of Minehead. House situated on A358 from Cross Keys, Taunton to Minehead rd. House in trees beside the Flaxpool Garage.* Spring garden, azaleas, rhododendrons, camellias. Fishpond. 1-acre area where dogs can run. Cream TEAS. *Adm £2.50, chd 50p. Sun 15 May (2.30-6)*

◆ Forde Abbey Gardens, Chard ⌗⊕

See Dorset.

Frankham Farm, Ryme Intrinseca ⌗⌗⊕

See Dorset.

㉙ ◆ Gants Mill & Garden, Bruton ⌗

(Alison & Brian Shingler) *½m SW of Bruton. Out of Bruton centre on Yeovil rd, A359, under railway bridge, 100yds uphill, fork R down Gants Mill Lane. ¾-acre garden.* Clematis, rose arches and pergolas;

DANGER
GIANT VENUS
FLY-TRAP

streams, ponds, bog garden; brick circle, grasses in gravel; garden sculpture exhibition; riverside walk to the top weir; colour-themed planting with many iris, oriental poppies, delphiniums, day lilies, dahlias; also vegetable, soft fruit and cutting flower garden. The garden is overlooked by the historic watermill, also open on NGS day. Accommodation. Featured in '25 Beautiful Gardens' 2003, 'Amateur Gardening' 2004. Home-made TEAS. *Garden adm £3, chd £1. Mill & garden £5, chd £1. Suns, Thurs & Bank Hols 15 May to end Sept.* **For NGS:** *Sat 27 Aug (2-5). Tel 01749 812393 www.gantsmill.co.uk*

㉚ ◆ Gaulden Manor, Tolland ⌗⌗⊕

(Mr & Mrs J Le G Starkie) *9m NW of Taunton. Nr Lydeard St Lawrence, off A358 & B3224.* Medium-sized garden made by owners. Herb, bog, scent and butterfly gardens. Bog plants, primulas and scented geraniums. Large stew pond with island. Secret garden beyond. Cream TEAS on NGS days. *Adm £3.25, chd £1. Suns & Thurs June to Aug.* **For NGS:** *Wed, Thur 8, 9 June (2-5). Tel 01984 667213*

㉛ Glencot House, Wookey Hole ⌗⊕

(Mrs Jenny Attia) *1m SW of Wells. From Wells follow signs to Wookey Hole. Through village, past the Wookey Hole Caves & take 1st turning L into Titlands Lane, signed WHCC. Proceed for approx ½m, entrance to Glencot cricket field is on LH-side. Drive across field and park.* 18 acres of parkland of which approx 4 acres are formal gardens with frontage to R Axe. Herbaceous borders, rose walk and terraced walk with water features. Accommodation. Home-made TEAS. *Adm £2, chd 50p. Sun 3 Apr (2-5)*

㉜ 190 Goldcroft, Yeovil ⌗⌗⊕

(Eric & Katrina Crate) *Take A359 from roundabout by Yeovil College, then 1st R. ¼ acre.* Colour-themed shrub and herbaceous borders and island beds, rose garden, raised pond, seaside deck, fernery, hosta walk, vegetable garden designed for the visually impaired. Home-made TEAS in aid of Yeovil Stroke Club. *Adm £2, chd 50p. Sat, Sun 11, 12 June (2-5)* **Evening Opening** *wine, £2, Mon 13 June (4-8). Private visits welcome by appt, groups welcome. Tel 01935 475535*

Grange Farm, Kilmington ♿❀☺
See Wiltshire.

㉝ ◆ Greencombe, Porlock
♿❀☺NCCPG
(Miss Joan Loraine) ½m W of
Porlock. L off rd to Porlock Weir.
59yr-old garden on edge of ancient
woodland, overlooking Porlock Bay.
Choice rhododendrons, azaleas,
camellias, maples, roses, hydrangeas,
ferns, and many other plants.
National Collections of *Polystichum*,
Erythronium, *Vaccinium* and
Gaultheria. Completely organic, with
compost heaps on show. *Adm £4.50,
chd £1. Sats to Weds, Apr to July.* For
NGS: *Sats 28 May; 25 June (2-6).
Tel 01643 862363*

㉞ ◆ Hadspen Garden, Castle
Cary ♿❀☺NCCPG
(N & S Pope) *2m SE of Castle Cary.
Entrance on A359.* 5-acre garden
featuring a 2-acre curved Georgian
walled garden with extensive
colourist borders of shrub roses and
choice herbaceous plants, many
originating in the garden, such as
hosta 'Hadspen Blue', astrantia
'Hadspen Blood' and lobelia
'Hadspen Purple'. Rectangular lily
pond set in a dramatic terrace of
Mediterranean planting and a
woodland of fine specimen trees.
National Collection of *Rodgersia*.
Featured in 'The English Garden'
2004. Light refreshments and TEAS.
*Adm £4, chd 50p, students £2. Thurs
to Suns & Bank Hol Mons 3 Mar to
end Sept.* For NGS: *Sun 24 Apr (10-5).
Tel 01749 813707
www.hadspengarden.co.uk*

㉟ Hangeridge Farm, Wrangway
♿❀☺
(Mrs J M Chave) *2m S of Wellington.
1m off A38 bypass signed
Wrangway. 1st L towards Wellington
Monument over motorway bridge 1st
R.* 1-acre garden, herbaceous borders,
flowering shrubs and heathers, raised
rockeries, spring bulbs. Lovely setting
under Blackdown Hills.
Accommodation. Home-made TEAS.
*Adm £1.50, chd free. Suns 24 Apr;
22 May; 17, 31 July (2-6). Private
visits welcome by appt. Tel 01823
662339*

㊱ Hapsford House, Great Elm ❀
(Mrs Angela Enthoven) *½m out of
Frome on A362 to Radstock. 1st L to
Great Elm, Mells & Hapsford,
approx ½m, house on L.* Large 14-
acre C19 Grade II listed garden runs
from Regency house (not open) to
lower-filled island on R Mells.
Woodland, riverside and meadow
walks; tranquil setting where an

abundance of wildlife flourishes
amongst naturalistic planting. Home-
made TEAS in aid of The Haven
Trust. *Adm £3, chd £2. Fris 20 May;
17 June (11-7). Private visits welcome
by appt 20 May to end June.
Tel 01373 463557*

㊲ Harptree Court, East Harptree
♿☺
(Mr & Mrs Richard Hill & Mr &
Mrs Charles Hill) *8m N of Wells.
A39 Bristol rd to Chewton Mendip,
then B3114 to E Harptree, gates on
L. From Bath, A368 Weston-super-
Mare rd to W Harptree.* Spacious
garden designed when the house was
built in 1797. Two ponds linked by a
romantic waterfall and a stream,
flanked by large trees. Herbaceous
borders, lily pond and formal garden
are among other features. Home-
made TEAS in aid of St Laurence
Church, East Harptree. *Adm £3, chd
free. Sun 29 May (2-6)*

㊳ Hartford Lodge, Brompton
Regis ☺
(John & Denzil Sims) *4½m NE of
Dulverton. From Dulverton, follow
signs Brompton Regis. Through
village, carry straight on to 1st R, at
Xrds straight over. From Taunton
B3224, follow signs. Bampton 1st L
after Beulah Chapel signed
Wimbleball Lake & Brompton Regis.
L after village sign, L to Hartford
1½m.* A plantsman's garden! A
terraced garden only 8yrs old. Lots of
unusual plants and shrubs, many
propagated by owners. Of particular
interest are trilliums, hellebores and
pulmonarias in spring, salvias and
lobelias in summer, asters, gladioli &
tritonias in autumn, plus many
varieties cornus, acer and salix. *Adm
£2, chd free. Suns 24 Apr; 24 July; 4
Sept. Thur 2 June (2-5). Private visits
welcome by appt. Tel 01398 371117*

㊴ NEW Heaven's Door, Rimpton
♿
(Virginia Dewhurst & William
Hopkinson) *4m N of Sherborne.
From Sherborne leave A30 on B3148
(Marston rd) towards Marston
Magna. After 4m and 140yds after
Welcome to Somerset sign, turn R
then 1st L to bottom of hill. From
A303 at Hazelgrove (Sparkford)
roundabout, leave S on A359 to
Queen Camel and Marston Magna.
In Marston Magna turn L on
Rimpton rd, R at Villa Farm, through
Rimpton and out other side. After 2
right-angled bends, Heaven's Door
¼m further S.* 1-acre garden with
mature trees, mixed borders and
island beds, predominantly
herbaceous perennials. Sculpted

hedges; terraced beds; pots; brick
circle. Adjoining wild flower area;
large and small natural ponds; oak
and hazel spinney; woodland walk;
long hazel tunnel. Interesting local
vistas and longer views to Corton
Ridge and Cadbury Castle. TEAS.
*Adm £2.50, chd £1. Sat 25 June
(11-6)*

㊵ Henley Mill, Wookey ♿❀☺
(Peter & Sally Gregson) *2m W of
Wells. Off A371. Turn L into Henley
Lane, driveway 50yds on L.* 2½ acres
beside R Axe. Traditional and
unusual cottage plants informally
planted in formal beds with roses,
oriental poppy borders, shady 'folly
garden' and late summer borders
with grasses and perennials.
Ornamental kitchen garden. *Adm
£2.50, chd under 16 free. Private
visits welcome by appt. Tel 01749
676966 mcp@tinyworld.co.uk*

㊶ ◆ Hestercombe Gardens,
Cheddon Fitzpaine ☺
(Mr P White, Hestercombe Gardens
Trust) *4m N of Taunton. Follow
tourist information daisy symbol.*
Encompasses over 3 centuries of
garden history in 50 acres of formal
gardens and parkland. Famous
Edwardian gardens designed by
Lutyens and Jekyll created in 1904-6,
together with landscape garden
designed by Coplestone Warre
Bampfylde in the 1750s. 40 acres of
lakes, temples and woodland walks.
Light refreshments and TEAS. *Adm
£5.75, chd £1.50, concessions £5.25.
Daily all yr.* For NGS: *Tues 8 Mar; 7
June (10-6, last adm 5). Tel 01823
413923 www.hestercombegardens.
com*

㊷ NEW Hewletts Mill,
Galhampton ♿☺
(Mrs Cindy Saunders) *15m from
Yeovil. From A303 Sparkford
roundabout continue towards
London. Take 2nd L signed N/S
Cadbury. Follow signs to N Cadbury,
through village. At bottom of hill
turn R on corner signed Galhampton.
Follow narrow lane approx 1m,
garden on R (stone wall surrounds
double gate).* 2½-acre garden, old mill
site, rockery, old garden in throes of
being re-established. Herbaceous
borders, shrubs, interesting trees,
tennis court. Children must be
supervised due to many open water
sites and working water wheel.
Limited wheelchair access. TEAS in
aid of NSPCC. *Adm £5, chd free. Sun
8 May (2-6)*

43 Hill Lodge, Northend, Batheaston ♿✂©
(Susan & Sydney Fremantle) 4m NE of Bath. Turn N in Batheaston village up steep, small rd signed Northend & St Catherine. Hill Lodge ¾m on L. Parking in courtyard for disabled only. 3-acre country garden used for work experience by horticultural students because of variety of features incl stream, small wildlife lake, 2 ponds, bog garden, herbaceous borders, alpine bed, rose/clematis pergola, small cottage garden room, vegetable garden, orchard, coppice and hill with trees and view. Plants for sale in aid of Children's Hospice of the South West. Home-made TEAS. Adm £2.50, chd 50p. Suns 22 May; 12, 19 June; 11 Sept (2-5)

44 Hinton St George Gardens, nr Crewkerne
3m N of Crewkerne. N of A30 Crewkerne-Chard; S of A303 Ilminster Town Rd, at roundabout signed Lopen & Merriott, then R to Hinton St George. Pretty village with thatched Hamstone houses and C15 church. TEAS at Hooper's Holding in aid of Cats Protection. Combined adm £5, chd free. Sat, Sun 4, 5 June (2-6)

End House, West Street ♿©
(Helen Ford) Old walls protect informal plantings of trees, shrubs, climbers and herbaceous plants in ½ acre. Two large pergolas emphasise courtyard garden.

Hooper's Holding, 45 High Street ♿
(Ken & Lyn Spencer-Mills) (See separate entry).

NEW **Mallards, Gas Lane** (Capt & Mrs T Hardy) Small, sheltered S-facing garden, well stocked with a wide variety of shrubs, grasses and herbaceous plants. Lovely view over rolling countryside. Some disabled access, not suitable for wheelchairs.

NEW **Niddons House, Green Street** ♿ (Leslie & Joan Farris) 1.3 acres of 'work in progress' in beautiful rural setting with stunning views. Mostly terraced hillside given over to semi-natural wildlife garden with mature trees. Borders, shrubs and cultivated area around house.

The Old Malt House, High Street ✂
(Lord & Lady Peyton) 1½-acre plantsman's garden with views to Mendips. Wide variety of interesting trees, shrubs and perennials. Formal pool, sculptures.

Rookwood, West Street (Ian & Betty Hudspith) ¼-acre modern

garden, herbaceous borders, pond, greenhouse, vegetable garden and fruit cage, fountain and obelisks. Accommodation.

45 The Hollies, Barton Road, Barton St David ✂©
(David & Geri Gibson) 4m E of Somerton. From village of Keinton Mandeville take turning to Barton St David. The Hollies approx ½m on RH-side. Recently televised for HTV, our garden has been reclaimed over approx 6 yrs from the local rabbit population. Our visitors are invited to roam through the cottage garden to the woodland and formal decking areas. The koi pond leads through the bog garden to the stream and waterfalls. Home-made TEAS. Adm £3, chd free. Suns 5 June; 10 July (2-6). Private visits welcome by appt. Tel 01458 850991 www.gardens-to-visit.co.uk

46 Holt Farm, Blagdon ✂©
(Mr & Mrs Tim Mead) 12m S of Bristol. Off A368 Weston-super-Mare to Bath rd, between the villages of Blagdon & Ubley. Entrance to Holt Farm is approx ½m outside Blagdon, on LH-side. Developing farmhouse garden bordering Blagdon lake with wild flower meadow, experimental annual meadow, stream, woodland walk, sunken walled garden, potager and new formal pool. Spring bulbs, herbaceous summer planting and late summer and autumn colour throughout 3-acre site. Home-made TEAS. Adm £2, chd free. Suns 1 May; 5 June; 9 Oct (2-5)

47 Hooper's Holding, 45 High Street, Hinton St George ♿
(Ken & Lyn Spencer-Mills) 3m NW of Crewkerne. N of A30 Crewkerne-Chard; S of A303 Ilminster Town Rd, at roundabout signed Lopen & Merriott, then R to one of Somerset's prettiest villages. ⅓-acre garden in colour compartments; lily pool; dwarf conifers, azaleas, rare herbaceous and shrubby plants, many exotics. Pedigree cats. Garden mosaics developing. Featured in 'Somerset Life' & 'Gardens Monthly' 2004. Home-made TEAS in aid of Cats Protection. Adm £3, chd free. Sat, Sun 14, 15 May (2-6). Also opening with **Hinton St George Gardens** Sat, Sun, 4, 5 June. Private visits welcome by appt May to mid Aug. Tel 01460 76389 kenlyn@eclipse.co.uk

◆ **Iford Manor, nr Bradford-on-Avon**
See Wiltshire.

48 Jasmine Cottage, 26 Channel Road, Clevedon ✂©
(Mr & Mrs M Redgrave) 12m W of Bristol. M5 J20. Follow signs to seafront & pier, continue N on B3124, past Walton Park Hotel, turn R at St Mary's Church. Mature densely-planted garden featuring specimen trees, flowering shrubs, herbaceous plants and selection of grasses in areas screened by evergreen hedges. Plantings of tender perennials and unusual climbers. Greenhouse display of pelargoniums. WC. Adjacent nursery open May to Sept. Featured in 'Somerset Country Gardener' 2003. Adm £2, chd free. Thurs 19 May to 30 June (2-5). Private visits welcome by appt. Tel 01275 871850 www.bologrew.pwp.blueyonder. co.uk

49 King Ina's Palace, Silver Street, South Petherton ♿✂
(Shirley & Trevor Brown) 6m E of Ilminster. Through village turn R opp the PO. Garden approx 50yds down Silver St on L. Parking outside or in one of several village car parks. Plantaholic's formal garden of 1 acre. Colour-themed borders, yew hedging and topiary, vegetable garden and a degree of ongoing restoration. Accommodation. Featured in 'Amateur Gardening, Gorgeous Gardens' 2004. Adm £3, chd free. Private visits welcome by appt for groups. Tel 01460 240603 trevor.brown2@tinyworld.co.uk

50 ◆ Kingsdon, Somerton ♿✂©
(Mrs Charles Marrow) 2m SE of Somerton. Off B3151 Ilchester rd. From Ilchester roundabout on A303 follow NT signs to Lytes Cary; L opp gates, ½m to Kingsdon. Drive through village, nursery signs on L, gate. 2-acre plantsman's garden and nursery garden. A large selection of carefully chosen trees, shrubs and herbaceous perennials - many of them rare and hard to come by. Knowledgeable help with new or established gardens. Adm £2.50, chd free. Apr to Oct 11-6. **For NGS:** Suns 10, 24 Apr (2-6). Tel 01935 840232

51 Kites Croft, Westbury-sub-Mendip ✂©
(Dr & Mrs W I Stanton) 5m NW of Wells. On A371 Wells to Cheddar rd, follow signs from Westbury Cross. 2-acre sloping garden planted for colour throughout season with fine views to Glastonbury Tor. Wander down winding paths to rockery where cypress-like columnas and yuccas lend a Mediterranean air, pass

ponds and lawn to densely-planted mixed borders, shrubs and perennials. Fruit trees incl figs, walnut and mulberry. In the wood primroses, bluebells and cyclamen thrive. TEAS. *Adm £2, chd free. Suns, Weds 15, 18 May; 28, 31 Aug (2-5). Private visits welcome by appt. Tel 01749 870328*

52 1 Lambrook Gate, West Lambrook ✖
(Mr & Mrs W J Martin) *2m NW of South Petherton. Leave A303 at S Petherton. Hamlet between Shepton Beauchamp & Stembridge nr Kingsbury. East Lambrook Gardens, pass public house, bear L then 2nd L bringing you into W Lambrook. Long garden approx 170ft x 40ft. Dry stone wall, gravel, scree with alpines and grasses. Lawn with flower beds designed for all-yr colour; garden rooms, pergola with enclosed fish pond. Climbers, shrubs, bulbs, bamboos, lilies and herbaceous, over 350 named plants and wildlife area. Adm £2.50, chd free. Suns 26 June; 17 July; 14, 28 Aug. Mon 18 July (11-5). Private visits welcome by appt. Tel 01460 240114*

53 Langford Court, Langford ♿✖
(Sir David & Lady Wills) *11½m S of Bristol. 150yds S of A38 Bristol to Bridgwater rd. 1½m N of Churchill T-lights. Signed Upper Langford. 3½ acres. Lawns and trees, good display of daffodil and crocus. Topiary. Pleasant setting and outlook. Water garden and woodland walk. Home-made TEAS in aid of Burrington PCC. Adm £3, chd free. Sun 13 Mar (2-5)*

54 Little Garth, Dowlish Wake ♿✖
(Roger & Marion Pollard) *2m S of Ilminster. Turn R off Ilminster to Crewkerne rd at Kingstone Cross, then L, follow Dowlish Wake sign. Turn L at Glebe Cottage (white cottage) before reaching church. Turn R following signs. Speke Hall car park in front of nearby church may be used. ½-acre plantsman's garden for all seasons with many interesting and unusual perennials. Although essentially cottage style, emphasis is placed on the artistic arrangement of plants, using foliage, grasses and colour themes. Featured in '25 Beautiful Gardens' 2004. Adm £2.50, chd free. Thurs 5 May to 15 Sept (10-5.30). Private visits welcome by appt. Tel 01460 52594*

55 Little Yarford Farmhouse, Kingston St Mary ♿✖
(Brian Bradley) *3½m N of Taunton. On Kingston St Mary rd. At 30mph sign turn L at Parsonage Lane. Continue 1¼m W, to Yarford sign. Continue 400yds. Turn R up concrete rd. Park on L. Creative landscaping around C17 farmhouse (not open). Interesting and specimen trees including pendulous and variegated cultivars, especially beech. 3 waterlily ponds, shrubs, climbers, herbaceous and grasses. Cream TEAS. Adm £3, chd free. Fri, Sat, Sun 12, 13, 14 Aug (12-6). Evening Opening £7.50, wine, Thur 11 Aug (6-8). Private visits welcome by appt. Tel 01823 451350*

56 ♦ Lower Severalls, Crewkerne ♿✖
(Audrey & Mary Pring) *1½m NE of Crewkerne. Signed off A30 Crewkerne to Yeovil rd or A356 Crewkerne to A303. 2½-acre plantsman's garden beside early Hamstone farmhouse. Herbaceous borders and island beds with collections of unusual plants, shrubs and interesting features incl dogwood basket, wadi, herb garden. Green roofed building. Home-made TEAS. Adm £3. Tues, Weds, Fris, Sats mid Mar to Sept (10-3). Please ring to check other times. For NGS: Suns 1 May to 5 June (2-5). Tel 01460 73234 www.lowerseveralls.co.uk*

57 Manor Farm, Middle Chinnock ✖
(Simon & Antonia Johnson) *3m ENE of Crewkerne. 4m SW of Yeovil, off A30. Garden of rooms, created over the last 14yrs; incl formal areas, mixed borders, pond garden; pool house with views down field to new pond, herb garden, vegetable and cutting garden and orchard. Home-made TEAS in aid of West Chinnock School. Adm £3, chd free. Sun 22 May (2-6). Private visits welcome by appt. Tel 01935 881706 aj@simonjohnson.co.uk*

58 Maple House, South Barrow, Yeovil ✖
(Mr & Mrs P K Shaw & Mrs E Verrinder) *6m SW of Castle Cary. Off A359 but best approached from Sparkford. Garden is 2m N of Sparkford. Follow rd sign to South Barrow & Lovington opp Haynes Publishers, then NGS sign. Gently sloping 5-acre site with fine view to Glastonbury Tor and Mendips. Developing garden begun in 1996, with lake, shrubberies, lawns, mown paths, pergola. 4-acre wild flower meadow (Somerset Wildlife site and private nature reserve) with mature*

and recently planted hedges, small wood of native trees and shrubs. Pond; garden around house with alpine bed and herbaceous borders. Conservation a priority. TEAS. *Adm £3, chd free. Sat, Sun 28, 29 May (2-6)*

♦ The Mead Nursery, Brokerswood ♿✖
See Wiltshire.

59 Meare Gardens, Meare
3m W of Glastonbury. B3151. Meare village has a long history of farming and drainage with several C14 ecclesiastical buildings. Home-made TEAS at Doran Lodge in aid of Macmillan Cancer Relief. *Combined adm £3, chd free. Sun 24 July (2-5.30)*

Doran Lodge, St Mary's Road ✖
(Peter Bentham) *Entrance 100yds past Meare PO into Great House Court Lane. Parking in St Mary's Rd.* Traditional 1770 house with walled plantsman's garden in the process of being replanted with interesting, cottage-style herbaceous perennials. 'Saraband' scented herb garden. Exceptionally large number of plants for sale, many unusual.

NEW The Laurels, St Mary's Road ♿✖
(Martin & Jane Bowe) *Opp Meare petrol station. Parking in field next to church cemetery.* Traditional C17 house extended during C19. 1-acre garden designed in garden rooms. Statuary woodland walk to river bank with C15 monk bridge.

NEW The New House, St Mary's Road ♿✖
(Joan & Ashley Middleton) *As for Doran Lodge, but entry and parking in St Mary's Rd, opp Great House Court Lane.* Cottage garden of approx ½ acre. Attractive landscaping with interesting plants and shrubs. Ornamental koi carp pond and marginal plants.

NEW Rotherslade, Stileway ♿✖
(Cathy & David Brunt) *From B3151 Glastonbury Rd turn L into Stileway at beginning of Meare. L fork, parking in field where lane forks. 4th house on L.* Country garden of approx ¾ acre. Interesting garden rooms with mixed plantings; vegetable plot; shrub borders. Ornamental koi carp pond.

The Wagon House, Stileway ✖
(Mollie King) *As for Rotherslade. 4th house on R.* Traditional English country garden. Stream,

pond and small bog garden. Raised bed vegetable plot.

Melplash Court, Melplash 🔵🌐
See Dorset.

60 The Mill, 21 Mill Lane, Cannington 🗑🌐 NCCPG
(Mr & Mrs J E Hudson) *4m W of Bridgwater. Off A39 in Cannington village. Turn opp Rose & Crown into Clifford Park. At end turn L into Mill Lane.* ¼-acre cottage-type plantsman's garden with waterfall and pond, over 130 clematis, National Collection of *Clematis texensis* hybrids. Many unusual plants. Featured on HTV Roots & Shoots 2003 and in 'Somerset Life' 2004. TEAS in aid of Cannington WI. *Adm £3, chd free. Sun, Mon 17, 18 July (11-5). Private visits welcome by appt. Tel 01278 652304*

61 ◆ Milton Lodge, Wells 🗑🌐
(D C Tudway Quilter) *½m N of Wells. From A39 Bristol-Wells, turn N up Old Bristol Rd; car park first gate on L.* Mature Grade II listed terraced garden with outstanding views of Wells Cathedral and Vale of Avalon. Mixed borders, roses, fine trees. Separate 7-acre arboretum. Home-made TEAS. *Adm £3.50, chd under 14 free. Tues, Weds, Suns & Bank Hols 25 Mar to 31 Oct.* **For NGS:** *Suns 15, 29 May; 12 June; 10 July (2-5). Tel 01749 672168*

62 ◆ Montacute House, Montacute 🔵🗑🌐
(The National Trust) *4m W of Yeovil. NT signs off A3088 & A303.* Magnificent Elizabethan house with contemporary garden layout. Fine stonework provides setting for informally planted mixed borders and old roses; range of garden features illustrates its long history. Light refreshments and TEAS. *House & garden adm £7.40, chd £3.70, family £17. Garden only £3.90, chd £1.80. Daily, not Tues, 18 Mar to 30 Oct (11-6, or dusk if earlier); 2 Nov to 18 Mar, not Mons & Tues (11-4).* **For NGS:** *Sun 19 June (11-6). Tel 01935 823956 floyd.summerhayes@nationaltrust. org.uk*

63 Montys Court, Norton Fitzwarren 🔵🗑
(Major & Mrs A Mitford-Slade) *4m W of Taunton. On B3227. 1m W of Norton Fitzwarren on LH-side.* Mature 4-acre garden around an historic family home (not open) with wide variety of shrubs and trees set in mature parkland with views to the Quantocks and Blackdowns. Large herbaceous border, Victorian rose garden filled with tulips in the spring and new wildlife pond. Accommodation. TEAS. *Adm £3, chd free. Sun 17 Apr (2-5)*

The Old Malthouse, Lower Westwood 🔵🌐
See Wiltshire.

64 Old Orchard, 14 Brook Lane, Catcott 🗑🌐
(Mr & Mrs V T Osmond) *8m E of Bridgwater. For parking, see Barton Farm details. Maps available at Barton Farm. For parking at other times, please contact direct.* Approx ¼-acre cottage garden. Main feature 100yr-old walnut tree. Shrub borders, peonies and hostas. Home-made TEAS in aid of CAFOD. *Combined adm £5, chd 50p with* **Barton Farm** *&* **Zool House.** *Suns 8 May; 5 June (2-6)*

65 NEW Old Rectory, Wootton Courtenay 🔵🌐
(Sue & Howard Shapland) *2½m SW of Minehead. From E take A39 towards Minehead. Turn onto A396 through Dunster. After 2m turn R at Cowbridge and follow signs, approx 2m. From W take A39 through Porlock towards Minehead. After 3m turn R at Venniford Cross and follow signs, approx 2½m. From S take A396 from Tiverton through Wheddon Cross to Timberscombe. At Cowbridge turn L and follow signs, approx 2m.* Old Rectory (built 1500) occupies an outstanding position on edge of Exmoor, with magnificent views of surrounding countryside. The present garden has been planted with colour-themed beds which peak at different times of the yr. Its many areas contain a great variety of interesting plants; it is a plantsman's garden. A plant guide will be supplied to help you appreciate the many different species in flower. Light

refreshments and Home-made TEAS in aid of Macmillan Cancer Relief. *Adm £2.50, chd free. Sat, Sun 16, 17 July (11-5). Private visits welcome by appt. Tel 01643 841001 sue.shapland@btinternet.com*

The Old Rectory, Netherbury 🗑🌐
See Dorset.

66 Olive Cottage, Langley Marsh, Wiveliscombe 🔵🗑🌐
(Mrs Frankie Constantine) *1m NW of Wiveliscombe. From Taunton take B3227 to Wiveliscombe. Turn R at T-lights. On entering the Square turn R past White Hart & continue on this rd for just over 1m. Olive Cottage on R going up hill just before Three Horseshoes PH.* An informal cottage garden of about ⅔ acre created by the owner over 27yrs. Small pond, rockery and bog garden, together with shrubs, perennials, climbers and trees create colour and interest throughout the yr. Productive kitchen garden and 2 greenhouses where many of the plants are raised. Home-made TEAS. *Adm £2, chd 50p (share to St Margaret's Hospice). Suns 26 June; 21 Aug (2-6). Private visits welcome by appt. Please write to Olive Cottage, Langley Marsh, Wiveliscombe TA4 2UJ*

67 Overbrook Cottage, Lower Cocklake, nr Wedmore 🔵🗑🌐
(Margaret & Stanley Castle) *1m E of Wedmore. Take B3151 from Wedmore towards Cheddar for 1m. Turn R following sign to Draycott & Nyland. Cottage after 3 bungalows on R.* ⅓₀-acre cottage garden redesigned 7yrs ago. Climbing roses over arbour, clematis, honeysuckles, old-fashioned plants continually being added to. Peaceful setting and pleasing outlook. Tearooms and inns at Wedmore for refreshment. Plant sales in aid of Greyhound Rescue. *Adm £2.50, chd free. Thurs 2, 9, 16, 23 June (10-4). Private visits welcome by appt 2 to 23 June. Tel 01934 712420*

68 3 Palmer's Way, Hutton 🔵🗑🌐
(Mary & Peter Beckett) *3m S of Weston-super-Mare. From A370 (N or S) follow signs to Hutton. In village turn L at PO, then 1st L into St Mary's Rd. Car park at St Mary's field, signed, 2 mins walk. From A371 turn R at PO. Private visits, 1st L off St Mary's Rd and 1st L into Palmer's Way. Very limited disabled parking at house.* Informal tapestry of densely-packed mixed planting. Cottage-style plants, unusual herbaceous perennials incl hardy

geraniums, fruit trees and herbs. Tropical plants in conservatory. New gravel bed, mini knot garden and pond area. Home-made TEAS. *Adm £1.50, chd free. Sun 10 July (2-6). Private visits welcome by appt, Weds in July only. Tel 01934 815110 macbeckett@clara.co.uk*

⑥⑨ Penwood Farm, Parchey, Chedzoy ✿❀
(Mr & Mrs E F W Clapp) *3½m E of Bridgwater. Take A39 Bath to Glastonbury rd. Immed after bridge over M5, turn sharp R into Chedzoy Lane. At T-junction in village turn L. Pass church approx ¾m. Penwood Farm seen facing you across sharp LH-bend. From Stawell to Glastonbury rd, cross bridge over King's Sedgemoor Drain (Parchey River). 1st house on L.* Plant lover's garden of approx ¾ acre. Terrace, patio, pergola, gravel, rock, water and kitchen gardens. Over 450 different varieties of rose - old, 'new' English and modern; collections of clematis, hosta, penstemon, shrubs and herbaceous perennials, many unusual plants and trees. Koi carp pond with Japanese-style bridge. Plant sales in aid of Chedzoy Playing Field Assoc, 10% to NGS. TEAS. *Adm £2, chd free. Suns, Mons 12, 13, 19, 20 June (2-5.30) . Private visits welcome by appt Mar to Sept. Coaches & large groups June & July only. Tel 01278 451631*

⑦⓪ Popinjays & Little Norton Mill, Little Norton
6m W of Yeovil. From A303 take A356. L to Norton-sub-Hamdon. Through village & follow signs. Park as for Little Norton Mill. Cream TEAS at Popinjays. Combined adm £3, chd free. Sun 19 June (2-6)
Little Norton Mill ❀ (Lynn & Tom Hart) 3 acres of landscaped gardens, meadow and orchard. Mill pond, ornamental ponds, marsh garden. Many mature trees and shrubs. Accommodation. *Private visits welcome by appt. Tel 01935 881337 te.hart@btinternet.com*

Popinjays (Eric & Jean Dunkley) Hamstone house with courtyard and long lushly-planted garden on the W slope of Ham Hill. Fish pools, sitting areas, fruits and vegetables, orchard and spinney. *Private visits welcome by appt. Tel 01935 881679*

⑦① ◆ Prior Park Landscape Garden, Bath ✿
The National Trust) *1m S of Bath. Visitors are advised to use public transport as there is no parking at*

Prior Park or nearby, except for disabled visitors. Telephone 01225 833422 for travel information leaflet. Beautiful and intimate C18 landscape garden created by Bath entrepreneur Ralph Allen (1693-1764) with advice from the poet Alexander Pope and Capability Brown. Sweeping valley with magnificent views of the city, Palladian bridge and lakes. Major restoration of the garden continues, summerhouse restoration now complete. *Adm £4, chd £2. Daily, not Tues, 1 Feb to 29 Nov (11-5.30). Fris, Sats, Suns 3 Dec to 31 Jan (11-dusk).* **For NGS:** *Sun 12 June. Tel 01225 833977 mathew.ward@nationaltrust.org.uk*

⑦② Rackley House, Rackley Lane, Compton Bishop ✿❀
(R & J Matthews) *2m W of Axbridge. SE Weston-super-Mare. Leave A38 at Cross & take rd to Loxton, Bleadon. Rackley Lane approx 1½m from Cross; Rackley House is only house on RH-side at end of lane.* ½-acre garden on S-facing slope with light alkaline soil. Features incl iris garden, rockery and lawns, small knot garden, pond and terrace. Some unusual plants and variety of cyclamen, snowdrops, old-fashioned roses and penstemons. TEAS in aid of Weare First School, Cream TEAS 11, 12 June only. *Adm £2, chd free. Weds 4, 11, 18, 25 May; Sat, Sun 11, 12 June (2-6). Private visits welcome by appt. Tel 01934 732311*

Regency House, Hemyock ✿❀
See Devon.

Saltford Farm Barn, 565a Bath Road, Saltford ✿❀
See Bristol & South Gloucestershire.

◆ Sherborne Garden, Litton ✿
See Bristol & South Gloucestershire.

⑦③ Somerfoss, Bath Road, Oakhill ❀❀
(Ewan & Rosemary Curphey) *3m N of Shepton Mallet. From Oakhill School ¼m N on A367. Parking in lay-by on R.* Recently developed 2-acre garden in secluded S-facing valley. Natural rocky outcrops provide a backdrop for planting with a Mediterranean feel. Borders with choice perennials. Woodland and meadow areas with native flora. Gravel garden. Fruit and vegetables. Large deck area with pots sets off an unusual 1970's house, not open. Steep access, slopes and steps; sensible shoes advised. Child-friendly. TEAS. *Adm £3, chd £1. Weds 23 Mar; 20 Apr; 25 May; 22 June; 24 Aug; Suns 24 Apr; 26 June; 4 Sept*

(2-6). **Evening Opening** *Fri 24 June, £3 wine (5-7.30). Private visits welcome by appt, Apr, May & June. Tel 01749 840542 ecurphey@aol. com*

⑦④ Stogumber Gardens
11m NW of Taunton. On A358. Sign to Stogumber, W of Crowcombe. Seven delightful gardens of interest to plantsmen in lovely village at edge of Quantocks. Home-made TEAS at village hall. *Combined adm £3, chd free. Sun 19 June (2-6)*
Brook Cottage ✿❀ (Mrs M Field) Good plants incl lilies in a lovely setting; small pond for added interest.

Butts Cottage ❀ (Mr & Mrs J A Morrison) Cottage garden with old roses, old-fashioned perennials, alpines, pond, small vine house and organic fruit and vegetable garden.

Cridlands Steep ❀ (Mrs A M Leitch) Large and interesting garden with collection of trees and wildlife pond.

Hill Farm (Mr & Mrs A Jeans) Large garden on 3 levels with attractive herbaceous beds and shrubberies, roses in profusion, vegetables, soft fruit, duck pond and tennis court.

Knoll Cottage ✿ (Mr & Mrs J D Leech) 2-acre garden started from fields in 1998. Extensive mixed borders, pond, young woodland, fruit and vegetable area. Accommodation.

Pitts Cottage (Mr & Mrs B Young) Pretty cottage garden with interesting herbaceous plants. Redeveloped rear garden with vegetables, herb bed and greenhouse.

Pound House ✿❀ (Mr & Mrs B Hibbert) Old orchard on terraced sloping site, garden started 2000. Young trees, shrub borders, herbaceous plants, rockery, organic vegetable garden and courtyard with climbing plants and herbs.

◆ Stourhead Garden, Stourton ✿❀
See Wiltshire.

⑦⑤ Stowleys, Bossington Lane, Porlock ✿❀❀
(Rev R L Hancock) *NE of Porlock. Off A39. 6m W of Minehead.* Medium-sized garden, approx 2 acres with magnificent views across Porlock Bay and Bristol Channel. Daffodils, roses, unusual tender plants incl leptospermum, drimys and

embothrium. Light refreshments and TEAS. *Adm £2, chd free. Sats 2 Apr; 18 June (2-6)*

76 Sunnyside, Yarley Hill, Yarley ⌘⌘
(Nigel Cox & Patsy Koeb) *3m W of Wells. 2m along B3139 Wedmore Rd. After Pheasant Inn at Wookey reach village sign for Yarley. 100yds beyond, turn L up Yarley Hill, house 200yds on L.* ½-acre cottage garden with large variety of plants, some rare. Collection of subtropical plants, incl bananas, cannas, hedychium, summer-flowering bulbs and many varieties of salvia. *Adm £3, chd free. Private visits welcome by appt, June & July only. Tel 01749 674905 nigel@deweycox.com*

77 Sutton Hosey Manor, Long Sutton ⌘⌘⌘
(Roger Bramble) *2m E of Langport, on A372. Gates N of A372 at E end of Long Sutton.* 3 acres, of which 2 walled. Lily canal through pleached limes leading to amelanchier walk past duck pond; rose and juniper walk from Italian terrace; Judas tree avenue; *Ptelea* walk. Ornamental potager. Drive-side shrubbery. Music by players from Sinfonia of Westminster. Home-made TEAS. *Adm £3, chd £2. Sun 17 July (2.30-6)*

78 Thurloxton Gardens
6m S of Bridgwater, 4m N of Taunton. Off A38, well signed. Ample parking. Three gardens in a hamlet and one next to Maypole Inn. Cream TEAS at Coombe Quarry. *Combined adm £3, chd under 12 free. Sun 1 May (2-6)*

Coombe Mill, West Monkton ⌘
(Hugh & Sheila Pollard) Garden has been created around C17 mill and the formal section incl an avenue of ornamental pears and water garden through which passes a natural stream. In the surrounding 2 acres there is a lime walk through the orchard and a woodland walk through adjacent disused quarry.

Coombe Quarry, West Monkton
(Miss Patricia Davies-Gilbert) Cottage garden with quarry walk. Roses and other shrubs, vegetables and animals.

Coombe Water, Coombe ⌘ (Mr & Mrs M K Paul) Cottage garden with stream and pond in a small valley.

Magnolias, Thurloxton ⌘⌘
(Heather Ambrose & Keith Brooks) *Next to Maypole Inn.* 1½ acres of informal mature mixed borders packed with yr-round

interest. A blaze of spring colour with divided rooms, incl 18 varieties of magnolias and over 30 varieties of camellias.

79 ◆ The Time-Trail of Roses, Westfield Road, Wells
(Mrs Susan Lee) *Centre of Wells. No site parking. Park Tucker St car park. Garden 2mins walk.* Magnificent collection, initially of roses (approx 1000 different), now interplanted with snowdrops (77), crocus (60), narcissus (65), hyacinths (20), tulips (130), iris (90), alliums (55), fritillaries (40), clematis (40), herbs (120), lilies (120), fruit (50), cyclamen (14), colchicums (26), nerines (12) etc, all in ½-acre garden, planted in date order of their introduction to show their beauty, diversity and evolution. £1 discount if you bring a child. Silver Award BBC Real Gardens 2004. Featured in 'Amateur Gardening' 2004. TEAS. *Adm £3 (May to July incl), £2 other months, chd free. 2nd & 4th Sun in month Feb to Oct, Suns to Weds May to July.* **For NGS:** *Suns 13 Feb; 13 Mar; 10 Apr; 8 May; 12 June; 10 July; 14 Aug; 11 Sept; 9 Oct (2-6) 12 Feb 2006. Tel 01749 674677*

80 ◆ Tintinhull, nr Yeovil ⌘⌘
(The National Trust) *5m NW of Yeovil. Tintinhull village. Signs on A303, W of Ilchester.* C17 and C18 house (not open). Famous 2-acre garden in compartments, developed 1900 to present day, influenced by Hidcote; many good and uncommon plants. Light refreshments and TEAS. *Adm £4.50, chd £2.10. Weds to Suns, Apr to Sept.* **For NGS:** *Sun 3 July (11-5). Tel 01935 823956*

81 Uplands, Glebelands, Minehead ⌘⌘
(Margaret & Malcolm Scott) *Wellington Square turn L into Park St signed Porlock. 2nd turning on R, Western Lane & at top turn L. Glebelands sign straight ahead. Please park in rd.* ¾-acre gently sloping garden with fine views. Colourful spring garden; alpina clematis, hellebores, epimediums, scillas, crocus and other bulbs. Variety of small trees and shrubs surround colour-themed herbaceous beds, with lilies, delphiniums and roses. Clematis and honeysuckles on trellises. Low retaining walls with unusual dwarf plants. Narrow paths and steps, unsuitable for pushchairs. *Adm £2, chd free. Sats, Suns 19, 20 Mar; 23, 24 Apr (11-4). Private visits welcome by appt. Tel 01643 704185*

82 Vellacott, Lawford, Crowcombe ⌘⌘
(Kevin & Pat Chittenden) *9m NW of Taunton. Off A358, signed Lawford.* Interesting 1-acre cottage garden on a S-facing slope with splendid views. Profusely stocked with a very wide selection of plants and trees for yr-round interest. The overall endeavour is to link the cottage and garden with the beautiful surroundings. WC. TEAS. *Adm £2, chd free. Sat 19, 21 May; Thur 16 to Sun 19 June incl; Thur, Sat 8, 10 Sept; Sat, Sun 1, 2 Oct (1-5). Also opening with* **Elworthy Cottage** *19, 21 May; 16, 18 June; 8 Sept; 1, 2 Oct. Private visits welcome by appt incl groups & coaches. Tel 01984 618249*

83 Walnut Farm, Yarley Hill, Yarley ⌘⌘
(Angela & John Marsh) *3m W of Wells. On B3139, 3m from Wells to Wedmore, turn L at Yarley Cross.* Island site 300yds up Yarley Hill. N-facing ⅔-acre garden with many unusual cottage garden perennials planted informally among shrubs, roses, climbers and 2 ponds. Yr-round interest. Splendid views of Mendips. 'Conservatory', small conservation area in adjoining field. Cream TEAS in aid of Diabetes UK. *Adm £3, chd free. Private visits welcome by appt, June & July only. Tel 01749 676942*

84 Watcombe, 92 Church Road, Winscombe ⌘⌘
(Peter & Ann Owen) *3½m NW of Cheddar. From Cheddar A371 to A38 N. 1st turn L into Winscombe Hill. After 1m reach The Square.* Pink house on L after further 150yds down hill. ¾-acre Italianate garden with colour-themed, informally planted mixed borders. Topiary, box hedging, lime walk, pleached hornbeams, orchard, vegetable plot, 2 small ponds. Featured in 'Water Gardener' 2003. Cream TEAS in aid of St James's Church. *Adm £2.50, chd free. Sun 22 May (10.30-5). Private visits welcome by appt. Tel 01934 842666*

Waterdale House, East Knoyle ⌘
See Wiltshire.

85 Wayford Manor, Crewkerne ⌘
(Mr & Mrs Robin Goffe) *3m SW of Crewkerne. Turning N off B3165 at Clapton; or S off A30 Chard to Crewkerne rd.* Fine Elizabethan manor house (not open). 3 acres, noted for magnolias and acers. Bulbs, flowering trees, shrubs, rhododendrons. Garden redesigned by Harold Peto in 1902. Featured in

'Somerset Life' 2003. Home-made TEAS. *Adm £2.50, chd 50p. Suns 10 Apr; 1, 22 May; 12 June. Mon 2 May (2-6)*

86 NEW **Wellfield Barn, Wells** ⊛
(David & Virginia Nasmyth) *½m N of Wells. From A39 Bristol to Wells rd turn R at 30mph sign into Walcombe Lane. Entrance at 1st cottage on R, parking signed.* 1½-acre gardens, made by owners over the past 8yrs from concrete farmyard. Ha-ha, wonderful views, pond, lawn, mixed borders, grass walks and interesting young trees. Structured design integrates house with landscape. New areas under development. TEAS. *Adm £2.50, chd free. Wed 1 June (2-6)*

Weston House, Buckhorn Weston ♿⊘⊛
See Dorset.

87 **Woodside, East Stoke, Stoke-sub-Hamdon** ♿⊛
(Mr & Mrs M Greenwood) *5m N of Yeovil. Follow A3088, take slip rd to Stoke-sub-Hamdon, turn R at T-junction. Garden lies behind Budgens shop. Please do not use car park nor other areas around the shop.* Recently developed 1-acre garden, with trees, shrubs, herbaceous border, all of easy maintenance and set in beautiful surroundings under Ham Hill. Most of the more unusual trees and shrubs are labelled. Varieties of fruit and vegetables are chosen for yr-round self-sufficiency. TEAS in aid of St Margaret's Hospice. *Adm £2, chd free. Sun 15 May (10-5)*

88 NEW **Zool House, 8 Steel Lane, Catcott** ♿⊘⊛
(Les Durston) *8m NE of Bridgwater. For parking, see Barton Farm details. Maps available at Barton Farm. For parking at other times, please contact direct.* ¾-acre garden, established from an old orchard (previously quarried) containing shrubs, bulbs and herbaceous planting, together with summer bedding. Home-made TEAS in aid of CAFOD. *Combined adm with* **Barton Farm** *&* **Old Orchard** *£5, chd 50p. Suns 8 May; 5 June (2-6). Private visits welcome by appt, most dates for groups of any size. Tel 01278 722267*

Evening Opening (See also garden description)

190 Goldcroft	13 June
Somerfoss	24 June
Little Yarford Farmhouse	
	11 August

Staffordshire & part of West Midlands

County Organisers:	Mr & Mrs Leslie Standeven, Smithy Cottage, Mucklestone, Market Drayton, Salop TF9 4DN Tel 01630 672677 email plantaholic@tiscali.co.uk
Press & Publicity Officer:	Mr Bert Foden, The Cottage, Tongue Lane, Brown Edge, Stoke on Trent ST6 8UQ Tel 01782 513033 email jeanandbert@btinternet.com

Maps: Numbers shown next to each garden entry refer to that garden's entry on the county map. This position is approximate; distance and directions from the nearest main town are generally shown in the garden text. A precise location is available for those gardens featured on the NGS website by visiting www.ngs.org.uk.

Symbols: Information relating to symbols is given on page 21

DATES OF OPENING

Evening openings
See end of county listing

Private gardens open regularly for NGS
Smithy Cottage, Mucklestone *(37)*

Gardens open to the public
For details see garden description
Biddulph Grange Garden, Biddulph *(4)*

By appointment only
For telephone number and other details see garden description.
Private visits welcomed
Arbour Cottage, Napley, Mucklestone *(1)*
Edgewood House, Stourton *(15)*

March 7 Monday
Stonehill Quarry Garden, Great Gate, Croxden *(39)*
March 14 Monday
Stonehill Quarry Garden, Great Gate, Croxden *(39)*
March 21 Monday
Stonehill Quarry Garden, Great Gate, Croxden *(39)*
March 25 Friday (Easter)
Smithy Cottage, Mucklestone *(37)*
March 27 Sunday (Easter)
Stonehill Quarry Garden, Great Gate, Croxden *(39)*
March 28 Monday (Easter)
Field House Farm, Pipe Gate *(17)*
Manor Cottage, Chapel Chorlton *(26)*
Stonehill Quarry Garden, Great Gate, Croxden *(39)*
April 4 Monday
Stonehill Quarry Garden, Great Gate, Croxden *(39)*
April 11 Monday
Stonehill Quarry Garden, Great Gate, Croxden *(39)*
April 23 Saturday
7 Beech Tree Road, Walsall Wood *(2)*
April 24 Sunday
7 Beech Tree Road, Walsall Wood *(2)*

May 1 Sunday
Yew Tree Cottage, Long Lane, White Cross, Haughton *(46)*
May 2 Monday (Bank Hol)
Manor Cottage, Chapel Chorlton *(26)*
May 5 Thursday
Smithy Cottage, Mucklestone *(37)*
May 8 Sunday
Heath House, nr Eccleshall *(22)*
May 12 Thursday
Smithy Cottage, Mucklestone *(37)*
May 14 Saturday
The Old Dairy House, Stoke-on-Trent *(30)*
The Old Rectory, Clifton Campville *(32)*
May 15 Sunday
The Beeches, Rocester *(3)*
Dorset House, Cheslyn Hay *(14)*
Little Onn Hall, Church Eaton *(25)*
The Old Dairy House, Stoke-on-Trent *(30)*
May 19 Thursday
Smithy Cottage, Mucklestone *(37)*
May 21 Saturday
Tanglewood Cottage, Wetley Rocks *(40)*
May 22 Sunday
12 Darges Lane, Great Wyrley *(12)*
Smithy Cottage, Mucklestone *(37)*
Tanglewood Cottage, Wetley Rocks *(40)*
May 26 Thursday
Smithy Cottage, Mucklestone *(37)*
May 29 Sunday
Field House Farm, Pipe Gate *(17)*
Yew Tree Cottage, Long Lane, White Cross, Haughton *(46)*
May 30 Monday (Bank Hol)
Manor Cottage, Chapel Chorlton *(26)*
June 1 Wednesday
The Old Orchard, Hammerwich *(31)*
June 2 Thursday
Smithy Cottage, Mucklestone *(37)*
June 4 Saturday
Birch Trees, Copmere End, Eccleshall *(5)*
Victoria Cottage, Yarnfield *(41)*
June 5 Sunday
The Garth, Milford *(18)*
Victoria Cottage, Yarnfield *(41)*
The Wombourne Wodehouse, Wolverhampton *(45)*
June 9 Thursday
Smithy Cottage, Mucklestone *(37)*

June 11 Saturday
Chuckery Gardens, Walsall *(10)*
June 12 Sunday
The Beeches, Rocester *(3)*
Heath House, nr Eccleshall *(22)*
Station Road Gardens, Rolleston on Dove *(38)*
June 16 Thursday
Smithy Cottage, Mucklestone *(37)*
June 19 Sunday
4 Dene Close, Penkridge *(13)*
Grafton Cottage, Barton-under-Needwood *(19)*
Lilac Cottage, Gentleshaw *(24)*
Pinfold Cottage, Shenstone *(33)*
Smithy Cottage, Mucklestone **(Evening)** *(37)*
June 23 Thursday
Smithy Cottage, Mucklestone *(37)*
June 26 Sunday
Biddulph Grange Garden, Biddulph *(4)*
The Garth, Milford *(18)*
Hales Hall *(20)*
High Trees, Longton *(23)*
Station Road Gardens, Rolleston on Dove *(38)*
Yew Tree Cottage, Long Lane, White Cross, Haughton *(46)*
June 27 Monday
15 St Johns Road, Pleck, Walsall **(Evening)** *(35)*
June 30 Thursday
Smithy Cottage, Mucklestone *(37)*
July 2 Saturday
The Bowers, Standon, nr Eccleshall *(7)*
July 3 Sunday
The Bowers, Standon, nr Eccleshall *(7)*
Grafton Cottage, Barton-under-Needwood *(19)*
July 7 Thursday
Smithy Cottage, Mucklestone *(37)*
July 9 Saturday
The Wickets, Wheaton Aston *(43)*
July 10 Sunday
The Mount, Gnosall *(29)*
Smithy Cottage, Mucklestone *(37)*
Station Road Gardens, Rolleston on Dove *(38)*
98 Walsall Road, Aldridge *(42)*
The Wickets, Wheaton Aston *(43)*

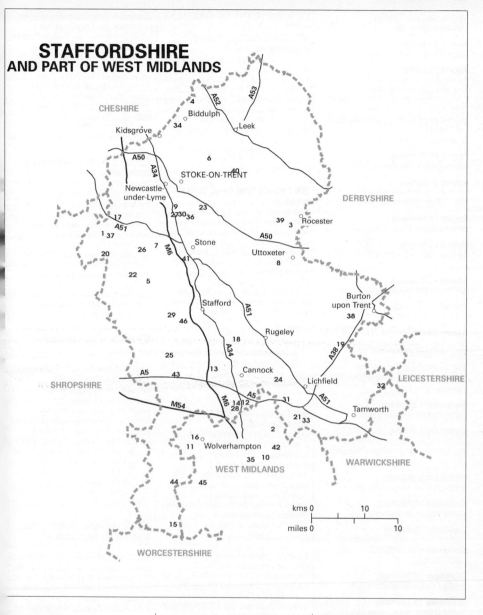

STAFFORDSHIRE
AND PART OF WEST MIDLANDS

55 Cornwall Road, Tettenhall, Wolverhampton *(11)*

August 4 Thursday
Smithy Cottage, Mucklestone *(37)*

August 7 Sunday
4 Dene Close, Penkridge *(13)*
Field House Farm, Pipe Gate *(17)*
Grafton Cottage, Barton-under-Needwood *(19)*
Manor Cottage Garden, Hanchurch, Stoke-on-Trent *(27)*
Silverwood, Trentham *(36)*

August 11 Thursday
Smithy Cottage, Mucklestone *(37)*

August 14 Sunday
Heath House, nr Eccleshall *(22)*
Lilac Cottage, Gentleshaw *(24)*

August 18 Thursday
Smithy Cottage, Mucklestone *(37)*

August 21 Sunday
34 Ennerdale Road, Tettenhall, Wolverhampton *(16)*

August 25 Thursday
Smithy Cottage, Mucklestone *(37)*

August 27 Saturday
Mind The Step, Cheslyn Hay *(28)*

August 28 Sunday
Birch Trees, Copmere End, Eccleshall *(5)*
Mind The Step, Cheslyn Hay *(28)*

August 29 Monday (Bank Hol)
Manor Cottage Garden, Hanchurch, Stoke-on-Trent *(27)*

September 1 Thursday
Smithy Cottage, Mucklestone *(37)*

September 4 Sunday
Smithy Cottage, Mucklestone *(37)*
The Willows, Trysull, nr Wolverhampton *(44)*

September 8 Thursday
Smithy Cottage, Mucklestone *(37)*

September 15 Thursday
Smithy Cottage, Mucklestone *(37)*

September 18 Sunday
Biddulph Grange Garden, Biddulph *(4)*
55 Cornwall Road, Tettenhall, Wolverhampton *(11)*

September 22 Thursday
Smithy Cottage, Mucklestone *(37)*

September 29 Thursday
Smithy Cottage, Mucklestone *(37)*

October 17 Monday
Stonehill Quarry Garden, Great Gate, Croxden *(39)*

October 23 Sunday
Stonehill Quarry Garden, Great Gate, Croxden *(39)*

October 24 Monday
Stonehill Quarry Garden, Great Gate, Croxden *(39)*

DESCRIPTIONS OF GARDENS

❶ Arbour Cottage, Napley, Mucklestone ⬛🐾⬛
(Mr & Mrs David Hewitt) *4m NE of Market Drayton. On Staffs-Shrops border. Take A53 then B5415 signed Woore, turn L 1¾m, unmarked lane.* Country garden of 2 acres with alpine screes, mixed perennials, shrub roses and many peonies, bamboos etc. All-yr colour from shrubs and trees of many species. Cream TEAS. *Adm £3, chd 50p. Private visits welcome by appt. Tel 01630 672852 hewitt1@clara.net*

❷ 7 Beech Tree Road, Walsall Wood 🐾⬛
(Mr & Mrs B Davis) *3m NE of Walsall. 6m SW of Lichfield. A461 Walsall to Lichfield rd. From Walsall turn R & immed R again just past church in Walsall Wood. From Lichfield turn L & immed R just before church. Car park 50yds.* Plantsman's garden approx 60ftx30ft. Rockeries and pool. No grass. First-class collection of alpines and primulas with miniature daphnes, rhododendrons and ferns. Dwarf conifers, some very rare species. Small plants underplanted with unusual bulbs. Fences covered with evergreen climbers. *Adm £2, chd free. Sat, Sun 23, 24 Apr (11-5). Private visits welcome by appt. Tel 01543 820921*

❸ The Beeches, Mill Street, Rocester ⬛🐾⬛
(Mr & Mrs K Sutton) *5m N of Uttoxeter. On B5030, turn R into village by JCB factory. By Red Lion PH take rd for Marston Montgomery. Garden 250yds on R.* Plant lover's garden of about ⅓ acre. Formal box garden; themed herbaceous borders containing many unusual varieties; shrubs incl rhododendrons, azaleas etc. Pools, roses, fruit trees, clematis and climbing plants. Yr-round garden. Cottage garden planting with a secret round every corner. Featured in 'Staffordshire Life' 2004. TEAS. *Adm £2.50, chd free. Suns 15 May; 12 June; 31 July (2-5). Private visits welcome by appt. Tel 01889 590631*

❹ ◆ Biddulph Grange Garden, Biddulph 🐾⬛
(The National Trust) *3½m SE of Congleton. 7m N of Stoke-on-Trent off the A527.* Exciting and rare survival of high Victorian garden extensively restored since 1988. Conceived by James Bateman, the 15 acres are divided into a number of smaller gardens designed to house

specimens from his extensive plant collection. An Egyptian Court, Chinese Temple and Willow Pattern bridge, pinetum and arboretum combine to make the garden a miniature tour of the world. Light refreshments and TEAS. *Adm £5, chd £2.50. 19 Mar to 30 Oct: Weds, Thurs, Fris (12-5.30) Sats, Suns (11-5.30). Closed Mons, Tues.* **For NGS:** *Suns 26 June; 18 Sept (11-5.30). Tel 01782 517999 biddulphgrange@nationaltrust.org.uk*

❺ Birch Trees, Copmere End, Eccleshall ⬛🐾⬛
(Susan & John Weston) *1½m W of Eccleshall. On B5026, turn at junction signed Copmere End. After ½m straight across Xrds by Star Inn.* Peaceful ½-acre country garden with views over surrounding countryside. Plant enthusiasts' garden with many unusual varieties, designed with wildlife in mind. Herbaceous borders, peat bed, water features and vegetable plot. TEAS. *Adm £2.50, chd free. Sats 4 June, 16 July; Sun 28 Aug (1.30-5.30). Private visits welcome by appt. Tel 01785 850448*

❻ Bleak House, Bagnall 🐾⬛
(Mr & Mrs J H Beynon) *4m NE of Stoke-on-Trent. A5009 to Milton Xrds, turn for Bagnall. 2m up hill past golf course to corner opp Bagnall Heights.* 1 acre on many levels. Natural stone quarry with jungle planting; various water features with emphasis on reclaimed materials. Many unusual plants. Featured in 'Country Living' 2003, '25 Beautiful Gardens' 2005. Home-made TEAS. *Adm £2.50, chd free. Sun 17 July (1-6). Private visits welcome by appt for groups of 10+, coaches permitted. Tel 01782 534713*

❼ The Bowers, Church Lane, Standon, nr Eccleshall 🐾⬛
(Maurice Thacker & Sheila Marriott) *5m N of Eccleshall. Take A519 & at Cotes Heath turn L signed Standon. After 1m turn R at Xrds by church, into Church Lane ½m on L. ⅓-acre* cottage-style garden in a rural setting. A plant lover's delight with massed planting of rare and unusual perennials in colour-themed borders. A large collection of clematis and hostas and over 200 hardy geraniums. Winner Stone in Bloom, best back garden, 2003 & 2004. Home-made TEAS. *Adm £2.50, chd free. Sat, Sun 2, 3 July (12.30-5). Private visits welcome by appt June & July only. Tel 01782 791244 metbowers@aol.com*

8 Brook House Farm, Dagdale, Bramshall, Uttoxeter &⊗⊕
(Jim & Zoe Barker) *2m W of Uttoxeter. On B5027 Stone rd. In Bramshall turn into Church Lane, go through village, turn 1st L past Robin Hood PH. ½m down lane.* 2½-acre prize-winning country garden. Hardy perennials and shrubs, formal rose garden with fountain. Parterre, grass garden. Double hot border, fernery with dry stone walls and folly, Mediterranean garden, natural stream, wild flower meadow, shrubberies, orchard. Organic vegetable garden. Rich in wildlife and unusual ideas, with strong emphasis on colour and plant associations. Wildlife observation tree house planned for 2005 and raised bed system for vegetable garden. Winner E Staffordshire Brighter Borough, best front garden, best back garden, gold medallist water features 2004. Cream TEAS in aid of Uttoxeter Gateway Club (Mencap). *Adm £2.50, chd free. Sun 17 July (2-5.30). Private visits welcome by appt June & July for individuals, groups & coaches. Tel 01889 562110*

9 Chetwynd House, 144 Northwood Lane, Clayton, Newcastle-under-Lyme ⊗
(Flavia Swann & John Sneddon) *2m S of Newcastle-under-Lyme. Off A519, ½m from M6 J15. From J15 take 1st L at roundabout to Newcastle A519, at 2nd roundabout turn R onto Northwood Lane. Entrance in Foxglove Lane on R.* Approx ½ acre of colourful garden recently developed from surviving S-facing terraces of original garden laid out in 1900. Herbaceous borders with many unusual and colourful plants, incl a collection of lavenders and architectural plants. Home-made TEAS in aid of Blackfriars Day Centre for disabled adults. *Adm £2.50, chd free. Sun 17 July (2-5)*

10 Chuckery Gardens, Walsall
1m E of Walsall town centre. On A4148 ring rd, 1m S of junction with A461, ½m N of junction with A34. Car park at arboretum/golf course car park in addition to rd. Country gardens in a suburban location. Home-made TEAS at 151 Broadway North in aid of Walsall Manor Hospital breast cancer unit. *Combined adm £2.50, chd free. Sat 1 June (1.30-5.30)*

151 Broadway North ⊗⊕ (Mose & John Hayward) Paths, trellis and archways separate mixed planting areas, mainly herbaceous. Ponds, variety of containers and hidden corners

add interest. Small woodland area.

58 Princes Avenue ⊗⊕ (Jo Toon) *Up Lincoln Rd (off ring rd, opp Grange Playhouse) then R at Xrds.* Interesting and unusual garden, using a steep site on 3 levels. Innovative use of containers/objets trouvés. A surprise around every corner.

11 NEW 55 Cornwall Road, Tettenhall, Wolverhampton &⊗⊕
(Eric Bateman & Tania Deans) *1½m W of Wolverhampton. A41 from J3 M54. Turn R onto Regis Rd at Tettenhall Green. Just before Mancroft Stores turn L into Cornwall Rd and park. House 3rd on L.* Small ex-Council house garden, thoughtfully designed and laid out over 8yrs. The traditional square shape has been changed to give the illusion of circles and curves. The back garden is terraced with a small pond and mixture of exotica and traditional bedding. A delight to see. Wolverhampton Housing Best Garden 2003. TEAS. *Adm £2, chd free. Suns 31 July; 18 Sept (2-5)*

12 12 Darges Lane, Great Wyrley ⊗⊕ NCCPG
(Mrs A Hackett) *2m SE of Cannock. From A5 take A34 towards Walsall. Darges Lane is 1st turning on R (over brow of hill). House on R on corner of Cherrington Drive.* ¾-acre well-stocked plantsman's and flower arranger's garden on two levels. Foliage plants a special feature. Mixed borders incl trees, shrubs and rare plants giving yr-round interest. Features constantly changing. National Collection of lamiums. Collection of 93 clematis. The overall effect is attractive and enticing to the plant lover. New for 2005 'Art in the Garden'. Light refreshments and TEAS. *Adm £2.50, chd 50p. Sun 22 May (2-6). Private visits welcome by appt. Tel 01922 415064*

13 4 Dene Close, Penkridge ⊗⊕
(David & Anne Smith) *6m S of Stafford. On A449 from Stafford. At far end of Penkridge turn L into Boscomoor Lane, 2nd L into Filance Lane, 3rd R Dene Close. Please park with consideration in Filance Lane. Disabled only in Dene Close.* Medium-sized plant lovers' garden created over the last 31yrs. Wide variety of herbaceous perennials, foliage plants and over 60 varieties of grasses in mixed borders and gravelled areas. Small water feature. Recently completed 54ft 'rainbow' border. Highly Commended, Stafford

in Bloom 2004. Home-made TEAS and plants in aid of County Air Ambulance. *Adm £2, chd free. Suns 19 June; 7 Aug (11-5). Private visits welcome by appt. Tel 01785 712580*

14 NEW Dorset House, 68 Station Street, Cheslyn Hay &⊗⊕
(Mary & David Blundell) *2m SE of Cannock. J11 M6. A462 towards Willenhall, L at island, follow rd to next island. R into one-way system (Low St), at T-junction L into Station St. A5 Bridgetown L over M6 toll rd to island, L into Coppice Rd. At T-junction R into Station St.* Inspirational ½-acre plantaholic's country garden giving all-yr interest. Many unique features, wealth of unusual rhododendrons, acers, shrubs and perennials, planted in mixed borders. Clematis-covered arches, intimate seating areas, hidden corners, water features, stream, all creating a haven of peace and tranquillity. Interesting and unusual plants for sale. Winners Cheslyn Hay Garden in Bloom 2004, Best Front & Rear Garden. *Adm £2.50, chd free. Suns 15 May; 17 July (10-5)*

15 Edgewood House, Greensforge Lane, Stourton &⊗
(Mr & Mrs G E Fletcher) *4m W of Stourbridge. 11m E of Bridgnorth. Take A458 from Stew Poney junction off A449 (Wolverhampton and Kidderminster) towards Bridgnorth. 1st lane on R, ¾m along lane on L.* 20 acres of woodland with winding paths, cultivated and natural garden with small pools. Rhododendrons and azaleas. Many steep steps through carpets of bluebells and lily of the valley. New enclosed garden within the grounds. Stout shoes recommended. Featured in 'Express & Star' & 'The Garden' 2004. Light refreshments and TEAS. *Adm £3, chd free. Private visits welcome by appt for groups of 10+. Tel 01384 872304 diana.fletcher@btopenworld.com*

ngs gardens open for charity

More than £20 million has been donated to charity since the NGS began in 1927

⑯ 34 Ennerdale Road, Tettenhall, Wolverhampton &🅖
(Yvonne & Stuart Stockley) *3m NW of Wolverhampton. On A41 into Wolverhampton, pass Tettenhall village paddling pool on L, then through deep stone cutting. At T-lights, turn L towards Pendeford, Codsall. Straight over mini-island, 2nd exit at next island towards Codsall. 3rd R into Windermere Rd, 2nd R into Ennerdale Rd.* Experience the Tropics in a unique urban environment. 115ft x 30ft garden featuring a wildlife pond with bog garden and Mediterranean area. Sit in 'The Retreat' and enjoy a variety of exotic plants incl collections of bananas, cannas, cordylines, echiums, lilies, phormiums and ricinus, as well as examples of cardoon, dasylirion, palms and small trees such as Indian bean and paulownia. Winners of 'Garden News' best newcomer garden 2003. Shortlisted and highly commended for 'Daily Mail' Garden of the Year 2004. Home-made TEAS in aid of Compton Hospice. *Adm £2, chd free. Sun 21 Aug (2-6). Private visits welcome by appt Aug only. Tel 01902 759922 stuartsvs@aol.com*

⑰ Field House Farm, Pipe Gate &
(Vicki & Brian Walker) *10m SW of Newcastle-under-Lyme. 11m E of Nantwich. On A51 at Pipe Gate. Turn at Chetwode Arms towards Norton in Hales. 100yds turn L, 50yds turn L.* Tranquil country house garden, with long garden vistas, seating and country views. Natural stream and willow grove, with cottage garden planting. Scented garden and auricula theatre. 350yd wild flower walk - spring bulbs in April, wild flowers in May in natural meadow, along brook course (uneven ground). Featured in 'The Sunday Sentinel' 2004. Home-made TEAS. *Adm £3, chd free. Mon 28 Mar; Suns 29 May; 7 Aug (2-6). Private visits welcome by appt. Tel 01630 647522*

⑱ The Garth, 2 Broc Hill Way, Milford 🅖
(Mr & Mrs David Wright) *4½m SE of Stafford. A513 Stafford to Rugeley rd; at Barley Mow turn R (S) to Brocton; L after ½m. ½ acre;* shrubs, rhododendrons, azaleas, mixed herbaceous borders, naturalised bulbs; plants of interest to flower arrangers. Rock hewn caves. Fine landscape setting. Cream TEAS. *Adm £2, chd free. Suns 5, 26 June (2-6). Private visits welcome by appt, coaches by arrangement. Tel 01785 661182*

⑲ Grafton Cottage, Barton-under-Needwood &🅖
(Margaret & Peter Hargreaves) *6m N of Lichfield. Leave A38 for Catholme S of Barton, follow sign to Barton Green, ¼m on L.* ¼-acre chocolate box cottage garden with secret behind every corner. Emphasis on scent and colour themes. Bridge over brook leads to summerhouse. Trellises covered with numerous old-fashioned roses and sweet peas. Over 90 clematis wander over and through plants in the borders to extend colour. Delphiniums, achilleas, salvias, phlox, hollyhocks and many other unusual perennials. Featured in BBC Gardeners' World, RHS 'Colour your Garden', 'Ideal Home' 2004. Cream TEAS. *Adm £2.50, chd free (share to Alzheimer's Research Trust). Suns 19 June; 3 July; 7 Aug (1.30-5.30). Private visits welcome by appt for groups. Tel 01283 713639 marpeter@onetel.com*

⑳ Hales Hall &🅖
(Mr & Mrs R N C Hall) *3m Market Drayton. Signed from A53 between Loggerheads & Market Drayton to Hales. Shropshire/Staffordshire border.* C18 house (not open) in wonderful setting. Restored walled organic vegetable garden. Woodland walks, bog garden, borders, Victorian yew garden. Many unusual plants and trees. All-yr-round interest. Cream TEAS in aid of Hales Church & Club. *Adm £3.50, chd free, OAP £2.50. Sun 26 June (2-5). Private visits welcome by appt for coaches and groups of 10+. Tel 01630 654144 jane@boreen.eclipse.co.uk*

㉑ Hammerwich Gardens, Burntwood
4m S of Lichfield. Turn off A461 onto A5190, L at lights. Limited parking & turning. Parking if busy at WI Hall in village centre (5mins walk), disabled at gardens. TEAS at The Mill House, samples of garden produce at The Old Orchard. *Combined adm £3.50, chd free. Sat 30 July (2-5)*

Mill House, Mill Lane &🅖 (Linda Skew) Pretty ½-acre flower arranger's cottage garden, in lovely country setting next to village windmill. Large well-stocked pool, shrubs, perennials, hostas, surprise herb garden and vegetable patch. Places to sit and relax. *Private visits welcome by appt for groups, garden clubs, flower arranging clubs, WI. No coaches. Tel 01543 672249 linda.skew@lineone.net*

The Old Orchard, 13 Stockhay Lane &🅖 (Mandy Tanna) (see separate entry).

㉒ Heath House, Offley Brook, nr Eccleshall &🅖
(Dr D W Eyre-Walker) *3m W of Eccleshall. Take B5026 towards Woore. At Sugnall turn L, after 1½m turn R immed by stone garden wall. After 1m straight across Xrds.* 1½-acre country garden of C18 miller's house in lovely valley setting, overlooking mill pool. Plantsman's garden containing many rare and unusual plants in borders, bog garden, woodland, alpine house, raised bed and shrubberies. TEAS. *Adm £3, chd free (share to Adbaston Parish Church). Suns 8 May; 12 June; 14 Aug (2-5). Private visits welcome by appt. Tel 01785 280318*

㉓ High Trees, 18 Drubbery Lane, Longton &🅖
(Peter and Pat Teggin) *5m S of Stoke-on-Trent. Situated in the S area of Stoke-on-Trent off A5035, midway between Trentham Gardens & Longton. Opp Longton Park.* Plantsperson's secluded suburban garden. Many unusual plants that flow easily from the gravel garden driveway, through arches and trellis of clematis and roses, to lush herbaceous planting. Also vibrant, hot, dry areas that contrast with the subdued tones of ferns and hostas in shade. Cream TEAS. *Adm £2, chd 50p. Suns 26 June; 17 July (2-5). Private visits welcome by appt for groups. Tel 01782 318453*

㉔ Lilac Cottage, Chapel Lane, Gentleshaw &&🅖
(Mrs Sylvia Nunn) *5m NW of Lichfield. Approx midway between Lichfield & Rugeley on A51 at Longdon, turn W into Borough Lane signed Cannock Wood & Gentleshaw. Continue 1m to T-junction. L for 1½m to Gentleshaw. From Burntwood, A5190 head N on Rugeley Rd at Burntwood Swan island; turn L at Xrds approx ½m past Nags Head PH, over Xrds to Gentleshaw. Parking only at Cannock Wood and Gentleshaw village hall. Roadside disabled parking only at Lilac Cottage.* Plant enthusiast's 1-acre country garden with emphasis on colour-themed borders and plant associations. Wealth of unusual perennials, especially geraniums, penstemons and achilleas, interspersed with English roses, interesting trees and shrubs. Small wildlife pool, bog garden, vibrant hot border, shady walks, tranquil sunken garden, sweeping

vistas. All-yr interest. Incl perennial nursery. Pleasant walks nearby on Gentleshaw Common, 'Castle Ring' and Cannock Chase. Featured in 'Midlands Journal' 2004. TEAS. *Adm £2.50, chd free. Suns 19 June; 17 July; 14 Aug (10-5). Private visits welcome by appt May to Aug for groups of 20+, coaches permitted. Tel 01543 675520 www.lilaccottagegarden.co.uk*

㉕ Little Onn Hall, Church Eaton 🚻

(Mrs A Kidson) 6m SW of Stafford. A449 Wolverhampton to Stafford; at Gailey roundabout turn W onto A5 for 1¼m; turn R to Stretton, 200yds turn L for Church Eaton; or Bradford Arms to Wheaton Aston & Marston 1¾m. 6-acre garden; herbaceous lined drive; abundance of rhododendrons; formal paved rose garden with pavilions at front; large lawns with lily pond around house; old moat garden with fish tanks and small ruin; fine trees; walkways. Paddock open for picnics. Cream TEAS. *Adm £3, chd 50p. Sun 15 May (2-5.30). Private visits welcome by appt. Tel 01785 840154*

㉖ Manor Cottage, Chapel Chorlton 🚻

(Mrs Joyce Heywood) 6m S of Newcastle-under-Lyme. On A51 Nantwich to Stone rd turn behind Cock Inn at Stableford; white house on village green. Good garden design with emphasis on plant association and outstanding collections of ferns, euphorbias, geraniums and unusual plants. *Adm £2, chd 50p. Mons 28 Mar; 2, 30 May (2-5). Private visits welcome by appt. Tel 01782 680206*

㉗ NEW Manor Cottage Garden, 2 Manor Cottage, Hanchurch, Stoke-on-Trent 🗖

(Dr & Mrs Clement) 4m S of Newcastle-under-Lyme. From J15 M6 follow A519 S towards Eccleshall. Straight on at T-lights, past Hanchurch village, under M6, 2nd R onto private rd. Welcome to 'the jungle'. This small semi-tropical garden comprises a small courtyard garden with phormiums and other architectural foliage plants. Off the courtyard the main garden, 'the jungle', incl bananas, bamboos, ferns, foxglove trees, cannas and day lilies in abundance. Small informal pond. Good end-of-season interest. Home-made TEAS. *Adm £2, chd free. Sun 7, Mon 29 Aug (11-5). Private visits welcome by appt for small groups, Aug only. Tel 01782 644112*

㉘ NEW Mind The Step, 26 Park Close, Cheslyn Hay 🗖

(Julie Guest & Ralph Partridge) 2½m SE of Cannock. From A5 take A34 Walsall. 1st R Darges Lane. At T-junction R into Station St (B4156), 4th L, next L and L again. Park Close off Glenthorne Drive, ignore Park St. Plantsman's garden. Tranquil stream provides serenity for study of unusual plants and grasses; ferns, hostas and acers offer consistency, moisture-loving and foliage plants complement the water garden, whilst bananas, cannas and gingers augment the tropical theme. Narrow pathways, possible congestion. Please be patient. TEAS in aid of County Air Ambulance. *Adm £2, chd 50p. Sat, Sun 27, 28 Aug (10-5)*

㉙ The Mount, Coton, Gnosall 🗖

(Andrew & Celia Payne) 8m W of Stafford. 4m E of Newport. From Stafford take A518 W towards Newport/Telford. Go through Gnosall, over canal. Garden on edge of Gnosall Village, on LH-side of A518. Parking approx 100yds signed up lane. Approx ¾-acre colourful developing plantsman's garden incl bog area with small wildlife pool, cottage-style front garden and herbaceous borders. Large variety of plants incl hardy geraniums, hostas, euphorbias, ferns, bamboos, plus numerous tender perennials. Home-made TEAS in aid of Macmillan Cancer Relief. *Adm £2.50, chd free. Sun 10 July (2-6). Private visits welcome by appt, July only. Tel 01785 242238 ac.payne@farming.co.uk*

㉚ NEW The Old Dairy House, Trentham Park, Stoke-on-Trent 🗖

(Philip & Michelle Moore) S edge of Stoke-on-Trent. Behind Trentham Gardens on rd to Trentham Church and Trentham Park Golf Club. From A34 turn into Whitmore Rd B5038. 1st L and follow NGS signs. Grade 2 listed house (not open) designed by Sir Charles Barry forms backdrop to this 2-acre garden set in peaceful parkland setting. TEAS. *Adm £2.50, chd free. Sat, Sun 14, 15 May (1.30-5)*

㉛ The Old Orchard, 13 Stockhay Lane, Hammerwich 🚻

(Mandy Tanna) 4m S of Lichfield. Turn off A461 onto A5190, L at lights. Limited parking & turning. Parking if busy at WI Hall in village centre (5mins walk), disabled at garden. ⅔-acre former orchard, now a family garden with something for everyone. Ponds, stream, shrubs, herbaceous plants, herbs and conservatory with exotics. Totally organic and wildlife-friendly. Treasure hunt and samples of garden produce. TEAS. *Adm £2. Wed 1 June (2-5). Also opening with* **Hammerwich Gardens** *Sat 30 July. Private visits welcome by appt, for groups and evening visits. Tel 01543 683364 mandytanna@aol.com*

㉜ The Old Rectory, Clifton Campville 🚻🗖

(Martin & Margaret Browne) 6m N of Tamworth. 2m W of M42 J11, in centre of Clifton Campville. Village signed off B5493 from Statfold or No Man's Heath. Entrance to garden on S side of Main St at top of hill, between bus shelter and school. Tranquil 2-acre garden around an historic former Rectory, developed over 21yrs by the present owners. Established trees underplanted with a diverse range of plants. Enjoy a garden on an ancient site, full of spring colour but with interest at all seasons. Paths give easy access to lawns, borders, fruit and vegetables. Small walled garden and gravel areas. Home-made TEAS. *Adm £2.50, chd £1. Sat 14 May (1-5). Private visits welcome by appt. Tel 01827 373533 mbrowne526@aol.com*

㉝ Pinfold Cottage, 6 Pinfold Hill, Shenstone 🗖

(Mrs Cherry Scobie) 6m N of Sutton Coldfield. 3m S of Lichfield. On A5127. For Pinfold Hill turn L at small island on A5127 if approaching from Sutton, or R if approaching from Lichfield. No 6 is an early C19 cottage set at R angles to rd on L, but proceed another 80yds to park at The Plough & Harrow PH. An enchanting cottage garden full of surprises with intriguing corners and hidden views to incl pond, rockery, some interesting trees and shrubs and a multitude of perennials. *Adm £2, chd free. Sun 19 June (2-6)*

㉞ 45 Rockside, off Church Street, Mow Cop 🗖

(Kath and Alan Myers) 3m N of Kidsgrove. 7m S of Congleton on A34. 3m N of Butt Lane on A34. Follow signs for Mow Cop/Mount Pleasant. Turn up Clare St and follow up the hill (Church St) approx 150 yds; garden on R. Plant lover's rugged country garden of about ¾ acre with herbaceous borders and island beds. Many varieties of shrubs and trees, hardy perennials. Water features, arches with roses, clematis and honeysuckles. Tiered gravel

garden with grasses, hosta bed, alpine troughs and beds. Bog garden, seating areas with views over the Cheshire Plain. Light refreshments and TEAS. *Adm £2.50, chd free. Sat, Sun 16, 17 July (1-5)*

㉟ 15 St Johns Road, Pleck, Walsall &⊕
(Maureen & Sid Allen) *2m W of Walsall. Off J10 M6. Head for Walsall on A454 Wolverhampton Rd. Turn R into Pleck Rd A4148 then 4th R into St Johns Rd.* Long narrow garden, 114ft long. Main garden packed with shrubs, small trees, perennials, tropical area; Japanese theme, with tea house, bridge over small stream and fish pool; lots of foliage planting; small features at every turn. New garden added this yr from derelict land, for wildlife with small pool, many grasses and small shady woodland walk. Runner up in 'Daily Mail' Garden of the Year 2003, from 3000 entries. TEAS. *Adm £2, chd free.* **Evening Opening** *Mon 27 June (6-9). Sun 17 July (11-5). Private visits welcome by appt for groups of 10+, coaches welcome. Tel 01922 441027*

㊱ Silverwood, 16 Beechfield Road, Trentham &⌖⊕
(Dr M & Mrs S Akhtar) *3m S of Stoke on Trent. From A34 Trentham Gardens roundabout take A5035 Longton Rd. After NatWest Bank take R turn into Oaktree Rd. From Longton (A50) follow A5035 into Trentham. After PH take L turn into Oaktree Rd, which becomes Beechfield Rd. Parking limited.* A plantsman's treat. Small town garden with an unexpected wealth of interesting plants. Woodland area, herbaceous beds and gravel area with tropical planting. Home-made TEAS in aid of Breast Cancer Campaign. *Adm £2.50, chd free. Sun 7 Aug (2-6)*

㊲ Smithy Cottage, Mucklestone ✿⊕
(Leslie & Diana Standeven) *8m SW of Newcastle-under-Lyme. On B5026 between Woore A51 & Loggerheads A53 opposite Mucklestone Church.* Country cottage garden ⅓-acre, with stream into pool, mixed borders, scree, alpine house. Eclectic collection of rarities in a unique conservation area of historical interest. All-yr interest. Featured in 'Amateur Gardening' & on Central TV 2004. TEAS. *Adm £2.50, chd free.* **Good Friday 25 Mar; Every Thur 5 May to 29 Sept. Suns 22 May; 10 July; 4 Sept (2-5).** **Evening Opening** *£3.50, wine, Sun 19 June (5-9). Private visits welcome by appt. Tel 01630 672677 plantaholic@tiscali.co.uk*

㊳ Station Road Gardens, Rolleston on Dove
3m N of Burton upon Trent. From A38 take Clay Mills exit, follow signs to Rolleston & Tutbury. Enter Rolleston 1½m from exit, past Jinny PH on R & Meadow View on L. Number 62 is 100yds further on L. Park on Meadow View or Station Rd. 2 unexpected gardens completely hidden from the rd. TEAS at 62 Station Rd. *Combined adm £3, chd free, concessions £2. Suns 12, 26 June; 10 July (1-5)*

60 Station Road &⌖ (Andy & Jackie Betteridge) Atmospheric plant lovers' garden, mixed borders, patio, trellises, gravel garden, containers, wildlife pond. Gold Award, E Staffs Brighter Borough gardening competition 2004.

62 Station Road &⌖ (John Cartwright & Anna Nickel) Plant lovers' garden being developed by new owners. Mixed borders in several contrasting areas. Wildlife areas and pond, native trees, dry river bed with grasses.

㊴ Stonehill Quarry Garden, Great Gate, Croxden &⌖⊕
(Mrs Caroline Raymont) *6m NW of Uttoxeter. A50 to Uttoxeter. Take B5030 to JCB Rocester, L to Hollington & Croxden Abbey. Third R into Keelings Lane & Croxden Abbey. At Great Gate, T-junction L to Stonehill.* 6-acre quarry garden incorporating numerous ornamental trees and shrubs (magnolias, acers, catalpa, Davidia, paeonias, azaleas) underplanted with unusual Asiatic and American woodlanders (lilies, trillium, erythroniums, paris, podophyllum, arisaemas, hellebores), bamboo 'jungle', rock garden, pond, mixed borders. Spring bulbs and hellebores. Autumn colour of

particular interest. Regret unsuitable for children. No videos, please. Coffee and TEAS. *Adm £2.50. Mons 7 Mar to 11 Apr incl; 17, 24 Oct; Suns 27 Mar; 23 Oct (2-5). Private visits welcome by appt Mar to 11 Apr only. Tel 01889 507202*

㊵ NEW Tanglewood Cottage, Consall Lane, Wetley Rocks &⌖⊕
(Paul & Deirdre Nicholls) *5m NE of Stoke-on-Trent. A52 to Cellarhead, A520 to Wetley Rocks, sharp R to A522 at Powys Arms. ¼m first L into Consall Lane, garden 50yds on R. Parking on lane, wheelchair users on drive.* Restored country garden of 2 acres. Many rhododendrons and woodland walks. Open borders and ponds, many shade-loving plants, protected trees and wildlife. Lovely spring clematis and wisteria. A garden to relax in. Home-made TEAS in aid of Wetley Rocks village hall extension fund. *Adm £2.50, chd free. Sat, Sun 21, 22 May (2-5.30)*

㊶ Victoria Cottage, Moss Lane, Yarnfield &⌖⊕
(John & Maureen Hammersley) *2m W of Stone. Approx 5m from Stafford town centre and 8m from Stoke-on-Trent off A34. Turn into Yarnfield Lane alongside Walton Inn. Approx 1m along Yarnfield Lane after motorway bridge turn R into Moss Lane & immed R into large driveway for parking.* Garden full of structure in approx 1 acre. Well-stocked borders incl raised bed around seated water feature. Large koi and fishpond with walk over bridge reached via gravelled pergola walks leading to decking area. Small bog garden, rockery and herb area, with large stone and slate feature. Cream TEAS in aid of Katherine Hospice, Stafford. *Adm £2.50, chd under 14 free. Sat, Sun 4, 5 June (11-5)*

㊷ 98 Walsall Road, Aldridge &⌖⊕
(Mr & Mrs A Atkins) *3m NW of Walsall. On A454, 300yds past White House Inn. ⅓-acre well-stocked small town garden, created over 26yrs, a tranquil haven behind a main rd.* All-yr garden. Mostly shrubs and perennials with informal pond. Light refreshments and TEAS in aid of Walsall breast cancer self-help group. *Adm £2, chd 50p (share to Walsall breast cancer self-help group). Sun 10 July (12-5)*

43 The Wickets, 47 Long Street, Wheaton Aston &⊗
(Tony & Kate Bennett) *8m W of Cannock. From M6 J12 turn W towards Telford on A5; across A449 Gailey roundabout; A5 for 1½m; turn R signed Stretton, 150yds turn L signed Wheaton Aston; 2½m turn L; ½m over canal bridge; garden on R. Or Bradford Arms Wheaton Aston 2m.* A garden of many themes, full of ideas. A more open front garden is contrasted by many features behind the house. This ½-acre garden incl pond, dry stream, prairie planting, clock golf, shrub borders, gravel beds and many hanging baskets and containers. Popular and pleasant walks along Shropshire Union Canal just 25yds away. TEAS. *Adm £2, chd free. Sat, Sun 9, 10 July (2-5.30). Private visits welcome by appt. Tel 01785 840233*

44 The Willows, Trysull, nr Wolverhampton &⊗
(Mr & Mrs Nigel Hanson) *7m SW of Wolverhampton. From A449 at Himley B4176 towards Bridgnorth, 2¼m turn R to Trysull. ¾m on L.* 2-acre plant lover's paradise created

and maintained by garden designers Nigel and Jane. Natural pool, tropical garden with dramatic flowers and foliage. Colour theme borders with an emphasis on exciting plant combinations using interesting and unusual plants. Featured on Central TV & in 'Country Homes and Interiors' 2003, 'Staffordshire Life' 2004. Home-made TEAS in aid of Trysull Church. *Adm £3, chd free. Sun 4 Sept (2-6). Private visits welcome by appt. Tel 01902 897557*

45 The Wombourne Wodehouse, Wolverhampton &⊗
(Mr & Mrs J Phillips) *4m S of Wolverhampton. Just off A449 on A463 to Sedgley.* 18-acre garden laid out in 1750. Mainly rhododendrons, herbaceous border, woodland walk, water garden and irises in walled kitchen garden. Partial wheelchair access. Home-made TEAS. *Adm £3, chd free. Sun 5 June (2-5.30). Private visits welcome by appt. Tel 01902 892202*

46 Yew Tree Cottage, Podmores Corner, Long Lane, White Cross, Haughton &⊗
(Clive & Ruth Plant) *4m W of Stafford. Take A518 W Haughton, turn R just before Shropshire Arms (signed Ranton) 1m, then turn R at Xrds.* Youthful cottage garden of ⅓acre designed by plantaholics to complement Victorian cottage. Many unusual perennials from snowdrops and hellebore to trillium, meconopsis and arisaema, lathyrus, peony and salvia, closing with crocosmia, verbena and aster. Gravel garden, vegetables, herbaceous borders. All in a peaceful countryside setting. Featured in 'Amateur Gardening', Gardener of the Year Stafford in Bloom 2004. Home-made TEAS. *Adm £2.50, chd free. Suns 1, 29 May; 26 June; 24 July (2-5). Private visits welcome by appt. Tel 01785 282516*

Evening Opening (See also garden description)	
Smithy Cottage	19 June
15 St Johns Road	27 June

ngs

gardens open for charity

Your garden in the Yellow Book?

The NGS is always interested to hear of gardens with potential, large or small, that might open in the future.

For more information about opening your garden, please contact the County Organiser in your area, preferably at the time of year that you would like your garden to open.

Suffolk

County Organisers:
(East)   Mrs Patricia Short, Ruggs Hall, Raydon, Ipswich IP7 5LW Tel 01473 310416
(West)   Mrs Elizabeth Seiffer, Garden House Farm, Rattlesden Road, Drinkstone, Bury St Edmunds
                                      IP30 9TN Tel 01449 736434
Assistant County Organisers:
(East)   Mrs Derek Brightwell, Bucklesham Hall, Bucklesham IP10 0AY Tel 01473 659263
(Press & Publicity Officer)   Mrs Jenny Reeve, 6a Church Walk, Mildenhall IP28 7ED Tel 01638 715289
(East)   Mrs Joby West, The Millstone, Friars Road, Hadleigh IP7 6DF Tel 01473 823154
County Treasurers:
(West)   Mr Hans Seiffer, Garden House Farm, Rattlesden Road, Drinkstone, Bury St Edmunds
                                      IP30 9TN Tel 01449 736434
(East)   Mr Robert Stone, Washbrook Grange, Washbrook, Ipswich IP8 3HQ Tel 01473 730244

Maps: Numbers shown next to each garden entry refer to that garden's entry on the county map. This position is approximate;
             distance and directions from the nearest main town are generally shown in the garden text.
             A precise location is available for those gardens featured on the NGS website by visiting www.ngs.org.uk.
Symbols: Information relating to symbols is given on page 21

DATES OF OPENING

Evening openings
See end of county listing

Gardens open to the public
For details see garden description
Blakenham Woodland Garden, Little
 Blakenham *(4)*
The Coach House, Assington *(11)*
Euston Hall, Thetford *(16)*
Ickworth House Park & Gardens, Horringer
 (24)
Melford Hall, Long Melford *(30)*
Shrubland Park Garden, Coddenham, nr
 Ipswich *(44)*
Somerleyton Hall & Gardens, Lowestoft *(45)*
Woottens, Wenhaston *(50)*
Wyken Hall, Stanton *(51)*

"You can come down now Henry,
they've all gone!"

By appointment only
*For telephone number and other
details see garden description.
Private visits welcomed*
Windmill Cottage, Capel St Mary *(49)*

February 12 Saturday
Treaclebenders, Drinkstone *(47)*

February 20 Sunday
Gable House, Redisham *(17)*

March 20 Sunday
East Bergholt Place, East Bergholt *(15)*

March 27 Sunday (Easter)
Rosemary, Rectory Hill, East Bergholt *(41)*

April 3 Sunday
The Beeches, Walsham-le-Willows *(3)*
Great Thurlow Hall, Haverhill *(19)*

April 5 Tuesday
Woottens, Wenhaston *(50)*

April 6 Wednesday
Woottens, Wenhaston *(50)*

April 7 Thursday
Woottens, Wenhaston *(50)*

April 10 Sunday
East Bergholt Place, East Bergholt *(15)*

April 12 Tuesday
Woottens, Wenhaston *(50)*

April 13 Wednesday
Woottens, Wenhaston *(50)*

April 14 Thursday
Woottens, Wenhaston *(50)*

April 17 Sunday
Brook Farm, Charsfield *(7)*
Corner Cottage, Gislingham *(14)*

April 19 Tuesday
Woottens, Wenhaston *(50)*

April 20 Wednesday
Woottens, Wenhaston *(50)*

April 21 Thursday
Woottens, Wenhaston *(50)*

April 23 Saturday
Blakenham Woodland Garden, Little
 Blakenham *(4)*
The Island House, Lavenham *(25)*

April 24 Sunday
The Island House, Lavenham *(25)*
The Rookery, Eyke *(39)*
Shrubland Park Garden, Coddenham, nr
 Ipswich *(44)*

April 26 Tuesday
Woottens, Wenhaston *(50)*

April 27 Wednesday
Woottens, Wenhaston *(50)*

April 28 Thursday
Woottens, Wenhaston *(50)*

May 1 Sunday
Brook Hall, Crowfield *(8)*
Rosedale, Bures *(40)*

May 2 Monday (Bank Hol)
Clematis Cottage Farm, Aldeby, Beccles
 (10)
Rosemary, Rectory Hill, East Bergholt *(41)*

May 3 Tuesday
Woottens, Wenhaston *(50)*

May 4 Wednesday
Woottens, Wenhaston *(50)*

May 5 Thursday
Woottens, Wenhaston *(50)*

May 8 Sunday
Bucklesham Hall, Bucklesham *(9)*
Magnolia House, Yoxford *(28)*
Priory Hall, Hadleigh *(35)*

May 10 Tuesday
Woottens, Wenhaston *(50)*

May 11 Wednesday
Woottens, Wenhaston *(50)*

May 12 Thursday
Woottens, Wenhaston *(50)*

May 15 Sunday
Ashlie, Knodishall, Saxmundham *(1)*
Highfields Farm, Bures *(21)*

SUFFOLK

May 17 Tuesday
Woottens, Wenhaston *(50)*

May 18 Wednesday
Woottens, Wenhaston *(50)*

May 19 Thursday
Woottens, Wenhaston *(50)*

May 21 Saturday
Mildenhall Gardens *(32)*
Woottens, Wenhaston *(50)*

May 22 Sunday
Gable House, Redisham *(17)*
The Hill House, Glemsford *(22)*
Kiln Cottage, Rickinghall *(26)*
Mildenhall Gardens *(32)*
The Priory, Stoke-by-Nayland *(34)*
Rockstead, Nacton nr Ipswich *(38)*
Sensory Garden, Sprites Lane, Ipswich *(43)*
Somerleyton Hall & Gardens, Lowestoft *(45)*
Woottens, Wenhaston *(50)*

May 23 Monday
Woottens, Wenhaston *(50)*

May 24 Tuesday
Woottens, Wenhaston *(50)*

May 25 Wednesday
Woottens, Wenhaston *(50)*

May 26 Thursday
Woottens, Wenhaston *(50)*

May 27 Friday
Woottens, Wenhaston *(50)*

May 28 Saturday
The White House, Clare *(48)*
Woottens, Wenhaston *(50)*

May 29 Sunday
Brook Hall, Crowfield *(8)*
Clematis Cottage Farm, Aldeby, Beccles *(10)*
Kiln Cottage, Rickinghall *(26)*
Woottens, Wenhaston *(50)*

May 30 Monday (Bank Hol)
Clematis Cottage Farm, Aldeby, Beccles *(10)*
Rosemary, Rectory Hill, East Bergholt *(41)*
Woottens, Wenhaston *(50)*

May 31 Tuesday
Woottens, Wenhaston *(50)*

June 1 Wednesday
Woottens, Wenhaston *(50)*

June 2 Thursday
Woottens, Wenhaston *(50)*

June 4 Saturday
Brampton Willows Gardens, Brampton *(5)*
Melton Hall, Melton, Woodbridge *(31)*
Woottens, Wenhaston *(50)*

June 5 Sunday
Barton Mere, Gt Barton *(2)*
Brampton Willows Gardens, Brampton *(5)*
Kiln Cottage, Rickinghall *(26)*
Woottens, Wenhaston *(50)*

June 7 Tuesday
Woottens, Wenhaston *(50)*

June 8 Wednesday
Woottens, Wenhaston *(50)*

June 9 Thursday
Woottens, Wenhaston *(50)*

June 11 Saturday
Brook Farm, Charsfield *(7)*
Wyken Hall, Stanton *(51)*

June 12 Sunday
Ashlie, Knodishall, Saxmundham *(1)*
Brook Farm, Charsfield *(7)*
Garden House Farm, Drinkstone *(18)*
Kiln Cottage, Rickinghall *(26)*
Wyken Hall, Stanton *(51)*
June 14 Tuesday
Woottens, Wenhaston *(50)*
June 15 Wednesday
Woottens, Wenhaston *(50)*
June 16 Thursday
Woottens, Wenhaston *(50)*
June 17 Friday
Hall Farm, Weston, Beccles *(20)*
June 18 Saturday
The Coach House, Assington *(11)*
Hall Farm, Weston, Beccles *(20)*
Reydon Grove House, Reydon, Nr
  Southwold *(37)*
Woottens, Wenhaston *(50)*
June 19 Sunday
Brook Hall, Crowfield *(8)*
The Coach House, Assington *(11)*
Hall Farm, Weston, Beccles *(20)*
Home Farm House, Rushbrooke *(23)*
Kiln Cottage, Rickinghall *(26)*
The Lucy Redman School of Garden
  Design, Rushbrooke *(27)*
Pightle Cottage, Milden *(33)*
Reydon Grove House, Reydon, Nr
  Southwold *(37)*
Rushbrooke Farm, Milden *(42)*
Woottens, Wenhaston *(50)*
June 21 Tuesday
Woottens, Wenhaston *(50)*
June 22 Wednesday
Woottens, Wenhaston *(50)*
June 23 Thursday
Woottens, Wenhaston *(50)*
June 25 Saturday
Melford Hall, Long Melford **(Evening)** *(30)*
Woottens, Wenhaston *(50)*
June 26 Sunday
Columbine Hall, Stowupland *(13)*
Woottens, Wenhaston *(50)*
June 28 Tuesday
Woottens, Wenhaston *(50)*
June 29 Wednesday
Woottens, Wenhaston *(50)*
June 30 Thursday
Woottens, Wenhaston *(50)*
July 2 Saturday
Brampton Willows Gardens, Brampton *(5)*
Rosedale, Bures **(Evening)** *(40)*
July 3 Sunday
Brampton Willows Gardens, Brampton *(5)*
July 5 Tuesday
Woottens, Wenhaston *(50)*
July 6 Wednesday
Woottens, Wenhaston *(50)*
July 7 Thursday
Woottens, Wenhaston *(50)*
July 9 Saturday
Thumbit, Walsham-le-Willows *(46)*

July 10 Sunday
Malt House, Higham *(29)*
Thumbit, Walsham-le-Willows *(46)*
July 12 Tuesday
Woottens, Wenhaston *(50)*
July 13 Wednesday
Woottens, Wenhaston *(50)*
July 14 Thursday
Woottens, Wenhaston *(50)*
July 16 Saturday
Woottens, Wenhaston *(50)*
July 17 Sunday
Ashlie, Knodishall, Saxmundham *(1)*
Redisham Hall, Beccles *(36)*
Woottens, Wenhaston *(50)*
July 19 Tuesday
Woottens, Wenhaston *(50)*
July 20 Wednesday
Woottens, Wenhaston *(50)*
July 21 Thursday
Woottens, Wenhaston *(50)*
July 23 Saturday
Woottens, Wenhaston *(50)*
July 24 Sunday
Bresworth House, Cotton *(6)*
Woottens, Wenhaston *(50)*
July 26 Tuesday
Woottens, Wenhaston *(50)*
July 27 Wednesday
Woottens, Wenhaston *(50)*
July 28 Thursday
Woottens, Wenhaston *(50)*
July 30 Saturday
Woottens, Wenhaston *(50)*
July 31 Sunday
Cobbs Hall, Great Saxham *(12)*
Woottens, Wenhaston *(50)*
August 2 Tuesday
Woottens, Wenhaston *(50)*
August 3 Wednesday
Woottens, Wenhaston *(50)*
August 4 Thursday
Woottens, Wenhaston *(50)*
August 7 Sunday
Rosedale, Bures *(40)*
August 9 Tuesday
Woottens, Wenhaston *(50)*
August 10 Wednesday
Woottens, Wenhaston *(50)*
August 11 Thursday
Woottens, Wenhaston *(50)*
August 14 Sunday
Ashlie, Knodishall, Saxmundham *(1)*
August 16 Tuesday
Woottens, Wenhaston *(50)*
August 17 Wednesday
Woottens, Wenhaston *(50)*
August 18 Thursday
Woottens, Wenhaston *(50)*
August 21 Sunday
Magnolia House, Yoxford *(28)*
August 23 Tuesday
Woottens, Wenhaston *(50)*

August 24 Wednesday
Woottens, Wenhaston *(50)*
August 25 Thursday
Woottens, Wenhaston *(50)*
August 30 Tuesday
Woottens, Wenhaston *(50)*
August 31 Wednesday
Woottens, Wenhaston *(50)*
September 1 Thursday
Woottens, Wenhaston *(50)*
September 3 Saturday
Brampton Willows Gardens, Brampton *(5)*
September 4 Sunday
Brampton Willows Gardens, Brampton *(5)*
September 6 Tuesday
Woottens, Wenhaston *(50)*
September 7 Wednesday
Woottens, Wenhaston *(50)*
September 8 Thursday
Woottens, Wenhaston *(50)*
September 11 Sunday
Highfields Farm, Bures *(21)*
September 13 Tuesday
Woottens, Wenhaston *(50)*
September 14 Wednesday
Woottens, Wenhaston *(50)*
September 15 Thursday
Woottens, Wenhaston *(50)*
September 20 Tuesday
Woottens, Wenhaston *(50)*
September 21 Wednesday
Woottens, Wenhaston *(50)*
September 22 Thursday
Woottens, Wenhaston *(50)*
September 25 Sunday
Ickworth House Park & Gardens, Horringer
  (24)
September 27 Tuesday
Woottens, Wenhaston *(50)*
September 28 Wednesday
Woottens, Wenhaston *(50)*
September 29 Thursday
Woottens, Wenhaston *(50)*
October 16 Sunday
East Bergholt Place, East Bergholt *(15)*

ngs gardens open for charity
Busy at work?
Try our evening openings

DESCRIPTIONS OF GARDENS

❶ NEW Ashlie, St Andrews Road, Knodishall, Saxmundham 🔾🚫🏠
(Mr & Mrs H Williams) *1m SW of Leiston. From A12 take A1094 signed to Aldeburgh. Turn L at sign for Leiston onto B1069, garden opp Butchers Arms PH. Some parking at garden, further parking on common land on Mill Rd at side of PH.* Approx ½-acre well-stocked garden; many unusual plants, trees and shrubs. Pond, young woodland area, herbaceous borders, old-fashioned climbing roses, many grasses, subtropical area. TEAS. *Adm £2, chd free. Suns 15 May; 12 June; 17 July; 14 Aug (11-5). Private visits welcome by appt. Tel 01728 831054*

Balsham Manor and Maze, 42 High St, Balsham 🔾🚫🏠
See Cambridgeshire.

❷ Barton Mere, Thurston Road, Gt Barton 🚫
(Mr & Mrs C O Stenderup) *4m NE of Bury St Edmunds. Take A143 towards Ixworth. After Gt Barton turn R at Bunbury Arms PH. Continue straight on past tourist signed turnings to Pakenham and Barton Hamlet . Entrance to drive 100yds after Barton Hamlet tourist sign, on L.* C16 house (not open) with later Georgian façade, set in parkland overlooking lake 'The Mere'. Mainly walled gardens with roses, herbaceous borders, shrubs, large vegetable garden and conservatory. Light refreshments and TEAS in aid of St Mary's Church, Pakenham. *Adm £2.50, chd free. Sun 5 June (2-5.30)*

❸ The Beeches, Grove Road, Walsham-le-Willows 🔾
(Dr A J Russell) *11m E of Bury St Edmunds. From A143 Bury to Diss take turning for Walsham-le-Willows. At Xrds in village R, church on L. After 100yds turn L. The Beeches is on L just over the bridge.* 150yr-old, 3-acre garden, which incl specimen trees, pond, stream, potager, memorial garden, lawns and a variety of beds. Home-made TEAS. *Adm £2.50, chd free. Sun 3 Apr (2-6)*

❹ ◆ Blakenham Woodland Garden, Little Blakenham 🚫
(Lord Blakenham) *4m NW of Ipswich. Follow signs at Little Blakenham, 1m off B1113.* 6-acre bluebell wood densely planted with fine collection of trees and shrubs; camellias, magnolias, cornus, azaleas, rhododendrons, roses, hydrangeas and a number of rarities. Landscape

features. *Adm £3, chd £1.50. Open daily 1 Mar to 30 June.* **For NGS:** *Sat 23 Apr (1-5). Tel 07760 342131*

❺ NEW Brampton Willows Gardens, Town Fen, London Road, Brampton 🚫🏠
(Mr & Mrs Robert Yates) *7m S of Beccles on A145. Brampton Willows sign at roadside, garden 200yds down track.* Flower and vegetable gardens created in 2000 and still evolving. Designed to show the extensive use of woven willow. Large woven willow features, pond and 15 acres of commercial willow beds. Home-made TEAS in aid of St Peter's Church, Brampton. *Adm £2.50, chd free. Sats (11-6), Suns (2-6) 4, 5 June; 2, 3 July; 3, 4 Sept*

❻ Bresworth House, Cotton 🔾🚫🏠
(Keith & Ann Bullock) *6m N of Stowmarket. Between B1113 & A140 close to Cotton Church.* 1-acre garden surrounded and sheltered by mature indigenous trees. Unique water feature and recycled iron sculptures. Island beds, mixed border, variety of ornamental trees and shrubs, vegetable plot, cows grazing next door. Light lunches 12-2 & Home-made TEAS. *Adm £2.50, chd free. Sun 24 July (11-5). Private visits welcome by appt Apr to July. Tel 01449 780102*

❼ NEW Brook Farm, Charsfield 🔾🏠
(Peter & Anne Tweddle) *2½m W of Wickham Market. On B1078, on junction of The Street and Church Rd, in centre of village.* Suffolk country garden set in the small valley of Potsford Brook. Home to a large and varied collection of plants which enjoy the light free-draining conditions. Herbaceous borders lead into small woodland and meadows. Owners are keen propagators. Home-made TEAS. *Adm £3, chd free, concessions £2.50. Sun 17 Apr; Sat, Sun 11, 12 June (2-5)*

❽ Brook Hall, Church Road, Crowfield 🔾🚫
(Mr & Mrs D S Pumfrey) *3m N of Coddenham. 1m S of Stonham Aspal, Pettaugh A1120, ¼m from Crowfield Church. Brook Hall is reached down a farm drive.* Tranquil 1½ acres surround a classic Suffolk farmhouse (not open). Relaxing country garden with informal mixed borders. Clematis, rambling roses, shrubs, trees and containers. Kitchen garden with polytunnel and greenhouse. Natural ponds and wildlife area. Home-made TEAS. *Adm £2.50, chd*

free. Suns 1, 29 May; 19 June (11-5). Private visits welcome by appt, May & June only; groups of 10+, coaches permitted. Tel 01449 711575 brookhall@freenetname.co.uk

❾ Bucklesham Hall, Bucklesham 🔾🚫🏠
(Mr & Mrs D R Brightwell) *6m NE of Ipswich. 1m E of village nr Bucklesham School on rd to Brightwell.* 7 acres of unusual plants, shrubs and trees with many rare rhododendrons, hydrangeas and acers; woodland; traditional rose garden; lakes and waterfalls. Home-made TEAS in aid of Bucklesham Primary School. *Adm £3, chd 50p. Sun 8 May (2-6)*

❿ NEW Clematis Cottage Farm, 4 Beccles Road, Aldeby, Beccles 🏠
(Dr Peter Harrison) *5m NE of Beccles. On A143 Yarmouth Rd from Beccles approx 1m after roundabout, R fork signed Aldeby. After approx 1m turn R signed Alderby St, this is Beccles Rd. Garden on R after Waveny Cottages and 2 bungalows, opp bus shelter.* New garden of about 1½ acres with 2 acres of field made from scratch over 5yrs. 300 meters maturing native hedging. Many trees, some grown from seed. Reconstructed pond, 1st recorded in Parish Register in 1800. Rare poultry and geese and other wildlife. A plantsman's garden. Hebe bed and unusual New Zealand plants. Cream TEAS in aid of Beccles Hospital. *Adm £2.50, chd free. Mons 2, 30, Sun 29 May (12-5.30). Private visits welcome by appt, June & July. Tel 01502 677319 peter@harrison198. freeserve.co.uk*

⓫ ◆ The Coach House, Assington 🔾🚫🏠
(Mrs Justine Ferrari) *5m S of Sudbury. On A134. Turn R into Assington village. On sharp LH-bend turn R into The Coach House.* Semi-formal 2-acre plantswoman's garden generously planted with herbaceous borders incl colour-themed beds. Pond garden, potager, woodland beds and wild flower areas. Many different shrubs, roses and climbers. Free range pure-bred hens. Featured in 'The Independent' 2003. Home-made TEAS. *Adm £2.50, chd free. Fris & Sats May & June.* **For NGS:** *Sat, Sun 18, 19 June (2-6). Tel 01787 211364 ferrarifrs@aol.com*

⓬ Cobbs Hall, Great Saxham 🔾🚫
(Dr & Mrs R H Soper) *4½m W of Bury St Edmunds. A14 exit to Westley. R at Westley Xrds. L fork at*

*Little Saxham signed Hargrave &
Chevington. Approx 1½m to sign on
R turn. Mustard-coloured house
300yds on L.* 2 acres of lawns and
borders; ornamental trees, large
fish/lily pond. Parterre, folly, walled
kitchen garden, grass tennis court and
pretty courtyard. Home-made TEAS.
*Adm £2.50, chd free. Sun 31 July
(2-6)*

⓭ Columbine Hall, Stowupland ♿

(Hew & Leslie Stevenson) *1½m NE
of Stowmarket. Turn N off A1120
opp Shell garage across village green,
then R at T-junction into Gipping
Rd. Garden on L just beyond
derestriction sign.* Formal gardens,
designed by George Carter, surround
moated medieval manor house (not
open). Also, outside the moat, bog
garden, Mediterranean garden,
colour-themed vegetable garden,
orchards and parkland. Gardens
developed since 1994 with constant
work-in-progress, incl transformed
farm buildings, wilderness and
eyecatchers. Home-made TEAS. *Adm
£3, chd free. Sun 26 June (2-6)*

⓮ Corner Cottage, Rickinghall Road, Gislingham ⊗✿

(Trevor & Pauline Cox) *5m W of
Eye. Situated approx 9m N of
Stowmarket or approx 2½m S of
Rickinghall on B1113.* Approx ¾-acre
plot containing areas of shrub and
herbaceous beds with orchard,
wildlife/lily pond, vegetable plot,
conservatory garden with paved area
and raised beds. Plantsman's garden
designed by owners to give feeling of
peace and tranquillity. TEAS. *Adm
£2. Sun 17 Apr (11-5). Private visits
welcome by appt May to Sept.
Tel 01449 781379*

⓯ East Bergholt Place, East Bergholt ♿⊗✿

(Mr & Mrs Rupert Eley) *On B1070
towards Manningtree, 2m E of A12.
Situated on the edge of East Bergholt.*
15-acre garden originally laid out at
the beginning of the century by the
present owner's great grandfather.
Full of many fine trees and shrubs
some of which are rarely seen in East
Anglia. Particularly beautiful in
spring when the rhododendrons,
magnolias and camellias are in full
flower, and in autumn with newly cut
topiary and autumn colours. Home-
made TEAS. *Adm £2.50, chd free.
Suns 20 Mar; 10 Apr; 16 Oct (2-5)*

⓰ ◆ Euston Hall, Thetford ♿⊗

(His Grace The Duke of Grafton)
*12m N of Bury St Edmunds. 3m S of
Thetford on A1088.* Terraced lawns,

herbaceous borders, rose garden, C17
pleasure grounds, lake and watermill.
C18 house open; famous collection of
paintings. C17 church; temple by
William Kent. Craft shop. Cream
TEAS. *House & garden adm £5, chd
£2, concessions £4. Garden only £3,
chd £2. Thurs 16 June to 15 Sept;
Suns 29 May (NCCPG Plant Sale);
26 June; 17 July; 4 Sept (2.30-5).
Tel 01842 766366 Sat & Sun eves to
book appts www.eustonhall.co.uk*

⓱ Gable House, Halesworth Road, Redisham ♿⊗✿

(Mr & Mrs John Foster) *5m S of
Beccles. Between Beccles &
Halesworth on Ringsfield/Ilketshall
St Lawrence rd.* 1-acre garden
contains a wide range of interesting
plants. In Feb visitors can see over
200 varieties of snowdrops together
with cyclamen, hellebore and other
early flowering bulbs. Wide range of
summer flowering plants. 3
greenhouses each contain plants from
alpines to tender species, many for
sale. Light refreshments and TEAS.
*Adm £2.50, chd free (share to St
Peters Church, Redisham). Suns 20
Feb (11-4); 22 May (11-5). Private
visits welcome by appt. Tel 01502
575298*

⓲ Garden House Farm, Drinkstone ⊗✿

(Mr & Mrs Seiffer) *10m E of Bury St
Edmunds. 3m from Woolpit. A14
turn off at Woolpit, village centre
turn L follow signs to Drinkstone,
then Drinkstone Green. Turn into
Rattlesden Rd then L down
unmarked lane.* 11-acre garden. Lake,
woodland gardens with rare trees and
shrubs. Summer borders, winter
garden. Colour and interest yr-round.
Featured in 'Gardens Illustrated'
2003. TEAS. *Adm £3. Sun 12 June
(2-6). Private visits welcome by appt
for groups of 10+. Tel 01449
736434
gardenhousefarm@dial.pipex.com*

⓳ Great Thurlow Hall, Haverhill ♿

(Mr & Mrs George Vestey) *10m S of
Bury St Edmunds. Great Thurlow
village on B1061 from Newmarket;
3½m N of junction with A143
Haverhill-Bury St Edmunds Rd.* 20
acres. River walk and trout lake with
extensive and impressive display of
daffodils and blossom. Spacious
lawns, shrubberies and roses. Walled
kitchen garden. TEAS in aid of All
Saints Church, Great Thurlow. *Adm
£2.50, chd free. Sun 3 Apr (2-5)*

⓴ Hall Farm, Weston, Beccles

(Mr & Mrs Peter Seppings) *1½m S of
Beccles. On A145. The entrance is
the same as for Winter Flora,
continue 300yds along the drive to
the private house.* The parterre is
crammed with shrub roses, many
favourite perennials, annuals and
ferns. Beyond the house is a large
pond surrounded by rushes and
moisture-loving plants. Terrace,
pergola and conservatory. Established
shrubs enclose the 1½-acre garden.
Lighty refreshments and TEAS. *Adm
£2.50, chd free. Fri, Sat, Sun 17, 18,
19 June (11-5.30). Private visits
welcome by appt, June & July only
for groups of 4+. Tel 01502 715065*

㉑ Highfields Farm, Bures ♿⊗✿

(Mr & Mrs John Ineson) *6m SE of
Sudbury. From Bures Church take
Nayland Rd. In 2m turn L signed
Assington. Take 1st R tarmac drive.
From other directions take Assington
to Wormingford rd.* 2-acre
plantsman's garden started in 1984
with mixed borders, shrubs,
camomile lawn and herbaceous beds.
Various flint features and lily pond.
Large selection of ornamental fowls.
Home-made TEAS. *Adm £2.50, chd
free. Suns 15 May; 11 Sept (2-5.30).
Private visits welcome by appt June
& July only. Tel 01787 227136
jpineson@aol.com*

㉒ The Hill House, Duffs Hill, Glemsford ♿⊗✿

(Sir John & Lady Mowbray) *100yds
N of Glemsford on the back rd to
Hawkedon & Boxted.* Pretty country
garden of 1 acre with interesting
mixed borders, planted conservatory
and kitchen garden. Home-made
TEAS in aid of St Nicholas Hospice.
*Adm £2.50, chd free. Sun 22 May
(2-6)*

㉓ Home Farm House, Rushbrooke ♿⊗✿

(Anita Wigan) *3m SE of Bury St
Edmunds. From A14 Bury St
Edmunds E Sudbury exit, proceed
towards town centre. After 50yds 1st
exit from roundabout & immed turn
R. Proceed ¾m to T-junction, turn L,
follow rd for 2m. Rushbrooke church
on L, turn R into paddock-railed
drive.* 3 acres: walled garden, mixed
borders, roses, lawns, incl 1¼-acre
kitchen garden (potager) and
glasshouses with stone fruit, figs,
vinery, orchids, general propagation.
Further 5 acres parkland and
orchard, moat garden. Ornamental
wattle and thatched summerhouse.
Home-made TEAS. *Adm £3, chd
free. Sun 19 June (2-5). Also open*
The Lucy Redman School of Garden

Design. *Private visits welcome by appt. Tel 01284 386276*

㉔ ◆ Ickworth House Park & Gardens, Horringer ⬧⬧
(The National Trust) *2m SW of Bury St Edmunds. Ickworth is in the village of Horringer on the A143 Bury to Haverhill Rd.* 70 acres of garden. South gardens restored to stylised Italian landscape to reflect extraordinary design of the house. Fine orangery, agapanthus, geraniums and fatsias. North gardens informal wild flower lawns with wooded walk; the *Buxus* collection, great variety of evergreens and Victorian stumpery. New planting of cedars. The Albana Wood, a C18 feature, initially laid out by Capability Brown, incorporates a fine circular walk. *House & garden adm £6.70, chd £3. Garden only £3.10, chd 90p. Open daily 25 Mar to 30 Oct; Mon-Fri 31 Oct to 23 Dec (10-5). For NGS: Sun 25 Sept. Tel 01284 735961 julia.vinson@nationaltrust.org.uk*

㉕ The Island House, Lower Road, Lavenham ⬧⬧
(Brian & Heather Massey) *7m NE of Sudbury. From the Market Place proceed to the bottom of Prentice St & turn R. The Island House is immed on L. Park in Lavenham car park or Market Square.* Garden of approx ¾ acres in woodland setting, through which the R Brett flows. Mixed island borders contain all-yr-round interest. Woodland and shaded areas. TEAS. *Adm £2.50, chd free. Sat 23 (2-6), Sun 24 Apr (11-5). Private visits welcome by appt. Tel 01787 248181 islandhouse@dial.pipex.com*

㉖ Kiln Cottage, Candle Street, Rickinghall ⬧⬧⬧
(Mrs Susan Archer) *5m SW of Diss. Candle St located approx 100yds from A143 Bury St Edmunds-Diss rd. Turn off on B1113 signed Stowmarket & Finningham.* Small thatched cottage (not open) surrounded by 8yr-old, 1-acre country garden, divided by archways and trellis. Formal beds with perennials and shrubs lead to young woodland area, nursery beds, greenhouse and courtyard. *Adm £2, chd free. Suns 22, 29 May; 5, 12, 19 June (2-5). Private visits welcome by appt 22 May to 19 June. Tel 01379 890684*

㉗ NEW The Lucy Redman School of Garden Design, 6 The Village, Rushbrooke ⬧⬧
(Lucy Redman & Dominic Watts) *3m E of Bury St Edmunds. From A14 Bury St Edmunds, E Sudbury exit, proceed towards town centre. After 50yds, 1st exit from roundabout and immed R. ¾m to T-junction, turn L, follow rd for 2m. Before church turn R between white houses, past brick wall, thatched house on L.* Thatched cottage (not open) surrounded by ½-acre quirky plantsman's garden divided into compartments with impressive colour-coordinated borders containing many interesting combinations of unusual shrubs, roses, grasses and perennials. Grass parterre, turf tree seat, sculptures. Wildlife pond in purple hazel meadow. Unusual bulb and rhizome garden. Home-made TEAS in aid of St Nicholas Church. *Adm £2, chd free. Sun 19 June (2-5). Also open* **Home Farm House**. *Private visits welcome by appt. Tel 01284 386250 www.lucyredman.co.uk*

㉘ Magnolia House, Yoxford ⬧⬧
(Mr Mark Rumary) *Centre of Yoxford on A1120.* Small, completely walled, romantic garden, tucked behind a pretty C18 village house (not open). Ingeniously designed to appear larger and planted to provide yr-round colour, scent and horticultural interest. Contains ancient mulberry, raised Moorish-style pool and attractive pots and urns. TEAS. *Adm £2.50, chd free. Suns 8 May; 21 Aug (2-5.30). Private visits welcome by appt. Tel 01728 668321*

㉙ Malt House, Higham ⬧⬧⬧
(Peter & Georgina Pharaoh) *7m W of Bury St Edmunds. From Bury St Edmunds take A14 W. Follow signposts to Higham village. Garden on R in village. Park in rd.* Plantsman's garden of approx ½-acre, with mixed shrubs and herbaceous borders; small pond with water feature and conservatory with unusual plants. Home-made TEAS. *Adm £2.50, chd free. Sun 10 July (2-6)*

㉚ NEW ◆ Melford Hall, Long Melford ⬧⬧⬧
(The National Trust) *3m N of Sudbury.* Romantic turreted brick Tudor mansion, in unspoilt village. Set in the confines of what was a medieval moated site, the garden is Edwardian in design. Clipped box hedges and topiary and some fine specimen trees, incl 2 copper beeches and an old mulberry. A long

herbacoeus border and a pleasant walk along a dry moat, together with a rare example of a Tudor Banqueting House. *Apr & Oct, Sats, Suns. May to Sept, Weds to Suns, Bank Hol Mons (2-5.30).* **For NGS: Evening Opening** *£2.50, chd £1, wine, Sat 25 June (6-8). Tel 01359 250632 www.nationaltrust.org.uk*

㉛ Melton Hall, Melton, Woodbridge ⬧⬧
(Colin & Cindy de la Rue) *1m N of Woodbridge. From A12 take A1152 signed to Orford/Bawdsey; turn R at T-lights after 1m; entrance to property 1st R; parking 75yds further at Coach & Horses PH.* Formal and informal gardens with Regency family house (not open). Wide lawns leading to wild flower meadow in parkland setting with wooded area. Large herbaceous bed/shrubbery. Formal kitchen garden with box hedging and serpentine walls. Roses are a particular feature with many varieties in a walled garden and several other beds. TEAS in aid of Sargent Cancer Fund for Children. *Adm £3, chd free. Sat 4 June (2-6)*

㉜ Mildenhall Gardens
15m W of Bury St Edmunds. 5 mins from Mildenhall centre. From Fiveways roundabout at Barton Mills on A11 follow signs to Mildenhall. Gardens all within 5 mins walk of town centre car parks. Historic market town with famous Suffolk church. Home-made TEAS at 28 Kingsway. *Combined adm £2.50, chd free. Sat, Sun 21, 22 May (2-5)*

6a Church Walk ⬧ (Mr & Mrs D G Reeve) Walled garden surrounding modern bungalow. Sunken paved area, raised bed with pond and waterfall. Patio with water feature, established rockery, many herbaceous plants and shrubs incl collection of hemerocallis. *Tel 01638 715289 jenny@dandjreeve.fsnet.co.uk*

28 Kingsway ⬧⬧ (Nick & Anne Berry) Varied garden containing 2 modern sculptures surrounded by bamboos, grasses and herbaceous borders. Ingenious irrigation system. Established grapevines in greenhouse. Conservatory contains collections of carnivorous plants and orchids. *Private visits welcome by appt. Tel 01638 714180 nickberry@eurobell.co.uk*

Tiggywinkle Cottage, Wamil Way ⬧⬧ (Mrs Marion Turner) Small cottage garden designed around a central courtyard containing a variety of unusual plants for both hot and shady areas. Climbing roses and clematis give height and seclusion to areas for relaxation. Winner Newmarket Gardening Society Best Back Garden 2004. *Private visits welcome by appt. Tel 01638 715827*

㉝ Pightle Cottage, Rectory Corner, Milden 🚽🖼
(Mrs Ann Prudden) *6m NE of Sudbury. Signs from A1141 & B1115.* 2 acres of cottage garden with mixed shrub and herbaceous borders; many old shrub and climbing roses. Hot gravel area and formal sunken garden. Featured in 'Country Life' 2004. Cream TEAS. *Adm £3, chd free. Sun 19 June (2-6). Also open* **Rushbrooke Farm**

㉞ The Priory, Stoke-by-Nayland 🚽🖼
(Mr & Mrs H F A Engleheart) *5m SW of Hadleigh. Entrance on B1068 to Sudbury (NW of Stoke-by-Nayland).* Interesting 9-acre garden with fine views over Constable countryside; lawns sloping down to small lakes and water garden; fine trees, rhododendrons and azaleas; walled garden; mixed borders and ornamental greenhouse. Wide variety of plants; peafowl. Home-made TEAS. *Adm £3, chd free. Sun 22 May (2-5.30)*

㉟ Priory Hall, Benton Street, Hadleigh 🚽🖼
(Mr & Mrs A V Hilton) *11m S of Ipswich. From A12 take B1070 to Hadleigh. After 4m pass Hook Lane on R. Priory Hall is next entrance on R. From Ipswich-Sudbury A1071: through Hadleigh High St, straight over junction to Benton St. Pass Cranworth Rd on L, 50yds further to Priory Hall on L.* 22 acres of woods, pasture and formal gardens, with lake and water meadows incl a covered picnic area. Special interest is the knot garden and topiary; walled terrace and orchards and new rose arbour. Cream TEAS. *Adm £3, chd/concessions £2.50. Sun 8 May (3-6)*

㊱ Redisham Hall, Beccles 🚽🖼
(Mr Palgrave Brown) *5m S of Beccles. From A145, turn W on to Ringsfield-Bungay rd. Beccles, Halesworth or Bungay, all within 5m.* C18 Georgian house (not open). 5-acre garden set in 400 acres parkland and woods. Incl 2-acre walled kitchen garden (in full production) with peach house, vinery and glasshouses. Lawns, herbaceous borders, shrubberies, ponds and mature trees. Home-made TEAS. *Adm £3, chd free. Sun 17 July (2-6)*

㊲ Reydon Grove House, Reydon, Nr Southwold 🚽🖼
(Cmdr & Mrs J Swinley) *1m W of Southwold. Situated ½m N of Reydon Church. Turnings off the Wangford to Southwold rd.* 1½-acre mature garden. Large collection of herbaceous plants and shrubs, many interesting and unusual. Old-fashioned roses. Emphasis on plants suitable for sandy soil and dry, coastal conditions. Large vegetable garden. Home-made TEAS in aid of Reydon Church. *Adm £2.50, chd free. Sat, Sun 18, 19 June (2-5.30). Private visits welcome by appt. Tel 01502 723655*

㊳ Rockstead, Nacton nr Ipswich 🚽🖼
(Jeremy & Angela Pratt) *5m E of Ipswich. In centre of Nacton village by War Memorial, approx 1m S of Seven Hills roundabout on A14.* 1-acre garden with informal plantings, mature trees and lawns on an undulating site. Numerous scree beds; raised beds; alpine house for cultivation of alpines and bulbs; vegetable and fruit gardens. Waterfall and reconstructed C19 rockery. Home-made TEAS in aid of Nacton Village Hall. *Adm £2.50, chd free. Sun 22 May (2-6). Private visits welcome by appt. Tel 01473 659423 jemanpratt@ukonline.co.uk*

㊴ The Rookery, Hollesley Road, Eyke 🚽🖼🖼
(Capt & Mrs Sheepshanks) *5m E of Woodbridge. Turn N off B1084 Woodbridge to Orford rd signed Rendlesham.* 10-acre garden. Many rare specimen trees and shrubs; landscaped on differing levels, providing views and vistas; the visitor's curiosity is constantly aroused by what is round the next corner: ponds, Japanese garden, rhododendrons, roses, bulbs, borders as well as Staverton vineyard. Free wine tastings, wine available for sale from vineyard. TEAS. *Adm £3, chd over 10 £1. Sun 24 Apr (2-5.30). Private visits welcome by appt. Tel 01394 460271*

㊵ Rosedale, 40 Colchester Road, Bures 🖼🖼
(Mr & Mrs Colin Lorking) *6m SE of Sudbury. 9m NW of Colchester on B1508. As you enter the village of Bures, garden on L. From Sudbury follow signs through village towards Colchester, garden on R as you leave village.* Approx ½-acre plantsman's garden; many unusual plants, herbaceous borders, pond, woodland area. Home-made TEAS. *Adm £2, chd free. Suns 1 May; 7 Aug*

(12-5.30). **Evening Opening** *£3, wine, Sat 2 July (6-9)*

㊶ Rosemary, Rectory Hill, East Bergholt 🚽🖼
(Mrs N E M Finch) *4m NE of Colchester. Turn off A12 onto B1070 to East Bergholt & follow rd round to church. Rosemary 100yds down from church on L.* This romantic garden, which appeals particularly to artists, has been developed over 33yrs. Planted to reveal paths and vistas. Over 100 old-fashioned roses. 2 bog beds, unusual trees, good bulbs and many unusual plants. Planted for all seasons. Accommodation. Home-made TEAS. *Adm £2.50, chd free. Sun 27 Mar; Mons 2, 30 May (2-5). Private visits welcome by appt. Tel 01206 298241*

㊷ Rushbrooke Farm, Church Road, Milden 🚽🖼
(Mr & Mrs Michael Hawkins) *6m NE of Sudbury. Take Boxford-Milden Rd off B1115, take Church Rd at Milden red tel box; Rushbrooke Farm ¼m on L.* Approx 1-acre garden. Mixed herbaceous and shrubs, conifers, 2 ponds with primulas and water plants. *Adm £3, chd free. Sun 19 June (2-6). Also open* **Pightle Cottage**

㊸ NEW Sensory Garden, Belstead School, Sprites Lane, Ipswich 🚽
(Mrs S Chesworth, Headteacher) *On outskirts of Ipswich. Close to junction of A12 and A14.* Ample parking in front of school. Our garden is a sensory garden specifically designed for people with disabilities. It is full of interesting colour, texture and smell. The garden also incl a bog garden. The whole garden is wheelchair-accessible. It is a sensory experience, whether or not you have disabilities. Featured on Gardeners' World 2004. Home-made TEAS in aid of Belstead School League of Friends. *Adm £2.50, chd free. Sun 22 May (11-4)*

㊹ ♦ Shrubland Park Garden, Coddenham, nr Ipswich 🚽🖼🖼
(Lord De Saumarez) *6m N of Ipswich. At junction of A14/A140, from roundabout take slip rd signed Ipswich A14 but turn L on slip rd signed Barham. Turn R at T-junction, after 1m entrance is on L at sawmill.* Extensive formal garden of Shrubland Park, one of the finest examples of an Italianate garden in England. Much use is made of evergreens clipped into architectural shapes to complement the hard landscaping of the masonry. Pines, cedars, holly and holm oak

soften this formal structure and add
to the Italian flavour. *Adm £3, chd
£2. Suns & Bank Hol Mons 27 Mar
to 4 Sept.* **For NGS:** *Sun 24 Apr (2-5).*
Tel 01473 830221
www.shrublandpark.co.uk

**45 ◆ Somerleyton Hall &
Gardens, Lowestoft** 🅿🚫♿
(The Hon Hugh Crossley) *5m NW of
Lowestoft. Off B1074.* 12 acres of
beautiful gardens contain a wide
variety of magnificent specimen trees,
shrubs, borders and plants providing
colour and interest throughout the yr.
Sweeping lawns and formal gardens
combine with majestic statuary and
original Victorian ornamentation.
Highlights incl the Paxton
glasshouses, pergola, walled garden
and famous yew hedge maze. House
and gardens remodelled in 1840s by
Sir Morton Peto. House created in
Anglo-Italian style with lavish
architectural features and fine state
rooms. Light refreshments and TEAS.
*Garden only £4.50, chd £2.50, OAP
£3.50. Hall & garden add £2 to each
garden price, plus additional £3.50,
chd £2, OAP £3 for guided tour of
Hall. Thurs & Suns Mar to Oct; Tues
& Weds July, Aug & Bank Hols.* **For**

NGS: *Sun 22 May (11-5.30).*
Tel 0871 222 4244
www.somerleyton.co.uk

**46 Thumbit, Badwell Road,
Walsham-le-Willows** 🅿
(Mrs Ann James) *10m NE of Bury St
Edmunds. Take turning for
Walsham-le-Willows. From A143
(Bury-Diss) to Xrds by church.
Follow Badwell Ash Rd to outskirts
of village ½m.* House is part of
thatched C16 one-time public house
(not open). Shared driveway (please
do not drive in). Small informal
garden with emphasis on design and
plant association. Pergola, pool,
topiary and potager. 500 choice
plants, shrubs, roses and climbers.
'25 Beautiful Gardens', 'The Lady',
'Amateur Gardening' & 'Times'
features 2003. Home-made TEAS.
*Adm £2, chd free. Sat, Sun, 9, 10 July
(2-6). Private visits welcome by appt.
Tel 01359 259414*

**47 Treaclebenders, Cross Street,
Drinkstone** 🚫
(Mrs Maureen Ridge) *10m E of Bury
St Edmunds. Leave A14 at Woolpit,
L at village pump, R opp Plough PH.
R at T-junction with grass triangle, L*

beside railings at Xrds into
Drinkstone. After 1m turn L opp
phone box into Rattlesden Rd.
200yds & L into Cross St. Garden on
R of lane. Park in Rattlesden Rd.
Plantsman's garden of about 1 acre
surrounding thatched Tudor cottage
(not open). All-yr colour, incl many
winter and spring bulbs; autumn and
winter cyclamen. Featured in
'Gardeners' World' 2004. Home-
made TEAS. *Adm £2.50, chd free.
Sat 12 Feb (11-4)*

**48 The White House, Nethergate
Street, Clare** 🅿🚫♿
(Mr & Mrs Patrick Daniels) *11m W
of Sudbury, 6m E of Haverhill. On
A1092 from Clare towards Haverhill.*
A garden of about 2 acres, well-
established, S-facing, partially walled,
bordered by R Stour, just within the
historic part of Clare and with views
of the castle. Part of garden is formal,
with box hedges, beds of irises; other
parts comprise lawns, mixed borders,
a wild meadow and orchard. The
trees incl mulberry, *Cornus kousa*,
medlar and weeping ash. Home-made
TEAS. *Adm £2.50, chd free. Sat 28
May (2-5)*

49 Windmill Cottage, Mill Hill, Capel St Mary
(Mr & Mrs G A Cox) 3m SW of Ipswich. Turn off A12 at Capel St Mary. At far end of village on R after 1¼m. ½-acre plantsman's cottage-style garden. Island beds, pergolas with clematis and other climbers. Many trees and shrubs, iris bed, ponds and vegetable area. TEAS. Adm £2.50, chd free. Private visits welcome by appt Apr to June gandemcox@lineone.net

50 ◆ Woottens, Blackheath Road, Wenhaston
(Mr M Loftus) 18m S of Lowestoft. On A12 & B1123, follow signs to Wenhaston. Small romantic garden, redesigned in 2003. Scented-leafed pelargoniums, violas, cranesbills, lilies, salvias, penstemons, primulas, etc. 2 acres of bearded iris, ¾ acre of iris sibiricas, 1 acre of hemerocallis. Featured in 'Gardens Illustrated' 2004. Adm £1, chd 50p. **For NGS:** Every Tues, Wed & Thur Apr to Sept. Bearded iris field Sat 21 to Mon 30 May incl; Sat, Sun 4, 5 June. Iris sibirica field Sats, Suns 18, 19, 25, 26 June. Hemerocallis field Sats, Suns 16, 17, 23, 24, 30, 31 July (9.30-5). Tel 01502 478258 www.woottensplants.co.uk

51 ◆ Wyken Hall, Stanton
(Sir Kenneth & Lady Carlisle) 9m NE of Bury St Edmunds. Along A143. Follow signs to Wyken Vineyards on A143 between Ixworth & Stanton. 4-acre garden much developed recently; knot and herb garden; old-fashioned rose garden, wild garden, nuttery, pond, gazebo and maze; herbaceous borders and old orchard. Woodland walk, vineyard. Country Store and Leaping Hare Restaurant. Light refreshments and TEAS. Adm £3, chd free, concessions £2.50. **For NGS:** Sat 11 (10-6), Sun 12 June (2-6). Tel 01359 250287 for restaurant bookings www.theleapinghare.co.uk

Evening Opening (See also garden description)

Melford Hall	25 June
Rosedale	2 July

THE ROYAL GARDENERS' ORPHAN FUND

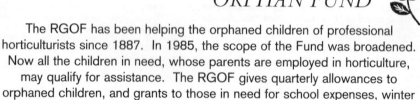

The RGOF has been helping the orphaned children of professional horticulturists since 1887. In 1985, the scope of the Fund was broadened. Now all the children in need, whose parents are employed in horticulture, may qualify for assistance. The RGOF gives quarterly allowances to orphaned children, and grants to those in need for school expenses, winter clothing, bedding and holidays.

The donation our Fund receives each year from The National Gardens Scheme is invaluable in enabling the continuation of our work.

For more information about the RGOF, please contact the Secretary,
Mrs Kate Wallis
14 Scholars Mews, Welwyn Garden City,
Hertfordshire AL8 7JQ
Tel/Fax: 01707 333663
email: rgof@btopenworld.com
web: www.rgof.org.uk

Surrey

County Organiser:	Mrs Gayle Leader, Stuart Cottage, East Clandon, Surrey GU4 7SF Tel 01483 222689
Assistant County Organisers:	
(County Leaflets)	Mr Keith Lewis, 41 Shelvers Way, Tadworth, Surrey KT20 5QJ Tel 01737 210707
	Mrs Caroline Norman, Spring Cottage, Mannings Hill, Cranleigh, Surrey GU6 8QN Tel 01483 272620
(Minutes Secretary)	Mrs Eileen Pearcy, Far End, Pilgrims Way, Guildford, Surrey GU4 8AD Tel 01483 563093
	Mrs Shirley Stoneley, Woodbury Cottage, Colley Lane, Reigate, Surrey RH2 9JJ Tel 01737 244235
	Mrs Averil Trott, Odstock, Castle Square, Bletchingley, Surrey RH1 4LB Tel 01883 743100
County Treasurer:	Mr Roger Nickolds, Old Post House, East Clandon, Surrey GU4 7SE Tel 01483 224027

Maps: Numbers shown next to each garden entry refer to that garden's entry on the county map. This position is approximate; distance and directions from the nearest main town are generally shown in the garden text. A precise location is available for those gardens featured on the NGS website by visiting www.ngs.org.uk.

Symbols: Information relating to symbols is given on page 21

DATES OF OPENING

Evening openings
See end of county listing

Gardens open to the public
For details see garden description

Clandon Park, West Clandon *(12)*
Claremont Landscape Garden, Esher *(13)*
Crosswater Farm, Churt *(17)*
Gatton Park, Merstham *(23)*
Hatchlands Park, East Clandon *(29)*
Loseley Park, Guildford *(38)*
Polesden Lacey, Bookham *(45)*
Ramster, Chiddingfold *(47)*
RHS Garden Wisley *(48)*
Titsey Place Gardens, Oxted *(60)*
Winkworth Arboretum, nr Godalming *(68)*

February 13 Sunday
Gatton Park, Merstham *(23)*

February 16 Wednesday
Gatton Park, Merstham *(23)*

March 13 Sunday
Albury Park, Albury *(2)*

March 20 Sunday
Clandon Park, West Clandon *(12)*

March 28 Monday (Easter)
Vann, Hambledon *(64)*

March 29 Tuesday
Vann, Hambledon *(64)*

March 30 Wednesday
Vann, Hambledon *(64)*

March 31 Thursday
Vann, Hambledon *(64)*

April 1 Friday
Vann, Hambledon *(64)*

April 2 Saturday
Vann, Hambledon *(64)*

April 3 Sunday
Vann, Hambledon *(64)*
Wintershall, Bramley *(69)*

April 7 Thursday
Knightsmead, Chipstead *(32)*

April 10 Sunday
Knightsmead, Chipstead *(32)*
Lodkin, Hascombe *(35)*

April 17 Sunday
Coverwood Lakes, Ewhurst *(16)*
Munstead Wood, Godalming *(40)*

April 24 Sunday
Coverwood Lakes, Ewhurst *(16)*
Dunsborough Park, Ripley *(19)*
Hatchlands Park, East Clandon *(29)*
41 Shelvers Way, Tadworth *(51)*
Vann, Hambledon *(64)*

April 25 Monday
Vann, Hambledon *(64)*

April 26 Tuesday
Vann, Hambledon *(64)*

April 27 Wednesday
Vann, Hambledon *(64)*

April 28 Thursday
Vann, Hambledon *(64)*

April 29 Friday
Vann, Hambledon *(64)*

April 30 Saturday
Vann, Hambledon *(64)*

May 1 Sunday
Coverwood Lakes, Ewhurst *(16)*
Nuthatch, Haslemere *(41)*
The Old Croft, South Holmwood *(44)*
Spring Cottage, Cranleigh *(54)*
Vann, Hambledon *(64)*
Winkworth Arboretum, nr Godalming *(68)*

May 2 Monday (Bank Hol)
The Old Croft, South Holmwood *(44)*
Spring Cottage, Cranleigh *(54)*
Walton Poor, Ranmore *(65)*

May 3 Tuesday
Spring Cottage, Cranleigh *(54)*

May 4 Wednesday
Spring Cottage, Cranleigh *(54)*

May 5 Thursday
Spring Cottage, Cranleigh *(54)*

May 6 Friday
Spring Cottage, Cranleigh *(54)*

May 7 Saturday
Crosswater Farm, Churt *(17)*
Spring Cottage, Cranleigh *(54)*
Titsey Place Gardens, Oxted *(60)*

May 8 Sunday
Coverwood Lakes, Ewhurst *(16)*
Crosswater Farm, Churt *(17)*
Loseley Park, Guildford *(38)*
Spring Cottage, Cranleigh *(54)*
Westways Farm, Chobham *(67)*
Wintershall, Bramley *(69)*

May 14 Saturday
Feathercombe, Hambledon *(21)*

"Is that a helter-skelter tree, Mum?"

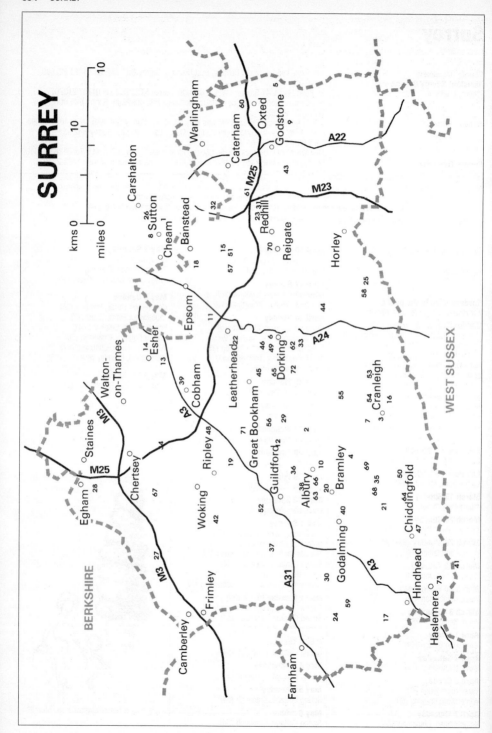

SURREY

kms 0
miles 0

10
10

BERKSHIRE

WEST SUSSEX

Camberley
Frimley
Egham 28
Staines
M3
M25
Chertsey
67
Walton-
on-Thames
Esher 14
13
Cobham 39
A3
Woking
42
Ripley 48
19
Guildford 2
52
A3
44
A31
37
Farnham
24 30
59
Godalming 40
17
A3
Hindhead
Haslemere 73
41
Chiddingfold 64
47
50
21
68 35 69
Albury 38
63 66 20
Bramley 4
10
36
Cranleigh 3
7 54 53
16
55
72 A24
Dorking 62 33
65 45
49 6
46
Leatherhead 22
Great Bookham 56
71
29
Epsom 11
18 57 51 15
Banstead
Cheam 1
Sutton 8 26
Carshalton
Warlingham
Caterham 60
Oxted 5
Godstone 9
A22
M25 61
M23
32
Redhill 23 31
70 Reigate
Horley
58 25
43

May 15 Sunday
Arden Lodge, Limpsfield *(5)*
Coverwood Lakes, Ewhurst *(16)*
Feathercombe, Hambledon *(21)*
Hethersett, Littleworth Cross, Seale *(30)*
Moleshill House, Cobham *(39)*
Quinneys, Westhumble *(46)*
Waterloo Pond Gardens, Albury *(66)*

May 16 Monday
Arden Lodge, Limpsfield *(5)*
Waterloo Pond Gardens, Albury *(66)*

May 18 Wednesday
Moleshill House, Cobham *(39)*

May 21 Saturday
Feathercombe, Hambledon *(21)*

May 22 Sunday
Alderbrook, Smithwood Common, Cranleigh *(3)*
Coverwood Lakes, Ewhurst *(16)*
Feathercombe, Hambledon *(21)*
Hall Grove School, Bagshot *(27)*
Longer End Cottage, Normandy *(37)*
Munstead Wood, Godalming *(40)*
Spurfold, Peaslake *(55)*
Vann, Hambledon *(64)*
Woodcote Park Nursery, Send *(71)*

May 23 Monday
Chauffeur's Flat, Tandridge *(9)*
Vann, Hambledon *(64)*

May 24 Tuesday
Chauffeur's Flat, Tandridge *(9)*
Vann, Hambledon *(64)*

May 25 Wednesday
Chauffeur's Flat, Tandridge *(9)*
Vann, Hambledon *(64)*

May 26 Thursday
Chauffeur's Flat, Tandridge *(9)*
Vann, Hambledon *(64)*

May 27 Friday
Chauffeur's Flat, Tandridge *(9)*
Vann, Hambledon *(64)*

May 28 Saturday
Chauffeur's Flat, Tandridge *(9)*
Vann, Hambledon *(64)*

May 29 Sunday
Chauffeur's Flat, Tandridge *(9)*
Culverkeys, Ewell *(18)*
22 Knoll Road, Dorking *(33)*
The Old Croft, South Holmwood *(44)*
Vann, Hambledon *(64)*
Yew Tree Cottage, Haslemere *(73)*

May 30 Monday (Bank Hol)
The Old Croft, South Holmwood *(44)*

June 1 Wednesday
Culverkeys, Ewell *(18)*
22 Knoll Road, Dorking *(33)*

June 3 Friday
58 Eastwood Road, Bramley **(Evening)** *(20)*

June 4 Saturday
Tilford Cottage, Tilford *(59)*

June 5 Sunday
Claremont Landscape Garden, Esher *(13)*
58 Eastwood Road, Bramley *(20)*
Rostellan, Westhumble *(49)*
Tilford Cottage, Tilford *(59)*
Walton Poor, Ranmore *(65)*

June 6 Monday
Tilford Cottage, Tilford *(59)*

June 8 Wednesday
Barhatch Farm, Cranleigh *(7)*
The Copse Lodge, Burgh Heath **(Evening)** *(15)*
Dunsborough Park, Ripley *(19)*
Vale End, Albury *(63)*

June 9 Thursday
Vale End, Albury **(Evening)** *(63)*

June 12 Sunday
Barhatch Farm, Cranleigh *(7)*
The Copse Lodge, Burgh Heath *(15)*
Munstead Wood, Godalming *(40)*
Polesden Lacey, Bookham *(45)*
Tollsworth Manor, Chaldon *(61)*

June 15 Wednesday
Shepherds Lane Gardens, Guildford *(52)*

June 18 Saturday
Titsey Place Gardens, Oxted *(60)*

June 19 Sunday
Chinthurst Lodge, Wonersh *(10)*
Langstone Cottage, Addlestone *(34)*
Lodkin, Hascombe *(35)*
6 Upper Rose Hill, Dorking *(62)*

June 20 Monday
Chauffeur's Flat, Tandridge *(9)*

June 21 Tuesday
Chauffeur's Flat, Tandridge *(9)*

June 22 Wednesday
Chauffeur's Flat, Tandridge *(9)*
Chinthurst Lodge, Wonersh *(10)*

June 23 Thursday
Chauffeur's Flat, Tandridge *(9)*

June 24 Friday
Ashleigh Grange, West Humble **(Evening)** *(6)*
Chauffeur's Flat, Tandridge *(9)*

June 25 Saturday
Chauffeur's Flat, Tandridge *(9)*
35 Tadorne Road, Tadworth *(57)*

June 26 Sunday
Ashleigh Grange, West Humble *(6)*
Chauffeur's Flat, Tandridge *(9)*
Chipchase, Ashtead *(11)*
Claygate Gardens *(14)*
Longer End Cottage, Normandy *(37)*
35 Tadorne Road, Tadworth *(57)*

June 29 Wednesday
Shepherds Lane Gardens, Guildford **(Evening)** *(52)*

July 1 Friday
Woodbury Cottage, Reigate **(Evening)** *(70)*

July 2 Saturday
Woodbury Cottage, Reigate *(70)*

July 3 Sunday
Arden Lodge, Limpsfield *(5)*
Woodbury Cottage, Reigate *(70)*

July 4 Monday
Arden Lodge, Limpsfield *(5)*
Polesden Lacey, Bookham *(45)*

July 7 Thursday
Stuart Cottage, East Clandon **(Evening)** *(56)*

July 9 Saturday
Appletrees, Shamley Green **(Evening)** *(4)*
The Old Croft, South Holmwood *(44)*

July 10 Sunday
Appletrees, Shamley Green *(4)*
Culverkeys, Ewell *(18)*
Nuthatch, Haslemere *(41)*
The Old Croft, South Holmwood *(44)*

July 13 Wednesday
Culverkeys, Ewell *(18)*
Vale End, Albury *(63)*

July 15 Friday
The Round House, Loxhill **(Evening)** *(50)*

July 16 Saturday
48 Gatesden Road, Fetcham *(22)*
Titsey Place Gardens, Oxted *(60)*

July 17 Sunday
Chipchase, Ashtead *(11)*
Gorse Cottage, Tilford *(24)*
47 Harvest Road, Englefield Green *(28)*
The Round House, Loxhill *(50)*
Tanhouse Farm, Newdigate *(58)*

July 20 Wednesday
Chipchase, Ashtead *(11)*

July 23 Saturday
123 Benhill Road, Sutton *(8)*
The Hopperty, Merstham *(31)*

July 24 Sunday
123 Benhill Road, Sutton *(8)*
The Hopperty, Merstham *(31)*
Long Barton, Guildford *(36)*
Longer End Cottage, Normandy *(37)*
19 Oak Tree Road, Knaphill *(42)*
Wotton House, Dorking *(72)*

July 27 Wednesday
48 Gatesden Road, Fetcham **(Evening)** *(22)*
The Hopperty, Merstham *(31)*

July 31 Sunday
72 Green Wrythe Lane, Carshalton *(26)*
Sky-Road Ranch, Ewhurst *(53)*
Walton Poor, Ranmore *(65)*
Wotton House, Dorking *(72)*

August 3 Wednesday
The Hopperty, Merstham **(Evening)** *(31)*
Sky-Road Ranch, Ewhurst *(53)*
Spurfold, Peaslake **(Evening)** *(55)*

August 4 Thursday
The Copse Lodge, Burgh Heath **(Evening)** *(15)*

August 6 Saturday
The Old Croft, South Holmwood *(44)*

August 7 Sunday
The Copse Lodge, Burgh Heath *(15)*
Odstock, Bletchingley *(43)*
The Old Croft, South Holmwood *(44)*
Wotton House, Dorking *(72)*

August 14 Sunday
Stuart Cottage, East Clandon *(56)*
Wotton House, Dorking *(72)*

August 21 Sunday
Green Lane Farm, Newdigate *(25)*

August 23 Tuesday
RHS Garden Wisley **(Evening)** *(48)*

August 24 Wednesday
Green Lane Farm, Newdigate *(25)*

August 27 Saturday
123 Benhill Road, Sutton *(8)*

August 28 Sunday
67 Albion Road, Sutton *(1)*
123 Benhill Road, Sutton *(8)*
41 Shelvers Way, Tadworth *(51)*

September 3 Saturday
Woodbury Cottage, Reigate *(70)*

September 4 Sunday
Claremont Landscape Garden, Esher *(13)*
Loseley Park, Guildford *(38)*
Woodbury Cottage, Reigate *(70)*

September 7 Wednesday
Woodbury Cottage, Reigate *(70)*

September 10 Saturday
Titsey Place Gardens, Oxted *(60)*

September 11 Sunday
Dunsborough Park, Ripley *(19)*

September 24 Saturday
123 Benhill Road, Sutton *(8)*

September 25 Sunday
123 Benhill Road, Sutton *(8)*
Hatchlands Park, East Clandon *(29)*

October 2 Sunday
Albury Park, Albury *(2)*

October 9 Sunday
Walton Poor, Ranmore *(65)*
Winkworth Arboretum, nr Godalming *(68)*

October 23 Sunday
Coverwood Lakes, Ewhurst *(16)*

2006

February 12 Sunday
Gatton Park, Merstham *(23)*

February 15 Wednesday
Gatton Park, Merstham *(23)*

DESCRIPTIONS OF GARDENS

❶ 67 Albion Road, Sutton ⬛
(Peter & Patricia Tremlin & Mr & Mrs A Tremlin) *¼m SE of Sutton. S from Sutton station, 4th turning L into Cavendish Rd, at mini roundabout straight across into Albion Rd.* Small attractive garden made and maintained by owners incl courtyard area with water feature, selection of trees, shrubs, bamboos and ferns chosen for their foliage variation. Various types of container plantings. Home-made TEAS in aid of Leukaemia Society for children. *Adm £2, chd free. Sun 28 Aug (11-5)*

❷ Albury Park, Albury ⬛⬛
(Trustees of Albury Estate) *5m SE of Guildford. From A25 take A248 towards Albury for ¼m, then up New Rd, entrance to Albury Park immed on L.* 14-acre pleasure grounds laid out in 1670s by John Evelyn for Henry Howard, later 6th Duke of Norfolk. ¼m terraces, fine collection of trees, lake and river. The gardens of Albury Park Mansion also open (by kind permission of Historic

House Retirement Homes Ltd) (house not incl, separate charge). Home-made TEAS in aid of Guts & Fossa. *Adm £3, chd free under 16. Suns 13 Mar; 2 Oct (2-5)*

❸ Alderbrook, Smithwood Common, Cranleigh ⬛
(Mr & Mrs Peter Van Den Bergh) *1m N of Cranleigh. A281 from Guildford turn L 1m out of Bramley. Turn R at roundabout then immed L. Drive on L just beyond far end of Smithwood Common.* Approx 8 acres of woodland walks with azaleas and rhododendrons. Rock garden with large pools linked by a stream filled with bog plants which is flanked by bamboo and Japanese maples. Terraces with magnificent views to S Downs. Home-made TEAS in aid of Cranleigh Village Hospital Trust. *Adm £3, chd free. Sun 22 May (2-6)*

NEW 23 Anglesey Road, Aldershot ⬛⬛
See Hampshire.

❹ Appletrees, Stonards Brow, Shamley Green ⬛⬛
(Mr & Mrs A Hodgson) *5m S of Guildford. A281 Guildford-Horsham rd, turn L at Shalford on B2128 via Wonersh to Shamley Green, turn R before Red Lion public house, then R into Sweetwater Lane. At top of lane turn R into Stonards Brow or follow signs to car park.* ¼-acre garden with many interesting features. Several small water features incl fish pond. Summerhouse, greenhouses, raised railway sleeper beds, pergolas. Shrub and perennial borders. Patio and gravel area with several colourful containers. Raised vegetable beds; new secret garden and white garden. Obelisks and clematis, all on a sandy loam soil. An ideas garden. Cream TEAS. *Adm £2, chd free. Sun 10 July (2-6).* **Evening Opening** *£3.50, cheese & wine, Sat 9 July (5-8). Private visits welcome by appt, groups of 20 or more July & Aug only, coaches permitted. Tel 01483 898779 ahodgson@arsenalfc.net*

❺ Arden Lodge, Pastens Road, Limpsfield ⬛⬛
(Mr & Mrs C Bruce-Jones) *1m E of Oxted. From A25 take B269 Edenbridge Rd for 200yds. R down Brick Kiln Lane. Pastens Rd 2nd turning L, house at end of rd.* 2-acre greensand garden with extensive views. Herbaceous border; rhododendrons, azaleas and much formal and informal mixed planting with interesting trees, shrubs, roses and containers. Home-made TEAS (May only) in aid of Oxted URC.

Adm £2.50, chd free. Suns Mons 15, 16 May; 3, 4 July (Suns 2-6, Mons 11-6). Private visits welcome by appt, groups also welcome, Apr to July. Tel 01883 722171

❻ Ashleigh Grange, off Chapel Lane, West Humble ⬛⬛
(Clive & Angela Gilchrist) *2m N of Dorking. From A24 at Boxhill/Burford Bridge follow signs to Westhumble. Through village & L up drive by ruined chapel (1m from A24).* 3½-acre sloping chalk garden in charming rural setting. Many areas of interest incl rockery and water feature; raised ericaceous bed; 'prairie-style' bank; mixed herbaceous and shrub borders; foliage plants; woodland walk and fernery. Home-made TEAS in aid of Barnardos. *Adm £2.50, chd free. Sun 26 June (2-5.30).* **Evening Opening** *£3.50, wine, Fri 24 June (6-8). Private visits welcome by appt May & June only. Tel 01306 884613 clive.gilchrist@btinternet.com*

❼ Barhatch Farm, Barhatch Lane, Cranleigh ⬛⬛⬛
(Mr & Mrs P M Grol) *2m N of Cranleigh. A281 from Guildford, L at B2128 to Cranleigh through village, take Ewhurst Rd for 1m, turn L into Barhatch Rd which becomes Barhatch Lane. Garden 1st on R after Cranleigh Golf & Leisure Club.* Created by present owners, 6 acres of rambling garden, surrounding listed Tudor farmhouse (not open). Herbaceous borders, abundance of old roses, walled pond, rose tunnel and ornamental pond. Wild flower meadow and sunken Zen garden; cutting garden and newly planted meadow. Home-made TEAS in aid of Cranleigh Village Hospital Trust. *Adm £2.50, chd free. Wed, Sun 8, 12 June (12-5). Private visits welcome by appt June & July only. Tel 01483 277968*

❽ NEW 123 Benhill Road, Sutton ⬛
(Mr Martyn Graham) *½m NE of town centre. Take A230 from Rosehill roundabout towards Sutton. After approx 2/3m turn L into All Saints Rd which becomes Benhill Rd.* Specialist garden 30 metres x 8 metres with a selection of exotic plants. This interesting collection incl 60 different types of palms and spiky plants with pseudopanaxes, bamboos, arundos, ferns, cannas, gunnera and climbing plants giving a wide variety of leaf colour and shape. Light refreshments and TEAS. *Adm £2, chd free. Sats, Suns 23, 24 July; 27, 28 Aug; 24, 25 Sept (11-5)*

NEW Bentley Village Gardens
See Hampshire.

Brocas Farm, Lower Froyle &⊗
See Hampshire.

Bury Court, Bentley &⊗☺
See Hampshire.

◆ **Charts Edge, Westerham** &☺
See Kent.

❾ Chauffeur's Flat, Tandridge Lane, Tandridge ⊗
(Mr & Mrs Richins) *2m E of Godstone. Turn off A25 for Tandridge. Take drive on L past church. Follow arrows to circular courtyard.* Enter 1-acre tapestry of magical secret gardens with magnificent views. Touching the senses, all surefooted visitors may explore the many surprises on this exuberant escape from reality. Imaginative use of recycled materials creates an inspired variety of ideas, while wild and specimen plants reveal an ecological haven. Home-made TEAS. (Sats & Suns only). *Adm £2.50, chd free. Mons to Suns 23 May to 29 May; 20 June to 26 June (10-5). Tel 01883 715937*

❿ Chinthurst Lodge, Wonersh Common Road, Wonersh &⊗
(Mr & Mrs M R Goodridge) *4m S of Guildford. A281. At Shalford turn E into B2128 towards Wonersh. Just after Wonersh rd sign, before village, garden on R.* 1-acre yr-round garden, herbaceous borders, white garden, specimen trees and shrubs; gravel garden with water feature; small kitchen garden; fruit cage; 2 wells; ornamental ponds, millennium parterre garden, herb area. Home-made TEAS in aid of Alzheimers' Society. *Adm £2.50, chd free. Sun 19, (2-5.30), Wed 22 June (2-5.30)*

⓫ Chipchase, Park Road, Ashtead &⊗☺
(Peter & Valerie Gray) *2m NE of Leatherhead. From A24 just S of Ashtead Village turn into Greville Park Rd (park here). Park Rd (disabled parking) is approx 100yds on L by post box.* Garden designed and constructed by owners since 2001, with emphasis on low maintenance and minimal digging by using membrane and mulch. Herbaceous border, trees, shrubs, pergola, rose rope, hanging baskets, troughs, water feature and large single area with grasses. Home-made TEAS in aid of Family Focus. *Adm £2, chd free. Suns 26 June; 17 July, Wed 20 July (11-5). Private*

visits welcome by appt, group visits June to Aug. Tel 01372 275106 chipchase@ashtead.net

⓬ NEW ◆ Clandon Park, West Clandon &
(The National Trust) *3m E of Guildford. On A247. From A3 follow signs to Ripley to join A247 via B2215.* The garden around the house is laid out informally, apart from the parterre beneath the south front. To the S a mid C18 grotto. The principal front faces parkland, laid out in the style of 'Capability Brown' around 1770. Created in 1901 a Dutch garden modelled on the pond garden at Hampton Court Palace. The large bulb field looks stunning in spring. Light refreshments and TEAS. *Adm by donation.* **For NGS:** *Sun 20 Mar (11-5). Tel 01483 222482 www.nationaltrust.org.uk/ clandonpark*

⓭ ◆ Claremont Landscape Garden, Portsmouth Road, Esher &⊗
(The National Trust) *1m SW of Esher. On E side of A307 (no access from A3 bypass).* One of the earliest surviving English landscape gardens; begun by Vanbrugh and Bridgeman before 1720; extended and naturalized by Kent and Capability Brown; lake; island with pavilion; grotto and turf amphitheatre; viewpoints and avenues. Light refreshments and TEAS. *Adm £5, chd £2.50.* **For NGS:** *Suns 5 June; 4 Sept (10-7). Tel 01372 467806 Andrew King www.nationaltrust.org.uk/claremont*

⓮ ◆ Claygate Gardens
2m E of Esher. Turn into Milbourne Lane from the A244 (Claremont Lane) continue into Hare Lane, turn R at Foley Arms or from S bound A3 take A309 into Woodstock Lane & follow yellow signs. Maps available at each garden. Light refreshments and TEAS at Clarebrook & 19 Glenavon Close. *Combined adm £3.50, chd under 12 free. Sun 26 June (11-5)*

Catari, 27 Stevens Lane &⊗☺
(Ruth & Keith Fowles) Small garden created by owners; shrubs and plants grown for keen flower arranger; unheated conservatory full of tender plants from all over the world; collection of Bonsai trees grown from seeds and cuttings.

Clarebrook, 3 Claremont Road &⊗☺ (Francis & Jennifer Boff) Paved area with formal pond enclosed by ornamental trellis and climbing plants features seasonal planting. An archway

leads to small garden with mixed borders planted for yr-round interest.

19 Glenavon Close ⊗ (Jean & Dennis Radley) Delightful ¼-acre summer garden artistically designed and constructed by owners with rockeries and ponds creating a tranquil setting; walkway across bridge to garden chalet; small woodland area; colourful planting in borders and containers.

⓯ The Copse Lodge, Brighton Road, Burgh Heath &⊗☺
(Marian & Edward Wallbank) *6m S of Sutton. On A217. 200yds past T-lights at junction with Reigate Rd. Turn L into Heathside Hotel, park in hotel car park courtesy of hotel. Proceed on foot 80yds to garden.* Very unusual 1 acre garden with architectural features and exciting planting. Large Japanese garden abounds with acers, bamboo, wisteria and bonsai. Wander it's paths past the tea house and emerge refreshed to enjoy the contrast of exotic planting of palms, bananas and beautiful tender specimens. TEAS. *Adm £2.50, chd free. Suns 12 June; 7 Aug (1.30-5.30).* **Evening Openings** *£3, wine, Wed 8 June; Thur 4 Aug (6-9)*

⓰ Coverwood Lakes, Peaslake Road, Ewhurst ⊗
(The Metson Family) *7m SW of Dorking. From A25 follow signs for Peaslake; garden ½m beyond Peaslake.* 14-acre landscaped garden in stunning position in the Surrey hills with 4 lakes and bog garden. Extensive rhododendrons, azaleas, primulas and fine trees. 3½-acre lakeside arboretum. Marked trail through the working farm with cows and calves, sheep and horses, extensive views of the surrounding hills. Home-made TEAS. *Adm £3.50, chd £2 (share to Coverwood Farm). Suns 17, 24 Apr; 1, 8, 15, 22 May (2-6); 23 Oct (11-4.30). Private visits welcome by appt. Tel 01306 731101*

⓱ ◆ Crosswater Farm, Crosswater Lane, Churt &⊗☺
(Mrs E G Millais & Family) *6m S of Farnham, 6m NW of Haslemere. From A287 turn E into Jumps Rd ½m N of Churt village centre. After ¼m turn acute L into Crosswater Lane & follow signs for Millais Nurseries.* Idyllic 6-acre woodland garden. Plantsman's collection of rhododendrons and azaleas, incl rare species collected in the Himalayas, hybrids raised by the owners. Everything from alpine dwarfs, to architectural large leaved trees. Ponds, stream and companion

plantings incl sorbus, magnolias & Japanese acers . Trial gardens of new varieties. Rhododendron nursery open throughout the year. Featured in 'Garden Answers' 2004. Home-made TEAS in aid of St Mary's Church, Frensham, NGS days only. *Adm £2.50, chd free. Daily 18 Apr to 10 June.* **For NGS:** *Sat, Sun 7, 8 May (10-5). Tel 01252 792698 www.rhododendrons.co.uk*

⑱ Culverkeys, 20A Longdown Lane North, Ewell 🅰🅳🅔
(Anne & Geoff Salt) *1m E of Epsom. 1m S of Ewell Village. Leave Ewell bypass (A24) by Reigate Rd (A240) to pass Nescot on L. Turn R in ¼m.* A romantic somewhat secret garden on the edge of Epsom Downs. Meandering paths pass borders planted to capacity with interesting and unusual plants. Arches smothered in climbers reveal secluded corners. Running water soothes the spirit and seats in sun and shade offer rest and reflection. Designed for yr-round interest, shrubs and trees play host to many clematis with viticellas ruling supreme in mid to late summer. Featured in 'Surrey Life' 2004. Home-made TEAS (Suns only). *Adm £2, chd free. Suns, Weds 29 May; 1 June; 10, 13 July (Suns 2-5.30) (Weds 2-5)*

⑲ Dunsborough Park, Ripley 🅰🅳🅔
(A J H Baron Sweerts de Landas Wyborgh) *6m NE of Guildford. Entrance across Ripley Green.* Extensive walled gardens redesigned by Penelope Hobhouse and Rupert Golby; herbaceous borders; 70ft ginkgo hedge, ancient mulberry tree, water garden. Restored Edwardian wooden glasshouses. TEAS in aid of charities. *Adm £3, chd £1.50. Suns 24 Apr; 11 Sept; Wed 8 June (1-5). Tel 01483 225366 info@sweerts. com*

⑳ 58 Eastwood Road, Bramley 🅳
(Ray & Kate Vernalls) *3m S of Guildford. From Guildford - S on A281 (signed Horsham) through Shalford village to Bramley. Turn L at BP Garage into Station Rd. Park in Bramley Business Centre on L. Walk along Downs Link path (approx 200yds).* ½-acre garden created and maintained by owners. Formal entrance with topiary; herbaceous borders, small fruit and vegetable plot. Sunken area with bog garden and large wildlife pond, semi-wild area leading to river. TEAS. *Adm £2.50, chd 50p. Sun 5 June (2-6).* **Evening Opening** *£3.50, wine, Fri 3 June (6-9)*

The Elms, 13 Wolverton Avenue, Kingston-on-Thames 🅳🅔
See London.

㉑ Feathercombe, Feathercombe Lane, Hambledon 🅔
(Mrs M E Campbell) *4m SW of Godalming. 2m from Milford station, on Feathercombe Lane, off Hambledon Rd, between Hydestile Xrds & Merry Harriers public house.* 12-acre garden of mature rhododendrons, azaleas, tree heathers, shrubs and topiary. Fine views. Garden designed and made by Surrey author and journalist Eric Parker and his wife Ruth (neé Messel) of Nymans. Now maintained by his grandchildren and has supported the NGS continually for over 60yrs. Some parts not suitable for wheelchairs owing to gradients. Featured in Surrey Monocle, 2004. *Adm £2.50, chd 50p (share to St Peter's Church, Hambledon). Sats, Suns 14, 15, 21, 22 May (2-5). Private visits welcome by appt May, groups welcome. Coaches not permitted. Tel 01483 860264*

Froyle Cottage Gardens
See Hampshire.

㉒ NEW 48 Gatesden Road, Fetcham 🅳
(Paul Bates) *1m W of Leatherhead. From Leatherhead take A246 towards Fetcham & Guildford, pass under railway bridge, with leisure centre on L, turn R at mini roundabout take A245 towards Cobham, straight over next mini roundabout, at double mini roundabout take L into School Lane at end turn R, take 1st L into Gatesden Rd.* Small interesting garden with Mediterranean influence, plenty of unusual plants incl various palms and collection of large agaves and succulents. Small ornamental pond and patio area with selection of plants in terracotta pots. Not suitable for young children. *Adm £2.50, chd free. Sat 16 July (11-5).* **Evening Opening** *£3.50, wine, Wed 27 July (6-9)*

㉓ ◆ Gatton Park, Merstham 🅔
(Royal Alexandra & Albert School) *3m NE of Reigate. Access via Rocky Lane. 5 mins from M25 junction 8 (A217) or from top of Reigate Hill, over M25 then follow sign to Merstham. Entrance is off Rocky Lane accessible from Gatton Bottom or A23 Merstham.* Formerly home to the Colman family (of mustard fame), now the grounds of the Royal Alexandra and Albert School. Hidden gardens within historic 'Capability'

Brown parkland. 1910 Edwardian, Japanese garden restored for Channel 4's 'Lost Gardens'. Dramatic 1912 Pulham rock garden, walled gardens, lakeside trail. Restoration of gardens ongoing and maintained by volunteers. Ivan Hick's children's trail behind main lake. Featured in 'The Times', 2004. Light refreshments and TEAS in Gatton Hall, NGS days only. *Adm £3, chd free. 1st Sun of each month Feb to Oct (1-5).* **For NGS:** *Sun 13 Feb (10-3), Wed 16 Feb (12-3); Sun 12 Feb (10-4), Wed 15 Feb (12-4) 2006. Tel 01737 649068 www.gattonpark.com*

㉔ Gorse Cottage, Tilford 🅰🅳
(A M How) *5m SE of Farnham. Midway between Farnham & Hindhead. Garden is opp The Grange, approx 1½m from Tilford Green at Rushmoor end of village.* Approx ¾-acre plantsman's informal garden in tranquil rural setting with lawns, mature trees, herbaceous borders and shrubs. Pond and stream with moisture loving plants. TEAS in aid of Brooke Hospital for Animals. *Adm £2, chd free. Sun 17 July (2-5.30)*

㉕ Green Lane Farm, Cudworth Lane, Newdigate 🅰🅳🅔
(Mr & Mrs P Hall) *8m S of Dorking. On A24 turn L at Beare Green roundabout - signposted Newdigate. R at T-junction, L at Church, R into Cudworth Lane - Farm ¼m on R.* 1½-acre garden created from a cow paddock in 2000. Emphasis on colour in mixed borders, containers, gravel area with many lovely grasses, unique oak summerhouse, beautiful restored gypsy vardo (caravan). Farm walk circling 3 lakes. Featured in 'Period Living', 2003; 'Surrey Life', 'Garden Style', 25 'Beautiful Gardens', 2004. Home-made TEAS. *Adm £2.50, chd free. Sun,21 (11-5), Wed 24 Aug (12-5). Private visits welcome by appt, groups of 15 or more, June & Aug. Coaches permitted. Tel 01306 631214*

㉖ 72 Green Wrythe Lane, Carshalton 🅰🅳🅔
(Mrs G Cooling) *1m E of Sutton in Carshalton. From Carshalton Ponds turn N across ponds into North St. Continue to Wrythe Green, then 1st R into Green Wrythe Lane.* 170ft x 50ft colourful cottage style garden o various habitats; incl herbaceous borders, woodland area, wildlife pond. A plantaholic's delight, work organically - an oasis in suburbia. Home-made TEAS. *Adm £2, chd fr*

*(share to Royal Marsden Hospital).
Sun 31 July (10.30-4.30)*

㉗ Hall Grove School, Bagshot
&🚫♿

(Mr & Mrs A R Graham & Mr &
Mrs P D Smithson) *6m SW of
Egham. M3 to junction 3, follow
A322 1m until sign for Sunningdale
A30, 1m E of Bagshot, opp Long
Acres garden centre, entrance at
footbridge. Ample car park.* Formerly
a small Georgian country estate, now
a co-educational preparatory school.
Grade II listed house (not open).
Mature parkland with specimen trees.
Tour comprises three contrasting
private gardens within the old estate.
Historical features incl ice house, old
walled garden, heated peach wall.
Much recent development. Lots of
ideas for keen gardeners. Home-made
TEAS served from 2pm in aid of
Sebastian Gates Action Trust. *Adm
£5, chd free. Sun 22 May (12-5)
www.hallgrove.surrey.sch.uk*

**㉘ 47 Harvest Road, Englefield
Green** 🚫

(Joan & Tony Faulkner) *1m SW of
Egham. Directly opp Royal
Holloway College on A30. Nearest
BR station is Egham. Car parking a
short walk away in Victoria St.*
A small garden but full of interest,
divided into a fisherman's cottage
garden, a more formal garden and
Japanese style garden. Home-made
TEAS. *Adm £2, chd free. Sun 17 July
(2-5.30). Private visits welcome by
appt. Tel 01784 435411*

**㉙ ◆ Hatchlands Park, East
Clandon** 🚫

(The National Trust) *4m E of
Guildford. In East Clandon, off
A246. A3 from London direction,
follow signposts to Ripley to join
A247 & proceed via West Clandon
to A246. From Guildford take A25
then A246 towards Leatherhead at
West Clandon.* Garden and park
designed by Repton in 1800. Follow
one of the park walks to the stunning
bluebell wood in spring. In autumn
enjoy the changing colours on the
long walk. S of the house is a small
parterre designed by Gertrude Jekyll
in 1913 to flower in early June.
House and restaurant also open.
Light refreshments and TEAS. *House
and Garden adm £6, garden only £3,
chd £1.50.* **For NGS:** *Suns 24 Apr; 25
Sept (11-6). Tel 01483 222482
www.nationaltrust.org.uk/hatchlands*

**㉚ Hethersett, Littleworth Cross,
Seale** 🚫

(Mr Adam Gordon & Mr Douglas
Gordon) *7m SE of Farnham. S of*

Hogs Back (A31) *1½m from Seale
Church on Elstead Rd or 1m N from
B3001 (Milford-Farnham rd) on
Seale Rd.* Historic woodland garden
created at end of C19 by H A
Mangles, an early hybridiser of
rhododendrons. In the 25-acre wood
are many mature trees and shrubs
incl many of his hybrids, species from
the earliest expeditions to the
Himalayas, as well as large drifts of
azaleas. TEAS in aid of local charity.
*Adm £3, chd under 12 free. Sun 15
May (11-5)*

239a Hook Road, Chessington
🚫♿

See London.

**㉛ The Hopperty, 59 London
Road South, Merstham**

(Stephen & Pamela Whiting) *3m E of
Reigate. From Redhill town centre
take A23 signed Croydon. After 1m
enter Merstham (London Rd Sth),
turn 1st R after New Battlebridge
Lane T-lights, into service rd. Please
park tactfully.* Creative, imaginative
suburban garden incorporating
formal and informal styles, pots,
pond, gazebo and greenhouse.
Colourful, vibrant planting leads to
gated rose arch and through to cool,
shady woodland area created to
encourage wildlife with man-made
stream, well and summerhouse. An
ideas garden with quirky touches.
140ft x 40ft. TEAS in aid of Croydon
Animal Samaritans. *Adm £2, chd
free. Sat, Sun, Wed 23, 24, 27 July
(1-5).* **Evening Opening** *£2.50, wine,
Wed 3 Aug (6-9)*

Kew Green Gardens
See London.

**㉜ Knightsmead, Rickman Hill
Road, Chipstead** 🚫♿

(Mrs Jones & Miss Collins) *5m N of
Reigate. From A23 in Coulsdon turn
W onto B2032. Through T-lights, L
fork into Portnalls Rd. Top of hill at
Xrds, R into Markedge Rd. R into
Lissoms Rd. R into Bouverie Rd.* ½-
acre garden on heavy clay, designed
and maintained by owners for
perfume, colour, form and foliage
giving yr-round interest. Hellebores,
spring bulbs, ferns and unusual
woodland plants; trees, shrubs,
perennials and climbers; raised beds,
water features, conservatory and
glazed pergola. Enjoy scent, sights,
seats and shelter. Small Craft
Exhibition. Light refreshments and
TEAS Thur; teas only Sun in aid of
Chipstead WI. *Adm £2.50, chd 50p.
Thur 7 (11-4); Sun 10 Apr (2-5).
Private visits welcome by appt.
Tel 01737 551694*

㉝ 22 Knoll Road, Dorking
🚫♿

(David & Anne Drummond) *From
one-way system after Mays Garage
turn L up the Horsham Rd (A2003
which runs to N Holmwood
roundabout A24). Knoll Rd on R just
beyond The Bush Inn.* ½-acre town
garden, interesting and unusual
plants and many artefacts (incl
unique works of art), mixed borders,
many alpines in raised beds, tufa and
sinks, mini-meadow and peat bed,
fern alley, lawn with cretan labyrinth,
fruit and vegetables, exotic front
garden; well stocked sub-tropical
conservatory. Wheelchairs may be
driven up short steep drive. TEAS in
aid of Dorking Amnesty Group. *Adm
£2, chd free. Sun 29 May; Wed 1
June (10.30-5.30). Private visits
welcome by appt. Tel 01306 883280*

**㉞ Langstone Cottage, 26 Hare
Hill, Addlestone** 🚫♿

(Sue & Dennis Millward) *5m NE of
Woking. Off B3121. From M25
junction 11 take A320 signed
Woking. L into B3121 & follow
yellow signs.* 175ft x 50ft slightly
sloping romantic cottage garden with
mixed plantings of hardy perennials
(some unusual). Bower planted with
variety of clematis; pond, shaped box
hedges and peaceful summer house.
Featured in 'Ideal Home' 2003. Plant
sales in aid of Brownbread Horse
Rescue Charity. Home-made TEAS.
*Adm £2, chd free. Sun 19 June
(2-5.30)*

**Little Coopers, Coopers Hill,
Eversley** 🚫♿
See Hampshire.

Little Lodge, Thames Ditton
🚫♿
See London.

㉟ Lodkin, Lodkin Hill, Hascombe
🚫♿

(Mr & Mrs W N Bolt) *3m S of
Godalming. Just off B2130
Godalming/Cranleigh, on outskirts of
Hascombe; take narrow lane
signposted to garden.* Country garden
of approx 4½ acres. Woodland, pond,
stream, extensively restored Victorian
greenhouses in full use. Kitchen
garden and flower borders. Spring
bulbs in profusion. Newly planted
shrub rose border; large azaleas,
rhododendrons and flowering trees.
Partial wheelchair access, garden is
very steep in parts. Featured in
'Countryside Magazine' 2003;
'Independent' 2004. Home-made
TEAS. *Adm £2.50, chd free. Suns 10
Apr; 19 June (2-5). Private visits*

welcome by appt. Tel 01483 208323
willibolt2@aol.com

㊱ Long Barton, 12 Longdown Road, Guildford
(Harry & Rose-Marie Stokes) *1m E of Guildford. A246 (Epsom Rd) from Guildford, after ½m turn R into Tangier Rd. At top turn L into Warren Rd - becoming One Tree Hill. At Xrds turn sharp R into Longdown Rd - last house on R in rd.* 2-acre S-facing hillside (450ft) garden with stunning views. Formal fish pond, knot garden, large collection of Japanese maples and tree peonies (May flowering), specimen trees, topiary, many annuals. Decorative wrought iron and stone work; babbling brook and large decorative screen. TEAS. *Adm £2.50, chd free (share to St Marthas Appeal). Sun 24 July (10-5.30)*

㊲ Longer End Cottage, Normandy Common Lane, Normandy &⌂
(Ann & John McIlwham) *4m W of Guildford. On A323 from Guildford. At War Memorial Xrds in Normandy turn R into Hunts Hill Rd then 1st R into Normandy Common Lane.* 1½-acre garden divided into rooms with a wide variety of plants, shrubs and trees incl roses, delphiniums, tree ferns, gunnera, grasses etc. Knot garden, laburnham walk, and wild flower meadow are features of particular interest. Home-made TEAS. *Adm £2.50, chd free. Suns 22 May; 26 June; 24 July (11-6). Private visits welcome by appt. Tel 01483 811858*

㊳ ◆ Loseley Park, Guildford &⌂✉
(Mr & Mrs M G More-Molyneux) *4m SW of Guildford. Leave A3 at Compton S of Guildford, on B3000 for 2m. Signposted. Guildford station 2m, Godalming station 3m.* Charming 2.5-acre walled garden. Award-winning rose garden with over 1,000 bushes, mainly old-fashioned varieties. Herb garden with sections for culinary, medicinal, household and decorative. Fruit and flower garden. White garden with water features. New organic vegetable garden. Moat walk, terrace, herbaceous borders, ancient wisteria, mulberry tree and magnificent vine walk. Featured in 'English Home' 2003; 'Monocle Magazine' 2004. Light refreshments and TEAS in Courtyard Tearoom. *House & Garden adm £6, chd £3, concesssions £5. Garden only £3, chd £1.50, concessions £2.50. Tues to Suns May to Sept (11-5), House open: Tues,*

Weds, Thurs & Suns May to Aug (1-4.30). **For NGS:** *Suns 8 May; 4 Sept (11-5). Tel 01483 304440*
www.loseley-park.com

NEW **Lowder Mill, Bell Vale Lane, Fernhurst** ✉⌂
See Sussex.

㊴ Moleshill House, The Fairmile, Cobham &✉⌂
(Penny & Maurice Snell) *2m NE of Cobham. On A307 Esher to Cobham Rd next to free car park by A3 bridge, at entrance to Waterford Close.* Flower arranger's romantic walled garden. Topiary and garlanded cisterns around house (not open); circular lawn surrounded by borders designed for drought tolerance; hot garden with railway sleeper feature; gravel bed; dovecote; bee alcoves; sorbus lutescens avenue, bog garden, paving and pots. Featured on Carlton TVs Garden Makers 2003. TEAS Sun only. *Adm £2.50, chd free. Sun, Wed 15, 18 May (2-5). Private visits welcome by appt for groups of 10 or more. Tel 01932 864532 pennysnellflower@aol.com*

㊵ Munstead Wood, Godalming &⌂
(Sir Robert & Lady Clark) *2m SE of Godalming. Take B2130 Brighton Rd out of Godalming towards Horsham. After 1m church on R, Heath Lane just thereafter on L. 400yds on R is entrance to Munstead Wood. Parking on L of Heath Lane. Limited parking on road.* 10 acres of rhododendrons, azaleas, woods, shrub and flower beds. House (not open) was designed by Edwin Lutyens and was the home of Gertrude Jekyll until her death. Home-made TEAS. *Adm £3, chd free, OAPs £2 (share to The Menieres Society). Suns 17 Apr; 22 May; 12 June (2-6). Private visits welcome by appt. Tel 01483 417867*

㊶ Nuthatch, Tennysons Lane, Haslemere ✉⌂
(Mr & Mrs S Vaughan) *1m S of Haslemere. From S end of Haslemere High St, turn L on B2131. 2nd R into Haste Hill. Straight on at Xrds, then L into Tennysons Lane. Garden 1m on L. Park in NT Blackdown car park (short walk).* 1¾-acre sloping wooded garden, developed since 1994. Herbaceous and mixed borders. Woodland areas linked by narrow (sometimes steep) paths threading through mature trees. New woodland walk for 2005. Unusual woodland plantings. Bulbs, ferns, camellias and magnolias and many

other interesting shrubs. Fine views. Blackdown walks close by. Home-made TEAS. *Adm £2, chd £1. Suns 1 May; 10 July (11-5)*

㊷ NEW 19 Oak Tree Road, Knaphill ✉
(Barry & Pam Gray) *5m NW of Guildford. From A3 take A322 Bagshot Rd, continue through Worplesdon, straight over at Brookwood Xrds. 1st turning on L into Oak Tree Rd (opp Sainsburys).* Colourful front garden of informal bedding, baskets and containers featuring tender perennials and annuals grown by owners. Back garden (approx 80' x 35') has lawn, patio, small pond, trees, shrubs and perennials for foliage, texture, scent and yr-round-interest. 3 greenhouses, fruit trees and vegetables some of which are grown to exhibition standard. No wasted space in this delightful garden.. 'Garden News' Gardener of the year 3rd overall; Winner of 'Gardens Monthly' Kitchen Gardener; 'Woking in Bloom' Front Garden 2003. TEAS in aid of Woking Hospice. *Adm £2, chd free. Sun 24 July (11-5)*

㊸ Odstock, Castle Square, Bletchingley &✉⌂
(Averil & John Trott) *3m W of Godstone. Just off A25 in Bletchingley. At top of village nr Red Lion public house. Parking in village no parking in Castle Square.* ⅔-acre plantsman's garden maintained by owners and developed for all-yr interest. Special interest in grasses and climbers, 76 at last count. Japanese features; dahlias. No-dig, low-maintenance vegetable garden. Children's quiz. Disabled please telephone first. Featured in '25 Beautiful Gardens' 2004. Home-made TEAS in aid of St Mary's Church, Bletchingley. *Adm £2.50, chd free. Sun 7 Aug (12.30-5.30). Private visits welcome by appt. Tel 01883 743100*

㊹ The Old Croft, South Holmwood &⌂
(David & Virginia Lardner-Burke) *3m S of Dorking. From Dorking take A24 S for 3m. Turn L at sign to Leigh-Brockham into Mill Road. ½m on L, 2 free car parks in NT Holmwood Common. Follow signs for 500yds along woodland walk.* 5 acre mature parkland garden with lake, swans, wild pond, bog gardens, herb garden, wild and formal areas, bamboo/ornamental grass maze; roses, pergolas. A peaceful garden o great beauty. Featured in 'Period Living & Traditional Homes' 2003.

Cream TEAS in aid of St Catherine's Hospice. *Adm £3, chd free. Suns, Mons 1, 2, 29, 30 May; Sats, Suns 9, 10 July; 6, 7 Aug (2-6).* **Disabled and elderly: for direct access** *Tel 01306 888224 www.lardner-burke.org.uk*

45 ◆ Polesden Lacey, Bookham &⊗

(The National Trust) *1½m S of Great Bookham. Nr Dorking. Off A246 Leatherhead-Guildford rd.* 30 acres formal gardens in an exceptional setting on the North Downs; walled rose garden, winter garden, lawns; magnificent views. Regency villa dating early 1820s, remodelled after 1906 by the Hon Mrs Ronald Greville. King George VI and Queen Elizabeth the Queen Mother spent part of their honeymoon here. (June roses, July S.S.S trail). Light refreshments and TEAS. *House and garden adm £8, garden only £5, chd £2.50. Garden: all year.* **For NGS:** *Sun, Mon 12 June; 4 July (11-5).* *Tel 01372 452048 polesdenlacey@ntrust.org.uk*

46 NEW Quinneys, Camilla Drive, Westhumble &⊗

(Peter & Jane Miller) *1m N of Dorking. Turn L off A24 (going north) into Westhumble St, just before Boxhill roundabout. After ¼m, pass Boxhill and Westhumble station & go through archway into Camilla Dr. House 3rd on L. Limited parking at garden. Parking available at Boxhill Station (3mins walk). Coming from Leatherhead (going south) on A24 turn R just after Boxhill roundabout signed Westhumble Station. Then as above.* 3 acres created at the breakup of the neighbouring great estate of Camilla Lacey. The garden incorporates some of the original cedar trees and the present owners have planted a mini arboretum, and have used the concept of 'tapestry' hedges to good effect. The garden incls some rare trees and shrubs, an ancient glorious wisteria, rhododerndrons and azaleas in full flower. Interesting water garden. Home-made TEAS in aid of St Michael's Church, Mickleham. *Adm £3, chd free, OAPs £2. Sun 15 May (2-6)*

47 ◆ Ramster, Chiddingfold &⊗

(Mr & Mrs Paul Gunn) *1½m S of Chiddingfold. On A283; large iron gates on R.* Mature 20-acre woodland garden of exceptional interest with lakes, ponds and woodland walks. Laid out by Gauntlett Nurseries of Chiddingfold in early 1900s. Fine rhododendrons, azaleas, camellias, magnolias, trees

and shrubs. Maturing bog garden and millennium garden. Picnic area. Light refreshments and TEAS in Cedar House Tearoom. *Adm £4, chd under 16 free (share to NGS). Daily 9 Apr to 26 June (10-5). Tel 01428 654167 Mrs M Gunn www.ramsterweddings.co.uk*

48 ◆ RHS Garden Wisley &⊗⊗

(Royal Horticultural Society) *1m NE of Ripley. SW of London on A3 & M25 (Junction 10). Follow signs with flower logo.* The primary garden of the RHS and centre of its scientific and educational activities. Arboretum, alpine and wild garden, rock garden, mixed borders, model gardens, model fruit and vegetable garden, rose garden, glasshouses, orchard and trial grounds. Picnics not allowed in the garden. *Adm (incl RHS members) £6, chd under 15 free (share to RHS Wisley Garden).* **For NGS:** *special* **Evening Opening** *with music Tue 23 Aug (6-9)*

49 NEW Rostellan, Pilgrims Close, Westhumble ⊗⊗

(Ron & Linda Stanton) *2m N of Dorking. From Dorking roundabout on A24 approx 1m N - take L turn signed Westhumble. 1st L into Pilgrims Way, then 1st R into Pilgrims Close. Park in field on L, house 2nd on R. ½-acre garden in 3 basic areas. Nearest the house are raised beds with mixed planting, lawn and pond. The middle garden has a raised seating area with an acer collection, lawn, fruit trees and summer house. At the end of the garden is a vegetable plot screened by a trellis with roses and clematis. TEAS in aid of SCOPE. Adm £2.50, chd free. Sun 5 June (1-5)*

50 NEW The Round House, Dunsfold Road, Loxhill

(Mrs Sue Lawson) *4m S of Bramley. On A281. At Smithbrook Kilns take R turn to Dunsfold. Follow to T-junction. Go R (B2130). After 1.2m Park Hatch on R, enter park, follow drive to garden.* 2.5-acre walled Victorian garden on sloping site. Extensive restoration project started in 2002 still in progress. Orchard with apple and plum trees. Herbaceous beds with varieties of annuals and perennials, roses and mixed planting. Former greenhouse beds with peonies and dahlias. Newly planted serpentine walks. Main feature 75 metre lavender walk. Far reaching views from top of garden. TEAS in aid of local charity. *Adm £2.50, chd free. Sun 17 July (11-5).* **Evening Opening** *£3.50, wine, Fri 15 July (5-dusk)*

NEW Shalford House, Square Drive, Kingsley Green ⊗

See Sussex.

51 41 Shelvers Way, Tadworth &⊗

(Mr & Mrs K G Lewis) *6m S of Sutton. Off the A217. 1st turning on R after Burgh Heath T-lights heading S. 400yds down Shelvers Way on L.* Against a background of mature trees this plantsman's garden with attractive cobbled and shingle area has something to offer for every season. Wide variety of herbaceous perennials and shrubs with over 80 varieties of daffodils plus other bulbs. Divided into rooms with plenty of seating giving pleasing aspects. Home-made TEAS. *Adm £2, chd free. Suns 24 Apr; 28 Aug (1-5.30). Private visits welcome by appt. Tel 01737 210707*

52 Shepherds Lane Gardens, Guildford

1m NW of Guildford. From A3 take A322 Worplesdon Rd. Turn L at T-lights (Emmanuel Church), Stoughton into Shepherds Lane. Gardens are L on brow of hill. Alternatively, via A323 Aldershot Rd and Rydes Hill Rd, Shepherds Lane is 2nd on R. Home-made TEAS. *Combined adm £2, chd free. Wed 15 June (1.30-5.30).* **Evening Opening** *£3, wine, Wed 29 June (6-9)*

67 Shepherds Lane ⊗⊗ (Charles & Gwen Graham) Suburban garden inviting a progress from forecourt alpine garden via fuchsia alley to rear gravel border, pond, lawns with mixed herbaceous and shrub borders. Specimen trees fern walk. White garden specimen grass circle and dwarf fruit tree bed. *Private visits welcome by appt. Tel 01483 566445 charlesadgraham@btinternet.com*

69 Shepherds Lane ⊗⊗ (Mrs J Hall) Maturing suburban garden designed with linked circular lawns, specimen trees, mixed shrub and herbaceous borders planted for yr-round colour in silver, pink and purple shades linked to No 67 by rose and clematis covered arched gates.

53 NEW Sky-Road Ranch, Horsham Lane, Ewhurst &⊗

(John & Liz Weller) *3m E of Cranleigh. Take B2127 from obelisk E end of Cranleigh. 3m to Ewhurst. Take 1st or 2nd signed Horsham Lane & Ewhurst Green. Park on S side of cricket green, 50yds S to garden. Tranquil 2¼ acre mainly* walled garden and meadow. Developed continuously over 45yrs by owners. Many flowering shrubs, large fuchsias and hydrangeas, wisteria covered moongate, rose festooned curved pergola. Different romantic aspects, mixed borders, varied island beds. Attractive colourful containers, vegetable potagers; large variety of good foliage plants. Yr round interest with many birds, butterflies and insects. Home-made TEAS. *Adm £2.50, chd free. Sun, Wed 31 July; 3 Aug (2-6)*

⑤ Spring Cottage, Cranleigh ♿🐕🎨

(Mr & Mrs D E Norman) *1m N of Cranleigh. From Cranleigh Cricket Ground take rd signed Cranleigh School. Garden is ¼m N of Cranleigh School entrance. From Guildford take A 281 towards Horsham, follow signs to Cranleigh, turn L immed after roundabout into Smithwood Common Road. Garden 1¼m on R.* Come and see our 1¾ acre garden at tulip time. Spring bulbs in the woodland area and small meadow. Lovely views. Enjoy a mix of flowers and foliage, colours and shapes. Accommodation. Home-made TEAS Suns & BH Mon only. *Adm £2.50, chd free (share to Cranleigh Village Hospital Trust). Sun 1 May to Sun 8 May (11-5). Private visits welcome by appt May & June only. Tel 01483 272620*

⑤ Spurfold, Peaslake 🎨🙂

(Mr & Mrs A Barnes) *8m SE of Guildford. Take A25 to Shere. Turn R through Shere village & up hill. Over railway bridge 1st L to Peaslake. In Peaslake turn L after village stores Radnor Rd. Approx 500yds up single track lane to car park.* Approx 4 acres of garden and woodland, rhododendrons, azaleas, herbaceous, mixed borders, woodland walk, formal pond and terraces; new garden created at rear of house in 2001. Featured in '25 Beautiful Gardens' 2004. Home-made TEAS in aid of Peaslake Village School. *Adm £2.50, chd free. Sun 22 May (11-5).* **Evening Opening** *£4, wine, Wed 3 Aug (5-8). Private visits welcome by appt May to Aug. Not suitable for large coaches. Tel 01306 730196*

◆ Squerryes Court, Westerham ♿
See Kent.

⑤ Stuart Cottage, East Clandon ♿♿

(Mr & Mrs J M Leader) *4m E of Guildford. Off A246 or from Ripley - Rose Lane, follow yellow signs.* ½-acre partly walled garden with a few recent, changes to reflect C16 cottage. Wisteria and rose walks, intertwined with clematis, provide shade in this perfumed garden. Unusual herbaceous plants hide amongst the cottage garden favourites whilst rosemary and lavender edge the old brick paths. From the decorative organic kitchen garden, walk through the annually planted tunnel to the chequerboard orchard. Featured in '25 Beautiful Gardens' 2003. Cream TEAS in aid of charity. *Adm £2.50, chd free. Sun 14 Aug (11-5).* **Evening Opening** *£3.50, wine, Thur 7 July (6-8.30). Private visits welcome by appt for groups of 15 or more. Tel 01483 222689*

Sunningdale Park, Larch Avenue, Ascot
See Berkshire.

⑤ 35 Tadorne Road, Tadworth 🙂

(Dr & Mrs J R Lay) *6m S of Sutton. On A217 to large roundabout, 3m N of Junction 8 on M25. Take B2220 signposted Tadworth. Tadorne Rd 2nd on R.* ⅓-acre hedged garden with a colourful herbaceous border, shrubby island beds, rose and clematis-covered pergola leading to secluded seating area, potager-style vegetable plot, soft fruit, woodland corner, varied patio display and plant-filled conservatory. Home-made TEAS. *Adm £2, chd free. Sat, Sun 25, 26 June (2-6)*

⑤ Tanhouse Farm, Rusper Road, Newdigate ♿🙂

(Mr & Mrs N Fries) *8m S of Dorking. On A24 turn L at roundabout at Beare Green. R at T-junction in Newdigate 1st farm on R approx 2/3m.* Garden created by owners since 1987. 1 acre of rambling gardens surrounding a C16 house (not open). Rose gardens; herbaceous borders; small lake and stream with ducks and geese. Vegetable gardens which supply our own farm shop. Farm has sheep and small herd of pedigree Aberdeen Angus. Picnic area. Cream TEAS. *Adm £2.50, chd free. Sun 17 July (2-6)*

⑤ Tilford Cottage, Tilford 🙂

(Mr & Mrs R Burn) *3m SE of Farnham. From Farnham station along the Tilford Rd. Tilford Cottage is opp Tilford House. Parking on village green.* Approx 2 acres created by owners in an area of outstanding natural beauty. Mediterranean terrace, conservatory with pot plants, many running water features, carp pond, wildlife water meadow with 15 species of butterflies noted, bog garden, river walk, gravel, topiary, knot and herb gardens, oriental garden, hosta bed, dove cote, heather bed, Victorian-style glasshouse, fruit and vegetable garden, orchard, formal lawns, and plenty of garden seats to sit and rest. Art exhibition as part of Surrey Open Studios. Bring and Buy plant sale. Home-made TEAS. *Adm £5, chd & concessions £2.50. Sat, Sun, 4, 5 June (10.30-4); Mon 6 June (2-7). Private visits welcome by appt for groups of 10 or more. Tel 01252 795423 bobsitybee@aol.com*

⑥ ◆ Titsey Place Gardens, Titsey Hill, Oxted 🙂

(The Trustees of the Titsey Foundation) *3m N of Oxted. A25 between Oxted & Westerham, turn ? into Limpsfield Village down High St, turn L (on sharp bend) into Bluehouse Lane & R into Water Lane. Follow road under M25 through park to walled garden car park. Brown signs from A25 at Limpsfield.* One of the largest surviving estates in Surrey. Magnificent ancestral home and gardens of the Gresham family since 1534. Walled kitchen garden restored early 1990's. Golden jubilee rose garden. Etruscan summer house adjoining picturesque lakes and fountains. 15 acres of formal and informal gardens idyllic setting with the M25. Featured in 'Country Life' 2003; 'Surrey Monacle' 2004. House and garden adm £5, garden only £2.50, chd £1. May & Aug Bank Hols. Weds, Suns 11 May to 29 Sep. Garden only on Easter Mon. **For NGS** Sats 7 May; 18 June; 16 July; 10 Sep (1-5). Tel 01273 407056 Kate Moisson www.titsey.com

61 NEW Tollsworth Manor, Rook Lane, Chaldon 🅰🚫🅗
(Carol & Gordon Gillett) *2m W of Caterham. From Caterham-on-the-Hill, take B2031 through Chaldon. 300yds out of Chaldon take concrete farm track on L. Parking in farmyard beyond house.* Old-fashioned country garden, created from derelict site over 20yrs by present owners. Well-stocked herbaceous borders with old-fashioned roses, peonies, delphiniums. Wildlife pond and duck pond with ducks. Lovely views over surrounding farmland. Shetland pony. Home-made TEAS in aid of St Cathrines Hospice. *Adm £2.50, chd free. Sun 12 June (11-5)*

Treetops, Upper Froyle 🚫🅗
See Hampshire.

62 6 Upper Rose Hill, Dorking 🚫🅗
(Peter & Julia Williams) *Town Centre. From roundabout at A24/A25 junction follow signs to town centre. Turn L after Pizza Piazza. Parking available in rd & behind Sainsburys (5 min walk). ½-acre informal plantsman's terraced garden on dry sand. Surprising secluded setting with striking outlook onto St Pauls Church. Planted for yr-round interest of foliage and form; fruit and vegetables, gravel bed and alpine troughs, borders and rockeries. Autumn colour, grasses attractive into Oct. Many unusual plants for sale. Home-made TEAS in aid of Mid Surrey Crossroads. Adm £2.50, chd free. Sun 19 June (11-5.30). Private visits welcome by appt. Tel 01306 881315*

63 Vale End, Albury 🅗
(Mr & Mrs John Foulsham) *4m SE of Guildford. From Albury take A248 W for ¼m.* 1-acre walled garden on many levels in beautiful setting overlooking mill pond. Richly diverse planting of roses, shrubs, annuals and perennials on light sandy soil. Clipped yew walk with festooned rope swag, tiny courtyard, fruit, vegetable and herb garden. Mantled water cascade. Featured in *The Times' 2003.* Home-made TEAS. *Adm £2.50, chd free. Weds 8 June; 13 July (1-5).* **Evening Opening** *3.50, wine, Thur 9 June (6-8.30). Also opening with Waterloo Pond Gardens 15, 16 May. Private visits welcome by appt. Tel 01483 202296*

64 Vann, Hambledon 🅰🚫🅗
(Mrs M Caroe) *6m S of Godalming. A283 to Wormley. Turn L at Hambledon. Follow yellow Vann signs for 2m.* An English Heritage

registered garden of 4½ acres surrounding Tudor and William and Mary house (not open) with later additions and alterations by W D Caröe. Old cottage garden, pergola, ¼-acre pond, Gertrude Jekyll water garden 1911, azaleas, spring bulbs and woodland, mixed borders. Island beds, crinkle crankle wall. Maintained by owner with 2 days' help per week. Partially suitable for wheelchairs. Featured in 'Which' garden readers favourite 2003; 'Countryside Magazine'; 'The Garden' RHS journal 2004. Home-made TEAS (Mon 28 Mar only). *Adm £3.50, chd 50p. Mon 28 Mar to Sun 3 Apr (28 Mar 2-6); Sun 24 Apr to Sun 1 May; Sun 22 May to Sun 29 May (10-6). Private visits welcome by appt for groups of 15 or more, Mar to July. Tel 01428 683413*

Walbury, Lower Froyle 🅰🅗
See Hampshire.

65 Walton Poor, Ranmore 🅰🅗
(Nicholas & Prue Calvert) *6m NW of Dorking. From Dorking take rd to Ranmore, continue for approx 4m, after Xrds in dip 1m on L. From A246 at East Horsley go S into Greendene, 1st L Crocknorth Rd, 1m on R.* A deeply tranquil, almost secretive garden in N Downs. Area of Outstanding Natural Beauty. Paths wind between 4 acres of fine mature trees and colourful shrubs. Pond fringed with bold foliaged plants; hideaway dell; formal herb garden linked with the well known herb nursery. TEAS. *Adm £2.50, chd 50p. Mon 2 May; Suns 5 June; 31 July (11-6); 9 Oct (2-5). Private visits welcome by appt. Tel 01483 282273 wnscalvert@clara.co.uk*

66 Waterloo Pond Gardens, Albury 🅗
4m SE of Guildford. From Albury take A248 W for ¼m. Situated in a setting of outstanding natural beauty with river, pond and woodlands. Home-made TEAS at Vale End in aid of The Lychgate Trust. *Combined adm £3.50, chd free. Sun, Mon 15, 16 May (1-5)*

Swan Cottage 🚫🅗 (Carol Elms) Sheltered garden beneath steep hillside with beautiful view of pond and St Martha's Church. 1-acre garden being redesigned since 2000, features stream and bog garden, live willow arches, screen and patio - colourful.

Tillingbourne 🚫🅗 (Jim & Shirley Farrar) 2-acre woodland garden bordered by the R Tillingbourne. Aviaries with ornamental pheasants; several unusual

natural features in the woodland walk.

Vale End, Albury 🅗 (Mr & Mrs John Foulsham) 1-acre walled garden on many levels. Richly diverse spring garden.

67 Westways Farm, Gracious Pond Road, Chobham 🅰🅗
(Paul & Nicky Biddle) *4m N of Woking. From Chobham church proceed over roundabout towards Sunningdale, 1st Xrds R into Red Lion Rd to junction with Mincing Lane. Woodland not suitable for wheelchairs.* Open 8-acre garden surrounded by woodlands planted in the 1930s with mature and some rare rhododendrons, azaleas, camellias and magnolias, underplanted with bluebells, erythroniums, liliums and dogwood; extensive lawns and sunken pond garden. Working stables and sandschool. Lovely Queen Anne House (not open) covered with listed magnolia grandiflora. Home-made TEAS. *Adm £2, chd 50p. Sun 8 May (10-4). Private visits welcome by appt. Tel 01276 856163 prbiddle@hotmail.com*

Wheatley House, between Binsted and Kingsley 🅰🚫🅗
See Hampshire.

68 ◆ Winkworth Arboretum, Hascombe Road, nr Godalming 🅰
(The National Trust) *2m S of Godalming. On B side of B2130. Entrance with car park - Coaches (by written arrangement). Station: Godalming 3m.* 110 acres of rolling Surrey hillside set in a valley leading down to a reservoir and wetland area. Planted with rare trees and shrubs leading to impressive displays in spring with magnolias, azaleas and bluebells matched by the dramatic reds, golds and browns of maples, cherries etc during autumn. Limited wheelchair access. Light refreshments and TEAS in Tearoom. *Adm £4.50, chd £2. Family ticket £10 (2 adults & 3 chd). For NGS: Suns 1 May; 9 Oct (11-5). Tel 01483 208477 Rob Tyler winkwortharboretum@nationaltrust.org.uk*

69 Wintershall, Bramley 🅰🚫
(Mr & Mrs Peter Hutley) *3m S of Bramley Village. On A281 turn R, then next R. Wintershall Drive next on L. Bus: AV33 Guildford-Horsham; alight Palmers Cross, 1m.* 2-acre garden and 200 acres of park and woodland; bluebell walks in spring; wild daffodils; rhododendrons; specimen trees; lakes and flight ponds; superb views. Chapel of St Mary, stations of Cross,

Rosary Walk and St Francis Chapel. Cream TEAS in aid of HASTE. *Adm £3, chd £1. Suns 3 Apr; 8 May (2-5). Private visits welcome by appt. Tel 01483 892167 Susan Babbington susan@hutleygroup.com*

70 Woodbury Cottage, Colley Lane, Reigate ⊗⊕
(Shirley & Bob Stoneley) *1m W of Reigate. M25 junction 8, A217 (direction Reigate). Immed before level Xing turn R into Somers Rd, cont as Manor Rd. At very end turn R into Coppice Lane & follow signs to car park. Garden is 300yds walk from car park.* Cottage garden just under ¾-acre made and maintained by owners. Garden is stepped on slope with mixed harmonious planting, enhanced by its setting under Colley Hill. Still attractive in Sept. Home-made TEAS. *Adm £2.50, chd free. Sats, Suns 2, 3 July; 3, 4, Wed 7 Sept (Sats, Wed 2-5) (Suns 11-5).* **Evening Opening** *£3.50, wine, Fri 1 July (5-8). Private visits welcome by appt, for groups of 10+. Tel 01737 244235*

71 Woodcote Park Nursery, Send ⊗⊕
(Mrs E Gibbison) *4m E of Guildford. On the A246. Turn L, through E Clandon & continue on Ripley Rd -* *Nursery is opp HM Prison. From A3, turn L in Ripley, Rose Lane, then take 2nd R for 1m.* Small private plantsman's garden with many unusual shrubs used as host to a variety of clematis. Herbaceous borders. Light refreshments and TEAS. *Adm £2.50, chd free. Sun 22 May (10-4)*

72 Wotton House, Guildford Road, Dorking ⊗
(Hayley Conference Centres Ltd) *3m W of Dorking. On A25 between Dorking & Guildford. Gravel driveway (signed), adjacent to Wotton Hatch public house.* 20 acres of parkland featuring Italian garden created in 1640 by George Evelyn and designed by his brother John, the eminent designer and diarist. Terraced mount, classical garden temple, statuary, tortoise house (uninhabited), and grottoes. Recently restored and widely held to be the first example of an Italian-style garden in England. Home-made TEAS. *Adm £2.50, chd free. Suns 24, 31 July; 7, 14 Aug (11-4) www.hayley-conf.co.uk*

73 Yew Tree Cottage, Bunch Lane, Haslemere ⬥⊗⊕
(Mr & Mrs E E Bowyer) *1m N of Haslemere. Turn off High St into* *Church Lane, leave church on L, carry on up High Lane, then steeply downhill to Xrds turn L into Bunch Lane. Yew Tree Cottage first house on L.* 2-acre garden created by owners since 1976 on hillside. Large variety of trees and shrubs, water garden, heather bed, alpines, kitchen garden, Jacob and Shetland sheep, rare breed poultry, Shetland pony in paddock beyond garden. TEAS in aid of Macmillan Cancer Relief Midhurst. *Adm £2, chd £1. Sun 29 May (2-6). Private visits welcome by appt June & July. Tel 01428 644130*

Evening Opening (See also garden description)

58 Eastwood Road	3 June
The Copse Lodge	8 June
Vale End	9 June
Ashleigh Grange	24 June
Shepherds Lane Gardens	29 June
Woodbury Cottage	1 July
Stuart Cottage	7 July
Appletrees	9 July
The Round House	15 July
48 Gatesden Road	27 July
The Hopperty	3 August
Spurfold	3 August
The Copse Lodge	4 August
RHS Garden Wisley	23 August

ngs gardens open for charity

Music in the Garden

Take a stroll around the wonderful garden at Wisley enjoying the various musical entertainments at a special charity evening for The National Gardens Scheme by kind permission of the Royal Horticultural Society

Tuesday 23rd August 2005
6.00 – 9.00 pm

The Wisley Flower Show marquee will be open from 7.00 – 8.30pm
The Wisley Shop and Plant Centre will close at 8.30 pm

Admission £6
Children 15 and under free
Admission also applies to RHS members

The Terrace Restaurant and Conservatory Cafe will be open and if you wish to reserve a table for dinner in the Terrace Restaurant, please phone 01483 211773

Also a Barbecue (weather permitting)
Suggestion: Bring a torch – it will be dark when you leave

ADEQUATE PARKING
SORRY NO PICNICS INSIDE THE GARDEN

Sussex

County Organisers:
(East & Mid Sussex)

Janet Goldsmith, Sunnymead, Tapsells Lane, Wadhurst, Sussex TN5 6RS
Tel 01892 783264

(Press & Publicity Officer) West Sussex   Carrie McArdle, Message Cottage, Kirdford, West Sussex RH14 0JR Tel 01403 820272
Assistant County Organisers:
(East & Mid-Sussex)

Julia Ball, Turf Lodge, Sheep Plain, Crowborough TN6 3ST Tel 01892 655505
Miriam Book, Appledore, 50 Hill Drive, Hove BN3 6QL Tel 01273 541600
Rosemary Collins, Windwhistle, Faircrouch Lane, Wadhurst TN5 6PP Tel 01892 782243
Matty & Richard Holmes, Beauchamps, Float Lane, Udimore, Sussex TN31 6BY
Tel 01797 223055
Inyca Humphreys, Witherenden Mill, Station Road, Stonegate TN5 7EU Tel 01435 883444
Sophie Neal, Legsheath Farm, East Grinstead, Sussex RH19 4JN Tel 01342 810230
Jan Newman, Graywood House, Graywood, East Hoathly, Sussex East BN8 6QP
Tel 01825 872623
Jeannette Perry, 4 Elmsdown Place, Hailsham BN27 2AN Tel 01323 842408
Carolyn Steel, Beeches, Cuckfield Lane, Warninglid, East Sussex RH17 5UB
Tel 01444 461262
Janet Wood, Woodhill, Cross in Hand, Heathfield TN21 0TP Tel 01435 868209

West Sussex

Jane Burton, Church Farmhouse, Ford Water Road, Lavant, Chichester, Sussex PO18 0AL
Tel 01243 527822
Margaret Dales, Sands, Warnham, Horsham, West Sussex RH12 3SQ Tel 01403 254843
Judith Dean, 8 Wimblehurst Road, Horsham, W Sussex RH12 2ED Tel 01403 268166
Consie Dunn, Wildham, Stoughton, Chichester, West Sussex PO18 9JG Tel 01243 535202
Suzanna Gayford, Rymans, Apuldram Lane, Chichester, West Sussex PO20 7EG
Tel 01243 783147
Jane Lywood, Battlehurst Farm, Wisborough Green, West Sussex RH14 0LJ
Tel 01403 820225
Claudia Pearce, 17 Sheridan Road, Worthing BN14 8EU Tel 01903 601655
Susan Pinder, 30 Townfield, Kirdford, West Sussex RH14 0LZ Tel 01403 820430
Sue Shipway, Badger's End, Northchapel, West Sussex GU28 9HX Tel 01428 707467

County Treasurers:
(East & Mid Sussex)

David Goldsmith, Sunnymead, Tapsells Lane, Wadhurst, E Sussex TN5 6RS
Tel 01892 783264

(West Sussex)

Peter Edwards, Quince Cottage, The Street, Bury, Pulborough, West Sussex RH20 1PA
Tel 01798 831900

Maps: Numbers shown next to each garden entry refer to that garden's entry on the county map. This position is approximate;
distance and directions from the nearest main town are generally shown in the garden text.
A precise location is available for those gardens featured on the NGS website by visiting www.ngs.org.uk.

Symbols: Information relating to symbols is given on page 21

DATES OF OPENING

Evening openings
See end of county listing

Private gardens open regularly for NGS
Bignor Park, Pulborough *(18)*
Whitehouse Cottage, Staplefield *(149)*

Gardens open to the public
For details see garden description
Alfriston Clergy House, Alfriston *(4)*
Arundel Castle, Arundel *(7)*
Bateman's, Burwash *(13)*
Charleston, Nr Firle *(30)*
Cookscroft, Earnley *(37)*
Great Dixter, Northiam *(56)*
High Beeches, Handcross *(63)*
Highdown, Goring-by-Sea *(64)*
Merriments Gardens, Hurst Green *(83)*
Moorlands, Friar's Gate, nr Crowborough
(85)

Nymans Garden, Handcross *(91)*
Parham Gardens, Storrington, nr
Pulborough *(98)*
The Priest House, West Hoathly *(111)*
Sheffield Park Garden, Sheffield Park *(126)*
St Mary's House & Gardens, Bramber *(132)*
Standen, East Grinstead *(133)*
Uppark, South Harting *(140)*
West Dean Gardens, West Dean *(144)*

By appointment only
*For telephone number and other
details see garden description.
Private visits welcomed*
Alcheringa, West Chiltington *(3)*
Eastergate House, Eastergate *(45)*
8 Felbridge Court, East Grinstead *(47)*
Pine Cottage, Pulborough *(109)*
Sherburne House, Eartham, nr Chichester
(127)
Whitehouse Cottage, Staplefield *(149)*

February 13 Sunday
Mitchmere Farm, Stoughton *(84)*

February 15 Tuesday
Mitchmere Farm, Stoughton *(84)*

February 17 Thursday
Mitchmere Farm, Stoughton *(84)*

February 20 Sunday
Mitchmere Farm, Stoughton *(84)*

March 6 Sunday
Champs Hill, Coldwaltham *(28)*
Dormers, West Marden *(41)*

March 13 Sunday
Champs Hill, Coldwaltham *(28)*

March 19 Saturday
The Manor of Dean, Pitshill, Tillington *(78)*
Rymans, Apuldram *(117)*

March 20 Sunday
The Manor of Dean, Pitshill, Tillington *(78)*
Penns in the Rocks, Groombridge *(104)*
Rymans, Apuldram *(117)*

March 27 Sunday (Easter)
Bignor Park, Pulborough *(18)*
March 28 Monday (Easter)
Bignor Park, Pulborough *(18)*
April 2 Saturday
Hampton Cottage, Fittleworth *(61)*
April 3 Sunday
Berri Court, Yapton *(16)*
Firle Place, Lewes *(49)*
Hampton Cottage, Fittleworth *(61)*
Northwood Farmhouse, Pulborough *(90)*
April 4 Monday
Berri Court, Yapton *(16)*
Northwood Farmhouse, Pulborough *(90)*
April 6 Wednesday
Bignor Park, Pulborough *(18)*
Bradstow Lodge, Ifold *(22)*
April 10 Sunday
Bates Green, Arlington *(14)*
Bradstow Lodge, Ifold *(22)*
Charleston, Nr Firle *(30)*
Newtimber Place, Newtimber *(89)*
April 13 Wednesday
Bignor Park, Pulborough *(18)*
April 20 Wednesday
Bignor Park, Pulborough *(18)*
April 23 Saturday
Hampton Cottage, Fittleworth *(61)*
The Manor of Dean, Pitshill, Tillington *(78)*
18 Pavilion Road, Worthing *(100)*
April 24 Sunday
Hampton Cottage, Fittleworth *(61)*
The Manor of Dean, Pitshill, Tillington *(78)*
Offham House, Offham *(92)*
The Old Post Office, Coldwaltham *(93)*
Sandhill Farm House, Rogate *(119)*
Warren House, Crowborough *(142)*
April 27 Wednesday
Bignor Park, Pulborough *(18)*
46 Westup Farm Cottages, Balcombe *(147)*
April 30 Saturday
Down Place, South Harting *(42)*
18 Pavilion Road, Worthing *(100)*
Sackville College Gardens, East Grinstead *(118)*
May 1 Sunday
4 Birch Close, Arundel *(19)*
Down Place, South Harting *(42)*
Frith Lodge, Northchapel *(54)*
Malt House, Chithurst *(77)*
Peasmarsh Place, Peasmarsh *(101)*
Sackville College Gardens, East Grinstead *(118)*
Stonehealed Farm, Streat *(135)*
May 2 Monday (Bank Hol)
Ashburnham Place, Battle *(8)*
4 Birch Close, Arundel *(19)*
Down Place, South Harting *(42)*
Malt House, Chithurst *(77)*
Stonehealed Farm, Streat *(135)*
Warren House, Crowborough *(142)*
May 3 Tuesday
Fittleworth House, Fittleworth *(51)*
Sheffield Park Garden, Sheffield Park *(126)*
May 4 Wednesday
Bignor Park, Pulborough *(18)*

May 5 Thursday
Meadow Cottage, Staplefield *(82)*
Uppark, South Harting *(140)*
May 6 Friday
Stone Cross House, Crowborough *(134)*
May 7 Saturday
Adur Lodge, Shoreham-by-Sea *(2)*
Meadow Cottage, Staplefield *(82)*
18 Pavilion Road, Worthing *(100)*
May 8 Sunday
Ansty Gardens *(6)*
Ashdown Park Hotel, Wych Cross *(9)*
Berri Court, Yapton *(16)*
Champs Hill, Coldwaltham *(28)*
Dormers, West Marden *(41)*
Framfield Grange, Framfield *(53)*
Hammerwood House, Iping *(60)*
Malt House, Chithurst *(77)*
Mountfield Court, nr Robertsbridge *(87)*
Palatine Gardens, Worthing *(97)*
Rosemary Cottage, Cross In Hand *(115)*
Stone Cross House, Crowborough *(134)*
May 9 Monday
Berri Court, Yapton *(16)*
Mountfield Court, nr Robertsbridge *(87)*
May 10 Tuesday
Fittleworth House, Fittleworth *(51)*
May 11 Wednesday
Bateman's, Burwash *(13)*
Bignor Park, Pulborough *(18)*
Hawkhurst House, Wisborough Green *(62)*
May 12 Thursday
Little Dene, Chelwood Gate *(74)*
Lowder Mill, Fernhurst *(76)*
May 13 Friday
Champs Hill, Coldwaltham **(Evening)** *(28)*
Little Dene, Chelwood Gate *(74)*
May 14 Saturday
Birchanger Gardens, Balcombe *(20)*
Champs Hill, Coldwaltham *(28)*
Ham Cottage, Highbrook, Ardingly *(59)*
The Manor of Dean, Pitshill, Tillington *(78)*
May 15 Sunday
Champs Hill, Coldwaltham *(28)*
Cowdray Park Gardens, Midhurst *(38)*
Ham Cottage, Highbrook, Ardingly *(59)*
Hammerwood House, Iping *(60)*
The Manor of Dean, Pitshill, Tillington *(78)*
Mount Harry House & Mount Harry Lodge, Offham *(86)*
Nymans Garden, Handcross *(91)*
Selehurst, Lower Beeding *(123)*
Trotton Old Rectory, Trotton *(139)*
May 17 Tuesday
Fittleworth House, Fittleworth *(51)*
Standen, East Grinstead *(133)*
May 18 Wednesday
Bignor Park, Pulborough *(18)*
Hawkhurst House, Wisborough Green *(62)*
May 21 Saturday
Ham Cottage, Highbrook, Ardingly *(59)*
May 22 Sunday
Baker's House, Shipley *(10)*
Bardown Oast Farm, Stonegate *(12)*
Coates Manor, Fittleworth *(34)*
Filliams Bungalow, Kirdford *(48)*
Fishers Farm, Etchingham *(50)*

Gardeners Cottage, West Dean *(55)*
Ham Cottage, Highbrook, Ardingly *(59)*
Legsheath Farm, nr Forest Row *(73)*
18 Pavilion Road, Worthing *(100)*
Tinkers Bridge Cottage, Ticehurst *(137)*
May 24 Tuesday
Fittleworth House, Fittleworth *(51)*
May 25 Wednesday
Bignor Park, Pulborough *(18)*
46 Westup Farm Cottages, Balcombe *(147)*
May 28 Saturday
Duckyls Holt, West Hoathly *(43)*
18 Pavilion Road, Worthing *(100)*
The Priest House, West Hoathly *(111)*
White Rock, West Hoathly *(148)*
May 29 Sunday
Brighton & Hove Clematis Gardens *(24)*
Cookscroft, Earnley *(37)*
Duckyls Holt, West Hoathly *(43)*
High Beeches, Handcross *(63)*
Rose Cottage, Hadlow Down *(114)*
Roundhill Cottage, East Dean **(Day & Evening)** *(116)*
Rymans, Apuldram *(117)*
White Rock, West Hoathly *(148)*
May 30 Monday (Bank Hol)
Cookscroft, Earnley *(37)*
Highdown, Goring-by-Sea *(64)*
Roundhill Cottage, East Dean *(116)*
Rymans, Apuldram *(117)*
Warren House, Crowborough *(142)*
May 31 Tuesday
West Dean Gardens, West Dean *(144)*
June 1 Wednesday
6 Plantation Rise, Worthing *(110)*
Sparrow Hatch, nr Newick *(131)*
Wildham, East Marden/Stoughton *(150)*
June 2 Thursday
Sparrow Hatch, nr Newick *(131)*
Uppark, South Harting *(140)*
Wildham, East Marden/Stoughton *(150)*
June 3 Friday
Five Oaks Cottage, West Burton *(52)*
Great Lywood Farmhouse, Ardingly *(57)*
Siggle Wriggle, Chiddingly/Hailsham *(128)*

ngs gardens open for charity
Your garden in the Yellow Book?
The NGS is always interested to hear of gardens with potential, large or small, that might open in the future.

For more information about opening your garden, please contact the County Organiser in your area, preferably at the time of year that you would like your garden to open.

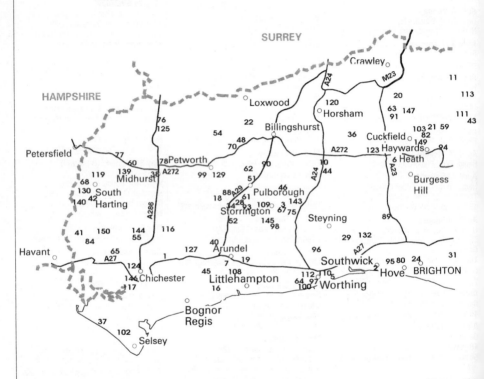

June 4 Saturday
Beauchamps, Udimore **(Evening)** *(15)*
51 Carlisle Road, Eastbourne *(27)*
Collington Gardens, Bexhill *(35)*
Hobbs Barton, Framfield, nr Uckfield *(66)*
Hurston Place, Pulborough *(67)*
King John's Lodge, Etchingham *(71)*
The Martlets Hospice, Hove *(80)*
Siggle Wriggle, Chiddingly/Hailsham *(128)*

June 5 Sunday
Beauchamps, Udimore *(15)*
Berri Court, Yapton *(16)*
Buckles, Burwash Common *(25)*
51 Carlisle Road, Eastbourne *(27)*
Clinton Lodge, Fletching *(33)*
Frith Lodge, Northchapel *(54)*
Great Lywood Farmhouse, Ardingly *(57)*
Hailsham Grange, Hailsham *(58)*

Hobbs Barton, Framfield, nr Uckfield *(66)*
Hurston Place, Pulborough *(67)*
King John's Lodge, Etchingham *(71)*
The Martlets Hospice, Hove *(80)*
Northwood Farmhouse, Pulborough *(90)*
Offham House, Offham *(92)*
6 Park Terrace, Tillington *(99)*
Sackville College Gardens, East Grinstead
   (118)

June 6 Monday
Berri Court, Yapton *(16)*
Buckles, Burwash Common *(25)*
Clinton Lodge, Fletching *(33)*
Hobbs Barton, Framfield, nr Uckfield *(66)*
Hurston Place, Pulborough *(67)*
Northwood Farmhouse, Pulborough *(90)*

June 7 Tuesday
Fittleworth House, Fittleworth *(51)*

June 8 Wednesday
Filliams Bungalow, Kirdford *(48)*
Parham Gardens, Storrington, nr
   Pulborough *(98)*

June 9 Thursday
Charleston, Nr Firle **(Evening)** *(30)*
Parham Gardens, Storrington, nr
   Pulborough *(98)*
6 Park Terrace, Tillington **(Evening)** *(99)*

June 10 Friday
Penland Farmhouse, Cuckfield *(103)*

June 11 Saturday
Chantry Green House, Steyning *(29)*
Frith Lodge, Northchapel **(Evening)** *(54)*
Kent House, East Harting *(68)*
The Old Post Office, Coldwaltham
   (Evening) *(93)*
Sennicotts, Chichester *(124)*

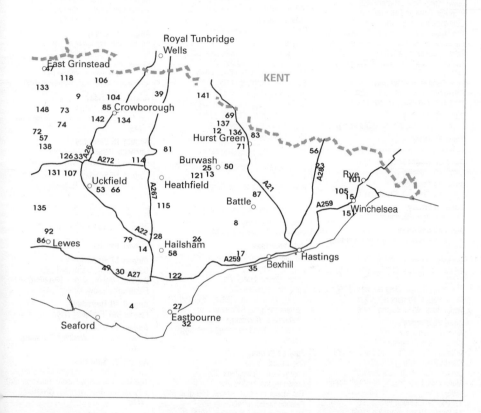

somerset Lodge, Petworth *(129)*
South Harting Gardens *(130)*
Swiftsden Farm Oast, Hurst Green *(136)*

June 12 Sunday
Ambrose Place Back Gardens, Richmond
Road, Worthing *(5)*
Chantry Green House, Steyning *(29)*
Dale Park House, Madehurst *(40)*
illiams Bungalow, Kirdford *(48)*
rith Lodge, Northchapel *(54)*
ent House, East Harting *(68)*
etleys, Flimwell *(69)*
Mayfield Gardens *(81)*
Park Terrace, Tillington *(99)*
8 Pavilion Road, Worthing *(100)*
enland Farmhouse, Cuckfield *(103)*
erryfield House, Udimore *(105)*

Sackville College Gardens, East Grinstead
(Evening) *(118)*
Sands, Warnham *(120)*
Somerset Lodge, Petworth *(129)*
South Harting Gardens *(130)*
Swiftsden Farm Oast, Hurst Green *(136)*
Town Place, Freshfield *(138)*

June 13 Monday
Somerset Lodge, Petworth *(129)*

June 14 Tuesday
Fittleworth House, Fittleworth *(51)*
4 Hillside Cottages, West Stoke **(Evening)**
(65)
Somerset Lodge, Petworth *(129)*

June 15 Wednesday
Rose Cottage, Hadlow Down **(Evening)**
(114)
Somerset Lodge, Petworth *(129)*

June 16 Thursday
Alfriston Clergy House, Alfriston **(Evening)**
(4)
Somerset Lodge, Petworth *(129)*
Town Place, Freshfield *(138)*

June 17 Friday
Clinton Lodge, Fletching *(33)*
Down Place, South Harting *(42)*
Ketleys, Flimwell **(Evening)** *(69)*
Somerset Lodge, Petworth *(129)*

June 18 Saturday
Bexhill Gardens *(17)*
Down Place, South Harting *(42)*
Hampton Cottage, Fittleworth *(61)*
The Manor of Dean, Pitshill, Tillington *(78)*
Old Scaynes Hill House, Scaynes Hill *(94)*
18 Pavilion Road, Worthing *(100)*

Penland Farmhouse, Cuckfield **(Evening)** *(103)*
The Pykle, Worthing **(Day & Evening)** *(112)*
Somerset Lodge, Petworth *(129)*
Winchelsea's Secret Gardens *(151)*

June 19 Sunday
Baker's House, Shipley *(10)*
Bexhill Gardens *(17)*
Chelmsford Lodge, Eastbourne *(32)*
Down Place, South Harting *(42)*
Hampton Cottage, Fittleworth *(61)*
Little Wantley, Storrington *(75)*
The Manor of Dean, Pitshill, Tillington *(78)*
Old Scaynes Hill House, Scaynes Hill *(94)*
Palatine Gardens, Worthing *(97)*
The Pykle, Worthing **(Day & Evening)** *(112)*
Rose Cottage, Hadlow Down *(114)*
Somerset Lodge, Petworth *(129)*
Trotton Old Rectory, Trotton *(139)*

June 20 Monday
Palatine Gardens, Worthing **(Evening)** *(97)*

June 21 Tuesday
Fittleworth House, Fittleworth *(51)*

June 22 Wednesday
Latchetts, Danehill *(72)*

June 23 Thursday
Latchetts, Danehill **(Evening)** *(72)*

June 24 Friday
Clinton Lodge, Fletching *(33)*

June 25 Saturday
51 Carlisle Road, Eastbourne **(Evening)** *(27)*
Duckyls Holt, West Hoathly *(43)*
18 Pavilion Road, Worthing **(Evening)** *(100)*
The Priest House, West Hoathly *(111)*
Ridge House, Turners Hill *(113)*
White Rock, West Hoathly *(148)*

June 26 Sunday
Ansty Gardens *(6)*
Bates Green, Arlington *(14)*
Brighton & Hove Clematis Gardens *(24)*
Chattri View, Hollingbury *(31)*
Duckyls Holt, West Hoathly *(43)*
Moorlands, Friar's Gate, nr Crowborough *(85)*
13 The Oval, Findon Village *(96)*
18 Pavilion Road, Worthing *(100)*
33 Peerley Road, East Wittering *(102)*
Pheasants Hatch, Piltdown *(107)*
Ridge House, Turners Hill *(113)*
Town Place, Freshfield *(138)*
White Rock, West Hoathly *(148)*

June 27 Monday
Pheasants Hatch, Piltdown *(107)*

June 28 Tuesday
Fittleworth House, Fittleworth *(51)*

June 29 Wednesday
Sands, Warnham **(Evening)** *(120)*
46 Westup Farm Cottages, Balcombe *(147)*

July 1 Friday
Clinton Lodge, Fletching *(33)*
Hampton Cottage, Fittleworth **(Evening)** *(61)*
Rose Cottage, Hadlow Down **(Evening)** *(114)*

July 3 Sunday
Hailsham Grange, Hailsham *(58)*
Nymans Garden, Handcross *(91)*
Town Place, Freshfield *(138)*

July 5 Tuesday
Fittleworth House, Fittleworth *(51)*

July 6 Wednesday
Sparrow Hatch, nr Newick *(131)*

July 7 Thursday
Berri Court, Yapton **(Evening)** *(16)*
Sparrow Hatch, nr Newick *(131)*

July 8 Friday
Clinton Lodge, Fletching *(33)*

July 9 Saturday
Bankton Cottage, Crawley Down *(11)*
Kent House, East Harting *(68)*
18 Pavilion Road, Worthing *(100)*
The Pykle, Worthing *(112)*

July 10 Sunday
Bankton Cottage, Crawley Down *(11)*
Filliams Bungalow, Kirdford *(48)*
Kent House, East Harting *(68)*
Merriments Gardens, Hurst Green *(83)*
The Pykle, Worthing *(112)*
Town Place, Freshfield *(138)*
Villa Elisabetta, Cousley Wood, Wadhurst *(141)*
West Chiltington Village Gardens *(143)*

July 12 Tuesday
Fittleworth House, Fittleworth *(51)*

July 14 Thursday
Town Place, Freshfield *(138)*

July 15 Friday
Latchetts, Danehill *(72)*

July 16 Saturday
Crown House, Eridge *(39)*
Latchetts, Danehill *(72)*
The Manor of Dean, Pitshill, Tillington *(78)*
Parham Gardens, Storrington, nr Pulborough **(Evening)** *(98)*
18 Pavilion Road, Worthing **(Evening)** *(100)*

July 17 Sunday
Ansty Gardens *(6)*
Chattri View, Hollingbury *(31)*
Crown House, Eridge *(39)*
The Manor of Dean, Pitshill, Tillington *(78)*
Palatine Gardens, Worthing *(97)*
18 Pavilion Road, Worthing *(100)*
Shalford House, Kingsley Green *(125)*
West Chiltington Village Gardens *(143)*

July 18 Monday
Palatine Gardens, Worthing **(Evening)** *(97)*

July 19 Tuesday
Fittleworth House, Fittleworth *(51)*

July 23 Saturday
18 Pavilion Road, Worthing *(100)*

July 24 Sunday
64 Old Shoreham Road, Hove *(95)*
Westgate Close, Chichester *(146)*

July 26 Tuesday
Westgate Close, Chichester **(Evening)** *(146)*

July 29 Friday
Ebbsworth, Nutbourne *(46)*
St Mary's House & Gardens, Bramber *(132)*

July 30 Saturday
Ebbsworth, Nutbourne *(46)*
St Mary's House & Gardens, Bramber *(132)*

July 31 Sunday
4 Hillside Cottages, West Stoke *(65)*
18 Pavilion Road, Worthing *(100)*

August 5 Friday
Clinton Lodge, Fletching *(33)*

August 6 Saturday
Bignor Park, Pulborough *(18)*
18 Pavilion Road, Worthing *(100)*
Sayerlands, Polegate *(122)*

August 7 Sunday
Bignor Park, Pulborough *(18)*
Champs Hill, Coldwaltham *(28)*
Charleston, Nr Firle *(30)*
13 The Oval, Findon Village *(96)*
33 Peerley Road, East Wittering *(102)*

August 12 Friday
Latchetts, Danehill *(72)*
West Lodge South, Rackham **(Evening)** *(145)*

August 13 Saturday
Latchetts, Danehill *(72)*
Perryhill Farmhouse, Hartfield *(106)*

August 14 Sunday
2 Adelaide Cottages, Halnaker *(1)*
Brickwall, Northiam *(23)*
Champs Hill, Coldwaltham *(28)*
Durrance Manor, Shipley *(44)*
Filliams Bungalow, Kirdford *(48)*
Penns in the Rocks, Groombridge *(104)*
Perryhill Farmhouse, Hartfield *(106)*

August 17 Wednesday
Colwood House, Warninglid *(36)*
Durrance Manor, Shipley **(Evening)** *(44)*
Filliams Bungalow, Kirdford *(48)*

August 18 Thursday
Lowder Mill, Fernhurst *(76)*

August 19 Friday
6 Plantation Rise, Worthing **(Evening)** *(110)*

August 20 Saturday
Butlers Farmhouse, Herstmonceux *(26)*
The Manor of Dean, Pitshill, Tillington *(78)*
6 Plantation Rise, Worthing **(Evening)** *(110)*

August 21 Sunday
Butlers Farmhouse, Herstmonceux *(26)*
Colwood House, Warninglid *(36)*
The Manor of Dean, Pitshill, Tillington *(78)*
18 Pavilion Road, Worthing *(100)*

August 26 Friday
Five Oaks Cottage, West Burton **(Evening)** *(52)*
Ham Cottage, Highbrook, Ardingly **(Evening)** *(59)*

August 27 Saturday
18 Pavilion Road, Worthing *(100)*

August 29 Monday (Bank Hol)
New Barn, Egdean *(88)*
Pindars, Lyminster *(108)*
Warren House, Crowborough *(142)*

September 3 Saturday
Five Oaks Cottage, West Burton *(52)*

September 4 Sunday
Newtimber Place, Newtimber *(89)*
6 Park Terrace, Tillington **(Day & Evening)**
(99)
18 Pavilion Road, Worthing *(100)*

September 7 Wednesday
Bateman's, Burwash *(13)*

September 10 Saturday
Hampton Cottage, Fittleworth *(61)*
18 Pavilion Road, Worthing *(100)*
Rymans, Apuldram *(117)*

September 11 Sunday
Bates Green, Arlington *(14)*
Hampton Cottage, Fittleworth *(61)*
Kiln Copse Farm, Kirdford *(70)*
Marchants Hardy Plants, Laughton *(79)*
Pindars, Lyminster *(108)*
Rymans, Apuldram *(117)*
Sarah Raven's Cutting Garden, Brightling
(121)
Stonehealed Farm, Streat *(135)*

September 12 Monday
Pindars, Lyminster *(108)*
Stonehealed Farm, Streat *(135)*

September 13 Tuesday
Fittleworth House, Fittleworth *(51)*

September 17 Saturday
The Manor of Dean, Pitshill, Tillington *(78)*
Sandhill Farm House, Rogate *(119)*

September 18 Sunday
The Manor of Dean, Pitshill, Tillington *(78)*
Merriments Gardens, Hurst Green *(83)*
18 Pavilion Road, Worthing *(100)*
West Lodge South, Rackham *(145)*

September 22 Thursday
Borde Hill Garden, Park & Woodland,
Haywards Heath *(21)*

September 24 Saturday
18 Pavilion Road, Worthing *(100)*

September 25 Sunday
Five Oaks Cottage, West Burton *(52)*

October 1 Saturday
High Beeches, Handcross *(63)*

October 2 Sunday
The Old Post Office, Coldwaltham *(93)*

October 4 Tuesday
Sheffield Park Garden, Sheffield Park *(126)*

October 5 Wednesday
Signor Park, Pulborough *(18)*

October 8 Saturday
The Manor of Dean, Pitshill, Tillington *(78)*

October 9 Sunday
The Manor of Dean, Pitshill, Tillington *(78)*

October 12 Wednesday
Signor Park, Pulborough *(18)*

October 18 Tuesday
Standen, East Grinstead *(133)*

October 19 Wednesday
gnor Park, Pulborough *(18)*

October 23 Sunday
Peasmarsh Place, Peasmarsh *(101)*

October 26 Wednesday
gnor Park, Pulborough *(18)*

2006
February 12 Sunday
Mitchmere Farm, Stoughton *(84)*

February 14 Tuesday
Mitchmere Farm, Stoughton *(84)*

February 19 Sunday
Mitchmere Farm, Stoughton *(84)*

DESCRIPTIONS OF GARDENS

❶ 2 Adelaide Cottages, Halnaker
🚻⊕
(Mrs Joan Mezulis) *3½m NE of
Chichester. On A285. 200yds on L
after Anglesey Arms PH. Off street
parking.* Unexpected, hidden garden
of ½ acre at end of path. Blaze of
summer colour in herbaceous
borders; vegetables from unusual
seeds brought from Latvia. Wide
variety of trees and shrubs, set in a
tranquil paddock. Small pond with
goldfish, frogs, water snails etc.
Owner maintained. TEAS. *Adm £2,
chd free. Sun 14 Aug (2-6). Private
visits welcome by appt. Tel 01243
773685*

**❷ NEW Adur Lodge, The Street,
Shoreham-by-Sea** 🚻🐕⊕
(Jeremy & Gilda Buckwell) *2m W of
Southwick. From A27 on Shoreham
bypass take A283 exit 5 signed
Shoreham. 1st L to Upper Shoreham
Rd, immed L into St Nicholas Lane
then R into The Street.* Walled garden
with herbaceous beds, shrubs,
vegetables and conservatory. Judas
tree a feature. Home-made TEAS in
aid of Macmillan Cancer Relief. *Adm
£2.50, chd free. Sat 7 May (11-5)*

❸ Alcheringa, West Chiltington
🐕⊕
(Trevor & Ksenia Watts) *3m N of
Storrington. From Pulborough turn
off A283 into West Chiltington Rd
then R into Monkmead Lane, L into
Nyetimber Lane. B2139 from
Storrington L into Fryern Rd; L into
Monkmead Lane, then R into
Nyetimber Lane.* Mature woodland
garden within ¾-acre site with
framework of unusual trees and
shrubs, providing sheltered
environment for many tender species.
Some outstanding specimen plants,
plant list exceeds 1000. Herb,
vegetable, fruit gardens, pond and
fernery. Featured in 'Garden News'
2003 & '25 Beautiful Gardens' 2004.
*Adm £2, chd £1. Private visits
welcome by appt, for 4 or more.
Tel 01798 812549*

**❹ ◆ Alfriston Clergy House,
Alfriston** 🐕⊕
(The National Trust) *4m NE of
Seaford. Just E of B2108, in Alfriston*
*village, adjoining The Tye & St
Andrew's Church. Bus: RDH 125
from Lewes, Autopoint 126 from
Eastbourne & Seaford.* Enjoy the
scent of roses and pinks in a tranquil
setting with views across the
meandering R Cuckmere. Visit this
C14 thatched Wealden 'Hall House',
the first building to be acquired by
the National Trust in 1896. Our
gardener will be available to talk to
you and welcome you to this peaceful
cottage garden. *Adm £3.10, chd
£1.55, family £7.25. Sat, Sun 5 Mar
to 13 Mar (11-4); 18 Mar to 31 Oct
(10-5) closed Tues & Fris; 2 Nov to
18 Dec (11-4) closed Tues & Fris .*
For NGS: Evening Opening *£3.10 soft
drink incl, Thur 16 June (5-8) .
Tel 01323 870001
alfriston@nationaltrust.org.uk*

**❺ Ambrose Place Back Gardens,
Richmond Road, Worthing**
*Take Broadwater Rd into town
centre, turn R at T-lights into
Richmond Rd opp Library; small
town gardens with entrances on L;
parking in rds.* TEAS at Way-In Cafe,
Worthing Tabernacle Church. Tea &
cake tickets only at 10 Ambrose Place
£1.50. *Combined adm £3, chd under
14 free. Sun 12 June (11-1 - 2-5)*

1 Ambrose Place 🐕⊕ (Mrs M M
Rosenberg) Walled garden;
shrubs, pond, climbing plants.

3 Ambrose Place 🐕 (Tim &
Fiona Reynoldson) Borders with
pond and summerhouse.

4 Ambrose Place 🐕 (Mrs J
Green) Paved garden, raised
herbaceous borders, lawn and
flowering summer plants.

5 Ambrose Place 🐕⊕ (Mr &
Mrs P Owen) Paved town garden
with raised borders, variety of
flowering shrubs and herbaceous
plants.

6 Ambrose Place 🚻 (Mrs S
Evans) Lawned garden with
charming colourful borders and
summerhouse.

7 Ambrose Place 🐕 (Mark &
Susan Frost) Small courtyard
garden, with conservatory.
Featured in 'Amateur Gardener'
2004.

9 Ambrose Place ⊕ (Mr & Mrs
D Irvine) Small town garden with
courtyard, greenhouse and
interesting water feature.

10 Ambrose Place 🐕⊕ (Mr &
Mrs A Pringle) Paved garden with
well stocked borders and pond.

11 Ambrose Place 🐕 (Mrs M
Stewart) Roses, summerhouse,
flowering plants.

13 Ambrose Place ⊠ (L Gamble) Courtyard garden with colourful seasonal flowers.

Ambrose Villa ⊠ (Mr & Mrs M Potter) Secluded town garden, pond, statues, shrubs and perennials.

❻ Ansty Gardens
3m W of Haywards Heath. On A272. 1m E of A23. Start in car park signposted in Ansty village. TEAS at The Barn House in May, Appletree Cottage in June, Whydown Cottage in July in aid of St Peter's & St James' Hospice, Ansty Village Hall Trust, Chichester Diocesan Assoc & Family Support Work (Knowles Tooth). Strawberry Cream Tea in June. Combined *adm £3, chd free. Suns 8 May, 26 June, 17 July (1.30-6)*

Apple Tree Cottage, Deaks Lane ⊠⊕ (Mr & Mrs G J Longfield) Cottage garden, herbaceous borders, mature trees, vegetable garden. '25 Beautiful Gardens' feature 2003.

NEW **The Barn House** 🕭 (Michael & Jackie Dykes) At the rear lovely views to Cuckfield across the valley. Wildlife pond surrounded by azaleas, through to a small pretty walled garden, formal design, informal planting.

Brenfield, Bolney Road 🕭⊕ (Dr & Mrs A Mace) Major private collection of cacti and succulents.

Leafield, Bolney Road ⊠⊕ (Mr & Mrs Paul Dupée) 2½ acres. Rockery and herbaceous borders, incl many hardy geraniums, acers, eucalyptus and young olive, lemon and fig trees. Meadow and woodland areas. Exhibition of owner's contemporary watercolours of flowers. *Not open 17 July*

Netherby (Mr & Mrs R Gilbert) Cottage garden.

Whydown Cottage, Bolney Road ⊠⊕ (Mrs M Gibson & Lance Gibson) 1-acre woodland garden, with water features. Many unusual trees, incl an embothrium. Ideas for the smaller garden. Featured in 'Amateur Gardening' 2003.

❼ ♦ Arundel Castle, Arundel 🕭🕭
(Arundel Castle Trustees Ltd) *In the middle of Arundel town.* Home of the Duke and Duchess of Norfolk. 40 acres of grounds and gardens. 2 restored Victorian glasshouses with exotic fruit and vegetables. Walled flower and kitchen gardens, with architectural plants and wrought iron features. Specialising in unusual

tender perennials and plants for mild climates. Fitzalan Chapel white garden. Light refreshments and TEAS. *House and Garden adm £11, chd/concessions £7.50, Garden only adm £6.50. Apr to Oct (11-5). Tel 01903 882173 www.arundelcastle.org*

❽ Ashburnham Place, Battle 🕭⊠⊕
(Mr Rhod Jones - Ashburnham Christian Trust) *5m W of Battle. On A271 (formerly B2204).* 220 acres of landscaped grounds and gardens originally designed by 'Capability' Brown. Glorious views over 3 lakes, with bridge and terraces designed by George Dance. Features incl scented prayer garden, working kitchen gardens within 4-acre walled garden and C19 winter garden. Lakeside and woodland walks. Cream TEAS. *Adm £2.50, chd 50p. Mon 2 May (1-5). Tel 01424 892244 www.ashburnham.org.uk*

❾ Ashdown Park Hotel, Wych Cross ⊠
(Mr Kevin Sweet) *6m S of E Grinstead. Take A22, 3m S of Forest Row turn L at Wych Cross by garage, 1m on R. From M25 take M23 S & leave at J10 taking A264 to E Grinstead. Approach from S on A22, turn R at Wych Cross.* 186 acres surrounding Ashdown Park Hotel. Parkland setting, mixture of woodland walks, water gardens and walled garden with glasshouse. Fine mature specimen trees, terraced lawns leading to carp-filled lake. Restored 'Secret Garden'. Peaceful oasis in the heart of Ashdown Forest. Gardens and grounds under 7yr restoration plan. TEAS. *Adm £2.50, chd free. Sun 8 May (2-6)*

❿ Baker's House, Shipley ⊠⊕
(Mr & Mrs Mark Burrell) *5m S of Horsham. Take A24 to Worthing, then A272 W, 2nd turn to Dragon's Green, L at George & Dragon PH, Baker's Lane then 300yds on L.* Large Wealden garden, lake, laburnum tunnel, shrubs, trees, rose walks of old-fashioned roses; scented knot garden, bog gardens, new lemon and olive walk. Home-made TEAS. *Adm £2.50, chd free (share to St Mary the Virgin, Shipley). Suns 22 May; 19 June (2-6). Private visits welcome by appt, Apr to June, groups 10+ & coaches. Tel 01403 741215*

⓫ Bankton Cottage, Turners Hill Road, Crawley Down 🕭⊠⊕
(Mr & Mrs Robin Lloyd) *4m W of East Grinstead. 2½m E of M23 J10.*

On B2028 1m N of Turners Hill Xrds. Almost unanimously described as a 'romantic' garden by visitors, the old walled kitchen garden has beds of herbaceous perennials, roses and clematis, box-edged lavender parterre and serpentine yew hedging. Beyond, lake, swans, bog garden and woodland. And as befits Pots and Pithoi's owners, plenty of terracotta pots throughout the 3½ acres. Home-made TEAS in aid of Heatherley Cheshire Home. *Adm £3, chd free. Sat, Sun 9, 10 July (2-6). Private visits welcome by appt, groups of 15+, late May to early Aug. Tel 01342 718907*

⓬ NEW Bardown Oast Farm, Bardown Road, Stonegate 🕭⊠⊕
(Mr & Mrs N Bowie) *3m N of Burwash. From S take A21. 1m after Hurst Green, L onto B2099 signed Ticehurst. Through the village, 2¼m L signed Stonegate. 1m on L by black milk churn. From Wadhurst on B2099. After 1m R signed Stonegate.* Delightful grounds of many 'rooms' for you to roam in at leisure. Ornamental ducks, well established borders and terraces. Unique attraction, not to be missed in the walled vegetable garden is the large Victorian greenhouse in working order. Fine views across an area of natural woodland to the R Lymden. Home-made TEAS in aid of Macmillan Cancer Relief. *Adm £3, chd free. Sun 22 May (11-5)*

⓭ ♦ Bateman's, Burwash 🕭⊠
(The National Trust) *6m E of Heathfield. ½m S (A265). From rd leading S at W end of Burwash, or N from Woods Corner (B2096).* Home of Rudyard Kipling from 1902-1936. Kipling planted yew hedges and rose garden, as well as constructing the pear alley and pond. The mill, within the grounds, grinds local wheat into flour. *Adm £5.90, chd £2.95. Sats to Weds Apr to Oct (11-5), Wed to Sun Nov, Dec (11-4). For NGS: Weds 11 May; 7 Sept (11-5). Tel 01435 882302 www.nationaltrust.org.uk*

⓮ Bates Green, Tyehill Road, Arlington 🕭⊠⊕
(Carolyn & John McCutchan) *3½m SW of Hailsham. 2½m SW of A22, 2½m from Wilmington on A27. Bates Green is on a small back rd (Tyehill Road) running from the Yew Tree Inn in the centre of Arlington village to Caneheath nr the Old Oak Inn.* Plantsman's tranquil garden of 2 acres; mixed borders with colour themes, shaded foliage garden giving yr-round interest from spring bulbs to autumn cyclamen and natural pond.

Organic vegetable garden with raised beds, double cordon fruit trees and glasshouse. Monocotyledon garden overlooks wild flower meadow with wood of anemones beyond. Light refreshments and TEAS in aid of Hellingly School PTA. *Adm £2.50, chd free. Suns 10 Apr; 26 June; 11 Sept (11-5). Also open* **Marchants Hardy Plants**, *11 Sept. Private visits welcome by appt. Tel 01323 485152*

⑮ Beauchamps, Float Lane, Udimore 🅰🈂🈁
(Matty & Richard Holmes) *3m W of Rye. 3m E of Broad Oak Xrds. Turn S off B2089 down Float Lane ½m.* Informal country garden, with wide range of unusual herbaceous plants, shrubs and trees incl fine specimens of *cornus controversa* 'Variegata' and Crinodendron hookeranum. Small orchard, kitchen garden and copse. Good views of beautiful Brede Valley. Cream TEAS in aid of Chernobyl Children, Rye. *Adm £2.50, chd free. Sun 5 June (2-6).* **Evening Opening** *£3, wine, Sat 4 June (6-8)*

⑯ Berri Court, Main Road, Yapton 🅰🈁
(Mr & Mrs J C Turner) *5m SW of Arundel. In centre of village between Shoulder of Mutton & The Olive Branch PHs. A2024 Littlehampton-Chichester rd. Car park is opp T-junction next to the Free Church chapel.* Intensely planted 2-acre garden of wide interest; trees, flowering shrubs, heathers, eucalyptus, daffodils, shrub roses, hydrangeas and lily pond. TEAS 5, 6 June only. *Adm £2.50, chd free. Suns, Mons 3, 4 Apr; 8, 9 May; 5, 6 June (2-6).* **Evening Opening** *£2.50, wine, Thur 7 July (6-9). Private visits welcome by appt. Tel 01243 551663*

⑰ Bexhill Gardens
½m W of centre of Bexhill. Proceed to Little Common roundabout on A259, 2m W of Bexhill. Light refreshments and TEAS at 99 Pear Tree Lane. *Combined adm £3, chd free* (share to St Michael's Hospice, St Leonards-on-Sea). *Sat, Sun 18, 19 June (11-5)*

The Clinches, Collington Lane East 🅰🈂 (Val & Ian Kemm) *Exit roundabout E through pelican lights. 1m over hill turn R into Sutherland Ave (signed town centre) & R into Collington Lane East.* A plantswoman's garden, ⅓-acre, which surrounds the house. Developed by owners; intensively planted with trees, shrubs, herbaceous borders, unusual plants and water features. Has variety of small seating areas each

with its own character. New features.

99 Pear Tree Lane, Little Common 🅰🈂🈁 (Marion Longhurst & Barbara Lenny) *Exit roundabout N into Pear Tree Lane. ½m on L.* Large cottage garden of mixed borders with perennials, shrubs and trees incl cranesbill geraniums, rockery, vegetables and water feature. Among the trees a Cornus kousa chinensis, considered to be one of the finest in the area.

Somerby Cottage, 97 Pear Tree Lane 🅰🈂 (Paula & Andrew Smith) *Exit roundabout N into Pear Tree Lane, ½m on L.* Informal ½-acre garden set amongst mature trees, incl rhododendrons, herbaceous borders, water feature and pond, roses, shrubbery and orchard. Present owners still developing further features in garden.

⑱ Bignor Park, Pulborough 🅰🈁
(Lord & Lady Mersey) *5m S of Petworth. On West Burton Rd. Nearest village Sutton (Sussex).* 11 acres of trees, shrubs, wild flowers and magnificent views of the S Downs, from Chanctonbury Ring to Bignor Hill. Plenty of shelter if it rains, in a temple, Greek pavilion or summerhouse. Short woodland walk, zen pond and bog garden. Newly developed potager in walled garden. Interesting modern sculptures and surprises for children. Featured in 'Chichester Observer' 2004. TEAS Easter & Aug only. *Adm £2.50, chd free. Sun, Mon 27, 28 Mar; Weds, 6 Apr to 25 May; Sat, Sun 6, 7 Aug; Weds, 5 Oct to 26 Oct (Sat, Sun, Mon 12-5), (Wed 2-5) www.bignorpark.co.uk*

⑲ 4 Birch Close, Arundel 🈂🈁
(Elizabeth & Mike Gammon) *1m S of Arundel. From A27/A284 roundabout at W end of Arundel take Ford Rd. After ½m turn R into Maxwell Rd. Follow signs for ½m.* ⅓-acre woodland garden containing a wide range of mature trees, shrubs and hardy perennials in a tranquil setting with secluded corners, meandering paths and plentiful seating. Particular emphasis on spring flowers and clematis, 100 at last count. Featured in '25 Beautiful Gardens' 2004. Home-made TEAS by Arundel Flower Club in aid of Sussex Kidney Trust. *Adm £2, chd free. Sun, Mon 1, 2 May (2-5). Private visits welcome by appt. Tel 01903 882722 e.gammon@tesco.net*

⑳ Birchanger Gardens, High Street, Balcombe 🅰
(Derek & Rae Worrall) *6m NW of Haywards Heath. On B2110 2m E of A23 at Handcross. 2m from Balcombe.* 7 acres of rhododendrons, camellias and magnolias, with many trees planted after the devastation of the Great Storm of 1987. Azalea avenue, lake lily pond with statue and fountains, Tuscan temple and pergola with many climbing plants. Recent successful clearance and replanting of 1½ acres of Rhododendron ponticum jungle. TEAS in aid of Macmillan Cancer Relief. *Adm £3, chd free. Sat 14 May (2-6). Private visits welcome by appt May only, coaches permitted. Tel 01444 811228*

㉑ Borde Hill Garden, Park & Woodland, Balcombe Road, Haywards Heath 🅰🈁
(Borde Hill Garden Ltd) *1½m N of Haywards Heath.* Heritage and collector's garden, set within 200 acres of spectacular Grade II parkland with renowned botanical collection of rare trees and shrubs, incl rhododendrons, azaleas, roses and herbaceous borders. Intimate 'garden rooms' with stunning views. Magical woodland and lakeside walks with picnic area. Autumn and winter splendour. Adventure playground and fishing. *Adm £6, chd £3.50, concessions £5. Thur 22 Sept (10-6 or dusk if earlier). Tel 01444 450326 info@bordehill.co.uk*

㉒ ⓃⒺⓌ **Bradstow Lodge, The Drive, Ifold** 🅰🈂🈁
(Ian & Elizabeth Gregory) *1m S of Loxwood. From A272/A281 take B2133 (Loxwood). ½m S of Loxwood take the Plaistow Rd, after 800yds turn R into The Drive (by village shop). Follow signs. Parking in The Drive only, please park considerately.* Young garden of approx 3 yrs old - still 'in the making'. Pond, bog garden, sunken formal area, herbaceous and greenhouse areas, many pots and containers, providing yr-round interest. Several 'developing' and experimental areas. TEAS. *Adm £2, chd free. Wed, Sun 6, 10 Apr (2-5.30)*

㉓ Brickwall, Rye Road, Northiam 🅰🈁
(The Frewen Educational Trust Ltd) *8m NW of Rye. S end of Northiam High St at A28/ B2088 junction. Rail: Rye. Bus: Rye - Northiam - Hastings service.* Listed garden surrounding a Grade I listed Jacobean Mansion (also open) and currently housing a school for dyslexic children. Gardens incl chess garden with topiary yew

pieces and number of Stuart characteristics: brick walls, clipped yew and beech are particular features. Dogs must be kept on leads. Home-made TEAS in aid of Frewen Educational Trust. *Adm £3, chd under 16 free. Sun 14 Aug (2-5). Tel 01797 253388 office@frewcoll. freeserve.co.uk*

㉔ Brighton & Hove Clematis Gardens
3 gardens 1m apart opening on 2 days to show how well clematis will grow in totally different soils and aspects. Home-made TEAS at 64 Old Shoreham Road. *No combined adm, £2 each garden, chd free. Suns 29 May; 26 June (2-5)*

Hove City Centre Garden, 27 Third Avenue, Hove 🗶☻ (Mrs Michael Fisher) *Third Avenue runs from Hove Town Hall in Church Rd to seafront. Pay parking in st.* Small hidden town garden sheltered by high walls, with an interesting collection of clematis and shrubs. Pots used extensively to provide changing colour and interest all through the yr.

64 Old Shoreham Road, Hove 🗶☻ (Brian & Muriel Bailey) (See seperate entry).

93 Wayland Avenue, Brighton 🗶☻ (Brian & Sylvia Jackson) *From Dyke Rd Ave into Tongdean Lane, R into Wayland Ave.* Garden on clay designed and built by owner. Emphasis on dense and varied planting. Roses, ornamental grasses, hostas, bamboos, perennials, over 125 clematis, trees provide shade planting; water feature in rockery areas. , Encouraging wildlife a priority. *Private visits welcome by appt June & Jul. Tel 01273 501027*

㉕ NEW Buckles, Burwash Common 🗶☻ (Giles & Nicola Dealtry) *3m E of Heathfield. From Heathfield take A265 E. In Burwash Common turn between Shanks Nursery and Ashwood Home (signed Stonegate Station). Garden 50yds on L.* After years of neglect the new owners began renovating this 4-acre garden 3yrs ago. Herbaceous borders with planting for sun and shade, orchard, enclosed kitchen and cutting garden, herb potager, woodland with rhododendrons and azaleas and magnificent 60ft Victorian glasshouse with tropical plants and fruits. Superb views over the Weald. Light refreshments and TEAS in aid of Burwash Common Playing Fields.

Adm £2.50, chd 50p. Sun, Mon 5, 6 June (11-5)

Burrswood, Groombridge 🗶
See Kent.

㉖ Butlers Farmhouse, Butlers Lane, Herstmonceux 🗶☻☻
(Irene Eltringham-Willson) *3m E of Hailsham. Take A271 from Hailsham, go through the village of Herstmonceux, turn R signed Church Rd then approx 1m turn R.* ½-acre garden surrounding C16 farmhouse (not open) with views of S Downs. Mainly herbaceous with rainbow border and small pond. Still being restored to its former glory, as shown in old photographs. Relax and listen to live jazz in the garden. Cream TEAS. *Adm £2.50, chd free. Sat, Sun 20, 21 Aug (2-5)*

㉗ 51 Carlisle Road, Eastbourne 🗶☻
(Mr & Mrs N Fraser-Gausden) *200yds inland from seafront (Wish Tower), close to Congress Theatre.* Walled, S-facing garden (82ft sq) with mixed beds intersected by stone paths and incl a small pool. Planting is profuse and diverse. Wide selection of shrubs, old roses, herbaceous plants and perennials mingle with specimen trees and climbers. NB Small but worth queueing for. Featured in 'Gardens Monthly' 2003 & '25 Beautiful Gardens' 2004. Home-made TEAS. *Adm £2, chd £1. Sat, Sun 4, 5 June (2-5). Evening Opening £3 wine, Sat 25 June (6-8). Private visits welcome by appt. Tel 01323 722545 fgausden@ic24.net*

㉘ Champs Hill, Waltham Park Road, Coldwaltham 🗶☻☻
(Mr & Mrs David Bowerman) *3m S of Pulborough. On A29, turn R to Fittleworth into Waltham Park Rd; garden 400yds.* 27 acres of acid-loving plants around sand pits and woodland. Superb views. Sculptures. Special Event Art Exhibition: 'The Newlyn School' (1880 to 1940): A Private Collection, May 13, 14. Featured in 'Sussex Life' & 'Chichester Observer' 2004. TEAS. *Adm £3, chd free. Suns 6, 13 Mar; 8, 15 May; 7, 14 Aug (2-5). Special Event Evening Opening £6, chd free, complimentary wine, Fri 13 May (6.30-8.30) & Sat 14 May (11.30-2.30). Private visits welcome by appt. Tel 01798 831868*

㉙ Chantry Green House, Steyning 🗶
(Mr R S Forrow & Mrs J B McNeil) *5m N of Worthing. 5m N of*

Worthing. Off A283. Turn into Church St from High St opp White Horse Inn. Garden 150yds down on L. Parking on Fletchers Croft car park, entrance opp church. Interesting 1-acre garden, redesigned by Jack Grant White. Features incl wall fountain, herbaceous borders and extensive shrub borders with a predominance of colourful evergreens providing interest throughout the yr. Small arboretum; rock and water garden. Home-made TEAS. *Adm £2, chd 50p. Sat, Sun 11, 12 June (2-5)*

㉚ ◆ Charleston, Nr Firle 🗶☻☻
(The Charleston Trust) *7m E of Lewes. Signed off A27, between villages of Firle & Selmeston.* Painters' garden. Plants chosen by Bloomsbury artists Vanessa Bell and Duncan Grant, to reflect their love of intense colour and silver foliage and for use in their still-life paintings. Walled cottage-style garden, influenced by S Europe, with mosaics, box hedges, ponds. Sense of luxuriance and surprise, heightened by various sculptures. TEAS. *House and garden adm £6, chd £4.50, concessions Wed & Thur £5, garden only adm £2.50, chd £1.50. Weds to Suns & Bank Hol Mons 23 Mar to 30 Oct (2-6 last entry 5), Weds to Sats July, Aug (11.30-6).* **For NGS:** *Suns 10 Apr; 7 Aug (2-6, last entry 5).* **Evening Opening** *£2.50, wine, Thur 9 June (6-8). Tel 01323 811626 www.charleston.org.uk*

㉛ Chattri View, 103 Cuckmere Way, Hollingbury 🗶☻
(Mr G Bourgoing) *2m N of Brighton City Centre. Off the Ditchling Rd turn L into Woodbourne Ave, immed R into Cuckmere Way. From A27(T) take Hollingbury exit onto Ditchling Rd.* Delightfully eccentric wildlife garden set on chalk downs on highest point in Brighton. Very unusual garden for Sussex NGS. Very steeply sloping (55 steps). Enter via side gate and themed seaside area. Only 5yrs old, this highly imaginative garden has been created from recycled wood and general household paraphernalia. Organic wildlife pond and wetland area with many native trees, shrubs and grasses. New features for 2005. No photography please. Home-made TEAS. *Adm £1.65, chd 50p. Suns 26 June; 17 July (3-6)*

㉜ Chelmsford Lodge, 12 Granville Road, Eastbourne 🗶☻☻
(David Stevens) *500yds from sea-front (Wish Tower), from Congress Theatre take Carlisle Rd L at Granville Rd Xrds. 100yds on R.*

Easy st parking. ¾ acre. Lawns with herbaceous beds, mature and unusual trees, shrubs, formal beds around pond; rockery; fruit trees and soft fruit area. Garden started in 1994 developing year by year. Former prep-school playing field and neglected garden. Home-made TEAS. *Adm £2.50, chd free. Sun 19 June (2-5)*

㉝ Clinton Lodge, Fletching
&❀✿

(Sir Hugh & Lady Collum) *4m NW of Uckfield. From A272 turn N at Piltdown for Fletching,* 1½*m.* 6-acre formal and romantic garden, overlooking parkland, with old roses, double herbaceous borders, yew hedges, pleached lime walks, copy of C17 scented herb garden, medieval-style potager, vine and rose allée, wild flower garden. Canal garden, small knot garden and shady glade. Caroline and Georgian house, not open. TEAS. *Adm £4, chd £2 (share to Fletching Parish Church). Sun, Mon, Fris 5, 6, 17, 24 June; 1, 8 July; 5 Aug (2-5.30). Private visits welcome by appt for groups of 15+ weekdays. Tel 01825 722952*

㉞ Coates Manor, Fittleworth
✿✿

(Mrs G H Thorp) 3½*m SE of Pulborough. Turn off B2138 at signed 'Coates'.* 1 acre, mainly shrubs and foliage of special interest, surrounding Elizabethan house (not open). Flowing design punctuated by clipped shrubs and specimen trees. Newly paved walled garden with interesting perennials, clematis, scented climbers and smaller treasures. Cyclamen, nerines, amaryllis, berries and coloured foliage give late season interest. Featured in various magazines & newspapers 2004. Light refreshments and TEAS in aid of Children's Society. *Adm £2.50, chd free. Sun 22 May (11-5). Private visits welcome by appt. Tel 01798 865356*

㉟ NEW Collington Gardens, Bexhill
½*m W of centre of Bexhill. Proceed to Little Common roundabout on A259.* Home-made TEAS at 64 Cranston Ave. *Combined adm £3, chd free (share to St Michael's Hospice). Sat 4 June (11-5)*

> NEW **1 Ashcombe Drive** &❀✿
> (Richard & Liz Chown) *Exit roundabout S into Cooden Sea Rd, 3rd L into Kewhurst Ave, 1st L into Ashcombe Dr, 400yds on R.* A charming garden featuring echiums, tree ferns, exotics, fish pond and rose arch. Although not

large this interesting garden contains a number of uncommon plants incl an *acacia baileyana* 'Purpurea'.

> NEW **64 Cranston Avenue** &❀
> (G & M Stokes) *From Little Common roundabout, take A259 E (towards Hastings), after approx 1m turn R into Sutherland Ave, 3rd turning on R into Cranston Ave.* Established town garden owned by avid plant collectors with an eye for the unusual.

> NEW **66 Cranston Avenue** ❀✿
> (Karen Hewgill) Surprising large town garden - definitely not formal but interesting, with themed areas to amuse. Potter around this quirky garden to discover hidden surprises.

> NEW **64 Cranston Avenue** &❀
> (G & M Stokes) *From Little Compton roundabout, take A259 towards Hastings. Approx 1m, turn R into Sutherland Ave (signed Bexhill Town Centre) 3rd turn on R into Cranston Ave.* An established town garden owned by avid plant collectors with an eye for the unusual.

㊱ Colwood House, Cuckfield Lane, Warninglid
&✿

(Mr & Mrs Patrick Brenan) *6m W of Haywards Heath. 6m SE of Horsham. Entrance on B2115 (Cuckfield Lane). Turn from A23, proceed W towards Warninglid for* ¾*m.* 6½ acres with mature and specimen trees from the last century. Lawns and woodland paths, formal and informal flower beds; 100ft terrace and herbaceous border overlooking flower-rimmed croquet lawn, parterre garden, herb and rose gardens. Cut turf labyrinth and forsythia tunnel. Water features and fountains; ornaments; gazebos and pavilions. Pets' cemetery and gypsy caravan. Home-made TEAS. *Adm £2.50, chd 50p. Wed, Sun 17, 21 Aug (2-6)*

㊲ ◆ Cookscroft, Earnley
&✿

(Mr & Mrs J Williams) *6m S of Chichester. At end of Birdham Straight take L fork to E Wittering. 1m on, before sharp bend, turn L into Bookers Lane. 2nd house on L.* 5-acre garden started from fields in 1988. Many trees grown from provenance seeds or liners. Collections of eucalyptus, birch, snake bark maples and unusual shrubs. 3 ponds with waterfalls. Cottage garden and Japanese garden. Interesting and developing garden, incl woodland area. TEAS (NGS days only). *Adm £2, chd under 16 free.*

Sats 26 Mar to 28 May; then last Sats in month to 26 Nov (10-4). **For NGS:** *Sun, Mon 29, 30 May (2-6). Tel 01243 513671 www.cookscroft. co.uk*

㊳ Cowdray Park Gardens, Midhurst
&✿

(The Viscount & Viscountess Cowdray) *1m E of Midhurst. S of A272. Entrance by East Front.* Avenue of wellingtonias, woodland walk; grass garden, rhododendrons, azaleas; lakes; large variety of trees and shrubs, herb parterre. Lebanon cedar 300yrs old; pleasure garden surrounded by ha-ha, new themed herbaceous border; laburnum tunnel and cherry avenue. 'Sussex Heritage' award 2003. Home-made TEAS. *Adm £3, chd under 16 free (share to RHS). Sun 15 May (2-5)*

㊴ Crown House, Eridge
&❀✿

(Major L Cave (Retd)) *3m SW of Tunbridge Wells. A26 Tunbridge Wells-Crowborough rd (29 bus route* ½ *hourly service); in Eridge take Rotherfield turn S, 1st R, house 1st on L, short walk from bus stop.* 1½ acres with pools; rose garden and rose walk; herbaceous borders and heather border; herb garden. Full size croquet lawn. Laid out as a series of 'Garden Rooms' in the style of Gertrude Jekyll. Panoramic views. Home-made TEAS. *Adm £2.50, chd under 14 free (share to Multiple Sclerosis Society). Sat, Sun 16, 17 July (2-6). Private visits welcome by appt May to Sept. Tel 01892 864389*

㊵ Dale Park House, Madehurst
❀✿

(Robert & Jane Green) *4m W of Arundel. Take A27 E from Chichester, or A27 W from Arundel, then A29 (London) for 2m, turn L to Madehurst & follow red arrows.* Set in parkland on S Downs with magnificent views to sea. Large walled garden with 200ft herbaceous border, mixed borders and rose garden. Rose and clematis arches, interesting collection of hostas, foliage plants and shrubs, orchard and kitchen garden. Home-made TEAS in aid of Madehurst Church. *Adm £2.50, chd free. Sun 12 June (2-5). Private visits welcome by appt. Tel 01243 814260*

㊶ Dormers, West Marden
&❀✿

(Mr & Mrs John Cairns) *10m NW of Chichester. On B2146. In centre of village turn up hill towards Rowlands Castle.* Village garden on chalk, started from scratch in 1997. Cottage-style planting, mainly herbaceous and bulbs, hellebores in early spring. Each area with a different colour scheme, small but productive vegetable patch. *Adm £2, chd free. Suns 6 Mar (12-4); 8 May (2-5)*

㊷ Down Place, South Harting 🐾⊕
(Mr & Mrs D M Thistleton-Smith) *1m SE of South Harting. B2141 to Chichester, turn L down unmarked lane below top of hill.* 7-acre hillside, chalk garden on the N side of S Downs with fine views of surrounding countryside. Extensive herbaceous, shrubs and rose borders on different levels merge into natural wild flower meadow renowned for its collection of native orchids. Fully stocked vegetable garden and greenhouses. Spring flowers and blossom. Cream TEAS. *Adm £2.50, chd free (share to Friends of Harting Church). Sat, Sun, Mon 30 Apr; 1, 2 May; Fri, Sat, Sun 17, 18, 19 June (2-6). Private visits welcome by appt Apr to July. Tel 01730 825374*

㊸ Duckyls Holt, Selsfield Road, West Hoathly 🐾⊕
(Mr & Mrs Kenneth Hill) *4m SW of East Grinstead, 6m E of Crawley. At Turners Hill take B2028. After 1m S fork L to West Hoathly.* Surprisingly intimate cottage garden of approx 2 acres on many different levels. Small herb garden, formal and informal plantings, herbaceous borders, rose border and new formal rose garden. Within walking distance of **The Priest House** & **White Rock** Combined adm £3. Home-made TEAS. *Adm £1, chd free. Sats, Suns 28, 29 May; 25, 26 June (11.5.30). Private visits welcome by appt May, June & July. Tel 01342 810282 sophie@duckylsholt.fsnet.co.uk*

㊹ NEW Durrance Manor, Smithers Hill, Shipley 🐾🐾
(Gordon & Joan Lindsay) *5m SW of Horsham. Take A245 to A272, turn W towards Billingshurst, go 1.7m & take rd signed Shipley & Countryman PH. Durrance Manor 2nd on L.* 2 acres of Wealden clay, surrounding C15 hall house (not open). Ha-ha overlooking Chanctonbury Ring. Long and colourful high summer border,

Mediterranean-style garden with grasses, espaliered fruit trees behind mixed border, gravelled courtyard with exotic planting, large pond with pondside planting, orchard with wild flowering meadow, other shrub borders, vegetable garden. Home-made TEAS in aid of St Mary's Church, Shipley. *Adm £2.50, chd free. Sun 14 Aug (1-5).* **Evening Opening** *£3, wine, Wed 17 Aug (6-9)*

㊺ Eastergate House, Church Lane, Eastergate 🐾⊕
(Michael & Jacintha Hutton) *7m E of Chichester. On A27 turn R at Fontwell roundabout onto A29. At War Memorial turn immed into Church Lane for approx 250yds.* 1-acre walled and hedged garden has herbaceous borders interplanted with shrubs and roses, water garden and paved potager; in spring superb magnolia and wisteria. *Adm £3.50 to incl TEA. Private visits welcome by appt. Tel 01243 544195*

㊻ Ebbsworth, Nutbourne 🐾⊕
(Mrs F Lambert) *2½m E of Pulborough. Take A283 E from junction with A29 (Swan Corner) 2m with 2 L forks signed Nutbourne. Pass Rising Sun & follow signs to garden.* Charming, well-planted, owner-maintained cottage garden, surrounding old cottage (not open). Roses and lilies, together with herbaceous borders. Man-made stream and ponds planted with water plants. TEAS. *Adm £2.50, chd free. Fri, Sat 29, 30 July (2-5)*

㊼ 8 Felbridge Court, Copthorne Road, East Grinstead 🐾⊕
(Jan & John Laskey) *2m NW of East Grinstead. From A22 at Felbridge (by Star Inn), take A264 Copthorne Rd, then 1st L.* Small cottage-style garden divided into compartments, overflowing with plants for yr-round interest. Formal hedging and topiary combine with informal planting, incl many native species to encourage wildlife. Many imaginative and unusual ideas for the smaller garden. Woodland/stream garden in bordering communal grounds. Seeds/cuttings available on request. TEAS. *Adm £2.50 incls guided tour not suitable for children. Private*

visits welcome by appt, weekdays May to Sept. Tel 01342 321965 jan.laskey@virgin.net

㊽ Filliams Bungalow, Plaistow Road, Kirdford 🐾🐾⊕
(Janet & Roger Green) *5m NE of Petworth. Between Kirdford & Plaistow villages. ½m N of Kirdford. 2½m S of Plaistow. Entrance with car park.* Approx 3-acre garden. 2 mazes, 1 of climbing and rambling roses, 1 of living willow. Mixed border with many unusual plants. Shrubs, trees, fish ponds, wild flower meadow, rockeries and grass garden. Many plants grown from seed and cuttings in extended plant propagation area. Vegetable area, greenhouses and much more. Home-made TEAS in aid of Special Care Baby Unit, Southampton Hospital. *Adm £2.50, chd £1.50. Suns, Weds 22 May; 8, 12 June; 10 July; 14, 17 Aug, Suns (11-5), Weds (2-5). Private visits welcome by appt. Tel 01403 820425*

㊾ NEW Firle Place, Lewes
(8th Viscount Gage) *3m E of Lewes. A27 turn R. Follow signs tourist signs. 'The Pleasure Grounds'.* Wild woodland garden dating back to C16 currently undergoing renovation, situated above Firle Place giving far reaching views over Firle Park towards the Sussex Weald. The garden consists of woodland paths and avenues leading to hidden glades. House also open. Featured on Country Ways (TV) 2005. TEAS. *Adm £2.50, chd /concessions £2. Sun 3 Apr (12-4)*

㊿ Fishers Farm, Etchingham 🐾🐾⊕
(Mr & Mrs David Pettman) *3½m W of Hurst Green. Take A265 to Etchingham from A21 at Hurst Green. 1st turning L after level Xing. After ½m turn R into Fontridge Lane, continue for 1m.* 3 acres incl walled garden, pond with golden orfe, formal rose garden and mixed borders with azaleas, acers and old-fashioned shrub roses. Small military memorabilia display. Home-made TEAS. *Adm £3, chd free. Sun 22 May (2-6)*

51 Fittleworth House, Bedham Road, Fittleworth 🐾⊕
(Edward & Isabel Braham) *3m SE of Petworth. Just off A283, 200yds along lane signed Bedham.* Mature 3-acre garden encompassing wisteria-covered Georgian House (not open). Working walled kitchen garden featuring a wide range of vegetables, apple tunnel, 150ft cutting borders.

ngs
gardens open for charity

Look out for the [NCCPG] National Plant Collections at some of our gardens

Magnificent cedar, rose garden, mixed borders, rhododendrons/shrub plantings, spring/wild garden, lawns, fountain, greenhouses, old potting shed. Gardener's cottage garden also open. Head Gardener on hand to answer questions. TEAS in aid of Fittleworth First School. *Adm £2.50, chd free. Tues 3 May to 24 May; 7 June to 19 July; 13 Sept (2-5). Private visits welcome by appt Apr to July, groups of 4+. Tel 01798 865074 Mark Saunders*

52 Five Oaks Cottage, West Burton 🕭⊕
(Jean & Steve Jackman) *5m S of Pulborough. From the A29 4m S of Pulborough, take the B2138 signposted to Fittleworth & Petworth. Turn immed L & L again at T-junction. 1m on the L. Please follow these directions to avoid coming through the village.* Artists' garden which is going through a metamorphosis this year. More grasses, more British natives and more space to move around! Lots of ideas and interesting corners. Totally organic; vegetable plot; unsuitable for children due to small pond and poisonous plants. No smoking garden. Adjacent nursery. Featured in 'Haven' (Denmark), 2003, 'Sussex Life' & 'Chichester Observer' 2004. *Adm £2, chd free. Tue 3 June (2-5); Sat, Sun 3, 25 Sept (11-5).* **Evening Opening** *£2, wine, Fri 26 Aug (6-8)*

53 Framfield Grange, Framfield 🕭⊕
(Mr & Mrs Jack Gore) *3m E of Uckfield. From Uckfield take B2102 to Framfield 2½m. Continue through Framfield on B2102. The Grange is approx ¼m E on R.* 10 acres of garden with shrub borders, wild flower meadow and lakes. Woodland walks, bluebell glades. Many hybrid and species of rhododendrons and azaleas. Beautifully kept walled kitchen garden. Home-made TEAS in aid of Macmillan Cancer Relief. *Adm £3, chd free. Sun 8 May (2-6)*

54 Frith Lodge, Northchapel ⊕
(Mr & Mrs Geoffrey Cridland) *7m N of Petworth. On A283 turn E in centre of Northchapel into Pipers Lane, ¾m turn L into bridleway.* 1-acre traditional English cottage garden divided into several rooms running off 2 principle axes incl rose tunnel, honeysuckle parterres in early May and hornbeam ave. In addition, 2-acre wild and woodland garden with outstanding views of the Sussex Weald. Created by garden designer owner. First time open in spring. Featured in 'The English Garden',

'The Garden' 2003. Home-made TEAS. *Adm £3, chd £2 (share to Cedar). Suns 1 May; 5; 12 June (2.30-5.30).* **Evening Opening** *£3.50, wine, Sat 11 June (5-7). Private visits welcome by appt May & June only. Tel 0776 9978 520*

55 Gardeners Cottage, West Dean 🕭
(Jim Buckland & Sarah Wain) *6m N of Chichester. Follow signs to West Dean Gardens and park in gardens car park. Follow signs to cottage N of car park.* Small serene and secluded theatrical retreat with strong emphasis on texture, foliage and good structure created by trees. Topiary, labyrinthine paths, interesting spaces. Separate courtyard, garden with pond. Home-made TEAS in aid of Christian Aid. *Adm £2.50, chd free. Sun 22 May (11-6)*

56 ◆ Great Dixter, Northiam 🕭🕭🕭
(Mr Christopher Lloyd) *8m NW of Rye. ½m N of Northiam off A28.* Designed by Lutyens and Nathaniel Lloyd whose son, Christopher, has now officiated over these gardens for 50yrs, creating one of the most experimental and constantly changing gardens of our time. Wide variety of interest from clipped topiary, wild meadow flowers, natural ponds, formal pool and the famous long border and exotic garden. A long and varied season is aimed for. Light refreshments and TEAS. *House and garden adm £6.50, garden only adm £5, chd £1.50. Suns to Suns 25 Mar to 30 Oct (2-5) . Tel 01797 252878 www.greatdixter.co.uk*

57 Great Lywood Farmhouse, Lindfield Road, Ardingly 🕭⊕
(Richard & Susan Laing) *2½m N of Haywards Heath. Take B2028 for Ardingly. 2m from centre of Lindfield, turn L down single track.* Approx 1½ acres. Terraced garden surrounding C17 Sussex farmhouse (not open). Landscaped and planted since 1997, with views to S Downs. Featuring lawns and grass walks, mixed borders, rose garden, kitchen garden and orchard, walled garden with dovecote. Home-made TEAS in aid of Ardingly Old Jeshwang Assoc. *Adm £2.50, chd free. Fri 3, Sun 5 June (2-6)*

58 Hailsham Grange, Vicarage Road, Hailsham 🕭🕭⊕
(Mr Noel Thompson) *Turn off Hailsham High St into Vicarage Rd, park in public car park.* Formal garden designed and planted in

grounds of former early C18 Vicarage (not open). Series of garden areas representing modern interpretation of C18 formality; Gothic summerhouse; pleached hedges; herbaceous borders, romantic planting in separate garden compartments. Featured in '25 Beautiful Gardens' 2003 & 'The English Garden' 2004. Home-made TEAS in aid of Roof Restoration Fund, St Mary's Church, Hailsham. *Adm £2.50, chd free. Suns 5 June; 3 July (2-5.30). Private visits welcome by appt. Tel 01323 844248*

59 Ham Cottage, Highbrook, Ardingly 🕭⊕
(Peter & Andrea Browne) *5m N of Haywards Heath. On B2028 1m S of Ardingly turn into Burstow Hill Lane. Signed to Highbrook, then follow NGS signs.* 8 acres being created from agricultural land. Wide variety of trees and shrubs, mainly rhododendrons, azaleas and camellias. 2 areas of woodland, bluebell wood and sandstone outcrop, part of which forms small natural amphitheatre. Stream-fed bog garden, large pond and formal garden all created by present owners. Home-made TEAS in aid of Breakthrough Breast Cancer. *Adm £2, chd free. Sats, Suns 14, 15, 21, 22 May (1-6).* **Evening Opening** *£3, wine, Fri 26 Aug (6-9)*

60 Hammerwood House, Iping 🕭⊕
(The Hon Mrs Lakin) *3m W of Midhurst. 1m N of A272 Midhurst to Petersfield rd. Well signed.* Large informal garden; fine trees, rhododendrons, azaleas, acers, cornus, magnolias; wild garden (¼m away), bluebells, stream. Home-made TEAS. *Adm £2.50, chd free. Suns 8, 15 May (2-5.30). Private visits welcome by appt. Tel 01730 813635*

61 Hampton Cottage, School Lane, Fittleworth ⊕
(Nick & Louise Elliott) *3m SW of Pulborough. Off the A283 between Pulborough & Petworth (3m), School Lane is equidistant between A283 & B2138. Parking in rd or at village hall a short walk away.* Picturesque cottage garden packed with interesting and unusual plants collected by plantaholic! Old summerhouse and garden memorabilia creating a nostalgic feel - additional land recently acquired being sympathetically restored - please come and see it develop over time. Featured on A Garden for all Seasons UK Style TV 2003. *Adm £2.50, chd free. Sats, Suns 2, 3, 23,*

24 Apr; 18, 19 June; 10, 11 Sept
(2-5). **Evening Opening** £2.50, wine,
Fri 1 July (7-9). Private visits
welcome by appt, groups of 15+.
Tel 01798 865491

62 **NEW** **Hawkhurst House,**
Wisborough Green ⊕
(Carolyn Bullard) 4m E of Petworth.
Turn S off A272 between Petworth
& Wisborough Green in direction of
Crimbourne. After 600yds turn R
signed Hawkhurst Court take R gate
to Hawkhurst House or follow car
park signs. 6 acres landscaped
grounds with 100yr history
dominated by 3 cedars of Lebanon,
numerous beds of unusual shrubs and
trees. Dramatic display of
rhododendrons and azaleas. Garden
surrounded by West Sussex Wildlife
Trust woodland. Adm £2.50, chd
50p, concessions £2. Weds 11, 18
May (2-5)

63 ◆ **High Beeches, Handcross**
⊗ NCCPG
(High Beeches Gardens Conservation
Trust) 5m NW of Cuckfield. Situated
on B2110 1m E of A23 at
Handcross. 20 acres of enchanting
landscaped woodland and water
gardens; spring daffodils; bluebells
and azalea walks; many rare and
beautiful plants; wild flower
meadows; glorious autumn colours.
Picnic area. National Collection of
Stewartia. Light refreshments and
TEAS. Adm £5, chd under 14 free.
Daily except Weds . **For NGS:** Sun 29
May; Sat 1 Oct (1-5). Tel 01444
400589 www.highbeeches.com

64 ◆ **Highdown, Goring-by-Sea**
(Worthing Borough Council) 2m N
of Worthing. A259, 3m W of
Worthing. Station: Goring-by-Sea,
1m. Famous garden created by Sir F
Stern situated in chalk pit and
downland area containing a wide
collection of plants. Spring bulbs,
peonies, shrubs and trees. Many
plants were raised from seed brought
from China by great collectors like
Wilson, Farrer and Kingdon-Ward.
Collection box. **For NGS:** Mon 30
May (10-6)

65 **4 Hillside Cottages, Downs**
Road, West Stoke ⊗
(Heather & Chris Lock) 3m NW of
Chichester. From A286 at Lavant,
head W for 1½m, nr Kingley Vale.
Garden 120ft x 27ft in established
rural setting, created from scratch
8yrs ago. Densely planted with mixed
borders and shrubs, large collection
of roses, clematis and fuchsias.
Profusion of colour and scent in an
immaculately maintained small

garden. TEAS. Adm £2, chd free. Sun
31 July (2-5). **Evening Opening** £2,
wine, Tue 14 June (6-9). Private visits
welcome by appt June, July & Aug.
Tel 01243 574802

66 **Hobbs Barton, Framfield, nr**
Uckfield �⊗⊕
(Mr & Mrs Jeremy Clark) 3m E of
Uckfield. From Uckfield take B2102
E to Framfield. Approaching from S
leave A22 at Pear Tree junction S end
of Uckfield bypass. Garden signed
from centres of Framfield & Buxted.
In a peaceful pastoral setting, typical
of rural Sussex and well removed
from the noise of traffic, this is a
mature garden of 2½ acres developed
by the present owners over the past
32yrs. Wide sweeping lawns lead to
areas planted with many types of
rose, shrubberies and herbaceous
borders; numerous specimen trees
incl Metasequoia glyptostroboides,
liriodendron, giant prostrate junipers;
pretty water features; part-walled
vegetable and fruit garden. New
woodland garden. Excellent plant
stall. Home-made TEAS in aid of
Macmillan Cancer Relief. Adm £3,
chd free. Sat, Sun, Mon 4, 5, 6 June
(2-5.30)

67 **Hurston Place, Pulborough**
(The Hon Mrs David Bigham) 1m W
of Storrington. Off the A283 between
Pulborough & Storrington. Approx
3m from Pulborough going towards
Storrington at 2 cottages turn L.
Straight down lane, over small bridge
round to R, garden on L behind
mature yew hedge. Garden divided
into 2 parts: one a walled, semi
formal garden with boxed edged
beds, vegetables and borders; the
other garden has 2 mixed herbaceous
beds using as a background the old
walls of the farm. There are a further
4 mixed beds of herbaceous and
shrubs. New yew hedges and topiary
shapes, and in the last 5yrs, a new
beech hedge planted at the back of
the croquet lawn. Home-made TEAS
in aid of St Peter's Church, Parham.
Adm £2.50, chd £1. Sat, Sun, Mon 4,
5, 6 June (2-5.30)

68 **Kent House, East Harting**
ð⊗⊕
(Mr & Mrs David Gault) 4m SE of
Petersfield. On the B2146 at South
Harting take the Elstead-Midhurst rd
E for ½m. Just W of Turkey Island,
turn N up no through road for
400yds. 1½-acre garden in old setting
with mixed shrub roses, shrubs and
herbaceous plants. Walled garden,
shade garden around an C18 classical
house (not open); exceptional views.
Home-made TEAS. Adm £2, chd

under 10 free (share to Friends of
Harting Church). Sats, Suns 11, 12
June; 9, 10 July (2-6). Private visits
welcome by appt May to Aug.
Tel 01730 825206

69 **Ketleys, Flimwell** ⊗⊕
(Helen Yemm & Chris Craib) 12m
SE of Tunbridge Wells. Between A21
& B2087. Please approach from
B2087 since Rosemary Lane is single
track. Garden writer Helen Yemm's
airy 2½-acre garden which has been
substantially replanted over the past
7yrs. Gravel gardens, imperfect
lawns, borders, small vegetable
garden and two ponds - one formal
and one very informal, in a
challenging wooded area which is
constantly the subject of valiant
efforts at greater control. The garden
is on several levels and there are
oblique views over Bewl Water and
surrounding farmland. Featured in
'The English Garden' 2004. TEAS in
aid of Friends of Ticehurst School.
Adm £3, chd 50p. Sun 12 June (2-7).
Evening Opening £3, wine, Fri 17 June
(6-9.30). Private visits welcome by
appt for groups of 20 or more, (no
coaches). Tel 01580 879300
helenyemm@ketleys.co.uk

70 **NEW** **Kiln Copse Farm,**
Kirdford ð⊗⊕
(Bill & Pat Shere) 4m NE of
Petworth. Take A283 from Petworth
then fork R signed Kirdford & Balls
Cross. Through Balls Cross, over
narrow bridge then 400yds on L. 1½-
acre garden on clay that has
gradually evolved to blend with its
natural woodland setting. Many
informal mixed shrub and herbaceous
borders combine with ponds, pergola,
low maintenance conifer border,
lawns and vegetable garden. Home-
made TEAS in aid of RABI. Adm
£2.50 , chd free. Sun 11 Sept (2-5.30)

71 **King John's Lodge,**
Sheepstreet Lane, Etchingham
ð⊗
(Mr & Mrs R A Cunningham) 2m W
of Hurst Green. Burwash to
Etchingham on the A265. Turn L
before Etchingham Church into
Church Lane which leads into
Sheepstreet Lane after ½m. L after
1m. 3-acre romantic garden
surrounding an historic listed house
(not open). Formal garden with water
features, rose walk, wild pond and
garden with rustic bridge to shaded
ivy garden, large herbaceous borders,
old shrub roses and secret garden.
Accommodation. TEAS. Adm £2.50,
chd free. Sat 4 (2-6), Sun 5 June
(11-5). Private visits welcome by

appt. Tel 01580 819232
www.kingjohnslodge.co.uk

72 Latchetts, Freshfield Lane, Danehill &⊗⊕
(Mr & Mrs Laurence Hardy) 5m NE of Haywards Heath. SW off A275. In Danehill turn into Freshfield Lane at War Memorial. 1m on R. 1414 visitors last year admired this beautifully-maintained country 4-5 acre garden. Over 1000 different trees, shrubs, roses, herbaceous and bedding plants set off by fine lawns. 'Fun' corners, ha-has, duck pond, walled millennium garden, raised vegetable beds, wild corner, terraces, stone and brick paving, water garden and a lovely view. Featured in 'English Garden' 2003. Cream TEAS. Adm £3.50, chd free. Wed 22 June; Fris, Sats 15, 16 July; 12, 13 Aug (1.30-5.30). **Evening Opening** £3.50, wine & refreshments, Thur 23 June (5.30-8.30). Private visits welcome by appt Weds to Sats, also coaches. Tel 01825 790237

73 Legsheath Farm, nr Forest Row &⊕
(Mr & Mrs M Neal) 4m S of E Grinstead. 2m W of Forest Row, 1m S of Weirwood Reservoir. Panoramic views over reservoir. Exciting 10-acre garden with woodland walks, water gardens and formal borders. Of particular interest, clumps of wild orchids, fine davidia, acers, eucryphia and rhododendrons. Mass planting of meconopsis on the way to new ponds. A new border has been created adjacent to the herbaceous border. Home-made TEAS. Adm £3.50, chd free. Sun 22 May (2-5.30). Private visits welcome by appt. Tel 01342 810230 legsheath@onetel.com

74 Little Dene, Stonequarry Road, Chelwood Gate &⊗
(Professor & Mrs D Anderson) 8m S of East Grinstead. Take A275 off A22 at Wych Cross, then 1st L & 2nd R. Plantsman's garden of yr-round interest. Many unusual shrubs and climbers, over 150 clematis, raised alpine bed. ½-acre very suitable for people who cannot walk far. Featured in 'Womens Weekly' 2003. TEAS by appointment only. Adm £2, chd free. Thur, Fri 12, 13 May (12-5). Private visits welcome by appt, coaches permitted. Tel 01825 740657

75 Little Wantley, Fryern Road, Storrington &⊗⊕
(Hilary Barnes) 1m W of Storrington. Follow signs to West Chiltington. Entrance approx 1m on R in Fryern

Rd. Parking in field. Close to the S Downs, naturalistic garden approx 3½ acres. Wide range of plants grown in neutral/acid soil with deep mixed herbaceous borders. Secret garden reached by pergola walk. 1½-acre lake excavated in 1997, water lilies, 2 islands for water fowl, unusual cantilevered jetty, impressive marginal planting. Children must be strictly supervised. Home-made TEAS. Adm £3, chd free. Sun 19 June (2-5.30)

76 NEW Lowder Mill, Bell Vale Lane, Fernhurst ⊗⊕
(Anne & John Denning) 1½m S of Haslemere. Follow A286 out of Midhurst towards Haslemere, through Fernhurst and take 2nd R after Kingsley Green into Bell Vale Lane. Lowder Mill approx ½m on R. Mill House and former water mill on Sussex/Surrey/Hampshire border. Set in 3 acres of gardens, lake, ponds, orchard and kitchen garden. The gardens had been neglected, but, redesigned by Bunny Guinness in 2002, they are being restored by the present owners, with work still ongoing. Unusual chickens, ducks and resident kingfishers. Home-made TEAS. Adm £3, chd £1.50. Thurs 12 May; 18 Aug (11-5). Private visits welcome by appt, groups 10+. Tel 01428 644822 johndenning@cyder.freeserve.co.uk

77 Malt House, Rogate, Chithurst &⊕
(Mr & Mrs G Ferguson) 3m W of Midhurst. From A272, 3½m W of Midhurst turn N signed Chithurst then 1½m; or at Liphook turn off A3 onto old A3 (B2070) for 2m before turning L to Milland, then follow signs to Chithurst for 1½m. 6 acres; flowering shrubs incl exceptional rhododendrons and azaleas, leading to 50 acres of arboretum and lovely woodland walks. TEAS in aid of Borden Wood Village Hall. Adm £3, chd free. Suns, Mon 1, 2, 8 May (2-6). Private visits welcome by appt. Tel 01730 821433

78 The Manor of Dean, Pitshill, Tillington &⊗⊕
(Miss S M Mitford) 3m W of Petworth. On A272 from Petworth to Midhurst. Pass through Tillington village. The A272 then opens up to a short section of dual carriageway. Turn R at end of this section and proceed N, entrance to garden is approx ½m. Approx 3 acres. Traditional English garden, Herbaceous borders, spring bulbs, grass walks, walled kitchen garden

with vegetables and fruit. Asparagus bed. Lawns, rose garden and informal areas. TEAS. Adm £2, chd 5 - 16 £1, under 5 free. Sats, Suns 19, 20 Mar; 23, 24 Apr; 14, 15 May; 18, 19 June; 16, 17 July; 20, 21 Aug; 17, 18 Sept; 8, 9 Oct (2-5). Private visits welcome by appt. Tel 01798 877555

79 Marchants Hardy Plants, 2 Marchants Cottages, Mill Lane, Laughton &⊗⊕
(Graham Gough & Lucy Goffin) 6m E of Lewes. From Laughton Xrds on B2124 (at Roebuck Inn), proceed E for ½m, at Xrds turn S signed Ripe down Mill Lane; on R. Young atmospheric 2-acre garden and nursery with remarkable backdrop of Firle Beacon and S Downs. Imaginatively designed and sensitively planted with rich tapestry of unusual plants, incl many graceful and noble grasses. Featured in 'Country Living' & '25 Beautiful Gardens' 2004. Adm £2.50, chd under 16 free. Sun 11 Sept (2-5). Also open **Bates Green**, 11 Sept

80 The Martlets Hospice, Wayfield Avenue, Hove &⊗⊕
(The Martlets Hospice) From Old Shoreham Rd (A270), 600yds W of A2023 junction turn N into Holmes Ave. ¼m L into Wayfield Ave. From A27T Hove exit. Take King George VI Ave. Turn L at 1st T-lights immed R into Holmes Ave, ½m turn R into Wayfield Ave. 1-acre garden with courtyard. Mainly informal plantings. Rose bower, water feature and wild flower bank. Peaceful garden with private secluded areas which are enjoyed by patients and their families. Maintained by volunteer gardeners who will greet visitors. Home-made TEAS. Adm £2, chd free. Sat, Sun 4, 5 June (2-5)

81 Mayfield Gardens
10m S of Tunbridge Wells. Exit A267 into Mayfield. At N end of village on sharp bend take minor road (Fletching St which leads into East St) signed Witherenden. Gardens within ¼m. All within easy walking distance. Attractive old Wealden village in conservation area dating back to Saxon times. TEAS at 3 Fingal Place. Combined adm £3, chd free. Sun 12 June (2-5.30)

3 Fingal Place, East Street
&⊗⊕ (Gina & Martin Osborne) Medium-sized family garden. Designed by owners from 1984, containing some remnants of pre-1900 orchard, mixed planting, herbs, vegetables, greenhouse and conservatory and a surprise piece of seaside.

Hopton, Fletching Street &⌖⊛
(Carolyn & Ian Goemans)
*Limited parking for disabled
only. Car park in village.*
Informal S-facing garden of about
¼ acre, with views. Formerly a
delphinium nursery now
redesigned with mixed beds and
borders. Established magnolias,
camellias and around 50 different
varieties of rhododendrons and
azaleas.

May Cottage, Fletching Street
&⊛ (Kathleen & Ian Lyle)
Cottage garden. Wide variety of
interesting plants, shrubs and
trees, raised beds, small pond.

**September Cottage, Fletching
Street** ⊛ (Colin Richard Wills)
Modest, pocket-handkerchief
garden with mixed borders and
spring bulbs.

1 Southview Villas ⊛ (Nick &
Angela Rowe) Arched hedge
leads to steps and terrace, cottage
garden with cherry and pear
trees, rambling roses, lilies and
azaleas. Views across the valley
and, every man's dream, a large
shed.

NEW **Sunnybank Cottage,
Fletching Street** ⊛ (Eve & Paul
Amans) S-facing informal garden
with views, feature bank with
numerous specimen shrubs.

**82 Meadow Cottage, Rose
Cottage Lane, Staplefield** ⊛
(Mrs D Nader) 1½m W of Cuckfield.
*Take B2114 towards Handcross.
Garden is 200yds from bottom of
Rose Cottage Lane.* Charming
cottage garden, set in 1 acre, designed
to provide yr-round interest. Featured
in 'Sussex Life' 2004. Home-made
TEAS. *Adm £2, chd free. Thur 5, Sat
7 May (12-5)*

**83 ◆ Merriments Gardens, Hurst
Green** &⊛
(Mr D Weeks & Mrs P Weeks) 1m N
*of Hurst Green. Between Hawkhurst
& Hurst Green.* In the garden we
offer you 4 acres of densely planted
borders where the plants grown in
the nursery are seen growing in a
garden context with a depth of
imagination which is truly
remarkable. This artistic wilderness
takes you through the colour
spectrum, explores textural and
tactile elements so often lacking in
gardens. Look deeply into our
endlessly imaginative planting
schemes. Light refreshments and
TEAS. *Adm £4, chd £2. Good Friday
25 Mar to 30 Sept.* **For NGS:** *Suns 10
July; 18 Sept (10.30-5.30).*

*Tel 01580 860666
www.merriments.co.uk*

84 Mitchmere Farm, Stoughton
&⊛⊕
(Neil & Sue Edden) 5½m NW of
*Chichester. Turn off the B2146 at
Walderton towards Stoughton. Farm
is ¾m on L, ¼m beyond the turning
to Upmarden.* 1½-acre garden started
in 1991 in lovely downland position.
Unusual trees and shrubs, many
coloured stems or catkins growing in
dry gravel, briefly wet most years
when the Winterbourne rises and
flows through the garden. Drifts of
snowdrops and crocuses. Small
collection of special snowdrops. New
small formal kitchen garden, free-
range bantams. Wellies. Featured in
Chichester Observer', Sussex Country
Life' 2003, 'Country Homes &
Interiors' 2004 & 'Ideal Home' 2005.
TEAS. *Adm £2.50, chd free. Suns 13,
20 Tues 15, Thur 17 Feb (11-4); Suns
12, 19, Tue 14, Feb 2006. Private
visits welcome by appt for groups Feb
only, minumum adm £25. Tel 02392
631456*

**85 ◆ Moorlands, Friar's Gate, nr
Crowborough** ⊕
(Dr & Mrs Steven Smith & Dr Lucy
& Mr Mark Love) 2m N of
*Crowborough. St Johns Rd to Friar's
Gate. Or turn L off B2188 at Friar's
Gate signed Horder Hospital.* 4 acres
set in lush valley deep in Ashdown
Forest; water garden with ponds,
streams and river; primulas,
rhododendrons, azaleas. River walk
with grasses and bamboos. Rockery
restored to original 1929 design. The
many special trees planted 25yrs ago
make this garden an arboretum.
Home-made TEAS. *Adm £3, chd
free. Weds 1 Apr to 1 Oct (11-5).* **For
NGS:** *Sun 26 June (2-6). Tel 01892
652474*

**86 Mount Harry House, Ditchling
Road, Offham** &⊕
(Lord & Lady Renton) & **Mount
Harry Lodge** (Mr & Mrs A K Stewart-
Roberts) (2 adjoining gardens) 2m N
*of Lewes. On S side of Ditchling Rd
B2116, ½m W of A275.* 7-acre and
1-acre terraced gardens on chalk;
herbaceous and shrubbery borders,
wild flower walk, specimen trees,
laburnum walks, walled garden, dell
garden, conservatory, ornamental
tree nursery. In beautiful downland
setting. TEAS in aid of Sussex Ouse
Conservation Society. *Adm £3.50,
chd free. Sun 15 May (2-5)*

**87 Mountfield Court, nr
Robertsbridge** ⊛
(Mr & Mrs Simon Fraser) 3m N of
*Battle. On A21 London-Hastings;
½m from Johns Cross.* 3-acre wild
woodland garden; walkways through
exceptional rhododendrons, azaleas,
camellias and other flowering shrubs;
fine trees and outstanding views.
Small paved herb garden. Home-
made TEAS in aid of All Saints'
Church, Mountfield. *Adm £2.50, chd
free. Sun, Mon 8, 9 May (2-5)*

88 New Barn, Egdean &⊛⊕
(Mr & Mrs Adrian Tuck) 2m SE of
*Petworth. ½m S of Petworth turn off
A285 to Pulborough, at 2nd Xrds
turn R into lane. Or 1m W of
Fittleworth take L fork to Midhurst
off A283. 150yds turn L.* Converted
C18 barn (not open) with 2-acre
garden in beautiful peaceful farmland
setting. Large natural pond and
stream. Owner-maintained and
planned for yr-round interest from
snowdrops, camellias, spring flowers,
masses of bluebells, azaleas, water-
irises, roses, shrubs and herbaceous
through to autumn colour. Trees
planted for flower, bark and leaf.
Seats and 2 swings. Featured in 'The
English Garden' 2003. Home-made
TEAS. *Adm £2.50, chd 50p. Mon 29
Aug (10.30-5.30). Private visits
welcome by appt. Tel 01798 865502*

89 Newtimber Place, Newtimber
&⊕
(Mr & Mrs Andrew Clay) 7m N of
*Brighton. Off A281 between
Poynings & Pyecombe.* Beautiful C17
moated house (not open). Gardens
and woods full of bulbs and wild
flowers in spring. In summer, roses,
herbaceous border and lawns. Moat
flanked by water plants. Mature
trees. Wild garden; ducks, chickens
and fish. Home-made TEAS in aid of
Newtimber Church. *Adm £2.50, chd
£1. Suns 10 Apr; 4 Sept (2-5.30)*

**90 Northwood Farmhouse,
Blackgate Lane, Pulborough** ⊛
(Mrs Pat Hill) 1m N of Pulborough.
*On A29, turn NW into Blackgate
Lane & follow lane for 2m then
follow signs.* Cottage garden with
bulbs, roses, pasture with wild
flowers and pond; all on Wealden
clay, surrounding Sussex farmhouse
(not open) dating from 1420. TEAS.
*Adm £2, chd £1. Suns, Mons 3, 4
Apr; 5, 6 June (2-5). Private visits
welcome by appt. Tel 01403 700740*

91 ◆ Nymans Garden, Handcross
&⊛⊕
(The National Trust) 4m NW of
Cuckfield. On B2114 at Handcross

signed off M23/A23 London-Brighton rd, SE of Handcross. Bus: 73 from Hove or Crawley & 271 from Haywards Heath. One of the great gardens of the Sussex Weald. Walled garden with fountain, hidden sunken garden, rose garden, romantic ruins and woodland walks. A few rooms in Nymans House are open. Light refreshments and TEAS. Adm £6.70, chd £3.30. Weds to Suns 16 Feb to 30 Oct. **For NGS:** Suns 15 May; 3 July (11-6). Tel 01444 400321 www.nationaltrust.org.uk/nymans

92 Offham House, Offham (&)(circle)
(Mr H N A Goodman & Mr & Mrs P Carminger) 2m N of Lewes. On A275. Cooksbridge station ½m. Fountains; flowering trees; double herbaceous border; long peony bed. Queen Anne house (not open) 1676 with well-knapped flint facade. Herb garden. Walled kitchen garden with glasshouses. Home-made TEAS. Adm £3, chd £1. Suns 24 Apr; 5 June (1-5)

93 NEW The Old Post Office, London Road, Coldwaltham (circle)(circle)
(Patrick & Stephanie Fane) 2m S of Pulborough. On A29. 300yds S of St Giles' Church. Parking in Sandham Hall car park next door. Enthusiastic plantaholic's garden, meandering through L-shaped plot. Designed to reveal itself in stages with planting for colour, form and texture. Plants for sandy soil or special areas (bog garden, loggery) incl trees, shrubs, roses, climbers, perennials and bulbs. 2 ponds, potager, hillock with summerhouse. Home-made TEAS. Adm £2.50, chd free (share to CHASE). Suns 24 Apr; 2 Oct (2-5). **Evening Opening** £2.50, wine, Sat 11 June (5-8)

94 Old Scaynes Hill House, Clearwater Lane, Scaynes Hill (circle)(circle)
(Sue & Andy Spooner) 2m E of Haywards Heath. On A272, 50yds down Sussex border path (no parking available), beside Shell Garage shop, & opp Farmers Inn. Public parking by village hall (300yds towards Haywards Heath). In memory of Sarah Robinson. Entrance archway with steps leading to 1-acre natural garden on S-facing slope of predominantly heavy clay. Mature trees and shrubs with some unusual specimens. Several colourful herbaceous borders and island beds with ornamental grasses. Many roses, small wild flower meadow with orchids, woodland walk, small orchard, fruit and vegetable area, bog garden and natural-looking pond.

Home-made TEAS. Adm £2, chd free. Sat, Sun 18, 19 June (2-5.30). Private visits welcome by appt July to Sept, groups of 10+. Tel 01444 831602

95 64 Old Shoreham Road, Hove (&)(circle)
(Brian & Muriel Bailey) A270. On S side between Shirley Drive & Upper Drive. 12.6 metres by 33.6 metres designed and built by owners. Automatic watering for 134 containers. 1,062 varieties incl 68 hostas and 164 clematis. Home-made TEAS. Adm £2, chd free. Sun 24 July (2-5). Also opening with **Brighton & Hove Clematis Gardens** Suns 29 May, 26 June

96 13 The Oval, Findon Village (&)(&)
(Ann & Phil Van Praag) 4m N of Worthing. N end of village past Fire Station just off A24. Plenty of parking on The Oval. An architectural garden with a subtropical feel. Adm £2, chd 50p. Suns 26 June; 7 Aug (10-5)

97 Palatine Gardens, Palatine Road, Worthing (&)(circle)
(Mrs Jennie Rollings) 1m W of Worthing. Turn S off A2032 at roundabout onto The Boulevard, signed Goring (A259). Take R turn at next roundabout into Palatine Rd. School approx 100yds on R. Award-winning school garden created by teachers, volunteers and pupils with special needs into a series of themed gardens: large and small pond with bog garden, wildlife area, rockeries, sea garden, mosaics, oriental garden and rare tree collection. The thinking garden, labyrinth and new dry garden are being developed this year. Lottery award 2003, Worthing in Bloom (Best School Garden) 2003/4, 'REEP', Alan Titchmarsh (Gardens for Schools) & Earthwatch awards 2004. TEAS in aid of St Barnabas Hospice (Suns). Adm £2.50, chd free. Suns 8 May; 19 June; 17 July (11-5). **Evening Opening** £2.50, wine, Mons 20 June; 18 July (7-9). Private visits welcome by appt for large groups, coaches permitted. Tel 01903 242835 www.goring-by-sea.com/palatine

98 ◆ Parham Gardens, Parham Park, Storrington, nr Pulborough (&)(circle)
(home of Lady Emma & Mr James Barnard) 4m SE of Pulborough. On A283 Pulborough-Storrington rd. 4 acres of walled garden with huge herbaceous borders providing a riot of colour throughout the summer and well into the autumn. Large areas of

cutting flowers providing material for wonderful arrangements throughout the house. Vegetables, fruit and a very beautiful greenhouse, brick and turf maze, lake - the whole set within an SSSI. Picnic area. Featured in 'The English Garden', 'Country House & Home', 'Kitchen Garden' 2003 & 'Sussex Life' 2004. Light refreshments and TEAS. House and garden adm £6.50, chd £2.50, OAP £5.50, garden only adm £5, chd £1, OAP £4.50. Weds, Thurs, Suns, Bank Hol Mons Easter to Sept; also Tues, Fris in Aug. **For NGS:** Wed, Thur 8, 9 June (12-5). **Evening Opening** £5, wine (not incl in adm), bring a picnic, Sat 16 July (3-9). Tel 01903 742021 www.parhaminsussex.co.uk

99 6 Park Terrace, Tillington (circle)
(Mr & Mrs H Bowden) 1m W of Petworth. On A272, between Midhurst & Petworth, 1m W of Petworth, turn uphill at sign to Tillington Village, past Horseguards PH and church, no 6 is past village hall. Please do not park in residents' spaces but further up the lane. A garden designed for entertaining or quiet retreats in complete privacy. Terrace under the vine; 2 ponds, aviary; archways of roses, wisteria, box hedges, dry beds surrounded by herbaceous and shrubs. Another leafy tunnel leads to the large dome covered by fruit trees and climbers. Terrace, pigsty, greenhouse, fern walk, more beds. Sunset terrace with S Downs views. The garden resounds with the water from all the fountains made by Humphrey. Featured on Joe Swift Meridian TV 2004. Home-made TEAS (June only). Adm £2, chd 50p (share to Tillington Village Hall). Suns 5, 12 June; 4 Sept (11-5); **Evening Openings** £3, wine, Thur 9 June; Sun 4 Sept (5-8). Private visits welcome by appt, groups of 10+, May, June, July (not Hampton Court Show week). Tel 01798 344114 isabellebowden@aol.com

100 18 Pavilion Road, Worthing (circle)(circle)
(Andrew Muggeridge) Nr Worthing main station. Town garden. This is a plantsmans garden, many unusual perennials, lots of grasses, alliums, many infill plants used throughout the season. Sunflowers, leonotis, seasonal pots, the design and planting is always changing, described as organised chaos, plenty to see. Not suitable for children. Featured in 'Sussex Life' 2004. Adm £1.50, chd free. Sats, Suns 23, 30 Apr; 7, 22, 28 May; 12, 18, 26 June; 9, 17, 23, 31 July; 6, 21, 27 Aug; 4, 10, 18, 24

Sept (2-5). **Evening Openings** *£2.50, wine, Sats 25 June; 16 July (6-8). Private visits welcome by appt. Tel 01903 821338 rewrew18@hotmail.com*

101 Peasmarsh Place, Church Lane, Peasmarsh ♿✿ NCCPG
(Viscount Devonport) *3½m NW of Rye. From A268 in Peasmarsh take Church Lane (signed Norman Church), garden 1m on R after church.* 7-acre garden surrounding Peasmarsh Place (not open). Yew-enclosed rose garden and various features with an 'Alice in Wonderland' connection. Fine display of spring flowers and autumn colour. Contains National Collection of limes and sweet chestnuts. Large and varied arboretum mostly planted since 1976 with fine walks and outdoor sculpture. Home-made TEAS. *Adm £2.50. Suns 1 May; 23 Oct (2-5)*

102 33 Peerley Road, East Wittering ✿✱
(Paul & Trudi Harrison) *7m S of Chichester. From A286 take B2198 to Bracklesham. Turn R into Stocks Lane then L at Royal British Legion into Legion Way & follow rd round to Peerley Rd halfway along.* Small garden 65ft x 32ft. 110yds from sea packed full of ideas and unusual plants using every inch of space to create unusual rooms and places for adults and children to play. Specialising in unusual plants that grow well in seaside conditions. A must for any suburban gardener. Featured in Garden Makers Meridian TV 2004. *Adm £2, chd free. Suns 26 June; 7 Aug (12-4). Private visits welcome by appt. Tel 01243 673215 www.coastalgardening.net*

103 NEW Penland Farmhouse, Hanlye Lane, Cuckfield ♿
(Chris & Anne French) *1m N of Haywards Heath. From Haywards Heath take Balcombe Rd, approx 1m from station L into Hanlye Lane.* 150

yds L into drive. Redeveloped since 1999, 8 connected garden areas set in 1 acre around converted farmhouse and cottage (not open). Stocked with trees, shrubs and herbaceous plants for yr-round interest. Walled garden with parterre, wisteria pergola walkway and overflowing colour-themed borders. Home-made TEAS in aid of St Peter & St James Hospice. *Adm £2.50, chd free. Fri, Sun 10, 12 June (2-5.30).* **Evening Opening** *£2.50, wine, Sat 18 June (5-8)*

104 Penns in the Rocks, Groombridge ♿✿✱
(Lady Gibson) *7m SW of Tunbridge Wells. On Groombridge-Crowborough rd just S of Plumeyfeather corner.* Large wild garden with rocks; lake; C18 temple; old walled garden with herbaceous, roses and shrubs. House (not open) part C18. Dogs under control in park only (no shade in car park). TEAS. *Adm £3, up to two chd 50p each, further chd free. Suns 20 Mar; 14 Aug (2.30-5.30). Private visits welcome by appt for parties. Tel 01892 864244*

105 Perryfield House, Udimore ✿✱
(Mr & Mrs Adam Hart) *3½m NW of Rye. On B2089 ½m E of Udimore. Opp phone box on R.* Approx 2-acre garden of wide interest, mixed borders of perennials, shrubs and trees, incl eucalyptus and acers. Wild flower meadow and small Mediterranean garden. Cream TEAS in aid of Chenobyl Children, Rye. *Adm £2.50, chd free. Sun 12 June (2-5)*

106 Perryhill Farmhouse, Hartfield ♿✿✱
(John & Diana Whitmore) *7m E of East Grinstead. Midway between E Grinstead & Tunbridge Wells. 1m N of Hartfield on B2026. Turn into unmade lane adjacent to Perryhill*

Nurseries. 1½ acres, set below beautiful C15 hall house (not open), with stunning views of Ashdown Forest. Herbaceous and mixed borders, formal rose garden and climbing rose species, water garden, parterre, pergola. Many varieties of unusual shrubs and trees. Croquet lawn (open for play). Top and soft fruit. Productive Victorian greenhouse. Dahlia mania corner. Home-made TEAS in aid of Cancer Research. *Adm £3, chd free. Sat, Sun 13, 14 Aug (2-5). Private visits welcome by appt. Tel 01892 770266*

107 Pheasants Hatch, Piltdown ♿✱
(Mrs G E Thubron) *3m NW of Uckfield. On A272.* 2 acres; rose gardens with ponds and fountains; beautiful herbaceous borders; foliage; wild garden; peacocks. Home-made TEAS. *Adm £2.50, chd free. Sun, Mon 26, 27 June (2-6). Private visits welcome by appt. Tel 01825 722960*

108 Pindars, Lyminster ♿✿✱
(Mr & Mrs Clive Newman) *2m S of Arundel. Lyminster on A284 between A27 & A259. 1m S of A27 Pindars is on L. Park beyond house on same side.* A garden that like Topsy, "just growed"! A flat bare field many yrs ago, the owners have tried to create a garden with interesting nooks and corners, hidden borders and benches, with a wide diversity of planting. New Mediterranean-style gravel and grasses area around swimming pool. Vegetable garden; mature trees. Accommodation. Home-made TEAS in aid of St Mary the Virgin Church, Burpham. *Adm £2, chd under £5 free. Mons, Sun 29 Aug; 11, 12 Sept (2-6)*

109 Pine Cottage, Rackham, Pulborough ♿✿✱
(Rob & Glenys Rowe) *4m E of Pulborough. From Pulborough take A283 to Storrington, after 4m turn into Greatham Rd. Follow Rackham signs. From Arundel take A284 then B2139 to Storrington. After Amberley turn L into Rackham St. Park by old school & walk through gate along the path into the woods.* The 4-acre garden has been sympathetically developed since 1995 to fit into the surrounding unspoilt landscape of the South Downs and Arun Valley. 3 large ponds, wild flower meadows, kitchen garden and orchard. Relaxed planting with native species is a feature to give naturalistic feel and to encourage as wide a range of wildlife as possible. Organic principles are applied throught out the garden. Not suitable for children.

"... but I distinctly remember asking for <u>Morris</u> dancers!"

Featured in 'Essential Water Garden' 2004. *Adm £2.50. Private visits welcome by appt, also groups May & June, visits at other times may be possible. Tel 01903 744115* glenysrowepc@aol.com

110 **NEW** **6 Plantation Rise, Worthing** (&)(※)(⊕)
(Mr & Mrs N Hall) *Outskirts of Worthing. A24 meets A27 at Offington roundabout. Proceed into Offington Lane. Take 1st R into The Plantation, 1st R again - Plantation Rise. Please park in The Plantation - short walk to Plantation Rise - no 6 top of close on L. Interesting garden* 70ft x 80ft lovingly landscaped by owners. Featuring pond, summerhouse, pergolas, various trees and shrubs. Perennial plants, all-yr colour. Winner 'Daily Mail' National Garden Competition 2004. TEAS in aid of St Barnabus Hospice, Worthing. *Adm £2, chd free. Wed 1 June (2-6).* **Evening Openings** *£2, wine, Fri, Sat 19, 20 Aug (5-8). Private visits welcome by appt May & June Weds only (2-5), groups maximum of 8. Tel 01903 262206* trixiehall@btinternet.com

111 ♦ **The Priest House, North Lane, West Hoathly** (⊕)
(Sussex Archaeological Society) *4m SW of East Grinstead. Turn E to West Hoathly 1m S of Turners Hill at the Selsfield Common junction on B2028. 2m S turn R into North Lane. Garden ¼m further on.* C15 timber-framed house with cottage garden. Large selection of culinary and medicinal herbs in small formal garden with mixed herbaceous borders, plus long-established yew topiary, box hedges and espalier apple trees. Small woodland garden with fernery. Featured in '25 Beautiful Gardens' 2003. Priest House Museum open at special price £1 for garden visitors. *Within walking distance of* **Duckyls Holt** *&* **White Rock** *Combined adm £3. House and garden adm £2, chd £1, garden only adm £1, chd free. Tues to Suns Mar to Oct (10.30-5.30).* **For NGS:** *Sats 28 May; 25 June (11-5.30). Tel 01342 810479* www.sussexpast. co.uk/priesthouse

112 **NEW** **The Pykle, 11 Salvington Road, Worthing** (&)(※)
(Alex Burt) *3m N of Worthing town centre. From Worthing on local bus route, 50 meters W of John Seldon PH.* Charming small town garden started from scratch in Oct 2003 by novice gardener, concentrating on annuals but with some interesting grasses & perennials. Changes every

year with different themes. Theme for 2005 is 'Bicentenary of Trafalgar'. Architectural features in wrought iron designed and made by garden owner, this year featuring 6' x 10' HMS Victory infilled with flowers - real nautical flavour. Home-made TEAS. *Adm £1.50, chd under 12 free. Sat, Sun 9, 10 July (11-5). Day* &**Evening Openings** *£1.50, Sat, Sun 18, 19 June (11-8). Private visits welcome by appt. Tel 01903 693223* alexpykle@aol.com

113 **Ridge House, East Street, Turners Hill** (&)
(Mr & Mrs Nicholas Daniels) *4m SW of East Grinstead. 3m E of Crawley. On B2110, 5m SE J10 of M23. Via A264 & B2028. 30yds E of CrownPH on Turners Hill Xrds. Parking in recreation ground E of Ridge House.* 1-acre garden with mixed borders, Victorian greenhouse, pond, dell and productive vegetable garden. Nigel's garden gives interest throughout the yr and offers a quite corner to absorb the beautiful view of the High Weald of Sussex. The garden offers interest, calm and unexpected vistas. Featured in 'Amateur Gardening' 2003. Home-made TEAS in aid of St Leonard's Church. *Adm £2, chd free. Sat, Sun 25, 26 June (2-6)*

114 **Rose Cottage, Hadlow Down** (※)(⊕)
(Ken & Heather Mines) *6m NE of Uckfield. Turn off A272 opp entrance to Wilderness Wood.* Plantsman's ⅔-acre garden using unusual plants combined with reclaimed materials, mouldering carvings from a Victorian church and contemporary sculptures to recreate childhood memories of secret places. Old-fashioned roses add nostalgia and scent. Self-seeding is encouraged resulting in a garden that is constantly changing. Luxuriance is valued above tidiness. All plants sold, incl HYDRA 'Heritage' vegetables are raised in the garden. Home-made TEAS. *Adm £2.50, chd free. Suns 29 May; 19 June (2-5.30).* **Evening Openings** *£2.50, wine, Wed 15 June; Fri 1 July (5-8). Private visits welcome by appt. Tel 01825 830314* kenmines@hotmail.com

115 **Rosemary Cottage, Firgrove Road, Cross In Hand** (※)(⊕)
(Mr & Mrs C Walker) *3m SW of Heathfield. From A267 (at Cross in Hand) turn onto B2102 opp Esso garage. After ½m turn L into Firgrove Rd, approx 1m on R. A* Peter Thurman garden of 2 acres with many features. Now in its 5th yr, the

sensitive brickwork terraces frame borders with exquisite plantings, incl a white border, cutting garden, topiary, spring rockery, with woodland and rose walks. Choice plants are hidden throughout. A reflective pond is beautifully enhanced by clipped yews and extensive collection of terracotta. Winner Assoc of Professional Landscapers competition 2003. Home-made TEAS in aid of James House Childrens Hospice At Home, Burwash Weald. *Adm £2.50, chd free. Sun 8 May (2-6)*

116 **Roundhill Cottage, East Dean**
(Mr Jeremy Adams) *7m NE of Chichester. Take A286 Chichester-Midhurst. At Singleton follow signs to Charlton/East Dean. In East Dean turn R at Star & Garter Inn, Roundhill is approx 100yd.* 1-acre country garden set in tranquil fold of the South Downs, designed in 1980 by Judith Adams whose inspiration came from French impressionists and continued by her daughter Louise, whose love of secret gardens, wild flower meadows and crumbly gothic ruins all shown to delightful effect in a garden full of surprises. Come and enjoy. Featured in Alan Titchmarsh's Garden Calender. TEAS. *Adm £2.50, chd free. Day &* **Evening Opening** *Sun 29 May (2-8). Mon 30 May (2-6). Private visits welcome by appt. Tel 01243 811447*

117 **Rymans, Apuldram**
(Mrs Michael Gayford) *1m S of Chichester. Take Witterings rd out of Chichester; at 1½m SW turn R signposted Apuldram; garden down rd on L.* Walled and other gardens surrounding lovely C15 stone house (not open); bulbs, flowering shrubs, roses, water feature, potager. Many unusual and rare trees. Featured on ITV Making Gardens 2004. Home-made TEAS in aid of Leukaemia Research. *Adm £3, chd free. Sats, Suns 19, 20 Mar; 29 May; 10, 11 Sept; Mon 30 May (2-5). Private visits welcome by appt. Tel 01243 783147*

118 **Sackville College Gardens, High Street, East Grinstead** (&)(※)
(Sackville College Trustees) *From High St turn into Church Lane (almost opp Dorset Arms public house). Public car park in Church Lane, just past college entrance.* Restoration (begun 2003) of almshouse garden, incl quadrangle. Herbaceous beds against old (1609) stone walls, lawns, bowling green, shrubs and trees. Warden's private garden with an area of steps, terraces

and low stone walls, is being restored with ferns, hostas, bulbs and rare plants. Grade I listed Jacobean almshouse also opens Adm £3. Home-made TEAS in aid of Sackville College Repairs Fund. *Adm £2, chd £1. Sat, Suns 30 Apr; 1 May; 5 June (2-6).* **Evening Opening** *£2.50, wine, Sun 12 June (5-8). Private visits welcome by appt. Tel 01342 326561 www.sackville-college.co.uk*

119 NEW **Sandhill Farm House, Rogate** ⬤⬤

(Rosemary Alexander) *4m SE of Petersfield. From A272 Xrds in Nyewood/Harting. Follow rd for approx 1m over small bridge. Sandhill Farm House on R, over cattle grid.* Both front and rear gardens are broken up into garden rooms. Front garden incl small woodland area planted with early spring flowering shrubs and bulbs, white garden, hot dry terraced area with Mediterranean type planting. Rear garden has mirror borders, small decorative vegetable garden and 'red' border. Featured in Evening Standard 'Homes & Property' & 'The Times' 2004. *Adm £3, chd free, concessions £1.50. Sun 24 Apr; Sat 17 Sept (2-5.30)*

120 Sands, Warnham ⬤⬤

(Professor & Mrs R P Dales) *3½m NW of Horsham. From A24 enter Warnham & follow signs to Northlands & Ockley.* Country garden of approx 1 acre on Wealden clay, surrounding C15 farmhouse (not open). Various areas from grassy orchard to pond, kitchen garden and herb garden are separated by hedges. Borders and beds contain mainly shrubs and herbaceous perennials; collection of hardy geraniums. Featured in 'West Sussex County Times' 2004. TEAS (Sun). *Adm £2, chd free. Sun 12 June (2-5.30).* **Evening Opening** *£3, wine & soft drinks, Wed 29 June (6-8). Private visits welcome by appt. Tel 01403 254843*

121 Sarah Raven's Cutting Garden, Perch Hill Farm, Willingford Lane, Brightling ⬤⬤

(Sarah Raven) *7m SW of Hurst Green. From A21 Hurst Green take A265 Heathfield Rd for 6m. In Burwash Weald turn L at Wheel Inn down Willingford Lane. 1m on L.* 1-acre working garden in Sussex Weald. Incl cutting garden with annuals and biennials, cleome, helianthus, amaranthus. Oast garden, extravagant mix of colour and structure. Salvias, cardoons,

artichokes; brilliantly coloured dahlia garden with zinnias, gladioli, cannas, jungly corn, banana foliage. Kitchen garden with unusual vegetables eg borlotti beans. Home-made TEAS. *Adm £3, chd free, concessions £2.50. Sun 11 Sept (11-5). Private visits welcome by appt for groups of 18+, Apr to Sept. Tel 0845 0504849 www.thecuttinggarden.com*

122 NEW **Sayerlands, Polegate**

2m S of Hailsham. From N take A22 Hailsham to Polegate. Just before Polegate bypass roundabout, L into Baytree Lane. At end L into Sayerland Lane. From S, at Polegate bypass roundabout take A22 signed Hailsham, immed L under underpass, R into Baytree Lane. Home-made TEAS, plant sales, tickets and car park at Sayerlands House. *Combined adm £3.50, chd free (share to All Saints Church, Eastbourne & SOS Sahel UK). Sat 6 Aug (2-6)*

NEW **Bay Tree Cottage** ⬤⬤ (Mrs Margot Adkins) *1st house in Sayerland Lane.* 1 acre mature cottage style garden. Brimming with colour, many containers with unusual annuals, fuchsias and begonias, several patio areas surrounded by beds thickly planted with mixed annuals and perennials.

NEW **Sayerland House** ⬤⬤⬤ (Penny & Kevin Jenden) *300yds down Sayerland Lane, 1st gate on L after Cat Hotel.* 5-acre garden surrounding listed C15 house (not open). Several distinct garden areas. Walled garden with colour-themed herbaceous borders, enclosed rose garden, ponds, kitchen garden, wild flower areas and new 'tropical' beds. Many mature shrubs and specimen trees.

123 Selehurst, Lower Beeding ⬤⬤⬤

(Mr & Mrs M Prideaux) *4½m S of Horsham. On A281 opp Leonardslee.* Woodland garden in romantic valley. Sham-Gothic tower on the skyline above a pebblework waterfall, chain of 5 ponds, further waterfalls, pretty bridge. Fine trees, tree-like rhododendrons, eucryphias, azaleas, camellias, stewartias. Formal features incl walled garden with borders, semicircular arbour of *Cytisus battandieri*, 60ft rose and laburnum tunnel. Chinoiserie pavilion over the lake decorated with Chinese balustrading, red lacquer, gold dragons and dolphins. Box and herb parterre. Featured in 'The English Garden' 2005. Home-made TEAS. *Adm £3, chd free (share to St*

John's Church, Coolhurst). Sun 15 May (2-6)

124 Sennicotts, Chichester ⬤

(Mr & Mrs James Rank) *2m NW of Chichester. From Chichester take B2178 signed Funtington for 2m. Entrance on R. Long drive, ample parking nr house. From Fishbourne turn N marked Roman Palace then straight on until T-junction. Entrance opp.* 6-acre mature garden with intriguing spaces; lawns, rhododendrons and azaleas. Pleached lime walk leading to large walled kitchen garden and cutting garden with herbaceous plants; greenhouses and an orchard. Featured in 'West Sussex Gazette' 2003. TEAS. *Adm £3, chd free. Sat 11 June (2-6)*

125 NEW **Shalford House, Square Drive, Kingsley Green** ⬤

(Vernon & Hazel Ellis) *2m S of Haslemere. Just S of border with Surrey on A286. Square Drive is at brow of hill, to the E. Turn L after 0.2m and follow rd to R at bottom of hill.* Garden created from scratch over last decade with designer Sally Court. Terraces, streams, ponds, waterfall, sunken and walled gardens, herbaceous borders, meadow with wild orchids. Wonderful hilly setting. 10-acre garden merging into 7 acres woodland with further 30 acres of woods with beeches, rhododendrons, ponds and clearing with new trees. Featured in 'The Modern Garden Makers' book by Sally Court. TEAS. *Adm £2.50, chd free. Sun 17 July (2-6)*

126 ◆ **Sheffield Park Garden, Sheffield Park** ⬤⬤⬤ NCCPG

(The National Trust) *10m S of E Grinstead. 5m NW of Uckfield; E of A275.* Magnificent 120 acres (40 hectares) landscaped garden laid out in C18 by Capability Brown and Humphry Repton. Further development in early yrs of this century by its owner Arthur G Soames. Centrepiece is original lakes, with many rare trees and shrubs. Beautiful at all times of the year, but noted for its spring and autumn colours. National Collection of Ghent azaleas. TEAS not NT. *Adm £5.50, chd £2.75. Sats, Suns 1 Jan to 13 Feb (10.30-4); Tues to Suns 15 Feb to 31 Oct (10.30-6) & 1 Nov to 22 Dec (10.30-4). Daily May to Oct.* **For NGS:** *Tues 3 May; 4 Oct (10.30-6 last entry 5). Tel 01825 790231 sheffieldpark@nationaltrust.org.uk*

⚑ Sherburne House, Eartham, nr Chichester ⬤⬤⬤
(Mr & Mrs Angus Hewat) *6m NE of Chichester. Approach from A27 Chichester-Arundel rd or A285 Chichester-Petworth rd, nr centre of village, 200yds S of church.* Chalk garden of approx 2 acres. Shrub and climbing roses, lime-tolerant shrubs, herbaceous, grey-leaved and foliage plants, pots, water feature, small herb garden, kitchen garden potager with octagonal pergola, wild flower meadow and conservatory. *Private visits welcome by appt, also groups, June & July best. Refreshments by arrangement. Tel/fax 01243 814261*

⚑ NEW Siggle Wriggle, Nash Street, Chiddingly/Hailsham ⬤⬤⬤
(Mr Paul Hastie) *3m NW of Hailsham. From A22 Eastbourne to Uckfield. 1m NW of Boship roundabout turn R into Nash St, signed Gun Hill. 400yds on L opp Marigolds Farm. Please park in Nash St.* Garden of shadows and light. Newly developing 2-acre garden planted and maintained by present owner since 1996. Garden fans out from C16 cottage (not open) bedecked with old roses. Hornbeam walk, pond, rose garden, 300ft mixed border, woodland garden, small fruit and vegetable garden, beech ave, yew roundel and rough meadow. Extensive bamboo collection. *Adm £2.50, chd free. Fri, Sat 3, 4 June (11-4). Private visits welcome by appt, no coaches. Tel 01825 873134 siggle1@aol.com*

⚑ Somerset Lodge, North Street, Petworth ⬤
(Mr & Mrs R Harris) *On A283 & A272 100yds N of church. Parking in town car park.* Charming ½-acre town garden with ponds and walled kitchen garden, small collection of old roses and wild flower garden. Cleverly landscaped on slope with beautiful views. Featured in '25 Beautiful Gardens' & on Meridian TV 2004. TEAS in aid of St Mary Petworth appeal. *Adm £2, chd 50p. Sat 11 to Sun 19 June (12-6). Private visits welcome by appt. Tel 01798 343842*

⚑ South Harting Gardens
4m SE of Petersfield. On B2146. Charming Downland village with notable and famous copper-spired church and wide village street. Cream TEAS at Malthouse in village (Sun). *Combined adm £3, chd free. Sat, Sun 11, 12 June (2-5.30)*

Ivy House ⬤ (Mr & Mrs David Summerhayes) *At S end of village*

opp Harting Church on B2146. 1½-acre terraced village garden, sloping down to brook with orchard and paddock beyond. Specimen trees, shrubs and roses. Views to Harting Down.

NEW Nyewood House ⬤⬤ (Mr & Mrs C J Wright) *From South Harting take rd N signed Rogate & Nyewood. At far end of Nyewood turn R beside pylon towards South Downs Hotel. Nyewood 2nd entrance on R between trees and over cattle grid.* Victorian country house (not open) garden, 3 acres, simplified and opened up over past 2yrs to maximise stunning views of South Downs. Added features incl shrub border, new rose arbour and Japanese style walkway over pond.

Pyramids, North Lane ⬤⬤ (Mrs Stephanie Morgan) *200yds on R up North Lane.* ½ acre with mainly chalk-loving plants; old-fashioned roses, clematis, rose arbour; pool with fountain; uniquely shaped old apple trees. Interesting house designed 1965 by Stout and Lichfield (not open) linked to garden by paved areas. Splendid views.

⚑ Sparrow Hatch, Cornwell's Bank, nr Newick ⬤⬤
(Tony & Jane Welfare) *5m E of Haywards Heath. From A272 turn R into Oxbottom Lane (signpost Barcombe), ½m fork L into Narrow Rd, continue to T-junction & park in Chailey Lane (no parking at house).* ¾-acre plantsman's cottage garden. Developed by owners over past 7yrs into various different areas allowing maximum space for plantaholic's diverse collection of plants, many unusual. *Adm £2. Weds, Thurs 1, 2 June; 6, 7 July (2-5). Private visits welcome by appt. Tel 01825 723057*

⚑ ◆ St Mary's House & Gardens, Bramber ⬤⬤
(Mr Peter Thorogood) *1m E of Steyning. 10m NW of Brighton in Bramber Village off A283.* Over 5 acres of gardens, incl charming formal topiary beds, pools and fountains, the ancient ivy-clad 'Monk's walk', large example of the prehistoric *Ginkgo biloba*, and magnificent *Magnolia grandiflora*; all around Grade I listed C15 timber framed medieval house, once a pilgrim inn. The Victorian 'Secret' gardens also incl splendid 140ft fruit wall, heated pineapple pits (awaiting restoration), circular orchard, rural museum, terracotta garden and the delightful Jubilee rose garden. TEAS.

Adm £3.50, chd £1. House & garden open Suns, Thurs Bank Hol Mons May to Sept (2-6). **For NGS:** *Fri, Sat 29, 30 July (2-5.30). Tel 01903 816205 www.stmarysbramber.co.uk*

⚑ ◆ Standen, East Grinstead ⬤⬤
(The National Trust) *1½m S of E Grinstead. Signed from B2110 & A22 at Felbridge.* Approx 12 acres of hillside garden, packed with surprises. Features incl quarry, bamboo gardens and 3 summerhouses. Lovely views over the Medway and Ashdown Forest. Private areas of garden open specially for NGS. TEAS. *Adm £3.90, chd £1.90. Weds to Suns & Bank Hols 18 Mar to 30 Oct (11-6).* **For NGS:** *Tues 17 May; 18 Oct (2-5). Tel 01342 323029 standen@nationaltrust.org.uk*

⚑ Stone Cross House, Crowborough ⬤
(Mr & Mrs D A Tate) *½m S of Crowborough. At Crowborough T-lights (A26) turn S into High St, & shortly R into Croft Rd. Straight over 2 mini roundabouts into Alice Bright Lane. Garden on L at next Xrds about 1½m from T-lights.* 1½-acre woodland spring garden with some unusual shrubs, azaleas and rhododendrons. Herbaceous borders, lovely views. Tours to be given by garden creator. TEAS in aid of St John Ambulance. *Adm £2.50, chd 50p. Fri, Sun 6, 8 May (2-5.30)*

⚑ NEW Stonehealed Farm, Streat Lane, Streat ⬤⬤⬤
(Lance & Fiona Smith) *2m SE of Burgess Hill. From B2116, 1m E of Westmeston, turn L (N) signed Streat, 2m on R immed after railway bridge.* Developing garden begun in 1996 surrounding C17 house (not open). Approx 1½ acres overlooking S Downs. Formal front garden, brick terrace with pool and seasonal pots, shady pond area with tree platform. Hot and cool borders, raised vegetable beds. Planted for all seasons balancing structure with informality. Home-made TEAS. *Adm £2.50, chd free. Suns, Mons 1, 2 May; 11, 12 Sept (2-5). Private visits welcome by appt. Tel 01273 891145 afionasmith@hotmail.com*

⚑ Swiftsden Farm Oast, Ticehurst Road, Hurst Green ⬤⬤
(John & Julie Gilbert) *2m NW of Hurst Green. On S side of B2099 approx 2m E of Ticehurst village & ½m W of A21. Short way along bridle path (unmade, single-track with passing places).* 8-acre steep

countryside site being developed. Oast House (not open) surrounded by small, intimate gardens and informal terraces. Extensive range of herbaceous plants, shrubs and trees. Vegetable garden and fruit trees. Chickens, bees, rare-breed sheep. Newly-planted native woodland. Conservation areas left for wildlife. Good views. Home-made TEAS in aid of Robertsbridge United Reformed Church. *Adm £2, chd free. Sat, Sun 11, 12 June (2-6)*

137 Tinkers Bridge Cottage, Tinkers Lane, Ticehurst 🏡
(Mrs M A Landsberg) *11m SE of Tunbridge Wells. From B2099 ½m W Ticehurst, turn N to Three Leg Cross for 1m, R after Bull Inn. House at bottom of hill.* 12 acres landscaped; stream garden nr house (not open) leading to herbaceous borders, wildlife meadow with ponds and woodland walks. TEAS. *Adm £3 incl tea, chd free. Sun 22 May (2.30-5.30). Private visits welcome by appt, no coaches. Tel 01580 200272*

138 Town Place, Freshfield 👥🎨🏡
(Mr & Mrs A C O McGrath) *3m E of Haywards Heath. From A275 turn W at Sheffield Green into Ketches*

Lane for Lindfield. 1¾m on L. 3 acres with over 600 roses, 150ft herbaceous border, walled herb garden, shrubbery, ancient hollow oak, orchard and potager. C17 Sussex farmhouse (not open). Featured in 'English Garden' 2003. Cream TEAS. *Adm £4, chd free. Suns, Thurs 12, 16, 26 June; 3, 10, 14 July (2-6). Private visits welcome by appt for groups of 20+. Tel 01825 790221*

139 Trotton Old Rectory, Trotton 🎨🏡
(Captain & Mrs John Pilley) *3m W of Midhurst. On A272.* Typical English garden with rose beds, designed by Hazel le Rougetel, framed in box and yew, has 2 levels with beautiful and interesting trees and shrubs running down to lake and R Rother. Newly planted pleached limes with formal planting. *Adm £3, chd free. Suns 15 May; 19 June (2-6)*

140 ◆ Uppark, South Harting 👥🎨
(The National Trust) *1½m S of S Harting. 5m SE of Petersfield on B2146.* Fine late C17 house situated high on the S Downs with magnificent views towards the Solent. Reptonian garden replanned and replanted since major fire in 1989.

Woodland walk. House open (1-5). Gardener Guided Tours. Post Fire Restoration Exhibition. Cream TEAS. *House and Garden adm £6, garden only adm £3, chd £1.50. Suns to Thurs Apr to Oct (11-5.30) (Oct 11-4.30). House (1-5), Suns in Aug (12-5).* **For NGS:** *Thurs 5 May; 2 June (11-5.30). Tel 01730 825415 uppark@nationaltrust.org.uk*

141 Villa Elisabetta, Newbury Lane, Cousley Wood, Wadhurst 👥🎨🏡
(Jim & Kathy Cooper) *8m SE of Tunbridge Wells. Proceed to Cousley Wood halfway between Wadhurst & Lamberhurst on B2100. Opp Old Vine Inn, take turning signed Bells Yew Green & Tunbridge Wells into Newbury Lane. 3rd house on L.* 1½ acre garden behind small semi-detached house (not open). Herbaceous beds, shrub borders, specimen trees, formal and woodland gardens. Developed from an old orchard and wild areas of bracken, nettles and brambles. Quiet location in the Sussex weald. Roses, dahlias, grasses and daylilies etc. Light refreshments and TEAS (share to British Diabetic Assoc). *Adm £2, chd free. Sun 10 July (2-5). Private visits welcome by appt. Tel 07803 134720 jim@elisabetta.co.uk*

142 Warren House, Warren Road, Crowborough 👥✂️🏠
(Mr & Mrs M J Hands) *1½m SW of Crowborough Cross. From Crowborough Cross towards Uckfield, 4th turning on R. 1m down Warren Rd. From South 2nd L after Blue Anchor.* Beautiful house (not open) steeped in history with 9-acre garden and views over Ashdown Forest. Series of gardens old and new, displaying wealth of azaleas, rhododendrons, impressive variety of trees and shrubs. Sweeping lawns framed by delightful walls and terraces, woodlands, ponds. Home-made TEAS in aid of Marie Curie. *Adm £2.50, chd free. Sun 24 Apr; Mons 2, 30 May; 29 Aug (2-5). Private visits welcome by appt for groups of 20+. Tel 01892 663502*

143 NEW West Chiltington Village Gardens
2m E of Pulborough. 3m N of Storrington. At Xrds in centre of West Chiltington opp Queens Head. 3 adjoining ½-acre gardens with contrasting designs. Plantsman's gardens with herbaceous and shrub borders. Home-made TEAS at Palmers Lodge in aid of Motor Neurone Disease. *Combined adm £3, chd free. Suns 10, 17 July (1.30-5.30)*

NEW **Hunters Barn, The Hollow** ✂️
(Ann & Derek Frost) Converted barn (not open). Completely reshaped and replanted in 3 different areas by present owners. Dry bed area, formal area for sitting and wild area still being developed.

NEW **Palmers, The Hollows** ✂️
(Norman & Barbara Vickers) Organic cottage garden, with mixed borders and many unusual plants. Cutting and kitchen gardens, fancy chickens, plus many mature trees, pond and water feature. All designed to attract wildlife.

Palmer's Lodge, Broadford Bridge Road ✂️ (Richard Hodgson) Charming plantsman's ½-acre garden with herbaceous and shrub borders. Fruit and vegetable garden, small greenhouse. *Private visits welcome by appt July only. Tel 01798 812751*

144 ◆ West Dean Gardens, West Dean 👥✂️🏠
(Edward James Foundation) *5m N of Chichester. On A286.* 35-acre historic garden in tranquil downland setting. 300ft long Harold Peto pergola, mixed and herbaceous borders, rustic summerhouses, redeveloped water and spring garden, specimen trees. Restored 2½-acre walled garden contains fruit collection, 13 Victorian glasshouses, apple store, large working kitchen garden, extensive plant collection. Circuit walk (2¼m) climbs through parkland to 45-acre St Roches Arboretum. Light refreshments and TEAS. *Adm £5.50, chd £2.50, OAP £5. Daily 1 Mar to 31 Oct.* **For NGS:** *Tue 31 May (10.30-5). Tel 01243 818209 www.westdean.org.uk*

145 West Lodge South, Rackham ✂️
(Mr Ray Gibbs & Mr Joe Reardon-Smith) *3m W of Storrington. From B2139 between Storrington & Amberly take rd signed Rackham (Rackham St). ¼m beyond village. From A283 Pulborough to Storrington rd. Follow signs. Parking at Rackham Old School. No rd-side parking.* Approx ¼ acre garden. Clipped box and gravel paths echo the formality of the lodge whilst the wild and informal planting carries the eye to the views beyond. Bold swathes of plants chosen for long trouble-free season. Striking use of colour. Herbs, vegetables and small pond in a garden teeming with wildlife. Featured in RHS Journal 2004. *Adm £2, chd free. Sun 18 Sept (2-6).* **Evening Opening** *£3, wine, Fri 12 Aug (4-8)*

ngs

gardens open for charity

Every time you visit a garden which opens for the NGS you are helping to raise money for

- Macmillan Cancer Relief
- Marie Curie Cancer Care
- Help the Hospices
- Crossroads – Caring for Carers
- The Queen's Nursing Institute
- The Nurses Welfare Service
- The Royal Gardeners' Orphan Fund
- NGS Gardeners' Bursaries – The National Trust Careership Scheme
- Perennial – Gardeners' Royal Benevolent Society
- County Nursing Associations
- Additional charities nominated by owners

⑯ Westgate Close, 68 Westgate, Chichester 🅰🖾🅰
(Anne & David Sparrow) ½m W of Chichester city centre. Take N exit from Donnington roundabout on A27 past Chichester Station. Follow A286 to Westgate roundabout, turn L into Westgate, past Henty Gdns and Parklands Rd, Garden on R. Secluded garden of ⅔acre with many hidden features, enclosed by walls and hedges. Drive leads to a variety of areas; lawns with mature trees, shrubs and herbaceous borders; pond and herb gardens, kitchen garden of raised beds with greenhouse and grapevine. Home-made TEAS in aid of St Wilfred's Hospice. Adm £2, chd free, concessions £1.50. Sun 24 July (2-6). **Evening Opening** £1.50, wine, Tues 26 July (6-9)

⑰ 46 Westup Farm Cottages, Balcombe 🖾🅰
(Chris Cornwell) 3m N of Cuckfield. ¼m N Balcombe station, take L off B2036 immed before Balcombe Primary School (signed). ¼m. Hidden in the Sussex countryside, this cottage garden combines the functionality of its origins with unique and unusual features, linked by intimate paths through lush and subtle planting. TEAS. Adm £2, chd free. Weds 27 Apr; 25 May; 29 June (12-5). Private visits welcome by appt, incl coach parties. Tel 01444 811891

⑱ White Rock, Selsfield Road, West Hoathly 🖾🅰
(Mrs J A Naylor) 4m SW of E Grinstead. 6m E of Crawley. At Turners Hill take B2028. After 1m S fork L to W Hoathly. Just under ½ acre of well-stocked hillside garden merging imperceptibly into N Downs. Designed for outdoor living. Wide variety of trees, shrubs, bulbs, herbaceous and aquatic plants. Artist's garden full of colour, form and texture. TEAS. Adm £1, chd free. Sats, Suns 28, 29 May; 25, 26 June (11-5.30). Within walking distance of **Duckyls Holt** & **The Priest House**. Combined adm £3. Private visits welcome by appt. Tel 01342 810540

⑲ Whitehouse Cottage, Staplefield Lane, Staplefield
(Mr Barry Gray) 5m NW of Haywards Heath. E of A23 & 2m S of Handcross. In Staplefield at Xrds by cricket pavilion take turning marked Staplefield Lane for 1m. 4-

acre woodland garden with mixed shrubs, paths beside stream linked by ponds. Home-made TEAS by arrangement, please call before your visit if possible. Adm £2, chd free. Private visits welcome by appt . Open daily. Day adm £2, chd free (9-6); **Evening** adm £2, wine (6-9). Tel 01444 461229 barry.gray@ukgateway.net

⑮⓪ NEW Wildham, East Marden/Stoughton
(Consie & Mark Dunn) 4m SE of South Harting. B2141 to Chichester, turn R to East Marden, in East Marden follow signs to Stoughton, garden up track on R 1m from wishing well. Very informal chalk garden on steep hill. Dripping with roses and clematis, unusual shrubs. Glorious position. God's garden with minor interference from an idle amateur. Adm £2, chd free. Wed, Thur 1, 2 June (11-5). Private visits welcome by appt. Tel 01243 535202 dunn.wildham@virgin.net

⑮① Winchelsea's Secret Gardens
2m W of Rye. Winchelsea is a beautiful medieval town, founded in 1288 by Edward I. Notable buildings incl the splendid C14 church and Court Hall. It is one of the few surviving C13 English towns where the streets are laid out in a grid system. Because of this, the gardens are hidden behind old walls. Many of the eight gardens open this year have lovely water features and wonderful views of the sea or across the beautiful Brede Valley. Town maps given to all visitors. Home-made TEAS at New Hall, Rectory Lane in aid of Friary Gardeners. Combined adm £4, chd under 12 free. Sat 18 June (2-6)

Alards Plat, 1 High Street (Cynthia & Richard Feast) Mature narrow paved garden on 2 levels.

Amerique, Castle Street 🅰🖾 (Mr & Mrs D O'Brien) Mature garden, partly walled, extending to a wild area with herb garden to attract bees and butterflies. Old-fashioned roses - ramblers, scramblers and bush varieties abound.

Chapel Plat, Hiham Green 🖾 (Mr & Mrs R D Cooper) Small enclosed town garden with climbers, shrubs, perennials and herbs.

Cleveland House 🅰 (Mr & Mrs J Jempson) 1½-acre mature walled garden with large potager, lawn with water feature. Long covered walk, rose garden, 2 formal ponds, large old indoor vine.

NEW Magazine House, Castle Street (Mr & Mrs Stradling) Walled cottage garden.

Mill Cottage, Rectory Lane 🖾 (Les & Sylvia Parker) Cottage garden with views over Brede valley.

New Cottage, Mill Lane (Mr Ken Chetwood) One of the larger gardens, split level with lawns and flowering shrubs. Medieval cellar (open).

Old Rectory, Rectory Lane 🅰 (June & Denis Hyson) Open lawned garden with views.

Evening Opening (See also garden description)	
Champs Hill	13 May
Roundhill Cottage	29 May
Beauchamps	4 June
Charleston	9 June
6 Park Terrace	9 June
Frith Lodge	11 June
The Old Post Office	11 June
Sackville College Gardens	
	12 June
4 Hillside Cottages	14 June
Rose Cottage	15 June
Alfriston Clergy House	
	16 June
Ketleys	17 June
Penland Farmhouse	18 June
The Pykle	18 June
The Pykle	19 June
Palatine Gardens	20 June
Latchetts	23 June
51 Carlisle Road	25 June
18 Pavilion Road	25 June
Sands	29 June
Hampton Cottage	1 July
Rose Cottage	1 July
Berri Court	7 July
Parham Gardens	16 July
18 Pavilion Road	16 July
Palatine Gardens	18 July
Westgate Close	26 July
West Lodge South	12 August
Durrance Manor	17 August
6 Plantation Rise	19 August
6 Plantation Rise	20 August
Five Oaks Cottage	26 August
Ham Cottage	26 August
6 Park Terrace	4 September

ngs gardens open for charity

Art in the Garden

Champs Hill, Coldwaltham (near Pulborough), West Sussex

A special viewing of a private collection of paintings – the NEWLYN SCHOOL 1880-1940, (including a complimentary glass of wine)

Friday 13th May 2005
6.30 pm – 8.30 pm

Saturday 14th May 2005
11.30 pm – 2.30 pm

Visitors can also enjoy 27 acres of acid-loving plants around sandpits and woodland. Superb views across the Arun Valley to the South Downs. Interesting and varied sculptures to be found in carefully chosen corners of the garden.

Admission £6

Children 15 and under free

ADEQUATE PARKING
NO DOGS

Warwickshire & part of West Midlands

County Organisers:
(Warwickshire)   Mrs Sandra Burbidge, Cedar House, Wasperton CV35 8EB Tel 01926 624304
(West Midlands)   Mrs Jackie Harvey, Ashover, 25 Burnett Road, Streetly, Sutton Coldfield B74 3EL
                                  Tel 0121 353 0547
Assistant County Organisers: Mrs Cynthia Orchard, Honington Glebe, Honington, Shipston-on-Stour, Warwickshire
                                  CV36 5AA Tel 01608 661693
                                  Mr Peter Pashley, Millstones, Mayfield Avenue, Stratford-on-Avon, Warwickshire
                                  CV37 6XB Tel 01789 294932
                                  Mrs Julia Sewell, Dinsdale House, Tysoe, Warwickshire CV35 0TX Tel 01245 680234

County Treasurers:
(West Midlands)   Mr Martin Harvey, Ashover, 25 Burnett Road, Streetly, Sutton Coldfield B74 3EL
                                  Tel 0121 353 0547
(Warwickshire)   Mr John Wilson, Victoria House, Farm Street, Harbury, Leamington Spa CV33 9LR
                                  Tel 01926 612572

Maps: Numbers shown next to each garden entry refer to that garden's entry on the county map. This position is approximate;
              distance and directions from the nearest main town are generally shown in the garden text.
              A precise location is available for those gardens featured on the NGS website by visiting www.ngs.org.uk.
Symbols: Information relating to symbols is given on page 21

DATES OF OPENING

Evening openings
See end of county listing

Gardens open to the public
For details see garden description
Baddesley Clinton Hall, Knowle, Solihull *(7)*
Bridge Nursery, Napton *(10)*
Castle Bromwich Hall Gardens, Castle
  Bromwich *(11)*
89 Harts Green Road, Harborne *(25)*
The Mill Garden, Warwick *(36)*
Newnham Paddox, Monks Kirby *(40)*
Packwood House, nr Hockley Heath *(43)*
Ragley Hall Gardens, Alcester *(48)*
Ryton Organic Gardens, nr Wolston Village
  (50)
University of Birmingham Botanic Garden at
  Winterbourne, Edgbaston *(52)*
Upton House, nr Banbury *(53)*
Victorian Pleasure Gardens at Hill Close,
  Warwick *(54)*

By appointment only
*For telephone number and other
details see garden description.
Private visits welcomed*
Woodpeckers, nr Bidford-on-Avon *(60)*
Wootton Grange, Henley-in-Arden *(61)*

ngs gardens open
for charity

£1.84 million
donated to national
nursing, caring and
gardening charities
in 2004

January 25 Tuesday
University of Birmingham Botanic Garden at
  Winterbourne, Edgbaston *(52)*
February 20 Sunday
Ragley Hall Gardens, Alcester *(48)*
February 22 Tuesday
University of Birmingham Botanic Garden at
  Winterbourne, Edgbaston *(52)*
February 27 Sunday
Elm Close, Welford-on-Avon *(19)*
March 22 Tuesday
University of Birmingham Botanic Garden at
  Winterbourne, Edgbaston *(52)*
March 27 Sunday (Easter)
Greenlands, Wellesbourne *(23)*
March 28 Monday (Easter)
Greenlands, Wellesbourne *(23)*
April 3 Sunday
Ilmington Gardens, nr Shipston-on-Stour
  (29)
April 10 Sunday
Newnham Paddox, Monks Kirby *(40)*
April 20 Wednesday
89 Harts Green Road, Harborne *(25)*
April 24 Sunday
Moseley Village Gardens - Salisbury Road,
  Moseley *(39)*
April 26 Tuesday
University of Birmingham Botanic Garden at
  Winterbourne, Edgbaston *(52)*
May 1 Sunday
50 Pereira Road, Harborne, Birmingham
  (46)
May 2 Monday (Bank Hol)
Earlsdon Gardens, Coventry *(17)*
May 14 Saturday
Edgbaston Garden Sculpture Trail,
  Edgbaston *(18)*
May 15 Sunday
Ashover, Streetly *(4)*

Cedar House, Wasperton *(12)*
Victorian Pleasure Gardens at Hill Close,
  Warwick *(54)*
Wits End, Shirley, Solihull *(58)*
Woodbrooke Quaker Study Centre, Selly
  Oak *(59)*
May 18 Wednesday
The Folly Lodge, Halford *(21)*
89 Harts Green Road, Harborne *(25)*
May 22 Sunday
Avon Dassett Gardens *(6)*
Grange Farm, Church Lawford, Rugby *(22)*
Lawford Hill Farm, Long Lawford *(31)*
May 29 Sunday
Alveston Gardens, Stratford-upon-Avon *(2)*
Barton House, Barton-on-the-Heath *(9)*
Greenlands, Wellesbourne *(23)*
Longdon Manor, nr Darlingscott *(34)*
Pebworth & Broad Marston Gardens,
  Stratford-upon-Avon *(45)*
May 30 Monday (Bank Hol)
Greenlands, Wellesbourne *(23)*
Pebworth & Broad Marston Gardens,
  Stratford-upon-Avon *(45)*
May 31 Tuesday
University of Birmingham Botanic Garden at
  Winterbourne, Edgbaston *(52)*
June 4 Saturday
Avon Cottage, Ashow, nr Kenilworth *(5)*
June 5 Sunday
Avon Cottage, Ashow, nr Kenilworth *(5)*
Elm Close, Welford-on-Avon *(19)*
Inglenook, Halesowen *(30)*
June 12 Sunday
Bridge Nursery, Napton *(10)*
The Cutting Gallery, Stockton *(15)*
Dorsington Gardens *(16)*
Hall Green Gardens, Birmingham *(24)*
Idlicote Gardens *(28)*
Ilmington Gardens, nr Shipston-on-Stour
  (29)

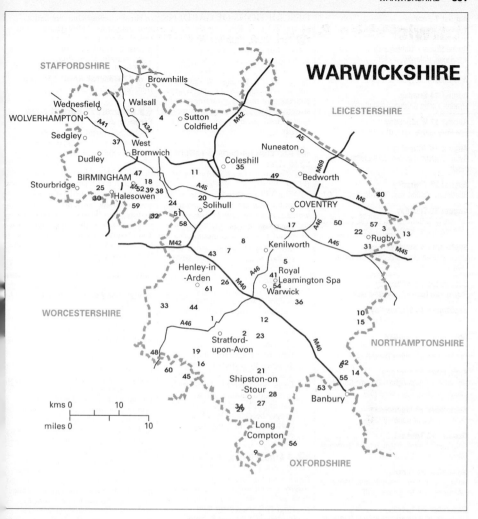

Pereira Road Gardens, Harborne,
Birmingham *(47)*

June 15 Wednesday
89 Harts Green Road, Harborne *(25)*

June 19 Sunday
Clifton-upon-Dunsmore Village Gardens, nr
Rugby *(13)*
Holywell Gardens, Claverdon, Warwick *(26)*
Maxstoke Castle, nr Coleshill *(35)*
Whichford & Ascott Gardens *(56)*

June 23 Thursday
Packwood House, nr Hockley Heath *(43)*
Ryton Organic Gardens, nr Wolston Village
(50)

June 26 Sunday
Balsall Common Gardens *(8)*
Honington Village Gardens, Shipston *(27)*

Moseley Gardens Reorganised, Birmingham
(38)
Pear Tree Cottage, Little Alne *(44)*
Roseberry Cottage, Fillongley *(49)*
Warmington Village Gardens *(55)*

June 28 Tuesday
University of Birmingham Botanic Garden at
Winterbourne, Edgbaston *(52)*

July 3 Sunday
Avon Dassett Gardens *(6)*
Wits End, Shirley, Solihull *(58)*

July 10 Sunday
Castle Bromwich Hall Gardens, Castle
Bromwich *(11)*
Stonor Road Gardens *(51)*

July 17 Sunday
Little Orchard, Great Alne *(33)*

70 Northumberland Road, Leamington Spa
(41)

July 20 Wednesday
The Folly Lodge, Halford *(21)*
89 Harts Green Road, Harborne *(25)*

July 23 Saturday
Moorlands Allotments, West Bromwich *(37)*

July 24 Sunday
Hall Green Gardens, Birmingham *(24)*

July 26 Tuesday
University of Birmingham Botanic Garden at
Winterbourne, Edgbaston *(52)*

July 31 Sunday
Alne View, Pathlow *(1)*
Little Indonesia, Kings Heath, Birmingham
(32)

August 7 Sunday
4 Arnold Villas, Rugby *(3)*
Ashover, Streetly *(4)*
Bridge Nursery, Napton *(10)*
Inglenook, Halesowen *(30)*
17 Whitehall Road, Rugby *(57)*
Wits End, Shirley, Solihull *(58)*

August 14 Sunday
Elmdon Exotic Garden, Solihull *(20)*

August 17 Wednesday
The Folly Lodge, Halford *(21)*

August 18 Thursday
Ryton Organic Gardens, nr Wolston Village *(50)*

August 25 Thursday
Baddesley Clinton Hall, Knowle, Solihull *(7)*

August 30 Tuesday
University of Birmingham Botanic Garden at Winterbourne, Edgbaston *(52)*

September 4 Sunday
Victorian Pleasure Gardens at Hill Close, Warwick *(54)*

September 7 Wednesday
Ragley Hall Gardens, Alcester *(48)*

September 14 Wednesday
89 Harts Green Road, Harborne *(25)*

September 18 Sunday
The Coach House, Avon Dassett *(14)*
Old Mill Cottage, Avon Dassett *(42)*

September 27 Tuesday
University of Birmingham Botanic Garden at Winterbourne, Edgbaston *(52)*

September 28 Wednesday
Upton House, nr Banbury *(53)*

October 25 Tuesday
University of Birmingham Botanic Garden at Winterbourne, Edgbaston *(52)*

November 29 Tuesday
University of Birmingham Botanic Garden at Winterbourne, Edgbaston *(52)*

December 20 Tuesday
University of Birmingham Botanic Garden at Winterbourne, Edgbaston *(52)*

DESCRIPTIONS OF GARDENS

❶ Alne View, Pathlow 🚻❀☺
(Mrs E Butterworth) *3m N of Stratford-upon-Avon. 5m S of Henley-in-Arden. On A3400.* Approx ⅓-acre. Shrubs, perennials, 3 ponds and rockery and raised beds. Aviary, collection of fuchsia, containers and streptocarpus; greenhouses. Home-made TEAS. *Adm £2, chd free. Sun 31 July (2-5)*

❷ Alveston Gardens, Stratford-upon-Avon
2m E of Stratford-upon-Avon. Off B4086, Stratford to Wellesbourne rd. TEAS at Village Malt House in aid of Macmillan Cancer Relief. *Combined adm £2, chd free. Sun 29 May (1-5)*
   The Bower House (Mr & Mrs P S Hart) 1-acre, owner-designed; unusual trees, water garden and rockeries, pergolas, alpine sinks, choice shrubs.
   Long Acre (Dr & Mrs N A Woodward) 1-acre, owner-designed; with a wide variety of trees and shrubs. Pergola, patios, rockery, water features, spinney walk.
   Parham Lodge (Mr & Mrs K C Edwards) 1-acre country garden designed by owners for colour, texture and scent at all seasons. Large pond, terrace, island beds, spring and summer bulbs. Wild flower apple orchard. Old cedars, copper beech and hornbeams. Beehives, so no sprays for 25 years.

❸ 4 Arnold Villas, Rugby ❀☺
(Mr Patrick Pratt) *From M1 take A428 towards Rugby town centre & Rugby School. After roundabout take 1st L into Horton Crescent for parking. Follow signs to Church Walk. Arnold Villas on R.* Small town garden containing wide variety

of shrubs, tender climbers and unusual plants. Mediterranean and exotic plants framed by mature palms. New addition of cobbled area and fountain. Home-made TEAS at 17 Whitehall Rd. *Combined adm with* **17 Whitehall Road**£2.50*, chd free. Sun 7 Aug (2-5)*

❹ Ashover, 25 Burnett Road, Streetly ❀☺
(Jackie & Martin Harvey) *8m N of Birmingham. Off B4138.* Secluded ⅓-acre, romantic country-style garden, profusion of mixed planting. Vibrant in May with tapestry of azaleas, tulips and complementary plants. In summer packed, colour-themed herbaceous borders, artistically planted with flowers and foliage to give maximum effect of colour, form and texture. Extended hot border a special feature. Established pond and waterfalls, grasses and ferns. Cream TEAS. *Adm £2.50, chd 50p. Suns 15 May; 7 Aug (1.30-5.30). Private visits welcome by appt for individuals and groups, coaches permitted. Tel 0121 353 0547*

❺ Avon Cottage, Ashow, nr Kenilworth ❀☺
(Neil Collett) *1½m E of Kenilworth. From A452 Kenilworth to Leamington rd take B4115 (signed Ashow & Stoneleigh). After ¼m turn R into Ashow. Cottage at far end of village adjacent to church (driveway opp village club). Limited parking only, please park outside village & walk to avoid congestion.* Charming cottage garden surrounding picturesque C18 Grade II listed building (not open). 1½ acres with extensive R Avon frontage. Diverse and interesting plantings for yr-round appeal. Orchard area with free-range domestic and waterfowl. *Adm £2, chd 50p (share to Beagle Welfare). Sat, Sun 4, 5 June (9-6). Private visits welcome by appt. Tel 01926 512850*

❻ Avon Dassett Gardens
7m N of Banbury. Off B4100 (use J12 M40). Car parking in village & at top of hill. Small, pretty Hornton stone village; 2 churches open for visitors. Home-made TEAS at The Old New House 22 May, Old Mill Cottage 3 July. *Combined adm £4, chd free (share to Myton Hamlet Hospice). Suns 22 May; 3 July (2-6)*
   Avon House 🚻 (Mr & Mrs E H Dunkley) Mature garden, principally shrubs, featuring hostas.
   The Coach House 🚻 (Mr & Mrs Rice) See separate entry. *Not open 3 July*

"Kenneth is a bit of a perfectionist when it comes to lawncare!"

Hill Top Farm 🚽⊕ (Mrs N & Mr D Hicks) 1 acre. Display of bedding plants, perennials, shrubs, conifers and heathers. Extensive kitchen garden. Greenhouses.

NEW The Limes 🚽 (Mr & Mrs B Anderson) Large ecological garden. Wide variety of roses, shrubs and trees.

4 Lower End 🚽 (Mrs M J Edginton) Interesting contrasts between cottage garden, courtyard and vegetable garden.

NEW Old Mill Cottage 🚽 (Mr & M J Mrs Lewis) see separate entry. *Not open 22 May*

The Old New House 🚽 (Mr & Mrs W Allen) 1 acre incl formal rose garden, herbaceous borders and specimen trees.

The Old Rectory 🚽 (Lily Hope-Frost) 2-acre mature garden with colourful terrace and wide stone steps leading to fountain and small wood, surrounding listed house (not open) mentioned in Domesday Book. Many places to sit. Entrance to church through walled garden.

Poppy Cottage 🚽 (Mr & Mrs R Butler) Newly established pretty cottage garden. Water feature and kitchen garden.

❼ ◆ Baddesley Clinton Hall, Knowle, Solihull 🚽⊗⊕
(The National Trust) *7½m NW of Warwick. ¾m W off A4141 Warwick to Birmingham rd nr Chadwick End.* Medieval moated manor house little changed since 1634; walled garden and herbaceous borders; natural areas; lakeside walk, nature trail. Light refreshments and TEAS. *House & garden adm £6.60, chd £3.30. Garden only £3.30, chd £1.65. Weds to Suns & Bank Hol Mons, Mar, Apr, Oct & Nov 12-5, May to Sept 12-5.30, Dec 12-4.30.* **For NGS:** *Thur 25 Aug. Tel 01564 783294*

❽ Balsall Common Gardens
6m W of Coventry. Balsall Common, 10m N of Warwick, 5m S of M42/M6 intersection. Junction of A452 & B4101. From T-lights of this intersection go W on B4101 towards Knowle for ¾m. Map available at each garden. Please note that a car or cycle is necessary in order to get round to all these gardens. TEAS at Silver Trees Farm and White Cottage Farm in aid of Helen Ley MS Respite Care Home. Combined adm £3, chd free. Sun 26 June (11-6)

The Bungalow 🚽⊗⊕ (Mr & Mrs G Johnson) *Fen End.* 2 acres

with mixed borders, pond and lawns.

NEW The Cottage 🚽⊗ (Enid & John Hinton) *Fen End.* Developing garden, 8yrs old. Mixed borders, wildlife pond with waterlilies, mature trees.

Firs Farm 🚽⊕ (Mr & Mrs C Ellis) *Windmill Lane.* ½-acre garden, courtyard with tubs, walled garden, formal garden with raised mixed borders. Grassed area with young ornamental trees.

Meriglen 🚽⊗⊕ (Mr & Mrs J Webb) *Windmill Lane.* Mixed borders of shrubs and perennials along with conservatory and greenhouse.

The Pines 🚽⊗⊕ (Mr & Mrs C Davis) *Hodgetts Lane.* 1½-acre formal garden divided into series of small ornamental areas; vegetables; fruit; herbs and apiary.

Silver Trees Farm ⊗⊕ (Mr & Mrs B Hitchens) 1½ acres, mixed borders, orchard, bog area, woodland garden. Large formal pond.

White Cottage Farm 🚽⊗ (Mr & Mrs J Edwards) *Off Holly Lane. Drive up the feeder lane to garden with ample parking.* 1½-acre cottage garden, mixed borders, pond, sunken garden.

32 Wootton Green Lane ⊗⊕ (Dr & Mrs Leeming) Lawns; water features; ornamental water fowl.

❾ Barton House, Barton-on-the-Heath 🚽⊗⊕
(Mr & Mrs I H B Cathie) *2m W of Long Compton. 2m off A3400 Stratford-upon-Avon to Oxford rd. 1¼m off A44 Chipping Norton to Moreton-in-Marsh rd.* 6 acres with mature trees, azaleas, species and hybrid rhododendrons, magnolias, moutan tree peonies. Japanese garden, catalpa walk, rose garden, secret garden and many rare and exotic plants. Vineyard planted 2000. Victorian kitchen garden. Exotic garden with palms, cypresses and olive trees established 2002. Manor house by Inigo Jones (not open). Featured in 'Warwickshire Today' 2004. Home-made TEAS in aid of St Lawrence Parish Church. *Adm £4, chd £2. Sun 29 May (2-6). Private visits welcome by appt for groups of 25+, May to July. Coaches welcome. Tel 01608 674303*

❿ ◆ Bridge Nursery, Napton 🚽⊕
(Christine Dakin) *3m E of Southam. Brown Tourist sign at Napton Xrds*

on the A425 Southam to Daventry rd. This challenging 1-acre garden (clay soil, exposed position) is home to an exciting range of rare and unusual plants. Grass paths meander round well-stocked informal borders. A haven for wildlife. Features incl large pond, bamboo grove (with panda sculptures) and willow dome. TEAS. *Adm £2, chd free. Fris, Sats, Suns Mar to Oct (10-4).* **For NGS:** *Suns 12 June; 7 Aug (2-6). Opening with* **The Cutting Gallery** *12 June. Combined adm £3, single garden £2, chd free. Tel 01926 812737 pmartino@beeb.net*

Burbage Gardens
See Leicestershire & Rutland.

⓫ ◆ Castle Bromwich Hall Gardens, Castle Bromwich 🚽⊕
(Castle Bromwich Hall Gardens Trust) *4m E of Birmingham. 1m from J5 of M6 (exit Northbound only).* Restored C18 formal walled gardens provide visitors with the opportunity to see a unique collection of historic plants, shrubs, medicinal and culinary herbs and fascinating vegetable collection. Intriguing holly maze. Several fruits within the orchards and along the paths incl apple, pear, apricot, quince, medlar, fig and cherry. Gifts and guided tours. Light refreshments and TEAS. *Adm £3.50, chd £1.50, concessions £2.50. Weds to Fris, Jan 12 to Mar 18 & October (11-2.30), 23 Mar to 30 Sept (12-4). 26 Mar to 25 Sept also Sats, Suns, Bank Hol Mons (1-5).* **For NGS:** *Sun 10 July (1-5). Tel 0121 749 4100 www.cbhgt.colebridge.net*

⓬ Cedar House, Wasperton 🚽⊗
(Mr & Mrs D L Burbidge) *4m S of Warwick. On A429, turn R between Barford & Wellesbourne, entrance nr end of village on L.* 3 acres; shrubs, herbaceous borders, ornamental trees, woodland walk. Cedar trees 200-300yrs old, fish pond, swimming pool area. Grass garden. Also open Gilbert Scott Church with Pugin window. Home-made TEAS. *Adm £2.50, chd free (share to St John's Church). Sun 15 May (2-5.30)*

⓭ Clifton-upon-Dunsmore Village Gardens, nr Rugby
2½m E of Rugby. From M6 leave at J1(S) and proceed on A426 towards Rugby. Take 1st L signed Clifton-upon-Dunsmore. From S leave M1 at J18 and proceed N on A5 for 3m. Take L-hand turn signed Clifton-upon-Dunsmore. Parking at village car park and Bull Inn. Teas and maps available at Townsend Memorial

Hall, Lilbourne Rd (opp church). Special flowers at St Mary's Church. Home-made TEAS. *Combined adm £2.50, chd free (share to St Marys Church and Clifton WI). Sun 19 June (2-5.30)*

NEW Clifton Mill (Denise & John Davies) Large farmhouse-style garden with mill pool and a series of interconnecting areas. Paved area. Gravel garden, orchard, wide herbaceous mixed borders, many clematis and mature trees. Parking available in farmyard.

NEW Jardin de Sol, 41 Rugby Road [symbols] (Mr & Mrs Murrell) Medium-sized garden. Paved area, lawn and large greenhouse. Developing garden, newly planted and designed by owners. Many interesting plants.

The Manor, Lilbourne Rd (Christine McKimmie & Andrew Kypri) Large garden surrounding manor house (not open). Newly-planted Edwardian sunken rose garden. Herbaceous borders recently designed and replanted. Series of pools, shade garden, mature trees.

NEW New Barn House (Annette & George Todd) Exuberant overgrown garden to encourage wildlife. Tolerant of selected weeds.

33 Shuttleworth Road (Margaret & Herbert Brockbank) Cottage-style front garden. Small colourful rear garden with paved area. Interesting plants, pond, bridge, pergola and vegetables. Winner Rugby in Bloom, medium/large section.

41 South Road [symbol] (Janice & Alan Duffin) Medium-sized garden. Arbour with pots, trellis and pergola with many named rambler roses and climbing plants. Colourful herbaceous borders.

🟢 The Coach House, Bitham Hall, Avon Dassett [symbol]
(Mr & Mrs G J Rice) *7m N of Banbury. From Leamington Spa take A462 to join Banbury rd (or J12 on M40). 3m after Gaydon turn L signed Avon Dassett. Entrance to garden on hill out of village. Parking on hill & in village.* 2 acres on sloping site, part of former Victorian garden overlooking Edge Hill. Walls give shelter and support to many climbers and more tender perennials and shrubs. Planting to give all-yr interest. Woodland area, alpines, fruit and vegetable plots. Home-made TEAS. *Adm £2, chd free. Sun 18 Sept (2-6). Opening with Avon Dassett*

Gardens *22 May & Old Mill Cottage 18 Sept. Private visits welcome by appt. Tel 01295 690255*

🔟 The Cutting Gallery, Station Road, Stockton [symbols]
(Julia & Tony Prior) *2m N of Southam. From Southam follow A426 towards Rugby. Take 1st R turn into Stockton, through the village then L after sports ground (Station Rd). After about ¾m turn L in front of Countrywide Stores. Garden is opp at Red Brick House.* Wooded wildlife garden of about 1 acre adjoining artists' studios. Part SSSI on the edge of an old cement quarry, incl organic kitchen garden, informal planting, ponds and sculpture trail with viewpoints overlooking lovely countryside. Home-made TEAS in aid of Multiple Sclerosis. *Combined adm with Bridge Nursery £3, single garden £2, chd free. Sun 12 June (2-6). Private visits welcome by appt for groups of 10+. Tel 01926 817572 tpriorart@aol.com*

🔟 Dorsington Gardens [symbols]
6m SW of Stratford-upon-Avon. On B439 from Stratford turn L to Welford-on-Avon, then R to Dorsington. Village maps given to all visitors. For information please ring 01789 720581. TEAS at The Old Manor and The Old Rectory. Combined adm £4.50, chd free (share to St Peter's Church). Sun 12 June (12-5)

Colletts Farm (Mr & Mrs D Bliss) Trees and shrubs. Container flowers. Highly productive kitchen garden with fan-trained fruit.

Dorsington Arboretum (Mr F Dennis) 12 acres with collection of several hundred trees from around the world; leading to Udde Well Pond (ancient well) and Willow Walk.

Glebe Cottage (Mr & Mrs A Brough) Over ¾-acre of land reclaimed into an uncomplicated garden which, over several yrs, has developed into interesting and varied garden rooms. A surprise at each turn.

Knowle Thatch (Mr & Mrs P Turner) Large garden; mature trees, shrubs and herbaceous borders.

Milfield (Mrs H Dumas) Small but beautifully planted cottage garden with a feeling of space and simplicity touched with a hint of grandeur in the form of the statuesque urns.

The Old Manor (Mr F Dennis) 3 acres with fairy walk, herb garden, ornamental fish pond, sunken water garden, leading to Highfield, with Mediterranean garden, container plants and bonsai collection.

The Old Rectory (Mr & Mrs N Phillips) 2-acre Victorian garden with mature trees incl old espalier fruit trees. Box hedges, herbaceous borders, many old roses, large pool, small wood.

NEW Sapphire House (Mrs D Sawyer) Newly laid-out garden with orchard, vegetable garden, shrub beds, lawns and large walnut trees.

The Welshman's Barn (Mr F Dennis) 5 acres with Japanese garden, Oz maze, statue garden of heroes, wild flower garden and stream.

Whitegates Shrubs, mature trees and shrub roses.

Windrush (Mrs M B Mills) Country garden with shrubs, cottage plants and roses.

🔟 Earlsdon Gardens, Coventry
Turn towards Coventry at A45/A429 T-lights. Take 3rd L turn into Beechwood Ave, Earlsdon Gardens. Maps available at all gardens. Light refreshments and TEAS. Combined adm £2.50, chd free. Mon 2 May (11-3)

NEW 3 Bates Road [symbols] (Victor & Judith Keene) Large established garden, with lots of spring interest incl rhododendrons, azaleas and mature trees, plus a kitchen garden.

NEW 155 Beechwood Avenue (Nigel & Jan Young) Garden with open traditional character - constantly being enhanced with intresting planting. Water feature.

40 Hartington Crescent (Viv & George Buss) Surprisingly large garden with interest for all ages; water feature and fern garden.

114 Hartington Crescent (Liz Campbell & Denis Crowley) Large, mature, pretty garden on several levels with hidden aspects.

36 Providence Street (Rachel Culley & Steve Shiner) Large, peaceful cottage garden. Water features, packed herbaceous borders, vegetable plot, yr-round interest and colour.

84 Rochester Road [symbol] (Peter & Bobby Harris) Interesting plantsman's garden with water

feature leading to large adjoining allotment.

87 Rochester Road (Edith Lewin) Peaceful, mature cottage garden.

⓳ Edgbaston Garden Sculpture Trail, 5 Farquhar Road East, Edgbaston
(John Alexander-Williams) *Under 1m from Birmingham Botanical Gardens. Farquhar Rd East is a triangle off Farquhar Rd, between Somerset & Richmond Hill Rds in Edgbaston.* Town garden of ½-acre. Evolved over 17 years to provide interlinking areas of interest with hidden walks and arches; designed to create sculpture trail. Some 60 sculptures by the owner provide surprise and amusement and set off very personal collection of shrubs, trees and plants. *Adm £2, chd free. Sat 14 May (1.30-5). Private visits welcome by appt. Tel 0121 454 1279 johnalexwill@tiscali.co.uk*

⓳ Elm Close, Binton Road, Welford-on-Avon
(Mr & Mrs E W Dyer) *5m SW of Stratford. Off B4390. Elm Close is between Welford Garage & The Bell Inn.* ⅔-acre packed with super plants and stocked for yr-round colour and interest. Clematis, daphnes, peonies and hellebores a particular speciality. TEAS in aid of British Red Cross. *Adm £2.50. Suns 27 Feb; 5 June (2-5). Private visits welcome by appt for groups of 10+. Tel 01789 750793 dyer@btclick.com*

⓴ Elmdon Exotic Garden, 88 Elmdon Park Road, Solihull
(Dennis Hennessy) *4m from Solihull town centre. Turn off A45 Coventry rd to Lode Lane. 1st L to Old Lode Lane, 4th L to Tanhouse Farm Rd, 3rd L to Elmdon Park Rd.* An exotic garden with semi-tropical plants. The garden is imaginatively set out with a sense of fantasy. From the dry, arid decked area, through a lush jungle of luxuriant bananas, bold coloured cannas, adjacent to tree ferns, gunneras and colocasias. Then onward to an area surrounded by a glass-walled water feature and steel-clad deck. Anglia TV Britain's Best Back Garden, regional finalist 2004. Light refreshments and TEAS. *Adm £2. Sun 14 Aug (12-5). Private visits welcome by appt. Tel 0121 688 3886*

Epwell Mill, nr Banbury
See Oxfordshire.

㉑ The Folly Lodge, Halford
(Mike & Susan Solomon) *9m NE Moreton in Marsh. 9m SE Stratford-upon-Avon. On A429 (Fosse Way). In Halford take turning opp PO to Idlicote. Garden on R past Feldon Edge.* Relaxed garden for plant lovers. Winding paths lead through colour-themed borders overflowing with a large variety of plants - some unusual, all interesting. The delights incl a potted garden, gravel gardens, pottery sculptures made by the owner and lots of seating areas for enjoying the atmosphere. TEAS. *Adm £2, chd free. Weds 18 May; 20 July; 17 Aug (2-5). Private visits welcome by appt. Tel 01789 740183*

㉒ Grange Farm, Coventry Road, Church Lawford, Rugby
(John & Lilian Reay) *4m W of Rugby. Between Church Lawford & Bretford with easy access. R on main A428 halfway between the 2 villages.* Frontage foliage garden of Victorian farmhouse (not open). Mature garden at rear with shrubs, unusual plants, succulents and vegetable area giving yr-round interest. Home-made TEAS. *Combined adm £3 with **Lawford Hill Farm**. Sun 22 May (12-5)*

㉓ Greenlands, Stratford Road, Wellesbourne
(Elizabeth Street) *4m E of Stratford-upon-Avon. Leave Stratford-upon-Avon due E on B4086. Garden on Xrds at Loxley-Charlecote by airfield.* 1 acre with mature trees, shrubs, herbaceous borders and semi-wild areas. TEAS. *Adm £1.50, chd free. Suns, Mons 27, 28 Mar; 29, 30 May (11-5)*

㉔ Hall Green Gardens, Birmingham
Off A34 approx 3m from city centre or 6m from M42 J4, near Hall Green station. TEAS at 28 Burnaston Rd & 36 Ferndale Rd in aid of County Air Ambulance & St Mary's Hospice. *Combined adm £3, chd free. Suns 12 June; 24 July (2-6)*

28 Burnaston Road (Mrs L Mole) Well-stocked borders with many unusual specimens. Small stream edged with moisture-loving plants runs into ornamental ponds. Shade area and small kitchen garden.

37 Burnaston Road (Mrs C M Wynne-Jones) Approx ⅓acre. Well-planted suburban garden, interesting array of plants by experienced propagator. Patio, lawn, mixed borders and shade area. Vegetables and soft fruit. *Not open 12 June*

36 Ferndale Road (Mrs A A Appelbe & Mrs E A Nicholson) Large suburban florists' garden. Well planted with many unusual plants. Garden divided into three distinct areas: large ornamental garden, small formal garden, small kitchen garden. Pool with small waterfall. *Private visits welcome by appt. Tel 0121 777 4921*

120 Russell Road (Mr D Worthington) *Turn off A34 E, by Methodist Church, down York Rd then L into Russell Rd.* Plantsman's sub-divided garden designed by owner. Features formal raised pool, shrubs, climbers, old roses, herbaceous and container planting. *Private visits welcome by appt. Tel 0121 624 7906 hildave@hotmail.com*

129 Southam Road (Stella & John Couper) Long, well-designed town garden, 150ft x 30ft. Shaped borders, pergola, wishing well and other unusual features. Good use of garden ornaments and artefacts as well as large number of well-grown plants.

Hanwell Gardens
See Oxfordshire.

㉕ ◆ 89 Harts Green Road, Harborne
(Mrs Barbara Richardson) *3m SE of Birmingham city centre. Off Fellows Lane-War Lane.* Wildlife-friendly, split-level garden protected by mature trees. Extensively planted with unusual herbaceous perennials, shrubs and climbers incl over 80 varieties of clematis. Rockery and pond. Large display of plants in containers featuring vegetables, half-hardy perennials and shade plants. Small nursery listed in Plant Finder. *Adm £2, chd free. Weds Apr to July, Sept (2-5).* **For NGS:** *Weds 20 Apr; 18 May; 15 June; 20 July; 14 Sept (2-5). Tel 0121 427 5200*

㉖ Holywell Gardens, Claverdon, Warwick
5m W of Warwick. Take A4189 towards Henley-in-Arden, turn R in Claverdon for Shrewley, take 2nd L for Holywell. A secluded, quiet hamlet. Home-made TEAS at Manor Farm in aid of Red Cross. *Combined adm £3, chd free. Sun 19 June (11-6)*

Holywell Farm (Ian and Ann Harper) 2½ acres with open views and now mature. *Private visits welcome by appt. Tel 01926 842331*

Manor Farm ⌀⊕ (Don & Margaret Hanson) Romantic garden surrounding Elizabethan farmhouse (not open) with natural duck pond. Yew and box hedges divide white border and cottage garden. Barn walls clothed with climbing roses. *Private visits welcome by appt for groups. Tel 01926 842331*

Home Farm, Balscote ⌀⊕
See Oxfordshire.

㉗ Honington Village Gardens, Shipston
1½m N of Shipston-on-Stour. Take A3400 towards Stratford then turn R signed Honington. A C17 village, recorded in Domesday, entered by old toll gate. Ornamental stone bridge over the Stour and interesting church with C13 tower and late C17 nave after Wren. Home-made TEAS at Honington Hall in aid of Honington Church Fund. *Combined adm £4, chd free. Sun 26 June (2.15-5.30)*

Holts Cottage (Mr & Mrs R G Bentley) Cottage garden being restored to original layout opening onto parkland. Interesting trees incl fruit trees and shrubs with herbaceous borders and ponds.

Honington Glebe (Mr & Mrs J C Orchard) 2-acre plantsman's garden consisting of rooms planted informally with yr-round interest in contrasting foliage and texture. Old walled garden laid out with large raised lily pool and parterre filled with violas and perennials.

Honington Hall ⊕ (B H E Wiggin) Extensive lawns and fine mature trees with river and garden monuments. Carolean house (not open); parish church adjoining house.

The Old House (Mr & Mrs I F Beaumont) Small structured cottage garden formally laid out with box hedging and small fountain. Informally planted, giving an almost billowing, frothy appearance.

Orchard House (Mr & Mrs Monnington) Small developing garden created in recent yrs by owners with informal mixed beds and borders.

㉘ Idlicote Gardens
3m NE of Shipston-on-Stour. Delightful hamlet with stunning views, large village pond and Norman church. Coaches please telephone 01608 661473 in advance.

Home-made TEAS at Badgers Farm. *Combined adm £4, chd free (share to St James the Great Church, Idlicote). Sun 12 June (2-6)*

Badgers Farm (Sir Derek & Lady Hornby) Lawns with panoramic views and herbaceous borders lead to enclosed rose garden, vegetable garden and pond and orchard walk.

2 Bickerstaff Cottages (Miss A Rickard) Delightful small enclosed cottage garden.

3 Bickerstaff Cottages (Miss A Cummins) Small cottage garden.

Bickerstaff Farm (Sir John & Lady Owen) Recently planted garden. Mainly shrub borders and roses. Colourful spring garden.

Home Farm (Mrs & Mrs G Menzies-Kitchen) Medium-sized garden with shrubs and interesting herbaceous planting. Tremendous views to the Malvern Hills.

Idlicote House (Mrs R P G Dill) Extensive gardens with mature trees and shrubs, formal area and spectacular views. Enclosed vegetable garden with flower borders. Norman Church and C18 dovecote in grounds. Grade II listed C18 house (not open).

NEW **The Old Forge** (Mr & Mrs J Terry) Newly-planted in 2003, easy maintenance garden.

The Old Rectory (Mr & Mrs G Thomson) Conventional old rectory garden with views of Idlicote Hill. Small fruit cage, one-third wilderness, conservatory.

Stone Cottage (Mr & Mrs C Rosser) Traditional cottage garden with some interesting shrubs and trees.

Woodlands (Captain & Mrs P R Doyne) Shrubs and herbaceous plants. Spectacular views beyond walled garden.

㉙ Ilmington Gardens, nr Shipston-on-Stour
8m S of Stratford-upon-Avon. 4m NW of Shipston-on-Stour on A3400 between Stratford-upon-Avon & Shipston-on-Stour. 3m NE of Chipping Campden. A most attractive Cotswold village with two inns and a Norman church. Ilmington traditional Morris dancers. Light refreshments and TEAS at Village Hall on 3 Apr only. *Combined adm £4, chd free. Suns 3 Apr; 12 June (2-6)*

The Bevingtons (Mrs N Tustain) Interesting cottage-style garden,

hedges dividing different areas which surround Cotswold stone thatched house (not open), daffodils under trees in orchard.

Crab Mill ⌀ (Mr & Mrs L Hodgkin) Terraced garden with dry stone walls and sunken courtyard round C18 house (not open). Daffodils, clematis and camellias. Paths through orchard with bluebells, cherry blossom and fritillaries. *Not open 12 June*

Foxcote Hill ⌀ (Mr & Mrs M Dingley) Garden developed on sloping site on edge of village. Retaining most of old orchard with naturalised bulbs. Paths through orchard give views over countryside towards Edge Hill. Paved courtyard with fountain.

Foxcote Hill Cottage ⌀ (Miss A Terry) Interesting garden on hillside with dry stone walls enclosing banks planted with alpines and spring bulbs. *Not open 12 June*

Frog Orchard ⌀ (M Naish) Open garden surrounding an interesting modern house (not open), with trees and flowers beds, bordered on one side by a pretty little stream. *Not open 12 June*

The Grey House ⌀ (Mr & Mrs B Blackie) Formal lawns and beds with orchard on elevated site surrounding Georgian farmhouse, overlooking village and distant views. *Not open 12 June*

Ilmington Manor ⌀ (Mr & Mrs M Taylor) Daffodils in profusion in April. Hundreds of old and new roses, ornamental trees, shrub and herbaceous borders, pond garden, topiary. House (not open) dates from 1600.

㉚ NEW Inglenook, 20 Waxland Road, Halesowen ⌀⊕
(Ron & Anne Kerr) ¼m from Halesowen town centre. M5 J3 take A456 to Kidderminster. Turn R at 1st island. 1st L into Dogkennel Lane. Waxland Rd 2nd turning on L. Charming garden featuring waterfalls which cascade over rocks down to ponds set within a woodland area. A path meandering through the trees brings you back to the lawn and patio. Hidden area hosts greenhouses, vegetable plots, asparagus beds and mixed borders. Enjoy panoramic views from the raised decked area with its semi-tropical planting overlooking terraces which display a wide variety of low-growing conifers. Limited roadside parking. 2 car parks in town centre. Home-made TEAS in aid of Mary Stevens Hospice. *Adm £2, chd 50p. Suns 5 June; 7 Aug (1-5)*

31 Lawford Hill Farm, Long Lawford 🅷
(Donald & Susan Moses) *2m W of Rugby. Outside village of Long Lawford. Lawford Heath Lane runs between A428 & A45, ½m off A428 or 2m off A45.* Gardens surround fine Grade II listed Georgian farmhouse (not open) in an acre of formal lawns, herbaceous borders, shrubberies and traditional walled vegetable and herb garden. Winner Rugby in Bloom 2003/04/05, Hotel section. TEAS in aid of St John's Church, Long Lawford. *Combined adm £3 with* **Grange Farm***, chd free. Sun 22 May (12-5). Private visits welcome by appt. Tel 01788 542001*

32 NEW Little Indonesia, 20 Poston Croft, Kings Heath, Birmingham 🅰
(Dave & Pat McKenna) *1½m from Kings Heath High St. Poston Croft is 5th on L off Broad Lane, which is off A435 Alcester Rd.* A garden that is the realisation of my dreams. An amazing plant paradise with the feel of entering a jungle, even though we are in the heart of Birmingham. Planted so that it seems to go on for ever. Plants of unusual leaf shapes and textures. Bananas, cannas and grasses jostle with one another for space. A plantaholic's paradise. 'Garden News' 2nd place Overall Gardener 2003. Light refreshments and TEAS. *Adm £2, chd 50p. Sun 31 July (11-4). Private visits welcome by appt. Tel 0121 628 1397 pat_mckenna66@hotmail.com*

33 Little Orchard, Henley Road, Great Alne 🅰🅸
(Sue Smith) *7m N of Stratford-upon-Avon. On B4089 between Wootton Wawen 4m & Alcester 2m. Parking at Village Hall 500yds.* A magical designer garden created in just 12 months. ½ acre of pleasant strolls comprising 6 garden vistas. Still and moving water with strong topical and tropical plantings from lakeside to woodland and formal garden, young trees, shrubs, perennials, eucalyptus screen. Dawn's piping pool, Sue's zen garden and even a cactus walk. Midsummer medley of bloom and butterflies. *Adm £2, chd free. Sun 17 July (2-5)*

34 NEW Longdon Manor, nr Darlingscott 🅰🅸
(Mrs J Brabyn) *3m WNW of Shipston-on-Stour. From Shipston-on-Stour take B4035 towards Chipping Campden for 1½m. Cross A429. Go further ½m, turn R at Darlingscott Gated Road sign. Go 1m. When rd goes sharp R, Longdon*

Manor drive straight on. Rambling old house, surrounded by barns and outhouses and rambling gardens. Lots of ground cover, wonderful old rambling roses, shrubs, climbers and honeysuckles; all tended by one rambling old woman. Light refreshments and TEAS. *Adm £3, concessions £2 (share to SPECAL - Special Early Care for Alzheimer's). Sun 29 May (2-6)*

35 Maxstoke Castle, nr Coleshill 🅳🅰🅼
(Mr & Mrs M C Fetherston-Dilke) *2½m E of Coleshill. E of Birmingham, on B4114. Take R turn down Castle Lane; Castle drive 1¼m on R.* Approx 5 acres of garden and grounds with herbaceous, shrubs and trees in the immed surroundings of this C14 moated castle (also open NGS day). No disabled access to house. TEAS. *Adm £5, chd £3, concessions £3. Sun 19 June (11-5)*

36 ◆ The Mill Garden, 55 Mill Street, Warwick 🅰🅷
(Open in memory of Arthur Measures) *Off A425 beside castle gate. Use St Nicholas car park.* ½-acre garden with abundance of plants, shrubs and trees beneath the walls of Warwick Castle beside the R Avon. Place of peace and beauty. Teas in Warwick. *Adm £1, chd free with adult. Daily early Apr to end Oct (9-6). Donation to NGS. Tel 01926 492877*

37 Moorlands Allotments, Hall Green Road, West Bromwich 🅳🅷
(Moorlands Allotment Association) *2½m N of West Bromwich. Exit J9 M6. Head for Wednesbury. At first T-lights turn L. To T-junction turn L. To island turn R into Hall Green Rd. Turn R into Manor House Drive. Car park at rear.* 1-acre site rented from Sandwell MBC comprising 19 gardens, 10 children's gardens and one garden with raised beds adapted for a wheelchair user. Flower borders front all gardens. Wide variety of fruit, soft fruit and vegetables grown. Considered one of the best kept sites in the country. Plants and vegetables for sale. Best allotment site in Sandwell 2004. Home-made TEAS. *Adm £2, chd free. Sat 23 July (11-4). Private visits welcome by appt. Tel 0121 502 4393 william.morrall@tesco.net*

38 Moseley Gardens Reorganised, Birmingham
Halfway between Kings Heath and Moseley village; 3m from city centre. From A435 turn at the main Moseley T-lights on to St Mary's Row/Wake

Green Rd. Grove Ave is 2nd on R. From here take 1st R, Oxford Rd, then 1st L, School Rd. Prospect Rd is 3rd on L, Ashfield Rd is 4th on R. Five gardens incl 2 shortlisted for BBC Gardener of the Year, and an Anglia TV regional Best British Back Garden. Plant sales at 33 School Rd. TEAS at Grove Avenue. *Combined adm £3, chd under 16 free. Sun 26 June (2-6)*

7 Ashfield Road 🅰🅷 (Mr & Mrs Bartlett) Small garden with secluded, cottage feel. Attractive pond with rockery, waterfall and shingle bank.

10 Grove Avenue (Mr & Mrs Harding) Suburban garden with herbaceous borders, pond area and beach house. Featured on Anglia TV Regional Best British Back Garden.

18 Grove Avenue 🅳🅸 (Richard & Judy Green) Small peaceful urban garden stocked with wide variety of unusual trees, shrubs and perennials, planted for colour and foliage.

19 Prospect Road (Mr A J White) Well planted suburban garden with plenty of colour.

33 School Rd 🅷 (Ms J Warr-Arnold) Mixed garden containing many plants with interesting histories and traditional uses. Come and spot the new dragons!

65 School Rd 🅰🅷 (Wendy Weston) Small shady garden with patio, pergola and pond. Designed for easy maintenance.

39 Moseley Village Gardens - Salisbury Road, Moseley
2½m S of Birmingham city centre. From A435 Alcester rd at Moseley village T-lights turn L down hill into Salisbury Rd on B4217 towards Edgbaston County Cricket ground. Please park in Amesbury Rd. Light refreshments and TEAS at 56 Salisbury Rd in aid of St Mary's Hospice, Selly Oak. *Combined adm £3, chd 50p. Sun 24 Apr (2-6)*

Brook House, 83 Salisbury Road 🅳🅰🅸 (John & Connie Andrews) *House approx 600yds on L nr junction with Amesbury Rd.* Medium-sized woodland garden with natural stream. Over 200 mature trees and shrubs. S-facing. *Private visits welcome by appt, no large groups, 10 persons max. Tel 0121 449 1029*

56 Salisbury Road 🅳🅸 (Peter & Wendy Binham) *House approx 300yds on R before junction with Amesbury Rd.* Approx ⅓-acre N-facing town garden, overlooking lake in private park. Terraced garden, mixed planting mainly shrubs. Patio, gazebo, rose trellis, gravel walk, raised beds, small and larger pond, water feature. *Private visits welcome by appt, no large groups, 10 persons max. Tel* 0121 449 7482

40 ◆ Newnham Paddox, Monks Kirby 🔣🔣
(The Earl & Countess of Denbigh) *7m NE of Rugby. 5m W of Coventry. From A5 Lutterworth roundabout, Willey exit, 2m on L. From Coventry B4027 towards Brinklow, turn L in Brinklow B4455 at 2nd Xrds turn R towards Willey. 3m on R. From Rugby B4112 to Pailton, in Pailton turn R B4027 - Lutterworth at roundabout 1st L to Willey 2m on L.* Created by Capability Brown in the C18, the beautiful classical landscape is enhanced by carpets of daffodils of many varieties, planted over generations. Rare and ancient trees will enchant. Entrance is through a newly cleared and planted oak wood, leading down towards the 2 lakes. Total distance approx 1m. Featured in 'Financial Times' and 'House & Garden' 2004. Home-made TEAS. *Adm £4.50, chd £1, concessions £3.50. Thurs to Suns, May to Oct (10-6, last adm 4). For NGS: Sun 10 Apr (12-4). Tel* 01788 833513 *www.newnhampaddox.com*

41 NEW 70 Northumberland Road, Leamington Spa 🔣
(Professor Tom & Doreen Whitehead) *N Leamington. Coming from N use A452. Just after Leamington Spa sign and 30mph sign take 1st R into Northumberland Rd. From the S on A452, go into Leamington keeping L of town centre. Cross over 2 T-light junctions, then a roundabout into Northumberland Rd.* Attractively divided long and narrow town garden containing colourful foliage plants and perennials. Also features a conifer bed, specimen trees, shrubs, an oriental pond and bamboo garden, water features incl a koi fish pond. Home-made TEAS in aid of Cancer Research UK. *Adm £2. Sun 17 July (2-5)*

42 Old Mill Cottage, Avon Dassett 🔣
(Mr & Mrs M J Lewis) *7m N of Banbury. From Leamington Spa take A462 to join Banbury rd (or J12 on M40). 3m after Gaydon turn L signed Avon Dassett. 200yds from The Coach House, further up lane on R.* Conservation garden of ¾ acre with shrubs, perennial borders and

rockeries. Collection of alpines and herbs. Pond and tropical garden. Mediterranean gravel garden. TEAS. *Adm £2, chd free. Sun 18 Sept (2-6). Also open* **The Coach House**. *Opening with* **Avon Dassett Gardens** *3 July*

43 ◆ Packwood House, nr Hockley Heath 🔣🔣
(The National Trust) *11m SE of Birmingham. 2m E of Hockley Heath.* Carolean yew garden representing the Sermon on the Mount. Tudor house with tapestries, needlework and furniture of the period. *House & garden adm £6, chd £3. Garden only £3, chd £1.50. Weds to Suns & Bank Hol Mons Mar, Apr, Oct, Nov (11-4.30), May to Sept (11-5.30). For NGS: Thu 23 June (11-5.30). Tel* 01564 783294 *www.nationaltrust.org.uk*

44 NEW Pear Tree Cottage, Little Alne 🔣🔣
(Norma Field) *6m N of Startford-upon-Avon. On B4089, Wootton Wawen to Alcester rd on the Shelfield junction.* Mature trees, colourful borders and 2 lily ponds abounding in goldfish, mostly spawned at home, welcome you to a flower safari. A serenade of blue pots and happy plants leads to an African thatched garden house. Sit here and enjoy sensational roses, cool clematis and borders overflowing with flowers and hostas. Not suitable for small children. Home-made TEAS. *Adm £2.50. Sun 26 June (11.30-5.30). Private visits welcome by appt in June & July for groups of 10+. Tel* 01789 488240

45 Pebworth & Broad Marston Gardens, Stratford-upon-Avon
9m SW of Stratford-upon-Avon. On B439 at Bidford turn L towards Honeybourne, after 3m turn L at Xrds signed Pebworth. Peaceful village with beautiful church and some thatched properties, particularly in Broad Marston. TEAS Nolan Cottage & Village Hall in aid of St Peter's Church, Pebworth. *Combined adm £3.50. Sun, Mon 29, 30 May (2-6)*

Ashlow 🔣🔣 (Mr & Mrs D Jarrett) New garden still being created but with a wealth of features already in place.

1 Elm Close 🔣🔣🔣 (Mr & Mrs G Keyte) Small cottage garden, very well stocked and with many features of interest.

NEW 2 Elm Close 🔣🔣 (E Osborn) Small garden containing herbs, ferns and assorted plants.

26 Elm Close 🔣🔣 (Mr J Power) Small tidy cottage garden - but come and see the orchids.

Icknield Barn 🔣🔣 (Sheila Davies) Very small walled cottage garden which almost becomes a part of the living room! Designed for relaxation and pottering, yet still full of interest.

Ivybank 🔣🔣 NCCPG (Mr & Mrs R Davis) ⅓-acre garden with ferns, ivies; roses and shrubs. Nursery holds National Collection of pelargoniums.

NEW The Knoll 🔣🔣 (Mr K Wood) Cottage-style walled garden.

Martins 🔣🔣🔣 (Mr & Mrs T Collins) ½-acre informal gardens with ponds, vegetable patch and unusual plants.

Nolan Cottage 🔣🔣🔣 (Mr & Mrs R Thomas) Cottage garden of ¾ acre with ponds, vegetable garden, ferns, mixed borders and wild garden area with many places to sit and contemplate.

Pebworth Barn 🔣🔣 (Mr & Mrs B O'Grady) An artist's garden and studio full of fascination, plants and creativity. An ancient stone water feature and ceramic works displayed with plants.

NEW Pebworth Manor 🔣🔣 (Mr & Mrs J Lloyd) Open lawns with extensive views across the Vale of Evesham towards the Malvern Hills. Herbaceous borders, mature trees. Large vegetable garden.

Pettifer House 🔣🔣 (Mr & Mrs M Veal) Traditional cottage garden, herbaceous beds, shrubberies, rock garden, lavender hedges and vegetable garden.

The Rowans 🔣🔣🔣 (Mr & Mrs D Fox) Gardens in a garden, looked after by 2 amateurs.

The White Cottage 🔣🔣 (Mr & Mrs R Woodthorpe Browne) 1½-acre garden full of different aspects planted with trees and shrubs and herbaceous borders. The garden leads to a paddock and newly-developed woodland.

46 50 Pereira Road, Harborne, Birmingham 🔣
(Peg Peil) *Birmingham A-Z p88 1C. Between Gillhurst Rd & Margaret Grove, ¼m from Hagley Rd or ½m from Harborne High St.* Plantaholic's garden with over 100 varieties, many unusual. Large bed of plants with African connections. Many fruits, vegetables, herbs, grasses. Over 100 varieties of plants on sale for

CAFOD. *Adm £1.50, chd free, OAP £1. Sun 1 May (2-5). Also opening with* **Pereira Road Gardens** *12 June. Private visits welcome by appt. Tel 0121 427 7573*

㊼ Pereira Road Gardens, Harborne, Birmingham
Between Gillhurst Rd & Margaret Grove, ¼m from Hagley Rd or ½m from Harborne High St. Home-made TEAS in aid of St Mary's Hospice. *Combined adm £3, chd free, OAP £1.50. Sun 12 June (2-5)*

> [NEW] **27 Pereira Road** (Mr John Hurdley) N-facing garden on 2 levels, with 2 ponds and a wide variety of plants and fruit.
>
> **50 Pereira Road** ㊒ (Prof Peg Peil) See separate entry.
>
> **84 Pereira Road** ㊒ (Mrs R E Barnett) Small garden with 30 degree sloping concreted bank, now extensive rockery, interesting shrubs, herbaceous borders.

㊽ ◆ Ragley Hall Gardens, Alcester ㊒㊛
(Marquess & Marchioness of Hertford) *2m SW of Alcester. Off A435/A46 8m from Stratford-upon-Avon.* 24 acres of gardens consisting predominantly of mature broadleaved trees, within which a variety of cultivated and non-cultivated areas have been blended to achieve a garden rich in both horticulture and biodiversity. Spring meadows and bulbs make way for summer meadows, herbaceous borders, annual bedding and rose beds to provide a rich tapestry of form, colour and contrast 12 months of the year. Light refreshments and TEAS. *Adm £3, chd free. Apr to Sept.* **For NGS:** *Sun 20 Feb (11-3); Wed 7 Sept (10-4). Tel 01789 762090 www.ragleyhall.com*

㊾ Roseberry Cottage, Sandy Lane, Fillongley ㊒㊛㊒
(Mr & Mrs Richard G Bastow) *6m N of Coventry. On B4098 Tamworth rd. Go under motorway bridge to top of hill, take Woodend Lane, sign on R. Turn L into Sandy Lane, opp triangle of beech trees. 1st house on R in Sandy Lane. Please use one-way system due to restricted parking.* 1¾ acres incl herbaceous border, rock garden, pool, peat and bog area, scree and small herb garden. Stone troughs, orchard with wild flowers, organically grown fruit and vegetables. TEAS. *Adm £1.50, chd 50p (share to NCCPG). Sun 26 June (2-5)*

㊿ ◆ Ryton Organic Gardens, nr Wolston Village ㊒㊛㊒
(HDRA - The Organic Organisation) *5m SE of Coventry. Gardens are on rd to Wolston, off the A45, 5m SE of Coventry. Coventry rail station is also approx 5m and offers an excellent taxi service. Also served by buses from Coventry and Rugby which stop in Wolston (approx 1m).* The UK's national centre for organic gardening offers visitors 10 acres of beautiful gardens from 'Vegetable Inspirations' to 'Diversity in Landscape'. Enjoy the Vegetable Kingdom exhibition for all the family. See how beautiful the organic approach can be. Enjoy our unique restaurant and unusual gifts in our shop. RHS Chelsea Gold Medal 2004, featured in 'Kitchen Garden' 2004. Light refreshments and TEAS. *Adm £4.50, chd £2, concessions £4. Daily except Christmas week.* **For NGS:** *Thurs 23 June; 18 Aug (9-5). Tel 024 7630 8211 events@hdra.org.uk*

� [NEW] Stonor Road Gardens
3m W of Solihull. From Robin Hood island on A34 Birmingham to Stratford rd, take Baldwins Lane exit. Stonor Rd is 2nd L. Four very different gardens demonstrating the variety of design and planting that can be achieved in a modest space. Home-made TEAS at 172 Stonor Road in aid of Warren Pearl Marie Curie Centre. *Combined adm £2.50, chd free. Sun 10 July (2-5.30)*

> [NEW] **154 Stonor Road** (Mrs J Seager) Small suburban garden with choice plants both in borders and containers. Large pool, with waterfalls and koi carp, bordered by alpine bed. Interesting collection of bonsai.
>
> [NEW] **166 Stonor Road** (Mrs & Mrs R Healey) Very colourful garden with well planted borders, immaculate lawn and a wealth of hanging baskets and containers. Very attractive sitting out areas at the bottom of the garden.
>
> **172 Stonor Road, Hall Green** (Mrs O Walters) Plantswoman's garden (approx 65ft x 24ft) with wide variety of plants, some not considered hardy in this area. Scree, containers, shade beds, ferns, climbers, conservatory. Always something new. *Private visits welcome by appt, Mar to Sept for individuals or small groups. Tel 0121 745 2894*
>
> [NEW] **188 Stonor Road** (Mrs J Mantle) Courtyard garden on several levels, paved and gravelled for ease of maintenance. Imaginative permanent planting

enlivened by hanging baskets. Delightful water feature.

㊓ ◆ University of Birmingham Botanic Garden at Winterbourne, Edgbaston ㊒㊛㊒ NCCPG
(University of Birmingham) *3m SW of Birmingham. Via A38; turn off at Edgbaston Park Rd. Situated on R nr junction with Pritchatts Rd. Buses: 61, 62, 63, 44. University station 10 mins.* 6 acres of themed gardens incl alpine troughs and scree garden. Sunken rock garden with stepping stones. Nut walk tunnel. Rhododendrons and unusual trees. Herbaceous borders, lawns and terraces. Ornamental features. National Collection of roses, anthemis and winter-flowering irises. Set around Grade II listed Winterbourne House (not open). Woodland walk, meadows, geographic beds and tropical beds. TEAS on NGS days. *Adm £2, chd free. Mon to Fri (11-4), not University closed days.* **For NGS:** *Tues 25 Jan; 22 Feb; 22 Mar; 26 Apr; 31 May; 28 June; 26 July; 30 Aug; 27 Sept; 25 Oct; 29 Nov; 20 Dec (11-4). Sun 24 Apr (2-5). Tel 0121 414 5590 Alison Darby www.unibotanic@bham.ac.uk*

㊔ ◆ Upton House, nr Banbury ㊛ NCCPG
(The National Trust) *7m NW of Banbury. On A422; 1m S of Edgehill.* Large terraced garden, S-facing valley with herbaceous borders, roses, water garden, kitchen garden, lawns. National Collection of asters, which should be at their best in the autumn. House contains an internationally important collection of paintings, porcelain and tapestries. No dogs in garden, little or no shade in car park. Light refreshments and TEAS. *House & garden adm £6.80, chd £3.50. Garden only £4, chd £2, groups of 15+ 20% discount.* **For NGS:** *Wed 28 Sept (11-5). Tel 01295 670266 www.nationaltrust.org.uk*

㊕ ◆ Victorian Pleasure Gardens at Hill Close, Warwick ㊒
(Hill Close Gardens Trust) *Park at Race Course; entrance Friars St. Enter on foot between Westgate School and Martinique Square, Bowling Green St.* 18 separate hedged gardens once enjoyed by prosperous townspeople. Derelict until 1998, now in process of restoration. Listed summerhouses, old fruit trees. NCCPG garden of unusual plants. TEAS. *Adm £1.50. 26 Mar to 2 Oct, Sats & Bank Hols 11-5, Suns 2-5.* **For NGS:** *Suns 15 May; 4 Sept (2-5). Tel 01926 493216*

www.hillclosegardens.warwick.uk.com

(55) Warmington Village Gardens

5m NW of Banbury. Off B4100. Village map given to all visitors. TEAS at Village Hall. *Combined adm £3, chd free (share to St Michael's Church Warmington Restoration Fund). Sun 26 June (2-6)*

Berka, Chapel Street (Mr & Mrs B J Castle) Country garden, fruit trees, flower beds, children's playing lawn.

3 Court Close (Mr & Mrs C J Crocker) Steep narrow terraced garden.

The Glebe House, Village Road (Mrs J Thornton) Village garden of ¼-acre with lawns, mature trees, roses, shrubs and perennials. Interesting conifer border established 1976. Flagstone terrace with distant views over countryside. Accommodation.

Little Dene Cottage, School Lane (Mr & Mrs M T J Tunstall) Bijou garden, very small, very colourful.

The Manor House, The Green (Mr & Mrs G Lewis) Large garden, fruit and vegetable plot, flower beds, knot garden. Featured on BBC 'Gardeners' World' 2003.

NEW **Old Manor Cottage, Church Hill** (Ms Jenny Andreae) Cottage garden with man-made stream, bridge and ponds. Pathways lead past mixed borders to quiet seating areas and on through archways to a terraced herb and kitchen garden.

Rotherwood, Soot Lane (Miss M R Goodison) Extensive garden with varied shrubs, views over fields.

Underedge, 1 Church Hill (Mr & Mrs J Dixon) Small colourful garden with pond and roses.

Westering, The Green (Mr & Mrs R Neale) Attractive medium-sized garden with vegetable plot, flower beds, patio area and chickens.

Wheelwright House, Long Compton

See Oxfordshire.

(56) Whichford & Ascott Gardens

6m SE of Shipston on Stour. Turn E off A3400 at Long Compton for Whichford. Two peaceful stone villages on the edge of the Cotswolds. Car park. Unusual plants for sale. TEAS in the Reading Room adjacent to Church in aid of St Michael's Church. *Combined adm £3.50, chd free. Sun 19 June (2-6)*

Ascott Lodge, Ascott (Charlotte Copley) Beautiful views, lawns sloping down to pond, well stocked shrub borders, courtyard garden. Many interesting plants.

Brook Hollow, Whichford (Mr & Mrs J A Round) Terraced hillside garden with large variety of trees, shrubs and plants; stream and water features. Competition for children.

The Old House, Whichford (Mr & Mrs T A Maher) Undulating, softly planted gardens spilling down through mature trees and shrubs to wildlife ponds.

The Old Rectory, Whichford (Mr & Mrs P O'Kane) Established family garden with sloping lawns, trees and shrubs. Wild flower paddock and waterside walks.

NEW **September House, Whichford** (Mrs J Clayton) Secluded peaceful garden, in full colour in June, with roses and other interesting plants.

The Whichford Pottery, Whichford (Mr & Mrs J B M Keeling) Secret walled garden, unusual plants, large vegetable garden and rambling cottage garden. Adjoining pottery also open. Featured in RHS 'The Garden' 2004.

(57) 17 Whitehall Road, Rugby

(Mary & Dick Illing) *From M1 take A428 towards Rugby town centre & Rugby School. After roundabout take 1st L into Horton Crescent for parking. Follow signs for Whitehall Rd.* Small, long, narrow (200ft x 35ft max) town garden, designed and created by owners over last few yrs. Areas of interest incl gravel and water features. Over 400 varieties of plants: clematis, ferns, bamboos and unusual shrubs chosen for yr-round interest. Hosta bed. Home-made TEAS. *Combined adm with* **4 Arnold Villas** *£2.50, chd free. Sun 7 Aug (2-5)*

(58) Wits End, 59 Tanworth Lane, Shirley, Solihull

(Sue Mansell) *2m SW of Solihull. Follow B4102 from Solihull for approx 2m. Turn R at island onto A34. After next island (Sainsbury's) Tanworth Lane is 1st L off A34.* Peaceful and interesting all-yr-round plantaholic's cottage-style garden. Hundreds of perennials, alpines and shrubs - many unusual - in various shaped beds and borders. Gravel area, alpine sinks, rockery, extensive shade areas and small waterfall, river and bog garden. Redesigned 2004 to incl 'Millennium Wheel' of sleepers and crazy paving. TEAS and extensive plants sale in aid of Alzheimer's Society. *Adm £1.50, chd free. Suns 15 May; 3 July; 7 Aug (2-5.30). Private visits welcome by appt. Tel 0121 744 4337*

59 Woodbrooke Quaker Study Centre, 1046 Bristol Road, Selly Oak &⊗⊕
4m SW of Birmingham. On A38 Bristol Rd, S of Selly Oak, opp Witherford Way. Buses: 143, 144, 61, 62 & 63. 10 acres of organically-managed garden and grounds. Grade II listed former home of George Cadbury (not open). Herbaceous and shrub borders, walled garden with herb garden, potager and cutting beds, orchard, arboretum, lake and extensive woodland walks. Very fine variety of trees. Light refreshments and TEAS in aid of Woodbrooke. *Adm £2, chd £1. Sun 15 May (2.30-5.30)*
www.woodbrooke.org.uk

60 Woodpeckers, Marlcliff, nr Bidford-on-Avon &⊗⊕
(Drs Andy & Lallie Cox) *7m SW of Stratford-upon-Avon. The Bank, Marlcliff. Off B4085 between Bidford-on-Avon & Cleeve Prior.* Peaceful 2½-acre plantsman's country garden designed and maintained by garden-mad owners since 1965. A garden for all seasons. Unusual plants, hidden surprises, interesting trees, colour-themed borders, potager and knot garden. Wooden sculptures of St Fiacre and The Green Man carved by the owner. Lovely garden buildings of framed green oak. *Adm £3.50, chd free. Private visits welcome by appt. Tel 01789 773416*

61 Wootton Grange, Pettiford Lane, Henley-in-Arden &⊕
(Mrs Jean Tarmey) *1m E of Henley-in-Arden. Take 1st R off A4189 Warwick Rd on to Pettiford Lane, garden is 300yds on R. From A3400 in Wootton Wawen turn by craft centre on to Pettiford Lane, garden 1m on L.* 1-acre farm garden with yr-round interest surrounding early Victorian farmhouse (not open). Wide variety of unusual plants incl bulbs, hellebores, clematis, roses and alpines. Bog garden, grass feature, kitchen garden. Home-made TEAS. *Adm £2. Private visits welcome by appt from early spring. Tel 01564 792592*

Wiltshire

County Organiser:	Brigadier Arthur Gooch, Manor Farmhouse, Chitterne, Warminster, Wiltshire BA12 0LG Tel 01985 850893
Assistant County Organisers:	Mrs David Armytage, Sharcott Manor, Pewsey, Wiltshire SN9 5PA Tel 01672 563485
	Mrs Anthony Heywood, Monkton House, Monkton Deverill, Wiltshire BA12 7EX Tel 01985 844486
Press Officer:	Mr Sean Magee, Byams House, Willesley, Tetbury, Gloucestershire GL8 8QU Tel 01666 880009
	Mrs Colin Shand, Ashton House, Worton, Devizes, Wiltshire SN10 5RU Tel 01380 726249
	Mrs John Surtees, Mitre Cottage, Snowhill, Dinton, Salisbury, Wiltshire SP3 5HN Tel 01722 716468

Maps: Numbers shown next to each garden entry refer to that garden's entry on the county map. This position is approximate; distance and directions from the nearest main town are generally shown in the garden text.
A precise location is available for those gardens featured on the NGS website by visiting www.ngs.org.uk.
Symbols: Information relating to symbols is given on page 21

DATES OF OPENING

Evening openings
See end of county listing

Private gardens open regularly for NGS
Enfield, Bromham *(16)*

Gardens open to the public
For details see garden description
Abbey House Gardens, Malmesbury Town Centre *(1)*
Bowood Rhododendron Walks, nr Chippenham *(5)*
Broadleas Gardens Charitable Trust Ltd, Devizes *(6)*
Corsham Court, nr Chippenham *(11)*
The Courts, Holt *(13)*
Great Chalfield Manor, nr Melksham *(21)*
Heale Gardens & Plant Centre, Middle Woodford *(25)*
Iford Manor, nr Bradford-on-Avon *(28)*
Lackham Gardens, Lacock *(31)*
Lacock Abbey Gardens, Chippenham *(32)*
The Mead Nursery, Brokerswood *(42)*
Mompesson House, Salisbury *(45)*
Pound Hill House, West Kington *(54)*
Stourhead Garden, Stourton *(59)*

February 6 Sunday
Great Chalfield Manor, nr Melksham *(21)*
February 12 Saturday
Lacock Abbey Gardens, Chippenham *(32)*
February 13 Sunday
Lacock Abbey Gardens, Chippenham *(32)*
February 19 Saturday
Lacock Abbey Gardens, Chippenham *(32)*
February 20 Sunday
Lacock Abbey Gardens, Chippenham *(32)*
The Old Rectory, Ham *(51)*
February 27 Sunday
Lower House, Whiteparish *(35)*
March 20 Sunday
Abbey House Gardens, Malmesbury Town Centre *(1)*

Corsham Court, nr Chippenham *(11)*
Fonthill House, nr Tisbury *(18)*
March 27 Sunday (Easter)
Littleton Drew Gardens *(34)*
March 28 Monday (Easter)
Littleton Drew Gardens *(34)*
April 3 Sunday
Mitre Cottage, Dinton *(44)*
April 6 Wednesday
Sharcott Manor, nr Pewsey *(57)*
April 10 Sunday
Broadleas Gardens Charitable Trust Ltd, Devizes *(6)*
Ridleys Cheer, Mountain Bower *(56)*
Sharcott Manor, nr Pewsey *(57)*
April 20 Wednesday
Home Covert Gardens & Arboretum, Roundway *(26)*
April 24 Sunday
Iford Manor, nr Bradford-on-Avon *(28)*
Inwoods, Farleigh Wick *(29)*
Little Durnford Manor, nr Salisbury *(33)*
Oare House, nr Pewsey *(48)*
May 1 Sunday
Waterdale House, East Knoyle *(60)*
May 4 Wednesday
Enfield, Bromham *(16)*
Sharcott Manor, nr Pewsey *(57)*
May 6 Friday
Mallards, Chirton *(36)*
May 8 Sunday
The Pound House, Little Somerford *(55)*
May 11 Wednesday
Enfield, Bromham *(16)*
Manor House, Stratford Tony *(39)*
The Old Mill, Ramsbury *(50)*
May 15 Sunday
The Courts, Holt *(13)*
Ridleys Cheer, Mountain Bower *(56)*
May 18 Wednesday
Enfield, Bromham *(16)*
Home Covert Gardens & Arboretum, Roundway *(26)*

May 20 Friday
Mallards, Chirton *(36)*
May 21 Saturday
Mompesson House, Salisbury *(45)*
May 22 Sunday
Conock Manor, Chirton *(10)*
The Grange, Winterbourne Dauntsey *(19)*
Manor Farm, Huish *(37)*
Sheldon Manor, nr Chippenham *(58)*
May 25 Wednesday
Enfield, Bromham *(16)*
May 29 Sunday
Guyers House, Pickwick, Corsham *(23)*
Hazelbury Manor Gardens, Wadswick, nr Box *(24)*
Hyde's House, Dinton *(27)*
June 1 Wednesday
Enfield, Bromham *(16)*
Sharcott Manor, nr Pewsey *(57)*
June 5 Sunday
Bowood Rhododendron Walks, nr Chippenham *(5)*
33 Calne Road, Lyneham *(7)*
Cantax House, Lacock *(8)*
Sheldon Manor, nr Chippenham *(58)*
June 8 Wednesday
33 Calne Road, Lyneham *(7)*
Enfield, Bromham *(16)*
June 10 Friday
Mallards, Chirton *(36)*
June 12 Sunday
Basset Down Farm Gardens, Salthrop, nr Wroughton *(2)*
Chisenbury Priory, East Chisenbury *(9)*
The Court House, Lower Woodford *(12)*
Dauntsey Gardens *(14)*
Edington Gardens *(15)*
Faulstone House, Bishopstone *(17)*
Grange Farm, Kilmington *(20)*
Lackham Gardens, Lacock *(31)*
Manor Farm, West Kington *(38)*
Manor House Farm, Hanging Langford *(40)*
Poulton House, Marlborough *(53)*
Ridleys Cheer, Mountain Bower *(56)*

WILTSHIRE

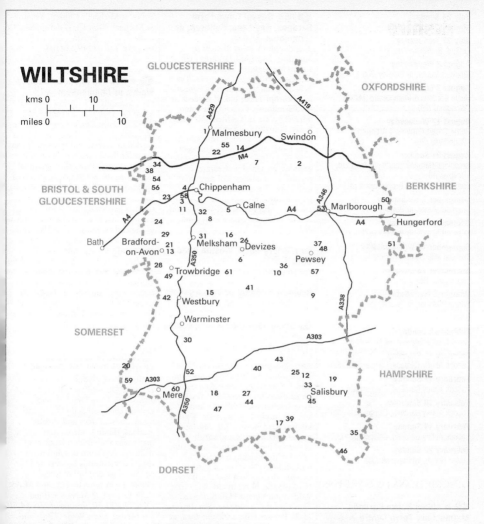

GLOUCESTERSHIRE

OXFORDSHIRE

BRISTOL & SOUTH GLOUCESTERSHIRE

BERKSHIRE

kms 0 — 10
miles 0 — 10

1 Malmesbury
Swindon
55 14
22 M4
7 2
34
38
54
56 4 Chippenham
23 58
3
11 32 8 5 Calne A4 53 Marlborough
24 A4 Hungerford
29 31 16
21 Melksham 26 Devizes 37 48
Bath Bradford- 13 A350 6 Pewsey
on-Avon 36 57
28 10
49 Trowbridge 61
42 Westbury 15 41 9
Warminster

SOMERSET

30
43
20 52 40 25 12 19 HAMPSHIRE
59 A303 33 Salisbury
60 Mere 18 27 44 45
47
17 39
35
46

DORSET

July 24 Sunday
Newland, Woodfalls *(46)*

July 27 Wednesday
Enfield, Bromham *(16)*

August 3 Wednesday
Sharcott Manor, nr Pewsey *(57)*

August 7 Sunday
Heale Gardens & Plant Centre, Middle Woodford *(25)*

August 17 Wednesday
Home Covert Gardens & Arboretum, Roundway *(26)*

August 21 Sunday
Broadleas Gardens Charitable Trust Ltd, Devizes *(6)*
The Mead Nursery, Brokerswood *(42)*

September 7 Wednesday
Sharcott Manor, nr Pewsey *(57)*

September 11 Sunday
Sharcott Manor, nr Pewsey *(57)*

September 14 Wednesday
The Old Mill, Ramsbury *(50)*

September 25 Sunday
The Courts, Holt *(13)*

October 5 Wednesday
Sharcott Manor, nr Pewsey *(57)*

2006

February 5 Sunday
Great Chalfield Manor, nr Melksham *(21)*

February 11 Saturday
Lacock Abbey Gardens, Chippenham *(32)*

February 12 Sunday
Lacock Abbey Gardens, Chippenham *(32)*

February 18 Saturday
Lacock Abbey Gardens, Chippenham *(32)*

February 19 Sunday
Lacock Abbey Gardens, Chippenham *(32)*

February 26 Sunday
Lower House, Whiteparish *(35)*

DESCRIPTIONS OF GARDENS

❶ ◆ Abbey House Gardens, Malmesbury Town Centre 🅷🅰🅷☺
(Barbara & Ian Pollard) *Beside C12 Abbey. Parking in town centre (short stay) or follow brown signs to long stay (via steps to gardens).* 5 beautiful acres planted by present owner. Over 60,000 spring bulbs especially tulips; 'medieval' herb garden; topiary; knot garden; herbaceous borders; laburnum walk; UK's largest private collection of roses; ornamental trees; rare plants; wooded walk to river, 'monastic' fish ponds, waterfall and fernery. 'The WOW factor is here in abundance', Alan Titchmarsh. Featured in 'The English Garden' 2003, 'The Times' 2004. TEAS. *Adm £5.50, chd £2, concessions £4.75. Daily 21 Mar to 21 Oct.* **For NGS:** *Sun 20 Mar (11-5.30). Tel 01666 822212 www.abbeyhousegardens.co.uk*

❷ NEW Basset Down Farm Gardens, Hay Lane, Salthrop, nr Wroughton 🅷🅰🅷☺
(Sue & John Hollis) *3m SW of Swindon. From M4 J16 take exit signed Wroughton. Straight on minor rd signed Salthrop. From A4361 turn NW at Wroughton Airfield hangars to Salthrop.* Three linked gardens at the Farmhouse, Coach House and adjacent cottage. Features incl formal areas, innovative greenhouse plantings, knot garden, rose garden, young orchard, woodland gardens, new wild flower meadows, vegetable gardens, pleached lime terraces, pond-side plantings, koi carp in a terrace pool and a new 'scented garden' area. Home-made TEAS in aid of Prospect Hospice, Wroughton. *Adm £3.50, chd free. Sun 12 June (12-6)*

Bath Priory Hotel, Weston Road, Bath 🅷🅰🅷☺
See Somerset.

Beverston Castle, nr Tetbury 🅷🅰☺
See Gloucestershire North & Central.

❸ Biddestone Manor, Biddestone 🅷🅰🅷☺
(Mr H Astrup) *5m W of Chippenham. On A4 between Chippenham & Corsham turn N. From A420, 5m W of Chippenham, turn S. Car park, please do not park on rd.* Peaceful 8-acre garden with extensive lawns, small lake and streams, topiary, arboretum. Walled kitchen garden, orchard, cutting garden, herbaceous and shrub borders. Fine C17 manor house (not open) with ancient dovecote and outbuildings. New round garden designed by Chelsea medal winner. Home-made TEAS in aid of Biddestone Village Hall & Recreation Trust. *Adm £3, chd free. Sun 26 June (2-5). Private visits welcome by appt for groups of 10+, Thurs only. Tel 01249 701305*

❹ Bolehyde Manor, Allington 🅷🅰☺
(The Earl & Countess Cairns) *1½m W of Chippenham. On Bristol Rd (A420). Turn N at Allington Xrds. ½m on R. Parking in field.* Series of gardens around C16 manor house (not open), enclosed by walls and topiary, densely planted with many interesting shrubs and climbers, mixed rose and herbaceous beds; inner courtyard with troughs full of tender plants; wild flower orchard, vegetable, fruit garden and greenhouse yard. Collection of tender pelargoniums; adventure tree house for children. Home-made TEAS in

aid of St Michael's Church, Kington St Michael. *Adm £3, chd 50p. Sun 19 June (2.30-6). Private visits welcome by appt. Tel 01249 652105*

❺ ◆ Bowood Rhododendron Walks, nr Chippenham 🅰☺
(The Marquis of Lansdowne) *3½m SE of Chippenham. Entrance off A342 between Sandy Lane & Derry Hill villages.* This 60-acre woodland garden of azaleas and rhododendrons is one of the most exciting of its type in the country. From the individual flowers to the breathtaking sweep of colour formed by hundreds of shrubs, surrounded by carpets of bluebells, this is a garden not to be missed. Planting first began in 1850 and some of the earliest known hybrids appear among the collection. Bowood House and Gardens a separate attraction, 2m from Rhododendron Walks. *Adm £3.70, chd free. Bowood House & Gardens and Rhododendron Walks on same day, deduct £1. Daily last week Apr to early June, depending on flowering season.* **For NGS:** *Sun 5 June (11-6) www.bowood.org*

❻ ◆ Broadleas Gardens Charitable Trust Ltd, Devizes 🅷☺
(Lady Anne Cowdray) *1m S of Devizes. On A360 or follow tourist signs from Long Street.* 9-acre garden; sheltered dell planted with many unusual trees and shrubs. Azaleas, rhododendrons and magnolias with underplantings of trilliums, erythroniums and many others. Herbaceous borders and perennial garden full of interesting plants. Light refreshments and TEAS. *Adm £5 (Apr & May), £4 (June to Oct), chd £1.50, groups of 10+ £4.50 per person. Suns, Weds, Thurs end Mar to end Oct.* **For NGS:** *Suns 10 Apr; 21 Aug (2-6)*

❼ 33 Calne Road, Lyneham 🅷🅰🅷☺
(Sue & Sam Wright) *7m N of Calne. Next to RAF Lyneham entrance.* Approx ¾-acre informal garden comprising modest collection of hostas, clematis and roses. Small kitchen garden, pond and mature orchard with bantams, chickens, geese, doves and dovecote. Green oasis surrounded by activity. Featured in 'Amateur Gardening' 2003. Home-made TEAS in aid of Lyneham Scout Hut. *Adm £1.50, chd 50p. Sun 5, Wed 8 June (1-5)*

Joe Swift

Garden designer
and TV presenter

Photograph: William Shaw

The best job in the world

I'm lucky enough to have one of the best jobs in the world. Over the last 18 months I've visited a total of 35 Yellow Book gardens whilst filming two series of Garden Makers, and sure it was very tiring work driving for miles, and filming long days, but I can honestly say that as a garden designer myself, I have never been so stimulated, inspired and energised as during the time I spent on these visits.

I love to see how each individual garden maker, or in many cases a formidable duo of garden makers, have creatively approached their particular plot with regards to existing site conditions, layout, colour, form, height, texture etc.- all the elements that combine to build up a highly individual space with its own unique mood.

Through the combination and balance of these elements the personality and identity of the garden owner becomes wonderfully and indelibly stamped onto their garden, and the two become deeply and irreversibly connected. To put it a little over dramatically, one cannot survive for long without the other.

Somerset Lodge, Sussex - one of the NGS gardens featured in Garden Makers
Photograph: Leigh Clapp

My tip (which may not go down too well with some of those who open their gardens) is to try to corner the garden owner and put simply, quiz them as much as possible. This is best done over the essential cup of tea and a slice of delicious homemade cake. You'll hear some fabulous tales of both success and failure (which we all know go hand in hand in gardening), and whilst drooling over one of the healthiest, most lush gardens you've ever seen in your life, you'll be told horror stories of battling against poor soil, strong winds, drought, too much rain, aphid infestations and next door's dog. And of course if you'd only been here last week, it looked so much better then, huh- the story of my life!

My own tour has proved that we truly are a nation of great gardeners, and the diversity and range never ceases to amaze me. Whether you want to visit a cottage garden or an urban 'outdoor room', a formal estate or a sculpture garden, the Yellow Book's got the lot. The creativity, commitment and sheer generosity of those who open their gardens is something we should be immensely proud of, and remember, it's all for charity. Enjoy.

Photographs: Ian Gowland

Caroline Donald

Garden Writer and Gardening
Editor of the Sunday Times

Learning from the masters

It is surely a dream of many British gardeners for their plot to be considered good enough, "with at least 40 minutes of interest", to open for The National Gardens Scheme. On my own part, I look at my electric shock of a cottage garden in Somerset and think, well, maybe next year.

Still, there is consolation in visiting other people's gardens, which are open to the NGS. What a treat to be allowed into someone's private heaven – be it an allotment in Gloucestershire, a hilltop or coastal garden or the Royal Family's resting ground at Frogmore in Windsor Park. And how very rarely they disappoint: even in the tiniest city garden you find breathtaking examples of plantsmanship and artistic creativity, the owners having made a haven from the bustling world outside the front door.

When people ask me what I do and I reply "I'm a journalist", an involuntary cloud often crosses their face, as if they think what they say will turn up on the front page of a scandal sheet. So I quickly tell them that I am a gardening writer and editor. Could there be a more benign area of hackdom – I've yet to meet a garden owner (certainly an NGS garden owner) who is anything other than friendly, informative and fun to be with. How often have I thought while walking round a garden chatting to the owner on a warm day in some far-flung part of the country, "lucky old me".

The next thing people ask is how I got into this area of work. I have to confess it is not through horticultural routes – I read history at university – but journalistic. I am a writer interested in gardening and most especially gardeners, rather than a horticulturalist who can string two words together. The two do overlap to some degree, however, in that I followed the familiar route via my mother dragging me round the garden to learn the names of plants as a child and through my own plots in London, then Somerset over the past 12 years or so. It was this and Dan Pearson that led me then to be Gardening Editor at the Sunday Times. Sitting in a department full of young urban things whose interests were in fashion and discussing their hangovers from some dreary lipstick press launch, I would plead to edit Dan's pieces, where I would take refuge in his dreamy prose, conjuring up his beautiful planting schemes in my head. And for endless inspiration here I am still leafing through the Yellow Book, knowing how many more lovely gardens in it there are to visit and write about. Lucky old me.

Photograph: Ian Gowland

NGS charity highlights

The National Gardens Scheme exists to support national nursing, caring and gardening charities, (see page 7). We feature here three of our charities, the Queen's Nursing Institute, Help the Hospices and the Nurses Welfare Service. For more detailed information on all our charities and the wonderful work they do visit our website www.ngs.org.uk

The Queen's Nursing Institute

The generosity of the NGS has enabled the Queen's Nursing Institute to provide funding for ground-breaking community nursing projects, which are transforming the lives of thousands of people throughout England, Wales and Northern Ireland.

Here a group of young mums and their babies take part in the first Ilkley post natal and toddler walk, a health promotion programme organised by two Yorkshire health visitors to help new mothers get fit and make new friends.

help the hospices

Help the Hospices

Staff and volunteers in hospices strive to offer terminally ill patients freedom from pain, dignity, peace and calm. They also give care and support for their loved ones. This work is endlessly rewarding but also very demanding - professionally and emotionally. Help the Hospices provides grants, training, education, information and advice to help ensure hospice staff can continue to give high quality care to those facing the end of their life.

The Nurses Welfare Service

Since 1975 the NGS has supported a unique charity - the Nurses Welfare Service. In fact from the very first garden opening in 1927 proceeds went towards assisting nurses in need. The NWS offers confidential support to nursing professionals with personal difficulties and uses NGS money to intervene before situations deteriorate too badly.

Photograph: Charlie Hopkins

ngs gardens open for charity

Sarah Raven
Garden Writer

My garden at Perch Hill Farm, Sussex

Perch Hill is all about being productive and bringing the garden into the house in the form of buckets and buckets of cut flowers and baskets of vegetables, herbs and salads. Ours is very much a working garden where we trial all our seeds for the mail order business, cut hard for the flower arranging courses and pick all the vegetables to eat in the cookery school and at home.

The idea is to get massive production from a relatively small area of ground. In the first part of the year we have hardy annuals which are put out in the autumn so that they flower in May and June. The second growing season is manned by half-hardy annuals which take us through high summer into autumn. We replace some of these, as they go over, with biennials such as wallflowers from March to May and white foxgloves from May until August. The edge beds in the cutting garden are used for trials of different species. We also have perennials and spring-flowering bulbs chock-a-block in these external beds. To give height to the garden we have a sweet pea tunnel which looks fantastic from May until early August when we replace them with climbing pumpkins, like 'munchkin' or French and runner beans.

Other parts of the garden to visit are the dahlia garden, the vegetable and herb garden and the oast garden. The dahlia garden is like a pantomime dame! A garden with too much make up, lots of colour and large bold clumps of foliage plants. It's a hot garden with brilliant-coloured dahlias, zinnias and tobacco plants set against exotic, jungley cannas and banana foliage. In the kitchen and herb gardens I grow interesting and unusual vegetables as well as many kitchen staples which we trial for flavour and ease of growth. The oast garden is vibrant and intense in colour with combinations of structural and extravagant foliage and flowers. Perch Hill is all at its best in spring and summer.

We opened the garden in aid of The National Gardens Scheme for the first time in 2004. It was a great day, full of interesting and appreciative visitors. The atmosphere was informal and friendly and even though the garden was humming with people it felt very relaxed. We all enjoyed the day and are looking forward to our next opening day for the NGS.

8 Cantax House, Lacock ⬡⬡⬡
(Andrew & Deborah van der Beek)
*3m S of Chippenham. Off A350
between Chippenham & Melksham.
Entrance to garden in Cantax Hill.*
Queen Anne former vicarage (not
open). Medium-sized garden of
colour, pattern and scent; designed
and maintained by artist owner;
interesting and unusual plants;
hornbeam spire and other topiary
projects in yew; old orchard wild
garden; sculpture by owner and
friends; brook with stepping stones;
good views of village. Cream TEAS.
*Adm £2.50, chd free (share to
Amnesty International). Sun 5 June
(2-6)*

**9 Chisenbury Priory, East
Chisenbury** ⬡⬡⬡
(Mr & Mrs John Manser) *3m SW of
Pewsey. Turn E from A345 at Enford
then N to E Chisenbury, main gates
1m on R.* Medieval Priory with
Queen Anne face and early C17 rear
(not open) in middle of 5-acre garden
on chalk; mature garden with fine
trees within clump and flint walls,
herbaceous borders, shrubs, roses.
Moisture-loving plants along mill
leat; carp pond, orchard and wild
garden, many unusual plants.
Featured in 'The English Garden',
2003. Cream TEAS in aid of Enford
Parish Church. *Adm £2.75, chd free.
Sun 12 June (2-6). Private visits
welcome by appt. Tel 07810 483984*

Conholt Park, Chute ⬡
See Hampshire.

10 Conock Manor, Chirton
⬡⬡⬡
(Mrs Bonar Sykes) *5m SE of Devizes.
Off A342.* Mixed borders, flowering
shrubs; extensive replanting incl new
arboretum; interesting decorative
brickwork with tiled water runnels to
replace old borders. C18 house in
Bath stone, not open. Cream TEAS.
*Adm £2.50, chd under 16 free (share
to St John's Church, Chirton). Sun 22
May (2-6)*

**11 ◆ Corsham Court, nr
Chippenham** ⬡⬡
(Mr James Methuen-Campbell) *4m
W of Chippenham. S of A4.* Park and
gardens laid out by Capability Brown
and Repton. Large lawns with fine
specimens of ornamental trees; lily
pond with Indian bean trees; spring
bulbs; young arboretum; C18 bath
house; Elizabethan mansion with
alterations. Wheelchair users and
necessary attendants free entry to
garden. TEAS NGS days only, or by
appt for groups of 15+. *House &
garden adm £5, chd £2.50, OAP*

*£4.50. Garden only £2, chd £1, OAP
£1.50. Daily (not Mons & Fris) incl
Bank Hols 20 Mar to 30 Sept
(2-5.30) ; Oct to 19 Mar weekends
only (2-4.30). Closed Dec.* **For NGS:**
*Sun 20 Mar; Sun 17 July (2-5.30, last
entry 5). Tel 01249 701610
www.corsham-court.co.uk*

**12 The Court House, Lower
Woodford** ⬡⬡
(Mr & Mrs J G Studholme) *3m N of
Salisbury. On Woodford Valley rd,
between A360 & A345.* 3½-acre
garden on the banks of the Avon.
Herbaceous borders, waterside
planting, yew hedges, rambler roses
and wild flowers. Ancient site of
Bishop's Palace in the time of Old
Sarum. TEAS in aid of Mothers'
Union. *Adm £2.50, chd free. Sun 12
June (2-6). Private visits welcome by
appt, June & July only. Tel 01722
782237*

13 ◆ The Courts, Holt ⬡⬡⬡
(The National Trust) *2m E of
Bradford-on-Avon. S of B3107 to
Melksham. In Holt follow National
Trust signs, park at Village Hall.* 3½
acres of formal gardens divided by
yew hedges and raised terraces.
Features incl conservatory, lily pond,
colour-themed herbaceous borders,
pleached limes, Venetian gates and
stone ornaments. 3½ acres wild
flower and arboretum; many fine
trees. C15 House (not open). Kitchen
garden under restoration. Cream
TEAS. *Adm £4.80, chd £2.50.* **For
NGS:** *Suns 15 May; 25 Sept (11-5.30).
Tel 01225 782340
www.nationaltrust.org.uk*

◆ Crowe Hall, Widcombe ⬡
See Somerset.

14 Dauntsey Gardens
*5m SE of Malmesbury. Approach via
Dauntsey Rd from Gt Somerford,
1¼m from Volunteer Inn.* Home-
made TEAS at Idover House in aid of
St James' Church, Dauntsey.
*Combined adm £5, chd 50p. Sun 12
June (2-6)*

Church Lodge ⬡⬡ (Mr & Mrs
Donald Farquharson) Garden
forms part of former walled
garden of Dauntsey Park adjacent
to St James' Church. Lawns,
shrub roses and herbaceous
borders.

The Coach House ⬡⬡ (Col &
Mrs J Seddon-Brown) Small
walled garden. Herbaceous
borders and well-established
climbing roses, clematis and other
trees and shrubs.

Garden Cottage, Dauntsey Park
⬡⬡ (Miss Ann Sturgis) 5-acre
garden, incl restored C19 walled
kitchen garden organically run;
greenhouses; cottage garden;
orchard and woodland walks.
*Private visits welcome by appt.
Tel 07000 278874
ann@daunteypark.co.uk*

Idover House ⬡ (Mr & Mrs
Christopher Jerram) Medium-
sized mature garden in
established setting with many
mature trees incl two large
wellingtonias; spacious lawns,
herbaceous borders, formal rose
garden; swimming pool garden,
duck pond; yew hedge walk to
kitchen garden and woodland
garden.

The Pond House ⬡⬡ (Mr & Mrs
Stephen Love) Informal 1½-acre
garden, currently being developed
(does it ever stop?); large lily
pond, lawns, wild flowers,
orchard with path leading to
Garden Cottage.

15 Edington Gardens
*4m NE of Westbury. On B3098
between Westbury & West
Lavington. Park off B3098 in church
car park or in Monastery Rd opp
Monastery Garden House.* Village
map marking gardens given to all
visitors. Home-made TEAS in Parish
Hall. *Combined adm £4, chd free.
Sun 12 June (2-6)*

Bonshommes Cottage (Mr
Michael Jones) *Through Old
Vicarage garden.* ¾-acre hillside
garden with mixed herbaceous,
roses, shrubs. Some long-
established Japanese knotweed
has been retained as a practical
feature.

Edington Priory (Mr R Cooper)
4-acre gardens with medieval
well, walls and carp lake.
Herbaceous borders, kitchen
garden and extensive lawns with
shrubs and roses.

The Grange ⬡ (Mr & Mrs
Charles Atterton) Architectural
and leafy garden composed of
themed rooms featuring unusual
trees, shrubs and herbaceous
plants.

The Monastery Garden (Mr & Mrs
Allanson-Bailey) 2½-acre garden
with many varieties of spring
bulbs and shrub roses; 3-acre
additional walled garden;
medieval walls of national
importance.

The Old Vicarage ⬡⬡ NCCPG
(Mr J N d'Arcy) 2-acre garden on
greensand on hillside, fine views;
intensively planted with

herbaceous borders; newly built wall borders; gravel garden; small waterfall; shrubs; arboretum with growing range of unusual trees; woodland plants; bulbs; lilies, recently introduced species from abroad. National Collection of evening primroses, with over 20 species.

⑯ NEW Enfield, 62 Yard Lane, Bromham ♿✂🏠
(Graham & Elizabeth Veals) *4m NW of Devizes. E off A342 into Yard Lane, garden ¼m on R. Limited parking.* ½-acre garden in a quiet location, intensively planted in 4 sections with alpines, shrubs, mini-woodland and herbaceous borders that incl many old favourites as well as several more unusual species. TEAS. *Adm £2, chd free. Every Wed, May, June & July (10-8). Private visits welcome by appt May & June only, for groups of 8-15. Tel 01380 859303 graham@vealsgd. freeserve.co.uk*

⑰ Faulstone House, Bishopstone ♿✂🏠
(Miss Freya Watkinson) *3m SW of Salisbury. Take minor rd W off A354 at Coombe Bissett, after 2m turn S into Harvest Lane 300yds E of White Hart Inn.* Separate smaller gardens in large garden surrounding Old Manor House (not open). C14 Defence Tower converted to pigeon loft in C18. Many old-fashioned roses, herbaceous plants (some unusual), vegetable garden. Meadow with river frontage set in rural surroundings, including the Faulstone herd of Belted Galloways. Home-made TEAS in aid of the Village Hall. *Adm £2.50, chd under 15 free. Sun 12 June (2-6)*

⑱ Fonthill House, nr Tisbury ♿🏠
(The Lord Margadale of Islay) *13m W of Salisbury. Via B3089 in Fonthill Bishop. 3m N of Tisbury.* Large woodland garden. Daffodils, rhododendrons, azaleas, shrubs, bulbs; magnificent views; formal garden. Limited wheelchair access. *Adm £3, chd free. Sun 20 Mar (2-6)*

ng's gardens open for charity

Look out for the NCCPG National Plant Collections at some of our gardens

⑲ The Grange, Winterbourne Dauntsey ♿✂🏠
(Mr & Mrs Rebdi) *4m NE of Salisbury. On the A338.* Spacious 6-acre garden with R Bourne running through. Immaculate lawns, clipped box, borders. Laburnum, rose and clematis arched walk, lily pond, vegetable and herb garden. Wild natural area. Restored C17 thatched barn, open. Cream TEAS in aid of The Glebe Hall. *Adm £2.50, chd £1. Sun 22 May (2-6)*

⑳ Grange Farm, Kilmington ♿✂🏠
(Mrs Carolyn Lissack) *4m NW of Mere. Follow signs off the B3092.* Established garden situated in delightful setting with views of the surrounding countryside. Various separate elements incl mixed perennial and shrub borders, lawns, white garden, pond, waterfall and vegetable garden providing interest throughout the yr. Home-made TEAS. *Adm £2, chd free. Sun 12 June (2-6)*

㉑ ◆ Great Chalfield Manor, nr Melksham ♿✂🏠
(Mr & Mrs R Floyd & The National Trust) *3m W of Melksham. Take B3107 from Melksham then 1st R to Broughton Gifford. Follow sign for Atworth, turn L for 1m to Manor.* Park on grass outside. Garden and grounds of 7 acres laid out 1905-12 by Robert Fuller and his wife to designs by Alfred Parsons, Capt Partridge and Sir Harold Brakspear. Incl roses, daffodils, spring flowers, topiary houses, borders, terraces, gazebo, orchard, autumn border. C15 moated manor (not open) and adjoining Parish Church. Snowdrops and aconites enhance moat walk in early spring. *House & garden adm £4.60. Garden only £2.50, chd £1. Apr to Oct, Tues to Thurs (11-5), Suns (2-5). For NGS: Sun 6 Feb (2-4.30); Sun 5 Feb 2006. Tel 01225 782239 patsy@greatchalfield.co.uk*

㉒ Great Somerford Gardens
4m SE of Malmesbury. 4m N of M4 between J16 & J17; 2m S of B4042 Malmesbury to Wootton Bassett rd; 3m E of A429 Cirencester to Chippenham rd. TEAS at The Mount House. *Combined adm £3.50, chd under 13 free (share to Helen Ley Care Centre). Sat, Sun 25, 26 June (1.30-5.30)*

1 Hollow Street (Bridget Smith) ¼-acre, next door to Old Maltings. Lilies, penstemon and other assorted perennials.

The Mount House (Mr & Mrs McGrath) Complete traditional

village manor house garden; 3 acres of lawns, herbaceous beds, shrubs. Large trees and fruit and vegetable garden. The Mount area and restored Coach House garden also open. Ancient barn restored in 2001.

The Old Maltings, Hollow Street 🏠
(Dr & Mrs S Jevons) Front garden with extensive and interesting herbaceous and shrub borders. Behind house is walk down to and across R Avon into conservation area with plantations of native trees and shrubs. River walk.

Somerford House ♿✂ (Mr & Mrs Martin Jones) 3-acre garden developed over the last 25yrs which incorporates the original orchard and features roses, shrubs, old wisteria, perennials, rockery and pool, vegetables and soft fruit.

㉓ Guyers House, Pickwick, Corsham ♿✂🏠
(Mr & Mrs Guy Hungerford) *4m SW of Chippenham. Guyers Lane signed directly off A4 opp B3109 Bradford-on-Avon turning.* 6-acre garden recently restored and being extended. Herbaceous borders, yew walks, pleached hornbeam walk. Extensive lawns, ponds, walled garden, rose hoops, climbing and shrub roses; walled kitchen garden, orchard, herbs. TEAS. *Adm £2.50, chd free. Sun 29 May (2-5)*

Hapsford House, Great Elm ✂
See Somerset.

㉔ Hazelbury Manor Gardens, Wadswick, nr Box ♿✂🏠
5m SW of Chippenham. 5m NE of Bath. From A4 at Box, A365 to Melksham, at Five Ways junction L onto B3109; 1st L, drive immed on R. 8 acres Grade II landscaped organic gardens around C15 fortified manor (not open). Impressive yew topiary and clipped beeches around large lawn; herbaceous and mixed borders ablaze in summer; laburnum and lime walkways; rose garden, stone circle and rockery. Walled kitchen garden. Home-made TEAS. *Adm £4, chd £1, concessions £3. Sun 29 May (2-6). Private visits welcome by appt all yr. Tel 01225 812952*

㉕ ◆ Heale Gardens & Plant Centre, Middle Woodford ♿✂🏠
(Mr & Mrs Guy Rasch) *4m N of Salisbury. On Woodford Valley Rd between A360 & A345.* 8 acres beside R Avon; interesting and varied collection of plants, shrubs; roses in

formal setting of clipped hedges and mellow stonework surrounding C17 manor house (not open) where Charles II hid after battle of Worcester. Water garden with magnolia and acer; frames; authentic Japanese Tea House and Nikko bridge. Adjacent nursery. Light refreshments and TEAS. *Adm £3.75, chd £1.50. Daily all year, not Mons.* **For NGS:** *Sun 7 Aug (10-5).* *Tel 01722 782504*

Hill Lodge, Northend, Batheaston ⓕⓧ⊕
See Somerset.

◆ Hilltop, Woodville, Stour Provost ⓧ⊕
See Dorset.

Hodges Barn, Shipton Moyne ⓕ
See Gloucestershire North & Central.

㉖ Home Covert Gardens & Arboretum, Roundway ⓕ
(Mr & Mrs John Phillips) *1m N of Devizes. On minor rd signed Roundway linking A361 to A342, 1m from each main rd.* Extensive garden on greensand created out of ancient woodland since 1960. Situated below the Downs with distant views. Formal borders around the house contrast with water gardens in the valley below. Wide range of trees, shrubs and plants grown for yr-round interest, incl erythroniums, magnolias, rhododendrons, camellias, eucryphias and hydrangea species. *Adm £3, chd free. Weds 20 Apr; 18 May; 15 June; 17 Aug (2-5.30). Private visits welcome by appt. Tel 01380 723407*

㉗ Hyde's House, Dinton ⊕
(Mr George Cruddas) *9m W of Salisbury. Off B3089 nr Dinton Church.* 3 acres of wild and formal garden in beautiful situation with series of hedged garden rooms. Numerous roses and borders. Large walled kitchen garden, herb garden and C13 dovecote (open). Charming C16/18 Grade I listed house (not open), with lovely courtyard. NT walks around park and lake. TEAS in aid of St Mary's church. *Adm £3, chd free. Sun 29 May (2-5)*

㉘ ◆ Iford Manor, nr Bradford-on-Avon
(Mr & Mrs Hignett) *7m S of Bath. Off A36, brown tourist sign to Iford 1m. Or from Bradford-on-Avon or Trowbridge via Lower Westwood village (brown signs).* Very romantic award-winning Italian-style terraced garden, listed Grade I, home of

Harold Peto 1899-1933; house not open. Home-made TEAS. *Adm £4.50, concessions £3.50. Suns Apr & Oct; May to Sept: Tues, Weds, Thurs, Sats, Suns & Bank Hol Mons (2-5).* **For NGS:** *Sun 24 Apr (2-5). Tel 01225 863146 www.ifordmanor.co.uk*

Inkpen House, Inkpen ⓧ⊕
See Berkshire.

㉙ Inwoods, Farleigh Wick ⓕ⊕
(Mr & Mrs D S Whitehead) *3m NW of Bradford-on-Avon. From Bath via A363 towards Bradford-on-Avon; at Farleigh Wick, 100yds past Fox & Hounds, R into drive.* 5 acres with lawns, borders, flowering shrubs, wild garden, wild flower wood. Home-made TEAS in aid of Home Farm Trust. *Adm £2.50, chd 50p. Sun 24 Apr (2-6)*

㉚ Job's Mill, Crockerton ⊕
(The Lady Silvy McQuiston) *1½m S of Warminster. Down lane E of A350, S of A36 roundabout.* Delightful medium-sized terraced garden through which R Wylye flows. Herbaceous border and water garden. Light refreshments and TEAS. *Adm £2.50, chd free (share to Warminster Hospital). Sun 26 June (2-6)*

Kirby House, Inkpen ⓧ⊕
See Berkshire.

㉛ ◆ Lackham Gardens, Lacock ⓕⓧ⊕ NCCPG
(Wiltshire College Lackham) *4m S of Chippenham. On A350, 7M S of M4 J17, between Chippenham and National Trust village of Lacock.* Walled garden with greenhouses, lawn paths separating plots, with variety of interesting shrubs, unusual vegetables, herbaceous plants, fruit. Pleasure gardens: sensory garden, ornamental pond, mixed borders; lawns; woodland walks. Gardens include laurel maze and various plant collections, with many mature trees, incl oaks - many 200yrs old. Museum of agriculture and rural life incl horticultural equipment. 17 July is also our woodcraft day. Large Gold Medal winner and Best in Show at Royal Bath & West of England Show 2004. Home-made TEAS NGS days. *Adm £2, chd free, concessions £1.50. Suns, Bank Hol Mons Easter to end Aug.* **For NGS:** *Suns 12 June; 17 July (10-5, last adm 4). Tel 01249 466800 daviaj@wiltscoll.ac.uk*

㉜ ◆ Lacock Abbey Gardens, Chippenham ⓕⓧ⊕
(The National Trust) *3m S of Chippenham. Off A350. Follow National Trust signs. Use public car park just outside Abbey.* Victorian woodland garden with pond, botanic garden and exotic tree specimens. Display of early spring flowers with carpets of aconites, snowdrops, crocuses and daffodils. C13 Abbey with C18 gothic additions. Light refreshments and TEAS in village. *Adm £2, chd free.* **For NGS:** *Sats, Suns 12, 13, 19, 20 Feb (11-5). Sats, Suns 11, 12, 18, 19 Feb 2006. Tel 01249 730141 sue.carter@nationaltrust.org.uk*

◆ Larmer Tree Garden, Nr Tollard Royal ⓧ⊕
See Dorset.

㉝ Little Durnford Manor, nr Salisbury ⓕⓧ
(The Earl & Countess of Chichester) *3m N of Salisbury. Just beyond Stratford-sub-Castle.* Extensive lawns with cedars, walled gardens, fruit trees, large vegetable garden, small knot and herb gardens, terraces, borders, sunken garden, water garden, lake with islands, river walks, labyrinth walk. TEAS. *Adm £3, chd £1. Suns 24 Apr; 26 June (2-6)*

㉞ Littleton Drew Gardens
6m W of Chippenham. Nr The Gibb PH on B4039. Car parking on rd to Littleton Drew and walk down to Goulters Mill, or drive or walk up to Barton Cottage. Cream TEAS at Goulters Mill in aid of Jewish immigrants to Israel from Russia. *Combined adm £3, chd 30p, concessions £2. Easter Sun, Mon 27, 28 Mar (2-5)*

Barton Cottage, Littleton Drew
(Beryl Willis) *Turn N off B3095, 2nd cottage on L. Park opp.* Small garden surrounding Elizabethan Cotswold cottage. Densely planted with many unusual perennials, topiary, pond with ferns and small potager incl espalier apples, standard redcurrant and gooseberries. Over 70 different clematis.

Goulters Mill Farm, The Gibb
ⓕⓧ⊕ (Mr & Mrs Michael Harvey) *Parking at top of 300yd drive; elderly/disabled at the Mill.* Approx ¾-acre cottage garden; mixed perennials, salvias, eremurus, old-fashioned roses; water garden, walk through woodland and wild flower-meadow. Topiary ligustrum and box. Anemone nemorosa, hellebores, prunus blossom and

some heathers. Featured in 'The English Garden', '25 Beautiful Gardens' 2005.

35 Lower House, Whiteparish ♿✿✿ NCCPG

(Mr & Mrs D J Wood) *7m SE of Salisbury. On N side of A27, Salisbury end of village, opp Newton Bungalows.* Informal garden of 1 acre containing part of National Collection of hellebores. *Adm £2, chd free. Sun 27 Feb (2-4); Sun 26 Feb 2006. Private visits welcome by appt Feb to mid Mar. Tel 01794 884306 jeremy.wood@ic24.net*

36 Mallards, Chirton ♿✿✿

(Tim & Jenny Pape) *4½m SE of Devizes. Just N of A342. Through village, garden on R.* 1-acre hidden garden in tranquil setting tucked into woodland beside upper R Avon. Herbaceous borders, gravel garden, riverside dell, shrubs and woodland glade all informally planted with many unusual plants. Woodland walk. *Adm £2, chd free. Fris 6, 20 May; 10, 24 June; 8, 22 July (2-5). Private visits welcome by appt for individuals & groups May, June and July. No coach access. Tel 01380 840593 jennypape@tiscali.co.uk*

37 NEW Manor Farm, Huish ♿✿

(Mr & Mrs J Roberts) *3m NW of Pewsey. Huish is signed from A345 by White Hart PH in Oare. Follow lane for 1m into Huish, turn R by dead-end sign.* Evolving garden in fine downland setting. Featuring woodland pond, gravel garden, standing stones and grotto. Good variety of clematis, herbaceous beds, shrubs, wisteria, clipped hedging and pleached lime walk. Interesting collection of trees planted in the last 10yrs. Landscaped farmyard with

38 Manor Farm, West Kington ♿✿

(Sir Michael & Lady Farquhar) *8m NW of Chippenham. 2m NE of Marshfield. J18 on M4, take A420 Chippenham to Bristol rd N signed West Kington. At village take No Through Road at Xrds.* Lovely setting, interesting design, many unusual features. Wide herbaceous border with large variety of plants; other beds with many varieties of shrubs. Central walk with standard roses, lavender, allium, box, divided by pergola, roses, clematis and honeysuckle. Garden partly enclosed by high wall with roses and other climbing plants; courtyard with standard arbutus, hollies and bay, many tender plants in pots. Attractive kitchen garden, enclosed by hornbeam hedge; newly created woodland walk. Featured in 'The English Garden' 2004. TEAS at Ridleys Cheer. *Adm £3.50, chd free. Sun 12 June (2-5.30). Also open Ridleys Cheer. Private visits welcome by appt. Tel 01249 782671*

39 NEW Manor House, Stratford Tony ♿✿✿

(Mr & Mrs H Cookson) *4m SW of Salisbury. Take minor rd W off A354 at Coombe Bissett. Garden on S after 1m.* Varied 4-acre garden; formal and informal areas; small lake fed from R Ebble; herbaceous beds; pergola-covered vegetable garden; parterre garden; orchards; shrubberies; contemporary gazebo and fountain; many areas designed for sitting to enjoy both internal and external views. *Adm £3, chd free. Weds 11 May; 15 June (2-6). Private visits*

welcome by appt, May & June only. *Tel 01722 718496*

40 Manor House Farm, Hanging Langford ♿✿

(Miss Anne Dixon) *9m NW of Salisbury. S of A36 Salisbury to Warminster rd. 3m SE of A303 Wylye interchange. Follow signs from Steeple Langford. Ample parking in paddock adjacent to house.* C14/16 Wiltshire manor house (not open). New early summer opening. Series of gardens within traditional Wiltshire 'hats and boots' walls, containing herbaceous plants, clematis, wisteria, roses and ponds. 250yr-old Bramley apple tree. Secret garden in walls of shearing barn. Orchard recently opened up with shrubs incl tree peonies. Lovely riverside walk to teas. Home-made TEAS at Village Hall. *Adm £2.50, chd free. Sun 12 June (2-6)*

41 NEW Market Lavington Gardens

5m S of Devizes. Gardens are off B3098 in Market Lavington. Large village on the edge of Salisbury Plain with C14 church and interesting local museum, also open. Home-made TEAS at The Old House in aid of St Mary's Church. *Combined adm £3, chd £1, concessions £2. Sun 19 June (2-6)*

NEW Clyffe Hall ♿✿ (William Hall) *Drive entrance on B3098, 300 metres bottom hill, E of junction with A360. Parking at Parsonage Mead.* Parkland setting with pond, water garden of woodland paths. Some herbaceous, set out circa 1900 in mini Capability Brown style. Traditional walled kitchen garden, Grade II listed house (not open) with crinkle crankle wall.

NEW The Old House, Parsonage Lane ✿✿ (Tom Gutteridge) *Parsonage Lane off B3098, 1m E of junction with A360.* Interesting 1½-acre garden of C13 Grade I manor, laid out in 2003 in late Victorian style. Large borders, formal rose garden, herbs, parterre, grasses, winter garden, small orchard. Adjacent to noteworthy village museum. Car parking at St Mary's Church.

NEW Parsonage Mead ♿ (Sally & Slater Reynolds) *On S of B3098, ¾m E from junction with A360.* Young garden of open nature on greensand, but poor topsoil in parts. Changing and developing at owner's new home.

Mayo Farm, Higher Blandford Road, Shaftesbury 🐕🎫
See Dorset.

㊷ ◆ The Mead Nursery, Brokerswood 🚾🐕🎫
(Mr & Mrs S Lewis-Dale) *3m WNW of Westbury. E of Rudge. Follow signs for Country Park at Brokerswood. Halfway between Rudge & Country Park.* 1¼-acre nursery and garden giving ideas on colour and design with herbaceous borders, raised alpine beds, sink garden and bog bed. Well-drained Mediterranean-style raised bed and small wildlife pond. Nursery grows an extensive range of herbaceous perennials, alpines, pot-grown bulbs and grasses. 'Daily Telegraph' Nursery of the Week 2003. *Adm £2.50, incl home-made TEAS, NGS day only. Weds to Sats & Bank Hol Mons Feb to mid Oct (9-5); Suns (12-5); closed Easter Sun. For NGS: Sun 21 Aug (12-5). Tel 01373 859990*

㊸ The Mill House, Berwick St James 🚾
(Diana Gifford Mead) *8m NW of Salisbury. S of A303 on B3083, S end of village.* Part of 13-acre Nature Reserve (recent SSSI) flanked by R Till and leat running through garden of wild appearance and abounding in wildlife. Speciality old-fashioned roses tumbling out of trees. 130 species wild flowers in meadow and 39 species of beetle surveyed under cow-pats. Some hatches restored. Two families of water voles, very tame. Cream TEAS in aid of the Village Hall. *Adm £2.50, chd free. Sun 26 June (2-6). Private visits welcome by appt for groups of 10+, Apr to Sept. Tel 01722 790331 www.millhouse.org.uk*

㊹ Mitre Cottage, Dinton 🎫
(Mrs John Surtees) *9m W of Salisbury. nr Dinton Church off B3089.* Peaceful garden round C17 cottage with great range of shrubs and plants; hellebores in spring; small kitchen garden. TEAS. *Adm £2, chd free. Suns 3 Apr; 19 June (2-6). Private visits welcome by appt. Tel 01722 716468*

㊺ ◆ Mompesson House, The Close, Salisbury 🚾🐕🎫
(The National Trust) *Enter Salisbury Cathedral Close via High St Gate & Mompesson House is on the R.* The appeal of this comparatively small but attractive garden is the lovely setting in Salisbury Cathedral Close, with a well-known Queen Anne house. Planting as for an old English

garden with raised rose and herbaceous beds around the lawn. Climbers on pergola and walls; shrubs and small lavender walk. Light refreshments and TEAS. *House & garden adm £4. Garden only £1, chd free. Sat to Wed, Apr to Nov. For NGS: Sat 21 May (11-4.30). Tel 01722 335659 mompessonhouse@nationaltrust. org.uk*

㊻ Newland, Lodge Drove, Woodfalls 🐕
(David & Christine Shergold) *9m SSE of Salisbury. Turn E off A338 in Downton. 3m on B3080 to Woodfalls.* Mature garden where colourful displays of perennials and annuals border the lawns. Large vegetable garden where many of the vegetables grown to show standard. Three greenhouses to accommodate a variety of salad crops. Area set aside for local Chrysanthemum Soc where they grow flowers for the National Show. Morning coffee & Home-made TEAS. *Adm £2, chd free. Fri , Sat, Sun 22, 23, 24 July (10.30-5). Private visits welcome by appt, July only, for groups of 10+. Tel 01725 511404*

㊼ NEW North Cottage & Woodview Cottage, Tisbury Row, nr Tisbury 🐕🎫
(Jacqueline & Robert Baker, Diane McBride) *12m W of Salisbury. From A30 turn N through Ansty, L at T-junction, then 1st R signed Tisbury Row. From Tisbury take Ansty rd then 1st L.* Two cottage gardens divided into rooms, designed and developed over many yrs to incl fruit and vegetable areas, greenhouses and allotment. 4-acre smallholding containing orchard, ponds and coppice wood. Attractive perennial and annual planting provides season-long colour and variety. Home-made TEAS. *Adm £2, chd £1, concessions £1. Sun 3 July (2-6)*

㊽ Oare House, nr Pewsey 🚾
(Mr Henry Keswick) *2m N of Pewsey. On Marlborough Rd (A345).* Fine house (not open) in large garden with fine trees, hedges, spring flowers, woodlands; extensive lawns and kitchen garden. Home-made TEAS. *Adm £3, chd free. Suns 24 Apr; 17 July (2-6)*

㊾ The Old Malthouse, Lower Westwood 🚾🎫
(Simon & Amanda Relph) *2m SW of Bradford-on-Avon. Take B3109 S from Bradford-on-Avon. R to Westwood at 1st X-rds after leaving Bradford-on-Avon; 300yds past The*

New Inn on R. 1 acre. At front, small garden with unusual water feature. To the side, long border against N-facing wall with mainly white flowering shrubs and herbaceous plants. Through the wall to 3 garden rooms: lawn surrounded by shrubs; another small lawn with semi-circular flame border facing splendid magnolia across pond; gravel courtyard with 6 island beds, 2 lily ponds and sculptured water feature enclosed by rose-covered pergola on two sides. Home-made TEAS in aid of Tulsi Trust. *Adm £2.50, chd 50p. Sun 19 June (2-5.30)*

㊿ The Old Mill, Ramsbury 🐕🎫
(Mr & Mrs James Dallas) *5m NE of Marlborough. From W go down High St, bear R at The Bell, signed Hungerford. Garden behind new hedge on R 100yds beyond The Bell.* Garden in grounds of disused mill house on R Kennet, built around large areas of water. Mill stream, millrace and pool take up nearly ½ acre of 5 acres. Side streams, criss-crossed by bridges, meander through mixture of wild and cultivated area. Nr house, colour-themed borders, gravelled areas full of unusual plants; garden being constantly added to, an exciting blend of traditional and contemporary features, in keeping with peaceful and pretty setting. TEAS in aid of Holy Cross Church, Ramsbury. *Adm £3.50, chd free. Weds 11 May; 14 Sept (2-5). Sun 19 June (2-6)*

51 The Old Rectory, Ham 🚾🐕🎫
(Mr & Mrs N Baring) *4m S of Hungerford. Take A338 S from Hungerford, bear L after 3m on minor rd signed Ham. Entrance 50yds from village green on N side of Inkpen Rd.* 4-acre garden incl wide expanse of lawn and yew-edged enclosures leading to informal area with fine old trees and some new planting. Drifts of bulbs, hellebores and cyclamen are features in early spring. Cottage garden also open. Home-made TEAS. *Adm £3, chd free. Sun 20 Feb (2-5)*

52 Pertwood Manor, Hindon 🚾🐕
(Mrs James Giles) *8m S of Warminster. Off A350 (1m N of A303) 7m N of Shaftesbury. Take signs marked Pertwood Manor farm.* 1½-acre part-walled garden surrounding manor house (not open) in elevated position with lovely views. Herbaceous borders, various trees and shrubs. Sunken rose garden. Short woodland walk, small vegetable garden. Recently restored Church of St Peter. Home-made

TEAS. *Adm £2.50, chd under 10 free. Sun 19 June (2-6)*

53 Poulton House, Marlborough ✿

(Tom & Jill Otley) *½m E of Marlborough centre. Take Ramsbury rd from The Green in Marlborough ½m, large white gates on L.* Approx 7-acre garden round fine Queen Anne manor house (not open). Much recent design and planting, ponds, rill; walled garden with topiary and sunken potager; long borders, extensive lawns and newly planted riverside woodland. Home-made TEAS in aid of Mildenhall Village Hall. *Adm £3, chd under 10 free. Sun 12 June (2-6). Private visits welcome by appt. Tel 01672 516506*

54 ◆ Pound Hill House, West Kington ✿

(Mr & Mrs Philip Stockitt) *7m WNW of Chippenham. From A420 Chippenham to Bristol rd turn R, follow brown signs West Kington-Nettleton, entrance at Pound Hill Plants, 2 m.* Series of well-designed small garden rooms in lovely setting around C16 Cotswold House (not open), to provide interest throughout yr. Old-fashioned roses, David Austin's English roses, clipped box

and yew, topiary, herbaceous borders, Victorian vegetable garden, pergola of wisteria and roses, water garden, thousands of spring bulbs, courtyard of interesting pots. Plant centre with unusual plants and Gardeners Gift Shop and Pantry. Featured in 'Homes & Gardens' 2004. Light refreshments and TEAS. *Adm £3.50, chd free. Daily Mar to Oct.* **For NGS:** *Sun 19 June (2-5). Tel 01249 782781*

55 The Pound House, Little Somerford ✿

(Mr & Mrs Michael Baines) *2m E of Malmesbury. On B4042. In village turn S, leave church on R. Car park on R before railway bridge.* Medium-sized garden surrounding former rectory. Mature trees, hedges and spacious lawns. Well-stocked herbaceous borders, shrubs, pergola, parterre, swimming pool garden, water, ducks and chickens. TEAS. *Adm £2.50, chd free. Suns 8 May; 19 June (2-6). Private visits welcome by appt. Tel 01666 823212*

56 Ridleys Cheer, Mountain Bower ✿

(Mr & Mrs A J Young) *9m WNW of Chippenham. At The Shoe, on A420 8m W of Chippenham, turn N then*

take 2nd L & 1st R. 1½-acre informal garden with unusual trees and shrubs, incl acers, liriodendrons, magnolias, daphnes, hellebores, hostas and euphorbias. Over 100 different shrub rose varieties incl hybrid musks, albas, tree ramblers and species roses, planted progressively over past 30yrs; also potager, miniature box garden, 2-acre arboretum planted 1989, and 3-acre wild flower meadow. Accommodation. Featured in 'The English Garden' 2003 & 'Western Daily Press' 2004. Home-made TEAS. *Adm £3, chd under 14 free (share to Clover House). Suns 10 Apr; 15 May; 12 June (2-6). Also open 12 June* **Manor Farm, West Kington.** *Private visits welcome by appt, coaches permitted. Tel 01225 891204 antonyoung@ridleyscheer. co.uk*

Rooksnest, Lambourn Woodlands ✿

See Berkshire.

Sandle Cottage, Sandleheath ✿

See Hampshire.

57 Sharcott Manor, nr Pewsey

🚗🛇🏵

(Captain & Mrs D Armytage) *1m SW of Pewsey. Via A345.* 6-acre plantsman's garden on greensand with water - planted for yr-round interest. Many young trees, bulbs, climbers and densely-planted mixed borders of shrubs, roses, perennials and unusual plants. Woodland walk round ½-acre lake. Small collection of ornamental water fowl. Home-made TEAS. *Adm £3, chd under 14 free. Suns 10 Apr; 11 Sept (2-6); Weds 6 Apr; 4 May; 1 June; 6 July; 3 Aug; 7 Sept; 5 Oct (11-5). Private visits welcome by appt, coaches permitted. Tel 01672 563485*

58 Sheldon Manor, nr Chippenham 🛇🏵

(Kenneth & Caroline Hawkins) *1½m W of Chippenham. Take A420 W from Chippenham. 1st L signed Chippenham RFC, entrance approx ½m on R.* Wiltshire's oldest inhabited manor house with a C13 porch and a C15 chapel. Gardens with ancient yews, a mulberry tree and a profusion of old-fashioned roses blooming in May and June. Light refreshments and TEAS. *Adm £4.50, chd under 12 free. Suns 22 May; 5 Jun (2-5)*

◆ Special Plants, Nr Cold Ashton 🛇🏵

See Bristol & South Gloucestershire.

59 ◆ Stourhead Garden, Stourton

🚗🛇

(The National Trust) *3m NW of Mere. On B3092.* One of the earliest and greatest landscape gardens in the world, creation of banker Henry Hoare in 1740s on his return from the Grand Tour, inspired by paintings of Claude and Poussin. Planted with rare trees, rhododendrons and azaleas over last 250yrs. Light refreshments and TEAS. *House & garden adm £9.90. Garden only £5.80, chd £3.20 (1 Nov to 17 Mar £4.30, chd £2.10). Garden daily all yr (9-7 or dusk if earlier). House 18 Mar to 31 Oct, Fri to Tues (11-5, or dusk if earlier). Garden daily all yr.* **For NGS:** *Sun 26 June (9-7). Tel 01747 842010*

60 Waterdale House, East Knoyle

🏵

(Mr & Mrs Julian Seymour) *8m S of Warminster. N of East Knoyle. Garden signed from A350.* 4-acre mature woodland garden with rhododendrons, azaleas, camellias, maples, magnolias, ornamental water, bog garden, herbaceous borders. Home-made TEAS. *Adm £2.50, chd free. Sun 1 May (2-5). Private visits welcome by appt. Tel 01747 830262*

Weston House, Buckhorn Weston

🚗🛇🏵

See Dorset.

61 Worton Gardens, Devizes

3m SW of Devizes. A360 Devizes to Salisbury, turn W in Potterne or just N of West Lavington. From Seend turn S at Bell Inn, follow signs to Worton. Home-made TEAS at Ivy House in aid of WI. *Combined adm £3.50, chd free. Sun 10 July (2-6)*

Ashton House 🚗🛇🏵 (Mrs Colin Shand) ½-acre garden in 3 sections with herbaceous borders, many shrubs and birch grove; walled courtyard, small gravel garden and raised vegetable garden.

Brookfield House 🚗🛇 (Mr & Mrs Graham Cannon) 1-acre garden owned since 1993. Part-walled garden with mixed borders and separate fruit and vegetable garden, rose garden and fine views.

Ivy House 🚗🛇🏵 (Lt Gen Sir Maurice & Lady Johnston) 2-acre series of gardens separated by yew hedges and walls; herbaceous borders; shrubs; pond garden with maples and many fine trees incl swamp cypress, holm and red oak, medlar and mulberry; interesting vegetable garden and large greenhouse.

Oakley House 🚗🛇🏵 (Mr & Mrs Michael Brierley) ½-acre village garden with herbaceous borders, roses, many shrubs; small pond within a rockery; planted by owners since 1974.

"We don't get much trouble from the neighbours now!"

Worcestershire

County Organiser: Mrs Judy Berrow, Tythe Barn House, Chaddesley Corbett DY10 4QB
Tel 01562 777014 email j.berrow@virgin.net
Assistant County Organisers: Mrs Jeanie Neil, Viewlands, Blakeshall, Wolverley, Kidderminster DY11 5XL
Tel 01562 850360 email theviewlands@aol.com
Press & Publicity Officer Mr Dick Armitage, 11 Myatts Field, Harvington, Evesham, Worcs WR11 8NG
Tel 01386 871211
County Treasurer: Mr Cliff Woodward, 11 Trehernes Drive, Pedmore, Stourbridge DY9 0YX
Tel 01562 886349

Maps: Numbers shown next to each garden entry refer to that garden's entry on the county map. This position is approximate; distance and directions from the nearest main town are generally shown in the garden text.
A precise location is available for those gardens featured on the NGS website by visiting www.ngs.org.uk.
Symbols: Information relating to symbols is given on page 21

DATES OF OPENING

Evening openings
See end of county listing

Private gardens open regularly for NGS
Barnard's Green House, Malvern *(6)*

Gardens open to the public
For details see garden description
Bodenham Arboretum, Wolverley, Kidderminster *(8)*
Burford House Gardens, Tenbury Wells *(11)*
Eastgrove Cottage Garden Nursery, Sankyns Green, Shrawley *(18)*
The Greyfriars, Worcester *(22)*
Hanbury Hall, Hanbury *(23)*
Harvington Hall, Harvington *(24)*
Little Malvern Court, Little Malvern *(28)*
Spetchley Park Gardens, nr Worcester *(43)*
Stone House Cottage Gardens, Stone *(45)*
Webbs of Wychbold, Wychbold, nr Droitwich *(50)*
Whit Lenge Gardens, Hartlebury *(52)*
White Cottage, Stock Green, nr Inkberrow *(54)*

By appointment only
*For telephone number and other details see garden description.
Private visits welcomed*
Conderton Manor, nr Tewkesbury *(16)*
Ivytree House, Clent *(27)*
Overbury Court, nr Tewkesbury *(34)*

ngs gardens open for charity

More than
£20 million has been donated to charity since the NGS began in 1927

February 5 Saturday
The Greyfriars, Worcester *(22)*

February 16 Wednesday
Dial Park, Chaddesley Corbett *(17)*

February 17 Thursday
Dial Park, Chaddesley Corbett *(17)*

February 20 Sunday
Hanbury Hall, Hanbury *(23)*

March 20 Sunday
Holland House, Cropthorne *(26)*
Little Malvern Court, Little Malvern *(28)*

March 25 Friday (Easter)
Spetchley Park Gardens, nr Worcester *(43)*

March 26 Saturday (Easter)
Stone House Cottage Gardens, Stone *(45)*
The Walled Garden, Worcester *(49)*

March 27 Sunday (Easter)
Barnard's Green House, Malvern *(6)*
1 Prickley Bungalows, Martley *(37)*
Whit Lenge Gardens, Hartlebury *(52)*

March 28 Monday (Easter)
Astley Towne House, Astley *(4)*
Gadfield Elm House, Staunton *(20)*
1 Prickley Bungalows, Martley *(37)*
Whit Lenge Gardens, Hartlebury *(52)*

April 2 Saturday
White Cottage, Stock Green, nr Inkberrow *(54)*

April 3 Sunday
White Cottage, Stock Green, nr Inkberrow *(54)*

April 7 Thursday
Barnard's Green House, Malvern *(6)*
Dial Park, Chaddesley Corbett *(17)*

April 9 Saturday
Stone House Cottage Gardens, Stone *(45)*
The Walled Garden, Worcester *(49)*

April 14 Thursday
Barnard's Green House, Malvern *(6)*

April 16 Saturday
White Cottage, Stock Green, nr Inkberrow *(54)*

April 17 Sunday
1 Prickley Bungalows, Martley *(37)*
Shuttifield Cottage, Birchwood, Storridge *(41)*

White Cottage, Stock Green, nr Inkberrow *(54)*

April 21 Thursday
Barnard's Green House, Malvern *(6)*

April 24 Sunday
24 Alexander Avenue, Droitwich Spa *(1)*

April 28 Thursday
Barnard's Green House, Malvern *(6)*

April 30 Saturday
White Cottage, Stock Green, nr Inkberrow *(54)*

May 1 Sunday
Astley Towne House, Astley *(4)*
The Cockshoot, Castlemorton Common *(14)*
March House, Broadway *(31)*
1 Prickley Bungalows, Martley *(37)*
Whit Lenge Gardens, Hartlebury *(52)*
White Cottage, Stock Green, nr Inkberrow *(54)*

May 2 Monday (Bank Hol)
The Cockshoot, Castlemorton Common *(14)*
Little Malvern Court, Little Malvern *(28)*
1 Prickley Bungalows, Martley *(37)*
Whit Lenge Gardens, Hartlebury *(52)*
White Cottage, Stock Green, nr Inkberrow *(54)*

May 4 Wednesday
Stone House Cottage Gardens, Stone *(45)*

May 5 Thursday
Barnard's Green House, Malvern *(6)*

May 7 Saturday
Eastgrove Cottage Garden Nursery, Sankyns Green, Shrawley *(18)*
Shuttifield Cottage, Birchwood, Storridge *(41)*

May 8 Sunday
Spetchley Park Gardens, nr Worcester *(43)*
Whitcombe House, Overbury *(53)*

May 12 Thursday
Barnard's Green House, Malvern *(6)*

May 14 Saturday
The Walled Garden, Worcester *(49)*
White Cottage, Stock Green, nr Inkberrow *(54)*

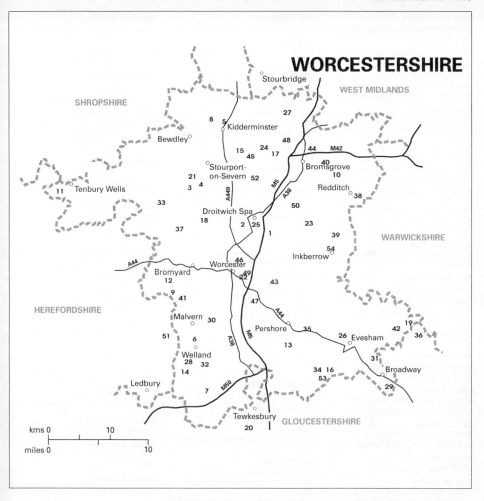

WORCESTERSHIRE

Stourbridge

WEST MIDLANDS

SHROPSHIRE

27

8 5
Kidderminster

Bewdley 48

15 24 44 M42
45 17

Stourport- 40
on-Severn Bromsgrove
21 52 10
3 4
Redditch
11 Tenbury Wells 38

33 50

Droitwich Spa
18 2 25 23

37 1 39

54
Inkberrow WARWICKSHIRE

A44 46
Worcester
Bromyard 22 49
12 43

9 41
HEREFORDSHIRE 47

Malvern 30 19
51 6 Pershore 35 42 36
28 32 13 26 Evesham
14 31
Welland 34 16 Broadway
53 29
Ledbury 7

kms 0 10
Tewkesbury 20
miles 0 10 GLOUCESTERSHIRE

May 15 Sunday
March House, Broadway *(31)*
White Cottage, Stock Green, nr Inkberrow *(54)*

May 19 Thursday
Barnard's Green House, Malvern *(6)*

May 21 Saturday
Gladderbrook Farm, High Oak, Heightington *(21)*
Shuttifield Cottage, Birchwood, Storridge *(41)*

May 22 Sunday
Hiraeth, Droitwich *(25)*
88 Rectory Road, Headless Cross, Redditch *(38)*
Red House Farm, Bradley Green *(39)*
Whitcombe House, Overbury *(53)*

May 26 Thursday
Barnard's Green House, Malvern *(6)*

May 28 Saturday
Gladderbrook Farm, High Oak, Heightington *(21)*
White Cottage, Stock Green, nr Inkberrow *(54)*

May 29 Sunday
1 Church Cottages, Defford *(13)*
16 Comberton Avenue, Kidderminster *(15)*
Luggers Hall, Broadway *(29)*
4 Poden Cottages, Honeybourne *(36)*
1 Prickley Bungalows, Martley *(37)*
South Littleton Gardens, nr Evesham *(42)*
Whit Lenge Gardens, Hartlebury *(52)*
White Cottage, Stock Green, nr Inkberrow *(54)*

May 30 Monday (Bank Hol)
Gadfield Elm House, Staunton *(20)*
March House, Broadway *(31)*
4 Poden Cottages, Honeybourne *(36)*
1 Prickley Bungalows, Martley *(37)*
South Littleton Gardens, nr Evesham *(42)*

Whit Lenge Gardens, Hartlebury *(52)*
White Cottage, Stock Green, nr Inkberrow *(54)*

June 2 Thursday
Barnard's Green House, Malvern *(6)*
Stone House Cottage Gardens, Stone *(45)*

June 4 Saturday
Gladderbrook Farm, High Oak, Heightington *(21)*
Orleton House, Orleton, Stanford Bridge *(33)*
White Cottage, Stock Green, nr Inkberrow *(54)*

June 5 Sunday
Frogs Nest, Honeybourne, Evesham *(19)*
Orleton House, Orleton, Stanford Bridge *(33)*
Whitcombe House, Overbury *(53)*
White Cottage, Stock Green, nr Inkberrow *(54)*

June 8 Wednesday
Burford House Gardens, Tenbury Wells *(11)*
June 9 Thursday
Barnard's Green House, Malvern *(6)*
June 11 Saturday
Shuttifield Cottage, Birchwood, Storridge *(41)*
The Walled Garden, Worcester *(49)*
June 12 Sunday
24 Alexander Avenue, Droitwich Spa *(1)*
Astley Country Gardens, Stourport-on-Severn *(3)*
27 Avill Grove, Kidderminster *(5)*
Birtsmorton Court, nr Malvern *(7)*
Frogs Nest, Honeybourne, Evesham *(19)*
Hiraeth, Droitwich *(25)*
March House, Broadway *(31)*
Pershore Gardens *(35)*
1 Prickley Bungalows, Martley *(37)*
White Cottage, Stock Green, nr Inkberrow *(54)*
June 13 Monday
White Cottage, Stock Green, nr Inkberrow *(54)*
June 16 Thursday
Barnard's Green House, Malvern *(6)*
June 18 Saturday
Eastgrove Cottage Garden Nursery, Sankyns Green, Shrawley *(18)*
Shuttifield Cottage, Birchwood, Storridge *(41)*
June 19 Sunday
Frogs Nest, Honeybourne, Evesham *(19)*
The Tynings, Stoulton, nr Worcester *(47)*
June 23 Thursday
Barnard's Green House, Malvern *(6)*
4 Poden Cottages, Honeybourne *(36)*
June 24 Friday
Hiraeth, Droitwich **(Evening)** *(25)*
Saranacris, Bromsgrove **(Evening)** *(40)*
June 25 Saturday
March House, Broadway *(31)*
June 26 Sunday
Bridges Stone Mill, Alfrick Pound *(9)*
Frogs Nest, Honeybourne, Evesham *(19)*
Gadfield Elm House, Staunton *(20)*
Luggers Hall, Broadway *(29)*
March House, Broadway *(31)*
1 Prickley Bungalows, Martley *(37)*
Tythe Barn House, Chaddesley Corbett *(48)*
June 30 Thursday
Barnard's Green House, Malvern *(6)*
4 Poden Cottages, Honeybourne *(36)*
July 2 Saturday
Burcot Grange, Burcot, Bromsgrove *(10)*
The Tynings, Stoulton, nr Worcester **(Evening)** *(47)*
July 3 Sunday
Harvington Hall, Harvington *(24)*
Holland House, Cropthorne *(26)*
Spetchley Park Gardens, nr Worcester *(43)*
July 6 Wednesday
Burford House Gardens, Tenbury Wells *(11)*
July 7 Thursday
Barnard's Green House, Malvern *(6)*

July 9 Saturday
The Walled Garden, Worcester *(49)*
July 10 Sunday
24 Alexander Avenue, Droitwich Spa *(1)*
Charlton House, Lulsley, Knightwick *(12)*
Hiraeth, Droitwich *(25)*
1 Prickley Bungalows, Martley *(37)*
Two Gardens in Beckett Drive, Northwick, Worcester *(46)*
July 14 Thursday
Barnard's Green House, Malvern *(6)*
Stone House Cottage Gardens, Stone *(45)*
July 15 Friday
Saranacris, Bromsgrove **(Evening)** *(40)*
July 16 Saturday
Eastgrove Cottage Garden Nursery, Sankyns Green, Shrawley *(18)*
Shuttifield Cottage, Birchwood, Storridge *(41)*
Stone Cottage, Bournheath, Bromsgrove *(44)*
July 17 Sunday
The Arles, Haye Lane, Hadley *(2)*
27 Avill Grove, Kidderminster *(5)*
Stone Cottage, Bournheath, Bromsgrove *(44)*
Weobley Cross Cottage, Mathon, nr Malvern *(51)*
July 21 Thursday
Barnard's Green House, Malvern *(6)*
July 24 Sunday
Barnard's Green House, Malvern *(6)*
July 27 Wednesday
Hiraeth, Droitwich *(25)*
July 28 Thursday
Barnard's Green House, Malvern *(6)*
July 30 Saturday
Orleton House, Orleton, Stanford Bridge *(33)*
88 Rectory Road, Headless Cross, Redditch *(38)*
July 31 Sunday
Gadfield Elm House, Staunton *(20)*
Orleton House, Orleton, Stanford Bridge *(33)*
88 Rectory Road, Headless Cross, Redditch *(38)*
August 4 Thursday
Barnard's Green House, Malvern *(6)*
August 6 Saturday
Gladderbrook Farm, High Oak, Heightington *(21)*
Stone House Cottage Gardens, Stone *(45)*
August 11 Thursday
Barnard's Green House, Malvern *(6)*
Stone House Cottage Gardens, Stone *(45)*
August 13 Saturday
Gladderbrook Farm, High Oak, Heightington *(21)*
Shuttifield Cottage, Birchwood, Storridge *(41)*
The Walled Garden, Worcester *(49)*
August 14 Sunday
Hiraeth, Droitwich *(25)*
August 18 Thursday
Barnard's Green House, Malvern *(6)*

August 21 Sunday
16 Comberton Avenue, Kidderminster *(15)*
Saranacris, Bromsgrove *(40)*
August 25 Thursday
Barnard's Green House, Malvern *(6)*
August 28 Sunday
Whit Lenge Gardens, Hartlebury *(52)*
August 29 Monday (Bank Hol)
Astley Towne House, Astley *(4)*
Whit Lenge Gardens, Hartlebury *(52)*
September 1 Thursday
Barnard's Green House, Malvern *(6)*
September 3 Saturday
Stone House Cottage Gardens, Stone *(45)*
White Cottage, Stock Green, nr Inkberrow *(54)*
September 4 Sunday
White Cottage, Stock Green, nr Inkberrow *(54)*
September 8 Thursday
Barnard's Green House, Malvern *(6)*
September 11 Sunday
Bodenham Arboretum, Wolverley, Kidderminster *(8)*
September 15 Thursday
Barnard's Green House, Malvern *(6)*
September 17 Saturday
White Cottage, Stock Green, nr Inkberrow *(54)*
September 18 Sunday
White Cottage, Stock Green, nr Inkberrow *(54)*
September 22 Thursday
Barnard's Green House, Malvern *(6)*
September 29 Thursday
Barnard's Green House, Malvern *(6)*
October 1 Saturday
White Cottage, Stock Green, nr Inkberrow *(54)*
October 2 Sunday
White Cottage, Stock Green, nr Inkberrow *(54)*
October 16 Sunday
Nerine Nursery, Welland *(32)*
October 23 Sunday
Madresfield Court, Madresfield nr Malvern *(30)*

DESCRIPTIONS OF GARDENS

❶ 24 Alexander Avenue, Droitwich Spa &⚫️❀
(Malley & David Terry) *South from Droitwich Spa towards Worcester A38, town centre approx 1m. Or from M5 junction 6 to Droitwich Town centre.* Plantswoman's garden in 140ft×40ft N-facing plot planted for yr-round interest. High hedges surrounding garden support part of collection of 150 clematis. Artistically designed colour-blended herbaceous borders. Alpine troughs and scree bed. Featured on ITV's 'Best Back Gardens' 2003. *Adm £2.50, chd free. Suns 24 Apr; 12 June; 10 July (2-6). Private visits welcome by appt. Tel 01905 774907 terrydroit@aol. com*

❷ The Aries, Haye Lane, Hadley &⚫️
(Linda Fernyhough) *3m W of Droitwich. 1m E of Ombersley on A4133. 7m S of Kidderminster on A449. Follow Woodland View Fishery signs along Haye Lane.* Approx ¾-acre garden in rural setting. Colourful garden with numerous beds and borders containing many unusual perennials and ornamental grasses. Daylilies are also a passion with a hybridizing programme underway. Parking in our adjoining field. Featured in 'Ideal Home' 2003. Home-made TEAS. *Adm £2.50, chd free. Sun 17 July (2-5.30)*

❸ Astley Country Gardens, Stourport-on-Severn
3m SW of Stourport-on-Severn. Start at Astley Village Hall where map and descriptions of gardens are available. Take A451 out of Stourport, turn L onto B4196 for Worcester. Interesting and diverse collection of gardens with lovely views. An entire afternoon's outing. Home-made TEAS at most gardens. *Combined adm £5, chd free. Sun 12 June (1-6)*

> **Astley Towne House** &⚫️❀ (Tim & Lesley Smith) (See separate entry).

> **Koi Cottage** &⚫️❀ (Melvin & Ann Raybould) A remarkable conversion of a small village garden into a classical Japanese one. The Japanese-style bridge leads to the front door over a pool with enormous Koi carp. Tea house, fernery and stream lead to pebble pond. Bonsai and many other features.

> **Little Yarhampton** &❀ (Skene & Petrena Walley) Beautiful views from very spacious upper garden

with a pretty walk down to a sizeable lake in a secluded valley, surrounded with a young arboretum with many different kinds of oak.

> **Pool House** &❀ (Betty & Gervase Elwes) Lawns, with flowering tulip and handkerchief trees, lead down from one of the few Strawberry Hill Gothic houses in the Midlands, to a lovely lake with large tame carp. Walled garden with tree peonies and old-fashioned roses.

> **Priors Mill** &❀ (Mike & Pat Haywood) The owners of this picturesque converted C17 watermill (not open) in a deep valley have created an upper and lower garden. Pools with waterfall and enchanting wildlife.

> **Swevenings, Dunley** &❀ (John & Sam Grazebrook) Connects to the White House. Sloping site with terraces and a natural stream. Cottage-style garden with vegetables and colourful borders, replanted in 2004.

> **The White House, Dunley** &❀ (Tony & Linda Tidmarsh) A classical-style garden divided by yew hedges, shrub borders and brick walls into separate gardens around a central lawn. Various features celebrate events in the owners' family. An Italian garden features a cascade made of copper. There are four other pools, one incorporating the former girls' entrance to Tipton Board School. Tree house.

❹ Astley Towne House, Astley &❀
(Tim & Lesley Smith) *3m W of Stourport-on-Severn. On B4196 Worcester to Bewdley Road.* Approx 2½ acres; evolving family garden to very ambitious design of the owners; formal kitchen garden with central fountain, grass paths winding through shrubs and herbaceous borders, children can see pets corner. Garden incorporates - pagoda bridge and tree-high Millennium sky deck, neo-classical style revolving summerhouse and stumpery garden and temple. Also expanding sub-tropical jungle garden with many interesting and unusual plants. Featured in RHS 'The Garden' and 'Your Cat' magazines 2004. Home-made TEAS in aid of Kidney Research. *Adm £2.50, chd free. Mon 28 Mar; Sun 1 May; Mon 29 Aug (1-5). Private visits welcome by appt. Tel 01299 822299*

❺ 27 Avill Grove, Kidderminster ⚫️❀
(Chris & Carol Cox) *1m N of Kidderminster. Off A442, R into Marlpool Lane beside Jacksons public house & 2nd R approx 250yds.* Limited parking in cul de sac. Small, steep suburban garden with herbaceous borders and shady courtyard with water feature and foliage plants. Open decked seating area. Wooden steps down to small patio and interesting vegetable and soft fruit area. Also small hydroponic and propagation units. Home-made TEAS. *Adm £1, chd free. Suns 12 June; 17 July (11-5)*

❻ Barnard's Green House, 10 Poolbrook Road, Malvern &⚫️❀
(Mr & Mrs Philip Nicholls) *1m E of Malvern. On E side of Malvern at junction of B4211 & B4208.* 3-acre garden; mature trees; herbaceous borders; rockery; heather beds; woodland, vegetable garden with old brick paths and box hedges. Unusual plants and shrubs. Old tennis court transformed into asphalt garden. Mrs Nicholls is a specialist and writer on dried flowers. 1635 half-timbered house, not open. TEAS. *Adm £2.50, chd free (share to Save The Children). Thurs, 7 Apr to 29 Sept; Suns 27 Mar; 24 July (2-6). Private visits welcome by appt, coaches permitted. Tel 01684 574446*

❼ Birtsmorton Court, nr Malvern &⚫️❀
(Mr & Mrs N G K Dawes) *7m E of Ledbury. On A438.* Fortified manor house (not open) dating from C12; moat; Westminster pool, laid down in Henry VII's reign at time of consecration of Westminster Abbey; large tree under which Cardinal Wolsey reputedly slept in shadow of ragged stone; white garden. Newly planted potager; topiary. TEAS in aid of church. *Adm £3.50, chd 50p. Sun 12 June (2-6)*

❽ ♦ Bodenham Arboretum, Wolverley, Kidderminster &❀
(The Binnian Family) *5m N of Kidderminster. Off the B4189. 2m N of Wolverley. Brown signs from Wolverley Church Island along B4189.* Arboretum landscaped in 156 acres during the last 30yrs, contains over 2600 species of trees and shrubs; 2 chains of lakes and pools; 5m of paths through glades; dawn redwoods and laburnum tunnel. Bring wellingtons or strong shoes. Best Small Tourist Attraction of the Year - Silver Award 2004. Home-made TEAS in Visitor Centre Sun 11 Sept. *Adm £5, chd £2, wheelchair*

users £2. Open Mar to Xmas (11-5) Closed Mons & Tues (except in May, June & Oct). **For NGS:** *Sun 11 Sept (2-5). Tel 01562 852444 www.bodenhamarboretum.co.uk*

❾ Bridges Stone Mill, Alfrick Pound 🚻🌳♿

(Sir Michael & Lady Perry) 6m NW of Malvern. From Worcester, take the A4103 Hereford rd to Bransford, at Bank House Hotel roundabout take minor rd towards Leigh & Suckley. After 200yds, fork L towards Suckley. After 3m sign announces arrival at Alfrick Pound. 300yds beyond that, entrance gate to Bridges Stone Mill on L. Formerly a cherry orchard adjoining the mainly C19 water mill, this is now a 2½-acre garden laid out with trees, shrubs and mixed beds and borders; small lake, stream and brook. The garden is bounded by 200yd stretch of Leigh Brook (an SSSI), and a mill stream from the mill's own weir. Extensive all-yr round planting. Ornamental vegetable parterre completes the picture. Home-made TEAS in aid of St Richard's Hospice, Worcester. *Adm £3. Sun 26 June (2-5.30)*

❿ Burcot Grange, Burcot, Bromsgrove

(Mr & Mrs Bales) 2m N of Bromsgrove. Approach Burcot village, once within village take rd called Greenhill signposted off only roundabout. Burcot Grange on L. 5 acres of mature garden incorporating water features, many mature trees and an abundance of summer colour. Home-made TEAS. *Adm £2. Sat 2 July (2-5)*

⓫ NEW **◆ Burford House Gardens, Tenbury Wells** 🚻🌳♿NCCPG

(Burford Garden Company) 1m W of Tenbury Wells. 8m from Ludlow on A456. 7 acres on the banks of the picturesque River Teme. Originally designed by the late John Treasure in 1952 around a Georgian mansion (not open). The Gardens contain the National Collection of clematis, the giant wisteria macrobotrys 'Burford' along with around 2000 other kinds of plants. Light refreshments and TEAS. *Adm £3.95, chd £1. Mons to Suns, Jan to Dec (9-6). Gardens close at dusk if earlier.* **For NGS:** *Weds 8 June; 6 July (9-6). Tel 01584 810777 www.burford.co.uk*

Caves Folly Nursery, Evendine Lane, Colwall 🚻🌳♿
See Herefordshire.

⓬ Charlton House, Hill Road, Lulsley, Knightwick 🌳

(Mr & Mrs Driver-White) 9m W of Worcester. Via A44, turn 1st L after Knightsford Bridge towards Alfrick, 1st L after Fox & Hounds signed Hill Rd, Lulsley; 1m at end of lane. ⅔-acre intimate garden of shrubs and shrub roses created by owner since 1970. Ducks and peacocks. No children or dogs owing to nesting waterfowl. Interesting collection of C16 barns. Unsuitable for wheelchairs. *Adm £2. Sun 10 July (1-5). Private visits welcome by appt. Tel 01886 821220*

⓭ NEW **1 Church Cottages, Church Road, Defford** 🌳

(John & Janet Taylor) 3m SW of Pershore. A4104 Pershore to Upton rd. Turn into Defford. Black & white cottage at side of church. Parking in village hall car park. True countryman's ⅓-acre garden, interesting layout. Specimen trees; water features; vegetable garden; aviary, poultry and ducks; cider making. TEAS. *Adm £2, chd free (share to Rotary International reg charity 'First Responders'). Sun 29 May (11-5)*

⓮ The Cockshoot, Castlemorton Common 🌳

(Clive & Elizabeth Wilkins) 2m S of Welland. On B4208 turn into New Rd opp Robin Hood public house. Take 1st L ½m. Follow signs. Paradise cottage garden set out in 'rooms' around a Georgian cottage (not open) in idyllic rural setting. Mixed planting with perennials, roses and clematis, flowering shrubs; trees; hosta garden, hosta terrace, orchard and pond. Many sitting areas. Hostas for sale. Home-made TEAS. *Adm £2, chd free. Sun 1, Mon 2 May (1-5)*

⓯ NEW **16 Comberton Avenue, Kidderminster** 🌳♿

(Sheila & Adrian James) 1m SE of Kidderminster. Off A448 L into Somerleyton Avenue, 2nd R into Comberton Avenue. Suburban garden packed with plants for all-yr interest. Water features. Exotics a feature in late summer. TEAS. *Adm £1.50, chd free. Suns 29 May; 21 Aug (11-5.30)*

⓰ Conderton Manor, nr Tewkesbury 🚻🌳

(Mr & Mrs W Carr) 5½m NE of Tewkesbury. On Bredon - Beckford rd or from A46 take Overbury sign at Beckford turn. 7-acre garden with magnificent views of Cotswolds. Flowering cherries and bulbs in spring; many unusual trees and shrubs giving yr-round interest. Formal terrace with clipped box

parterre; huge rose and clematis arches underplanted with perennials; mixed borders of roses and herbaceous plants in former kitchen garden; bog bank and quarry garden. *Adm £4. Private visits welcome by appt. Tel 01386 725389 carrs.conderton@virgin.net*

⓱ Dial Park, Chaddesley Corbett 🌳♿

(David & Olive Mason) 4½m from Kidderminster, 4½m from Bromsgrove. On A448 midway between Kidderminster & Bromsgrove. Limited parking at garden, or park in village or at village hall. Approx ¾-acre garden in rural setting in conservation area on edge of attractive village. Large collections of snowdrops, daffodils and hardy ferns. Very wide range of plants planted for yr-round interest. Small collection of country tools and bygones. Featured in 'The English Garden' and 'Amateur Gardening' 2004. TEAS. *Adm £2.50, chd free. Wed 16, Thur 17 Feb; (11-4) Thur 7 Apr (2-5). Private visits welcome by appt for groups & individuals. Tel 01562 777451 olivemason@btinternet.com*

⓲ ◆ Eastgrove Cottage Garden Nursery, Sankyns Green, Shrawley 🚻🌳♿

(Malcolm & Carol Skinner) 8m NW of Worcester, between Shrawley (B4196) & Great Witley (A443). Follow brown tourist signs to Sankyns Green. RHS partnership garden, this much loved country cottage flower garden with arboretum surrounds C17 half-timbered yeoman farmhouse (not open). Very personal and intimate yet unpretentious, the garden is stuffed with a tumbling abundance of plants, many unusual, full of colour and fascination at all seasons. New meadow planting. Excellent nursery. Featured in 'The Garden', 'Daily Telegraph'; BBC TV Gardeners' World, all 2004. *Adm £3.50, chd free, RHS members free. Thurs, Fris, Sats 14 Apr to 30 July and Bank Hol Suns & Mons (closed Aug) 8 Sept to 15 Oct (all 2-5).* **For NGS:** *Sats 7 May; 18 June; 16 July (2-5). Tel 01299 896389 www.eastgrove.co.uk*

Edgewood House, Greensforge Lane, Stourton 🚻🌳
See Staffordshire & part of West Midlands.

⓳ Frogs Nest, 8 Stratford Road, Honeybourne, Evesham 🏵️⌖
(Nina & Steve Bullen) *6m E of Evesham. 5m N of Broadway, 5m S of Bidford. Parking at the Gate Inn.* Small cottage garden with many sitting points for any weather to enjoy the varied features inc pools, herbaceous borders, old-English roses, shrubs etc. Home-made TEAS. *Adm £3. Suns 5, 12, 19, 26 June (11-6)*

⓴ Gadfield Elm House, Malvern Road, Staunton ⌖
(Canon John Evans & Mrs Jane Evans) *9m NW of Gloucester. 1m from Staunton Cross (A417) on B4208.* Garden created over 25yrs from scratch. Vistas, temples, statues, herbaceous borders. Field walk with view of Malverns, Bredon Hill and the Cotswolds. Rare breed poultry. Home-made TEAS. *Adm £2, chd free. Mons 28 Mar; 30 May; Suns 26 June; 31 July (2-6)*

㉑ NEW Gladderbrook Farm, High Oak, Heightington 🏵️⌖
(Mike & Sue Butler) *3m W of Stourport-on-Severn. Take A451 from Stourport. At Dunley turn R signposted Heightington. After 2m turn R signposted High Oak. Parking after ¾m at High Oak Farm by kind permission of Mr & Mrs T Sprague. Garden 100yds down lane.* Approx 1-acre garden with stunning views developed by owners since 2001. Full of colour all-yr with trees, shrubs, perennials, grasses, water feature, 2-acre spring wild flower meadow, developing arboretum, small orchard, vegetable plot and nursery. Stout shoes advisable. TEAS in aid of Heightington Church Restoration Fund. *Adm £2. Sats 21, 28 May; 4 June; 6, 13 Aug (11-4.30). Private visits welcome by appt, groups welcome. No coaches. Tel 01299 879923*

㉒ ◆ The Greyfriars, Friar Street, Worcester 🏵️⌖
(The National Trust) *In Friar Street within the centre of Worcester. Please use city car parks.* Delightful city garden created from the clearance of back to back housing. An archway leads through to the walled garden containing a beautiful display of spring bulbs incl snowdrops and daffodils. TEAS. *Adm £1.50, chd free.* **For NGS:** *Sat 5 Feb (1-4). Tel 01527 821014 Neil Cook*

㉓ ◆ Hanbury Hall, Hanbury ⌖🏵️⌖
(The National Trust (Neil Cook)) *3m NE of Droitwich. 6m S of Bromsgrove. Signed off B4090 and B4091.* Re-creation of C18 formal garden by George London. Parterre, Fruit garden and Wilderness. A Mushroon house, Orangery and Ice house, William and Mary style house dating from 1701, (not open for NGS event). Rare opening to see some of the first flowers of the year. *Adm £2 (also applies to NT members), chd free.* **For NGS:** *Sun 20 Feb (11-4). Tel 01527 821014 Neil Cook*

㉔ ◆ Harvington Hall, Harvington ⌖🏵️⌖
(The Roman Catholic Archdiocese of Birmingham) *3m SE of Kidderminster. ½m E of A450 Birmingham to Worcester Rd & about ½m N of A448 from Kidderminster to Bromsgrove.* Romantic Elizabethan moated manor house with island gardens. Small Elizabethan-style herb garden, tended by volunteers from the Hereford and Worcs Gardens Trust. The Hall gardens are looked after by volunteers who 'adopt' a bed. Tours of the Hall, which contains secret hiding places and rare wall paintings, are also available. Elizabethan re-enactors in hall and garden. Light refreshments and TEAS. *House and garden adm £4.50, OAP £3.80, chd £3, family £12.50, garden only adm £2, chd 50p. Weds to Suns Apr to Sept; w/ends Mar & Oct (11.30-4.30).* **For NGS:** *Sun 3 July (11.30-4.30). Tel 01562 777846 Mrs S Breedon www.harvingtonhall.com*

㉕ Hiraeth, 30 Showell Road, Droitwich ⌖🏵️⌖
(Sue & John Fletcher) *1m S of Droitwich. On The Ridings estate. Turn off A38 roundabout into Addyes Way, 2nd R into Showell Rd, 500yds on R.* Small traditional cottage garden incorporating pool and waterfall feature. Time is needed to inspect the hundreds of new and unusual varieties. Good collection of hostas and herbaceous plants. Spring garden incl heathers, azaleas, ferns. Water plants surround the pool. Featured in 'Amateur Gardening' 2004 and local newspapers. Home-made TEAS. *Adm £2, chd free. Suns 22 May; 12 June; 10 July; 14 Aug (1-5) Wed 27 July (12-5)* **Evening Opening** *£3.50, wine, Fri 24 June (5-9). Private visits welcome by appt. Tel 07752 717243*

㉖ Holland House, Main Street, Cropthorne 🏵️
(Mr Peter Middlemiss) *5m W of Evesham. Equidistant between Evesham and Pershore. Travel on B4084 (old A44) & take turning* signed Cropthorne village centre (on R from Evesham, on L from Pershore). Follow road round to R & then Holland House car park signed to the L . Please park in the car park & not on the rd. Formal gardens laid out by Lutyens in 1904 with rose garden; thatched house dating back to C16 (not open). Lovely riverside setting with banks of early daffodils in March and roses in June. TEAS. *Adm £3 (share to United Society For The Propagation Of The Gospel). Suns 20 Mar; 3 July (2-5)*

㉗ Ivytree House, Bromsgrove Road, Clent 🏵️ NCCPG
(Linda Eggins) *3m SE of Stourbridge & 5m NW of Bromsgrove. Off A491 Stourbridge to Bromsgrove dual carriageway. Car parking next door behind the French Hen Inn.* Over 1,000 varieties of small trees, shrubs and herbaceous plants in approx ½-acre plantsman's cottage garden; tree ivies and ivytrees, National Collection of aucubas, small conservatory with fuchsia trees; pond garden; fruit and vegetables; bantams and bees. *Adm £2.50, chd free. Private visits welcome by appt. Tel 01562 884171*

Kilima Lodge, Evendine Lane, Colwall ⌖🏵️
See Herefordshire.

Lakeside, Gaines Road, Whitbourne ⌖🏵️
See Herefordshire.

㉘ ◆ Little Malvern Court, Little Malvern ⌖🏵️⌖
(Mrs T M Berington) *3m S of Malvern. On A4104 S of junction with A449.* 10 acres attached to former Benedictine Priory, magnificent views over Severn valley. Intriguing layout of garden rooms and terrace round house designed and planted in early 1980's; water garden below feeding into chain of lakes; wide variety of spring bulbs, flowering trees and shrubs. Notable collection of old-fashioned roses. Topiary hedge and fine trees. TEAS Sun 20 Mar (in aid of SSAFA); Mon 2 May (in aid of The Friends of Little Malvern Priory). *Adm £3.50, chd 50p. Weds & Thurs afternoons mid Apr to mid July (2.15-5) .* **For NGS:** *Sun 20 Mar; Mon 2 May (2-5). Tel 01684 892988*

The Long Barn, Eastnor 🏵️⌖
See Herefordshire.

Longacre, Evendine Lane, Colwall Green ♿✂
See Herefordshire.

㉙ Luggers Hall, Springfield Lane, Broadway ♿☺
(Kay & Red Haslam) *Turn off Broadway High St by Swan Hotel, bear L into Springfield Lane. Luggers Hall is on the L approx 300yds along. Some parking but limited - if possible use car parks which are close by.* 2½-acre formal garden originally designed by the famous Victorian garden artist Alfred Parsons. Features incl rose garden; parterre; walled garden; potager; white garden; koi pool and herbaceous borders, all connected by gravel paths with seating areas. An abundance of clipped box and yew hedging; plus Victorian hazel walk. Children with caution due to deep water feature. Cream TEAS. *Adm £2.50, chd free. Suns 29 May; 26 June (2-6)*

㉚ Madresfield Court, Madresfield nr Malvern ♿
(Lady Morrison) *2m E of Malvern. In Madresfield village.* 60 acres formal and parkland garden incl rare species of mature trees, Pulhamite rock garden, maze; majestic avenues and beautiful autumn colours. TEAS. *Adm £5, school age chd £5 (pre-school free), concessions £2 (share to Madresfield Primary School). Sun 23 Oct (2-5)*

㉛ March House, Evesham Road, Broadway ✂☺
(Jim & June Cowan) *2m NW of Broadway. On A44, 1st house on R after roundabout going towards Evesham turn into unmarked lane. From Evesham approx. 3m, pass Murcot junction turn into unmarked lane 10yds past house sign 'The Slinget'.* ½ acre of herbaceous borders; extended water feature; young specimen trees; roses; small orchard; soft fruit; vegetable plots and heather garden. The garden was started from scratch in 1993. Featured in 'Worcestershire Life', 'Gloucester Echo' 2004; Natureza San Paulo, Brazil 2005. TEAS. *Adm £2, chd free. Sun 1, 15, Mon 30 May; Sun 12, Sat 25, Sun 26 June (2-5). Private visits welcome by appt.* Tel 01386 852993 2toads174@beeb.net

㉜ Nerine Nursery, Brookend House, Welland ✂☺ NCCPG
(Mr & Mrs I L Carmichael) *1m E of Welland. Brookend House,* ½*m towards Upton-on-Severn from Welland Xrds (A4104 × B4208).* Internationally famous National

Collection of nerines, 30 species and some 800 named varieties in 5 greenhouses and traditional walled garden; hardy nerines. Coaches by appt only. Featured in 'Gardens Illustrated', 'Garden Answers', BBC Gardeners' World all 2004. TEAS. *Adm £2.50, chd free. Sun 16 Oct (2-5). Private visits welcome by appt.* Tel 01684 594005

The Orchards, Golden Valley, Bishops Frome ✂☺
See Herefordshire.

㉝ Orleton House, Orleton, Stanford Bridge ♿✂☺
(Jenny & John Hughes) *6m E of Tenbury Wells. 15m NW of Worcester. A443 from Worcester for 10m then B4203 towards Bromyard. Cross R Teme at Stanford Bridge then next R turn. 1m down this lane.* 4 acres of garden adjoining paddocks and wooded areas nestling in the Teme Valley. C19 grade II listed house (not open) surrounded by superb herbaceous borders, bog garden, walled swimming pool and richly planted gravel terrace. Abundance of unusual plants, shrubs and roses providing exotic colour and perfume from May to Oct. Shaded walks follow the path of a fast-flowing natural stream as it tumbles down a damp wooded valley which is guarded by majestic oaks and a magnificent copper beech tree. Croquet lawn and putting green. Jenny's pottery shop. Light lunches and TEAS in aid of Stanford Village Hall & Church. *Adm £3, chd free. Sat 4, Sun 5 June; Sat 30, Sun 31 July (11-5). Private visits welcome by appt for groups of 10 or more.* Tel 01584 881253 www.orletonhouse.co.uk

㉞ Overbury Court, nr Tewkesbury ♿
(Mr & Mrs Bruce Bossom) *5m NE of Tewkesbury. Village signed off A46.* Georgian house 1740 (not open); landscape garden of same date with stream and pools; daffodil bank and grotto. Plane trees, yew hedges; shrubs; cut flowers; coloured foliage; gold and silver, shrub rose borders. Norman church adjoins garden. *Adm £2.50, chd free. Private visits welcome by appt and also combined with Conderton Manor & Whitcombe House by appt. Minimum charge for groups £15.* Tel 01386 725111 Fax 01386 725528 www.overbury.org

Pebworth & Broad Marston Gardens, Stratford-upon-Avon
See Warwickshire & part of West Midlands.

㉟ Pershore Gardens ☺
(Ross & Jan Garratt) *Centre of Pershore. On the B4084 bet Worcester and Evesham. Gardens located nr to centre of Pershore, in Bridge St, Broad St, High St and a few gardens nr to Abbey Park.* Many of the gardens are tucked away behind Georgian townhouses. Some gardens sweep down to the R Avon, others are large walled gardens with orchards and formal areas. There are gardens with interesting collections of perennials, shrubs and alpines and 'Weir Gardens' is an attractive, modern riverside development with views of Pershore Lock. Maps locating the gardens can be collected at any garden. Cream TEAS at and in aid of 'Number 8', Pershore's Community Arts Centre. *Adm £5, chd free. Sun 12 June (2-6)*

The Picton Garden, Old Court Nurseries, Colwall ♿✂☺ NCCPG
See Herefordshire.

㊱ 4 Poden Cottages, Honeybourne ♿✂☺
(Patrick & Dorothy Bellew) *6m E of Evesham. At the Gate Inn take the Pebworth, Long Marston rd, turn R at end of the Village for Mickleton. 1m on Mickleton Rd.* ⅓-acre cottage and rose garden which has been planted by the owners. Grass paths wind through mixed herbaceous borders. 100 different roses old and modern, shrubs, small terrace and pond. Fine views over the Cotswold Hills. Home-made TEAS. *Adm £2, chd free. Sun 29, Mon 30 May (12-5); Thurs 23, 30 June (11-6). Private visits welcome by appt.* Tel 01386 438996 pots@poden. freeserve.co.uk

㊲ 1 Prickley Bungalows, Martley ✂☺
(Megan Griffiths) *7m NW of Worcester. On the B4204, 2m from Martley on the B4197. Turn off R into Hockhams Lane. Parking at Prickley Farm (250yds) by kind permission of Mr & Mrs Nott.* ¼-acre cottage garden with many unusual plants. The garden is designed in 'rooms' to include two ponds, woodland area and herbaceous plants. Colour all-yr. Limited wheelchair access. *Adm £2.50, chd free. Suns 27 Mar; 17 Apr; 1 May; 29 May; 12, 26 June; 10 July; Mons 28 Mar; 2, 30 May (2-6). Private visits welcome by appt, coaches permitted.* Tel 01886 812523

38 **88 Rectory Road, Headless Cross, Redditch** ✿
(Richard & Carole Poolton) *1m S of Redditch. From A448 take the exit signed Headless Cross, Walkwood etc, turn L at island. Turn opp Archers public house. Rectory Rd on RH-side.* 130ft by 25ft garden at rear of Victorian end terraced property divided into four separate, intimate 'rooms'. Created by present owners over 10 yrs. Aromatic courtyard, formal pond in evergreen setting. Tranquil oriental-style garden leading to herb border, 'mockery' (a log garden, herbaceous beds and fruit cage. Redditch Best Garden 2004 - Area Winners, overall 2nd. Home-made TEAS. *Adm £2, chd free. Sun 22 May; Sat 30, Sun 31 July (11-4.30)*

The Red House, Staunton, nr Gloucester ✿
See Gloucestershire North & Central.

39 **Red House Farm, Flying Horse Lane, Bradley Green** ✿✿
(Mrs M M Weaver) *7m W of Redditch. On B4090 Alcester to Droitwich Spa. Ignore signpost to Bradley Green. Turn opp The Red Lion PH.* ½-acre plantsman's cottage garden in C18 farmhouse setting. Mixed planting with mature trees, shrubs, roses, herbaceous perennials giving all yr-round colour and interest. Adjacent nursery. *Adm £2, chd free. Sun 22 May (11-4.30). Private visits welcome by appt. Tel 01527 821269 www.redhousefarmgardenandnursery. co.uk*

40 **Saranacris, 28A Braces Lane, Bromsgrove** ✿✿
(John & Janet Morgan) *1m N of M42 J1, follow B4096 signposted Rednal, turn L at Xrds into Braces Lane. 1m S of M5 J4, follow A38 signposted Bromsgrove, turn L at T-lights into Braces Lane. Car park in recreation ground.* Unusual and challenging terraced garden created by owners in old sand quarry. Avid plant collectors; hostas, crocosmias, kniphofia and hedychium. Pools, stream and mature trees, patio, roof garden and conservatory overflowing with subtropical plants. Very steep garden. Featured in 'Amateur Gardening' 2005. Home-made TEAS in aid of County Air Ambulance. *Adm £2.50, chd free. Sun 21 Aug (2-6).***Evening Opening** *£4, wine, Fris 24 June; 15 July (6-9)*

41 **Shuttifield Cottage, Birchwood, Storridge** ✿✿
(Mr & Mrs David Judge) *8m W of Worcester. Turn R off A4103 opp Storridge Church to Birchwood. After 1¼m L down steep tarmac drive. Please park on roadside but drive down if walking is difficult.* Superb position and views. 3-acre garden with extensive herbaceous borders and many unusual trees, shrubs and perennials, colour-themed for interest throughout the year. Walks in the 20-acre wood with ponds and natural wild areas where anemones, bluebells, rhododendrons and azaleas are a particular feature in spring. Large old rose garden with many spectacular mature climbers. Small deer park and vegetable garden. Home-made TEAS. *Adm £2.50. Sun 17 Apr; Sats 7, 21 May; 11,18 June; 16 July; 13 Aug (1-5). Private visits welcome by appt. Tel 01886 884243*

42 **South Littleton Gardens, nr Evesham** ✿✿
(Lady Harford) *4m NE of Evesham. On B4085. Car parking and toilets on recreation ground. Transport provided to outlying gardens. Coaches welcome. Map available.* About 10 gardens around South Littleton. in the heart of the beautiful Vale of Evesham and - for the first time, the recently revitalised allotments, with 15-20 plots under culivation. Gardens vary in size and character from the traditional to the highly unusual - a great afternoon's outing. Home-made TEAS and plant sales in aid of St Michael's Church. *Combined adm £4, chd free. Sun 29, Mon 30 May (12-6)*

43 ♦ **Spetchley Park Gardens, nr Worcester** ✿✿
(Mr R J Berkeley) *2m E of Worcester. On A44.* 30-acre garden containing large collection of trees; shrubs and plants, many rare and unusual; new garden within kitchen garden. Red and fallow deer in nearby park. A wonderful display of spring bulbs, but masses of colour throughout spring and summer. Light refreshments and TEAS. *Adm £5, chd £2, prebooked parties 25+ adults £4.50, chd £1.90. Tues to Fris (11-6), Suns (2-6), Bank Hols (11-6). 25 Mar to 30 Sept. Last entry each open day 4pm.* **For NGS:** *Fri 25 Mar(11-6); Suns 8 May; 3 July (2-6). Tel 01905 345224 / 213 Mr R J Berkeley www.spetchleygardens.co.uk*

44 NEW **Stone Cottage, Valley Road, Bournheath, Bromsgrove** ✿✿✿
(Mr G A Webb) *3m NW of Bromsgrove. On B4091 to Rocky Lane, L into Valley Rd. M5 J4, M42 J4A. Stone Cottage on L opp Dodford sign.* Garden developed by present owner over last 30 yrs. Large organic vegetable garden. Raised beds, heated greenhouse and frames. Fruit trees, flower garden on two levels, ornamental pool. Herbaceous and shrub borders, water features. Outstanding display of lilies arranged in unusual BBQ area. TEAS. *Adm £2.50, chd free. Sat 16, Sun 17 July (2-5.30)*

45 ♦ **Stone House Cottage Gardens, Stone** ✿✿
(James & Louisa Arbuthnott) *2m SE of Kidderminster. Via A448 towards Bromsgrove next to church, turn up drive.* A beautiful and romantic walled garden adorned with unusual brick follies, exuberantly and richly planted. Holds one of the largest collections of rare plants in the country. Adjacent nursery, climbers a speciality. Featured in 'Sunday Telegraph', 'Daily Telegraph', 'Gardens Illustrated' 2003-2004. *Adm £3, chd free. Weds to Sats Mar to 17 Sept (10-5.30).* **For NGS:** *Sats 26 Mar; 9 Apr; Wed 4 May; Thurs 2 June; 14 July; Sat 6, Thurs 11 Aug; Sat 3 Sept (10-5.30). Tel 01562 69902 Louisa Arbuthnot www.shcn. co.uk*

46 **Two Gardens in Beckett Drive, Northwick, Worcester**
1½m N of Worcester city centre. Cul-de-sac off A449 Ombersley Rd directly opp Granthams garage, 1m S of Claines roundabout on A449. Two individual but contrasting gardens both with an abundance of plants. Home-made TEAS at 6 Beckett Drive. *Combined adm £2.50. Sun 10 July (10-5)*

5 Beckett Drive ✿✿ (Jacki & Pete Ager) A peaceful haven in a city suburb. An unusual and interesting garden with shrubs, perennials and alpines in a landscaped setting. Overall Winners Worcester in Bloom 2004.

6 Beckett Drive ✿ (Guy Lymer) Eclectic mix of planting, modern sculpture and water features. Established shrubs for yr-round interest are complemented by exotic plants, ornamental grasses and a natural arbour.

47 **The Tynings, Church Lane, Stoulton, nr Worcester** 🏵️🅿️

(John & Leslie Bryant) *5m S of Worcester; 3m N of Pershore. On the B4084 (formerly A44) between M5 junction 7 & Pershore. The Tynings lies beyond the church at the extreme end of Church Lane.* A plantsman's ½-acre garden in a rural setting with views of Stoulton Church, generously planted with unusual shrubs and trees. Island beds, herbaceous borders and water features contain a large collection of species and hybrid lilies (member of RHS Lily Group), euphorbias and ferns. Tree ferns, bamboos and a bog garden add to the surprises round every corner. Planting list available. TEAS in aid of Friends of Stoulton Church. *Adm £2.50, chd free.* **Evening Opening** *£4, wine, Sat 2 July (6-8.30). Private visits welcome by appt June & July only. Tel 01905 840189*

48 **Tythe Barn House, Chaddesley Corbett** 🏵️🅿️

(Judy & John Berrow) *4½m from Bromsgrove; 4½m from Kidderminster. On A448. 150yds towards Kidderminster from the turn into Chaddesley Corbett village. Parking in village or at village hall (200 yds).* ¾-acre romantic garden created in old farm rickyard, within old farm building complex in conservation area. Incl old and modern roses; herbs and herbaceous borders. Small terrace garden. Shrubs and trees together with a small vegetable plot. Lovely view of the church and surrounding countryside. Featured in 'Herefordshire & Worcestershire Life', 2003. Home-made TEAS. *Adm £2.50, chd free. Sun 26 June (2-5.30). Private visits welcome by appt, coaches permitted. Tel 01562 777014 j.berrow@virgin.net*

49 **The Walled Garden, 6 Rose Terrace, off Fort Royal Hill, Worcester** 🏵️🅿️

(Julia & William Scott) *Nr city centre. ½m from cathedral. Via Fort Royal Hill, off London Rd (A44). Park on first section of Rose Terrace & walk the last 20yds down track.* Hidden away, but close to city centre, this ½-acre C19 kitchen garden is developing along the lines of the 1886 original garden plan. Herb gardens, flower gardens, potager, old and newly planted fruit trees, all grown organically, provide colour and scent in an ever changing tapestry. TEAS. *Adm £2, chd 50p. Sats 26 Mar; 9 Apr; 14 May; 11 June; 9 July; 13 Aug (1-5)*

50 ◆ **Webbs of Wychbold, Wychbold, nr Droitwich** ♿🏵️🅿️ NCCPG

(Webbs of Wychbold) *2m N of Droitwich Spa. 1m N of M5 junction 5 on A38. Follow tourism signs from motorway.* Riverside gardens occupy 2½-acres of themed gardens incl National Collection of *Potentilla fruticosa*, colour spectrum garden, white garden, dry garden, David Austin roses, grass garden and many others under continual development. The New Wave section opened in 2004; designed by Noel Kingsbury, this area features a series of plantings of naturalised perennials for differing situations. These are both eye catching and wildlife friendly. Once established they will require minimum maintenance. Dogs welcome on site - designated walking area and drinking water provided, but not permitted in show gardens. Featured in 'Daily Telegraph' - Modern Gardens & 'Country Homes & Interiors', 2004. Light refreshments and TEAS. *Adm free, chd free, concessions free. Open daily all year except Christmas Day, Boxing Day & Easter Sun; Mons to Sats (9-6); Suns (10.30-4.30). Tel 01527 860000 www.webbsofwychbold.co.uk*

51 **NEW** **Weobley Cross Cottage, South End Lane, Mathon, nr Malvern** ⊗
(Mr & Mrs P Haywood) *4m W of Great Malvern. From Malvern town centre proceed S along Wells Rd A449 towards Ledbury. After approx ½m turn R signposted Colwall on B4208. After passing through the Wyche Cutting, turn R into West Malvern Rd. After 1m turn L into Harcourt Rd & continue down to T-junction. Proceed straight on for approx ¼m to South End Lane. Weobley Cross Cottage is on the L at the entrance to this lane. Parking down South End Lane. Approx ¾ of an acre.* 4 general areas. Restored cottage garden with stunning views, pond, variety of borders and winding paths, variety of shrubs, perennials and fruit trees. Suburban-style garden with planted wall, rockery and herbaceous border. Interesting pots. Kitchen/vegetable garden yet to be restored. Lawned area with old outbuilding, yet to be developed. TEAS. *Adm £1.50, chd 50p. Sun 17 July (1-5)*

52 ◆ **Whit Lenge Gardens, Hartlebury** ⑤⊗⊕
(Mr & Mrs K J Southall) *5m S of Kidderminster. Take A449 from Kidderminster towards Worcester, then A442 (signposted Droitwich) over small island, ¼m, 1st R into Whitlenge Lane. Follow signs.* Professional landscaper's garden with over 600 varieties of trees, shrubs etc. Water features, twisted pillar pergola, scree gardens, rockeries. 3 acres of plantsman's garden. Adjacent nursery. TEAS on NGS days. *Adm £2, chd free. Open all yr except Xmas, Mon to Sat (9-5), Sun (10-5).*

For NGS: *Suns 27 Mar; 1, 29 May; 28 Aug (10-5); Mons 28 Mar; 2, 30 May; 29 Aug (9-5). Tel 01299 250720 Lorraine Shuck www.creativelandscapes.co.uk*

53 **Whitcombe House, Overbury** ⑤⊗⊕
(Faith & Anthony Hallett) *5½m NE of Tewkesbury, 8m E of Upton Upon Severn, 7m SE of Pershore. Overbury lies on B4080 between Bredon & Beckford (1m from Kemerton). Turn up the hill opp bus shelter.Whitcombe is first house on L.* An acre of walled garden set in the beautiful Cotswold village of Overbury. Large herbaceous borders, around the pergola, comprise a variety of schemes, plantings and colour. Two shrubberies and a further five formal borders set beside gravel paths complement the informality and the surpise. A fast flowing stream is another feature, surrounded by primulas, arum lilies and bog plants, where the sound of water makes peaceful and idyllic reflection easy. Featured in 'Gloucester Echo' 2004, 'Evesham Journal' 2003 & 2004. TEAS in aid of Overbury School. *Adm £3, chd free, OAP £2. Suns 8, 22 May; 5 June (2-5.30). Private visits welcome by appt. Tel 01386 725206 tonyhallett@mailsaq.net*

54 ◆ **White Cottage, Stock Green, nr Inkberrow** ⑤⊗⊕
(Mr & Mrs S M Bates) *2m W of Inkberrow, 2m E of Upton Snodsbury. A422 Worcester to Alcester, turn at brown sign for Cottage Garden also Stock Green, 1½m to T- junction, turn L.* 2 acres, herbaceous and shrub beds, stream

and spring wild flower area, rose garden, raised woodland bed, large specialist collection of hardy geraniums. Adjacent nursery. TEAS Sats & Suns. *Adm £2, chd free, concessions £1.50. Mons, Tues and Fris 18 Mar to 2 Oct (10-5) and most w/ends. By appt in Aug.* **For NGS:** *Sats 2, 16, 30, Suns 3, 17 Apr; Mons 2, 30, Sats 14, 28, Suns 1, 15, 29 May; Mon 13, Sat 4, Suns 5, 12 June; Sats 3, 17, Suns 4, 18 Sept; Sat 1, Sun 2 Oct (10-5). Tel 01386 792414 Mrs S M Bates www.cranesbillnursery.com*

Evening Opening (See also garden description)

Hiraeth	24 June
Saranacris	24 June
The Tynings	2 July
Saranacris	15 July

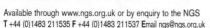

Yorkshire

County Organisers:
(N Yorks- Districts of Hambleton, Richmond, Ryedale, Scarborough & Cleveland)

Mrs Jane Baldwin, Riverside Farm, Sinnington, York YO62 6RY Tel/Fax 01751 431764

(E Yorks)

Mrs Sally Bean, Saltmarshe Hall, Saltmarshe, Howden, Goole, Yorkshire DN14 7RX Tel 01430 430199 Fax 01430 431607 email pmegabean@aol.com

(West & South Yorks & North Yorks District of Craven, Harrogate, Selby & York)

Mrs Bridget Marshall, The Old Vicarage, Whixley, York YO26 8AR Tel 01423 330474

Assistant County Organisers:
West & South Yorks

Mrs Jane Hudson, Lower Crawshaw, Emley, Huddersfield HD8 9SU Tel 01924 840980

(Press & Publicity Officer: West & South Yorks)

Mrs Elizabeth Tite, Field Cottage, Littlethorpe, Nr Ripon, Yorkshire HG4 3LG Tel 01765 690996

Maps: Numbers shown next to each garden entry refer to that garden's entry on the county map. This position is approximate; distance and directions from the nearest main town are generally shown in the garden text. A precise location is available for those gardens featured on the NGS website by visiting www.ngs.org.uk.

Symbols: Information relating to symbols is given on page 21

DATES OF OPENING

Evening openings
See end of county listing

Private gardens open regularly for NGS
Hunmanby Grange, Wold Newton *(47)*
Londesborough Cross, Shiptonthorpe *(53)*

Gardens open to the public
For details see garden description
Burton Agnes Hall, Driffield *(11)*
Castle Howard, nr York *(12)*
Constable Burton Hall Gardens, nr Leyburn *(18)*
Harewood House, nr Leeds *(41)*
Land Farm, Colden, nr Hebden Bridge *(51)*
Newby Hall & Gardens, Ripon *(69)*
Norton Conyers, Wath, nr Ripon *(70)*
Parcevall Hall Gardens, Skyreholme *(76)*
RHS Garden Harlow Carr, Harrogate *(81)*
Shandy Hall, Coxwold *(88)*
Stillingfleet Lodge, Stillingfleet, nr York *(92)*
The Walled Garden at Scampston *(98)*
Woodlands Cottage, Summerbridge *(104)*
Wytherstone Gardens, Pockley *(105)*
York Gate, Adel, Leeds 16 *(106)*

By appointment only
For telephone number and other details see garden description.
Private visits welcomed
Deepdale, Boston Spa *(24)*
8 Dunstan Lane, Adel, Leeds 16 *(29)*
East Wing, Thorp Arch Hall, Thorp Arch *(30)*
Evergreens, Bilton *(32)*
Field Cottage, Littlethorpe, nr Ripon *(34)*
The Mews Cottage, Harrogate *(64)*
Parkview, South Cave *(77)*
55 Rawcliffe Drive, York *(80)*
Tan Cottage, Cononley *(93)*
The White House, Husthwaite *(101)*

February 20 Sunday
Rose Cottage, nr Denby Dale *(82)*

February 23 Wednesday
Bridge Farm House, Great Heck, Goole *(9)*

February 27 Sunday
Rose Cottage, nr Denby Dale *(82)*

March 16 Wednesday
Londesborough Cross, Shiptonthorpe *(53)*

March 23 Wednesday
Londesborough Cross, Shiptonthorpe *(53)*

March 30 Wednesday
Londesborough Cross, Shiptonthorpe *(53)*

April 3 Sunday
Acorn Cottage, Boston Spa *(1)*
Londesborough Cross, Shiptonthorpe *(53)*
Ness Hall, Nunnington *(68)*

April 6 Wednesday
Acorn Cottage, Boston Spa *(1)*
Hunmanby Grange, Wold Newton *(47)*
Londesborough Cross, Shiptonthorpe *(53)*
Ness Hall, Nunnington *(68)*

April 10 Sunday
Acorn Cottage, Boston Spa *(1)*
Orchard House, Appleton Roebuck *(72)*

April 13 Wednesday
Hunmanby Grange, Wold Newton *(47)*
Londesborough Cross, Shiptonthorpe *(53)*

April 17 Sunday
Hotham Hall, Hotham *(46)*

April 20 Wednesday
Hunmanby Grange, Wold Newton *(47)*
Londesborough Cross, Shiptonthorpe *(53)*

April 24 Sunday
Ling Beeches, Scarcroft *(52)*
Londesborough Cross, Shiptonthorpe *(53)*
Parcevall Hall Gardens, Skyreholme *(76)*
Rose Cottage, nr Denby Dale *(82)*
Rye Hill, Helmsley *(84)*
Vicarage House, Kirkby Wharfe *(97)*

April 27 Wednesday
Hunmanby Grange, Wold Newton *(47)*
Londesborough Cross, Shiptonthorpe *(53)*
Rye Hill, Helmsley *(84)*

May 1 Sunday
Hunmanby Grange, Wold Newton *(47)*

May 4 Wednesday
Hunmanby Grange, Wold Newton *(47)*
Londesborough Cross, Shiptonthorpe *(53)*

May 7 Saturday
Outwood House, Horsforth *(75)*

May 8 Sunday
Londesborough Cross, Shiptonthorpe *(53)*
Orchard House, Appleton Roebuck *(72)*
Outwood House, Horsforth *(75)*
RHS Garden Harlow Carr, Harrogate *(81)*
Secret Garden, York *(86)*
The Spaniels, Hensall *(90)*
Stillingfleet Lodge, Stillingfleet, nr York *(92)*

May 11 Wednesday
Beacon Hill House, Nr Ilkley *(4)*
Hallgarth, Ottringham *(40)*
Hunmanby Grange, Wold Newton *(47)*
Londesborough Cross, Shiptonthorpe *(53)*
Low Askew, Cropton *(55)*

May 15 Sunday
Blackbird Cottage, Scampston *(7)*
The Court, North Ferriby *(19)*
Hallgarth, Ottringham *(40)*
Hillbark, Bardsey *(44)*
Kelberdale, Knaresborough *(50)*
Tregonning, Ellerton *(96)*
Woodlands Cottage, Summerbridge *(104)*

May 18 Wednesday
Hunmanby Grange, Wold Newton *(47)*
Londesborough Cross, Shiptonthorpe *(53)*

May 20 Friday
Shandy Hall, Coxwold **(Evening)** *(88)*

May 22 Sunday
Denwell, Wheldrake *(25)*
Hallcroft Hall, Addingham *(39)*
Highfields, Skelmanthorpe *(43)*
Lower Crawshaw, Emley, nr Denby Dale *(56)*
Rose Cottage, nr Denby Dale *(82)*
Rye Hill, Helmsley *(84)*
Saltmarshe Hall, Saltmarshe *(85)*

May 25 Wednesday
Hunmanby Grange, Wold Newton *(47)*
Londesborough Cross, Shiptonthorpe *(53)*
Rye Hill, Helmsley *(84)*

May 28 Saturday
Nawton Tower Garden, Nawton *(67)*
Pennyholme, Fadmoor *(78)*
Sleightholmedale Lodge, Fadmoor *(89)*

May 29 Sunday
Bolton Percy Gardens *(8)*
Cruckhouse Farm, Norwood, nr Otley *(21)*
High Farm, Bilton *(42)*
Londesborough Cross, Shiptonthorpe *(53)*
Nawton Tower Garden, Nawton *(67)*
The Old Rectory, Nunburnholme *(71)*
26 West End, Walkington *(100)*
Wytherstone Gardens, Pockley *(105)*

May 30 Monday (Bank Hol)
Croft Cottage, Green Hammerton *(20)*
Nawton Tower Garden, Nawton *(67)*
Whixley Gardens *(102)*

June 1 Wednesday
Cleaves House, Thirlby **(Day & Evening)**
(15)
Hunmanby Grange, Wold Newton *(47)*
Londesborough Cross, Shiptonthorpe *(53)*

June 3 Friday
Shandy Hall, Coxwold **(Evening)** *(88)*

June 4 Saturday
Pennyholme, Fadmoor *(78)*
Sleightholmedale Lodge, Fadmoor *(89)*

June 5 Sunday
Dunnington Manor, Dunnington, nr Driffield
(28)
Hillbark, Bardsey *(44)*
Home Farm, nr Easingwold *(45)*
Hunmanby Grange, Wold Newton *(47)*
Jacksons Wold, Sherburn *(48)*
Jasmine House, Wheatley Hills, Doncaster
(49)
Lullaby, Hull *(57)*
Secret Garden, York *(86)*

June 8 Wednesday
Cleaves House, Thirlby **(Day & Evening)**
(15)
The Grange, Carleton *(35)*
Hunmanby Grange, Wold Newton *(47)*
Londesborough Cross, Shiptonthorpe *(53)*

June 11 Saturday
Burton Agnes Hall, Driffield *(11)*

June 12 Sunday
Burton Agnes Hall, Driffield *(11)*
Derwent House, Osbaldwick *(26)*
Dowthorpe Hall, Skirlaugh *(27)*
Dunnington Manor, Dunnington, nr Driffield
(28)
Elvington Gardens, nr York *(31)*
Kelberdale, Knaresborough *(50)*
Maspin House, Hillam *(62)*
Norton Conyers, Wath, nr Ripon *(70)*
Orchard House, Appleton Roebuck *(72)*
Tregonning, Ellerton *(96)*
Yorke House, Dacre Banks, Nidderdale
(107)

June 15 Wednesday
Hunmanby Grange, Wold Newton *(47)*

June 18 Saturday
Mansion Cottage, Bempton *(61)*

June 19 Sunday
Birstwith Hall, Nr Harrogate *(6)*
Cold Cotes, Nr Kettlesing, Harrogate *(17)*
Darley Gardens, nr Harrogate *(23)*
Great Ouseburn Gardens *(36)*
Greencroft, Littlethorpe, nr Ripon *(37)*
Mansion Cottage, Bempton *(61)*
Millgate House, Richmond **(Day &
Evening)** *(65)*
Saltmarshe Hall, Saltmarshe *(85)*
Stillingfleet Lodge, Stillingfleet, nr York *(92)*
Woodlands, Littlethorpe *(103)*

June 22 Wednesday
The Grange, Carleton *(35)*
Hunmanby Grange, Wold Newton *(47)*
Rye Hill, Helmsley *(84)*

June 25 Saturday
Long Marston Hall, Long Marston *(54)*

June 26 Sunday
Bankfield, Huddersfield *(2)*
Beamsley Hall, Bolton Abbey, nr Skipton *(5)*
Brookfield, Oxenhope *(10)*
Cobwebs, Netherton *(16)*
Denwell, Wheldrake *(25)*
High Farm, Bilton *(42)*
Hillbark, Bardsey *(44)*
Jacksons Wold, Sherburn *(48)*
Long Marston Hall, Long Marston *(54)*
Makin's Cottage, Patrington *(59)*
Morefield, nr Holmfirth *(66)*
Orchard House, Hunton, Bedale *(73)*
Wytherstone Gardens, Pockley *(105)*

June 29 Wednesday
Brookfield, Oxenhope *(10)*
Hunmanby Grange, Wold Newton *(47)*

July 3 Sunday
72 Church Street, Oughtibridge *(14)*
Fernwood, Cropton *(33)*
Grimston Manor Farm, Gilling East *(38)*
Hunmanby Grange, Wold Newton *(47)*
Maidens Folly, Youlton, nr Easingwold *(58)*
Rose Cottage, nr Denby Dale *(82)*

July 5 Tuesday
Outwood House, Horsforth **(Evening)** *(75)*

July 6 Wednesday
Hunmanby Grange, Wold Newton *(47)*
Outwood House, Horsforth **(Evening)** *(75)*

July 7 Thursday
Grimston Manor Farm, Gilling East *(38)*

July 9 Saturday
Long Marston Hall, Long Marston
(Evening) *(54)*

July 10 Sunday
Cawood Gardens, Cawood *(13)*
Dacre Banks Gardens, Nidderdale *(22)*
Rudston House, Rudston, nr Driffield *(83)*
Secret Garden, York *(86)*
Tranmere Park Gardens, Guiseley *(95)*

July 13 Wednesday
Hunmanby Grange, Wold Newton *(47)*

July 16 Saturday
Sleightholmedale Lodge, Fadmoor *(89)*

July 17 Sunday
Darley Gardens, nr Harrogate *(23)*
Manor Farm, Thixendale *(60)*
130 Prince Rupert Drive, Tockwith, nr York
(79)

Sleightholmedale Lodge, Fadmoor *(89)*
Springfield House, Tockwith *(91)*
3 Weelsby Way, Hessle, E Yorkshire *(99)*

July 20 Wednesday
Hunmanby Grange, Wold Newton *(47)*
Rye Hill, Helmsley *(84)*

July 24 Sunday
Thorpe Lodge, nr Ripon *(94)*

July 27 Wednesday
Hunmanby Grange, Wold Newton *(47)*
The Walled Garden at Scampston *(98)*

July 31 Sunday
4 Shaftesbury Court, Bradford West *(87)*
The Spaniels, Hensall *(90)*

August 3 Wednesday
Denwell, Wheldrake *(25)*
Hunmanby Grange, Wold Newton *(47)*

August 7 Sunday
Woodlands Cottage, Summerbridge *(104)*

August 10 Wednesday
Hunmanby Grange, Wold Newton *(47)*

August 13 Saturday
Mansion Cottage, Bempton *(61)*

August 14 Sunday
Barley Mow, Moor Monkton *(3)*
Mansion Cottage, Bempton *(61)*
Mayroyd Mill House, Hebden Bridge *(63)*
RHS Garden Harlow Carr, Harrogate *(81)*
Wytherstone Gardens, Pockley *(105)*

August 17 Wednesday
Hunmanby Grange, Wold Newton *(47)*

August 21 Sunday
Ornamental Grass & Foliage Garden,
Rillington *(74)*

August 24 Wednesday
Hunmanby Grange, Wold Newton *(47)*

August 28 Sunday
Londesborough Cross, Shiptonthorpe *(53)*
Lullaby, Hull *(57)*

August 29 Monday (Bank Hol)
72 Church Street, Oughtibridge *(14)*

August 31 Wednesday
Hunmanby Grange, Wold Newton *(47)*
Londesborough Cross, Shiptonthorpe *(53)*

September 4 Sunday
Bridge Farm House, Great Heck, Goole *(9)*
Cold Cotes, Nr Kettlesing, Harrogate *(17)*
Cruckhouse Farm, Norwood, nr Otley *(21)*

September 7 Wednesday
Hunmanby Grange, Wold Newton *(47)*
Londesborough Cross, Shiptonthorpe *(53)*

September 11 Sunday
Ornamental Grass & Foliage Garden,
Rillington *(74)*
130 Prince Rupert Drive, Tockwith, nr York
(79)

September 14 Wednesday
Hunmanby Grange, Wold Newton *(47)*

September 21 Wednesday
Hunmanby Grange, Wold Newton *(47)*

September 28 Wednesday
Hunmanby Grange, Wold Newton *(47)*

DURHAM

CUMBRIA

Richmond ○ 65

73
18

Leyburn ○

○ Northallerton

A19

A1

Thirsk ○

15

88

101

Ingleton ○

Pateley Bridge ○

Ripon ○
34
69
103

22
37
94

45

A19

Settle ○

A65

76

107 104

23
17
6

64

Harrogate ○

Knaresborough
102
36 58

50

20
3

A59

A1(M)

81

91 54

1

79

30
24

A64

Tadcaster ○

Skipton ○
Ilkley ○
5
4
39

35

Wetherby

21

Otley ○

41

106
29

44
52

97 8

Keighley ○
93
95

75

BRADFORD
87

LANCASHIRE

Hebden 10
Bridge
51 ○
63
Halifax ○

M621

LEEDS ○

A1

62

M62

Pontefract ○

M62

16 ○ 2
HUDDERSFIELD

○ Wakefield

GREATER
MANCHESTER

66
Denby Dale ○
43 56
82

○ Barnsley

M1

Rotherham ○

14 ○
SHEFFIELD

M18

DERBYSHIRE

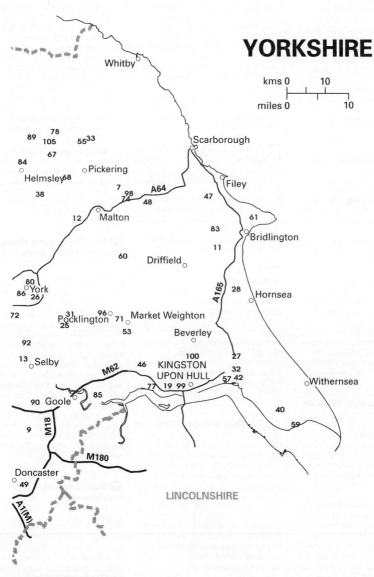

YORKSHIRE

Whitby

kms 0   10
miles 0   10

89   78
  105   55 33
  67

84

Scarborough

Pickering

Helmsley 68

38   7
   98   A64
  74   48

Filey

47

12   Malton

61

83

Bridlington

11

60   Driffield

80
86 York
  26

28   Hornsea

A165

72

31   96
Pocklington 71   Market Weighton
25   53

Beverley

92

13 Selby

M62

46

100

27

KINGSTON
UPON HULL

32

57 42

Withernsea

90 Goole

85

77   19 99

M18

9

40

59

M180

Doncaster

49

A1(M)

LINCOLNSHIRE

NOTTINGHAMSHIRE

DESCRIPTIONS OF GARDENS

❶ Acorn Cottage, 50 Church Street, Boston Spa ⊗
(Mrs C M Froggatt) *1m SE of Wetherby. Off A1 on A659 Church St opp Central Garage.* Small walled alpine garden of outstanding quality. Alpine plant collection est over 80yrs and two generations. Good range of small flowering bulbs and alpine flowers, Mar to May, attractively planted in local limestone formations. TEAS. *Adm £2, chd 50p. Suns, Wed 3, 6, 10 Apr (10-5). Private visits welcome by appt Mar & Apr, coaches permitted. Tel 01937 842519*

❷ Bankfield, 4 Queens Road, Huddersfield ⊗⊕
(Norma & Mike Hardy) *½m N of Huddersfield. From Huddersfield ring rd follow A629 to Halifax for ½m. Cross T-lights at Blacker Rd, turn R after 100yds. From M62, turn S at junction 24 to Huddersfield on A629. After ¾m pass 30mph sign, turn L after 200yds.* Substantial cottage garden has evolved from neglected Victorian town garden. Recently expanded to ¾-acre, contains a wide range of unusual and rare perennials, many unexpected this high in the Pennines and of interest to plant collectors. Rambling paths, informal beds, pond, gazebo, conifer area, terraced beds around lawned areas, large tree sculpture. Home-made TEAS. *Combined with **Cobwebs** Adm £2.50. Sun 26 June (11-5)*

❸ Barley Mow, Moor Monkton ⊗⊗⊕
(Dr & Mrs M Ashford) *5m NW of York. Off A59.* This plant enthusiasts ¾-acre garden has wide range of interesting plants both ornamental and edible. Garden peaks in late summer with vivid herbaceous borders and bold subtropical planting. Other features incl trellis draped with colourful climbers; formally trained apples and pears; pond, greenhouses, vegetable garden and wide range of less usual fruit. Featured in '25 Beautiful Gardens' 2004. Home-made TEAS in aid of Moor Monkton & Hessay LEP. *Adm £2, chd free. Sun 14 Aug (11-6)*

❹ Beacon Hill House, Langbar, Nr Ilkley ⊗⊕
(Mr & Mrs D H Boyle) *4m NW of Ilkley. 1¼m SE of A59 at Bolton Bridge.* Fairly large garden, facing S and sheltered by woodland, on the slopes of Beamsley Beacon at 900ft above sea-level. An old fernery and

big windbreak survive from original Victorian garden. Today, features of particular interest are early flowering rhododendrons in spring, and enormous climbing and rambling roses in July. Some unusual flowering trees and shrubs, several mixed borders, 2 ponds, which attract wildlife, small kitchen garden and cool greenhouse. Difficult for wheelchairs. Featured in 'Yorkshire Today' 2004. Home-made TEAS. *Adm £2.50, chd under 7 free, concessions £2 (share to Riding for the Disabled). Wed 11 May (2-6.30). Private visits welcome by appt. Tel 01943 607544*

❺ Beamsley Hall, Bolton Abbey, nr Skipton ⟨&⟩⊕
(The Duke & Duchess of Devonshire) *5m E of Skipton. Beamsley. On A59 at Bolton Abbey.* 6-acre traditional English garden with new plantings; incl extensive herbaceous border and kitchen garden. Minor restrictions for wheelchairs. Home-made TEAS. *Adm £3, chd under 15 free, concessions £2. Sun 26 June (1.30-5)*

❻ Birstwith Hall, High Birstwith, Nr Harrogate ⊕
(Sir James & Lady Aykroyd) *5m NW of Harrogate. Between Hampsthwaite & Birstwith villages, close to A59 Harrogate/Skipton rd.* Large 8-acre garden nestling in secluded Yorkshire dale with newly planted formal garden and ornamental orchard, extensive lawns, picturesque stream, large pond and Victorian greenhouse. Home-made TEAS. *Adm £3, chd free. Sun 19 June (2-5)*

❼ Blackbird Cottage, Scampston ⟨&⟩⊕
(Mrs Hazel Hoad) *5m E of Malton. Off A64 to Scarborough through Rillington, turn L signed Scampston only. Follow signs.* ⅓-acre plantswoman's garden made from scratch since 1986. Great wealth of interesting plants, with shrub and herbaceous border. Alpines a speciality. Please visit throughout the day to ease pressure on small but inspirational garden. TEAS in aid of St Peter's Church, Scampston. *Adm £2. Sun 15 May (10-5)*

❽ Bolton Percy Gardens
5m E of Tadcaster. 10m SW of York. From W follow Bolton Percy signs from Tadcaster, no R turn off A64. Light lunches and TEAS at Bolton Percy Parish Room available from 12.30, in aid of All Saints Church. *Combined adm £3.50, chd free. Sun 29 May (12.30-5)*

Bolton Percy Cemetery ⊗⊕ NCCPG
(Bolton Percy All Saints) An opportunity to meet Roger Brook who gardens an acre of old village churchyard where garden plants are naturalised. Beautiful 15th century church with acclaimed millennium window. Plants sale incl Dicentras from National Collection. Limited wheelchair access. Featured in 'The Times', 2003. Light refreshments and TEAS in aid of Bolton Percy Church. *Adm £1.50, chd free. Private visits welcome by appt, guided tours for groups of 20 or more. Tel 01759 319156*

Windy Ridge ⊗⊕ (Mr & Mrs J S Giles) *Marsh Lane.* Natural cottage style garden sloping down to the Ings, greatly influenced by Margery Fish. Paths meander through plantings of wild and unusual hardy plants.

❾ NEW Bridge Farm House, Long Lane, Great Heck, Goole ⟨&⟩⊗⊕
(Barbara & Richard Ferrari) *6m S of Selby. 3m N of M62 (J34) A19 turn E at roundabout to Snaith. Take 2nd R turn to Great Heck. House 1st on L, park in adjacent field.* Large garden with some mature trees under extensive redevelopment by previous owners of The Cottage, Kellington. Long double herbaceous borders backed by newly planted hedges. Plantsman's collection of perennials, hardy and half-hardy shrubs, bulbs and plants in pots. Pond, developing small woodland area, spring interest borders and named varieties of snowdrops and hellebores. TEAS. *Adm £2, chd 50p. Wed 23 Feb (12-3); Sun 4 Sept (11-4). Private visits welcome by appt. Tel 01977 661277*

❿ Brookfield, Jew Lane, Oxenhope ⊗⊕
(Dr & Mrs R L Belsey) *5m SW of Keighley. Take A629 towards Halifax. Fork R onto A6033 towards Haworth. Follow signs to Oxenhope. Turn L at Xrds in village. 200yds after PO fork R, Jew Lane.* 1-acre, intimate garden, incl large pond with island and mallards. Many varieties of candelabra primulas and floridaes, azaleas, rhododendrons. Unusual trees and shrubs, screes, greenhouse and conservatory. New series of island beds. Home-made TEAS. *Adm £2.50, chd free. Sun 26 (1-5), Wed 29 June (1-6). Private visits welcome by appt. Tel 01535 643070*

⑪ ◆ Burton Agnes Hall, Driffield
&⬜❀

(Mrs S Cunliffe-Lister) *Between Driffield & Bridlington. Burton Agnes is on A614.* 8 acres. Lawns with clipped yew and fountains; woodland gardens and walled garden containing potager; herbaceous and mixed borders; maze with thyme garden; jungle garden; campanula collection garden and coloured gardens containing giant games boards. Collections of hardy geraniums, clematis, penstemons and many unusual perennials. Light refreshments and TEAS. *House and garden adm £5.50, garden only £2.75, chd £1.30, concessions £2.50.* **For NGS:** *Sat, Sun 11, 12 June (11-5). Tel 01262 490324*

⑫ ◆ Castle Howard, nr York
&⬜❀

(Castle Howard Estate Ltd) *15m NE of York, 6m W of Malton. Off the A64.* Partially suitable for wheelchairs. Formal grounds laid out from C18 to present, incl fountains, lakes, cascades and waterfalls. Woodland garden, Ray Wood, has collection of rhododendron species and hybrids amounting to 800 varieties. Notable collection of acers, nothofagus, arbutus, styrax, magnolia and conifers. Formal rose gardens incl old, China and Bourbon roses, hybrid teas and floribunda. New plant centre, offering plants grown on the estate. Featured in 'Daily Telegraph'; 'Yorkshire Life' 2004. Light refreshments and TEAS. *House and garden adm £9.50, chd £6.50, concession £8.50. Garden & grounds £6.50, chd £4.50, concession £6. Daily 1 Mar to 6 Nov (10-4.30). Tel 01653 648333 www.castlehoward.co.uk*

⑬ Cawood Gardens, Cawood
5m N of Selby. On B1223 5m NW of Selby & 7m SE of Tadcaster. Between York & A1 on B1222. 4 gardens in attractive riverside village. Village maps given at all gardens. Home-made TEAS in aid of Selby Animal Sanctuary, at 9 Anson Grove; All Saints Church & Martin House Childrens Hospice, at Ash Lea. *Combined adm £4, chd free. Sun 10 July (12-5)*

9 Anson Grove ⬜❀ (Tony & Brenda Finnigan) Small orientally influenced garden with winding paths and raised areas; 4 pools, water features, mosaics and over 30 grasses. Contemplate in the Zen garden or sit in the Pagoda to enjoy the tranquility. Crafts.

Ash Lea &⬜ (Michael & Josephine Welbourn) Shrubs and

fernery lead to colourful formal borders, in contrast to a relaxed atmosphere by a clear pool. Bridge or woodland walk lead to a dining area and traditional vegetable garden edged in clipped box.

37 Broad Lane ⬜❀ (Rod & Margaret Carter) ⅔-acre atmospheric garden full of enchantment. Follow winding paths through areas in sunlight and shade which incorporate many different design features using natural materials set amongst lovely plantings of extensive variety. Dry, stream bed, scree slope, ponds and small pools and herb bed.

21 Great Close ⬜❀ (David & Judy Jones) Gravelled front garden leads to the contrasting colourful flower arranger's garden. New vegetable garden, extended borders and new water feature. Stream, pools, summerhouse and terrace with exotic planting.

⑭ NEW 72 Church Street, Oughtibridge ⬜

(Linda & Peter Stewart) *6m N of Sheffield. M1 (J36) A61 (Sheffield). Turn R at Norfolk Arms PH. In Oughtibridge follow one-way system turning L immed after zebra crossing.* Wildlife friendly ⅓-acre garden on N-facing slope. Informal beds providing yr-long interest have mixed plantings of trees, shrubs, phormiums, bamboos, grasses, ferns, bulbs and perennials which lead to a natural stream with a backdrop of native woodland. Home-made TEAS. *Adm £2, chd free. Sun 3 July; Mon 29 Aug (2-5). Private visits welcome by appt. Tel 0114 286 3847*

⑮ Cleaves House, Thirlby
&⬜❀

(Margaret & Tony May) *3m NE of Thirsk. From A170 in Sutton under Whitestone Cliff take turning signed Felixkirk. Almost immed take rd R signed Thirlby.* Large 2-acre garden on sloping site with beautiful views. Bold, interesting planting with many old-fashioned roses, shrubs, trees, pond and bog area. Enthusiastically gardened and planted since 1991. Home-made TEAS in aid of Teesside & Scarborough Hospices. **Day & Evening Opening** £3, chd free, wine, *Weds 1, 8 June (2-4.30) (7-9). Private visits welcome by appt . No access for coaches. Cleaves House Thirlby YO7 2DQ*

⑯ NEW Cobwebs, 24 Lavender Court, Netherton ⬜❀

(Roxanne & Nick Walker) *2½m SW of Huddersfield. M62, J25 or J23 to Huddersfield. From ring road take A616 (Sheffield), after 3rd set of T-lights take B6108 towards Meltham. In Netherton village turn L at chemist then 2nd R (Coppice Drive).* Narrow access past gravelled area with grasses and ferns leads to small SW-facing wildlife-friendly garden. Two ponds and an abundance of shrubs and perennials, layer planted, jostle to create a tapestry of colour and textured foliage with unusual plant combinations. Containers with Mediterranean planting. TEAS. *Adm £1.50. Combined with Bankfield Adm £2.50. Sun 26 June (11-5)*

⑰ Cold Cotes, Cold Cotes Road, Nr Kettlesing, Harrogate ⬜❀

(Penny Jones, Ed Loft, Doreen Russell) *7m W of Harrogate. Off A59. After Black Bull public house turn R to Menwith Hill/Darley.* Large peaceful garden set in rural landscape developed since mid-1990s with expansive views to White Horse and Hambleton Hills. Series of discreet gardens, formal and informal water, streamside walk, woodland glade and large sweeping herbaceous borders (at their height in Aug and Sept) influenced by designer Piet Oudolf. Accommodation. Featured in 'The English Garden' & 'Yorkshire Life' 2004. Home-made TEAS in aid of Christ Church Community Centre, Darley. *Adm £2, chd 50p. Suns 19 June; 4 Sept (1-5). Private visits welcome by appt, 19 June to 4 Sept for groups of 10+. Tel 01423 770937 www.coldcotes.com*

⑱ ◆ Constable Burton Hall Gardens, nr Leyburn &⬜❀

(Mr Charles Wyvill) *3m E of Leyburn. Constable Burton Village. On A684, 6m W of A1.* Large romantic garden with terraced woodland walks. Garden trails, shrubs, roses and water garden. Display of daffodils and over 5000 tulips planted annually amongst extensive borders. Fine John Carr house (not open) set in splendour of Wensleydale countryside. *Adm £3, chd 50p, concessions £2.50. Daily 19 Mar to 16 Oct (9-6). Tel 01677 450361 www.constableburtongardens.co.uk*

⑲ The Court, Humber Road, North Ferriby &⬜❀

(Guy & Liz Slater) *7m W of Hull. Travelling E on A63 towards Hull, follow sign for N Ferriby after large T-lights at Melton. Through village to*

*Xrds with war memorial, turn R &
follow rd to T-junction with Humber
Rd. Turm L & immed R into
unmarked cul-de-sac, last house on
LH-side.* Restful and secluded,
informal garden with yr-round
interest. Hidden seating areas and
summerhouses, small pond and
waterfall. ⅔-acre garden surrounded
by trees contains laburnum and
wisteria tunnel which leads to well-
planted shady woodland area, around
tennis court. Many interesting
features, courtyards and a 'pretty
potty patio'. Home-made TEAS. *Adm
£2, chd free. Sun 15 May (1-5).
Private visits welcome by appt.
Tel 01482 633609*

**㉑ Croft Cottage, Green
Hammerton** ⌘
(Alistair & Angela Taylor) *6m E of
Knaresborough. 3m E of A1M
adjacent to A59. Entrance through
orchard off Harrogate rd.* Secluded ½-
acre cottage garden divided into a
number of 'garden rooms'.
Conservatory, clipped yew, old brick,
cobbles and pavers used for formal
areas leading to water feature, mixed
borders and orchard with wild
flowers. Home-made TEAS. *Adm £2.
Combined with* **Whixley Gardens** *Adm
£4.50, chd free. Mon 30 May (12-5).
Private visits welcome by appt.
Tel 01423 330330 a.b.t@btinternet.
com*

**㉑ NEW Cruckhouse Farm, Lower
Norwood Road, Norwood, nr Otley**
⌘
(Miles & Julie Gill) *6m W of
Harrogate. Between Otley & A59 off
B6451. After Farnley turn L before
Norwood signed Dob Park (narrow
rd). Car park in field adjacent to
house.* Within this 20-acre
smallholding a series of sloping
gardens incl orchard, vegetable
parterre, herbaceous border, water
garden, herb knot, rose trellis, loggia
and rockery. Double predominately
white-flowering shrub borders lead to
wildlife ponds all surrounded by
ancient wild flower meadows with
superb views over the Washburn
valley. Home-made TEAS. *Adm £2.
Suns 29 May; 4 Sept (2-5)*

**㉒ Dacre Banks Gardens,
Nidderdale**
*4m SE of Pateley Bridge, 10m NW
of Harrogate. On B6451. Limited
wheelchair access. Parking at each
garden.* Lovely walk between gardens
along Nidderdale valley. Picnic area
at Yorke House. Map provided.
Home-made TEAS at Low Hall &
Yorke House. *Combined adm £4.50,
chd free. Sun 10 July (11-5)*

Low Hall ⌘ (Mrs P A Holliday)
Romantic walled garden on
different levels around a C17
family home (not open) with
shrubs, climbing roses, tender
plants, herbaceous borders and
pond garden. Mature yews and
beech hedges.

Orchard House ⌘⌘ (Mr & Mrs J
T Spain) 2 acres of simple natural
uncontrived garden blending into
beautiful surrounding countryside
and providing a haven for
wildlife. Shrub and perennial
plantings from shade to full sun
together with productive fruit
and vegetables. *Private visits
welcome by appt, May to Aug
incl. Coaches permitted.
Tel 01423 780502*

Stud Cottage, Oak Lane (Mr &
Mrs J M Kent) ½-acre planted to
complement C18 cottage (not
open). Herbaceous, rockery,
kitchen garden and orchard with
small fish pond. Patio with
seating area and water feature
added, with large parasol. *Private
visits welcome by appt, coaches
permitted. Tel 01423 780495*

Yorke House ⌘⌘ (Mr Anthony
& Mrs Pat Hutchinson) (See
separate entry). *Private visits
welcome by appt, June July &
August. Coaches permitted.
Tel 01423 780456
hutchinson@yorkehouse.co.uk*

㉓ Darley Gardens, nr Harrogate
*6m W of Harrogate. Off A59. Take
B6451 to Pateley Bridge. Turn R at
Wellington Inn into Darley. Ample
good parking in adjacent field at
Graylings.* . Winner RHS Gold Medal
National Britain in Bloom large
village category, 2003; Gold Medal
Entente Forale 2004. Home-made
TEAS available at both gardens.
*Combined adm £3.50, chd 50p. Suns
19 June; 17 July (12-5)*

Graylings, Niddside ⌘⌘⌘ (Phil
& Paddy Mayes) *Bottom of
Station Rd.* 1-acre tranquil rural
garden bordered by farmland on
banks of R Nidd designed and
maintained by owners since
1995. Immaculate lawns meander
through borders planted for yr-
round interest. Forest and
ornamental trees, shrubs, roses,
'hot' borders and many
containers planted with half-
hardy perennials. Greenhouses,
small courtyard and canal, both
with fountains. *Private visits
welcome by appt, groups of 10+.
Coaches permitted. Tel 01423
781531 paddymayes@darley93.
freeserve.co.uk*

The Old Vicarage ⌘⌘ (Judi &
Steve Smith) *Next to Christ
Church.* ¾-acre garden, owner
made and maintained since 1996.
Gravel paths set with decorative
cobbles wind between large
herbaceous island beds through
extensive rustic archways and
pergolas creating smaller garden
rooms all enclosed by dry stone
walls. Small greenhouse alpines,
herbs, grasses, annuals, roses,
clematis and colourful perennials.
Yorkshire in Bloom trophy
winner for last 5 yrs. *Private
visits welcome by appt.
Tel 01423 780526
judi@darley33.freeserve.co.uk*

**㉔ Deepdale, Deepdale Lane,
Boston Spa** ⌘⌘⌘
(Mr & Mrs F Umpleby) *1m SE of
Wetherby. Off A1. Take A659 turn L
after ½m Deepdale Lane.*
Inspirational ¾-acre garden offering
yr-round interest. Mixed planting, 2
ponds, one with bridge the other with
purpose made stream. Patio with
unusual potted plants, pergola and
gazebo. Restful garden in country
surroundings. *Private visits welcome
by appt, groups & coaches welcome
Apr to June/July. Tel 01937 842227*

**㉕ Denwell, 2 Derwent Park,
Wheldrake** ⌘⌘⌘
(Jill & Peter Tait) *4m S of York, 10m
N of Selby. Turn off A19 at Crockey
Hill into village. Derwent Park is 2nd
turning L off Church Lane
(Thorganby Rd).* Mature garden
created over 16yrs by enthusiastic
plant collecting owners (125
clematis). Mixed shrub and
herbaceous borders, hosta and fern
border. Patio, pots and tubs, pond
with rockery, water feature and small
gravel garden. TEAS. *Adm £2, chd
free. Suns 22 May; 26 June; Wed 3
Aug (1-5). Private visits welcome by
appt . Coaches permitted. Tel 01904
448884*

**㉖ Derwent House, 59
Osbaldwick Village, Osbaldwick**
⌘⌘
(Dr & Mrs D G Lethem) *2m E of
York. On village green at
Osbaldwick off A1079.* ¾-acre,
attractive village garden extended in
1984 to provide new walled garden
with yew hedges and box parterres.
Conservatories, terraces, rose garden,
hardy geraniums and pelargoniums.
Double herbaceous borders leading to
meadow with plantings of eucalyptus.
TEAS. *Adm £2, chd free. Sun 12 June
(1.30-5). Private visits welcome by
appt. Tel 01904 410847
davidlethem@tiscali.co.uk*

㉗ Dowthorpe Hall, Skirlaugh &
(Mr & Mrs J Holtby) *6m N of Hull, 8m E of Beverley. On the A165 Hull to Bridlington Rd halfway between Coniston & Skirlaugh on the RH-side travelling N. Signed at the bottom of drive which has white railings.* 3½ acres owned by professional garden designer. Kitchen garden, orchard, Mediterranean-style planting, small gravel garden and main lawn area surrounded by shrubs, beautiful mature trees and sumptuous herbaceous borders. Pond with island. *Adm £3, chd under 16 free. Sun 12 June (11-5). Private visits welcome by appt. Tel 01964 562235 john.holtby@farming.co.uk*

㉘ NEW Dunnington Manor, Dunnington, nr Driffield & ✿
(Marygold & Eric Baines) *12m N of Beverley. Take the Dunnington turn on the A165 between Brandsburton & Beeford. The house is 1st after the village sign. Parking directions willl be given.* Areas of different interest open up in 2 acres of traditional borders, lawns, hedges and orchard, surrounded by superb mature trees. Cream TEAS in aid of St Nicholas Church, Dunnington. *Adm £2, chd free. Suns 5, 12 June (2-5)*

㉙ 8 Dunstarn Lane, Adel, Leeds 16 &
(Mrs R Wainwright) *3m N of Leeds centre. From Leeds ring rd A6120 exit Adel, up Long Causeway. 4th junction R into Dunstarn Lane. 28 bus from Leeds centre stops nr gate.* 2 acres of long herbaceous and rose borders of exceptional variety. 60 varieties of delphiniums and wide range of July/August blooming plants giving magnificent display of summer colour. Large lawns for picnics. *Adm £2. Private visits welcome by appt. Tel 0113 267 3938*

㉚ East Wing, Thorp Arch Hall, Thorp Arch ✿ ⊕
(Fiona & Chris Royffe) *1m S of Wetherby. Take A659 into Boston Spa centre. Turn at HSBC over bridge to Thorp Arch, at end of Main St turn L into Thorp Arch Park & R over cattle grid.* ¾-acre surrounding the East Wing of C18 John Carr house (not open), being imaginatively developed. Inspiring garden arranged to link spaces and emphasize views. Courtyards, water features, potager, earth sculpture and dry garden. Dramatic combinations of plants, unusual bamboos and climbers. Photographic exhibition and small nursery. *Private visits welcome by appt, May to Sept, groups of 15+. Coaches permitted. Tel 01937*

843513 plantsbydesign@btinternet. com

㉛ Elvington Gardens, nr York
8m SE of York. From A1079, immed after leaving York's outer ring rd, turn S onto B1228 for Elvington. Delightful Yorkshire village set round a village green on the R Derwent. Light lunches and TEAS at Village Hall. *Combined adm £4, chd free. Sun 12 June (11-5)*

Brook House & ⊕ (Mr & Mrs C Bundy) Old established garden with fine trees. Kitchen garden and pond garden. Large mixed and shrub borders, spectacular climbing roses.

The Old Coach House & ⊕ (Simon & Toni Richardson) Delightful atmospheric owner-made 2-acre garden, most plants grown from cuttings. Trees, ponds and summerhouse.

Red House Farm & (Professor & Mrs E Macphail) Developing garden created from field 18yrs ago. Fine collection of hardy perennials, shrubs and roses. Courtyard with interesting plantings and ½-acre young wood.

㉜ Evergreens, 119 Main Road, Bilton &
(Phil & Brenda Brock) *5m E of Hull. Leave city by A165. Exit B1238.* Bungalow ½m on L nearly opp Asda. 1 acre with mosaics and sundials, tower, raised beds, rockeries and landscaped pond. Japanese garden, seaside garden, summerhouse, heather and mixed beds. Collection of dwarf conifers. 'Fun' items. Photographs showing development of garden. Featured in 'The Journal' 2003. *Adm £1.50, chd free. Private visits welcome by appt, incl group evening visits. Light buffet £3.25, full buffet £4.25 incl garden entry. Tel 01482 811365*

㉝ Fernwood, Cropton ⊕
(Dick & Jean Feaster) *4m NW of Pickering. From A170 turn at Wrelton signed Cropton.* 1-acre garden created by owners containing series of individual gardens, herbaceous borders, large collection of species and old roses, wide variety of interesting and unusual plants, with view of N Yorkshire moors beyond. Large stall of home propagated plants. Cream TEAS share to Village Hall. *Adm £2, chd free. Sun 3 July (1-5). Private visits welcome by appt. Tel 01751 417692*

㉞ Field Cottage, Littlethorpe Road, Littlethorpe, nr Ripon & ✿
(Richard & Liz Tite) *1m SE of Ripon. Off A61 Ripon bypass follow signs to Littlethorpe continue straight on at church, round sharp LH-bend 250yds on LH-side by derestriction sign.* 1-acre plantsman's garden with walled garden and small pond, raised sleeper beds and gravel garden. Perennials incl late flowering autumn bed, vegetable plot, Victorian style greenhouse with pelargoniums and extensive range of unusual and tender plants in containers. TEAS. *Adm £2.50. Private visits welcome by appt, groups of 10+. Tel 01765 690996 liz.tite@talk21.com*

㉟ The Grange, Carla Beck Lane, Carleton & ✿ ⊕
(Mr & Mrs R N Wooler) *1½m SW of Skipton. Turn off A56 (Skipton-Clitheroe) into Carleton. Keep L at Swan PH, continue through to end of village & turn R into Carla Beck Lane. From Skipton town centre follow A6131. Turn R to Carleton.* Large walled mid C19 garden with original ha-ha and many mature, unusual trees from different continents and developing woodland garden. Lovely sweeping herbaceous border, shrubs, ornamental pools, raised vegetable beds and greenhouse in full use, reached by long rose and clematis walk. Cream TEAS. *Adm £2.50, chd free. Weds 8, 22 June (1.30-5)*

㊱ NEW Great Ouseburn Gardens
13m NW of York. Off B6265. 4m E of A1 (M) J47 (A59). Before Green Hammerton take B6265 towards Boroughbridge. Follow signs to Great Ouseburn. Car parking at each garden, please use field. Home-made TEAS. *Combined adm £3, chd free. Sun 19 June (2-5)*

NEW Cedar Croft, Main Street & ✿ (Jane & Nick Butler) ½-acre garden created by owners over last 25yrs on S side of listed Georgian house (not open) with mature trees and lovely views over Ousebeck towards Whixley Moor. 3 large herbaceous, mixed shrub and rose borders provide foliage interest and colour throughout the yr. Summerhouse, terrace with pots and small parterre to N side.

NEW Tinkers Hollow, Church Field Lane & ✿ ⊕ (Heather & Eric Sugden) Originally a permanent pasture paddock. Tinkers Hollow is just over 1 acre in area, long and narrow in shape (175 x 35 yds). Beginning in 1978, the now hidden gardens and connecting walks have through time and nature transformed the former open space. Hopefully today's layout and diverse features will appeal to a wide range of gardener taste and are left undescribed for first time visitors to explore.

㉗ Greencroft, Pottery Lane, Littlethorpe, nr Ripon ⌖
(Mr & Mrs David Walden) *1m SE of Ripon. Off A61 Ripon bypass, follow signs to Littlethorpe. Turn R at church to Bishop Monkton for 1½m. On RH-side after Littlethorpe Pottery.* ½-acre informal garden made and built by owners. Special ornamental features incl gazebo, temple, pavilion, stone wall with mullions, pergola and formal pool. Long herbaceous borders lead to circular enclosed garden planted with late flowering perennials, annuals and exotics. Log cabin with shingle roof built alongside large pond. Limited wheelchair access. Home-made TEAS. *Adm £2. Combined with* **Woodlands** *£3. Sun 19 June (12.30-5.30). Private visits welcome by appt. Tel 01765 602487*

㉘ Grimston Manor Farm, Grimston, Gilling East ♿✿⌖
(Richard & Heather Kelsey) *7m S of Helmsley, 17m N of York. York - Helmsley rd B1363. 1m S of Gilling East & 3m N of Brandsby. Turn off at Grimston.* ¾-acre garden, mostly 40yrs old. Intricate design, profusely planted with wide collection of herbaceous plants, trees and shrubs, incorporating fine country views and

old farm buildings. A well-seated garden with millennium fountain. TEAS. *Adm £2, chd free. Sun 3, Thur 7 July (1.30-5.30)*

㉙ Hallcroft Hall, Ilkley Road, Addingham ♿⌖
(Brian & Linda Burrows) *2m W of Ilkley. Between Ilkley & Addingham on Ilkley Rd adjacent to junction of A65 & B6160.* 3-acre garden restored and developed over 18yrs surrounding wisteria clad Georgian house (not open). Courtyard with fountain and conservatory, laburnum tunnel, small formal parterres, pool and summerhouse. Scented garden with stream and romantic gothic arches, wild flower area, new cutting garden and English roses. Home-made TEAS. *Adm £2.50, chd free (share to Riding for the Disabled & WSSR - Welsh Springer Spaniel Rescue). Sun 22 May (11-5)*

㉚ Hallgarth, Station Road, Ottringham ♿✿⌖
(Mr & Mrs John Hinchliffe) *10m E of Hull, 4½m W of Withernsea. Turn N in Ottringham on A1033 Hull to Withernsea Rd, towards Halsham. ¾m 1st L over former railway Xing.* Large informal garden of interesting corners hidden in Holderness countryside. Main garden developed from a plan (on display) of John Brookes. Wooded area with candelabra primulas, meconopses and giant echiums. Entrance and pond gardens, long walk border. Secluded patio, bulbs, grasses, roses. Featured in 'Amateur Gardening' 2004. Cream TEAS in aid of St Wilfrid's Church,

Ottringham. *Adm £2.50, chd free. Wed, Sun 11, 15 May (1.30-5). Private visits welcome by appt for groups. Tel 01964 622230 john.hinchliffe@tiscali.co.uk*

㉛ ♦ Harewood House, nr Leeds ♿⌖
(Harewood House Trust) *7m N of Leeds. On A61.* 160 acres of gardens within 1000 acres of 'Capability' Brown landscaped parkland. Elaborate Victorian terrace comprising box scrolls filled with seasonal bedding, enhanced by Italianate fountains and statues all framed by extensive flower borders. Charming informal walks through woodland gardens around 32 acre lake to walled vegetable garden. Cascade and picturesque rock garden with an array of exotic plants. Silver award, England National Awards, 2003. Light refreshments and TEAS in Courtyard Café. *House and garden adm £11, chd £6.50, OAP £9, garden only £8.25, chd £5.50, OAP £7.50. Daily 4 Feb to 4 Nov (10-6). Tel 01132 181010 www.harewood.org*

㊷ High Farm, Lime Tree Lane, Bilton ♿✿⌖
(Mr & Mrs G R Cooper) *5m E of Hull City Centre. Take A165 Brid Rd, turn onto B1238 to Bilton. Turn L opp church. High Farm is at bottom of Limetree Lane.* Large enchanting all-yr garden with distinctive design features, displaying extensive range of plants. Mature trees festooned with cascades of rose and clematis. Many contrasting seasonal sections unfolding with intricate tapestry of colours, shapes and textures, provided by outstanding collection of shrubs, ornamental grasses, succulents and rare herbaceous plants. Spectacular autumn garden. Picnic area in paddock, with car park. Featured in 'NFU Countryside', 'Dalesman' & 'Gardeners Weekly' 2004. Teas locally. *Adm £2.50, chd free. Suns 29 May; 26 June (1-5). Private visits welcome by appt, for groups of 10+. Tel 01482 811431*

㊸ [NEW] **Highfields, Manorstead, Skelmanthorpe** ⌖
(Julie & Tony Peckham) *8m SE of Huddersfield. M1 (J39) A636 towards Denby Dale. Turn R in Scissett village (B6116) to Skelmanthorpe. After 2nd Police Speed Check sign turn L (Barrowstead), continue to top of hill.* Overlooking open countryside this small garden, commenced in

DANGER
GIANT VENUS
FLY-TRAP

2000, shows creativity within metres rather than acres! Two ponds, gravel bed, box parterre with obelisk water feature, arbours, arches and vertical structures create small garden rooms and vistas. TEAS in aid of The Promised Land charity. *Adm £1.50, chd free. Combined opening with* **Lower Crawshaw** *Adm £3. Sun 22 May (2-5)*

❹❹ Hillbark, Church Lane, Bardsey 🌿👥

(Tim Gittins & Malcolm Simm) *4m SW of Wetherby. Turn W off A58 into Church Lane. The garden is on L before church. Car parking at village hall (Woodacre Lane).* 1-acre country garden, on open S-facing slope, started in 1987. Shrubs and perennials with interesting foliage, and some annuals, provide yr-round colour. Hidden arbours and surprising views amongst lively plantings. Descent to a number of interconnecting ponds and large natural pond with ducks and marginal planting. Woodland area, approached by bridges across stream gradually evolving. Some unusual garden ceramics. Featured in 'Yorkshire Ridings' 2004. TEAS. *Adm £2, chd 50p. Suns 15 May; 5, 26 June (11-5). Tel 01937 572065 www.hillbark.co.uk*

◆ Hodsock Priory Gardens, Blyth 👤🌿👥

See Nottinghamshire.

❹❺ Home Farm, Hawkhills, nr Easingwold 👤👥

(Sir Ben & Lady Gill) *10m N of York. A19 2m S of Easingwold. 1st L after roundabout, signed Hawkhills.* 1-acre garden made from farmland over the last 8yrs, containing a great variety of unusual plants in mixed borders, interesting flowers and foliage. Small walled white garden. Cream TEAS. *Adm £2.50, chd free. Sun 5 June (1.30-5). Private visits welcome by appt June only, groups of 5 or more. Coaches permitted. Tel 01347 821344*

❹❻ Hotham Hall, Hotham 👤

(Stephen & Carolyn Martin) *15m W of Hull. Nr North Cave, junction 38 of M62 turn towards North Cave, follow signs for Hotham.* C18 Grade II house (not open), stable block and clock tower in mature parkland setting with established gardens. Lake with bridge over to newly planted island (arboretum). Garden with Victorian pond and mixed borders. Selection of spring flowering bulbs. TEAS in aid of local charity. *Adm £2.50, chd free. Sun 17 Apr (1-4).*

Private visits welcome by appt. Tel 01430 422054 themartins@hotham1745. freeserve.co.uk

❹❼ Hunmanby Grange, Wold Newton 👤🌿👥

(Tom & Gill Mellor) *12½m SE of Scarborough. Hunmanby Grange is a farm between Wold Newton & Hunmanby on the rd from Burton Fleming to Fordon.* 3-acre garden created from exposed open field, on top of Yorkshire Wolds nr coast. Hedges and fences now provide shelter from wind making series of gardens with yr-round interest and seasonal highlights. Featured in 'The Dalesman', 'Gardens Monthly' 2004. Home-made TEAS in aid of St Cuthbert's Church, Burton Fleming. *Adm £2.50. Suns 1 May; 5 June; 3 July (11-5); Weds, 6 Apr to 28 Sept (1-5) . Combined £3 with* **Jacksons Wold** *Sun 5 June . Private visits welcome by appt. Tel 01723 891636 www.hunmanbygrange. co.uk*

❹❽ Jacksons Wold, Sherburn 👤🌿👥

(Mr & Mrs Richard Cundall) *11m E of Malton, 10m SW of Scarborough. A64 in Sherburn. T-lights take Weatherthorpe Rd. R fork to Hesterton Wold.* 2-acre garden with stunning views of the Vale of Pickering. Walled garden with mixed borders, numerous old shrub roses underplanted with unusual perennials. Woodland paths lead to further shrub and perennial borders. Lime avenue with wild flower meadow. Traditional vegetable garden with roses, flowers and box edging framed by Victorian greenhouse. Adjoining nursery. Featured in 'The English Garden' magazine 2004. Cream TEAS in aid of St Hilda's Church, Sherburn. *Adm £2.50, chd free. Sun 26 June (11-5). Combined £3 with* **Hunmanby Grange** *Sun 5 June . Private visits welcome by appt, Tues May & June (1-5). Tel 01944 710335*

❹❾ Jasmine House, 145 The Grove, Wheatley Hills, Doncaster 🌿👥

(Mr & Mrs R J Breame) *1m E of Doncaster Royal Infirmary. Off A18. Turn R into Chestnut Ave (Motor Save on corner).* Small plantsman's garden with wealth of unusual plants, many grown from seed by owner. Garden rooms with water features, Japanese garden, climbers, shrubs, alpine troughs and bonsai. Patio area with pots and baskets full of half hardy and tender plants, all within a

typically narrow town garden. Doncaster in Bloom Gold Awards - Grassless & Environmental 2004. TEAS. *Adm £1.50, chd free (share to Bluebell Wood Children's Hospice). Sun 5 June (1-5). Private visits welcome by appt. Tel 01302 361470*

❺⓿ Kelberdale, Wetherby Road, Knaresborough 🌿👥

(Stan & Chris Abbott) *1m from Knaresborough. On B6164 Wetherby rd. House on L immed after new ring rd (A658) roundabout.* Owner-made and maintained, inspirational medium-sized plantsman's garden with river views. Full of yr-round interest with large herbaceous border, conifer and colour beds. Alpines and pond. Vegetable and wild garden with wildlife pond. Featured in 'Gardening Which' top 30 gardens & runner up 'The Sunday Times' Garden of the Year 2004. TEAS in aid of Joshua's Ambulance Appeal. *Adm £2.50. Suns 15 May; 12 June (11-5). Private visits welcome by appt. Tel 01423 862140 chris@kelberdale.fsnet.co.uk*

❺❶ ◆ Land Farm, Colden, nr Hebden Bridge 🌿👥

(Mr J Williams) *8m W of Halifax. From Halifax at Hebden Bridge go through 2 sets T-lights. Take turning circle to Heptonstall. Follow signs to Colden. After 2¾m turn R at 'no thru' rd, follow signs to garden.* 4 acres incl alpine, herbaceous, formal and newly developing woodland garden. Elevation 1000ft N-facing. C17 house (not open). Art Gallery. Featured in 'Open Country', BBC Radio 4, 2003. 'The Garden' 2004. *Adm £3, chd free. Weekends & Bank Hols May to end Aug (10-5). Parties welcome evenings by prior arrangement. Tel 01422 842260*

❺❷ Ling Beeches, Ling Lane, Scarcroft 👤🌿👥

(Mrs Arnold Rakusen) *7m NE of Leeds. A58 mid-way between Leeds & Wetherby. At Scarcroft turn W into Ling Lane, signed to Wike on brow of hill. Garden ½m on R.* 2-acre enchanting woodland garden designed by owner. Emphasis on labour-saving planting. Unusual trees and shrubs, ericaceous plants, some species roses, conifers, ferns and interesting climbers. Several garden seats. Interesting composting system. Featured in 'The Garden', 2003. Home-made TEAS. *Adm £2.50. Sun 24 Apr (2-5). Private visits welcome by appt. Tel 0113 289 2450*

53 Londesborough Cross, Shiptonthorpe ⬥⬥⬥

(Mr & Mrs J W Medd) *2m From Market Weighton, 5m from Pocklington. A1079 Hull to York rd . Turn off in Shiptonthorpe down the side of church. Londesborough Cross is at bottom of Town St.* In 20yrs railway goods yard transformed by owners into delightful garden with ponds and other water features, bog area, island beds, large herbaceous borders, screes and rock garden. Pergola and arches planted with roses and clematis and collection of hostas. New woodland garden with large collection of hardy ferns, many rare. Good collection of woodland plants. Cream TEAS in aid of British Heart Foundation (Weds), Shiptonthorpe Church & Chapel (Suns). *Adm £2.50, chd free. Weds, 16 Mar to 8 June; 31 Aug; 7 Sept (1-4). Suns 3, 24 Apr; 8, 29 May; 28 Aug. Private visits welcome by appt. Tel 01430 873908 sylvia.medd@btopenworld.com*

54 Long Marston Hall, Tockwith Road, Long Marston ⬥⬥⬥

(Alison Agnew & Brian Yule) *7m W of York. On B1224 between York & Wetherby turn N at Xrds towards Tockwith.* 1-acre garden surrounding C16-C18 house (not open). Small orchard, walled flower gardens, formal pool, terrace with raised beds, vegetable garden and games lawn. Major interest is that most of the garden was re-landscaped and planted only 7yrs ago and has established quickly. Some interesting trees but the focus is on large borders containing a range of perennials and shrubs (more than 700) chosen to exploit the sandy loam soils. Home-made TEAS in aid of Long Marston Church. *Adm £2. Sat, Sun 25, 26 June (11-6).* **Evening Opening** *£2.50, wine, Sat 9 July (6-8)*

55 Low Askew, Cropton ⬥

(Mr & Mrs Martin Dawson-Brown) *5m W of Pickering. Signed to Cropton from A170. Between the villages of Cropton & Lastingham.* Situated in the beautiful valley of the R Seven, this sloping garden with stream merges gently into the landscape beyond. Thoughtful planting has produced impact throughout the yr. Old-fashioned pelargoniums and auriculas for sale. Home-made TEAS. *Adm £2.50, chd free. Wed 11 May (2-6)*

56 Lower Crawshaw, Emley, nr Denby Dale ⬥⬥

(Mr & Mrs Neil Hudson) *8m E of Huddersfield. From Huddersfield*

turn R to Emley off A642 (Paul Lane). M1 junction 39 (A636) direction Denby Dale, 1m after Bretton roundabout turn R to Emley, ½m beyond Emley village turn R (Stringer House Lane) continue for ¾m. 3-acre developing country garden created over past 9yrs surrounding C17 farmhouse (not open). 2 large ponds and natural stream with lush planting of moisture-loving plants; courtyard; enclosed rose garden with double borders, topiary, perennials, shrubs, wilderness garden and orchard; potager with raised beds set within old barn framework. Limited wheelchair access. Home-made TEAS in aid of Kirkwood Hospice. *Adm £2.50, chd free. Combined with* **Highfields** *£3. Sun 22 May (12-5). Private visits welcome by appt May, June, July for groups of 10-30. No coaches. Tel 01924 840980*

57 Lullaby, 22 Barra Close, Hull ⬥⬥⬥

(Michael & Linda Whitton) *From A165 (Holderness Rd), take Salthouse Rd towards Sutton Village. Turn R into Dunvegan Rd, R into Barra Close & R again.* Small peaceful retreat with planting to attract wildlife. Architectural features incl obelisks, summerhouse, courtyard garden, pergolas, small woodland walk. Colourful herbaceous borders, shrubs and unusual plants. New water feature, pond with rill. Cream TEAS. *Adm £1.50, chd free. Suns 5 June; 28 Aug (2-5). Private visits welcome by appt. Tel 01482 783517 lindamwhitt@aol.com*

58 Maidens Folly, Youlton, nr Easingwold ⬥⬥⬥

(Mr & Mrs Henry Dean) *11m NW of York. 2m E of Aldwark tollbridge. 4m SW of Easingwold. Off A19 to Tollerton follow Helperby rd, turn L at Alne Xrds. Car parking in adjacent paddock.* Large cottage garden comprising 4 different themes. Double herbaceous borders bounded by beech hedges and divided by stone pathway; enclosed white garden with central feature inspired by Gertrude Jekyll surrounded by flower beds, arches and trellis festooned with climbers; walled area with lavender walk, rose and penstemon border; attractive courtyard garden. Home-made TEAS in aid of Aldwark Church. *Adm £2.50. Sun 3 July (11.30-5.30). Private visits welcome by appt. Tel 01347 838289*

59 Makin's Cottage, Patrington ⬥⬥

(Roy & Elaine O'Brien) *15m E of Hull. Coming E on A1033 take 1st R in Patrington (signed Caravan Park). After 300yds L at T-junction, white cottage 1st on R. Care with parking please.* ½-acre S-facing informal garden hidden behind pretty C18 cottage with open views to Humber Estuary. Paved/gravelled area with lots of pots, extensive herbaceous borders with old favourites and many less common plants, sunken herb garden, gravelled area with grasses, small pond and vegetable garden. Public toilets in village. TEAS. *Adm £2, chd free. Sun 26 June (1.30-5). Private visits welcome by appt June & July only. Tel 01964 630819 robpatrington@aol.com*

60 Manor Farm, Thixendale ⬥⬥⬥

(Charles & Gilda Brader) *10 m SE of Malton. Unclassified rd through Birdsall, ½m up hill, turn L at Xrds for Thixendale - 3m, 1st farm on R. 17m E of York, turn off A166 rd at the top of Garrowby Hill, follow signs for Thixendale, 4m turn into village, drive through to end, farm on L.* Created in the last 15yrs nestling in a frost pocket and wind tunnel! 1-acre garden featuring two pergolas and a traditional conservatory, courtyard, two alpine areas, one with large rocks, running water and ruined shed which stands by a small knot garden. Large lawns surrounded by mixed beds of interesting plants. Shaded area with many special hellebores and bulbs. The garden is continually changing and developing. Accommodation. Home-made TEAS in aid of Breast Cancer & St Leonard's Hospice. *Adm £2.50, chd 50p. Sun 17 July (10-6)*

61 Mansion Cottage, 8 Gillus Lane, Bempton ⬥

(Polly & Chris Myers) *2m NE of Bridlington. From Bridlington take B1255 to Flamborough. 1st L at T-lights, go up Bempton Lane, turn 1st R after houses then L at T-junction. Cross railway into Bempton, Gillus Lane is L fork at church.* Peaceful, secluded truly hidden garden with many different views. Herbaceous and shrub borders with wide variety of architectural planting. This variety is enhanced by water features, ponds, shady border, bog garden, scented border and patio, grasses, vegetable plot, pergola and climbers, decks and lawns, summerhouse and late-flowering tender perennial bed. Featured in 'The Journal' 2003. Light refreshments and TEAS. *Adm £2, chd free (share to St Michael's Church, Bempton). Sats, Suns 18, 19 June; 13, 14 Aug (10-4). Private visits welcome by appt, incl groups, end May to Sept. Tel 01262 851404*

62 Maspin House, Hillam Common Lane, Hillam 🅰🛇
(Howard & Susan Ferguson) *7m W of Selby. 4m E of A1 on A63. Turn R after leaving Monk Fryston signed Birkin, Beale, Kellington. L at T junction. House 1m on L.* 2-acre garden packed with interest and large variety of plants. Orchard with old roses; gravel garden, cottage garden, cutting garden; woodland, formal and informal water features; clipped hedges and grass walkway. TEAS in aid of Barkston Ash School. *Adm £2, chd free. Sun 12 June (2-6) www.maspin-house.co.uk*

63 Mayroyd Mill House, Mayroyd Lane, Hebden Bridge 🛇🌣 NCCPG
(Richard Easton & Steve Mackay) *At Hebden Bridge (A646) follow signs to Railway Station. Car parking at station.* Steep steps lead down to approx ½-acre S-facing designers' garden with bold herbaceous and ornamental grass plantings created for naturalistic effect peaking in late summer. Many rare and unusual plants; woodland shade; bog areas and riverbank walk. National Collection of astrantias. Featured in 'Gardens Illustrated' & 'The Garden' 2004. Home-made TEAS. *Adm £2, chd 50p. Sun 14 Aug (1-5.30). Private visits welcome by appt, June & Aug only, groups of 10+. Tel 01422 845818*

64 The Mews Cottage, 1 Brunswick Drive, Harrogate 🛇🌣
(Mrs Pat Clarke) *W of Harrogate town centre. From Cornwall Rd, N side of Valley Gardens, 1st R (Clarence Dr), 1st L (York Rd), 1st L (Brunswick Dr).* Small garden on sloping site of particular interest to hardy planters. Full of unusual and familiar plants but retaining a feeling of restfulness. Courtyard with trompe 'oeil and gravelled area enclosed by trellising provide sites for part of large collection of clematis. *Private visits welcome by appt. Tel 01423 566292 patriciamclarke@hotmail.com*

65 Millgate House, Millgate, Richmond 🛇
(Tim Culkin & Austin Lynch) *Centre of Richmond. House is located at bottom of Market Place opp Barclays Bank. Next to Halifax Building Soc.* E walled town garden overlooking R Swale. Although small, the garden is

full of character, enchantingly secluded with plants and shrubs. Foliage plants incl ferns and hostas. Old roses, interesting selection of clematis, small trees and shrubs. RHS associate garden. Immensely stylish, national award winning garden. Featured in '25 Beautiful Gardens' 2003; BBC 'Gardeners' World' magazine 2005. *Adm £2, chd £1. Day & Evening Opening Sun 19 June (8.30-8). Tel 01748 823571 www.millgatehouse.com*

66 NEW Morefield, 44 Springwood Road, nr Holmfirth 🛇
(Peter Broadbent) *5m S of Huddersfield. Halfway between New Mills & Holmfirth (A635). Turn down Springwood Rd opp Sycamore Inn PH.* 150 different cultivars of trees, rarely seen in the North, planted in this large garden over the last 40yrs make this a most unusual tree garden. Set within 20 acres of farmed parkland also planted with interesting trees which leads to a small wood containing examples of all British native trees. TEAS. *Adm £2, chd free. Sun 26 June (2-6)*

67 Nawton Tower Garden, Nawton 🅰🌣
(Douglas Ward Trust) *5m NE of Helmsley. From A170, between Helmsley & Nawton village, at Beadlam turn N 2½m to Nawton Tower.* Large garden; heathers, rhododendrons, azaleas, shrubs. Partially suitable for disabled. *Adm £1.50, chd 50p. Sat, Sun, Mon 28, 29, 30 May (2-6). Private visits welcome by appt May & early June. Tel 01439 771218*

68 Ness Hall, Nunnington 🅰
(Mr & Mrs D Murray Wells) *6m E of Helmsley, 22m N of York. From B1257 Helmsley-Malton rd turn L at Slingsby signed Kirkbymoorside, 3m to Ness.* Large walled garden, mixed and herbaceous borders, undergoing reconstruction; orchard with shrubs and climbing roses. Home-made TEAS in aid of Nunnington Church. *Adm £2.50. Sun, Wed 3, 6 Apr (2-5). Private visits welcome by appt. Tel 01439 748223*

69 ◆ Newby Hall & Gardens, Ripon 🅰🛇🌣 NCCPG
(Mr R C Compton) *2m E of Ripon. Signposted from A1 & Ripon town centre.* 40-acres extensive gardens laid out in 1920s. Full of rare and beautiful plants. Formal seasonal gardens, stunning double herbaceous borders to R Ure and National Collection holder *Cornus.* Miniature railway and adventure gardens for

children. Sculpture Park (June to Sept). Light refreshments and TEAS. *House and garden adm £8.20, chd/disabled £5.70, OAP £7.20, garden only £6.70, chd/disabled £5, OAP £5.70. Tues to Sun; Bank & Summer Hols Mons; 25 Mar to end of Sept (11-5.30). Tel 0845 4504068 www.newbyhall.com*

70 ◆ Norton Conyers, Wath, nr Ripon 🅰🛇🌣
(Sir James & Lady Graham) *4 m N of Ripon. Take Melmerby & Wath sign off A61 Ripon-Thirsk.* Large C18 walled garden of interest to garden historians. Interesting iron entrace gate; borders, yew hedges and (newly repaired) orangery with an attractive little pond in front. House, which was visited by Charlotte Brontë, and is an original of 'Thornfield Hall' in 'Jane Eyre', also open. House and garden have a friendly, quiet and unspoilt atmosphere. Featured in 'Country Life', 2003. Home-made TEAS in Summerhouse 12 June only. *Adm garden only £3, chd free; house only £5, OAP £3.50, chd under 17 free. Easter Sun & Bank Hol Suns & Mons; Suns 24 Apr to 21 Aug. Daily 27 June to 2 July (2-5 last adm 4.40). For NGS: Sun 12 June (2-5). Tel 01765 640333 norton.conyers@ripon.org*

71 The Old Rectory, Nunburnholme 🅰🛇🌣
(Mr & Mrs M Stringer) *13m SE of York. Turn off Hull-York A1079 at Hayton (between Beverley & York). Follow signs to Nunburnholme.* Large informal garden for chalk-loving plants with natural stream running through. Shrubs and herbaceous beds blending into attractive surrounding countryside. Owner-maintained. Adjacent nursery. Please park in field. Home-made TEAS. *Adm £2.50, chd free. Sun 29 May (1.30-5). Private visits welcome by appt. Tel 01759 302295*

72 Orchard House, Appleton Roebuck 🅰🛇🌣
(David & Sylvia Watson) *8m SW of York. Off A64. 6m E of Tadcaster, via Oxton (no R turn off A64).* Fascinating 1½-acre garden created and maintained by owners in harmony with surrounding countryside. Brimming with unusual features and ideas. Old oak revolving summerhouse, exposed tree roots leading to sunken garden and grotto. Parasol bed, 'Torr' with Chapel of Rest, lily pond, rill, stream, wildlife pond. Brick and cobble paths wind through extensive plantings. Featured in 'Gardens Monthy', 'The Lady',

2003; 'Yorkshire Ridings' 2004. Home-made TEAS in aid of Yorkshire Cancer Research. *Adm £2.50, chd free. Suns 10 Apr; 8 May; 12 June (11-5). Private visits welcome by appt, groups of 10+, Apr, May & June, coaches permitted. Tel 01904 744460*

73 Orchard House, Hunton, Bedale &⊗⊕
(Mr & Mrs Lincoln) *6m S of Richmond. Just off Leyburn Rd. Centre of village almost opp village hall.* Gently-sloping, S-facing, ½-acre garden bordered by farmland in pleasant dales village. Stone walls, mature trees with sweeping lawn, 2 patios and pond. Borders feature great variety of flowering shrubs, evergreens and perennials. The upper garden contains organically grown fruit and vegetables, greenhouse and further colourful planting. TEAS in aid of church funds. *Adm £2, chd/concessions £1. Sun 26 June (11-4)*

74 NEW Ornamental Grass & Foliage Garden, Rillington &⊗⊕
(Mrs Angela Kilby) *5m E of Malton. On A64 5m E of Malton in centre of village. Turn L at signs. Before T-lights.* Garden developed around traditional farm buildings planted in informal and creative designs. Great emphasis on late summer interest in the garden, incl use of grasses, foliage and north American herbaceous species. The garden reflects the use of space to create individual areas such as the gravel, foliage and healing gardens. Light refreshments and TEAS. *Adm £2, chd free. Suns 21 Aug; 11 Sept (12-4). Private visits welcome by appt. Tel 01944 758247 www.ornamentalgrass.co.uk*

75 Outwood House, Outwood Lane, Horsforth &⊗⊕
(David & Ruth Hanson) *4m W of Leeds. From Leeds ring rd (A6120) turn towards the city at A65 junction roundabout. Outwood Lane ¾m on L. Please park away from garden entrance.* 1-acre traditional English walled garden with carriage drive, lawns and productive kitchen garden disposed around mature beech and sweet chestnut; borders, courtyard garden, scree bed and ornamental pool; many wall-trained and standard fruit trees incl figs, pears, peaches; greenhouse, fruit cages and vegetable beds to provide yr-round produce. Light refreshments and TEAS in aid of 'Thinking Space' Gap Year Programme. *Adm £2.50, chd free. Sat, Sun 7, 8 May (1-5).* **Evening**

Opening £3.50, wine, Tue, Wed 5, 6 July (6-8)

76 ◆ Parcevall Hall Gardens, Skyreholme ⊕
(Walsingham College, Yorkshire Properties Ltd) *9m N of Skipton. Signs from B6160 Bolton Abbey-Burnsall rd or off B6265 Grassington-Pateley Bridge.* 16 acres in Wharfedale sheltered by mixed woodland; terrace garden, rose garden, rock garden, fish ponds. Mixed borders, daffodils, tender shrubs (desfontainea, crinodendron, camellias); autumn colour. Birdwatching, old apple orchard for picnics. Light refreshments and TEAS in Tea Rooms adjacent to Garden Office. *Adm £3.50, chd 50p. Daily Good Friday to 31 Oct.* **For NGS:** *Sun 24 Apr (10-6 last entry 5). Tel 01756 720311 Phillip Nelson www.parcevallhallgardens.co.uk*

77 Parkview, 45 Church St, South Cave &⊗⊕
(Mr Christopher Powell) *12m W of Hull. On A63 turn N to S Cave on A1034. In centre of village turn L by chemists, 250yds on L black gates under arch.* ½-acre sheltered garden of perennial and shrub packed beds, pond and bog bed. Rose/honeysuckle pergola underplanted with varieties of hosta. Organic fruit and vegetable garden. New courtyard garden and developing hosta and acer border. *Private visits welcome by appt. Tel 01430 423739 chrispowell@supanet.com*

78 Pennyholme, Fadmoor
(Mr & Mrs P R Wilkinson) *7m NE of Helmsley. From A170 between Kirkbymoorside & Nawton, turn N. ½m before Fadmoor turn L, signed 'Sleightholmedale only' continue N up dale, across 3 cattle grids, to garden. No buses.* Enchanting 10-acre country garden. Unique river and dale setting. Extensive collection of magnificent rhododendrons and azaleas in mature oak wood circular walk. Currently developing traditional rose/mixed borders, water features, wildlife garden and tree garden. TEAS in aid of All Saints Church, Kirkbymoorside. *Adm £2.50. open with* **Sleightholmedale Lodge.** *Sats 28 May; 4 June (1-5)*

79 130 Prince Rupert Drive, Tockwith, nr York ⊗⊕
(Mr & Mrs B Wright) *7m E of Wetherby. From B1224 Wetherby/York rd turn N to Cattal, after 1m turn R at Xrds to Tockwith. 1st turning on R in village. Please do not park in the cul-de-sac.* ½-acre

enthusiast's garden planted for yr-round interest, containing many unusual and rare plants, some from wild-collected seed. Gravel paths through shrubs, perennials, grasses and a large fern collection. Rock and bog gardens with pond; glasshouses, shade house and large kitchen garden with vegetables and trained fruit. Home-made TEAS in aid of Tockwith Church. *Adm £2, chd free. Suns 17 July; 11 Sept (1-5)*

80 55 Rawcliffe Drive, Clifton, York ⊗⊕
(Mr & Mrs J Goodyer) *A19 from York centre, turn R at Clifton Green T-lights (Water Lane). Rawcliffe Drive is 1st L after roundabout.* 30yd x 10yd suburban garden on 2 levels. Planted for yr-round interest with excellent use of foliage and colour. Many unusual shrubs, herbaceous plants, bulbs and large number of clematis. TEAS. *Adm £1.50, chd free. Private visits welcome by appt, April to July. Tel 01904 638489*

81 ◆ RHS Garden Harlow Carr, Harrogate &⊗⊕
(Royal Horticultural Society) *1m W of Harrogate town centre. On B6162 (Harrogate - Otley).* The newest RHS garden with many exciting recent developments. This beautiful and peaceful 58-acre garden draws inspiration from the local scenery. Highlights incl streamside garden; flower and vegetable trials; contemporary grass border; scented, herb and foliage gardens; woodland, arboretum and wild flower meadow. Spectacular 'Gardens through Time' - seven fascinating historical gardens created to mark RHS Bicentenary, televised on BBC2. Museum of Gardening, courses and events programme, Plant Centre & Gift Shop, picnic areas. Light refreshments and TEAS in (new) Bettys Garden Cafe. *Adm garden only £5.50, chd £1.50 6-16. Open all yr.* **For NGS:** *Suns 8 May; 14 Aug (9.30-6). Tel 01423 565418 www.rhs.org.uk*

82 Rose Cottage, High Hoyland, nr Denby Dale ⊗⊕
(Mrs M & Dr A Owen Griffiths) *4m NE of Denby Dale. Nr Cannon Hall Country Park, Barnsley. M1 junction 38 (A637-Huddersfield). Turn L after 75yds (Jebb Lane). After 2m L at T junction. L in High Hoyland (Upperfield Lane).* ¾-acre garden designed and started June 2000 on hillside by previous owners of Joan Royd House. Extensive trelliswork and arbours provide protection for rose gardens, topiary, sun and shade borders, clematis, rhododendrons,

ferns perennials incl meconopsis, hellebores, bulbs, trilliums, collection of 140 varieties of galanthus. 'Black' border, new wild flower meadow and copse. Please confirm Feb dates if weather doubtful (frost/snow) tel 01226 391667. Featured in and cover of 'Gorgeous Gardens' 2004. TEAS in aid of St Andrew's Methodist/URC Church, Penistone. *Adm £2.50, chd 50p. Suns 20, 27 Feb(1-4); 24 Apr; 22 May; 3 July (2-5)*

83 Rudston House, Rudston, nr Driffield 🚫🏵
(Mr & Mrs Simon Dawson) *5m W of Bridlington. On B1253. S at Bosville Arms for approx 300yds.* Birthplace of authoress Winifred Holtby. Victorian farmhouse (not open) and 3 acres of exuberant garden with fine old trees, lawns, paths with clipped box hedges, conifers, shrubs, greenhouses, roses, interesting potager with named vegetable varieties, hosta beds with lilies, and short woodland walk, with pond. Plenty of seats and interesting corners and features. Featured in 'Period Living' & Traditional Homes' 2004. Cream TEAS in aid of All Saints Church, Rudston. *Adm £2.50, chd free. Sun 10 July (11-5)*

84 Rye Hill, Helmsley 🏵🏵
(Dr & Mrs C Briske) *Centre of Helmsley. Signed at Helmsley bridge on A170 (Thirsk-Scarborough).* Plantswoman's garden designed, constructed and maintained by owners. Divided into interlinking compartments, each planted in different style: formal, woodland and cottage. Intense planting using unusual plants for yr-round colour and interest. Conservatory, well stocked with tender species, ponds and many architectural features. New projects each yr. TEAS. *Adm £2, chd free. Suns, Weds 24, 27 Apr; 22, 25 May; Weds 22 June; 20 July (2-5). Private visits welcome by appt, please write to Rye Hill, 15 Station Rd, Helmsley YO62 5BZ*

85 Saltmarshe Hall, Saltmarshe 🚫🏵🏵
(Mr & Mrs Philip Bean) *6m E of Goole. From Howden (M62, junction 37) follow signs to Howdendyke & Saltmarshe. House in park W of Saltmarshe village.* Large lawns, fine old trees, R Ouse and a Regency house (not open) with courtyards provide setting for shrubs, climbers, herbaceous plants and roses. Of special interest to plantsmen and garden designers are pond garden, walled garden and large herbaceous border. Approx 10 acres. Featured in

'Country Life' 2003. Home-made TEAS in aid of Laxton Church. *Adm £2.50. Suns 22 May; 19 June (12-5). Private visits welcome by appt, May & June only. Tel 01430 430199 pmegabean@aol.com*

86 Secret Garden, 10 Sherwood Grove, Acomb, York 🏵🏵
(Mr & Mrs A C Downes) *2m W of York centre. From York on A59, turn L into Beckfield Lane opp Manor School at mini roundabout, ¼m before Western ring rd. Take 1st R, 2nd L.* ¾-acre hidden garden developed and extended over 25yrs. Features rockery, large pond with stream. Extensive mixed plantings incl many unusual plants. 6 greenhouses with vine, cactus, succulent and tender plant collections. Hosta, euphorbia and grass collections. Small nursery. Featured in 'Yorkshire Today' 2003; 'Northern Glories ITV 2005. *Adm £2, chd free. Suns 8 May; 5 June; 10 July (10-5). Private visits welcome by appt. Tel 01904 796360 chrisdownes15@hotmail.com*

87 4 Shaftesbury Court, Shaftesbury Avenue, Bradford West 🏵🏵
(Mrs Pam Greenwood) *Between Bradford Royal Infirmary & Allerton. Follow Duckworth Lane W into Pearson Lane. Shaftesbury Avenue 3rd turn on R off Pearson Lane. Please park in Shaftesbury Avenue, access to Shaftesbury Court by foot.* ¼-acre plant lover's garden for all seasons especially concentrating on late summer colour. Narrow paths divide borders full of many rare and unusual perennials, small shrubs and bulbs for both sun and shade, the boundary walls are festooned with climbers. Limited wheelchair access. Home-made TEAS. *Adm £2, chd free. Sun 31 July (11-5). Private visits welcome by appt 4 Shaftesbury Court, Shaftesbury Ave, Bradford BD9 6BQ*

88 ◆ Shandy Hall, Coxwold 🏵
(The Laurence Sterne Trust) *N of York. From A19, 7m from both Easingwold & Thirsk, turn E signed Coxwold.* Home of C18 author Laurence Sterne. 2 walled gardens, 1 acre of unusual perennials interplanted with tulips and old roses in low walled beds. In old quarry, another acre of trees, shrubs, bulbs, climbers and wild flowers. Wheelchairs with help. *House and Garden adm £4.50. Garden only £2.50, chd £1. Suns to Fris 1 May to 30 Sept (11-4.30). For NGS: Evening Opening, £2.50, wine, Fris 20 May; 3*

June (6.30-8.30). Tel 01347 868465 Patrick Wildgust www.asterisk.org.uk

89 Sleightholmedale Lodge, Fadmoor
(Dr & Mrs O James) *6m NE of Helmsley. Parking can be limited in wet weather.* Hillside garden, walled rose garden and herbaceous borders. Not suitable for wheelchairs. No coaches. Accommodation. TEAS 16, 17 July only. *Adm £2.50, chd 50p. Sat, Sun 16, 17 July (2-6). Opening with **Pennyholme** Sats 28 May; 4 June (1-5). Private visits welcome by appt. Tel 01751 431942*

90 The Spaniels, Field Lane, Hensall 🚫🏵🏵
(Janet & Dennis Tredgett) *5m S of Selby. 2m N of M62. Turn E off A19 to Hensall. Field Lane is last turn on R in Hensall Village.* Immaculately tended garden of ⅔-acre. Long mixed borders in colour themes with island beds, wildlife pond and bog gardens. Garden layout amended in 2004 to provide additional interest. The wide range of plants available for sale is also a popular attraction that should not be missed. TEAS in aid of RSPCA. *Adm £2, chd free. Suns 8 May; 31 July (12-4). Private visits welcome by appt. Tel 01977 661858 dennis.tredgett@btopenworld.com*

91 Springfield House, Tockwith 🚫🏵🏵
(Mr & Mrs S B Milner) *5m E of Wetherby. 1m off B1224. Garden at W end of village.* 1½ acres. Well established walled garden, new herbaceous borders, pretty stream, water and rock gardens. Roses, conifers and shaded shrub walk. Wide variety of interesting plants. TEAS. *Adm £2, chd free. Sun 17 July (2-5)*

92 ◆ Stillingfleet Lodge, Stillingfleet, nr York 🚫🏵🏵 NCCPG
(Mr & Mrs J Cook) *6m S of York. From A19 York-Selby take B1222 towards Sherburn in Elmet.* Plantsman's garden subdivided into smaller gardens, each based on colour theme with emphasis on use of foliage plants. Wild flower meadow and natural pond. 55yds double herbaceous borders; holders of National Collection of Pulmonaria. Organic garden. Adjacent nursery. Featured in 'Country Homes & Interiors', 'The English Garden', 'The Garden', 'Daily Telegraph' 2003. 'The Journal', 'Gardens Illustrated', 'Gardening Which' 2004. TEAS in aid of church. *Adm £2.50, chd under 5 free, 5-16yrs 50p. Weds, Fris May*

to end Sept; Sats May & June (1-4).
For NGS: *Suns 8 May; 19 June
(1.30-5). Tel 01904 728506
www.stillingfleetlodgenurseries.co.uk*

93 Tan Cottage, West Lane, Cononley 🚫NCCPG
(Mrs Denis Shaw) *2¾m S of Skipton.
Take A629; turn off to Cononley; top
of village turn R onto Skipton rd.
West Lane turning on L. ¼-acre
plantsman's garden adjoining C17
house (not open). Interesting plants,
many old varieties. National
Collection of primroses. Private visits
welcome by appt. Tel 01535 632030*

**94 Thorpe Lodge, Knaresborough
Road, nr Ripon** 🚫
(Mr & Mrs T Jowitt) *1m S of Ripon.
On Ripon-Bishop Monkton-
Knaresborough rd ¾m from Ripon
bypass. Large country garden of 12
acres with extensive colour themed
flower borders, walled rose garden,
pleached hornbeam walk and allées
leading to mature woodland with
vistas and ponds. Courtyard with
exotic shrubs and tender plants in
pots. Area for picnics.
Accommodation. Featured in 'English
Garden' 2004. TEAS. Adm £3, chd
free. Sun 24 July (2-6). Private visits
welcome by appt. Tel 01765 602088
jowitt@btinternet.com*

**95 NEW Tranmere Park Gardens,
Guiseley**
*8m NW of Leeds. From Harry
Ramsdens on A65 Leeds to Skipton
rd take A6038 for Bradford. After
¼m turn R into Southway, Tranmere
Park. Residential development
situated on the SE flank of Ilkley
Moor. Home-made TEAS at 48
Southway in aid of The
Neurofibromatosis Association.
Combined adm £2, chd free. Sun 10
July (1-5)*

NEW 11 Southway, Tranmere Park
🚫 (Mike & Pat
Hargreaves) Formal suburban
garden with 200 - 300 sweet pea
plants grown for exhibition;
colourful bedding and mixed
borders.

NEW 48 Southway, Tranmere Park
(Harold & Maureen
Woodworth) The garden extends
to ⅓-acre. Deliciously scented old
roses from miniatures to giants
tumbling from the treetops. Regal
spires of heavenly blue
delphiniums; numerous clematis,
hostas, lilies, geraniums,
pulmonarias, fruit trees etc.
Recently-installed well-stocked
17ft Hartley Clear Span
Greenhouse. 1st prize Guiseley in

Bloom Best Front Garden Award
2004.

96 Tregonning, Ellerton 🚫
(Deirdre Falcon & John Barwick)
*12m S of York. On B1228 to
Elvington & Howden. 10m N of
M62 junction 37. Next to village
pond.* 1½-acres created over 30yrs,
organic garden with fruit, vegetables
and wild flower meadow. Annual and
perennial wild flower borders. Over
60 species of old roses, climbers and
dovecote. Large herbaceous border.
Pergola walk, wild-life ponds, bog
gardens, Victorian wells, rockeries
and terrace. Large collection of seed-
grown bonsai, together with garden-
grown specimens of same age and
variety. Featured in 'Yorkshire
Today' 2003; 'Yorkshire Wildlife'
2004. Home-made Cornish Cream
TEAS in aid of WWF. Adm £2, chd
free. Suns 15 May; 12 June (2-5).
Private visits welcome by appt,
groups of 10+. Coaches welcome.
Tel 01757 288578
deirdrefalcon@hotmail.com*

**97 Vicarage House, Kirkby
Wharfe** 🚫
(Mr & Mrs R S A Hall) *1m S of
Tadcaster. (A162) turn L (B1223)
after 1m turn L to Kirkby Wharfe.*
Secluded 1-acre country garden
surrounded by mature trees; extensive
herbaceous borders, raised beds.
Species primulae and Elizabethan
polyanthus. Jacqueline Giles's
polyanthus on sale (Elizabethan).
Home-made TEAS in aid of CLIC.
Adm £2, chd free. Sun 24 Apr (1-5).
Private visits welcome by appt,
groups of 5+ May & June -
Aquilegias. Tel 01937 835458

**98 ◆ The Walled Garden at
Scampston** 🚫
(Sir Charles & Lady Legard) *5m E of
Malton. ½m N of A64, signed
Scampston only.* An exciting new
garden designed by Piet Oudolf,
winner of Gold and 'Best in Show' at
Chelsea. The contemporary layout in
the 4½-acre walled garden incl
perennial meadow planting and
grasses in Oudolf's signature style in
addition to spring borders. Described
by Stephen Anderton in 'The Times'.
'Oudolf offers a dazzling display of
modern planting, structure, form and
space handling. The garden is a gem'.
Featured in 'The Times', 'Daily
Telegraph', 'The Garden' 2004. Light
refreshments and TEAS. *House and
garden adm £11, garden only £5, chd
£3, concessions £4.50. House: 23
June to 24 July, daily, (closed Mons).
Garden: 26 Mar to 16 Oct, (closed
Mons except Bank Hols (10-5). For*

NGS: *Wed 27 July (10-5). Tel 01944
758224 www.scampston.co.uk*

**99 3 Weelsby Way, Hessle, E
Yorkshire** 🚫
(Martin Thornton) *4m W of Hull.
From W turn off A63 to
Hessle/Humber Bridge. At 1st
roundabout take exit to Humber
Bridge. At 2nd roundabout take exit
to Hull A1105. Take 1st L from
Boothberry Rd.* Small lawnless
garden (approx 65ft x 30ft) packed
with rare and interesting plants. Lily
pond, rose pergola, cottage-style
areas. TEAS. *Adm £1.50, chd free.
Sun 17 July (1-5). Private visits
welcome by appt. Tel 01482 641388*

100 26 West End, Walkington 🚫
(Miss Jennifer Hall) *2m SW of
Beverley. On the B1230, 100yds
beyond Xrds in centre of village on
the R.* Charming and interesting 1-
acre cottage garden opening into old
wooded gravel pit still being
developed by owner. Many rare
plants collected over 20yrs. Featured
in '25 Beautiful Gardens' 2004.
TEAS. *Adm £2.50, chd free. Sun 29
May (1.30-5). Private visits welcome
by appt, preferably June & July.
Tel 01482 861705*

101 The White House, Husthwaite
🚫
(Dr & Mrs A H Raper) *5m S of
Thirsk. Turn R off A19 signposted
Husthwaite. 1½m to centre of village
opp parish church.* Come and meet
the gardener, an enthusiastic
plantswoman. Exchange ideas and
visit a 1-acre country garden with
herb garden, conservatory and
gardens within the garden.
Herbaceous, particularly a hot
summer border and shrubs and many
fascinating unusual plants. New
landscaping and planting in the old
orchard. *Private visits welcome by
appt, groups and coaches permitted.
Tel 01347 868688*

102 Whixley Gardens
*Between York & Harrogate. 3m E or
A1 off A59 York-Harrogate. Follow
signs to Whixley.* Light refreshments
and TEAS at The Old Vicarage.
*Combined adm £4.50, chd free. Also
opening* **Croft Cottage** *(See separate
entry). Mon 30 May (12-5)*

Ash Tree House, High Street 🚫
(Mr & Mrs E P Moffitt) Well
designed unusual garden of
approx ¼-acre with extensive
rockeries making full use of
sloping site. Est excellent
plantings of heathers, alpines,
hardy plants, climbers and
shrubs.

NEW **The Bay House, Stonegate**
⚘ (Mr & Mrs John Beckett)
Densely planted courtyard garden
on differing levels.

Cobble Cottage, Rudgate ⚘⊕
(John Hawkridge & Barry
Atkinson) Imaginatively designed,
constantly changing, small
cottage garden full of decorative
architectural plants and old
family favourites. Interesting
water garden, containers and use
of natural materials. Secret
courtyard garden and new
Japanese garden. Featured in '25
Beautiful Gardens', 2003. *Private
visits welcome by appt, groups of
8+ June & July only. Tel 01423
331419*

The Old Vicarage ⚘⊕ (Mr &
Mrs Roger Marshall) Delightful
¾-acre walled flower garden with
mixed borders, unusual shrubs,
climbers, roses, hardy and half-
hardy perennials, bulbs and
hellebores. Paths and garden
structures lead to new vistas and
hidden areas using the garden's
natural contours.

103 **NEW** **Woodlands, Green Lane,
Littlethorpe** ♿⚘⊕
(John & Jane Beadle) *1m SE of
Ripon. Off A61 Ripon bypass, follow
signs to Littlethorpe, turn R at
church to Bishop Monkton for ½m.
Turn L into Green Lane after red
brick wall. Car parking in adjacent
field.* 1-acre informal garden
developed by owners incl courtyard,
extensive kitchen garden with raised
beds, gravel terrace, lawns and newly
created garden from old tennis court.
Limited wheelchair access. Home-
made teas at Greencroft. *Adm £2.
Combined with* **Greencroft** *Adm £3.
Sun 19 June (12.30-5.30)*

104 ◆ **Woodlands Cottage,
Summerbridge** ♿⊕
(Mr & Mrs Stark) *4m E of Pateley
Bridge, 10m NW of Harrogate. On
the B6165 (Ripley-Pateley Bridge)*

½m W of Summerbridge. 1-acre
plantsman's garden, featured on Tyne
Tees television. Informal areas with
natural stone outcrops, woodland
and wild flowers; also cottage garden
herbaceous planting and more formal
areas with a 'garden room', herb and
vegetable areas and newly revamped
front garden. Home-made TEAS.
Adm £2, chd 50p. Groups by appt.
For NGS: Suns 15 May; 7 Aug (1-5).
Tel 01423 780765
www.woodlandscottagegarden.co.uk

105 ◆ **Wytherstone Gardens,
Pockley** ♿⚘⊕
(Lady Clarissa Collin) *2m NE of
Helmsley. Signpost from A170.* Large
garden, consisting of interlinked
compartments, with choice and hard-
to-find shrubs and perennials.
Constantly expanding, always
something new to see. Large variety
of lavenders and salvias, terracotta
pots, Mediterranean garden, peat
terracing, rock garden of rare alpines.
Arboretum of rare trees with pond to
woodland walk. Conservatory garden
with climbing roses, herbaceous
borders. Newly created railway
sleeper border. Several plants not
normally hardy in North thrive and
flower yr after yr. Adjacent nursery.
Featured in 'Yorkshire Life' 2003;
'Country Life', 'The Journal' 2004.
TEAS. *Adm £2.50, chd £1. Weds 1
June to 31 Aug; Suns 12 June; 17
July.* **For NGS:** *Suns 29 May; 26 June;
14 Aug (1-5). Tel 01439 770012*
www.wytherstonegardens.co.uk

106 ◆ **York Gate, Back Church
Lane, Adel, Leeds 16** ⚘⊕
(Perennial) *5m N of Leeds centre.
From Leeds take A660. Turn R at 1st
set of T-lights after intersection with
A6120. Turn L into Church Lane &
park nr church. Public footpath
through churchyard & straight on
passes garden gate.* 1-acre
masterpiece and outstanding example
of C20 English garden design. Within
a series of inner gardens are shrubs

and herbaceous borders, ponds,
pinetum, dell, fern border, nut walk,
white and silver borders, kitchen
garden and famous herb garden with
topiary. Each area has its own unique
architectural features and evergreens
are used to great effect throughout.
Redevelopment of 'Sybil's Garden'
due for completion early 2005.
Featured in 'TV's City Gardener'
2003, 'Gardening Which' 2003 &
2004, 'Small Town Gardens' 2004.
TEAS June to Sept. *Adm £3, chd free.
Thurs, Suns & Bank Hol Mons, Apr
to Sept (2-5); Thurs evenings July
(6.30-9). Tel 0113 267 8240*
www.perennial.org.uk

107 **Yorke House, Dacre Banks,
Nidderdale** ♿⊕
(Anthony & Pat Hutchinson) *4m SE
of Pateley Bridge, 10m NW of
Harrogate. On B6451. Limited car
parking available.* Flower arranger's
2-acre garden with colour-themed
borders full of flowering and foliage
plants and shrubs. Extensive water
feature incl large ornamental ponds
and stream. Other features incl nut
walk, rose pergola, patios, gazebo,
Millennium garden and wildlife area.
The garden enjoys beautiful views
across Nidderdale. Picnic area.
Home-made TEAS. *Adm £2.50, chd
free (share to Harrogate & District
Society for the Blind). Sun 12 June
(11-5). Private visits welcome by appt
June, July & Aug, coaches permitted.
Tel 01423 780456*
hutchinson@yorkehouse.co.uk

Evening Opening (See also garden description)	
Shandy Hall	20 May
Cleaves House	1 June
Shandy Hall	3 June
Cleaves House	8 June
Millgate House	19 June
Outwood House	5 July
Outwood House	6 July
Long Marston Hall	9 July

WALES

Carmarthenshire & Pembrokeshire

County Organiser: Mrs Jill Foster, Heron Cottage, Picton Ferry, The Rhos, Haverfordwest, Pembrokeshire SA62 4AR Tel 01437 751241
Assistant County Organiser: Mrs Jane Stokes, Llyshendy, Llandeilo, Carmarthenshire SA19 6YA
County Treasurer: Mrs Jo Hammond, Ashdale, Llanmill, Narberth, Pembrokeshire SA67 8UE

Maps: Numbers shown next to each garden entry refer to that garden's entry on the county map. This position is approximate; distance and directions from the nearest main town are generally shown in the garden text. A precise location is available for those gardens featured on the NGS website by visiting www.ngs.org.uk.
Symbols: Information relating to symbols is given on page 21

DATES OF OPENING

Evening openings
See end of county listing

Gardens open to the public
For details see garden description

Blaen y Wawr, Bryn (2)
Colby Woodland Garden, Amroth (5)
Dyffryn Fernant, Llanychaer, Fishguard (10)
Moorland Cottage Plants, Brynberian (19)
Norwood Gardens, Llanllwni (20)
Picton Castle Woodland Gardens, The Rhos (22)

By appointment only
For telephone number and other details see garden description.
Private visits welcomed
Blaen y Wawr, Bryn (2)
Cwm Pibau, New Moat (7)
Glandwr, Pentrecwrt (13)
Llwyn Cyll, Trap (14)
Millinford, Millin Cross (18)

April 3 Sunday
Pembrey & Burry Port Gardens (21)

April 24 Sunday
Norwood Gardens, Llanllwni (20)

May 2 Monday (Bank Hol)
Balandra, Manorbier (1)

May 8 Sunday
Maesquarre, Llandeilo (16)
Picton Castle Woodland Gardens, The Rhos (22)

May 11 Wednesday
Maesquarre, Llandeilo (16)

May 14 Saturday
Maesquarre, Llandeilo (16)

May 15 Sunday
Colby Woodland Garden, Amroth (5)
Ffynone, Boncath (12)

May 29 Sunday
Dyffryn Farm, Lampeter Velfrey, Narberth (9)

June 5 Sunday
The Cors, Laugharne (6)
Mapsland, Laugharne (17)
Pembrey & Burry Port Gardens (21)

June 12 Sunday
Maesquarre, Llandeilo (16)

June 15 Wednesday
Maesquarre, Llandeilo (16)

June 18 Saturday
Maesquarre, Llandeilo (16)

June 19 Sunday
Disgwylfa, Abergorlech (8)

June 26 Sunday
Coed-y-Ffynnon, Lampeter Velfrey (4)
Erwlon, Llanboidy (11)
Rhosygilwen Mansion, Cilgerran, Cardigan (23)

July 2 Saturday
Coed-y-Ffynnon, Lampeter Velfrey (4)

July 3 Sunday
Balandra, Manorbier (1)

July 9 Saturday
Llysnewydd, Llangadog (15)

July 10 Sunday
Llysnewydd, Llangadog (15)
Norwood Gardens, Llanllwni (20)

July 17 Sunday
Cilgwyn Lodge, Llangadog (3)
Picton Castle Woodland Gardens, The Rhos (22)

August 7 Sunday
Dyffryn Fernant, Llanychaer, Fishguard (10)

August 21 Sunday
Rhosygilwen Mansion, Cilgerran, Cardigan (23)

August 28 Sunday
Erwlon, Llanboidy (11)

September 11 Sunday
Norwood Gardens, Llanllwni (20)

DESCRIPTIONS OF GARDENS

❶ Balandra, 6 Pembroke Road, Manorbier ⊗
(Janet Bell) 7m W of Tenby. From Tenby ignore 1st turning into Manorbier, but take the 2nd. Bungalow is 7th property on R. Park in Pembroke Rd. ½-acre plantsman's garden divided into compartments for pictorial effect and richly planted: arisaemas, hellebores, primulas, fritillaria, black tulips. Unusual trees, shrubs and climbers, particularly clematis. Dramatic use of pots and screens, colours and textures. Adm £2, chd free. Mon 2 May; Sun 3 July (11-5)

❷ ◆ Blaen y Wawr, 4 Heol Penllwyngwyn, Bryn ⊗⊞
(Alan & Justine Clarke) 2½m N of Llanelli. 2.7m from M4 J48, on B4297 towards Llanelli. Adjacent to Bryn Breakfast Café (on R, white house with green roof). Garden developed by plantsman. ½-acre site with unusual trees and shrubs, sunny border, water garden, orchard and small nursery garden. Also bonsai and container plants. Designed for ease of maintenance and dramatic effect with high emphasis on intrigue and relaxation. TEAS available on request. Adm £2, chd free. Private visits welcome by appt. Tel 01554 821274

NEW Brynderi, Llechryd ⊗⊗⊞
See Ceredigion/Cardiganshire.

❸ Cilgwyn Lodge, Llangadog ⊗⊞
(Keith Brown & Moira Thomas) 3m NE of Llangadog village. 4m SW of Llandovery. Turn off A40 into centre of Llangadog. Bear L in front of village shop then 1st R towards Myddfai. After 2½m pass Cilgwyn

CARMARTHENSHIRE & PEMBROKESHIRE

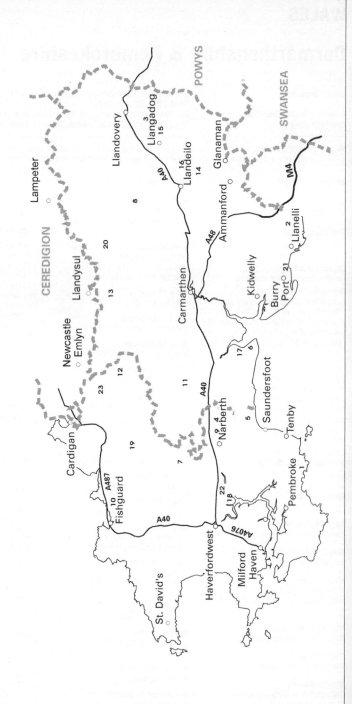

POWYS

SWANSEA

CEREDIGION

Llandovery

Llangadog 3
15

Glanaman
16
Llandeilo 14

Lampeter

A40

Ammanford

M4

8

A48

Llanelli 2

Llandysul

20

Kidwelly

Burry
Port 21

13

Carmarthen

Newcastle
Emlyn

12

23

17 6

Saundersfoot

11

A40

19

7

4
Narberth
9

5

Tenby

Cardigan

A487

10
Fishguard

22
18

Pembroke
1

A40

A4076

Haverfordwest

Milford
Haven

St. David's

kms 0   10
miles 0   10

Manor on L then 1st L by tel kiosk. Garden ¾m on L. Fascinating 1-acre garden set in glorious countryside comprising 2 separate gardens incl fruit and vegetables, shrubs and a wide variety of herbaceous plants, especially hostas and hardy geraniums, displayed in extensive colour-themed borders. Large waterlily and wildlife pond and formal koi pond. Plenty of seating to enjoy the garden. Featured in '25 Beautiful Gardens' 2004. Home-made TEAS. Adm £2. Sun 17 July (1-5). Private visits welcome by appt. Tel 01550 777452

④ Coed-y-Ffynnon, Lampeter Velfrey ♿⌖

(Col R H Gilbertson) 2½m SE of Narberth. From Penblewin roundabout on A40 follow signs to Narberth & then to crematorium. Straight on through Llanmill & Lampeter Velfrey. Garden ½m on L. 1-acre garden which incl collection of historic roses at their best mid-June to mid-July. Tranquil rural setting. Talk and guided tour available. Cream TEAS in aid of Lampeter Velfrey Village Hall Project. Adm £2.50, chd free. Sun 26 June; Sat 2 July (2-6). Private visits welcome by appt. Tel 01834 831396 rh.gilbertson@virgin.net

⑤ ◆ Colby Woodland Garden, Amroth ♿⌖

(The National Trust) 6m N of Tenby. 5m SE of Narberth. Signed by brown tourist signs on coast rd & A477. 8-acre woodland garden in a secluded and tranquil valley with fine collection of rhododendrons and azaleas. Walled garden open by kind permission of Mr and Mrs A Scourfield Lewis. TEAS. Adm £3.60, chd £1.80. Open daily 18 Mar to 30 Oct. For NGS: Sun 15 May (10-5), walled garden 11-5. Tel 01834 811885

⑥ NEW The Cors, Newbridge Road, Laugharne ♿⌖⌖

(Nick Priestland) 12m SW of Carmarthen. From Carmarthen, turn R in centre of Laugharne at The Mariners PH. At bottom of Newbridge Rd on R. Public car parks 5 mins walk. Approx 2½ acres set in beautiful wooded valley bordering river. Large bog garden with ponds, gunnera, bamboos and tree ferns. Well-designed plantsman's garden with unusual architectural and exotic planting and sculptures. The Cors is also a restaurant with rooms, Thur, Fri & Sat eves. Light refreshments and TEAS. Adm £2. Sun 5 June (11-5). Also opening **Mapsland**.

Private visits welcome by appt. Tel 01994 427219

⑦ Cwm Pibau, New Moat

(Mrs Duncan Drew) 10m NE of Haverfordwest. 3m SW of Maenclochog. 5-acre woodland garden surrounded by old deciduous woodland and streams. Created in 1978, contains shrubs and trees from Chile, New Zealand and Europe, set on S-facing sloping hill. Adm £2, chd free. Private visits welcome by appt. Tel 01437 532454

⑧ Disgwylfa, Abergorlech ⌖⌖

(Mrs Ann MacGregor) 17m NE of Carmarthen. Between Brechfa & Llansawel. From Carmarthen, take A40 (Llandeilo). At Nantgaredig turn L (signed Brechfa-Llansawel). Abergorlech is 4m from Brechfa. Disgwylfa 1st house on L. Please park tidily on same side. No small children. Unsuitable for severely disabled. Artist's garden of ¾-acre with artist's eye for colour, comprising wonderful terraces with springtime heathers, bulbs and multitude of shrubs and perennials for all-yr interest. A delight for the discerning gardener, with conditions from dry to bog area and pond. Set into the forest with superb views over Cothi Valley. Featured in 'Amateur Gardening' 2004. Home-made TEAS. Adm £2, chd 75p. Sun 19 June (10.30-4). Private visits welcome by appt Apr to Aug. Tel 01558 685302

⑨ Dyffryn Farm, Lampeter Velfrey, Narberth ♿⌖⌖

(Dr & Mrs M J R Polson) 3m E of Narberth. From junction of A40 & A478 follow signs for crematorium, continue down into Llanmill. Then uphill, at brow turn L at Bryn Sion Chapel Xrds (before Lampeter Velfrey). After ½m rd turns R under railway bridge. Dyffryn Farm straight ahead, parking under bridge and immed on R. Fair-sized relaxed garden developed into 9 distinct areas, some on different levels with 'statement' plants to draw the eye. More than 60 bamboos and many other grasses. Sympathetic herbaceous planting, shrubs; climbers; pond, bog and woodland areas. Wheelchair access limited in wet weather. Home-made TEAS. Adm £2.50, chd free. Sun 29 May (1-6)

⑩ NEW ◆ Dyffryn Fernant, Llanychaer, Fishguard ⌖⌖

(Christina Shand & David Allum) 3m E of Fishguard, then ½m inland. A487 Fishguard to Cardigan. After approx 3m, at end of long straight

hill, turn R signed Llanychaer with blue rd signs 'unsuitable for long vehicles'. After exactly ½m is Dyffryn track, on L behind LH bend, with wooden sign. 3½-acre plantsman's garden with abundance of plants, opening out into wildflower meadows, pond and ancient rush pasture. Comprising quarry, courtyard, bog, rickyard, fernery with tree ferns, azalea bank, kitchen garden and orchard. Circular woodland and younger woodland plantings. A romantic garden set in wild N Pembrokeshire landscape. Parking spaces nr house. Adm £2, chd free. Open Mar to Oct, please ring for dates or see website. For NGS: Sun 7 Aug (10-6). Tel 01348 811282 www.genuslocus.net

⑪ NEW Erwlon, Llanboidy ⌖

(John & Liz Rees) 15m SW of Carmarthen. A40 from Carmarthen. Make for Llanboidy roundabout near Whitland signed Llanboidy 4m. When nearing village turn L at Xrds. Erwlon in centre of village next to school. ⅓ acre surrounding modern bungalow. Water feature in spacious front garden. Ingenious use of space and levels, plus grass, gravel and stone landscaping to create a variety of planting areas. Many interesting and developing shrubs, particularly roses with good underplanting. Water and changes of level, so unsafe for young children. TEAS. Adm £2 (share to Wales Air Ambulance). Suns 26 June; 28 Aug (11-5). Private visits welcome by appt for groups of 10+. Tel 01994 448353

"You can come down now Henry, they've all gone!"

◆ **Farmyard Nursery Woodland Garden, Llandysul** ⊛ NCCPG
See Ceredigion/Cardiganshire.

⓬ **Ffynone, Boncath** ⊛
(Earl & Countess Lloyd George of Dwyfor) *9m SE of Cardigan. 7m W of Newcastle Emlyn. From Newcastle Emlyn take A484 to Cenarth, turn L on B4332, turn L again at Xrds just before Newchapel. Large woodland garden designated Grade I on CADW register of historic gardens in Wales. Lovely views, fine specimen trees, rhododendrons, azaleas, woodland walks. House (also Grade I) by John Nash (1793), not open. Later additions and garden terraces by F Inigo Thomas c1904. TEAS in aid of Fishguard Sea Cadets. Adm £2.50, chd under 14 free. Sun 15 May (2-6). Private visits welcome by appt. Tel 01239 841610*

⓭ **Glandwr, Pentrecwrt** ⊛
(Mrs Jo Hicks) *15m N of Carmarthen. 2m S of Llandysul. On A486. At Pentrecwrt village, take minor rd opp Black Horse PH. After bridge keep L for ¼m. Glandwr is on R. Delightful 1-acre cottage garden with stream. Natural woodland walk for spring and summer, with surprises. Featured in 'Amateur Gardening' 2004. Adm £2, chd 50p. Private visits welcome by appt. Tel 01559 363729*

⓮ **Llwyn Cyll, Trap** ⊛⊛
(Liz & John Smith) *3m SE of Llandeilo. In Trap turn towards Glanaman & Llandybie (at The Cenan Arms). Llwyn Cyll is ½m on L adjoining Llwyn Onn. Parking limited. 3½-acre garden of yr-round interest. Abundant and colourful terraced and walled borders, small arboretum, orchard and vegetable garden. Sun and shade areas with sympathetic planting. Adm £2, chd £1. Private visits welcome by appt, daily 16 Apr to 17 Sept, small coaches permitted. Tel 01558 822398*

⓯ **Llysnewydd, Llangadog** ⊛⊛
(Jan Jones & Nick Voyle) *6m E of Llandeilo. Midway between Llandeilo & Llandovery turn off A40 into centre of Llangadog. Bear L in front of village shop. Turn 1st R. After approx ½m turn R. Garden approx 600yds on R. 1-acre oasis of tranquillity set in scenic Towy Valley. Quiet, relaxing garden evolving from the need to prevent river erosion. Planted for yr-round interest in areas ranging from full sun to deep shade. Productive vegetable garden; woodland garden and fernery.*

Unsuitable for children. TEAS. Adm £2. Sat, Sun 9, 10 July (11-5). Private visits welcome by appt. Tel 01550 777432 jllysnewydd@aol.com

⓰ NEW **Maesquarre, Bethlehem Road, Llandeilo** ⊛⊛
(Mr & Mrs Geoffrey Williams) *1½m E of Llandeilo. From Llandeilo take A483 across R Towy. At Ffairfach Xrds turn L along unclassified Bethlehem Rd, garden on R after 2m. Parking nearby. Spacious and peaceful garden attempting to combine the owners' interest in unusual shrubs and trees and local flora and fauna. Large closely-planted pond area, slopes of developing and maturing shrubs and trees, natural woodland, with an attractive stream flowing throughout, form the main features of the garden. TEAS in aid of Cancer Research UK. Adm £2, chd 50p. Sun 8, Wed 11, Sat 14 May; Sun 12, Wed 15, Sat 18 June (2-6). Private visits welcome by appt. Tel 01558 822960*

⓱ NEW **Mapsland, Laugharne** ⊛⊛
(Picton & Jane Gibbin) *13m SW of Carmarthen. 3½m from St Clears. ½m before town of Laugharne off A4066 turn L signed to Ants Hill Caravan Park. Garden 2nd entrance after Caravan Park on R. Mature 1½-acre garden with superb views of Gower Peninsula. Gravel terrace garden. Prairie-style mixed grass slopes, woodland and walled vegetable gardens. Fish pond and bog planting. Formal lawn and borders planted with a wide variety of shrubs, herbaceous plants and trees. Georgian house, not open. Home-made TEAS. Adm £2, chd 50p. Sun 5 June (11-5). Also opening **The Cors***

⓲ **Millinford, Millin Cross** ⊛
(Drs B & A Barton) *3m E of Haverfordwest. From Haverfordwest on A40 to Carmarthen, turn R signed The Rhos, take turning to Millin. Turn R at Millin Chapel then immed L over river bridge. Spacious, undulating and peaceful garden of 4 acres on bank of Millin Creek. Varied collection of over 125 different trees, plus shrubs, herbaceous plants and bulbs in beautiful riverside setting. Worth visiting in spring, summer and early autumn. TEAS. Adm £2, chd free. Private visits welcome by appt. Tel 01437 762394*

⓳ ◆ **Moorland Cottage Plants, Rhyd-y-Groes, Brynberian** ⊛⊛
(Jennifer & Kevin Matthews) *12m SW of Cardigan. 16m NE of Haverfordwest, on B4329, ¾m*

downhill from cattlegrid (from Haverfordwest) and 1m uphill from sign post to Brynberian (from Cardigan). Country garden of approx ½ acre, situated at 720ft on NE slopes of the Preseli mountains. Extensive and diverse plantings linked by meandering paths. Cottage garden borders, bamboo and grass borders; shade planting incl small fern garden. Adjacent nursery specialising in hardy perennials. Featured in 'Amateur Gardening', 'Daily Telegraph' Nursery of the Week 2004. Adm £1.50, chd free. Daily, not Weds, 23 May to 4 Sept (10-6). Tel 01239 891363 www.moorlandcottageplants.co.uk

⓴ ◆ **Norwood Gardens, Llanllwni** ⊛⊛
(The Norwood Gardens Partnership) *8m SW of Lampeter. On A485 Carmarthen to Lampeter rd in village of Llanllwni between Talardd Arms and Belle Vue PH. Recently created 3-acre garden. Consists of individual gardens, each with its own character, linked by paths and borders, plus sculpture. Over 70 Varieties of daffodil flood the garden with spring colour. Shrubs and herbaceous plants continue to provide colour throughout the yr. Growing collection of hemerocallis and alliums. Light refreshments and TEAS. Adm £3, chd £1.50, under 12 free, concessions £2.50. Daily Easter to Oct. For NGS: Suns 24 Apr; 10 July; 11 Sept (10-6). Tel 01559 395386 www.norwoodgardens.co.uk*

Old Cilgwyn Gardens, Newcastle Emlyn ⊛
See Ceredigion/Cardiganshire.

The Old Vicarage, Llangeler ⊛⊛
See Ceredigion/Cardiganshire.

㉑ **Pembrey & Burry Port Gardens**
4m W of Llanelli. On A84 (follow signs for Pembrey Country Park). All parking at Bryn Illtyd, minibus to Brynheulog. 2 very different gardens nr Pembrey Country Park. Home-made TEAS at Bryn Illtyd in aid of Friends of Bryn Illtyd. Combined adm £4 incl minibus from Bryn Illtyd to Brynheulog. Suns 3 Apr; 5 June (2-6)

Bryn Illtyd Residential Home, Ar-y-Bryn, Pembrey ⊛⊛ (Richard & Marion James) *Turn R at St Illtyd's Church, 2nd R into Ar-y-Bryn. Traditional S-facing garden around Edwardian house, in about 1 acre, now a residential home. Mixed shrub and* herbaceous borders planted with old favourites. Fine magnolia, holm oaks and willow, small pond, S-facing raised bank, lawns. ½m Pembrey Country Park. Plant sale, % to Friends of Bryn Illtyd. *Private visits welcome by appt. Tel 01554 832462*

Brynheulog, Y Graig, Burry Port ⊕ (Huw & Lynda Morse) *Turn 1st R immed after pelican crossing on hill signed Y Graig. Pass Farmers Arms PH on L. 2nd turning on R up hill. Bear L up next hill for 250yds.* 1-acre garden with splendid views to Gower Peninsula, containing several different terraced gardens, lawns, patios, ponds, productive fruit/vegetable garden. Herbaceous borders, heather and conifer beds, Mediterranean-style patio, tender shrubs, palms, trees and herbs. Unsuitable for the less

mobile. *Private visits welcome by appt Apr to end Sept, groups of up to 10. Tel 01554 833490*

㉒ ◆ Picton Castle Woodland Gardens, The Rhos 🅷🅰 (Picton Castle Trust) *3m E of Haverfordwest. On A40 to Carmarthen, signed off main rd.* Mature 40-acre woodland garden with unique collection of rhododendrons and azaleas, many bred over 38yrs, producing hybrids of great merit and beauty; rare and tender shrubs and trees incl magnolia, myrtle, embothrium and eucryphia. Wild flowers abound. Walled garden with roses; fernery; herbaceous and climbing plants and large clearly-labelled collection of herbs. TEAS. *Grounds & Gallery adm £4.95, chd £2.50, senior citizens £4.75. Castle extra. Daily 1 Apr to 30 Sept (except Mons, but open Bank Hol Mons). For* **NGS:** *Suns 8 May; 17 July (10.30-5).*

Tel 01437 751326 www.pictoncastle.co.uk

㉓ NEW Rhosygilwen Mansion, Cilgerran, Cardigan 🅷🅰 (Glen Peters & Brenda Squires) *5m S of Cardigan. From Cardigan follow A478 signed Tenby. After 6m turn L at Rhoshill towards Cilgerran. After ¼m turn R signed Rhosygilwen. Mansion gates ½m.* 20 acres of garden in 55 acre estate. Pretty ½m drive through woodland planting. Spacious lightly wooded grounds for leisurely rambling, 1-acre walled garden fully productive of fruit, vegetables and flowers, authentically restored Edwardian greenhouses, many old and new trees, small formal garden. BBC Radio Wales 2004. Light refreshments and TEAS. *Adm £3, chd under 14 free. Sun 26 June; Sun 21 Aug (10.30-4). Private visits welcome by appt. Tel 01239 841387 rhosygilwen@btconnect.com*

Ceredigion/Cardiganshire

County Organiser:
Mrs Joy Neal, Llwyncelyn, Glandyfi, Machynlleth SY20 8SS
Tel 01654 781203 email joy@glandyfi.fsnet.co.uk

Assistant County Organiser:
(Press & Publicity Officer)
Mrs Jennifer Dyer, Robin Hill, Coed y Garth, Furnace, Machynlleth SY20 8PG
Tel 01654 781223 email jenny@cornardtye.freeserve.co.uk

County Treasurer:
Mrs Sheila Latham, Garreg, Glandyfi, Machynlleth SY20 8SS Tel 01654 781251

Maps: Numbers shown next to each garden entry refer to that garden's entry on the county map. This position is approximate;
distance and directions from the nearest main town are generally shown in the garden text.
A precise location is available for those gardens featured on the NGS website by visiting www.ngs.org.uk.

Symbols: Information relating to symbols is given on page 21

DATES OF OPENING

Evening openings
See end of county listing

Private gardens open regularly for NGS
Winllan Wildlife Garden, Talsarn *(18)*

Gardens open to the public
For details see garden description
Cae Hir, Cribyn *(6)*
Farmyard Nursery Woodland Garden,
Llandysul *(8)*
Llanerchaeron *(10)*
Ty Glyn Walled Garden *(17)*

By appointment only
*For telephone number and other
details see garden description.
Private visits welcomed*
Old Cilgwyn Gardens, Newcastle Emlyn *(14)*

March 27 Sunday (Easter)
Farmyard Nursery Woodland Garden,
Llandysul *(8)*

April 10 Sunday
Farmyard Nursery Woodland Garden,
Llandysul *(8)*

May 1 Sunday
Cwmrhaiadr Garden & Nursery, Glaspwll,
Machynlleth *(7)*

May 8 Sunday
Farmyard Nursery Woodland Garden,
Llandysul *(8)*
Llwyncelyn, Glandyfi *(12)*
The Mill House, Glandyfi *(13)*
Pant-yr-Holiad, Rhydlewis *(16)*

ngs gardens open for charity

Look out for the [NCCPG]
National Plant
Collections at some
of our gardens

May 21 Saturday
The Bungalow, Plwmp *(4)*

May 29 Sunday
Alltyrodyn Mansion, Capel Dewi, Llandysul
(1)

June 1 Wednesday
Winllan Wildlife Garden, Talsarn *(18)*

June 2 Thursday
Winllan Wildlife Garden, Talsarn *(18)*

June 3 Friday
Winllan Wildlife Garden, Talsarn *(18)*

June 4 Saturday
Winllan Wildlife Garden, Talsarn *(18)*

June 5 Sunday
Arfron, Talsarn, Lampeter *(2)*
Winllan Wildlife Garden, Talsarn *(18)*

June 6 Monday
Winllan Wildlife Garden, Talsarn *(18)*

June 7 Tuesday
Winllan Wildlife Garden, Talsarn *(18)*

June 8 Wednesday
Winllan Wildlife Garden, Talsarn *(18)*

June 9 Thursday
Winllan Wildlife Garden, Talsarn *(18)*

June 10 Friday
Winllan Wildlife Garden, Talsarn *(18)*

June 11 Saturday
Winllan Wildlife Garden, Talsarn *(18)*

June 12 Sunday
Bwlch y Geufford, Bronant *(5)*
Cae Hir, Cribyn *(6)*
Farmyard Nursery Woodland Garden,
Llandysul *(8)*
Winllan Wildlife Garden, Talsarn *(18)*

June 13 Monday
Winllan Wildlife Garden, Talsarn *(18)*

June 14 Tuesday
Winllan Wildlife Garden, Talsarn *(18)*

June 15 Wednesday
Winllan Wildlife Garden, Talsarn *(18)*

June 16 Thursday
Winllan Wildlife Garden, Talsarn *(18)*

June 17 Friday
Winllan Wildlife Garden, Talsarn *(18)*

June 18 Saturday
Winllan Wildlife Garden, Talsarn *(18)*

June 19 Sunday
Llanllyr, Talsarn, Lampeter *(11)*
Pant-yr-Holiad, Rhydlewis *(16)*
Winllan Wildlife Garden, Talsarn *(18)*

June 20 Monday
Winllan Wildlife Garden, Talsarn *(18)*

June 21 Tuesday
Winllan Wildlife Garden, Talsarn *(18)*

June 22 Wednesday
Winllan Wildlife Garden, Talsarn *(18)*

June 23 Thursday
Llanerchaeron **(Evening)** *(10)*
Winllan Wildlife Garden, Talsarn *(18)*

June 24 Friday
Winllan Wildlife Garden, Talsarn *(18)*

June 25 Saturday
Winllan Wildlife Garden, Talsarn *(18)*

June 26 Sunday
Brynderi, Llechryd *(3)*
The Old Vicarage, Llangeler *(15)*
Winllan Wildlife Garden, Talsarn *(18)*

June 27 Monday
Winllan Wildlife Garden, Talsarn *(18)*

June 28 Tuesday
Winllan Wildlife Garden, Talsarn *(18)*

June 29 Wednesday
Winllan Wildlife Garden, Talsarn *(18)*

June 30 Thursday
Winllan Wildlife Garden, Talsarn *(18)*

July 3 Sunday
The Bungalow, Plwmp *(4)*
The Old Vicarage, Llangeler *(15)*
Ty Glyn Walled Garden *(17)*

July 10 Sunday
Landring, Rhydlewis *(9)*

July 31 Sunday
Arfron, Talsarn, Lampeter *(2)*

September 4 Sunday
Cwmrhaiadr Garden & Nursery, Glaspwll,
Machynlleth *(7)*

CEREDIGION/CARDIGANSHIRE

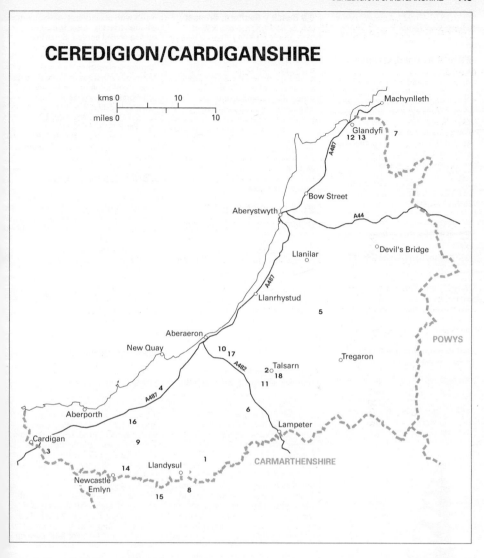

DESCRIPTIONS OF GARDENS

❶ Alltyrodyn Mansion, Capel Dewi, Llandysul 🔥⊛
(Mr & Mrs Donald Usher) *8m W of Lampeter. Off A474. B4459 at Rhydowen to village of Capel Dewi. Entrance on R by South Lodge.* Early C19 garden. Approx 8 acres, mostly mature woodland with many fine trees. Old walled garden. Rare stone-built gothic cold bathhouse. Early C20 lake, Dutch garden and rhododendron plantings. Garden is best viewed in spring when rhododendrons and azaleas are in

bloom. Home-made TEAS. *Adm £2, chd 50p (share to Capel Dewi Church). Sun 29 May (11-5). Private visits welcome by appt. Tel 01545 590206*

❷ Arfron, Talsarn, Lampeter ✗⊛
(Mr & Mrs T Richardson) *8m NW of Lampeter. A482 from Lampeter towards Aberaeron, after approx 5m turn R onto B4337. Pass through Talsarn & Trefilan, continue up hill until you reach tel box on the R outside white house. Turn immed R, Arfron is 1st house on R, ½m from*

junction. Limited parking. The garden is just under 1 acre, consisting of a formal section of terraced lawns, dry stone walls and mature herbaceous borders that gradually slope away from the house and surround a central pool. The lower garden has a woodland setting descending more steeply along a narrow winding path, with a bridge over a tumbling stream. Gunnera, iris and a wealth of trees and shrubs. Home-made TEAS. *Adm £2, chd 50p. Suns 5 June; 31 July (11-5). Private visits welcome by appt.*

Tel 01570 470923 termar@arfrontalsarn.fsnet.co.uk

❸ NEW Brynderi, Llechryd
👦♿✉

(Geoff & Pauline Palmer) 3m E of Cardigan. From Cardigan take A484 Carmarthen rd towards Newcastle Emlyn. Take 1st R at Xrds, Croes-y-llan. After 1 ½m Brynderi is 1st white cottage on L. Limited parking. Approx 1 acre of mixed herbaceous island beds and borders, shrubs, trees, rose garden with arched walkway. Small pond, vegetable plot and fruit trees. Light refreshments and TEAS. Adm £2.50, chd free. Sun 26 June (11-5)

❹ NEW The Bungalow, Plwmp
♿✉

(Mr & Mrs Barry Crutchley) 14m N of Cardigan. Take the lane to Post Bach opposite Plwmp PO. Entrance 100yds on L. This ½-acre garden comprises a wide variety of trees, shrubs and herbaceous perennials and, being positioned high on a ridge overlooking Cardigan Bay, the groomed hedges play an important part in giving wind protection. These feature hedges divide the garden into four rooms which are entered through clipped arches providing the visitor with many surprises. Large plant sale. Light refreshments and TEAS. Adm £2, chd free. Sat 21 May, Sun 3 July (11-5) . Private visits welcome by appt. Tel 01239 654281

"Is that a helter-skelter tree, Mum?"

❺ Bwlch y Geufford, Bronant ✉
(Mr & Mrs J Acres) 6m NW of Tregaron. 12m SE of Aberystwyth off the A485. Take turning opp Bronant school for 1 ½m then turn L up a ½m track. 1000ft high, 2-acre wildlife garden featuring lake with water lilies and a series of pools linked by waterfalls, a number of theme gardens, from mediterranean to woodland and from oriental to exotic jungle with hut. Plenty of sympathetic seating and large sculptures. TEAS in aid of Tregaron Hospital. Adm £2.50. Sun 12 June (11-6). Private visits welcome by appt June to Sept incl. Tel 07891 658520 gayacres@aol.com

❻ ◆ Cae Hir, Cribyn 👦✉
(Wil Akkermans) 5m W of Lampeter. Take A482 from Lampeter towards Aberaeron. After 5m turn S on B4337. Cae Hir is 2m on L. No blabla this time. Just wonderful! Come and see it. 6 acres of sheer delight from colour themed sub-gardens and bonsai enclosure to wild flower bog areas. Limited wheelchair access. Featured on BBC Wales TV I love Wales, 2003. TEAS. Adm £4, chd 50p. Open daily, except Suns. Open Bank Hols. For NGS: Sun 12 June (1-6). Tel 01570 470839

❼ Cwmrhaiadr Garden & Nursery, Glaspwll, Machynlleth ✉
(Mr & Mrs Glynne Jones) 5 ½m S of Machynlleth. From Machynlleth head S on A487, after 2m turn L signposted Glaspwll. Continue for 3 ½m, narrow in parts with few passing places. Turn L at 2nd junction, R at next junction, L at next, continue & turn R at junction signposted To the Falls, continue uphill to nursery. Park in farmyard. 1-acre garden planted for yr-round effect with many species of evergreen trees and shrubs, incl rhododendron, eucryphia, hoheria, with rarities such as Leptospermum scoparium, Myrtus chequen, Acacia dealbata var subalpina. The garden is situated in a spectacular and peaceful setting. TEAS. Adm £2, chd free. Suns 1 May; 4 Sept (1-5). Private visits welcome by appt Jun & Sept only. Tel 01654 702223 glynne.jones@btinternet.com

❽ ◆ Farmyard Nursery Woodland Garden, Llandysul ✉ NCCPG
(Mr Richard Bramley) ½m S of Llandysul. Off Carmarthen rd B4336, 2nd L opp Valley Services garage. Approx 1m following signs. Established 1-acre shaded woodland and herbaceous garden. Peaceful

walks with magnificent views, natural wildlife, friendly water features, sunken walled garden. Extensive hosta, fern and bulb planting providing all-yr-round interest. Adjoining plantsman's nursery. National Collection of Tricyrtis and biggest collection of hand-pollinated hellebores in the country. 'Daily Telegraph' 2003, 'Carmarthan Journal' 2004. TEAS. Adm £2, chd free. For NGS: Suns 27 Mar; 10 Apr; 8 May; 12 June (9-6). Tel 01559 363389 richard@farmyardnurseries.co.uk

❾ NEW Landring, Rhydlewis ♿✉
(Tracey Davis & Andy Walsh) 5m N of Newcastle Emlyn. Look for Garden Open signs in the village of Rhydlewis. A plantsman's garden of 2 acres created from an overgrown field. The garden contains rhododendrons, azalea, magnolia, clethra, styrax to name but a few, herbaceous perennials, grass area, scree hill and 2 ponds. All set in small Welsh valley. Light refreshments and TEAS. Adm £2, chd free. Sun 10 July (11-6). Private visits welcome by appt. Tel 01239 851138

❿ ◆ Llanerchaeron 👦♿✉
(The National Trust) 2 ½m E of Aberaeron. On the A482 Lampeter to Aberaeron. Llanerchaeron is a small C18 Welsh gentry estate set in the beautiful Dyffryn Aeron. The estate survived virtually unaltered into the C20. 2 extensive restored walled gardens produce home-grown vegetables, fruit and herbs for sale. The kitchen garden sits at the core of the estate with a John Nash villa built in 1795 and home farm, all virtually unaltered since its construction. Evening in The Walled Garden with Madrigals. Light refreshments and TEAS. Adm £5.20, chd £2.60. Weds to Suns & Bank Hol Mons, 18th Mar to 30th Oct (11-5). For NGS: Evening Opening £2, Thur 23 June (6-9). Tel 01545 570200 www.nationaltrust.org.uk

⓫ Llanllyr, Talsarn, Lampeter 👦♿✉
(Mr & Mrs Robert Gee) 6m NW of Lampeter. On B4337 to Llanrhystud. Large early C19 garden on site of medieval nunnery, renovated, replanted and extended since 1989. Shrub rose borders. Large pond with bog and water plants; formal water garden. Laburnum arbour; avenues of flowering trees; allegorical labyrinth. Formal box garden. Many interesting and unusual plants.. Winner Clwb Garddio S4C TV 2004. Home-made

TEAS. *Adm £3, chd 50p, Prams and wheelchairs free. Sun 19 June (2-6). Private visits welcome by appt Apr to Oct. Tel 01570 470900*

12 Llwyncelyn, Glandyfi &⌀☺
(Mr & Mrs Stewart Neal) *12m N of Aberystwyth. On A487 Machynlleth (5½m). From Aberystwyth (12m), turn R just before Glandyfi sign.* 8-acre hillside garden/arboretum alongside Dyfi tributary. Collections of hybrid/species rhododendrons, azaleas, camellias, bluebells in oak woodland, hydrangea collection, fernery. Formal garden contains parterre, potager, soft fruits and unusual plants. Large plant sale. Limited wheelchair access. Featured in 'Gardening Which' 2003. Home-made TEAS. *Combined with* **The Mill House** *adm £3, chd free. Sun 8 May (11-6). Private visits welcome by appt inc groups and coaches. Tel 01654 781203 joy@glandyfi.fsnet.co.uk*

13 The Mill House, Glandyfi ⌀
(Professor & Mrs J M Pollock) *12m N of Aberystwyth. On A487 Machynlleth 5½m. From Aberystwyth 12m; turn R up lane almost directly opp sign for Glandyfi (on L). 2nd house up lane, approx 150yds.* Picturesque garden of a former water mill with millstream, millpond, and several waterfalls in woodland setting, about 1½ acres. Azaleas, rhododendrons and spring colour enhance waterside vistas, which have a Japanese theme. Featured in '25 Beautiful Gardens' Spring Issue 2004. *Combined with* **Llwyncelyn** *adm £3, chd free. Sun 8 May (11-6). Private visits welcome by appt May only. Tel 01654 781342 jpol781342@aol.com*

14 Old Cilgwyn Gardens, Newcastle Emlyn &
(Mr & Mrs Fitzwilliams) *1m N of Newcastle Emlyn. On B4571, turn R into entrance.* 14-acre woodland garden SSSI; snowdrops, daffodils, bluebells, rhododendrons, large tulip tree, well trained fremontodendron, crinodendron and many hydrangeas make this a plantsman's garden of great interest. *Adm £2, chd free. Private visits welcome by appt coaches welcome. Tel 01239 710244 mary.fitzwilliams@virgin.net*

15 The Old Vicarage, Llangeler ⌀☺
(Mr & Mrs J C Harcourt) *4m E of Newcastle Emlyn. From N Emlyn turn down lane on L in Llangeler before church.* A garden gem created since Sept 1993. Less than 1 acre divided into 3 areas of roses, shrubs and a semi-formal pool with an interesting collection of unusual herbaceous plants. Cream TEAS. *Adm £2, chd 50p. Suns 26 June; 3 July (11-8). Private visits welcome by appt. Tel 01559 371168*

16 Pant-yr-Holiad, Rhydlewis ⌀☺
(Mr & Mrs G H Taylor) *10m NE of Cardigan. From coast rd (A487) take B4334 at Brynhoffnant S towards Rhydlewis, after 1m turn L, driveway 2nd L.* 5 acres embracing walled garden housing tender plants, alpine beds, water features, rare trees and shrubs with further 15 acres of woodland setting; extensive collection rhododendron species. Home of Holiad rhododendron hybrids. TEAS. *Adm £2.50, chd £1. Suns 8 May; 19 June (2-5). Private visits welcome by appt Groups of 10 or more. Tel 01239 851493*

17 NEW ◆ **Ty Glyn Walled Garden** &⌀☺
(Ty Glyn Davis Trust) *3m SW of Aberaeron. Turn off A482 Aberaeron to Lampeter at Ciliau Aeron signposted to Pennant. Entrance 700m on L.* Secluded L-shaped walled garden in beautiful woodland setting alongside R Aeron developed specifically for special needs children. S-facing productive terraced kitchen garden overlooks herbaceous borders, orchard and ponds with child orientated features and surprises amidst unusual shrubs and perennials, newly planted fruit trees selected from former gardener's notebook of C19. Home-made TEAS. *Adm £2.50, chd free (share to Ty Glyn Davis Trust). Daily 11-5.* **For NGS:** *Sun 3 July (11-5). Tel 01970 832268 tyglyndavistrust@care4free.net*

18 Winllan Wildlife Garden, Talsarn
(Mr & Mrs Ian Callan) *8m NNW of Lampeter. On B4342, Talsarn-Llangeitho rd.* 6-acre wildlife garden owned by botanists happy to share their knowledge with visitors. Garden incl large pond, herb-rich meadow, small woodland and 600yds of river bank walk. Over 200 species of wild flowers incl many orchids with attendant butterflies, dragonflies and birds. Limited suitability for wheelchairs. *Adm £2, chd 50p. Daily Wed 1 June to Thur 30 June (2-5). Tel 01570 470612*

Evening Opening (See also garden description)

Llanerchaeron — 23 June

ngs gardens open for charity
The Yellow Book 2006
£7.99 including UK p&p
Available through **www.ngs.org.uk** or by enquiry to the NGS.
T +44 (0)1483 211535 **F** +44 (0)1483 211537 **E** email ngs@ngs.org.uk
Cheques should be in £ sterling, made payable to The National Gardens Scheme and sent to:
The National Gardens Scheme, Hatchlands Park, East Clandon, Guildford, Surrey GU4 7RT
The book will be posted on publication (Feb/Mar 2006)

Denbighshire & Colwyn

County Organiser:	Mrs Sue Rathbone, Bryn Celyn, Llanbedr, Ruthin, Denbighshire LL15 1TT Tel 01824 702077 email rathbones@bryncelyn.fsnet.co.uk
Assistant County Organisers:	Miss Marion MacNicoll, Trosyffordd, Ystrad Road, Denbighshire LL16 4RL Tel 01745 812247 macnicoll@netbreeze.co.uk
	Mrs Maggie Watkins, Parc Bach, Llanrhaeadr, Denbighshire LL16 4RY Tel 01745 890409 m-watkins@parc-bach.freeserve.co.uk
County Treasurer:	Mrs Anne Rowley Williams, Glyn Arthur, Llandyrnog, Denbighshire LL16 4NB Tel 01824 790511

Maps: Numbers shown next to each garden entry refer to that garden's entry on the county map. This position is approximate; distance and directions from the nearest main town are generally shown in the garden text. A precise location is available for those gardens featured on the NGS website by visiting www.ngs.org.uk.

Symbols: Information relating to symbols is given on page 21

DATES OF OPENING

Evening openings
See end of county listing

By appointment only
For telephone number and other details see garden description. Private visits welcomed

Aberclwyd Manor, Derwen, nr Corwen *(1)*
Arfryn, Pentrecelyn *(2)*
Bryn Celyn, Llanbedr *(5)*
Donadea Lodge, Babell *(11)*
Parc Bach, Llanrhaeadr, Denbigh *(21)*
Tan y Graig, Henllan *(24)*

February 13 Sunday
Rûg, Corwen *(22)*

April 17 Sunday
The Old Rectory, Llanfihangel Glyn Myfyr *(19)*

May 1 Sunday
Caereuni, Godre'r Gaer, nr Corwen *(7)*

May 2 Monday (Bank Hol)
Caereuni, Godre'r Gaer, nr Corwen *(7)*

May 6 Friday
Dibleys Nurseries, Cefn Rhydd, Llanelidan *(9)*

May 7 Saturday
Dibleys Nurseries, Cefn Rhydd, Llanelidan *(9)*

May 8 Sunday
Dibleys Nurseries, Cefn Rhydd, Llanelidan *(9)*

May 15 Sunday
Beaver Grove House, Betws-y-Coed *(3)*
The Old Rectory, Llanfihangel Glyn Myfyr *(19)*

May 21 Saturday
Dolhyfryd, The Lawnt **(Evening)** *(10)*

May 22 Sunday
Dolhyfryd, The Lawnt *(10)*
Maesmor Hall, Maerdy *(17)*

May 29 Sunday
Caereuni, Godre'r Gaer, nr Corwen *(7)*
Trosyffordd, Ystrad *(26)*

May 30 Monday (Bank Hol)
Caereuni, Godre'r Gaer, nr Corwen *(7)*
Garthewin, Llanfair TH *(13)*

June 3 Friday
33 Bryn Twr & Lynton, Abergele **(Evening)** *(6)*

June 5 Sunday
Caereuni, Godre'r Gaer, nr Corwen *(7)*
Isguerwen, nr, Pentrellyncymer *(15)*

June 10 Friday
The Old Rectory, Llangynhafal **(Evening)** *(20)*

June 11 Saturday
The Old Rectory, Llangynhafal *(20)*

June 12 Sunday
33 Bryn Twr & Lynton, Abergele *(6)*

June 19 Sunday
Caereuni, Godre'r Gaer, nr Corwen *(7)*
Green Garth, Rhos on Sea *(14)*
Nantclwyd Hall, Ruthin *(18)*

June 26 Sunday
The Old Rectory, Llanfihangel Glyn Myfyr *(19)*
Trosyffordd, Ystrad *(26)*

July 3 Sunday
Caereuni, Godre'r Gaer, nr Corwen *(7)*
Tal-y-Bryn Farm, Llannefydd *(23)*

July 10 Sunday
Waen Wen, Llandyrnog *(27)*

July 17 Sunday
Caereuni, Godre'r Gaer, nr Corwen *(7)*
Ffynnon y Milgi, Llanelidan *(12)*

July 24 Sunday
Llandegla Village Gardens *(16)*

August 7 Sunday
Caereuni, Godre'r Gaer, nr Corwen *(7)*
Green Garth, Rhos on Sea *(14)*
Tan yr Onnen, Graigfechan *(25)*

August 8 Monday
Bodysgallen Hall & Spa, nr Llandudno *(4)*

August 28 Sunday
Caereuni, Godre'r Gaer, nr Corwen *(7)*

August 29 Monday (Bank Hol)
Caereuni, Godre'r Gaer, nr Corwen *(7)*

September 4 Sunday
Caereuni, Godre'r Gaer, nr Corwen *(7)*
Castanwydden, Fforddlas, Llandyrnog *(8)*

"... but I distinctly remember asking for <u>Morris</u> dancers!"

DENBIGHSHIRE & COLWYN

DESCRIPTIONS OF GARDENS

❶ Aberclwyd Manor, Derwen, nr Corwen
(Miss Irene Brown & Mr Giuliano Sparvoli) *7m S of Ruthin. From Ruthin take A494 to Bala. At Bryn SM service station turn R, follow sign to Derwen. Before village, black wrought iron gates on L.* 4 acres with mature trees incl monkey puzzle in new Italianate garden, wild flower meadow, 3 ponds, potager, rose pergola, hornbeam avenue. Peacocks, shrubs and herbaceous. Feb for snowdrops. *Adm £2.50, chd 25p. Private visits welcome by appt. Tel 01824 750431*

❷ Arfryn, Pentrecelyn 🌷🅷
(Mr & Mrs A O Davies) *4m S of Ruthin. On A525 Wrexham rd. At Llanfair Dyffryn Clwyd take B5429 to Graigfechan. Mold-Ruthin A494 to Llanbedr Dyffryn Clwyd turn L after village B5429 to Graigfechan. Follow signs from village.* Situated on hillside 800ft above sea level. 1½-acre garden designed for yr-round interest. Divided into separate rooms - secret garden filled with old roses and hardy geraniums, cottage garden, wild flower bank and lawned gardens with herbaceous and shrub beds. Featured in 'Farmers Guardian' 2003 & 'Farmers Weekly' 2004. *Adm £2.50, chd free. Private visits welcome by appt June, July only, groups of 10+. Tel 01978 790475 arfryn@pentrecelyn.fsnet.co.uk*

❸ Beaver Grove House, Betws-y-Coed 🌷🅷
(Mr J Heminsley) *½m S of Betws-y-Coed. Opp side of R Conwy from Betws-y-Coed, one entrance drive on A470, 200yds N of Waterloo Bridge; other entrance 800yds N of bridge on same rd.* Magic of a lost, old, unrestored garden; grass paths winding between wonderful old magnolias, azaleas and rhododendrons, leading to small arboretum. Approx 5 acres. Light refreshments and TEAS. *Adm £2.50, chd 50p (share to Colwyn Bay Leukaemia Research). Sun 15 May (12-6)*

❹ Bodysgallen Hall & Spa, nr Llandudno 🌷🅷
(Historic House Hotels Ltd) *2m from Llandudno. Take A55 to its intersection with A470 towards Llandudno. Proceed 1m, hotel is 1m on R.* Garden is well known for C17 box-hedged parterre. Stone walls surround lower gardens with rose gardens and herbaceous borders.

Outside walled garden is cascade over rocks. Enclosed working fruit and vegetable garden with espalier-trained fruit trees, hedging area for cut flowers with walls covered in wineberry and Chinese gooseberry. Newly restored Victorian woodland, walks with stunning views of Conwy and Snowdonia. House, cottages & outbuildings not open. Featured in 'The English Garden', 'The Garden' & S4C 2004. TEAS. *Adm £2.50, chd 50p. Mon 8 Aug (2-5)*

❺ Bryn Celyn, Llanbedr 🅷🌷🅷
(Mrs S Rathbone) *2m N of Ruthin. From Ruthin take A494 towards Mold. After 1½m, turn L at Griffin PH onto B5429. Proceed 1½m; garden on R.* 2-acre garden with lawns surrounded by mixed borders. Walled garden with old-fashioned roses, clematis, pond, fruit trees. New design features. Pergola leading to Mediterranean garden and woodland area. *Adm £2.50, chd 25p. Private visits welcome by appt, anybody, any time. Tel 01824 702077 rathbones@bryncelyn.fsnet.co.uk*

❻ 33 Bryn Twr & Lynton, Abergele 🌷🅷
(Mr & Mrs Colin Knowlson & Mr & Mrs K A Knowlson) *From A55 heading W, take slip rd to Abergele. Turn L at roundabout then over T-lights; 1st L signed Llanfair T H. 3rd rd on L, No. 33 is on L.* 2 connected gardens of totaly differing styles, one cottage style of planting, the other quite formal. Approx ¾ acre in total, containing patio and pond areas; mixed herbaceous and shrub borders, many unusual plants. Not suitable for wheelchairs. TEAS. *Adm £2.50, chd free, concessions £2 (share to St Kentigern Hospice). Sun 12 June (12-5).* **Evening Opening** *£2.50, wine, Fri 3 June (7-9.30). Private visits welcome by appt. Tel 01745 828201 apk@slaters.com*

Caerau Uchaf, Sarnau 🅷🌷🅷
See Gwynedd.

❼ Caereuni, Godre'r Gaer, nr Corwen 🅷🌷
(Mr & Mrs Steve Williams) *1m N of Corwen. Take A5 to Bala. Turn R at T-lights onto A494 to Chester. 1st R after lay-by; house ¼m on L.* Exotic themed garden. Rare tropical plants; Japanese water garden; old ruin and miniature pine garden; woodman's lodge; dry stream and tree fern jungle. Lost Welsh gold mine; Mexican chapel; seaside beach and Spanish patio area with over 100 pots and containers. S4C Wales Garden of the Year 2003. Home-made TEAS in

aid of Hope House, Oswestry. *Adm £2.50, chd 50p. Suns, Mons 1, 2, 29, 30 May; 5, 19 June; 3, 17 July; 7, 28, 29 Aug; 4 Sept (2-5)*

❽ Castanwydden, Fforddlas, Llandyrnog 🅷🌷🅷
(Mr A M Burrows) *4m E of Denbigh. Take rd from Denbigh due E to Llandyrnog approx 4m. From Ruthin take B5429 due N to Llandyrnog.* 1 acre overflowing with unusual cottage garden plants; sunken patio garden with stone troughs; newly replanted rock garden, gravel bed with grasses; trellises covered in roses and clematis; unusual trees, wonderful colour and interest all summer, late flowering salvias, autumn cyclamen. Adjacent nursery. Home-made TEAS. *Adm £2.50, chd 50p (share to Llangynhafal Parish Church). Sun 4 Sept (2-6). Private visits welcome by appt. Tel 01824 790404*

❾ Dibleys Nurseries, Cefn Rhydd, Llanelidan 🌷🅷
(Mr & Mrs R Dibley) *7m S of Ruthin. Take A525 to Xrds by Llysfasi Agricultural College. Turn onto B5429 towards Llanelidan. After 1½m turn L, 1m up lane on L. Brown tourist signs from A525.* 9-acre arboretum with wide selection of unusual trees, many becoming mature, others newly planted. Glasshouses of streptocarpus and other pot plants open Mar to Oct. Beautiful views of Vale of Clwyd. Miniature railway running through arboretum. Home-made TEAS. *Adm £2, chd 50p (share to ActionAid). Fri, Sat, Sun 6, 7, 8 May (10-5) www.dibleys.com*

❿ Dolhyfryd, The Lawnt 🅷🌷
(Captain & Mrs Michael Cunningham) *1m SW of Denbigh. On B4501 to Nantglyn, from Denbigh - 1m from town centre.* Established garden set in small valley of R Ystrad. Acres of crocuses in late Feb/early Mar. Paths through wild flower meadows and woodland of magnificent trees, shade-loving plants and azaleas; mixed borders; walled kitchen garden. Cream TEAS. *Adm £2.50, chd £1.50. Sun 22 May (2-6).* **Evening Opening** *£2.50, wine, Sat 21 May (5-7.30). Private visits welcome by appt early March for crocus & winter garden + all other dates. Tel 01745 814805 virginia@dolhyfryd.com*

⓫ Donadea Lodge, Babell 🅷🌷🅷
(Mr & Mrs P Beaumont) *7m NE of Denbigh. Turn off A541 Mold to*

Denbigh at Afonwen, signed Babell; T-junction turn L. A55 Chester to Conway take B5122 to Caerwys, 3rd turn on L. 1-acre shady garden showing 25yrs of imaginative planting to enhance the magic of dappled shade, moving through different colour schemes, with each plant complementing its neighbour. Over 100 clematis also a medlar tree over 100yrs old. *Adm £2.50, chd free. Private visits welcome by appt May, June & July. Tel 01352 720204*

⑫ NEW Ffynnon y Milgi, Llanelidan 🌿
(Mr & Mrs Charles Davey) *4m S of Ruthin. On A525 S of Ruthin at Xrds with B5429, before Llysfasi Agricultural College, turn R (signed to Llanelidan), take 4th lane on R (2¼m from Xrds). This is a very narrow lane for 1000 metres. Take 2nd on R.* Unusual country garden nestling around limestone outcrop where nature is allowed to complement the relaxed planting of shrubs, herbaceous borders, gravel garden and rockeries. Natural rock water feature and pond together with grass and gravel paths make this a garden for meandering. Home-made TEAS in aid of Cancer Research UK Cymru. *Adm £2.50, chd 50p. Sun 17 July (2-6)*

⑬ NEW Garthewin, Llanfair TH
(Mr Michael Grime) *6m S of Abergele & A55. From Abergele take A548 to Llanfair TH & Llanrwst. Car park & entrance to garden ½m W of Llanfair TH on A548 to Llanrwst.* Valley garden with ponds and woodland areas. Much of the 8 acres have been reclaimed and redesigned providing a younger garden with a great variety of azaleas, rhododendrons and young trees, all within a framework of mature shrubs and trees. Small chapel open. TEAS n the old theatre. *Adm £3, chd £1 (share to St Mary's Church, Llanfair TH). Mon 30 May (2-6). Private visits welcome by appt. Tel 01745 720288*

⑭ Green Garth, 86 Dinerth Road, Rhos on Sea 🌿🏡
(Eryl & Tricia Williams) *1m W of Colwyn Bay. Exit A55 at J20. Take B5115 Rhos on Sea/Llandudno for 1m. Turn L at garage. Garden ½m on L.* ½-acre garden on steep S-facing limestone hillside backing onto Bryn Euryn Nature Reserve. Pond, gravel and bog gardens. Large limestone rockery, many unusual plants. Designed for yr-round interest with shrub and herbaceous borders. TEAS.

Adm £2, chd free (share to St David's Hospice). Suns 19 June; 7 Aug (11-5)

⑮ NEW Isguerwen, nr, Pentrellyncymer 🌿🏡
(Michael Williams) *10m W of Ruthin. 10m SW of Denbigh. From Ruthin take B1505 towards Cerrigydrudion, ½m (Cross Keys PH) fork R to Bontuchel & Cyffylliog, 5m through Cyffylliog towards Glocaenog forest, 3m straight over small Xrds at edge of forest, 2m straight over Xrds at top of forest, 50yds fork R, garden ½m.* At 1500ft, isolated with stunning views, 2-acre garden balances the formal and informal with areas of shrubbery, woodland copses, bog, herbaceous gardens and open spaces. The maturity belies the fact that the garden is only 17yrs old and shows what can be grown in a windy area with a short growing season. Home-made TEAS. *Adm £2.50, chd free. Sun 5 June (1.30-5.30)*

⑯ NEW Llandegla Village Gardens
(Mr Keith JAckson) *10m W of Wrexham. Off A525 at Llandegla Memorial Hall.* Small picturesque village surrounded by moorland. Church with interesting features. Communal leisure area by river. Maps available at Memorial Hall. Llandegla Village achieved merit awards in both Wales in Bloom & Neighbourhood awards 2004. Light refreshments and TEAS at & in aid of Llandegla Village Hall, Sports & Social Group. *Combined adm £5. Sun 24 July (2-6)*

> **NEW Sŵn y Gwynt** 🏡 (Phil Clark) *Situated in Llandegla Village.* ¼-acre plantsmans' garden, shrubs and associated plants for shade.

> **NEW Ty'n y Llidiart** 🌿🏡 (Janet & Ian Robinson) *On A5104 half way between The Crown Hotel (A525) & roundabout leading to The Horseshoe Pass (A542).* ¾ acre int trees, hedges and bushes for birds, ferns, rockery, plants for butterflies. 1000sq ft cactus collection (cacti for sale), ditch with tadpole pond, brick maze, vegetables. Has won local awards as wildlife garden.

NEW Tyn y Pwll 🏡 (R & S M Percival) *12m from Wrexham on A525 W of Llandegla before the Nant-y-Garth Pass.* ¾-acre organic garden, hardy plants, sheltered areas, herbs, soft fruits, vegetables and wild area.

⑰ Maesmor Hall, Maerdy ♿🌿🏡
(Mr & Mrs G M Jackson) *4m W of Corwen. On A5 going to Bangor. Towards Betws-y-Coed go through 2 sets of T-lights, opp Goat PH (on A5 at Maerdy) turn L, over Ancient Rd bridge, hall gates in front. Ample parking.* Extensive woodlands with idyllic river walks through an 11-acre garden. Enormous mature trees incl avenue of lime trees, wonderful rhododendrons, tennis court walk, picnics welcomed. Unique tumulus surrounded by beech trees, embryonic water and white garden with fountains, azaleas, parkland, nut arch, secret gardens and the beginnings of a reinstated rose garden. Home-made TEAS in aid of Diabetics UK. *Adm £2.50, chd £1, concessions £1.50. Sun 22 May (11-5)*

⑱ Nantclwyd Hall, Ruthin 🌿🏡
(Sir Philip & Lady Isabella Naylor-Leyland) *4m S of Ruthin. Take A494 from Ruthin to Corwen. Garden is 1½m from Pwllglas on L, through stone gateway in beech hedge.* Approx 3 acres of formal gardens incl Italian garden, parkland with lake and further grounds. Temples and follies by Sir Clough Williams-Ellis. Grotto by Belinda Eade. Rustic bridge over R Clwyd. *Adm £3, chd 50p. Sun 19 June (2-6). Private visits welcome by appt Nantclwyd Hall, Ruthin, Denbighshire, LL15 2PR*

⑲ The Old Rectory, Llanfihangel Glyn Myfyr ♿🌿🏡
(Mr & Mrs E T Hughes) *2½m E of Cerrigydrudion. From Ruthin take B5105 SW for 12m to Llanfihangel Glyn Myfyr. Turn R just after Crown PH (follow signs). Proceed for ½m, garden on L.* 14 yr-old garden of approx 1 acre set in beautiful, tranquil, sheltered valley. A garden for all seasons; hellebores; abundance of spring flowers; mixed borders; water, bog, and gravel gardens;

walled garden with old roses, pergola and bower and garden of meditation . Also incl garden created 9yrs ago by son (now aged 16) which features hardy orchids and gentians. Accommodation. Home-made TEAS. *Adm £2.50, chd 50p (share to Cancer Research UK (Men's Cancers only). Suns 17 Apr; 15 May; 26 June (2-6). Private visits welcome by appt. Tel 01490 420568 elwynthomashughes@hotmail.com*

⓴ The Old Rectory, Llangynhafal &⟐
(Mr & Mrs Henry Dixon) *3½m N of Ruthin. From Ruthin take A494; Llanbedr take B5429. After ½m turn R signed 2½m Llangynhafal. Entrance on R at Xrds.* Extensive grounds centred on traditional walled gardens, with unusual plants, orchards and vegetables. Installations, sculptures and water features link the C18 and C21. Yr-round colour and interest. Home-made TEAS. *Adm £2.50, chd 50p (share to Llangynhafal Parish Church). Sat 11 June (2-5.30); Evening Opening £2.50, wine, Fri 10 June (6-8.30)*

㉑ Parc Bach, Llanrhaeadr, Denbigh &⟐
(Mrs Ivor Watkins) *2½m SE of Denbigh. 5m NW of Ruthin. On the A525, turn off for Llanrhaeadr. At war memorial follow the Prion Rd, up the hill. Parc Bach 1st turning on R (200yds). ½-acre* garden making max use of all available space. Beds crammed full of unusual plants, making beautiful picture, framed by wonderful views across the Vale of ClwydIt would be a pleasure to share my garden with small groups of people. Picnics possible or pub nearby. *Adm £2.50, chd free. Private visits welcome by appt May to Sept, groups of 10+. Tel 01745 890409 m-watkins@parc-bach.freeserve.co.uk*

Pen-y-Bryn, Llangollen &⟐⟐
See Flintshire & Wrexham.

㉒ Rûg, Corwen &
(Jennifer, Lady Newborough) *½m W of Corwen. Follow A5 from Corwen over R Dee bridge to T-lights. About ¼m turn R off A5 by Lodge.*

Snowdrops carpeting the woods in Feb, beneath beautiful trees, some of which are the oldest sequoias and Douglas firs in the country. Woodland walk with views of the lake. Knot garden progressing with several additions. Dogs on leads under the control of owners are allowed to walk round lake. Light refreshments and TEAS in aid of League of Friends of the Robert Jones & Agnes Hunt Orthopaedic Hospital. *Adm £2.50, chd free. Sun 13 Feb (12-3)*

㉓ Tal-y-Bryn Farm, Llannefydd &⟐
(Mr & Mrs Gareth Roberts) *3m W of Henllan. From Henllan take rd signed Llannefydd. After 2½m turn R signed Bont Newydd. Garden ½m on L.* Medium-sized working farmhouse cottage garden. Incorporating ancient privy festooned with honeysuckle and roses. Terraced arches, sunken garden pool and bog garden, fountains and old water pumps. Herb wheels, shrubs and other interesting features. Lovely views of the Clwydian range. Home-made TEAS. *Adm £2.50, chd free. Sun 3 July (2-6)*

㉔ Tan y Graig, Mill Lane, Llannefydd Road, Henllan &
(Jim & Barbara Buchanan) *2m W of Denbigh. On B5382 Denbigh to Henllan rd. Mill Lane is 100yds below Church Tower off the Llannefydd rd. Garden is top bungalow in Mill Lane.* Elevated ½-acre garden with panoramic views over surrounding countryside, disected by terraced walks and backed by a high limestone cliff abundant with wildlife. Large rockery, shrub and perennial beds containing over 500 varieties of plants - many unusual. Small adjacent nursery with all plants propagated from the garden. Featured in 'Liverpool Daily Post' 2003. *Adm £2.50, chd free. Private visits welcome by appt. Tel 01745 816161*

㉕ NEW Tan yr Onnen, Graigfechan ⟐⟐
(Anthony & Susan Shaw) *3m S of Ruthin. On A525 Wrexham rd. At Llanfair Dyffryn Clwyd B5429 to Graigfechan. Mold-Ruthin A494 to*

Llanbedr Dyffryn Clwyd, turn L after village to Graigfechan. Parking 40yds below Three Pigeons PH on roadside. 1½ acres of landscaped gardens on different levels, providing yr-round colour. Features incl lilypond, waterfall; Yorkstone patio, pergola, herb garden, lawned area, stunning containers and hanging baskets. Clever use of slate and gravel enhancing the many shrubs and perennials on display. A developing garden constantly changing. Abundance of plants for sale. Garden owner featured in 'The Cheshire Life' 2004. Light refreshments and TEAS in aid of Ruthin Community Hospital. *Adm £2.50, chd free. Sun 7 Aug (11-6)*

㉖ Trosyffordd, Ystrad &⟐⟐
(Miss Marion MacNicoll) *1½m W of Denbigh. From A525 Denbigh to Ruthin rd, turn R in outskirts of Denbigh by swimming pool, on Ystrad rd signed Prion & Saron. Follow for 1½m, Trosyffordd is 2nd drive on R after 1st hill.* Medium-sized real gardener's garden. Wide selection of shrubs, herbaceous, roses, trees and grasses. Home-propagated plants for sale. Home-made TEAS. *Adm £2.50, chd free (share to Cancer Research (May), St Kentigern Hospice (June)). Suns 29 May (2-6); 26 June (12-5). Private visits welcome by appt May to Oct. Tel 01745 812247 macnicoll@netbreeze.co.uk*

㉗ Waen Wen, Llandyrnog &⟐
(Mr & Mrs David Lloyd) *4m E of Denbigh. ¾m E from Llandyrnog on B5429.* 1-acre garden with informal mixed borders surrounding farmhouse (not open). Exciting features around every corner of farm buildings. Pond and bog area. Short walk to 7yr-old copse. Dogs may be walked in designated fields. Home-made TEAS in aid of Llandyrnog Parish Church. *Adm £2.50, chd 50p. Sun 10 July (2-5.30)*

Evening Opening (See also garden description)	
Dolhyfryd	21 May
33 Bryn Twr & Lynton	3 June
The Old Rectory	10 June

Flintshire & Wrexham

County Organiser: Mrs Gwen Manuel, Tir y Fron, Ruabon, Wrexham LL14 6RW
     Tel 01978 821633 email gwen.manuel@micro-plus-web.net
Assistant County Organiser: Mrs Rosemary Ffoulkes Jones, Bryn Hafod, Ffordd y Blaenau, Treuddyn, Mold CH7 4NS
     Tel 01352 771620
Press & Publicity Officer: Mrs Angela Wilson, Penley Hall Stables, Penley, Wrexham, Flintshire LL13 0LU
     Tel 01948 830439 email wilsons.penley@virgin.net
County Treasurer: Mr Peter Manuel, Tir y Fron, Ruabon, Wrexham LL14 6RW Tel 01978 821633

Maps: Numbers shown next to each garden entry refer to that garden's entry on the county map. This position is approximate; distance and directions from the nearest main town are generally shown in the garden text. A precise location is available for those gardens featured on the NGS website by visiting www.ngs.org.uk.
Symbols: Information relating to symbols is given on page 21

DATES OF OPENING

Evening openings
See end of county listing

Gardens open to the public
For details see garden description
Dolwen, Cefn Coch, Llanrhaeadr-ym-Mochnant *(5)*
Erddig Hall, nr Wrexham *(7)*
The Garden House, Erbistock *(8)*

By appointment only
For telephone number and other details see garden description.
Private visits welcomed
Leeswood Green Farm, Leeswood *(11)*

April 3 Sunday
Hawarden Castle, Hawarden *(9)*
April 17 Sunday
Park Cottage, Penley *(13)*
April 18 Monday
57 Wyndham Drive, Cefn-y-Bedd *(17)*
April 19 Tuesday
57 Wyndham Drive, Cefn-y-Bedd *(17)*
April 20 Wednesday
57 Wyndham Drive, Cefn-y-Bedd *(17)*
April 21 Thursday
57 Wyndham Drive, Cefn-y-Bedd *(17)*
April 22 Friday
57 Wyndham Drive, Cefn-y-Bedd *(17)*
April 25 Monday
57 Wyndham Drive, Cefn-y-Bedd *(17)*
April 26 Tuesday
57 Wyndham Drive, Cefn-y-Bedd *(17)*
April 27 Wednesday
57 Wyndham Drive, Cefn-y-Bedd *(17)*
April 28 Thursday
Erddig Hall, nr Wrexham *(7)*
57 Wyndham Drive, Cefn-y-Bedd *(17)*
April 29 Friday
57 Wyndham Drive, Cefn-y-Bedd *(17)*
May 1 Sunday
Tir-y-Fron, Ruabon *(16)*

May 2 Monday (Bank Hol)
Tir-y-Fron, Ruabon *(16)*
57 Wyndham Drive, Cefn-y-Bedd *(17)*
May 3 Tuesday
57 Wyndham Drive, Cefn-y-Bedd *(17)*
May 4 Wednesday
57 Wyndham Drive, Cefn-y-Bedd *(17)*
May 5 Thursday
Bryn Hafod, Treuddyn, Nr Mold *(3)*
57 Wyndham Drive, Cefn-y-Bedd *(17)*
May 6 Friday
57 Wyndham Drive, Cefn-y-Bedd *(17)*
May 9 Monday
57 Wyndham Drive, Cefn-y-Bedd *(17)*
May 10 Tuesday
57 Wyndham Drive, Cefn-y-Bedd *(17)*
May 11 Wednesday
57 Wyndham Drive, Cefn-y-Bedd *(17)*
May 12 Thursday
57 Wyndham Drive, Cefn-y-Bedd *(17)*
May 13 Friday
57 Wyndham Drive, Cefn-y-Bedd *(17)*
May 15 Sunday
Dolwen, Cefn Coch, Llanrhaeadr-ym-Mochnant *(5)*
May 16 Monday
57 Wyndham Drive, Cefn-y-Bedd *(17)*
May 17 Tuesday
57 Wyndham Drive, Cefn-y-Bedd *(17)*
May 18 Wednesday
57 Wyndham Drive, Cefn-y-Bedd *(17)*
May 19 Thursday
57 Wyndham Drive, Cefn-y-Bedd *(17)*
May 20 Friday
57 Wyndham Drive, Cefn-y-Bedd *(17)*
May 22 Sunday
Argoed Cottage, Overton *(1)*
Bryn Amma Cottage, Wrexham *(2)*
May 23 Monday
57 Wyndham Drive, Cefn-y-Bedd *(17)*
May 24 Tuesday
57 Wyndham Drive, Cefn-y-Bedd *(17)*
May 25 Wednesday
57 Wyndham Drive, Cefn-y-Bedd *(17)*
May 26 Thursday
57 Wyndham Drive, Cefn-y-Bedd *(17)*

May 27 Friday
57 Wyndham Drive, Cefn-y-Bedd *(17)*
May 29 Sunday
The Garden House, Erbistock *(8)*
Pen-y-Bryn, Llangollen *(14)*
June 5 Sunday
Pen-y-Bryn, Llangollen *(14)*
June 9 Thursday
Bryn Hafod, Treuddyn, Nr Mold *(3)*
June 12 Sunday
Dolwen, Cefn Coch, Llanrhaeadr-ym-Mochnant *(5)*
The Garden House, Erbistock *(8)*
Llangedwyn Hall, Llangedwyn *(12)*
Park Cottage, Penley *(13)*
Plas-yn-Llan, Llanrhaeadr-ym-Mochnant *(15)*
June 26 Sunday
The Garden House, Erbistock *(8)*
July 10 Sunday
The Cottage Nursing Home, Mold *(4)*
The Garden House, Erbistock *(8)*
July 17 Sunday
Knolton Villa, Knolton Bryn *(10)*
August 7 Sunday
Dove Cottage, Penyffordd, Nr Chester *(6)*
August 25 Thursday
Erddig Hall, nr Wrexham *(7)*
September 4 Sunday
The Garden House, Erbistock *(8)*
September 18 Sunday
Park Cottage, Penley *(13)*

FLINTSHIRE & WREXHAM

DESCRIPTIONS OF GARDENS

❶ **Argoed Cottage, Argoed Lane, Overton** 🔗🏵
(Mr & Mrs C J Billington) *3m S of Wrexham. Approach Overton from Wrexham on A528, cross over Overton Bridge & in about ¾m on brow of hill turn L into Argoed Lane.* Well cared for garden of 1¼ acres with a wide range of beds full of interesting herbaceous plants and shrubs. There are many other idea-

giving features set amongst beautiful trees and lawns. Home-made TEAS in aid of Nightingale House Hospice. *Adm £2.50, chd free. Sun 22 May (2-5.30)*

❷ NEW **Bryn Amma Cottage, Frondeg, Wrexham** 🏵🏵
(Gillian & Roger Nock) *3m W of Wrexham. From A483 turn onto A525 towards Ruthin, after Coedpoeth Village turn L in Minera on B5426 (Minera Hall Rd), 2m turn*

R into unnamed lane with passing places, follow signs to field parking. Approx 1½-acre garden on hillside at over 900ft, near moorland. Planted for yr-round interest, woodland slopes to stream with cataracts, flag iris, naturalised ferns and moisture-loving plants. Lawned areas with informal borders, spring daffodils, perennials, rhododendrons, azaleas, ornamental trees and shrubs. Home-made TEAS in aid of Muscular Dystrophy. *Adm £2.50, chd free. Sun 22 May (2-5.30)*

❸ Bryn Hafod, Ffordd-y-Blaenau, Treuddyn, Nr Mold 🌿📷

(Mr & Mrs Ffoulkes Jones) *1m W of Treuddyn. Turn S off A5104 into Ffordd-y-Blaenau (signed). Follow lane for 1¼m.* 1-acre country garden with extensive views lying in an elevated position amidst farmland. Wide variety of perennials and shrubs are grown in this plant lovers' garden. Home-made TEAS in aid of Cancer Research UK. *Adm £2, chd free. Thurs 5 May; 9 June (2-5.30)*

❹ The Cottage Nursing Home, 54 Hendy Road, Mold ♿📷

(Mr & Mrs A G & L I Lanini) *10m W of Chester. Mold town centre take A494 to Ruthin. 2nd R into Hafod Park. Straight on to T-junction. Turn R on Hendy Rd. Garden at junction of Hendy Rd & Clayton Rd.* Beautiful garden set in approx 1 acre. Well established shrubs, herbaceous plants and abundance of colourful window boxes and tubs. Heart-shaped patio, incl water feature and pergola, with natural reclaimed stone walling. Mold in Bloom Business Property Garden Winner 2003. Cream TEAS. *Adm £1.50, chd 50p (share to British Heart Foundation). Sun 10 July (2-5)*

❺ ◆ Dolwen, Cefn Coch, Llanrhaeadr-ym-Mochnant 📷

(Bob Yarwood & Jeny Marriott) *14m W of Oswestry. Take B4396 (or B4580 - narrow) W to Llanrhaeadr-ym-Mochnant. Turn R at W end of village opp The Plough Inn & up narrow lane for approx 1km. Garden on R.* 2 acres of hillside garden with pools, stream, small wood and many different types of unusual plants all backed by a stupendous mountain view. TEAS. *Adm £2.50, chd free. Fris and last Sun in month May to Aug (2-4.30).* **For NGS:** *Suns 15 May; 12 June (2-5). Tel 01691 780411, J Marriott*

Donadea Lodge, Babell ♿🌿📷
See Denbighshire & Colwyn.

❻ Dove Cottage, Rhos Road, Penyffordd, Nr Chester ♿🌿📷

(Chris and Denise Wallis) *6m SW of Chester. From Chester A55 S exit A550 follow signs for Corwen. Turn L immed opp Penyffordd railway station. From Wrexham A541 for Mold, R at Pontblyddyn for Chester, turn R immed opp Penyffordd railway station.* Approx 1½-acre garden, many shrubs and herbaceous plants set informally around lawns. Small kitchen garden, 2 ponds (1 wildlife), summerhouse, pergola.

Home-made TEAS in aid of Capricorn Animal Rescue. *Adm £2, chd free. Sun 7 Aug (2-5.30)*

❼ ◆ Erddig Hall, nr Wrexham ♿🌿 NCCPG

(The National Trust) *2m S of Wrexham. Signed from A483/A5125 Oswestry rd; also from A525 Whitchurch rd.* Garden restored to its C18 formal design incl varieties of fruit known to have been grown there during that period and now incl the National Ivy Collection. Also Victorian parterre roses and wild flower meadows. TEAS. *Adm £2.50, chd free. 19 Mar to 30 Oct daily except Thurs & Fris (11-4).* **For NGS:** *Thurs 28 Apr; 25 Aug (12-4). Tel 01978 355314, Glyn Smith glyn.smith@nationaltrust.org*

❽ ◆ The Garden House, Erbistock ♿🌿 NCCPG

(Mr & Mrs S Wingett) *5m S of Wrexham. On A528 Wrexham to Shrewsbury rd. Follow signs at Overton Bridge to Erbistock Church.* Shrub and herbaceous plantings in monochromatic, analogous and complementary colour schemes. Rose pergolas, National Collection of hydrangea (over 300 species and cultivars). Sculpture Garden. Large lily pond, Victorian dovecote. TEAS. *Adm £2, chd free. Mon to Sat (10-5) Sun (2-5) Apr to Oct.* **For NGS:** *Suns 29 May; 12, 26 June; 10 July; 4 Sept (2-5). Tel 01978 781149, Simon Wingett www.simonwingett.com*

❾ Hawarden Castle, Hawarden ♿

(Sir William & Lady Gladstone) *6m W of Chester. On B5125 just E of Hawarden village. Entrance via farm shop.* Large garden and picturesque ruined castle. Dogs must be on short leads. *Adm £3, chd £2. Sun 3 Apr (2-6)*

❿ Knolton Villa, Knolton Bryn 🌿📷

(Stephen Smith) *3m W of Ellesmere. 14m SE of Wrexham. On A528 Ellesmere-Overton rd, turn L signposted Knolton Bryn. 2m from Overton towards Ellesmere turn R signposted Knolton Bryn. ¾m down lane on RH-side.* Gentle sloping 1-acre garden with island beds, pool, summerhouse, small orchard. Area surrounding bungalow specialising in bamboos, grasses and hemerocallis. TEAS. *Adm £2, chd free. Sun 17 July (2-6)*

⓫ Leeswood Green Farm, Leeswood ♿📷

(Anne Saxon) *3m SE of Mold. 9m NW of Wrexham. Off A541 W. At Pontblyddyn, from Wrexham turn L after garage into Dingle Rd. After ½m at T-junction turn L then almost immed R down farm track ¼m long. Drive with care, no passing places. Signed public footpath. Limited parking.* Approx 1-acre garden surrounding C15 farmhouse and barn in rural location. Many trees, shrubs and interesting perennials set informally around lawns. Orchard, vegetable garden and paved areas with some unusual features. *Private visits welcome by appt Apr to Sept. Tel 01352 771222*

⓬ Llangedwyn Hall, Llangedwyn ♿🌿📷

(Mr & Mrs T M Bell) *8m W of Oswestry. On B4396 to Llanrhaeadr-ym-Mochnant about 5m W of Llynclys Xrds.* Approx 4-acre formal terraced garden on 3 levels, designed and laid out in late C17 and early C18. Unusual herbaceous plants, sunken rose garden, small water garden, walled kitchen garden and woodland walk. TEAS in aid of Llangedwyn Church. *Adm £2.50, chd 50p. Sun 12 June (2-6)*

⓭ Park Cottage, Penley 📷

(Dr & Mrs S J Sime) *3m E of Overton on Dee. 12m SE Wrexham. LH-side of Penley village post office on A539. Roadside parking in village involves 250yd walk to garden. Please no parking at house.* Relaxed garden emerging on site of 5 acres. Incl large natural pond, small formal water garden, double herbaceous border, labyrinth garden, several shade gardens and new wild flower area. Growing plant collection has 1500 plus species and cultivars, with special interest in the hydrangeaceae. Autumn border and grass garden look good in mid Sept. Home-made TEAS. *Adm £2.50, chd £1 (share to Penley Parish Church). Suns 17 Apr; 12 June; 18 Sept (2-5)*

ngs gardens open for charity

Look out for the NCCPG National Plant Collections at some of our gardens

⑭ Pen-y-Bryn, Llangollen
♿🐕☻
(Mr & Mrs R B Attenburrow) *14m SW of Wrexham. Located above centre of Llangollen. Signs at T-lights on A5 in centre of Llangollen to field parking on open days. Groups by appt should apply for directions.* 3-acre garden on wooded plateau overlooking town with panoramic view. On site of old hall with established trees, shrubs and rhododendrons; walled garden; water features; new folly; extensive lawns and herbaceous borders. Home-made TEAS. *Adm £2.50, chd free (share to Llangollen International Musical Eisteddfod (Floral)). Suns 29 May; 5 June (2-5.30). Private visits welcome by appt for groups. Tel 01978 860223*

⑮ Plas-yn-Llan, Llanrhaeadr-ym-Mochnant ♿🐕
(Mrs Frances Denby) *12m SW of Oswestry. From Oswestry take B4396 going W to Llanrhaeadr.* House in square 2nd from the Bank. Plantswoman's garden in courtyard of an old coaching inn (not open). Tender climbing plants in courtyard and orangery. Slate pathed garden at rear. *Adm £2, chd free. Sun 12 June (2-5). Private visits welcome by appt May to Aug incl. Tel 01691 780236*

⑯ Tir-y-Fron, Ruabon ♿🐕☻
(Mr & Mrs P R Manuel) *5m W of Wrexham. Llangollen rd. Take A539 from Ruabon bypass, signed Llangollen, after 500yds turn R on brow of hill.* 1¾-acre garden with shrubs and herbaceous plants surrounded by mature trees with quarry. Offa's Dyke separates garden from drive. Cream TEAS. *Adm £2.50, chd free (share to Llangollen Canal Boat Trust). Sun, Mon 1, 2 May (2-6). Private visits welcome by appt for groups. Tel 01978 821633*

⑰ NEW 57 Wyndham Drive, Cefn-y-Bedd ♿🐕☻
(Mr & Mrs M Morrow) *4m NW of Wrexham. On A541 towards Mold. Please park with consideration.* Small and interesting plantsman's garden for yr-round interest. Shrubs, perennials, scree, troughs, conservatory, alpine house. Restricted wheelchair access. *Adm £2.50 incl tea. Private visits welcome by appt afternoons or evenings Mon to Fri 18 Apr to 27 May, warm welcome to individuals or small groups.* **By appointment only** *tel 01978 760122*

ngs gardens open for charity

The National Trust Careership Scheme

In 2004, five more gardeners commenced a three-year National Trust vocational training programme in historic gardening with a bursary from The National Gardens Scheme. Fifteen trainees at different Trust gardens throughout England and Wales receive support from the NGS. The trainees range from school leavers to those looking to change their careers. The National Trust's scheme, known as Careership, combines day-to-day practical experience under the guidance of a head gardener with periods of residential training and study at Reaseheath College, Cheshire.

Applications for places are available from March 2005, and the three year course commences in early September 2005.

For more information on Careerships, contact:

HR Service Centre – Careership Scheme,
The National Trust, Rowan, Kembrey Park, Swindon, Wiltshire SN2 8YL
or visit the National Trust Website **www.nationaltrust.org.uk**

ngs gardens open for charity

Every time you visit a garden which opens for the NGS you are helping to raise money for

- **Macmillan Cancer Relief**
- **Marie Curie Cancer Care**
- **Help the Hospices**
- **Crossroads – Caring for Carers**
- **The Queen's Nursing Institute**
- **The Nurses Welfare Service**
- **The Royal Gardeners' Orphan Fund**
- **NGS Gardeners' Bursaries – The National Trust Careership Scheme**
- **Perennial – Gardeners' Royal Benevolent Society**
- **County Nursing Associations**
- **Additional charities nominated by owners**

Glamorgan

County Organiser: Mrs Rosamund Davies, Slade, Southerndown, Glamorgan CF32 0RP
                             Tel 01656 880048 email ros@daviesslade.plus.com
County Treasurer: Mr Peter Davies, Slade, Southerndown, Glamorgan CF32 0RP
                             Tel 01656 880048 email peter@daviesslade.plus.com

Maps: Numbers shown next to each garden entry refer to that garden's entry on the county map. This position is approximate; distance and directions from the nearest main town are generally shown in the garden text.
A precise location is available for those gardens featured on the NGS website by visiting www.ngs.org.uk.
Symbols: Information relating to symbols is given on page 21

DATES OF OPENING

Evening openings
See end of county listing

Gardens open to the public
For details see garden description

Bordervale Plants, Ystradowen *(4)*
Dyffryn Gardens, nr Cardiff *(8)*

By appointment only
For telephone number and other details see garden description.
Private visits welcomed

Coedargraig, Newton, Porthcawl *(6)*
11 Eastcliff, Southgate *(9)*

February 27 Sunday
11 Arno Road, Little Coldbrook, Barry *(2)*
April 3 Sunday
Slade, Southerndown *(14)*
April 17 Sunday
The Beachouse, Cardiff *(3)*
May 1 Sunday
Ridler's Garden, Cockett, Swansea *(13)*
May 2 Monday (Bank Hol)
Ridler's Garden, Cockett, Swansea *(13)*
May 7 Saturday
Llanmadoc & Cheriton Gardens, Llanmadoc, Gower *(12)*

May 15 Sunday
6 Alma Road, Penylan, Cardiff **(Evening)**
(1)
May 18 Wednesday
Ty Nant Corrwg, Rhydyfelin, Pontypridd *(15)*
19 Westfield Road, Glyncoch, Pontypridd *(16)*
May 22 Sunday
11 Arno Road, Little Coldbrook, Barry *(2)*
Greenfield Kennels, Llangyfelach *(10)*
Killay: Cottages & Columbines, Killay, Swansea *(11)*
June 5 Sunday
Bordervale Plants, Ystradowen *(4)*
Ty Nant Corrwg, Rhydyfelin, Pontypridd *(15)*
June 12 Sunday
11 Arno Road, Little Coldbrook, Barry *(2)*
June 15 Wednesday
Ty Nant Corrwg, Rhydyfelin, Pontypridd *(15)*
19 Westfield Road, Glyncoch, Pontypridd *(16)*
June 19 Sunday
The Clock House, Llandaff *(5)*
July 10 Sunday
Bordervale Plants, Ystradowen *(4)*
July 17 Sunday
6 Alma Road, Penylan, Cardiff **(Evening)**
(1)
July 19 Tuesday
6 Alma Road, Penylan, Cardiff **(Evening)**
(1)
July 20 Wednesday
19 Westfield Road, Glyncoch, Pontypridd *(16)*
July 31 Sunday
Cottrell Park Golf Club, St Nicholas, Cardiff *(7)*

DESCRIPTIONS OF GARDENS

❶ 6 Alma Road, Penylan, Cardiff
🌳🏵
(Mr Melvyn Rees) *1½m NE of Cardiff. N from Cardiff city centre off Marlborough Rd. Take Cardiff E J29 from M4, Llanedeyrn exit from Eastern Ave, then towards Cyncoed & down Penylan Rd. S-facing terraced house garden 30ft x 15ft with many species from the S and E*

hemispheres, incl *Dicksonia antarctica, D. squarosa* and *Sophora* in a riot of exotic foliage. Slate used as paving material with gravel infill. Decking provides a raised seating area. **Evening Openings** *£2.50, chd 50p, concessions £1 (share to Alzheimer's Society), wine, light refreshments and TEAS, Suns 15 May; 17 July, Tues 19 July (5-9). Private visits welcome by appt. Tel 01633 813586 work mel@tymel.demon.co.uk*

❷ 11 Arno Road, Little Coldbrook, Barry 🌳🏵
(Mrs D Palmer) *6m SW of Cardiff. On A4050 Cardiff to Barry, take roundabout marked Barry Docks & Sully. Then 2nd R into Coldbrook Rd, 2nd L into Langlands Rd, then 6th R into Norwood Cres; 1st L into Arno Rd. Restricted parking.* Plantaholic's small paradise garden. Herbaceous borders, slate scree planted with dwarf hardy geraniums. New alpine bed, ponds and fernery. Formal front garden, informally planted with perennials. Developing winter garden. Home-made TEAS. *Adm £1.50, chd 50p. Suns 27 Feb; 22 May; 12 June (12-4.30). Private visits welcome by appt, small groups welcome (under 20). Tel 01446 743642 deb.palmer@ntlworld.com*

❸ NEW The Beachouse, 10 Clos y Bryn, Cardiff 🕊🌳🏵
(Annie Jones) *2m N of Cardiff. From M4 J32 head S on A470. 1st L, R at mini-roundabout, follow signs for Wenallt Reservoir and Woodland (3rd L). Then 2nd L, 1st R.* Designed in 1999 as lakeland beach with several wooden outbuildings with a view. Planted with specimen plants. Designed for all-yr interest and weather, for horticultural excitement and soothing peace. Light refreshments and TEAS in aid of MS Trust. *Adm £2.50, chd free, concessions £1. Sun 17 Apr (2-6).*

GLAMORGAN

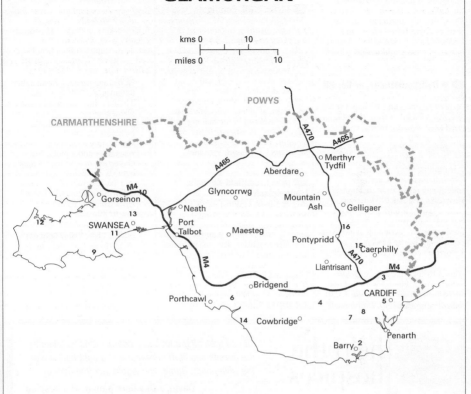

GLAMORGAN

Private visits welcome by appt.
Tel 02920 655272

4 ◆ Bordervale Plants, Ystradowen 🚫☺
(Mrs Claire Jenkins) *8m W of Cardiff. 10 mins from M4. Take A4222 from Cowbridge. Turn R at Ystradowen postbox, then 3rd L & proceed ½m. Garden on R. Parking in rd past corner.* Within mature woodland valley (semi-tamed), with stream and bog garden, extensive mixed borders; wild flower meadow, providing diverse wildlife habitats. Children must be supervised. The nursery specialises in unusual perennials and cottage garden plants. 10% of plant sales to NGS. Home-made TEAS on NGS days only, in aid of Bopath Children's Therapy Centre. *Adm £2, chd free. Fris, Sats, Suns, Bank Hols 11 Mar to 9 Oct.* **For NGS:**

Suns 5 June; 10 July (10-5).
Tel 01446 774036
www.bordervale.co uk

5 The Clock House, Cathedral Close, Llandaff ♿🚫☺
(Professor & Mrs Bryan Hibbard) *2m N of Cardiff. Follow signs to Cathedral via A4119. Bus: Cardiff alight Maltsters Arms.* Small walled garden; fine old trees; wide variety of shrubs and plants; important collection of shrub, species and old roses. TEAS. *Adm £2, chd free. Sun 19 June (2-6)*

6 NEW Coedargraig, Newton, Porthcawl ♿🚫
(Philip & Caroline Vaughan) *2m from centre of Porthcawl. Take hill out of Porthcawl (A4106 Bridgend rd). House on L opp Respite Centre.* 9 acres in the process of reclamation and renovation. A huge variety of

plants for every season: masses of spring flowers - daffodils, tulips, crocus; sweeping bluebell woods; primrose banks; azaleas, rhododendrons; formal terraced gardens; perennial garden; lavender path; orchard with hens; duck pond; broad spectrum of trees and shrubs. TEAS. *Adm £3, chd free. Private visits welcome by appt Sats, Suns, Mons 26, 27, 28 Mar; 30 Apr; 1, 2 May. Tel 01656 772222*

7 NEW Cottrell Park Golf Club, St Nicholas, Cardiff ♿🚫
(Cottrell Park Ltd) *4m W of Cardiff. M4 J33, take exit signed Cardiff International Airport off A4232. 4th exit off roundabout signed Cowbridge A48. Go through St Nicholas, entrance on RH-side 200 yds after village.* Set in historic parkland that has been landscaped over several centuries. It boast 2

magnificent championship golf courses. Views sweep N towards Brecon Beacons and S over Bristol Channel to the Mendips. Gentle rolling parkland and stately trees combine to create a special charm. The Clubhouse patio has seasonal borders. Light refreshments and TEAS. *Adm £2.95, chd 95p. Sun 31 July (10-8) www.golfwithus.com*

8 ◆ Dyffryn Gardens, nr Cardiff 🚻🌳

(Vale of Glamorgan Council) *5m N of Cardiff. Exit J33 from the M4, on the A4232 signed Barry; 1st interchange 4th exit A48 signed Cowbridge. In St Nicholas village turn L, Dyffryn is signed.* Outstanding Grade I listed Edwardian garden. Currently undergoing restoration to Thomas Mawson's original 1904 design. Formal lawns; fountains and pools; seasonal beds; trees and shrubs. Garden rooms, incl Pompeian, Paved Court and Theatre garden. Arboretum contains trees from all over the world incl 13 champion trees - one is the original *Acer griseum* collected by 'Chinese' Wilson. Light refreshments and TEAS. *Adm £3.50, chd/concessions £2.50. Daily: Easter*

to Sept (10-6); Oct (10-5); Nov to Easter (10-4). Tel 029 2059 3328 www.dyffryngardens.org.uk

9 11 Eastcliff, Southgate 🚻🌳🐕

(Mrs Gill James) *7m SW of Swansea. Take the Swansea to Gower rd & travel 6m to Pennard. Through village of Southgate & take 2nd exit off roundabout. Garden 200yds on L.* Seaside garden, approx ⅓ acre, and developed in a series of island and bordered beds for all-yr interest. Large number of white, blue-green and unusual plants, woodland area and a gravel bed in the making. *Adm £2, chd free. Private visits welcome by appt.* Tel 01792 233310 blgpfjames@pennard.yrfree.net

10 NEW Greenfield Kennels, Llangyfelach

(Mr & Mrs A Jenkins) *4m N of Swansea. M4 J46, Morriston Hospital Rd, after crossing cattle grid approx 150yds on R.* Approx 1-acre re-designed garden. Rhododendrons, azaleas, mixed borders, Cornus, dicksonia, unusual trees. Cascade. Home-made TEAS. *Adm £2, chd free. Sun 22 May (2-6). Private visits welcome by appt 1 May to 31 Oct.* Tel 01792 771839

11 NEW Killay: Cottages & Columbines, Killay, Swansea *W edge of Swansea. Take A4118 (Gower rd) past Killay shops and over mini-roundabout. 2nd L (halfway down hill) into Clyne Valley Road, which leads to cottages.* Brickworkers' cottages in historical country park. Close to Clyne Gardens, Singleton Botanical Gardens and coastline. *Combined adm £2, chd £1 incl quiz. Sun 22 May (11-5)*

NEW Touchwood, 4 Clyne Valley Cottages 🌳🐕 NCCPG (Carrie Thomas) Intimate, exuberant plantsman's garden, most items grown from seed. Annuals, biennials, perennials, bulbs, shrubs, grasses, climbers, herbs, vegetables and alpines. National Collection of Aquilegia *vulgaris*, hybrids and cultivars flower May and 1st half June. Plant sale in aid of Action for ME. *Private visits welcome by appt £1.* Tel 01792 522443 carrie.thomas@ntlworld.com

NEW 5 Clyne Valley Cottages 🌳🐕 (Anne Christie) Lovely cottage-style front garden featuring many typical cottage garden flowers incl a profusion of columbines (granny's bonnets, aquilegias). Plant sale in aid of Cats Protection, Swansea.

help the hospices

"If you took all the love and companionship given by the nurses and staff here, put it in a light bulb under the Millennium Dome, you would see it in Sydney."
David, a Day Care patient at a hospice

Hospice care is based on the simple idea that a dying patient is a living person; someone who deserves peace, respect and calm until the very end of their life. Hospice staff and volunteers seek to help people live life to the full, for whatever time they have left – no matter how long or how short. All hospice care is given free of charge.

Help the Hospices is the national charity for the hospice movement. Our role is to complement and enhance the wonderful care hospices give to patients and their loved ones. We do this by making grants to fund training of hospice staff particularly doctors and nurses; support new services; offer hospices advice and information and promote the issues affecting them and those who need their care to government and the media and running fundraising campaigns to support hospice care. Funds raised by the National Gardens Scheme are a vital source of income to help us in our work.

For further information, please call us on 020 7520 8200; www.helpthehospices.org.uk

Charity no: 1014851

⑫ NEW Llanmadoc & Cheriton Gardens, Llanmadoc, Gower
15m W of Swansea. M4 J47. Take A483 signed Swansea. Next roundabout R A484 signed Llanelli. 2nd roundabout L B4296 signed Gowerton. R at 1st T-lights onto B4295. 10m after Bury Green, R to Llanmadoc. Pass Britannia Inn, L at T-junction uphill past red tel box. 100 yds turn R. Honesty car park on R. Charming villages on Gower with spectacular coastal views. Home-made TEAS at Big House Farm. Combined adm £5, chd free (share to Ty-Hafan Children's Hospice). Sat 7 May (12-6)

NEW Big House Farm, Llanmadoc
(Mark & Sheryl Mead) Mainly walled coastal garden, just under 1 acre, with stunning views. A variety of interesting plants and shrubs in mixed borders. Small Mediterranean garden and walled kitchen garden.

NEW Cwm Ivy Court Farm, Llanmadoc 🌢 (Mrs Christine Roberts) Set in approx 2½ acres, incl a interestingmixed orchard. Garden is arranged in several separate areas with quiet seating and beautiful views. Something to catch your eye around every corner. Private visits welcome by appt Sats June & July (not July 2) (12-4). Tel 01792 386251

NEW Sycamores, Llanmadoc 🌢
(Professors G & J Chamberlain) Small garden, (⅓ acre), with numerous special features. Rose garden, fernery, topiary, stream crossed by bridge, gravel garden, alpines. Mixed borders. Some unusual trees, shrubs and perennials. Spectacular views across Loughor estuary and

Carmarthen Bay. Private visits welcome by appt, 15 June to 15 July, groups welcome. Tel 01792 386325

⑬ Ridler's Garden, St Peters Terrace, Cockett, Swansea 🌢
(Mr & Mrs Tony Ridler) 4m W of Swansea. M4 J47, follow A483 towards Swansea. After several sets of T-lights, at Bob Hughes Carpets on L, turn R onto A4216. Next T-lights L into St Peters Terrace. Formal ½-acre garden with box topiary and yew hedges. Regret no children. TEAS. Adm £2. Sun, Mon 1, 2 May (2-5)

⑭ Slade, Southerndown 🌢🌢
(Mr & Mrs Peter Davies) 5m S of Bridgend. M4 J35. Follow A473 to Bridgend. Take B4265 to St Brides Major. Turn R in St Brides Major for Southerndown. At Southerndown turn L opp 3 Golden Cups PH on to Beach Rd. Follow rd into Dunraven Park. Turn 1st L over cattle grid on to Slade drive. Woodland garden. Display of early spring flowers: snowdrops, daffodils, crocus, cyclamen, bluebells. Mature specimen trees. Beginnings of a garden sculpture collection. Heritage Coast wardens will give guided tour of adjacent Dunraven Gardens with slide show from 4pm. Home-made TEAS. Adm £2. Sun 3 Apr (2-6). Private visits welcome by appt. Tel 01656 880048 ros@daviesslade.plus.com

⑮ NEW Ty Nant Corrwg, 7 Heol-y-Bryn, Rhydyfelin, Pontypridd 🌢🌢
(Sue & Les Budd) 3m S of Pontypridd. From Pontypridd take

A470 S for 2m. Exit Upper Boat junction, signed Gellihirion Estate, from roundabout take A4054 Hawthorn Rd. 2nd R into Dynea Rd, up hill, turn R (still Dynea Rd), R into Heol-y-Bryn. A newly-created and developing garden, located on a difficult ⅓-acre hillside site. Incl wide variety of shrubs, plants, herbs, fruit and flowers. Garden divided into separate themed areas connected by a series of paths, steps and terraces. Light refreshments and TEAS. Adm £2.50, chd free. Wed 18 May; Sun, Wed 5, 15 June (11-6). Also open 18 May & 15 June **19 Westfield Road**. Private visits welcome by appt. Tel 01443 407628 susieabudd@aol.com

⑯ 19 Westfield Road, Glyncoch, Pontypridd 🌢
(Mr & Mrs Brian Dockerill) 10m NW of Cardiff. From Pontypridd travel 1½m N along B4273. Take L turn by school. From Pontypridd follow rd to L. Take 1st R & R again into Westfield Rd. Garden of approx ¾ acre designed as series of interlinked enclosures each of different character. Varying habitats in sun and shade permit wide range of plants to be grown extending the interest through the yr. TEAS. Adm £2, chd free. Weds 18 May; 15 June; 20 July (10-7). Also open 18 May & 15 June **Ty Nant Corrwg**. Private visits welcome by appt. Tel 01443 402999 brian.dockerill@btinternet.com

Evening Opening (See also garden description)	
6 Alma Road	15 May
	17 July
	19 July

"We don't get much trouble from the neighbours now!"

Gwent (Blaenau Gwent, Caerphilly, Monmouthshire, Newport and Torfaen)

County Organiser: Mrs Joanna Kerr, Glebe House, Llanvair Kilgeddin, Abergavenny, Gwent NP7 9BE
Tel 01873 840422

Assistant County Organiser: Mrs Sue Carter, St Pega's, 47 Hereford Road, Monmouth, Gwent NP25 3HQ
Tel 01600 772074

Maps: Numbers shown next to each garden entry refer to that garden's entry on the county map. This position is approximate; distance and directions from the nearest main town are generally shown in the garden text.
A precise location is available for those gardens featured on the NGS website by visiting www.ngs.org.uk.

Symbols: Information relating to symbols is given on page 21

DATES OF OPENING

Evening openings
See end of county listing

Gardens open to the public
For details see garden description
The Nurtons, Tintern *(19)*
Penpergwm Lodge, nr Abergavenny *(22)*
Tredegar House & Park, Newport *(24)*
Veddw House, Devauden *(27)*

March 13 Sunday
North Monmouth Gardens *(18)*

March 20 Sunday
Llanover, nr Abergavenny *(12)*

March 27 Sunday (Easter)
Llwyn-y-Wen Farm, Crumlin *(13)*

April 3 Sunday
Llwyn-y-Wen Farm, Crumlin *(13)*

April 17 Sunday
Llwyn-y-Wen Farm, Crumlin *(13)*

May 1 Sunday
Wyastone Estate *(28)*

May 8 Sunday
High House, Penrhos *(9)*
Llwyn-y-Wen Farm, Crumlin *(13)*

May 15 Sunday
Llwyn-y-Wen Farm, Crumlin *(13)*
Porthycarne Street Gardens, Usk *(23)*

May 22 Sunday
Llwyn-y-Wen Farm, Crumlin *(13)*
The Nurtons, Tintern *(19)*
The Old Vicarage Penrhos, Raglan *(21)*

May 29 Sunday
Barn Farm, Earlswood, Chepstow *(1)*
Cefntilla, Usk *(4)*
Magor Village Gardens *(14)*

May 30 Monday (Bank Hol)
Cefntilla, Usk *(4)*
Magor Village Gardens *(14)*

June 5 Sunday
Llwyn-y-Wen Farm, Crumlin *(13)*
Trostrey Lodge, Bettws Newydd *(25)*
Wyndcliffe Court, St Arvans *(29)*

June 11 Saturday
Hillcrest Bungalow, Cefn Fforest, Blackwood *(10)*

June 12 Sunday
Barn Farm, Earlswood, Chepstow *(1)*
Hillcrest Bungalow, Cefn Fforest, Blackwood *(10)*
Llanfoist Village Gardens *(11)*
Llwyn-y-Wen Farm, Crumlin *(13)*

June 18 Saturday
Monmouth Open Gardens Scheme, Bridges Community Centre, Drybridge Park *(16)*

June 19 Sunday
Llwyn-y-Wen Farm, Crumlin *(13)*
Monmouth Open Gardens Scheme, Bridges Community Centre, Drybridge Park *(16)*
Mulberry House, St Arvans, nr Chepstow *(17)*

June 25 Saturday
Usk Gardens, Usk Town *(26)*

June 26 Sunday
Usk Gardens, Usk Town *(26)*

June 27 Monday
Veddw House, Devauden **(Evening)** *(27)*

July 3 Sunday
Gardd-y-Bryn, Abergavenny *(7)*
Llwyn-y-Wen Farm, Crumlin *(13)*
Monmouth Allotments, Monmouth Town *(15)*

July 5 Tuesday
Veddw House, Devauden **(Evening)** *(27)*

July 9 Saturday
Magor Village Gardens *(14)*

July 10 Sunday
Barn Farm, Earlswood, Chepstow *(1)*
Castell Court, Llanelen *(2)*
Llwyn-y-Wen Farm, Crumlin *(13)*
Magor Village Gardens *(14)*
Ochran Mill *(20)*

July 17 Sunday
Clytha Park, Abergavenny *(5)*
Llwyn-y-Wen Farm, Crumlin *(13)*

July 24 Sunday
Glebe House, Llanvair Kilgeddin *(8)*

August 13 Saturday
Croesllanfro Farm, Rogerstone *(6)*

August 20 Saturday
Hillcrest Bungalow, Cefn Fforest, Blackwood *(10)*

August 21 Sunday
Hillcrest Bungalow, Cefn Fforest, Blackwood *(10)*
Llwyn-y-Wen Farm, Crumlin *(13)*

August 28 Sunday
Cefntilla, Usk *(4)*

August 29 Monday (Bank Hol)
Cefntilla, Usk *(4)*
Tredegar House & Park, Newport *(24)*

September 4 Sunday
The Nurtons, Tintern *(19)*

September 18 Sunday
Llanover, nr Abergavenny *(12)*

DESCRIPTIONS OF GARDENS

❶ Barn Farm, Earlswood, Chepstow ✿✿
(Stephen & Felicity Hunt) *6m SE of Usk, 7m NW of Chepstow. Off B4235 Chepstow to Usk rd. Turn off at Gaerllwyd Xrds. 1m from main rd.* ¾-acre secluded garden overlooking Wentwood forest. Herbaceous borders brimming with plants. Many varieties of penstemon, iris, hemerocallis and lilies provide spectacular summer colour. Vegetable garden on raised beds. Several water features. New additions incl 'hot' gravel and terrace area, fruit area and clematis walk. Featured on UK Style Series A Garden For All Seasons, 2003. 'Amateur Gardening' Mar 2003. Home-made TEAS in aid of Devauden Green WI. *Adm £3, chd free. Suns 29 May, 12 June, 10 July (2-6). Private visits welcome by appt Jun & Jul, groups 10+. Tel 01291 650604*
steve.hunt@forestry.gsi.gov.uk

❷ NEW Castell Court, Castell Prydydd, Llanelen ♿✿✿
(Lorna & John McGlynn) *1m S of Abergavenny. From*

GWENT

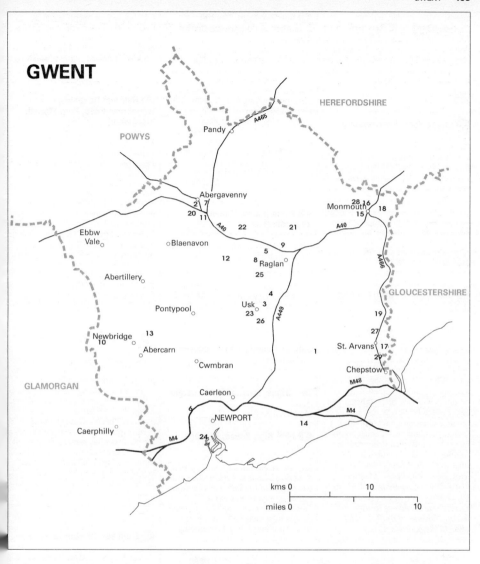

POWYS

HEREFORDSHIRE

Pandy

A465

Abergavenny

2 7
20 11

Monmouth 28 16
15 18

A40

22

21

A40

Ebbw
Vale

Blaenavon

9

12

5

8 Raglan

25

Abertillery

4

A466

GLOUCESTERSHIRE

Pontypool

Usk 3
23
26

A449

19

Newbridge
10

13

27

Abercarn

Cwmbran

1

St. Arvans 17
29

Chepstow

GLAMORGAN

Caerleon

M48

NEWPORT

M4

Caerphilly

M4 24

14

kms 0   10

miles 0   10

Abergavenny/Llanfoist take B4269 signed Llanelen. After passing Grove Farm turn R up single track rd. Rd climbs steeply up over canal. Approx 500yds entrance to Castell Court on L. Large informal family garden in rural surroundings with fine views overlooking Abergavenny. Lawns, established trees, shrubs and herbaceous borders. Organic kitchen and vegetable gardens. Newly planted orchard and tree walk. Hay meadow, family pets and livestock in fields. Due to narrow rd and steep hill, one way system out of Castell Court to

Ochran Mill - well signed route through narrow lane. Home-made TEAS in aid of Llanfoist Primary School. *Adm combined £3.50, chd free, with* **Ochran Mill**. *Sun 10 July (2-6)*

❸ Castle House, Usk 🚼🐕
(Mr & Mrs J H L Humphreys) *200yds from Usk centre. Turn up lane opp fire station off Monmouth Rd.* Romantic garden set around ruins of Usk Castle. Medieval herb garden, humorous topiary, herbaceous border, vegetable garden

and some imaginative garden structures. *Adm £2.50, chd free. Combined with* **Usk Gardens** *Sat 25, Sun 26 June (10-5). Private visits welcome by appt. Tel 01291 672563 www.uskcastle.com*

❹ Cefntilla, Usk 🚼🐕
(Lord Raglan) *3m NE of Usk. From S, take B4235 Usk to Chepstow rd to Gwernesney & follow signs N to Cefntilla, about 1m. From N, take Chepstow rd S from Raglan & follow signs through Llandenny.* Rectangular former Jacobean garden

area at rear extended with a circumambulatory in the 1850s. About 5 acres of trees, lawns, shrubs, flowers, topiary walk and lily pond. Home-made TEAS in aid of St John's Church, Llandenny. *Adm £2.50, chd free. Sun, Mon 29, 30 May; 28, 29 Aug (12-5)*

⑤ Clytha Park, Abergavenny ♿⊞

(Sir Richard Hanbury-Tenison) *Halfway between Abergavenny (4m) and Raglan (4m). On B4598 (not A40).* Large C18 garden around a 1½-acre lake with wide lawns and good trees. Visit the 1790 walled garden or walk around the lake on a serpentine path laid out over 250 yrs ago; a 'secret' garden at the furthest point. TEAS. *Adm £2.50, chd 8+ £1. Sun 17 July (2-6). Private visits welcome by appt May-Sept. Tel 01873 840300*

⑥ Croesllanfro Farm, Rogerstone ✂⊞

(Barry & Liz Davies) *3m W of Newport. From M4 J27 take B4591 to Risca. Take 2nd R, Cefn Walk (also signed 14 Locks Canal Centre). Proceed over canal bridge, continue approx ½m to island in middle of lane. White farm gate opp.* Limited parking. Approx 1½ acres of garden on different levels, created by garden designer Liz Davies. Wide variety of plants concentrating on form and texture, and interesting focal points incl grotto and folly. Colourful late summer borders. Featured in 'The English Garden' Sept 2004. Design featured in 'The Book of Garden Plans' 2004. Home-made TEAS. *Adm £3, chd free. Sat 13 Aug (2-5). Private visits welcome by appt June to Aug. Groups of 6+. Tel 01633 894343 lizplants@aol.com*

⑦ Gardd-y-Bryn, The Hill Education & Conference Centre, Abergavenny ✂⊞

(Coleg Gwent) *¼m N of town centre. From A40 in Abergavenny, follow signs to Hill College.* 1-acre Victorian walled garden, undergoing restoration since 1996, on S-facing slope overlooking Abergavenny and surrounded by mature woodland. Divided into various gardens; vegetables, fruit, flowers, wild garden and mixed borders. Ongoing developments incl Mediterranean garden. Used for teaching horticultural courses. Home-made TEAS. *Adm £2.50, chd free. Sun 3 July (2-6)*

⑧ Glebe House, Llanvair Kilgeddin ♿✂⊞

(Mr & Mrs Murray Kerr) *Midway between Abergavenny (5m) and Usk (5m). On B4598.* 1½ acres with small ornamental vegetable garden and summerhouse. Colourful herbaceous borders, climbers and S-facing terrace - all set in the picturesque Usk Valley. Home-made TEAS in aid of Bettws Group Parishes. *Adm £2.50, chd free. Sun 24 July (2-6)*

Gliffaes Country House Hotel, Crickhowell ♿
See Powys.

The Griggs, Newton St Margarets ♿✂
See Herefordshire.

⑨ NEW High House, Penrhos ♿✂⊞

(Mr & Mrs R Cleeve) *4m N of Raglan. From roundabout on A40 at Raglan take exit to Clytha. After 50 yds turn R to Llantilio Crossenny and follow garden open signs to High House - 10mins through lanes.* 3-acre garden in wonderful hidden part of rural Monmouthshire surrounding

C17 house (not open). Spacious lawns with natural pond, fruit trees, borders and spring bulbs. Home-made TEAS in aid of Penrhos Church. *Adm £3, chd free. Sun 8 May (2-6)*

⑩ Hillcrest Bungalow, Waunborfa Road, Cefn Fforest, Blackwood ♿✂

(Mr M O'Leary and Mr B Price) *3m W of Newbridge. Follow A4048 to Blackwood town centre. Take Pentwyn rd, follow Sports Centre signs to Waunborfa Rd.* 1½-acre garden with view over valley. Informal, perennial borders, established shrubs and trees, box parterre, octagonal gazebo. Annual displays, herb wheel with water feature and fig tree. New lower level with hedge-enclosed vegetables; ornamental conifers and interesting young trees. Light refreshments and TEAS. *Adm £2.50, chd free. Sat, Sun 11, 12 June; 20, 21 Aug (2-6). Private visits welcome by appt May-Sept. Tel 01443 837029*

⑪ Llanfoist Village Gardens ♿✂⊞

(Brian Barnes) *1m S of Abergavenny. On B4246 SW of Abergavenny. Map provided with ticket.* Most gardens within easy walking distance of the village centre. Free minibus to others. Limited wheelchair access to some gardens. This is our third annual event. Approx 12 gardens, some open for the first time, ranging from small to large, idiosyncratic to idyllic, in historic village of Llanfoist situated below the Blorenge Mountain. Home-made TEAS. *Adm £4, chd £1 (share to Local Charities). Sun 12 June (12-6)*

⑫ Llanover, nr Abergavenny ♿✂

(Mr & Mrs M R Murray) *4m S of Abergavenny. On A4042. Bus: Abergavenny-Pontypool, alight at drive gates.* 15 acres of gardens landscaped in C18 to create streams, ponds, cascades and a walled circular garden with herbaceous borders. Modern planting includes a large collection of magnolias and camellias for spring interest. No professional photography. Home-made TEAS in aid of St Bartholomew's Church, Llanover. *Adm £3, chd free. Suns 20 Mar; 18 Sept (2-5). Private visits welcome by appt groups 10+. Ty Uchaf, Llanover, Abergavenny, NP7 9EF elizabeth@llanover.com*

"Kenneth is a bit of a perfectionist when it comes to lawncare!"

⑬ Llwyn-y-Wen Farm, Hafodyrynys Road, Crumlin ✿🕮 (Mrs Helen Lewy) *11m NW of Newport and 6m W of Pontypool. M4 J28, take A467 to Risca. 11m to Crumlin T-lights, turn R on A472 to Pontypool. Entrance ¼m on R. Limited parking; lay-by available on road close to entrance.* 2-acre Welsh hillside garden with own spring providing large trout pond and bog garden. Many shade and damp-loving plants on different levels and over 150 tubs and troughs. Additional fields with beautiful bluebell walks in May. A haven for wildlife. Accommodation. Prize-winner, Caerphilly in Bloom Awards, 2003. HTV's Grassroots 2004. Cream TEAS. *Adm £3, chd free. Suns 27 Mar; 3, 17 Apr; 8, 15, 22 May; 5, 12, 19 June; 3, 10, 17 July; 21 Aug (2-5)*

⑭ Magor Village Gardens (Mrs C Davies) *9m W of Chepstow. M4 J23A and follow signs to Magor Village Square on B4245, ¼m. Good parking near village square, limited parking at some individual gardens. Map provided at first garden.* Group of gardens with wide appeal. Home-made TEAS at Myrtle Cottage in May, The Hawthorns in July. *Combined adm £2.50, chd 10+ 50p. Sun, 29, Mon 30 May; Sat 9, Sun 10 July (11-6)*

Courtney 🕮 (Joyce Escott) Mediterranean-style garden with water features, figs, olives and oleanders. *Not open 9,10 July*

The Hawthorns (John & Rosemary Skinner) Formal bedding scheme with standard fuchsias, summer bedding and conifers shaped into domes and archways, perennial garden with covered walkway, water-feature and garden seat with passion flower canopy. Please park in Queen's Gardens as sign-posted. No parking at The Hawthorns. Featured in 'Beautiful Gardens' 2004. *Not open 29,30 May*

Merevale House 🕮🕮 (Judy & Kevin Marris) Borders and beds; patio and parterre; still water, running water; shrubs and trees; fruit and vegetables; all in ¼-acre.

Myrtle Cottage 🕮✿ (Cecilia & Michael Davies) Cottage garden with broad range of plants. *Not open 9,10 July*

⑮ NEW Monmouth Allotments, Monmouth Town ✿🕮 *Follow Garden Open signs from public toilets at bottom of Monnow St (main street in Monmouth) along river bank and under the dual*

carriageway. Parking at allotments. Many allotments on site since 1940 gardened by people of all ages with a very wide variety of vegetables, fruit, flowers and sheds. Home-made TEAS. *Adm £2.50, chd free. Sun 3 July (10-4)*

⑯ Monmouth Open Gardens Scheme, Bridges Community Centre, Drybridge Park ✿🕮 (Mrs E Blow & Mrs N. Emery) *Take exit off A40 for town centre. Free parking. Pay at Bridges Community Centre, Drybridge Park. Free minibuses. Map provided.* The historic and picturesque town of Monmouth will be opening approx 25 gardens, from a terrace of cottages with original brick privies to a large country cottage garden and gardens with views. Light refreshments and TEAS. *Adm £5, weekend ticket £6, chd free (share to Local Charities). Sat, Sun 18, 19 June (10-5)*

⑰ Mulberry House, St Arvans, nr Chepstow ✿🕮 (Sir Alan & Lady Cox) *2½m N of Chepstow. Turn L off A466 from Chepstow, into St Arvans, 300yds on R.* 2-acres, inc ha-ha, vegetable garden, recently created lawns and parterres. 2000+ shrubs of huge variety, roses everywhere particularly the old and striped varieties. Rose arbour and two mulberry trees. Cream TEAS. *Adm £3, chd free. Sun 19 June (2-6)*

⑱ North Monmouth Gardens *N of town centre on A446 towards Hereford from T-lights in town.* Two spring gardens in historic town of Monmouth within walking distance of each other and town centre. TEAS at St Pega's. *Combined adm £3, chd free. Sun 13 Mar (2-6)*

St Pega's ✿🕮 (Mrs Sue Carter) Large steep ½-acre town garden not for the faint-hearted. Special features inc bog garden, dry stone walls and special alpine troughs. Collection of Barnhaven primulas.

Ty Gwyn, Dixton Road 🕮✿🕮 (Dr C Jones) ¾-acre garden. Unusual plants, bulbs, fruit cage, vegetable garden, pond, trees, shrubs.

⑲ ◆ The Nurtons, Tintern ✿🕮 (Adrian & Elsa Wood) *7m N of Chepstow. On A466 opp Old Station.* Exciting 2½ acre garden on a secluded historical site with stunning views of the Wye Valley. Very colourful with a large collection of choice plants in hot mediteranean,

cool woodland and water feature settings. 'English Garden' and 'Telegraph' features, 2003. *Adm £2.50, chd free. Wed to Mon, Mar to Oct (10.30-5).* **For NGS:** *Suns 22 May; 4 Sept (10.30-5). Tel 01291 689253 www.thenurtons.co.uk*

⑳ NEW Ochran Mill 🕮✿🕮 (Mr & Mrs D Rolfe) *3m S of Abergavenny. Approx 3m S of Abergavenny on A4042 midway between Llanellen & Llanover. Well signed one way route from Castell Court to Ochran Mill.* Grade II listed water mill (not working) approx 1½-acres in all. Large colour themed herbaceous borders, bog area, shrub borders, original leat, aviary, many different species of plants, all created in the last 3-yrs from a field. New areas being developed. Home-made TEAS in aid of Llanover PTA. *Adm combined £3.50, chd free with* **Castell Court.** *Sun 10 July (2-6). Private visits welcome by appt. Tel 01873 852227 www.ochranmill.org.uk*

㉑ The Old Vicarage Penrhos, Raglan 🕮✿🕮 (Professor & Mrs Luke Herrmann) *3m N of Raglan. At Raglan turn off A40 for Mitcheltroy. Almost immediately turn L for Tregare. Follow signs for Tregare, then Penrhos.* 1½ acres in rural surroundings with fine views. Garden being redeveloped. Informal mixture of shrubs, roses, perennials and annuals in varied settings; vegetable garden, wooded pond area, mature and newly planted trees; ornamental pots. *Adm £2.50, chd free under 12. Sun 22 May (2-5)*

Penmyarth, Glanusk Park, nr Crickhowell 🕮 See Powys.

㉒ ◆ Penpergwm Lodge, nr Abergavenny 🕮✿ (Mr & Mrs Simon Boyle) *3m SE of Abergavenny, 5m W of Raglan. On B4598. Turn opp King of Prussia Inn. Entrance 150-yds on L.* 3-acre garden with lawns, mature trees, Italianate parterre and brick-pillared vine walk. New Jubilee tower overlooks ornamental vegetable garden and S-facing terrace with sun-loving plants. 19th yr of Catriona Boyle's Garden School & special plant nursery. Accommodation. *Adm £3, chd free. Thurs to Suns 25 Mar to 25 Sept (2-6). Tel 01873 840208 www.penplants.com*

㉓ NEW Porthycarne Street Gardens, Usk
Porthycarne St leads N (Abergavenny direction) from the central Xrds in Usk at The Three Salmons Hotel. 3 gardens within easy walking distance of each other and of the centre of Usk. Park in town car-park, Maryport St. A small picturesque town with riverside walks by the Usk and numerous quaint pubs. Home-made TEAS at Plas Newydd if fine or Catholic Church Hall if wet in aid of Usk Catholic Church. Combined £3, chd free. Sun 15 May (2-5.30)

NEW **The Laurels** 🌿 (Dr & Mrs J Davies) Walled town family garden with large sheltered herbaceous border, ancient yew tree with tree house, vegetable and herb gardens and informal orchard/woodland area. Cobbled entry yard has magnificent wisteria and other climbers. *Also open with* **Usk Gardens** 25,26 June

NEW **Plas Newydd** ♿ (Dr & Mrs Owain Gibby, Mr Hugh Rose) Garden surrounding early victorian house with lawns, herbaceous border and specimen trees, mainly Japanese maples. Interest in Japanese plants collected by Philipp Von Siebold. Woodland area, small walled white garden.

NEW **Porthycarne House** ♿ (Mr & Mrs T Crawley) Large informal garden, interesting trees and shrubs, river view.

㉔ ◆ Tredegar House & Park, Newport ♿🌿🍃
(Newport City Council) *2m SW of Newport town centre. Signposted from A48 (Cardiff rd) & M4 J28. Series of C18 walled formal gardens surrounding magnificent late C17 house (also open). Early C18 orangery garden with coloured mineral parterres. Open on NGS day; private gardens maintained by Growing Space. Also by appointment tel 01633 810718. Light refreshments and TEAS. House and Garden Adm*

adm £5.40, concessions £3.85, chd free, Garden only Adm £2, chd free. **For NGS:** *Mon 29 Aug (11-5).* Tel 01633 815880

㉕ Trostrey Lodge, Bettws Newydd ♿🌿🍃
(Roger & Frances Pemberton) *4m W of Raglan. 7m E of Abergavenny. Off the old A40 (unnumbered). 1m S of Clytha Gates and 1½m N of Bettws Newydd. This intensely planted stone walled scented garden and orchard is set in a tranquil rolling landscape with fine old trees. It is approached through a picturesque iron gate over a ha-ha. The surrounding fields are perfect for picnics. Flowers, herbs and climbing roses are in profusion, peppered with poppies and garnished with guinea fowl. Home-made TEAS in aid of Llanfair Kilgeddin Primary School - the smallest school in Monmouthshire. Adm £2.50, chd free. Sun 5 June (12-6). Private visits welcome by appt. Tel 01873 840352*

㉖ Usk Gardens, Usk Town ♿🌿🍃
(Mrs Margaret Capel) *From M4 J24 take A449, proceed 8m to Usk exit. Good free parking in town. Map of gardens provided with ticket. Limited wheelchair access to some gardens. 20+ gardens from small cottages packed with colourful and unusual plants to large gardens with wonderful herbaceous borders. Roam around the ramparts of our romantic castle garden. New this year - visit our gardener's market for books and plants. Featured on HTV news 2004. Home-made TEAS. Adm £5, weekend ticket £7.50 (10-5), chd under 14 free (share to Local Charities). Sat , Sun 25, 26 June (10-5)*

㉗ ◆ Veddw House, Devauden 🌿
(Anne Wareham & Charles Hawes) *5m NW of Chepstow. Off B4293. Signed from PH on the green at Devauden. A modern romantic garden: "Only rarely does one come across a garden as ambitious and successful as that of Veddw House....*

These four acres combine all the achievements of a great garden ....." Stephen Anderton, the Times. Featured in 'The Times' 2003, 'English Garden' 2004, 'Telegraph' 2004, '25 Beautiful Gardens' 2004. *Adm £4, chd £1.50. Suns & Bank Hol Mons 5 Jun - 4 Sept (2-5).* **For NGS: Evening Opening** *£5, wine, Mon 27 June; Tue 5 July (6-7.30). Tel 01291 650 836 www.veddw. co.uk*

㉘ NEW Wyastone Estate 🌿
(Mrs Blow, Monmouth Open Gardens Scheme) *2m N of Monmouth. Take A40 from Monmouth towards Ross-on-Wye for 2m. L at sign for Ganarew & Wyastone Concert Hall and follow Concert Hall signs. Large S-facing hillside garden with views over the Wye Valley. Restored stone folly, woodland paths with mature trees, bluebells, wood anenomes, wild garlic and ferns. Some new planting for spring and autumn interest, guided walks and talk on the conservation of the area. Home of the Wyastone Concert Hall and a herd of fallow deer. Home-made TEAS. Adm £2.50, chd free (share to Local Charities). Sun 1 May (11-4)*

㉙ Wyndcliffe Court, St Arvans ♿
(Mr H A P Clay) *3m N of Chepstow. Off A466, turn at Wyndcliffe signpost. Bus: Chepstow-Monmouth, alight at St Arvans, Wyndcliffe stop, then ¼m. Medium-sized garden designed by Avray Tipping and Eric Francis; herbaceous borders; views, topiary, sunken garden and walled garden. One of the historic gardens of Wales. TEAS. Adm £3, chd free. Sun 5 June (2-6). Private visits welcome by appt. Tel 01291 622352*

Evening Opening (See also garden description)	
Veddw House	27 June
Veddw House	5 July

ngs
gardens open for charity

Look out for the NCCPG National Plant Collections at some of our gardens

Gwynedd

County Organisers:
(Anglesey, North Caernarfonshire, Aberconwy) Mrs Jenny Osborne, Fox Brush, Port Dinorwic, Y Felinheli, Gwynedd LL56 4JZ
01248 670463
(South Gwynedd) Mrs Marian Osselton, Felin y Ffridd, Friddgate, Machynlleth, Powys SY20 8QG
Tel 01248 670463
Assistant County Organiser: Mrs W N Jones, Waen Fechan, Islaw'r Dref, Dolgellau LL40 1TS Tel 01341 423479
Mr John Osselton, Felin y Ffridd, Ffriddgate, Machynlleth, Powys SY20 8QG
Tel 01654 702548
County Treasurers:
(South Gwynedd) Mr Michael Bishton, Bronclydwr, Rhoslefain, Tywyn, Gwynedd LL36 9LT
Tel 01654 710882
(North Gwynedd) Mrs Grace Meirion-Jones, Parc Newydd, Rhosgadfan, Caernarfon, Gwynedd LL54 7LF
Tel 01286 831195

Maps: Numbers shown next to each garden entry refer to that garden's entry on the county map. This position is approximate; distance and directions from the nearest main town are generally shown in the garden text.
A precise location is available for those gardens featured on the NGS website by visiting www.ngs.org.uk.
Symbols: Information relating to symbols is given on page 21

DATES OF OPENING

Evening openings
See end of county listing

Private gardens open regularly for NGS
Tir Mab Cynan Nursery, Brithdir *(34)*

Gardens open to the public
For details see garden description
Antur Waunfawr, Waunfawr *(1)*
Crug Farm, Griffiths Crossing *(13)*
Hotel Maes-y-Neuadd, Talsarnau, nr Harlech *(21)*
Penrhyn Castle, Bangor *(28)*
Pensychnant, nr Conwy *(29)*
Plas Newydd, Anglesey *(30)*
Tir Mab Cynan Nursery, Brithdir *(34)*

By appointment only
For telephone number and other details see garden description.
Private visits welcomed
Foxbrush, Felinheli *(16)*
Llys-y-Gwynt, Llandygai *(24)*

February 6 Sunday
Penrhyn Castle, Bangor *(28)*

March 13 Sunday
Bryniau, Boduan, nr Pwllheli *(7)*

March 25 Friday (Easter)
Plas Newydd, Anglesey *(30)*

March 27 Sunday (Easter)
Bont Fechan Farm, Llanystumdwy *(2)*
Bryniau, Boduan, nr Pwllheli *(7)*
Crug Farm, Griffiths Crossing *(13)*

March 28 Monday (Easter)
Bont Fechan Farm, Llanystumdwy *(2)*

April 24 Sunday
Maenan Hall, Llanrwst *(25)*

April 30 Saturday
Gwelfor, Rhostryfan *(19)*

May 1 Sunday
Bryniau, Boduan, nr Pwllheli *(7)*
Llanbedr Spring Festival Gardens - Gwyl Wanwyn Llanbedr *(22)*
Tir Mab Cynan Nursery, Brithdir *(34)*

May 2 Monday (Bank Hol)
Tir Mab Cynan Nursery, Brithdir *(34)*

May 3 Tuesday
Tir Mab Cynan Nursery, Brithdir *(34)*

May 4 Wednesday
Tir Mab Cynan Nursery, Brithdir *(34)*

May 5 Thursday
Tir Mab Cynan Nursery, Brithdir *(34)*

May 6 Friday
Tir Mab Cynan Nursery, Brithdir *(34)*

May 7 Saturday
Tir Mab Cynan Nursery, Brithdir *(34)*

May 8 Sunday
Bryn Gwern, Llanfachreth *(6)*
Gilfach, Rowen *(17)*
Tir Mab Cynan Nursery, Brithdir *(34)*

May 9 Monday
Tir Mab Cynan Nursery, Brithdir *(34)*

May 10 Tuesday
Tir Mab Cynan Nursery, Brithdir *(34)*

May 11 Wednesday
Tir Mab Cynan Nursery, Brithdir *(34)*

May 12 Thursday
Tir Mab Cynan Nursery, Brithdir *(34)*

May 13 Friday
Tir Mab Cynan Nursery, Brithdir *(34)*

May 14 Saturday
Megans Wood Gwernoer Farm, Nantlle *(27)*
Tir Mab Cynan Nursery, Brithdir *(34)*

May 15 Sunday
Bont Fechan Farm, Llanystumdwy *(2)*
Megans Wood Gwernoer Farm, Nantlle *(27)*
Tir Mab Cynan Nursery, Brithdir *(34)*

May 16 Monday
Tan Dinas, Llanfairpwll *(32)*
Tir Mab Cynan Nursery, Brithdir *(34)*

May 17 Tuesday
Tir Mab Cynan Nursery, Brithdir *(34)*

May 18 Wednesday
Tir Mab Cynan Nursery, Brithdir *(34)*

May 19 Thursday
Tir Mab Cynan Nursery, Brithdir *(34)*

May 20 Friday
Tir Mab Cynan Nursery, Brithdir *(34)*

May 21 Saturday
Tir Mab Cynan Nursery, Brithdir *(34)*

May 22 Sunday
Coron, Llanbedrog *(11)*
Craig y Ffynnon, Dolgellau *(12)*
29 Tan-y-Bwlch, Mynydd Llandegai *(33)*
Tir Mab Cynan Nursery, Brithdir *(34)*

May 23 Monday
Tir Mab Cynan Nursery, Brithdir *(34)*

May 24 Tuesday
Tir Mab Cynan Nursery, Brithdir *(34)*

May 25 Wednesday
Tir Mab Cynan Nursery, Brithdir *(34)*

May 26 Thursday
Tir Mab Cynan Nursery, Brithdir *(34)*

May 27 Friday
Tir Mab Cynan Nursery, Brithdir *(34)*

May 28 Saturday
Tir Mab Cynan Nursery, Brithdir *(34)*
Ty Ficerdy a Capel Gardens, Llanfachreth *(36)*

May 29 Sunday
Bryn Eisteddfod, Glan Conwy *(5)*
Bryniau, Boduan, nr Pwllheli *(7)*
Crug Farm, Griffiths Crossing *(13)*
Maesneuadd Farm, Llanfachreth *(26)*
Rhyd, Trefor *(31)*
Tir Mab Cynan Nursery, Brithdir *(34)*

May 30 Monday (Bank Hol)
Crug Farm, Griffiths Crossing *(13)*
Tir Mab Cynan Nursery, Brithdir *(34)*

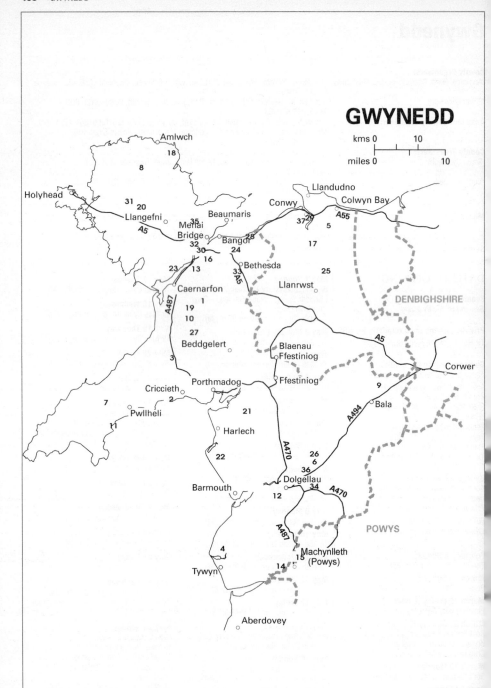

GWYNEDD

kms 0   10

miles 0   10

Amlwch

18

8

Holyhead

31

20

Llangefni

A5

35

Menai Bridge

32

Beaumaris

Bangor

28

30

16

24

23

13

33

A5

Bethesda

Caernarfon

1

19

10

27

Beddgelert

3

Criccieth

2

7

Pwllheli

1

Conwy

37

29

5

A55

Llandudno

Colwyn Bay

17

25

Llanrwst

DENBIGHSHIRE

A5

Blaenau
Ffestiniog

Ffestiniog

Corwer

9

Porthmadog

Bala

A494

21

Harlech

22

A470

26

6

36

Dolgellau

34

A470

12

Barmouth

A487

POWYS

4

14

15

Machynlleth
(Powys)

Tywyn

Aberdovey

May 31 Tuesday
Tir Mab Cynan-Nursery, Brithdir *(34)*

June 5 Sunday
Pensychnant, nr Conwy *(29)*

June 12 Sunday
Caerau Uchaf, Sarnau *(9)*
29 Tan-y-Bwlch, Mynydd Llandegai *(33)*

June 18 Saturday
Antur Waunfawr, Waunfawr *(1)*

June 19 Sunday
Esgairweddan, Pennal *(14)*

June 25 Saturday
Llanidan Hall, Brynsiencyn *(23)*

June 26 Sunday
Gilfach, Rowen *(17)*
Glanrafon Isaf, Penysarn *(18)*
Gwyndy Bach, Llandrygarn *(20)*
Maesneuadd Farm, Llanfachreth *(26)*
Treffos School, Llansadwrn *(35)*

July 3 Sunday
Bryniau, Boduan, nr Pwllheli *(7)*

July 9 Saturday
Llanidan Hall, Brynsiencyn *(23)*

July 10 Sunday
Braich-y-Foel, Bwlch Derwin *(3)*
Bronclydwr, Rhoslefain *(4)*
Cae Newydd, Rhosgoch, Anglesey *(8)*
Crug Farm, Griffiths Crossing *(13)*

July 12 Tuesday
Carmel Village Gardens *(10)*

July 17 Sunday
29 Tan-y-Bwlch, Mynydd Llandegai *(33)*
Ty Mawr, Gyffin *(37)*

July 24 Sunday
Rhyd, Trefor *(31)*
Ty Mawr, Gyffin *(37)*

July 30 Saturday
Hotel Maes-y-Neuadd, Talsarnau, nr Harlech *(21)*

July 31 Sunday
Bryn Gwern, Llanfachreth *(6)*

August 7 Sunday
Maenan Hall, Llanrwst *(25)*
29 Tan-y-Bwlch, Mynydd Llandegai *(33)*

August 14 Sunday
Felin y Ffridd, Ffriddgate, Machynlleth *(15)*
Gilfach, Rowen *(17)*

August 28 Sunday
Bryniau, Boduan, nr Pwllheli *(7)*
Crug Farm, Griffiths Crossing *(13)*

August 29 Monday (Bank Hol)
Hotel Maes-y-Neuadd, Talsarnau, nr Harlech *(21)*

September 18 Sunday
Bryniau, Boduan, nr Pwllheli *(7)*

October 9 Sunday
Bryniau, Boduan, nr Pwllheli *(7)*

DESCRIPTIONS OF GARDENS

❶ ◆ Antur Waunfawr, Waunfawr ⓰⊛
(Menna Jones Chief Executive) *4½m SE of Caernarfon. On A4085. Waunfawr village, turn L following signs, bear L for approx ½m.* Gardens and 7-acre Nature Park developed by Antur Waunfawr, a community venture providing employment opportunities for people with learning disabilities. Meadows, woodland walks, wildlife and ornamental ponds, soft fruit garden, herbaceous perennial beds. Well stocked wildlife plant nursery, greenhouses. New sensory garden open 2003. Light refreshments and TEAS Café at Antur. *Donations. Open all yr.* **For NGS:** *Sat 18 June (11-3). Tel 01286 650721 heullen@anturwaunfawr.org.uk*

❷ Bont Fechan Farm, Llanystumdwy ⓰⊛
(Mr & Mrs J D Bean) *2m W of Criccieth. On the A497 to Pwllheli on L of main rd.* Cottage garden with rockery, fish pond, herbaceous border, steps to river. Large variety of plants. Nicely planted tubs; good vegetable garden and poultry. Featured in 'Amateur Gardening' 2003. Home-made TEAS. *Adm £1.50, chd 50p. Suns, Mon 27, 28 Mar; 15 May (11-5). Private visits welcome by appt, also groups & coaches permitted. Tel 01766 522604 bontfechan.llanystumdwy@freeserve.co.uk*

❸ Braich-y-Foel, Bwlch Derwin 🗶⊛
(Mr & Mrs & Miss Ros Cooper) *9m S of Caernarfon. Take the A487 Caernarfon-Porthmadog rd. Leave the A487 at Pant Glas & follow signs.* Overstuffed cottage garden with little paths and nooks incl flowers, fruit and vegetables. Plenty of seating. Lovely setting and views over Anglesey. A variety of poultry at liberty in farm and garden. Thanks to Sally Crooks for her help. Light refreshments and TEAS. *Adm £1.50, chd free. Sun 10 July (12-4)*

❹ Bronclydwr, Rhoslefain 🗶⊛
(Mr & Mrs Michael Bishton) *5m N of Tywyn. Take A493 Dolgellau to Tywyn rd. At Rhoslefain take Tonfanau rd for about ½m. Fork L along private rd to end of tarmac rd then take unmade rd to large house on edge of wood.* Unique plantsman's garden of a peaceful historic farmhouse overlooking Cardigan Bay. Many unusual and tender plants are grown incl protea, puya, amicia, echiums, watsonias, arums, *Beschorneria yuccoides,* euryops, restios etc. Interesting trees, shrubs, bamboos. Extending to 1 acre; bog garden and wild wooded area. TEAS. *Adm £2, chd free. Sun 10 July (1-5)*

❺ Bryn Eisteddfod, Glan Conwy ⓰⊛
(Dr Michael Senior) *3½m SE of Llandudno. 3m W Colwyn Bay. Up hill (Bryn-y-Maen direction) from Glan Conwy Corner where A470 joins A55.* 8 acres of landscaped grounds incl mature shrubbery, arboretum, old walled 'Dutch' garden, large lawn with ha-ha. Extensive views over Conwy Valley, Snowdonia National Park, Conwy Castle, town and estuary. TEAS in aid of Friends of the Royal Cambrian Academy. *Adm £2.50, chd 50p. Sun 29 May (2-5). Private visits welcome by appt. Tel 01492 581175*

❻ Bryn Gwern, Llanfachreth ⓰🗶⊛
(Mrs H O & P D Nurse) *3m NE of Dolgellau. A494 Bala-Dolgellau rd: 13m from Bala. Take 1st Llanfachreth turn R. From Dolgellau 4th Llanfachreth turn L.* 2½ acres of trees, shrubs, flower beds, azaleas and rhododendrons. Garden has semi-wild feel. Many wild birds visit and nest. Ducks, chickens, Hawaiian geese, Guinea fowl, cats and dogs live here. Cream TEAS. *Adm £2, chd 50p. Suns 8 May; 31 July (10-5)*

❼ Bryniau, Boduan, nr Pwllheli ⊛
(P W Wright & J E Humphreys) *4m W of Pwllheli. Off A497. ½m down lane opp St Buan's Church.* Bryniau is a Grade II listed C18 Welsh farmstead (not open). Garden created since 1988 on pure sand. Over 100 families and over 300 genera of trees and shrubs, many unusual, showing that with little effort, one can grow virtually anything anywhere. Many tender and Australasian plants, truly a plantperson's garden. TEAS. *Adm £1.50, chd free. Suns 13, 27 Mar; 1, 29 May; 3 July; 28 Aug; 18 Sept; 9 Oct (11-5). Private visits welcome by appt, coaches permitted. Tel 01758 721338*

❽ NEW Cae Newydd, Rhosgoch, Anglesey ⓰🗶⊛
(Hazel & Nigel Bond) *3m SW of Amlwch. L immed after Amlwch Town sign on A5025 from Benllech, follow signs for leisure centre & Lastra Farm. L at next main T-junction follow rd for approx 3m, pass through Rhosgoch, keep to main*

rd, Sportsman PH on RH-side, follow signs for Llyn Alaw. Garden/car park 300yds on L. Recently created from an exposed 2½-acre S-facing field, overlooking Llyn Alaw with panoramic views of Snowdonia. Garden has mixed beds of interesting shrubs, grasses and perennials; large wildlife pond, meadow area with cut paths and buddleias, vegetable garden with polytunnel and chicken run. Paved area near house with raised beds and formal pond. Sheltered mature paddock garden with pond/bog area, formal herb bed and walled former pigsty providing additional shelter. Home-made TEAS in aid of Amwlch WI. *Adm £2.50, chd 50p. Sun 10 July (11-5). Private visits welcome by appt May to Sept, also small groups. Tel 01407 831354*

9 Caerau Uchaf, Sarnau 🅱🌂🏠
(Mr & Mrs Toby Hickish) *3m NE of Bala. From A5 N of Corwen turn L A494 to Bala. Approx 5m turn R into Sarnau, keep R up hill approx 1m. From Bala take A494 NE. After approx 3m turn L into Sarnau, keep R up hill approx 1m.* Herbaceous borders, lawns, ornamental vegetable garden, woodland walks - some paths rather steep. New developments every yr. Wonderful views. Home-made TEAS in aid of St Derfel Church. *Adm £2.50, chd free, concessions £1. Sun 12 June (2-5). Private visits welcome by appt. Tel 01678 530493 www.summersgardens.co.uk*

10 NEW Carmel Village Gardens
(Pwyllor Pentref Village Committee) *7m SE of Caernarfon. On A487 Porthmadog Rd, at Dinas roundabout exit 1st L to Groeslon, turn L at PO for 1½m.* Light refreshments and TEAS at St John the Baptist & St George in aid of DGAA. *Combined adm £2. Tue 12 July (2-5)*

NEW Gardd y Coleg 🅱🌂
(Pwyllor Pentref Carmel Village Committee) *Garden at Carmel village centre. Parking on site.* Approx ½-acre featuring raised beds planted with ornamental and native plants mulched with local slate. Benches and picnic area, wide pathways suitable for wheelchairs. Spectacular views. Garden created by volunteers. S4C Clwb Garddio 2004.

St John the Baptist & St George, Carmel 🏠 (Bishop Abbot Demetrius) *At village centre turn L & L again at Xrds.* Holy community in the making under the authority of The Orthodox Catholic Church of America. This is not a garden in the traditional sense but a spiritual retreat from

the stresses and strains of modern life, surrounded on all sides by space and rural tranquillity. We are privileged to share a glimpse of a more contemplative life.

11 NEW Coron, Llanbedrog 🅱🌂🏠
(Mr & Mrs B M Jones) *3m SW of Pwllheli. Turn R off A499 opp Llanbedrog Village sign, before garage, up private drive.* 6 acre mature garden featuring *Davidia involucrata*, overlooking Cardigan Bay. Pathways leading through extensively planted areas with rhododendrons, embothriom, azaleas, camellias, bluebell walks, wooded slopes and rock outcrops providing shelter for tender plants, lakes and bog gardens; orchards, walled vegetable and formal garden. Cream TEAS. *Adm £2.50, chd free. Sun 22 May (11-5.30). Private visits welcome by appt. Tel 01758 740296*

12 Craig y Ffynnon, Ffordd y Gader, Dolgellau 🌂
(Jon & Shân Lea) *Take A493 Tywyn rd from Dolgellau main sq. Park on rd by Penbryn Garage. Walk up rd signed Cader Idris. Garden entrance on L 50yds from junction.* N-facing 2-acre Victorian garden set out in 1870s. Majority of garden planted with mature specimen trees, rhododendrons and azaleas predominate. More formal herbaceous borders and greenhouse enclosed by box hedges. Wildlife pond; unusual shade-loving plants and ferns a feature. Steep uneven paths and steps. Home-made TEAS. *Adm £2, chd free (share to North Wales Air Ambulance Appeal). Sun 22 May (11-5). Private visits welcome by appt May & June only. Tel 01341 423445 jonlea@lycos.co.uk*

13 ◆ Crug Farm, Griffiths Crossing 🅱🌂🏠
(Mr & Mrs B Wynn-Jones) *2m NE of Caernarfon. ¼m off main A487 Caernarfon to Bangor rd. Follow signs from roundabout.* 3 acres; grounds to old country house (not open). Gardens filled with choice, unusual collections of climbers and herbaceous plants; over 300 species of hardy geraniums. Gold Medal at Tatton 2004. TEAS. *Adm £2.50, chd free. Walled garden & new woodland garden only + nursery Thurs to Suns 26 Feb to 31 Sept.* **For NGS:** *Sun 27 Mar; Sun, Mon 29, 30 May; Suns 10 July; 28 Aug (10-6). Tel 01248 670232 www.crug-farm.co.uk*

14 Esgairweddan, Pennal 🅱🌂
(Mr & Mrs John & Annie Parry) *4m W of Machynlleth. From Machynlleth take A493 towards Aberdovey. Esgairweddan is on R between Pennal & Cwrt.* Small garden with 400yr-old farmhouse (not open), ¾m drive from rd entrance leading through oak woodland with wonderful view of Dovey estuary. Home-made TEAS. *Adm £2, chd free. Sun 19 June (2-6)*

15 Felin y Ffridd, Ffriddgate, Machynlleth 🌂
(Mr & Mrs J W Osselton) *1m N of Machynlleth. From S, take A487 from Machynlleth to Dolgellau. After approx 1m turn R at B4404 to Llanwrin. Garden short distance on L before the bridge. From N, take A487, turn L on B4404.* Garden approx 1 acre, borders N Afon Dulas, and consists mainly of grassy paths and island beds of mixed plantings, trees, shrubs and herbaceous. Pond and gravel bed. Woodland edge being developed behind old mill. Hydrangeas, crocosmias and grasses. Home-made TEAS. *Adm £2, chd free. Sun 14 Aug (2-5.30)*

16 Foxbrush, Felinheli 🌂🏠
(Mr & Mrs B S Osborne) *3m SW of Bangor. On Bangor to Caernarfon rd, entering village opp lay-by with Felinheli sign post.* Fascinating 3-acre country garden created around winding river; ponds and small wooded area. Rare and interesting plant collections incl rhododendrons, ferns, clematis and roses; 45ft long pergola; fan-shaped knot garden. Dogs welcome. Winner Snowdonia National Park Wildlife Garden 2004. *Adm £2, chd free. Private visits welcome by appt Apr to end June only. Tel 01248 670463*

17 Gilfach, Rowen 🅱🌂🏠
(James & Isoline Greenhalgh) *4m S of Conwy. At Xrds 100yds E of Rowen S towards Llanrwst, past Rowen School on L; turn up 2nd drive on L, signposted.* 1-acre country garden on S-facing slope with magnificent views of the R Conwy and mountains; set in 35 acres of farm and woodland. Collection of mature shrubs is added to yearly; woodland garden, herbaceous border, small scree bed and pool. TEAS. *Adm £2, chd free. Suns 8 May; 26 June; 14 Aug (2-5.30). Private visits welcome by appt. Tel 01492 650216*

18 Glanrafon Isaf, Penysarn 🏠
(Mr & Mrs P E Hewitt) *15m NW of Bangor. On A5025, ¼m after village*

of Penysarn. Turn R across double white lines at bus stop on brow of incline. Parking in field, 100yds walk to garden. Medium-sized cottage garden with rockery, pond, alpines and greenhouse; vegetable garden and polytunnel. TEAS in aid of N Wales Air Ambulance Service. Adm £1.50, chd under 12 free. Sun 26 June (11-4). Private visits welcome by appt May to Sept, also small groups. Tel 01407 831642

⑲ NEW Gwelfor, Rhostryfan ⚘
(Mair & Dewi Tomos) 3½m S of Caernarfon. Follow A487 southwards through Caernarfon and Bontnewydd. 1st L signed Rhostryfan 1¼m. Park at chapel on R in village square. Follow signs to garden, 150 metre walk. Mature cottage garden with all-yr round interest. Kitchen garden, fruit trees, greenhouse and rockeries. Many interesting features. Finalist in S4C Garden of the Year 2004. Home-made TEAS in aid of local charities. Adm £1.50, chd free. Sat 30 Apr (11-5)

⑳ Gwyndy Bach, Llandrygarn ♿⚘❀NCCPG
(Keith & Rosa Andrew) 5m W of Llangefni. From Llangefni take the B5109 towards Bodedern, cottage is exactly 5m out on the L. ¾-acre artists garden, set amidst rugged Anglesey landscape. Romantically planted in intimate rooms developed over 30yrs. Many unusual plants, trees and shrubs. Featuring old roses, topiary, Japanese garden, large koi pond, bonsai and miniature Japanese palm display. National Collection of Rhapis. Studio attached. Home-made TEAS in aid of local charity. Adm £2, chd free. Sun 26 June (11.30-4.30) www.kannonchiku.co.uk

㉑ ◆ Hotel Maes-y-Neuadd, Talsarnau, nr Harlech ⚘❀
(Mr & Mrs P Jackson & Mr & Mrs P Payne) 3m NE of Harlech. Take B4573 old Harlech rd at T-junction with A496. Hotel signed ¼m on L. Take small lane on L immed after sign, just before small bridge on bend. Hotel entrance & car park ½m up hill, through small hamlet (tel box on L). Follow brown signs. Gardens and grounds of country house hotel, parts of which C14. Views towards Snowdon, Cardigan Bay and Lleyn Peninsula. 6 acres, meadows, woodland walks, 2 working walled gardens, unusual cultivars, cut flower borders; innovative, intensive, organic gardening methods with aesthetic appeal. TEAS. Adm £2, chd under 12 free, concessions £1.50. Open daily except Christmas and

New Year. **For NGS:** Sat 30 July; Mon 29 Aug (10-5). Tel 01766 780200/780319 www.neuadd.com

㉒ Llanbedr Spring Festival Gardens - Gwyl Wanwyn Llanbedr 7m N of Barmouth. On A496. Glorious, stylish, varied spring gardens in coastal micro-climate. Festival of gardens, music and walking. Sat to Mon 30 Apr to 2 May (2-5 Sat - 11-5 Sun & Mon). Home-made TEAS at Aber Artro Hall & Plas Gwynfryn in aid of Wales Air Ambulance & Llanbedr Community Fund. Combined adm £10 (valid 3 days), chd free. Sat 30 Apr to Mon 2 May. **For NGS:** Sun 1 May (11-5)

Aber Artro Hall ♿⚘❀ (Paul & Carolyn Morgan) Turn R off A496 in front of Victoria Inn in Llanbedr (L if coming from Harlech). After 1m turn R at sign Cwm Nantcol & follow arrows. Arts and Crafts 5-acre garden 1910 by architect Charles Edward Bateman. Terraced borders; riverside walk; fine trees, ponds. Hillside rock and wild garden leads to ancient woodland. Kitchen garden incl fruit pergola; secret Tuscan garden; William Morris 'wallpaper' garden. Adm £3 individual garden.

Llwyn ⚘ (Mr & Mrs Rodney Payne) Park on A496. Short walk uphill or shuttle service 11-4 on the hour. Mature 2-acre sloping garden, terrace leading down to formal lawn and pond. Herbaceous borders; wildlife pond, sunken garden, parterre, kitchen garden; woodland. Interesting variety of flowering trees, shrubs and plants, especially beautiful in spring. Adm £2.50 individual garden.

Plas Gwynfryn (J D S Evans) Spectacular 7-acre landscaped glacial rock garden. Sweeping lawns surrounded by rhododendrons, azaleas, magnolias, fine specimen trees incl taxodium, ginkgo, palms; fish pond, bamboo jungle; herbaceous borders, kitchen garden; woodland paths. Coastal and mountain scenery. Adm £3 individual garden.

Tyn y Wern (Mrs N Williams) Delightful small garden. Mature trees and shrubs, full of spring colour and interest, lawned area with pond bordered by shrubs, patio, gravel garden, small orchard, many varieties of clematis, rhododendrons, azaleas,

underplanted with spring bulbs. Adm £2 individual garden.

Uwchlaw'r Coed (Bernard & Caroline Roberts) Follow NGS signs from Llanbedr. Single track with passing places. Mountain setting (600ft) medium-sized garden with stream. Orchard bordered by 60yd working model steam railway. Camellias, irises, primulas. Adm £2 individual garden.

㉓ Llanidan Hall, Brynsiencyn ⚘❀
(Mr J W Beverley) 5m E of Llanfair Pwll. From Llanfair PG (Anglesey) follow A4080 towards Brynsiencyn for 4m. Turn at/opp Groeslon PH. Continue for 1m, garden entrance on R. Walled garden of 1¾ acres. Physic and herb gardens, ornamental vegetable garden, herbaceous borders, water features and many varieties of old roses. Children must be kept under supervision. Llanidan Church will be open for viewing. TEAS. Adm £2.50, chd £1. Sats 25 June; 9 July (10-4). Private visits welcome by appt. Tel 01248 852121 beverley.family@btinternet.com

㉔ Llys-y-Gwynt, Pentir Road, Llandygai ♿❀
(Jennifer Rickards & John Evans) 3m S of Bangor. 300yds from Llandygai roundabout at junction of A5 & A55. Take A5, then A4244 signed to Llanberis. 100yds from entrance to Esso service station, Little Chef & Travel Lodge, Take 'No Through Road' sign for 50yds. Turn L. Rambling 2 acre garden in harmony with and incl magnificent views of Snowdonia. Incorporating large Bronze Age Cairn. Designed to wander with paths to provide shelter and interest. The exposed site planted for wind - tolerance, yr-round colour and wildlife. Pond, waterfall and N-facing rockery. Featured in RHS 'The Garden' & 'Gardening in Harmony' - Wind 2003. Adm £2, chd free. Private visits welcome by appt, coaches permitted. Tel 01248 353863

㉕ Maenan Hall, Llanrwst 👤🎖️
(The Hon Mr & Mrs Christopher
Mclaren) *2m N of Llanrwst. On E
side of A470, ¼m S of Maenan
Abbey Hotel.* Gardens created since
1956 by the late Christabel, Lady
Aberconway and then present
owners; 10 acres; lawns, shrub, rose
and walled gardens; rhododendron
dell; many species of beautiful and
interesting plants, shrubs and trees set
amongst mature oaks and other
hardwoods; fine views across
Conway valley. A garden of
distinctive aspects incl fine rose
garden. Light refreshments and TEAS
in aid of St Davids Hospice (24 Apr)
& Red Cross (7 Aug). *Adm £3, chd
£2, concessions £2. Suns 24 Apr;
7 Aug (10.30-5.30) last entry 4.30.
Private visits welcome by appt.
Tel 020 7602 1983
cmmclaren@clara.co.uk*

**㉖ Maesneuadd Farm,
Llanfachreth** 👤🎖️
(Mr E & Mrs W Smith) *3½m NE of
Dolgellau. From Dolgellau take A494
Bala rd for 3m. 1/3m after Brithdir
junction turn L uphill. Go straight
across 1st junction. Farm ½m on L.
From Bala take A494 for 13m. At
2nd sign 'Llanfachreth' turn sharp R.
Cross 1st junction. Farm ½m on L.*
An old garden being renovated.
Ongoing new plantings. Small
areas of trees, shrubs, herbaceous.
Pond with bog-loving plants. Small
areas where frost-hardy plants thrive.
A naturally evolving flower meadow
where orchids have seeded. Beautiful
views. Steeply banked deciduous
Welsh woodland where bluebells,
ferns, mosses, lichen and whinberries
grow, dissected by a tumbling stream
and alive with birdsong. Home-made
TEAS. *Adm £2, chd free. Suns 29
May; 26 June (1-5.30)*

**㉗ NEW Megans Wood Gwernoer
Farm, Nantlle** 🎖️
(Mr & Mrs R Black) *2m E of
Penygroes. On B4418 Penygroes to
Rhyd-Ddu rd, past big house on L,
1st house on R after cattle grid.* 3
acre woodland garden set on steep
hillside. Panoramic views of the
Nantlle valley and Snowdon.
Woodland underplanted with over
1000 rhododendrons, azaleas and
camellias planted over the last 18yrs.
Ornamental pond and waterfall on
site of mines. TEAS. *Adm £2. Sat,
Sun 14, 15 May (10-4) . Private visits
welcome by appt. Tel 01286 880913*

㉘ ◆ Penrhyn Castle, Bangor 👤
(The National Trust) *3m E of
Bangor. On A5122. Buses from
Llandudno, Caernarvon, Betws-y-*

Coed; alight: Grand Lodge Gate.
Large grounds incl Victorian walled
garden; fine trees, shrubs, wild
garden, good views. Light
refreshments and TEAS. *Adm £1, chd
free.* For NGS: *Sun 6 Feb (12-4).
Tel 01248 353084
www.nationaltrust.org.uk*

**㉙ NEW ◆ Pensychnant,
Sychnant Pass, nr Conwy** 👤🎖️
(Pensychant Foundation Wardens
Julian Thompson & Anne Mynott)
*2½m W of Conwy. At top of
Sychnant Pass between Conwy &
Penmaenmawr. From Conwy turn L
into Upper Gate St by Heddlu/Police;
after 2½m Pensychnant's drive signed
on R. From Penmaenmawr, fork R
by Mountain View PH; summit of
Sychnant Pass after walls,
Pensychnant's drive on L.* Diverse
herbaceous borders surrounded by
mature shrubs, banks of
rhododendrons, ancient and
Victorian woodlands. 12 acre
woodland walks with views of
Conwy Mountain and Sychnant.
Woodland birds. Picnic tables,
archaelogical trail on mountain. A
peaceful little gem. Large Victorian
gothic house (open) with art
exhibition. Home-made TEAS in aid
of Pensychnant Foundation (NGS day
only). *Adm £2, chd 50p. Open Weds
to Suns Apr to Sept .* For NGS: *Sun 5
June (11-5). Tel 01492 592595
julian@pensychnant.fsnet.co.uk*

㉚ ◆ Plas Newydd, Anglesey
👤🎖️
(The National Trust) *2m S of
Llanfairpwll. A55 junctions 7 & 8 on
A4080.* Gardens with massed shrubs,
fine trees, lawns sloping down to
Menai Strait. Magnificent views to
Snowdonia. Woodland walk leading
to Marine Walk. Australasian
arboretum and wild flowers. Terrace
garden with summer display and
water features. Very good area for
bird-watching and fungi in autumn.
Rhododendron garden Mar to early
June only. C18 house by James Wyatt
contains Rex Whistler's largest
painting; also Military Museum.
Light refreshments and TEAS. *House
and Garden adm £5, chd £2.50,
family £12, Garden only adm £3, chd
£1.50 under 5 free. Sats to Weds 19
March to 2 Nov.* For NGS: *Fri 25 Mar
(11-5.30 last entry 4.30). Tel 01248
714795 www.nationaltrust.org.uk*

㉛ Rhyd, Trefor 👤🎖️
(Ann & Jeff Hubble) *7m W of
Llangefni. Nr Holyhead. From
Bodedern 2¼m along B5109 towards
Llangefni, turn L. 2½ acres of gardens
and nature walks.* Garden in areas

containing many unusual plants in
herbaceous beds; rhododendrons,
clematis and climbing roses abound;
grounds contain ponds, pergolas,
rockery, arboretum and garden room.
Walk through the nature reserve and
pause in the haven and see how many
wild flowers you can identify. Garden
bordered by stream. Finalist in Clwb
Garddio Best Garden Competion
2004. Home-made TEAS. *Adm £2,
chd free. Suns 29 May; 24 July
(11-5). Private visits welcome by
appt. Tel 01407 720320
jeff@jhubble.freeserve.co.uk*

㉜ Tan Dinas, Llanfairpwll 🎖️
(Charles Ellis) *2m W of Menai
Bridge. On main rd between
Llanfairpwll & Britannia Bridge,
250yds from the Marquess of
Anglesey's column. Parking in
Column car park, access via path
through Column woods. Visitors cars
can unload but not park at garden.*
An interesting 1½-acre cottage
garden. Overlooked by the Marquess
of Anglesey's column, 200yds from
the Menai Straits. Carefully designed
and planted on 3 levels; shrubbery,
large pond garden, vegetable and
fruit areas, heather garden. Careful
planting ensures all-yr colour.
Interesting specimens of *Echium
pininana*, other unusual plants.
TEAS. *Adm £2, chd 50p (share to
Llanfairpwll WI). Mon 16 May
(11-5). Private visits welcome by
appt. Tel 01248 714373
charles.ellis@tesco.net*

**㉝ 29 Tan-y-Bwlch, Mynydd
Llandegai** 👤🎖️
(Chas & Ilona Sewell) *5m S of
Bangor. From A55 J11, A5
roundabout follow A4244 signed
Llanberis for 5m then L towards
Deiniolen, next L up hill (Marchlyn),
then next L over moor. Take next R
down Tan-y-Bwlch Rd.* Despite the
land being infertile and exposed with
very high rainfall, a unique 1-acre
garden, plus 1½ acre wildlife area,
both with panoramic views, has been
created 1,000ft up in Snowdonia with
over 2,000 different plants.
Herbaceous beds, mature and young
trees, shrubs, grasses, roses, stream,
ponds and bog areas. Home-made
TEAS. *Adm £2. Suns 22 May; 19
June; 17 July; , 7 Aug (11-5). Private
visits welcome by appt, coaches
permitted. Tel 01248 600702
chas@dryll.com*

**㉞ NEW ◆ Tir Mab Cynan
Nursery, Brithdir** 🎖️NCCPG
(Anne & Jim Haunch) *3m E of
Dolgellau. From Dolgellau take A494
E towards Bala for 2m then R*

B4416. From Bala take A494 W towards Dolgellau then L B4416. Towards Dolgellau on A470, turn sharp R B4416, signed Brithdir. Between 2 chapels turn N through gate down lane for ¼m, then R to garden/nursery & car park. New garden in progress well stocked with many unusual rare and new introductions incl hardy geraniums. National Collection of Geranium Phaeum Cultivars. TEAS at Ty Glas Farm (top of lane). Adm £2, chd free. Nursery open daily Apr to Sept . **For NGS:** Daily Sun 1 May to Tue 31 May (10-5). Tel 01341 450339 after 6pm

 **Treffos School, Llansadwrn**

(Dr & Mrs Humphreys) 2 ½m N of Menai Bridge. A5025 Amlwch/Benllech exit from the Britannia Bridge onto Anglesey. Approx 3m turn R towards Llansadwrn. Entrance to Treffos School is 200yds on LH-side. 7 acres, child-friendly garden, in rural location, surrounding C17 house now run as school. Garden consists of mature woodland, underplanted with spring flowering bulbs and rhododendrons, ancient beech avenue leading down to rockery, herbaceous

borders and courtyards. Children's garden trails. Cream TEAS. Adm £1.50, chd free. Sun 26 June (12-4)

36 NEW Ty Ficerdy a Capel Gardens, Llanfachreth
4m NE of Dolgellau. 18m SW of Bala. From A470 nr Dolgellau take A494 towards Bala. Turn L in 200yds, signed Dolgellau. Take 1st R signed Llanfachreth. 2m uphill to village. Turn L at T-junction, war memorial on L. Ger-y-Llan garden 100yds on R. Continue for ½m to Capel garden. Park nr chapel and walk 30yds downhill. Small isolated village 1m from the famous 'Precipice Walk'. Spectacular views of Cader Idris and the Arans. Home-made TEAS at Ty Capel Ffrwd, Llanfachreth. Combined adm £3, chd free. Sat 28 May (11-5)

NEW Ger-y-Llan, Llanfachreth
(Carys & Aneurin Lewis) 1½ acre garden created over 25yrs, hillside garden to rear of house with bluebell woods. Formal garden in front of house. Terrace; koi pond; rose garden. Planters, trees, shrubs, azaleas, rhododendrons, heathers and mixed borders.

NEW Ty Capel Ffrwd (Revs Mary & George Bolt) 1 acre cottage garden on several levels with stream running through. Azaleas fill the bank with colour in spring. Garden in areas, containing many unusual plants. Large collection of hardy geraniums. Hosta and lilies in woodland area. Cardiocrinum giganteum flowering in June. Collection of shrub roses and climbers. Small bluebell wood. Some paths steep. Private visits welcome by appt June & July only. Tel 01341 422006

37 Ty Mawr, Henryd Road, Gyffin
(Mrs M P Davies) ½m S of Conwy. Gyffin Village S of Conwy on B5106 (½m). Garden in Henryd Rd next to Gyffin church. Small garden with good selection of plants and many interesting places to explore and sit in. Still a work in progress - much of the planting is 3yrs old. This will be our 2nd yr with the NGS and we hope you will come and enjoy the changes we have made. Not suitable for young children. TEAS. £1.50, chd 50p (share to St David's Hospice, Llandudno). Suns 17, 24 July (2-6)

Powys

County Organisers:
(South Powys)   Miss Shân Egerton, Pen-y-Maes, Hay-on-Wye, Hereford HR3 5PP
                   Tel 01497 820423 email sre@waitrose.com
(North Powys)   Mrs Angela Hughes, Castell y Gwynt, Montgomery, Powys SY15 6HR
                   Tel 01686 668317 email roghughes@aol.com
Press & Publicity Officers:
(South Powys)   Mrs Evelyn Evans, Ffrwdgrech House, Brecon, Powys LD3 8LB
                   Tel 01874 622519 email ffrwdgrech@btinternet.com
(North Powys)   Mrs Mary Lovegrove, Upper FFinnant, Llandinam, Newtown, Powys SY17 5AA
                   Tel 01686 688927 email mary.lovegrove@virgin.net
County Treasurers:
(South)   Mrs Joan McGrath, 1 Baskerville Court, Clyro, Hereford HR3 5SS Tel 01497 821465
(North Powys)   Capt Ray Watson (Ret'd), Westwinds, Common Road, Kerry, Newtown SY16 4NY
                   Tel 01686 670605

Maps: Numbers shown next to each garden entry refer to that garden's entry on the county map. This position is approximate; distance and directions from the nearest main town are generally shown in the garden text. A precise location is available for those gardens featured on the NGS website by visiting www.ngs.org.uk.

Symbols: Information relating to symbols is given on page 21

DATES OF OPENING

Evening openings
See end of county listing

Gardens open to the public
For details see garden description
Ashford House, Talybont-on-Usk *(2)*
Dingle Nurseries & Garden, Welshpool *(11)*
Glansevern Hall Gardens, Berriew *(15)*
Grandma's Garden, Plas Dolguog Estates, Machynlleth *(19)*
Powis Castle Garden, Welshpool *(32)*

By appointment only
For telephone number and other details see garden description.
Private visits welcomed
Cwm-Weeg, Dolfor *(10)*
Lower House, Cusop, Hay-on-Wye *(27)*
The White House, Groesffordd, nr Brecon *(39)*
Woodhill, Moelfre *(40)*

April 24 Sunday
Abernant, Fron, Garthmyl *(1)*

April 30 Saturday
Mill Cottage, Abbeycwmhir *(29)*

May 1 Sunday
Maesllwch Castle, Glasbury-on-Wye *(28)*
Mill Cottage, Abbeycwmhir *(29)*
Penmyarth, Glanusk Park, nr Crickhowell *(30)*

May 2 Monday (Bank Hol)
Mill Cottage, Abbeycwmhir *(29)*

May 7 Sunday
Tan-y-Llyn, Meifod *(33)*

May 8 Sunday
Gliffaes Country House Hotel, Crickhowell *(17)*

Grandma's Garden, Plas Dolguog Estates, Machynlleth *(19)*
Tan-y-Llyn, Meifod *(33)*

May 13 Friday
3 Church Terrace, Berriew *(6)*
Glansevern Hall Gardens, Berriew *(15)*

May 14 Saturday
Dingle Nurseries & Garden, Welshpool *(11)*

May 15 Sunday
The Chestnuts, Llanfyllin *(5)*
Dingle Nurseries & Garden, Welshpool *(11)*
Glanwye, Builth Wells *(16)*
Tinto House, Hay-on-Wye *(34)*

May 22 Sunday
Felindre Mill, Llanidloes *(12)*
Pen-y-Maes, Hay-on-Wye *(31)*

May 29 Sunday
Bodynfoel Hall, Llanfechain *(4)*
Ffrwdgrech House, Brecon *(13)*
Lower Cefn Perfa, Kerry *(26)*
Ty Capel Deildre, Llanidloes *(36)*

May 30 Monday (Bank Hol)
Llysdinam, Newbridge-on-Wye *(24)*

June 4 Saturday
Tan-y-Llyn, Meifod *(33)*

June 5 Sunday
Tan-y-Llyn, Meifod *(33)*
The Walled Garden, Knill *(37)*

June 10 Friday
Mill Cottage, Abbeycwmhir *(29)*

June 11 Saturday
Mill Cottage, Abbeycwmhir *(29)*

June 12 Sunday
Clawdd-y-Dre, Montgomery *(8)*
Mill Cottage, Abbeycwmhir *(29)*
Tretower House, Tretower, nr Crickhowell *(35)*

June 19 Sunday
Llowes Gardens *(23)*

June 25 Saturday
Abernant, Fron, Garthmyl *(1)*

June 26 Sunday
Crickhowell Gardens *(9)*
Fraithwen, Tregynon *(14)*

July 2 Saturday
Tan-y-Llyn, Meifod *(33)*

July 3 Sunday
Kerry Gardens *(21)*
Llangorse Gardens, nr Brecon *(22)*
Tan-y-Llyn, Meifod *(33)*

July 10 Sunday
Felindre Mill, Llanidloes *(12)*
Glyn Celyn House, Felinfach, nr Brecon *(18)*

July 11 Monday
Powis Castle Garden, Welshpool *(32)*

July 15 Friday
Mill Cottage, Abbeycwmhir *(29)*

July 16 Saturday
Mill Cottage, Abbeycwmhir *(29)*

July 17 Sunday
Hay-on-Wye Gardens *(20)*
Mill Cottage, Abbeycwmhir *(29)*

July 24 Sunday
Battle House, Battle *(3)*

July 30 Saturday
Cil y Wennol, Berriew *(7)*

July 31 Sunday
Cil y Wennol, Berriew *(7)*
Lonicera, Talybont-on-Usk *(25)*

August 6 Saturday
Tan-y-Llyn, Meifod *(33)*

August 7 Sunday
Tan-y-Llyn, Meifod *(33)*

August 14 Sunday
Llysdinam, Newbridge-on-Wye *(24)*

August 17 Wednesday
Grandma's Garden, Plas Dolguog Estates, Machynlleth *(19)*

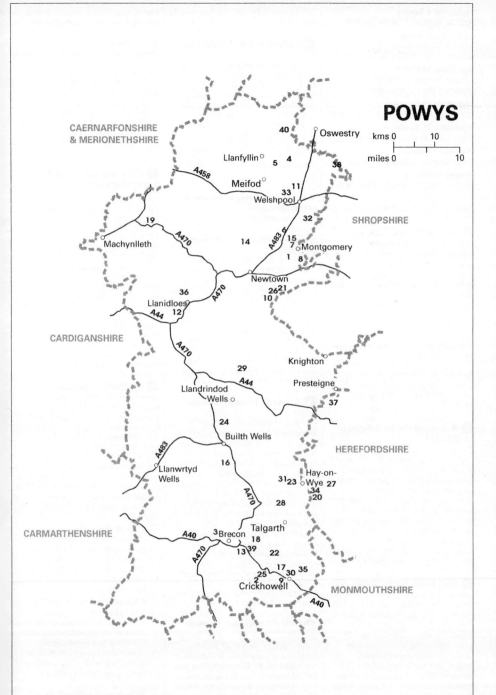

POWYS

CAERNARFONSHIRE
& MERIONETHSHIRE

Oswestry

40

Llanfyllin 5 4

38

Meifod 11

33

Welshpool

32

SHROPSHIRE

19

A458

A470

Machynlleth

14

A483

15
7

1 8

Montgomery

Newtown

36

A470

Llanidloes

26 21
10

12

A44

A470

CARDIGANSHIRE

Knighton

29

A44

Presteigne

Llandrindod
Wells

37

24

Builth Wells

HEREFORDSHIRE

A483

16

Llanwrtyd
Wells

A470

31 23
34
20

Hay-on-
Wye 27

28

CARMARTHENSHIRE

A40

3 Brecon

Talgarth

18

A470

13 39

22

17
25 30 35
2 9

Crickhowell

MONMOUTHSHIRE

A40

kms 0   10
miles 0   10

September 4 Sunday
Westlake Fisheries, Four Crosses *(38)*

September 9 Friday
3 Church Terrace, Berriew *(6)*
Glansevern Hall Gardens, Berriew *(15)*

September 16 Friday
3 Church Terrace, Berriew *(6)*
Glansevern Hall Gardens, Berriew *(15)*

September 24 Saturday
Dingle Nurseries & Garden, Welshpool *(11)*

September 25 Sunday
Dingle Nurseries & Garden, Welshpool *(11)*

October 22 Saturday
Dingle Nurseries & Garden, Welshpool *(11)*

October 23 Sunday
Dingle Nurseries & Garden, Welshpool *(11)*

DESCRIPTIONS OF GARDENS

❶ Abernant, Fron, Garthmyl ⌾
(J A & B M Gleave) *Mid-way between Welshpool (9m) & Newtown (9m). On A483. 1½m S of Garthmyl. Approached over steep humpback bridge, then straight ahead through gate.* Approx 2½ acres incl cherry orchard, lawns, pond, knot garden, roses, lavender, rockery, ornamental shrubs and trees, specimen fern garden, ornamental pond, potager; additional woodland area with natural pond and stream. Home-made TEAS. *Adm £2. Sun 24 Apr; Sat 25 June (2-6). Private visits welcome by appt, small groups. No parking for coaches. Tel 01686 640494*

❷ ◆ Ashford House, Talybont-on-Usk ⌾⌾
(Mr & Mrs D A Anderson) *6½m SE of Brecon. Off A40 on B4558. 1m SE of Talybont-on-Usk.* 1-acre walled garden surrounded by woodland and wild garden approx 4-acres altogether; restored and developed since 1979. Mixed shrub and herbaceous borders; meadow garden and pond; alpine house and beds; vegetables. Light refreshments and TEAS. *Adm £2.50, chd free. Tues, Apr to Sept (2-6). Tel 01874 676271*

❸ NEW Battle House, Battle ⌾⌾
(Mr & Mrs Roger Jones) *3m NW of Brecon. On Craddoc Rd. In Craddoc follow sign to Battle. Battle House is ¼m after the village on L.* Large terraced garden, surrounding C18 house (not open), developed over 12yrs but much done recently. Herbaceous and mixed borders, lawns, pond and bog garden, young arboretum and pleached limes, lakes, dovecote (new) and fine walling. Spectacular views of the Brecon Beacons. Home-made TEAS in aid of

Usk House. *Adm £3, chd free. Sun 24 July (2-5)*

❹ Bodynfoel Hall, Llanfechain ⌾⌾
(Mr & Mrs Bonnor-Maurice) *10m N of Welshpool. Via A490 towards Llanfyllin. Take B4393, follow signs.* Approx 3½ acres of garden and woodland, with ponds. Young and mature trees, woodland walks; formal and wild, rhododendrons, azaleas, lovely views, garden sculptures. TEAS in aid of Llanfechain Church. *Adm £2.50, chd 50p, concessions £1. Sun 29 May (2-6)*

◆ Bryan's Ground, Stapleton, nr Presteigne ⌾⌾⌾
See Herefordshire.

❺ The Chestnuts, High Street, Llanfyllin ⌾
(Mr & Mrs B Pawley) *In town centre, down lane opp telephone kiosk.* 1½ acres well established garden with unusual trees and shrubs. Herbaceous borders, planted for all-yr colour and interest. Rock garden with specialist alpines, grasses and herb garden. Extensive all-round views. No parking at garden. Free parking in town. Home-made TEAS. *Adm £2.50, chd free. Sun 15 May (2-6). Private visits welcome by appt. Tel 01691 648179*

❻ 3 Church Terrace, Berriew ⌾⌾
(Mr Jimmy Hancock) *5m S of Welshpool. In village centre, behind the Church.* ¾-acre garden with river below. A plantsman's garden with trees, shrubs, climbers and a diverse range of rare and unusual plants to create interest throughout the year; keen gardeners who feel they need something different to stimulate their garden will see what can be achieved in a small garden. 30ft x 12ft greenhouse with a good range of tender, interesting plants. Visitor numbers limited due to size of garden, personal tour incl with owner, Head Gardener, Powis Castle 1972-96. *Adm £1.50. Fris 13 May; 9, 16 Sept (2-6). Private visits welcome by appt. Tel 01686 640774*

❼ NEW Cil y Wennol, Berriew ⌾⌾
(Lady Carlile) *5m SW of Welshpool. Berriew is off the A483 Welshpool to Newtown rd. By Berriew School take B4385 towards Castle Caereinion. Cil y Wennol is ¾m along the B4385.* 3½-acre established garden set around Tudor cottage (not open). Long curving drive, wild grasses and trees

lead to oval lawn surrounded with sorbus. Front garden: traditional, formal cottage design with more recent influences. Rear gardens: sweeping array of new-style perennial prairie planting, spectacular views, enclosed vegetable garden and croquet lawn. Entire site combines wildness with smooth line and features crescent-shaped hedges, walks, slate walls and congruent sculptures. Some steep slopes involved. TEAS at Glansevern Hall (Sat only). *Adm £2.50, chd free. Sat 30, Sun 31 July (2-6)*

❽ Clawdd-y-Dre, Lions Bank, Montgomery ⌾⌾
(Mr E & Mrs J K Bowen-Jones) *From centre of Montgomery (parking) proceed up hill along Church Bank past St Nicholas Church. Turn R into Lions Bank past Spider Cottage.* ¾-acre town garden sitting on the old town walls with panoramic views across the valley and Offa's Dyke. Terrace with containers; conservatory housing succulents and exotics. Gravel paths and steps down to croquet lawn. Wild flower meadow in preparation. Yew screens. Wide range of shrubs and herbaceous perennials. Wildlife pond, rockeries. Home-made TEAS in aid of St Nicholas Church. *Adm £2.50, chd 50p. Sun 12 June (2-5.30)*

❾ Crickhowell Gardens
14m SE of Brecon. Travelling E from Brecon on A40 turn R for Tower St in centre of Crickhowell at Balti restaurant. Castle Rd is the last R turn leaving Crickhowell E on A40. Turn R at Bear Hotel for High Street which continues into Castle Rd. 5 small town gardens packed with interesting planting esp climbers and containers. Home-made TEAS at 6 Tower Street & Tremyrafon. *Combined adm £3, chd free. Sun 26 June (2-6)*

2 Tower Street ⌾ (Penelope & Geoffrey Harris) *Off A40 beside Balti restaurant.* Small walled town garden. Paved courtyard, statuary, water feature and containers. 50 varieties of plants incl many climbers.

5 Tower Street ⌾⌾ (Mr T G Horley) *Off A40 beside Balti restaurant.* Charming, densely planted Victorian town garden. Climbing and shrub roses, clematis, cistus and wisteria mix beautifully with other shrubs and perennials. Good container planting.

NEW Bwthyn-y-Castell, High Street ⌾ (Roger & Diana White) *Corner of High St and Castle Rd*

opp police station. Small cottage garden above the street, backing on to the bailey wall of the castle, with views up the Usk valley.
6 Tower Street 🔵🚫🏠 (Mr & Mrs Peter Davey) *Off A40 beside Balti restaurant.* Small stone walled and trellised Victorian town garden, with climbing and shrub roses, clematis, cistus, wisteria; other shrubs and perennials, surrounding flagstoned patio; containers.

NEW **Rose Cottage** 🚫 (Mrs K Price-Rees) *On bend in rd where High Street becomes Castle Rd, opp Ty Dan y Castell House.* Small, terraced cottage garden with wide variety of shrubs, climbers and bulbs. Views into castle grounds.

Tremyrafon, Castle Road 🔵🚫🏠 (Mrs P Williams) *Off Castle rd. Opp tennis courts.* Small, easy to maintain garden facing SW. Lawn, shrubs and bulbs surrounded by low beech hedge with views of Beaufort Mountain and River Usk.

Cwmrhaiadr Garden & Nursery, Glaspwll, Machynlleth 🏠
See Ceredigion/Cardiganshire.

🔟 **Cwm-Weeg, Dolfor** 🚫
(Dr W Shaefer & Mr K D George) *4½m SE of Newtown. Take A489 E from Newtown for 1½m, turn R towards Dolfor. After 2m turn L down farm track.* 2½-acre garden set within 12 acres of wild flower meadows and bluebell woodland with stream centred around C15 farmhouse (not open). The formal garden commenced in the 1990s in the English landscape tradition with vistas, grottos, lawns and extensive borders terraced with stone walls, translates older garden vocabulary into an innovative C21 concept. *Adm £2.50. Private visits welcome by appt from 15 May to 15 Sept. Tel 01686 628992 wolfgang@dial1.co.uk*

Diamond Cottage, Buttington, nr Welshpool 🚫🏠
See Shropshire.

⓫ ◆ **Dingle Nurseries & Garden, Welshpool** 🏠
(Mrs Kerry Hamer) *2m NW of Welshpool. From Welshpool, take A490 towards Llanfyllin and Guilsfield. After 1m turn L at sign for Dingle Nurseries & Garden.* 4-acre garden on a S-facing site, sloping down to a lake. The beds are mostly colour themed with a huge variety of rare and unusual trees and shrubs. Set

in the hills of mid Wales this beautiful and well known garden attracts visitors from Britain and abroad. TEAS. *Adm £2.50. Open all yr (9-5), closed Tues am (9-2) & Xmas wk.* **For NGS:** *Sats, Suns 14, 15 May; 24, 25 Sept; 22, 23 Oct (9-5). Tel 01938 555145 kerry@dinglenurseries.co.uk*

Felin y Ffridd, Ffriddgate, Machynlleth 🏠
See Gwynedd.

⓬ **NEW** **Felindre Mill, Llanidloes** 🏠
(Mr Noel & Mrs Joyce Benbow) *1m W of Llanidloes town centre. From Old Market Hall, Llanidloes, take Short Bridge St over river. Turn L, after ½m turn L at fork to Llangurig, 1st R over bridge.* Woodland garden created on the banks of R Severn with mill race feeding pond, streams and bog gardens. Narrow paths and steps meander through rich marginal plantings and mature trees. Rhododendrons, azaleas and herbaceous borders follow paths leading up to new arboretum and vegetable garden. Wonderful spring and summer colour. Unfenced river and streams, possibly unsuitable for children. Home-made TEAS in aid of Meningitis Research Foundation. *Adm £2.50, chd £1. Suns 22 May; 10 July (2-6). Private visits welcome by appt May to July. Tel 01686 413370*

⓭ **Ffrwdgrech House, Brecon** 🔵🏠
(Mr & Mrs Michael Evans) *½m W of Brecon. Enter Brecon from A40 by-pass at W roundabout. Take 3rd turning on R, Ffrwdgrech Rd. In ¾m oak gate & lodge on L.* 7-acre Victorian pleasure garden; lake, species trees incl fine examples of ginkgo, swamp cyprus, *Davidia involucrata,* subtropical shrubs, rhododendrons and azaleas. Stream and waterfall, woodland walks. Walled kitchen garden restoration programme. Views of Brecon Beacons. Home-made TEAS in aid of L'Arche. *Adm £3, chd free. Sun 29 May (2-5). Private visits welcome by appt, coaches & garden groups. Tel 01874 622519 Ffrwdgrech@btinternet.com*

⓮ **Fraithwen, Tregynon** 🚫🏠
(Mr & Mrs David & Sydney Thomas) *6m N of Newtown. On B4389 mid-way between villages of Bettws Cedewain & Tregynon.* 1½-acre established garden with herbaceous borders, rockeries and ponds. Packed with interesting and rare plants for yr-round colour.

Display of antique horse-drawn machinery and house implements. Featured on Welsh TV 'Brynhawn Da' 2004. TEAS in aid of Bettws Community Centre. *Adm £2.50. Sun 26 June (2-6). Private visits welcome by appt. Tel 01686 650307*

⓯ ◆ **Glansevern Hall Gardens, Berriew** 🔵🏠
(G & M Thomas) *5m SW of Welshpool. On A483 at Berriew.* 18-acre mature garden situated nr banks of R Severn. Centred on Glansevern Hall, a Greek Revival house dated 1801 (not open). Noted for variety of unusual tree species; much new planting; lake with island; woodland walk; large rock garden and grotto. Roses and herbaceous beds. Water garden and large walled garden, with fruit, vegetable and ornamental planting. Interesting shelters and follies. Walk down to R Severn. Light refreshments and TEAS. *Adm £3.50, concessions £3. Thurs, Fris, Sats & Bank Hol Mons May to Sept (12-6).* **For NGS:** *Fris 13 May; 9, 16 Sept (12-6). Tel 01686 640200 Mr & Mrs N Thomas www.glansevern.co.uk*

⓰ **Glanwye, Builth Wells** 🔵🏠
(Mr & Mrs David Vaughan, & H Kidston) *2m SE Builth Wells. On A470.* Large garden, rhododendrons, azaleas; herbaceous borders, extensive yew hedges, lawns, long woodland walk with bluebells and other woodland flowers. Magnificent views of upper Wye Valley. Home-made TEAS in aid of Llandewi Cwm Church. *Adm £3, chd free. Sun 15 May (2-5)*

⓱ **Gliffaes Country House Hotel, Crickhowell** 🔵
(Mr & Mrs N Brabner & Mr & Mrs J C Suter) *2½m NW of Crickhowell. 1m off the A40.* Large garden; spring bulbs, azaleas and rhododendrons; ornamental pond; heathers, shrubs and ornamental trees; fine maples; superb position high above R Usk. Home-made TEAS. *Adm £2.50, chd free. Sun 8 May (2-5)*

⓲ **Glyn Celyn House, Felinfach, nr Brecon** 🔵🏠
(Mr & Mrs N Paravicini) *4m NE of Brecon. On A470 east of Brecon on hill above Felinfach.* 10-yr-old 7-acre sloping garden still in the making. 2 streams supply water to fountains and lake. Mixed planting within yew and hornbeam hedges. Woodland walks lead to lake and unusual grotto. Well-established trees among newly-planted shrubs and trees. Pretty kitchen garden with raised beds and rose and sweet pea covered

arches. Glorious views over the Black Mountains. Home-made TEAS. *Adm £3, chd free. Sun 10 July (2-5). Private visits welcome by appt, also garden groups. Tel 01874 624836*

⓳ NEW ◆ Grandma's Garden, Plas Dolguog Estates, Machynlleth ♿⊕
(Diana & Richard Rhodes) *1½m E of Machynlleth. Turn L off A489 Machynlleth to Newtown rd. Follow brown tourist signs to Plas Dolguog Hotel.* 9 acres, stunning views of Snowdonia National Park and Dyfi Valley. Peace garden, arboretum and sculpture park, a place to find inner peace. Seven sensory gardens, riverside walk, rhododendrons, shrubberies and new mixed plantings. Easily accessible by wheelchair. Great for children. Featured on BBC2 'I love Wales' 2004. David Bellamy Gold Award for Conservation 2003. Home-made TEAS at Plas Dolguog Hotel. *Adm £2.50, chd 50p. Weds & Suns throughout the year for charity (10-late).* **For NGS:** *Sun 8 May; Wed 17 Aug (10.30-6). Tel 01654 702244 Diana Rhodes diana@sol-star.fsnet. co.uk*

The Griggs, Newton St Margarets ♿⊗
See Herefordshire.

⓴ Hay-on-Wye Gardens
One opp Clock Tower in centre and other 150yds on B4350 towards Brecon beyond Swan Hotel on R exactly opp Capel-y-Fin rd. Two large town gardens crammed with interesting planting and good design. Light refreshments and TEAS at The Granary opp Tinto House. *Combined adm £2.50, chd free. Sun 17 July (2-5)*

The Old Presbytery ♿⊕ (Sue & Duncan Graham) ¾-acre arboriferous town garden. Dense informal planting. Pond area and small wet garden.

Tinto House, Broad Street ♿⊗
(John Evans & Anne Skilbeck) (See separate entry).

◆ Hergest Croft Gardens, Kington ♿⊕NCCPG
See Herefordshire.

ngs gardens open for charity
Busy at work?
Try our evening openings

Ivy Cottage, Kinsham ⊗⊕
See Herefordshire.

㉑ Kerry Gardens
3m E of Newtown. On A489 Newtown to Churchstoke rd. Turn R in village onto Common Rd. Parking behind village hall. Village map given to all visitors. Home-made TEAS at and in aid of Kerry Village Hall. *Combined adm £3.50. Sun 3 July (2-6)*

23 Dolforgan View ⊗ (Margaret Olwen Hughes) Terraced garden with natural stream commanding good view of surrounding hills and woods. Comprising flower beds, borders, rockery and lawns. Variety of ornamental trees, shrubs, dwarf conifers, flowers, rock plants, ferns and climbers.

15 The Village ⊗ (Mr E Pugh) *On A489 in village centre opp church.* Small cottage-style garden planted with shrubs and herbaceous plants, small pond and arch covered with clematis. Patio with many tubs and baskets planted with fuchsias, geraniums, begonias and perennials.

Westwinds, Common Road ⊗
(Ray & Margaret Watson) *300yds from car park.* Terraced gardens with ponds, stream and patios. Narrow paths weave through conifers, heathers, shrubs and perennials for yr-round interest and colour.

Little Heldre, Buttington
See Shropshire.

㉒ Llangorse Gardens, nr Brecon
6½m E of Brecon. For Old Vicarage & The Neuadd, Llangorse take B4560 off A40 at Bwlch. Park in village. For Treberfydd also take B4560 off A40 but then L for Penorth. From Brecon, leave A40 at Llanhamlach. 2¼m sign for Llangasty Church, entrance over cattle grid. 3 very different gardens near Llangorse Lake in the Brecon Beacons National Park. Home-made TEAS at Treberfydd in aid of Llangasty WI. *Combined adm £3, chd free. Sun 3 July (2-5)*

The Neuadd, Llangorse, nr Brecon ♿⊗⊕ (Mr & Mrs Paul Johnson) 1-acre, informal garden; mixed borders, interesting trees incl cornus; shrubs, species and old roses and herbaceous plants; copse. Emphasis on good foliage and unusual forms of cottage garden and native plants. Maintained by owners on organic lines. *Private visits welcome by*

appt, also garden groups. Tel 01874 658670

The Old Vicarage, Llangorse, nr Brecon ♿⊗⊕ (Major & Mrs J B Anderson) Small family garden maintained by owners; interesting herbaceous and shrub borders; lawns, trees and vegetables. *Private visits welcome by appt, also garden groups. Tel 01874 658639*

Treberfydd, Bwlch, nr Brecon ♿⊕ (Lt Col D P Garnons Williams) Large garden surrounding impressive Victorian house (not open); lawns, roses, herbaceous borders, trees, rock garden.

㉓ Llowes Gardens
3½m W of Hay-on-Wye. On A438 bet Clyro and Glasbury-on-Wye at Llowes follow yellow signs. 3 very interesting, very different gardens nr C12 church (Celtic cross & Kilvert associations). Light refreshments and TEAS at Llowes Court in aid of St Meilog's Church. *Combined adm £3.50, chd free, wheelchair users free. Sun 19 June (11-6)*

Llowes Court ♿⊗⊕ (Mr & Mrs Briggs) *On L of rd at Llowes coming from Hay-on-Wye.* Low lying garden of walled courtyards, lawns, woodland, meadows, deep pools and stream surrounding striking C16 house (not open). Grotto, rill, mounts, box and yew alley. Formal garden in reclaimed farmyard, relaxed planting, rose tunnel, fruits, vegetables and useful herbs. Greenhouse, vinehouse and roaming ducks and hens.

2 Mill Cottages ⊗⊕ (Lyn & Chris Williams) *In village.* A fascinating long narrow garden in a series of individual areas imaginatively planted, featuring a variety of unusual stonework, interesting collection of grasses and many hidden surprises.

Plas Wye ⊗⊕ (Helen & Geoff Hardy) *On R of road at Llowes coming from Hay-on-Wye.* Mature 1-acre densely planted garden in a series of interconnecting areas cleverly linked over different levels. Water features, roses, laburnum arch, old apple trees and views of the Black Mountains.

Llwyncelyn, Glandyfi ♿⊗⊕
See Ceredigion/Cardiganshire.

❷ Llysdinam, Newbridge-on-Wye ⊕

(Lady Delia Venables-Llewelyn & Llysdinam Charitable Trust) *5m SW of Llandrindod Wells. Turn W off A470 at Newbridge-on-Wye; right immed after crossing R Wye; entrance up hill.* Large garden. Azalea, rhododendrons, water garden and herbaceous borders, shrubs, woodland garden, kitchen garden, greenhouses. Fine view of Wye Valley. Cream TEAS in aid of NSPCC. *Adm £2.50, chd free. Mon 30 May; Sun 14 Aug (2-6). Private visits welcome by appt, garden clubs & groups. Tel 01597 860200 mary@elster.demon.co.uk*

❷ Lonicera, Station Road, Talybont-on-Usk ⓹⊗⊕

(Mr & Mrs G Davies) *6m SE of Brecon. ¼m off A40, signposted Talybont-on-Usk. 1st bungalow on L.* RHS lecturer's ¼-acre garden of varied interest incorporating several small feature gardens. Modern roses; heather garden with conifers; herbaceous and woody perennials; colourful summer bedding displays; window boxes, hanging baskets and patio tubs forming extensive house frontage display; greenhouses. Home-made TEAS. *Adm £2.50, chd free (share to Arthritis & Rheumatism Council). Sun 31 July (2-6)*

❷ NEW Lower Cefn Perfa, Kerry ⊗⊕

(Mr & Mrs J Dugdale) *3m E of Newtown. From Newtown, turn R off A489 onto Gilfach Lane, just before 30mph sign in Kerry. Follow signs for ½m.* 2-acre garden bordered by R Mule. Mixed borders, rhododendrons, roses, exochordas, ornamental trees and lawns lead down to river with viewing area. Waterfall and stream crossed by bridges lead to woodland walk with pools and waterside planting, azaleas and red oak grove. Vegetable garden. NB River, streams and unfenced bridges. Children must be accompanied by an adult. *Adm £2.50, chd free. Sun 29 May (2-6). Private visits welcome by appt. Tel 01686 626470*

❷ Lower House, Cusop, Hay-on-Wye ⊗⊕

(Nicky & Pete Daw) *½m SE of Hay-on-Wye. Leave Hay-on-Wye on B4352. Turn R signposted Cusop Dingle. (No through road). After ¾m driveway on R. Parking in orchard if dry.* Sheltered valley garden, designed and maintained by owners since 1986 around C18 farmhouse (not open). Luxuriant planting and formal pools,

shady courtyard with tree fern and bamboos. Cedar conservatory, terrace with exotic planting. Ornamental vegetable garden with topiary, stream and evolving wild garden, woodland walk. Long season of interest, best in May/June and Sept. Featured in 'Daily Telegraph' 2004. *Adm £3, chd free. Private visits welcome by appt, between Apr & Sept. Also garden clubs & groups. Tel 01497 820773 nicky.daw@btinternet.com*

❷ Maesllwch Castle, Glasbury-on-Wye ⊕

(Walter & Iona de Winton) *4½m W of Hay-on-Wye. Turn off A438 immed N of Glasbury Bridge. Through Glasbury, ½m turn R at church.* Medium-sized, owner-maintained garden. Exceptional views from terrace across R Wye to Black Mountains. Woodland walk to old walled garden now used for growing trees. Fine trees include C18 ginkgo tree. Home-made TEAS. *Adm £3, chd free (share to All Saints' Church, Glasbury). Sun 1 May (2-5)*

❷ Mill Cottage, Abbeycwmhir ⊕

(Mr & Mrs B D Parfitt) *8m N of Llandrindod Wells. Turn L off A483 1m N of Crossgates roundabout, then 3½m on L, signposted Abbeycwmhir.* One third of an acre garden crammed with unusual and rare shrubs, small trees and climbers. Numerous ericaceous plants. Streamed side garden with water feature. Narrow paths and steps; limited parking. TEAS. *Adm £2. Sat 30 Apr; Sun 1, Mon 2 May; Fri 10, Sat 11, Sun 12 June; Fri 15, Sat 16, Sun 17 July (dawn to dusk)*

The Mill House, Glandyfi ⊗

See Ceredigion/Cardiganshire.

❸ Penmyarth, Glanusk Park, nr Crickhowell ⓹

(Hon Mrs Legge-Bourke) *2m NW of Crickhowell. On A40.* 11-acre rose, rock and wild garden. Bluebells, azaleas, rhododendrons and water garden. Specimen trees, particularly oaks. Home-made TEAS. *Adm £3, chd free. Sun 1 May (2-5)*

❸ Pen-y-Maes, Hay-on-Wye ⓹⊕

(Miss Shân Egerton) *1m SW of Hay-on-Wye. On B4350 towards Brecon.* 2-acre garden. Mixed borders; young topiary; walled formal kitchen garden; roses, irises, peonies, espaliered pears. Fine mulberry. Large variety of tulips. Beautiful dry stone walling. Home-made TEAS in

aid of St Eigon's Church, Llanigon. *Adm £3, chd free. Sun 22 May (2-5)*

❸ ◆ Powis Castle Garden, Welshpool ⓹⊗⊕ NCCPG

(The National Trust) *1m S of Welshpool. Turn off A483 ¾m out of Welshpool, up Red Lane for ¼m.* Laid out in early C18 with finest remaining examples of Italian terraces in Britain. Richly planted herbaceous borders; enormous yew hedges; lead statuary, large wild flower areas. One of the National Trust's finest gardens. National Collection of Aralia, Laburnum. Manual wheelchairs only, some steep gradients. Garden staff, incl Careership Students, will lead escorted tours at 11am and 2pm. 6th in 'Britain's Finest Gardens', Channel 5, 2003. Light refreshments and TEAS. *House and garden adm adult £8.80, chd £4.40; concessions £7.80 group visit; £22 family ticket. Garden only adm £6.20, chd £3.10, concessions £5.20 if group of 15+; £15.20 family ticket. Thurs to Mons incl 21 Mar to 30 Oct.* **For NGS:** *Mon 11 July (11-6). Tel 01938 551929 Rebecca Hammond www.nationaltrust.org.uk*

◆ Staunton Park, Staunton Green ⓹⊗⊕

See Herefordshire.

❸ Tan-y-Llyn, Meifod ⊗⊕

(Callum Johnston & Brenda Moor) *1m SE of Meifod. From Oswestry on A495 turn L in village, cross R Vyrnwy & climb hill for ½m bearing R at Y-junction.* S-facing sheltered 3-acre garden, surrounded by small hills, fields and forest. Steeply sloping, the paths, beds and hedges have been laid out to complement the contours of the hill. Extensive collection of plants in containers, herb garden, thorn grove, pond, orchard and wilderness. Exhibitions, events and entertainments. Home-made TEAS. *Adm £2.50 (share to Dolon Ffermio Goat Improvement Scheme). Sats, Suns 7, 8 May; 4, 5 June; 2, 3 July; 6, 7 Aug (2-5)*

❸ Tinto House, Broad Street, Hay-on-Wye ⊕

(John Evans & Anne Skilbeck) *Opp the Clock Tower in centre of Hay-on-Wye.* Large town garden densely planted with spring bulbs, tulips, roses and herbaceous. Vegetable and greenhouse area. End of garden overlooks the R Wye. Light refreshments and TEAS at The Granary. *Adm £2, chd free. Sun 15 May (2-5)*

35 Tretower House, Tretower, nr Crickhowell
(Lt Col & Mrs P K Cracroft) 2½m NW of Crickhowell. Leave Crickhowell on A40 towards Brecon. Take R fork for Builth Wells. Garden 1m in Tretower village. Charming 2½-acre garden maintained by owners. Mainly herbaceous. Conservatory. Views of Black Mountains and Tretower Castle. Home-made TEAS in village hall. *Adm £2.50. Sun 12 June (2-5)*

36 Ty Capel Deildre, Clywedog Reservoir, Llanidloes &⊕
(Dr Beverley Evans-Britt) 4½m N of Llanidloes. Go N from Llanidloes on B4518. 2m turn L on Clywedog rd, signed scenic route, 2½m on R by nature walk lay-by. 2-acre garden of almost 100% organic plants has been personally created on a former waste site over 30 years. A 1350ft windy location with stunning views of Llyn Clywedog. It consists of ponds surrounded by walks and marginal gardens, herbaceous borders containing many rare perennials, rose and tuberous begonia gardens and lawns. Games for children. Bring plastic bags, scissors for free cuttings. Light refreshments and TEAS in aid of Chernobyl Children's Project. *Adm £2.50, chd 50p, concessions 50p. Sun 29 May (2-5.30). Private visits welcome by appt June to Aug only. Tel 01686 412602*

Upper Tan House, Stansbatch ✗⊕
See Herefordshire.

37 The Walled Garden, Knill &⊕
(Dame Margaret Anstee) 3m W of Presteigne. On B4362 Walton-Presteigne rd. In Knill village turn R over cattle grid, keep R down drive. 4 acres: walled garden; river, bog garden and small grotto; primulas; over 100 varieties of roses, shrub, modern and climbing; peonies; mixed and herbaceous borders; many varieties of shrubs and mature trees; lovely spring garden. Nr C13 church in beautiful valley. *Adm £3, chd free. Sun 5 June (2-5). Private visits welcome by appt, incl garden groups. Tel 01544 267411 / 01544 260331*

38 NEW Westlake Fisheries, Domgay Road, Four Crosses &⊕
(Lynn Mainwaring) 9m N of Welshpool. Turn off A483 in Four Crosses, signed Westlake Fisheries. Follow brown tourist signs. Domgay Rd approx 1m. A quiet scenic environment of 38 acres, managed organically on the R Vyrnwy with lakes and pools. 2-acre garden containing mixed borders, fish lawn, orchard, potager, herb and cutting garden, large vegetable plot, greenhouses and fruit cage. Birch walk and newly planted purple hazel walk lead to lake walks and wildlife area. NB Deep water, children must be accompanied by adults. Home-made TEAS in aid of local charity. *Adm £2.50, chd 50p. Sun 4 Sept (2-6). Private visits welcome by appt. Tel 01691 831475*

39 The White House, Groesffordd, nr Brecon ✗
(P H Barker & E Dowman) 2½m E of Brecon. On A40 turn L on B4558, at T-junction turn R, go through village, last house on L (opp sign to Llechfaen). 2½-acre garden in process of refurbishment. Spring bulbs, azaleas, camellias, rhododendrons, acers and magnolia. Pond, stream, bog garden, unusual trees and lightly wooded area, views to Brecon Beacons. No toilets available. *Adm £3, chd free. Private visits welcome by appt, also garden groups, 4 Apr to 4 June; 19 Sept to 31 Oct only. Tel 01874 665 421*

40 Woodhill, Moelfre &
(Janet Randell) 9m W of Oswestry. 6 acres. Informal garden designed with wheelchair users in mind set amidst wonderful views of the surrounding hills and mountains on the foothills of The Berwyns nr Snowdonia. Footpaths for disabled access totalling ¾m, young arboretum, picnic spot overlooking stream, ponds and wetlands. Sheltered arbour in more formal setting. All-yr interest: bluebell wood in spring; roses in summer; trees, shrubs and berries in autumn; scented winter shrubs. To date approx 1000 trees and shrubs planted informally. Electric/push wheelchairs may be available on request. *Adm £2.50, chd 50p, disabled free (share to Woods, Hills & Tracks). Private visits welcome by appt, open all yr. Short notice OK. Tel 01691 791486 www.pco.powys.org.uk/woodhill*

EARLY OPENINGS 2006

Derbyshire

February 19 Sunday
Cherry Tree Cottage, Hilton

Devon

February 5 Sunday
Cherubeer Gardens, Dolton
Little Cumbre, Exeter

February 12 Sunday
Little Cumbre, Exeter

February 19 Sunday
Little Cumbre, Exeter

February 26 Sunday
Little Cumbre, Exeter

Gloucestershire North & Central

February 19 Sunday
Tinpenny Farm, Fiddington

Hampshire

February 12 Sunday
Little Court, Crawley, nr Winchester

February 19 Sunday
Bramdean House, Bramdean
Little Court, Crawley, nr Winchester
The White Cottage, Beech, Alton

February 20 Monday
Little Court, Crawley, nr Winchester

February 21 Tuesday
Little Court, Crawley, nr Winchester

Herefordshire

February 2 Thursday
Ivy Croft, Ivington Green, Leominster

February 9 Thursday
Ivy Croft, Ivington Green, Leominster

February 16 Thursday
Ivy Croft, Ivington Green, Leominster

February 23 Thursday
Ivy Croft, Ivington Green, Leominster

Lincolnshire

February 18 Saturday
21 Chapel Street, Hacconby, Bourne

February 19 Sunday
21 Chapel Street, Hacconby, Bourne

London

February 26 Sunday
Myddelton House Gardens, Enfield

Northamptonshire

February 26 Sunday
Dolphins, Great Harrowden

Somerset

February 12 Sunday
The Time-Trail of Roses, Wells

Surrey

February 12 Sunday
Gatton Park, Mersham

February 15 Wednesday
Gatton Park, Mersham

Sussex

February 12 Sunday
Mitchmere Farm, Stoughton

February 14 Tuesday
Mitchmere Farm, Stoughton

February 19 Sunday
Mitchmere Farm, Stoughton

Wiltshire

February 5 Sunday
Great Chalfield Manor, nr Melksham

February 11 Saturday
Lacock Abbey Gardens, Chippenham

February 12 Sunday
Lacock Abbey Gardens, Chippenham

February 18 Saturday
Lacock Abbey Gardens, Chippenham

February 19 Sunday
Lacock Abbey Gardens, Chippenham

February 26 Sunday
Lower House, Whiteparish

gardens open
for charity

Every time you visit a garden which opens for the NGS you are helping to raise money for

- Macmillan Cancer Relief
- Marie Curie Cancer Care
- Help the Hospices
- Crossroads – Caring for Carers
- The Queen's Nursing Institute
- The Nurses Welfare Service
- The Royal Gardeners' Orphan Fund
- NGS Gardeners' Bursaries – The National Trust Careership Scheme
- Perennial – Gardeners' Royal Benevolent Society
- County Nursing Associations
- Additional charities nominated by owners

National Plant Collections in the NGS

NCCPG

Nearly 120 gardens opening for The National Gardens Scheme are also part of the National Plant Collections, although these collections are not always noted in their garden descriptions.

These important collections of plants belong to each individual garden owner, but are brought together under the auspices of the independent charity - the National Council for the Conservation of Plants and Gardens (NCCPG).

The owner has responsibility for collecting, growing and studying their chosen plant. It is also up to the owners to decide how they display their plants taking into account the type of plants, the size and style of their gardens and their own personal preferences. In many private gardens the plant collections may be spread about amongst other plants, whereas in other locations they may be grown together, often in pots, although often in the ground.

The NCCPG began in the 1970s when it seemed there was a risk of losing good garden plants because the flourishing garden centre trade was limiting the variety of plants available. The remit of NCCPG is to encourage the promotion of these plant collections and ensure they are saved for future enjoyment. The success of their work has seen a reduction in the loss of plant varieties, and a growth in specialist nurseries now specialising in some of the varieties that were previously at risk.

There is still a need to monitor the situation, although, thankfully there is a growing number of gardeners now wanting some of these plants in their gardens thus helping protect their future.

The NCCPG can be contacted at The Stable Courtyard, Wisley Gardens, Woking, Surrey, GU23 6QP
T 01483 211465   F 01483 212404   W www.nccpg.com

Buckinghamshire
Catalpa
Cliveden (National Trust)

Cambridgeshire
Lathyrus
Weaver's Cottage, West Wickham
Walnuts
Wimpole Hall, Arrington

Cheshire & Wirral
Adiantum
Tatton Park (National Trust)
Brunnera
12 Burnham Close, Cheadle Hulme

Cornwall
Azara, Photinia
Trelissick (National Trust)
Clematis
Roseland House, Chacewater

Grevillea
Pine Lodge Gardens, Cuddra

Cumbria
Aconitum, Aruncus, Filipendula
Windy Hall, Windemere
Astilbe, Hydrangea, Polystichum (ferns)
Holehird Gardens, Windermere
Ligularia
Fell Yeat, Casterton, nr Kirkby Lonsdale
Styracaceae
Holker Hall Gardens, Cark-in-Cartmel

Derbyshire
Yuccas
Renishaw Hall, Renishaw
Argyranthemums
Sycamore Farm, Foston

Devon
Abelia, Salvia
Pleasant View Nursery, Newton Abbot
Agapanthus, Pittosporum
Bicton College, East Budleigh
Agapanthus,
Pine Cottage, Eggesford
Astilbe, Iris Ensata, Tulbaghia
Marwood Hill, Marwood
Caltha, Polygonum, Ranunculus Ficaria, Water Iris
Rowden Gardens, Brentor
Cornus, Ilex
Rosemoor (RHS)
Crocosmia, Tulbaghia, Chasmanthe, Eucomis, Galtonia, Amaryllis, Anomatheca
The African Garden, Estover, Plymouth
Dianthus
Dippers, Shaugh Prior

Gentianas
  Newton Farm, Hemyock

Helenium
  Sampford Shrubs, Sampford Peverell

Heucheras, Schizostylis
  Cliffe, Lee, Ilfracombe

Hostas
  Cleave House, Sticklepath

Magnolias and Knap Hill azaleas
  Sherwood, Newton St Cyres

Primula (sect. Cortusoides)
  Plant World, Newton Abbott

Rodgersia
  The Gate House, Lee, Coastal Village

Shasta Daisies, Leucanthemum superbum
  Shapcott Barton Estate, East Knowstone

Dorset

Anemone nemorosa, Convallaria
  Kingston Lacy, Wimborne Minster

Caenothus, Phygelius
  Knoll Gardens, Hampreston

Hoheria
  Abbotsbury Gardens, Weymouth

Penstemon
  Mews Cottage, Portland

Penstemons, Salvias
  Kingston Maurward Gardens, Dorchester

Durham

Polemoniums
  28 Sunnyside Terrace, Trimdon Grange

Essex

Malus
  Barnards Farm, West Horndon

Pyracantha
  Writtle College, Writtle

Viburnum
  RHS Garden Hyde Hall, Rettendon

Gloucestershire North & Central

Paeonia
  Green Cottage, Lydney

Rambler roses
  Moor Wood, Woodmancote

Rosmarinus officinalis
  Rosemary Cottage, Frocester

Hampshire

Buddleia, Clematis viticella
  Longstock Park Gardens, nr Stockbridge

Daphnes, Galanthus
  Brandy Mount House, Alresford

Eucalyptus
  Meon Orchard, N of Wickham

Helleborus
  Longthatch, Warnford

Japanese Anemones
  Heathlands, Locks Heath, nr Fareham

Native Sorbus
  Mount Joy, Cadnam

Old-fashioned Roses
  Mottisfont Abbey & Garden, Romsey

Salvia
  2 Hillside Cottages, North Boarhunt

Trilliums
  Spinners, Boldre

Herefordshire

Autumn Flowering Asters (Michaelmas Daisies)
  The Picton Garden, Colwall

Maples, Birches, Zelkova
  Hergest Croft Gardens, Kington

Dianthus
  Kingstone Cottages, Weston under Penyard, nr Ross-on-Wye

Hertfordshire

Elaeagnus, Hornbeam cultivars
  West Lodge Park, Hadley Wood

Sarcocca
  Capel Manor, Enfield

Kent

Apples, Cherries, Cobnuts, Currants, Gooseberries, Grapes, Pears, Plums, vitis vinifera
  Brogdale Horticultural Trust, Faversham

Hellebore, Japanese Anemone
  Broadview Gardens, Hadlow College

Mentha, Nepeta, Origanum
  Iden Croft Herb Gardens, Staplehurst

Leicestershire & Rutland

Astrantias
  Warren Hills Cottage, Coalville

Aubrieta, Lawson Cypress, Hardy Fuchsia, Skimmia
  University of Leicester 'Harold Martin' Botanic Garden, Oadby

Heliotropes
  The Homestead, Normanton-by-Bottesford

Liriope, Ophiopogon
  Brooksby Melton College, Melton Mowbray

Tradescantia andersoni
  1700 Melton Road, Rearsby

London

Bearded Irises
  Myddelton House Gardens, Enfield

Ceanothus
  Eccleston Square, SW1

Norfolk

Colchicum
  Felbrigg Hall, Cromer

Northamptonshire

Penstemons
  Froggery Cottage, Desborough

Northumberland & Tyne and Wear

Brunnera Macrophylla
  9 Grenville Court, Darras Hall

Centaurea
  Bide-a-Wee Cottage, Stanton

484

Thyme, Marjoram
  Chesters Walled Garden,
  Chollerford
Sambucus
  Wallington, Cambo

Nottinghamshire
Berberis
  Mill Hill House, East Stoke
Cannas
  University of Nottingham
  Gardens

Oxfordshire
Euphorbia
  University of Oxford Botanic
  Gardens, Oxford
Herbaceous Clematis
  Clematis Corner, Shillingford
Saxifraga
  Waterperry Gardens, Wheatley

Shropshire
Brugmansias (Angel's Trumpets)
  Valducci Flower & Vegetable
  Gardens, Meole Brace
Galanthus
  Moortown, Wellington
Hamamelis, Russell Lupins
  Swallow Hayes, Albrighton

Somerset
Arbutus
  Dunster Castle (National Trust)
Clematis Texensis, Hybrids, Caltha
  The Mill, Cannington
Geraniums
  East Lambrook Manor
  Gardens, East Lambrook
Polystichum, Erythronium,
Vaccinium, Gaultheria
  Greencombe, Porlock
Rodgersia
  Hadspen Garden, Castle Cary

Staffordshire
Lamium
  12 Darges Lane, Great Wyrley

Suffolk
Buxus
  Ickworth House (National Trust)

Surrey
Sorbus
  Winkworth Arboretum
  (National Trust)

Sussex
Aesculus, Liriodendron
  West Dean Gardens,
  Chichester
F. Stern Plants
  Highdown, Goring-by-Sea
Hardy Geraniums
  Coombland, Coneyhurst
Rhododendron (Ghent Azaleas)
  Sheffield Park Gardens
  (National Trust)
Stewartia
  High Beeches, Handcross
Tilia, Castanea
  Peasmarsh Place,
  Peasmarsh

Warwickshire
Asters (autumn flowering)
  Upton House, nr Banbury
Pelargoniums
  Ivybank, Pebworth
Roses, Anthemis, Winterflowering
Irises
  University of Birmingham
  Botanic Garden at
  Winterbourne, Edgbaston

Wiltshire
Acanthus
  Iford Manor, Bradford-on-Avon
Evening Primroses
  The Old Vicarage, Edington
Hellebores
  Lower House, Whiteparish
Populus
  Lackham Gardens, Lacock

Worcestershire
Aucuba
  Ivytree House, Clent

Clematis
  Burford house Gardens.
  Tenbury Wells
Nerines
  Nerine Nursery, Welland
Potentilla fruticosa
  Webbs of Wychbold, Wychbold

Yorkshire
Dicentras
  Bolton Percy Cemetery
  Garden, Bolton Percy
Astrantias
  Mayroyd Mill House, Hebden
  Bridge
Campanula
  Burton Agnes Hall, Driffield
Cornus
  Newby Hall & Gardens, Ripon
Dryopteris, Fuchsia sect. quelusia
(prov)
  Harlow Carr (RHS)
Primroses
  Tan Cottage, Cononley
Pulmonaria
  Stillingfleet Lodge, Stillingfleet,
  nr York

Wales

Ceredigion &Cardiganshire
Tricyrtis
  Farmyard Nursery, Llandyssul

Flintshire & Wrexham
Hedera
  Erddig Hall (National Trust)
Hydrangea
  The Garden House, Erbistock

Gwynedd
Coriaria, Paris
  Crug Farm, Caernafon
Miniature Japanese palms
  Gwyndy Bach, Llandrygarn

Powys
Aralia, Laburnum
  Powis Castle Garden

Accommodation available at NGS Gardens

We feature here a list of NGS garden owners or county team members who offer accommodation. We have listed them by county and indicated whether they offer Bed & Breakfast (**B&B**), Self-Catering (**SC**), or Hotel (**H**) accommodation. You will also find a reference to accommodation in the main directory with their garden entry.

Bristol & South Gloucestershire

Woodland Cottage,
Chapel Road, Oldbury-on-Severn, Bristol, South Glos BS35 1PL
Jane Perkins
T 01454 414570
1 double room, 1 twin room with shared bathroom. Price £20 per person per night.
Member of NGS County Team.
B&B

Cornwall

Bonython Manor
Cury Cross Lanes, nr Helston Cornwall, TR12 7BA
Richard & Sue Nathan
T 01326 240234
E sue@bonythonmanor.co.uk
W www.bonythonmanor.co.uk
3 properties sleeping 10, 6 and 4. All 5* accommodation with en-suite facilities and private gardens. Bookings through 'Rural Retreats', T 01386 701177. W www.ruralretreats.co.uk.
Cottage refs:
Bonython Farmhouse - CW042,
Mews Cottage - CW047,
St Corantyn Cottage - CW048.
See Cornwall for details of garden.
SC

Carwinion
Mawnan Smith, Falmouth
Cornwall TR11 5JA

A & J Rogers
T 01326 250258
F 01326 250903
E jane@carwinion.freeserve.co.uk
W www.carwinion.co.uk
1 double, 2 twin/double en-suite rooms in quiet country house set in 14 acres of valley garden. Children & dogs welcome. Rooms £70 per night. Single occ. £40. SC flat sleeps 2. Cottage sleeps 6.
See Cornwall for details of garden.
B&B SC

Creed House
Creed, Grampound, Truro
Cornwall TR2 4SL
Mr & Mrs William Croggon
T 01872 530372
Georgian Rectory, 2 bedrooms with super king beds, 1 with twin beds, all with private or en-suite bathrooms. Prices £80 per night. Single occ. £60.
See Cornwall for details of garden.
Member of NGS County Team.
B&B

Hidden Valley Gardens
Treesmill, Nr Par
Cornwall PL24 2TU
Patricia Howard
T 01208 873225
W www.hiddenvalleygardens.co.uk
Comfortable B & B accommodation in a stone barn conversion set in a 'hidden' valley with a 4 acre display garden. 2 double, 1 twin all en-suite, TV and tea making facilities. Price £24 per person per night. Single occ. £32.
See Cornwall for details of garden.
B&B

Tregoose
Grampound, Truro
Cornwall TR2 4DB
Anthony & Alison O'Connor
T 01726 882460
1 double room (four-poster), en-suite. 1 twin, en-suite bath with shower over. I double with private bath/ shower. Prices from £37 per person.
Member of NGS County Team.
B&B

Cumbria

Lakeside Hotel
Lake Windermere, Newby Bridge
Cumbria LA12 8AT
Mr N R Talbot
T 015395 30001
F 015395 31699
E sales@lakesidehotel.co.uk
W www.lakesidehotel.co.uk
The best 4* hotel in the Lake District, with a spectacular location on the southern shores of Lake Windermere. Guests enjoy exclusive use of our luxury health and leisure spa. Great value breaks all year round (78 rooms).
See Cumbria for details of garden.
H

Lindeth Fell Country House Hotel
Bowness-on-Windermere
Cumbria LA23 3JP
Air Cdr & Mrs P A Kennedy
T 01539 443286

F 015394 47455
E kennedy@lindethfell.co.uk
W www.lindethfell.co.uk
On a tree lined drive above Lake Windermere, standing in magnificent private gardens. 14 bedrooms, singles, doubles and family rooms. Price from £60 for B&B to £80 for dinner, B & B. Single occ. from £60. Many awards including AA Top 200 hotel and Gold Award. See Cumbria for details of garden.
H

The Miller Howe Hotel
Rayrigg Road, Windermere
Cumbria LA23 1EY
Mr Charles Garside
T 015394 42536
F 015394 45664
E lakeview@millerhowe.com
W www.millerhowe.com
Set in 5½ acres of magnificent gardens, the hotel is stylishly furnished. Quality service in country house splendour, with commanding panoramic views of Lake Windermere and the Langdale Pikes beyond.
See Cumbria for details of garden.
H

Denbighshire & Colwyn

The Old Rectory
Llanfihangel Glyn Myfyr
Cerrigydrudion
Denbighshire LL21 9UN
Mr & Mrs E T Hughes
T 01490 420568
E elwynthomashughes@hotmail.com
Luxury rural retreat set in idyllic garden and countryside. 1 family room, en-suite, 1 family room with private bathroom. Guest lounge. Price from £26 per person per night. Single occ. £32.
See Denbighshire & Colwyn for details of garden.
B&B

Derbyshire

The Riddings Farm
Kirk Ireton, Ashbourne
Derbyshire DE6 3LB
Mr & Mrs P R Spencer
T 01335 370331
ETC 3*. Delightful, peacefully situated barn conversion looking over Carsington Water. Spacious 2 bedroomed, accommodation, sleeps 3-4. Sorry no pets, no smoking. Towels, linen and electricity included. £200-£320 per week.
See Derbyshire for details of garden.
SC

Devon

The Cider House
Buckland Abbey, Yelverton
Devon PL20 6EZ
Mrs Sarah Stone
T 01822 853285
E sarah.stone@cider-house.co.uk
W www.cider-house.co.uk
House formerly part of Cistercian monastery of Buckland; 1 double & 1 twin room each with private bathroom, plus extra twin room if required. Price £35 per person per night, single occ. £45. Cottage sleeps 5 in 3 bedrooms; sitting room with log fire, dining room, kitchen. Walled garden, use of tennis court.
See Devon for details of garden.
Member of NGS County Team.
B&B SC

Kingston House
Staverton, Totnes
Devon TQ9 6AR
Michael & Elizabeth Corfield
T 01803 762235
F 01803 762444
E info@kingston-estate.co.uk
W www.kingston-estate.co.uk
Kingston House, 5 Diamonds - Gold award, has 3 beautiful suites and 9 Five Star cottages. The house is set in the gardens, offering delicious food using garden produce whenever possible, excellent wine list. Price on application.
See Devon for details of garden.
B&B SC

Little Ash Farm
Fenny Bridges
Devon EX14 3BL
Sadie & Robert Reid
T 01404 850271
En-suite family room sleeps 4. Family suite, twin and double with bathroom. Single, en-suite. All rooms have TV and tea tray. Full breakfast in large conservatory overlooking garden. From £21. Non smoking.
See Devon for details of garden.
B&B

Regency House
Hemyock, Cullompton
Devon EX15 3RQ
Mrs Jenny Parsons
T 01823 680238
E jenny.parsons@btinternet.com
Regency House is the most beautiful, spacious, Georgian rectory. Accommodation: double room, en-suite, 1 twin with private bathroom. Price £40 per person per night.
See Devon for details of garden.
B&B

Westcott Barton
Middle Marwood,Barnstaple
Devon EX31 4EF
Heidi Amschwand & Howard Frank
T 01271 812842
E westcottbarton@connecting business.com
Pretty bedrooms (5 double, 2 twin), all en-suite, all with colour TV and tea/coffee making facilities. Breakfast is a movable feast and evening meals are available on request. No smoking or pets. Not suitable for children under 14 yrs. £35 per person.
See Devon for details of garden.
B&B

Whitstone Farm
Whitstone Lane,Bovey Tracey
Devon TQ13 9NA
Katie & Alan Bunn
T 01626 832258
F 01626 836494

E katie@whitstonefarm.co.uk
W www.whitstonefarm.co.uk
Country house: 1 super king-sized (or twin) room, 1 king-sized room, 1 double room - all en-suite. Prices from £60 per night. Single occ. from £40. Evening meals by arrangement.
See Devon for details of garden
B&B

Winsford Walled Garden
Winsford Lane, Halwill Junction
Devon EX21 5XT
Aileen Birks & Michael Gilmore
T 01409 221477
E muddywellies@winsfordwalled garden.freeserve.co.uk
W www.winsfordwalledgarden.co.uk
AA four diamond double en-suite accommodation, located within Victorian walled garden containing 3000 varieties of plants and restored Victorian greenhouses built of teak.
See Devon for details of garden
B&B

Dorset

The Old Rectory
West Compton, Dorchester
Dorset DT2 0EY
Susan Wreford
T 01300 320007
2 king-size rooms, en-suite, in hamstone country house (1865) in rolling hills near Eggardon Hill iron-age fort. 9 miles from coast, equidistant Dorchester and Bridport. Continental breakfast. Dogs possible. £25 single, £45 double. Member of NGS County Team
B&B

Gloucestershire North & Central

Grange Cottage
Mill Lane, Blockley
Gloucestershire GL56 9HT
Guy & Alison Heitmann

T 01386 700251
E info@gardendesigner.biz
2 doubles, en-suite. On a peaceful lane in the centre of the old part of the village. A great area for walking.
See Gloucestershire North & Central for details of garden
B&B

Kempsford Manor
High Street, Kempsford
Fairford, Glos GL7 4EQ
Mrs Z Williamson
T 01285 810131
E ipek@lineone.net
W http://members.lycos.co.uk /kempsford_manor
C17-18 manor house set in peaceful gardens. Fine reception rooms. 3-4 double bedrooms. Price from £30 single occ. Home grown organic vegetables. Suitable for small conferences and marquee receptions.
See Gloucestershire North & Central for details of garden
B&B

Mill Dene
School Lane, Blockley
Moreton-in-Marsh,Glos GL56 9HU
Mrs Wendy Dare
T 01386 700457
F 01386 700526
E info@milldene.co.uk
W www.milldene.co.uk
The Dares and their cats welcome you to their Cotswold stone water mill, which is mostly C17 but converted to Silver award standard. Every room has views and sounds of the mill-pond and garden. See website or phone for tariff and availability.
See Gloucestershire North & Central for details of garden
B&B

The Old Chequer
Draycott, Moreton-in-Marsh
Glos GL56 9LB
Mr & Mrs H Linley
T 01386 700647
E g.f.linley@tesco.net
W www.smoothHound.co.uk/ hotels/oldchequer.html

Original ex- C17 inn, this country house combines genuine charm with modern comforts. 1 double, 2 twin rooms, all en-suite. TV, tea/coffee facilities. Quiet village location. Prices from £48 per night. Single occ. £40.
See Gloucestershire North & Central for details of garden
B&B

Gwent

Llwyn-y-Wen Farm
Hafodyrynys Road, Crumlin
Gwent NP11 5AX
Mrs H Lewy
T 01495 245115
E Helen@lefray.eclipse.co.uk
W www.lefray.eclipse.co.uk
1 single/twin and 1 double sharing large bath/shower room in self contained wing. Also available on request 1 double, en-suite; 1 double with shower and basin and 1 single.
Prices: double, £45 and single, £25.
See Gwent for details of garden
B&B

Penpergwm Lodge
Abergavenny,Gwent NP7 9AS
Mr & Mrs S Boyle
T 01873 840208
F 01873 840208
E boyle@penpergwm.co.uk
W www.penplants.com
A large rambling Edwardian house in the lovely Usk valley. Pretty bedrooms have garden views, bathrooms share a corridor, breakfast and relax in the spacious and comfortable sitting room. Great walking in nearby Brecon Beacons National Park.
See Gwent for details of garden
B&B

Hampshire

Forest Edge
Andover Down, Andover
Hampshire SP11 6LJ
Annette & David Beeson

T 01264 364526
E david@forest-edge.co.uk
W www.forest-edge.co.uk
2 double and 2 twin rooms, all en-suite.
Garden room for breakfast and relaxation.
Extensive menu including vegetarian
options. Quiet, abuts ancient forest. Car
park. Rated 4 diamonds, Silver Award.
See Hampshire for details of garden.
B&B

Herefordshire

Garnstone House
Weobley, Herefordshire HR4 8QP
Michael & Dawn MacLeod
T 01544 318943
F 01544 318197
1 double, 1 twin room, private
bathroom for these 2 rooms. Colour TV
and hand basin in each room. Central
heating. Prices from £60. Single occ.
£35 per night.
See Herefordshire for details of garden.
B&B

The Great House
Dilwyn, Hereford
Herefordshire HR4 8HX
Tom & Jane Hawksley
T 01544 318007
W www.herefordshireaccommodation.com
2 double/twin, en-suite bathrooms. Large
twin with private bathroom. Private sunny
sitting room with door to garden. Beams,
panelling, flagstone floors and enormous
log fires. Price £70. Single occ. £40.
Dinner by arrangement from £20.
See Herefordshire for details of garden.
B&B

Isle of Wight

Clatterford House
Clatterford Shute, Carisbrooke
Isle of Wight PO30 4NE
Sylvia Clare & David Hughes
T 01983 537338
E sylvia.clare@btinternet.com

W www.claritybooks.co.uk
Family, double and single rooms available
- no en-suite. £25 per person per night.
Vegetarian breakfasts, full board available
for retreats, and meditation. Central
island location with easy access to island
gardens of special interest.
See Isle of Wight for details of garden.
B&B

Northcourt Gardens
Shorwell, Isle of Wight PO30 3JG
Mr & Mrs J Harrison
T 01983 740415
E christine@northcourt.info
W www.northcourt.info
B & B in large C17 manor house in 15
acres of exotic gardens, on edge of the
downs. 6 double/ twin rooms, all en-
suite. Price from £60 per room. Also
wing of house for up to 14 self-catering.
See Isle of Wight for details of garden.
B&B SC

Kent

Hoath House
Chiddingstone Hoath
Edenbridge, Kent TN8 7DB
Mervyn & Jane Streatfield
T 01342 850362
F 01342 850362
E janesteatfeild@hoath-house.
freeserve.co.uk
Rambling medieval and Tudor house in
extensive gardens (most picturesque in
daffodil and rhododendron season) with
fine views. Convenient for Penshurst,
Chartwell and Hever and
recommendations for NGS openings
across Kent. Good access to London
and Gatwick.
Member of NGS County Team.
B&B

Stowting Hill House
Stowting, Ashford, Kent TN25 6BE
Richard and Virginia Latham
T 01303 862881
F 01303 863433
E vjlatham@hotmail.com

2 twins, both with bath. 1 double. A
Georgian Manor house set in beautiful
North Downs, with walks from our door
in quiet rolling valleys and plenty of
gardens to visit. Prices from £65.
Member of NGS County Team.
B&B

Boyton Court
Sutton Valence, Kent ME17 3BY
Richard & Patricia Stileman
T 01622 844065
F 01622 843913
E richstileman@aol.com
2 double rooms (1 king-size, 1 twin) with
en-suite bathrooms. Both with spectacular
south facing garden and Wealden views.
£75 per night. Single Occ. £45.
See Kent for details of garden.
B&B

Cottage Farm
Cackets Lane, Cudham,
Nr Sevenoaks, Kent TN14 7QG
Phil & Karen Baxter
T 01959 534048/532506
F 01959 532604
E karen@cottagefarmturkeys.co.uk
Delightful country cottage: 1 double and
1 twin room, living room, kitchen and
bathroom. Full central heating. From
£350 per week self catering. B&B £60
per night double or twin. £35 single occ.
See Kent for details of garden.
B&B SC

Mistral
Oxenturn Road, Wye
Kent TN25 5BH
G.P & S.M Chapman
T 01233 813011
F 01233 813011
E geoff@chapman.invictanet.co.uk
W www.chapman.invictanet.co.uk
4 Diamond. Small B & B enterprise
offering high quality in a central but
secluded part of Wye. Special diets
catered for. Train and bus service.
Excellent restaurants nearby. Price £25
per person per night. In garden, 450
plant varieties labelled. Owners -
botanist and flower arranger.
See Kent for details of garden.
B&B

Lancashire, Merseyside & Greater Manchester

The Ridges
Weavers Brow, Limbrick
Chorley, Lancashire PR6 9EB
John & Barbara Barlow
T 01257 279981
E barlow.ridges@virgin.net
W www.bedbreakfast-gardenvisits.com
Self-contained accommodation, immediately adjacent to "The Ridges". 3 double/twin bedrooms. 1 en-suite, 2 sharing a private bathroom. Second toilet in hallway. Guest lounge, dining room and kitchen. Prices from £50 per night. Single occ. £35. Self catering available, prices on request.
See Lancashire, Merseyside & Greater Manchester for details of garden.
B&B SC

Lincolnshire

Bleasby House
Legsby, Bleasby, Market Rasen
Lincolnshire LN8 3QN
John & Janet Dring
T 01673 842383
F 01763 844808
E dring@farmersweekly.net
W www.bleasbyhouse.com
Enjoy hearty breakfasts, en-suite rooms and flower filled sun lounge in spacious farmhouse. Ideal for touring Lincolnshire Wolds and coast. Fishing and hard tennis court on site. 2 twin, en-suite and 1 single with shower from £25 per night.
See Lincolnshire for details of garden.
B&B

London

239a Hook Road
Chessington, Surrey KT9 1EQ
Dawn & Derek St Romaine
T 020 8397 3761
F 020 8397 4187

E dawn@gardenphotolibrary.com
W www.gardenphotolibrary.com
Luxurious accommodation, 1 double, 1 twin room both en-suite. Direct access and beautiful views of the garden. Prices double occ. from £70. Single occ. from £45. 15 mins from RHS Wisley.
See London for details of garden.
B&B

38 Killieser Avenue
London SW2 4NT
Winkle Haworth
T 020 8671 4196
F 020 8671 4196
E winklehaworth@hotmail.com
1 twin bedded room, 1 single - private or shared bathroom. Price from £80. Single occ. £50. English breakfast incl.
See London for details of garden.
Member of NGS County Team.
B&B

Norfolk

The Old Rectory
Ridlington, North Walsham
Norfolk NR28 9NZ
Peter & Fiona Black
T 01692 650247
E blacks7@email.com
W www.oldrectory.northnorfolk.co.uk
House: 1 double bedroom, en-suite; 1 double with wash basin and private bathroom. Garden room: large studio, double/twin beds, plus sofa bed, kitchen and bathroom. Prices from £50 per night. 1 1/2 miles from East Ruston Old Vicarage Gardens.
Member of NGS County Team
B&B SC

Northamptonshire

The Old Fountain
25 High Street, Long Buckby
Northampton NN6 7RE
Anne & David Croston
T 01327 842345

F 0871 6610927
E fountainplants@tiscali.co.uk
Central location for Midland gardens. 45 mins from NEC. Easy access from M1. Comfortable en-suite double bedrooms, full English breakfast and affable hosts. Open May - end September. Price from £60 per night. Single occ. £40.
See Northamptonshire for details of garden.
B&B

Oxfordshire

South Newington House
South Newington, Banbury
Oxfordshire OX15 4JW
Roberta & John Ainley
T 01295 721207
F 01295 722165
E rojoainley@btinternet.com
Cottage annexe: 1 king-size bedroom, sitting room, shower room & kitchen. House: 1 king-size bedrooms & 1 twin all with private bathrooms. Prices from £70 per night. Single occ. £40.
See Oxfordshire for details of garden.
Member of NGS County Team.
B&B

Shropshire

Angel Barn
Angel Lane, Springfield, Bitterley
Ludlow, Shropshire SY8 3HZ
Dr K C Elliott & Ms J A V Roberts
T 01584 890381
F 01584 890381
E angelgardens@sy83hz.fsnet.co.uk
Situated in Angel Gardens, idyllic detached stone cottage. Sleeps 2 + cot in balconied double room. Beautifully furnished and fully equipped. Sitting room, kitchen, and bathroom. No smoking. No pets. Short breaks £50 per day, otherwise £45 per day.
See Shropshire for details of garden.
SC

Brownhill House
Ruyton XI Towns, Nr. Shrewsbury
Shropshire SY4 1LR
Yoland & Roger Brown
T 01939 261121
F 01939 260626
E brownhill@eleventowns.co.uk
W www.eleventowns.co.uk
Old world standards, modern facilities & relaxed atmosphere. Unique 2 acre garden - must be seen to be believed. Easy access - Chester to Ludlow, Snowdonia to Ironbridge and loads of wonderful gardens. Find out all about us on our website.
See Shropshire for details of garden.
B&B

Somerset

Montys Court
Norton Fitzwarren, Somerset TA4 1BT
Maj & Mrs A Mitford-Slade
T 01823 432255
F 01823 433623
E tonymitford-slade@montyscourt.freeserve.co.uk
2 double rooms en-suite. 1 twin room with private bathroom. Prices from £62- £68. Single occ. £37. Also available, self-catering farmhouse for 14 people.
See Somerset for details of garden
B&B SC

Gants Mill & Garden
Gants Mill Lane, Bruton
Somerset BA10 0DB
Alison & Brian Shingler
T 01749 812393
E shingler@gantsmill.co.uk
W www.gantsmill.co.uk
C18 farmhouse in rural valley, by historic watermill now generating electricity. Large comfortable pretty bedrooms with four-poster or lace canopy. Wide choice of familiar and unusual breakfasts with best local ingredients. £30 per person per night. Also self catering Miller's Cottage – sleeping 6.
See Somerset for details of garden.
B&B SC

Glencot House
Glencot Lane, Wookey Hole
Wells, Somerset BA5 1BH
Mrs M J Attia
T 01749 677160
F 01749 670210
E relax@glencothouse.co.uk
W www.glencothouse.co.uk
Elegantly furnished Victorian mansion offering high class accommodation, good food and friendly service, set in 18 acres of gardens and parkland with river frontage. Children welcome, dogs by arrangement. Special breaks available.
See Somerset for details of garden.
H

Hangeridge Farm
Wrangway, Wellington
Somerset TA21 9QT
Mrs J M Chave
T 01823 662339
F 01823 662339
Situated at the foot of the Blackdown Hills within 5 mins drive from M5 (jn 25 or 26). 1 twin and 1 double room with private bathroom. B& B £20 pp per night, B&B and evening meal £28 pp per night.
See Somerset for details of garden.
B&B

King Ina's Palace
Silver Street, South Petherton
Somerset TA13 5BY
Trevor & Shirley Brown
T 01460 240603
E trevor.brown2@tinyworld.co.uk
Grade 2* listed medieval house - 1 twin room en-suite. Prices £64 based on 2 sharing. £60 for three or more nights. £50 single occ.
See Somerset for details of garden.
B&B

Knoll Cottage
Stogumber, Taunton
Somerset TA4 3TN
Elaine & John Leech
T 01984 656689
E email@knoll-cottage.co.uk
W www.knoll-cottage.co.uk
Secluded rural location between the Quantocks and Exmoor. Beautiful 2 acre garden. 2 king-sized double

rooms, en-suite in recently converted stables. Full English breakfast using best quality local ingredients. Double £50, Single £30. Dogs welcome.
See Somerset for details of garden.
B&B

Little Norton Mill
Little Norton,Norton Sub Hamdon
Somerset TA14 6TE
Lynn Hart
T 01935 881337
F 01935 881337
E te.hart@btinternet.com
W www.littlenortonmill.co.uk
6 x 2 bedroomed cottages and 4 x 1 bedroom apartments around an old watermill in rural Somerset. ETC inspected 4 & 5 star. Prices from £190 to £650 per cottage per week. Short breaks available out of high season.
See Somerset for details of garden.
SC

Rookwood
West Street, Hinton St George
Somerset TA17 8SA
Mrs Betty Hudspith
T 01460 73450
E betty.hudspith@virgin.net
Situated at the end of a quiet cul-de-sac in pretty village. 2 twin rooms, 1 en-suite. Price £22 per person per night. Member of NGS County Team.
B&B

Suffolk

Tilbrook Farm Cottage
Station Road, Dullingham
Newmarket, Suffolk CB8 9UP
Ailah & Peter Loup
T 01638 508115
F 01638 508115
Quiet location with ample parking. Twin, en-suite, sitting room and bathroom, (£40 per person per night). Double with adjacent bathroom (£35 per person per night). Full English breakfast. Kitchen supper by prior arrangement. (£15 per person)
See Suffolk for details of garden.
B&B

Rosemary
Rectory Hill, East Bergholt
Colchester, Essex CO7 6TH
Mrs Natalie Finch
T 01206 298241
Situated in the heart of Constable
country within easy reach of Harwich
and Flatford. Garden featured on
Gardener's World. 3 twin rooms - with
hand basins, 1 single room. Shared
bathroom. Price £26 single, £52 twin.
See Suffolk for details of garden.
B&B

Surrey

Spring Cottage
Mannings Hill, Cranleigh
Surrey GU6 8QN
Mr & Mrs David Norman
T 01483 272620
E cjn@springcottage67.freeserve.co.uk
1st floor accommodation in newly built
barn. 1 double bedroom, bathroom,
large sitting room with TV. Lovely views
towards N and S downs. Good walking
and cycling. Enjoy garden in all seasons.
Prices from £60 per night. Single occ. £40.
See Surrey for details of garden.
Member of NGS County Team.
B&B

Sussex

King John's Lodge
Sheepstreet Lane, Etchingham
East Sussex TN19 7AZ
Jill & Richard Cunningham
T 01580 819232
F 01580 819562
E kingjohnslodge@aol.com
W www.kingjohnslodge.co.uk
Country house accommodation. 2
double, 2 twin rooms all with own
bathroom. Full English breakfast. Price
£40 per person per night. Self
contained converted barn in garden
giving 3 varying sized units.
See Sussex for details of garden.
B&B SC

Pindars
Lyminster, Arundel
Sussex BN17 7QF
Jocelyne & Clive Newman
T 01903 882628
F 01903 882628
House - 1 double, en-suite shower
room. 1 twin, en-suite WC and private
bathroom. Both south facing over
looking garden. Comfortable guest
sitting room. Evening meals usually
available. Prices from £55 per night.
See Sussex for details of garden.
B&B

73 Sheepdown Drive
Petworth, West Sussex GU28 0BX
Mrs Angela Azis
T 01798 342269
F 01798 342269
2 twin with shared bathroom. Prices
from £50 per room. Single occ. £30. A
short walk from the centre of the historic
town, no. 73 lies in a quiet 70s cul-de-
sac and has glorious garden views.
B&B

Turf Lodge
Sheep Plain, Crowborough
E Sussex TN6 3ST
Julia Ball
T 01892 655505
F 01892 665525
E IBALL20@aol.com
Off the beaten track on Crowborough
golf course. Peaceful tennis court/
swimming pool. 1 double room, en-
suite. 1 double room, 1 single room
shared bathroom. £30 per person per
night. NGS garden with fantastic views
5 minutes walk across fields.
Member of NGS County Team.
B&B

Warwickshire & part of West Midlands

The Glebe House
Village Road, Warmington,
Banbury,Oxfordshire OX17 1BT
Mrs J Thornton

T 01295 690642
Welcoming comfortable en-suite
accommodation serving traditional
breakfasts. Stone residence set in a
beautiful village beneath the Edgehills
in the heart of the English countryside.
Close for visiting Warwick, Cotswolds
and Stratford-on-Avon.
See Warwickshire & part of West
Midlands for details of garden.
Member of NGS County Team.
B&B

Wiltshire

Ridleys Cheer
Mountain Bower, Chippenham
Wiltshire SN14 7AJ
Sue & Antony Young
T 01225 891204
F 01225 891139
E sueyoung@ridleyscheer.co.uk
1 double with private bathroom. 1 double
and 1 twin bedded room with shared
bathroom. Prices from £80 per night.
Single occ. £40. Dinner £30 per head.
See Wiltshire for details of garden.
B&B

Yorkshire

Green House
Stone Man Lane, Gayles
Richmond, North Yorkshire DL11 7JB
Elizabeth Carrick
T 01833 621199
E elizabeth@ecarrick.fsnet.co.uk
Barn conversion: 1 double, en-suite and
1 twin with private bathroom. Scotch
Corner - 8 miles, A66 - 3 miles. Dogs
welcome. Price £22 per person per night.
Member of NGS County Team.
B&B

Manor Farm
Thixendale, Malton
North Yorkshire YO17 9TG
Charles & Gilda Brader
T 01377 288315

F 01377 288315
E info@manorfarmthixendale.co.uk
W www.manorfarmthixendale.co.uk
Private spacious wing of the
farmhouse. Hot deep baths and comfy
sofas. Situated west end of isolated
village. Substantial breakfasts, fresh
fruit, cereals, home-made bread. Buff
Orpington eggs. Proper meat cooked in
the aga. Relax in a bygone era.
See Yorkshire for details of garden.
B&B

Riverside Farm
Sinnington, Nr Pickering
York, North Yorkshire YO62 6RY
William and Jane Baldwin
T 01751 431764
F 01751 431764
E wnbaldwin@yahoo.co.uk
1 king-sized double, en-suite. 1 twin with
private bathroom. I single room. Price: £30
per person per night. Single occ. £40.
Member of NGS County Team.
B&B

Cold Cotes
Cold Cotes Road,Fellisbridge
Harrogate,North Yorks HG3 2LW
Ed Loft
T 01423 770937
F 01423 779284
E coldcotes@btopenworld.com
W www.coldcotes.com
Situated in the picturesque Yorkshire
Dales. Cold Coates provides superior
guest room and breakfast en-suite
accommodation in peaceful, tranquil
surroundings for 6 people and their
appetites. Price: double £60, single £40.
See Yorkshire for details of garden.
B&B

Sleightholmedale Lodge
Fadmoor, Kirbymoorside
York, Yorkshire YO62 6JG
Mrs R James
T 01751 431942
F 01751 430106
E info@shdcottages.co.uk
W www.shdcottages.co.uk

Peaceful, warm cottages round a stone
courtyard, adjoining a working farm and
garden. Max price – high season -
£450 per week.
See Yorkshire for details of garden.
SC

Thorpe Lodge
Knaresborough Road, Ripon
Yorkshire HG4 3LU
Mr & Mrs T Jowitt
T 01765 602088
F 01765 602835
E jowitt@btinternet.com
W www.thorpelodge.co.uk
Listed Georgian house with 2 large
double/twin rooms, both en-suite with
bath and shower, television and
tea/coffee making facilities. Own sitting
room and entrance. Dogs kept and
welcome. £80 per night including full
English breakfast, £55 single occ.
Excellent pubs nearby.
See Yorkshire for details of garden.
B&B

Disclaimer

The descriptions provided in this section have been given to the NGS by the garden owners. The NGS cannot
guarantee the accuracy of the information given to us, and accepts no responsibility for any error or
misrepresentation. All liability for loss, disappointment, negligence or other damage caused by reliance on the
information contained in this listing, or in the event of bankruptcy or liquidation or cessation of trade of any company,
individual or firm mentioned, is hereby excluded. We strongly recommend that you carefully check prices and other
details when you book your accommodation.

The NGS has no statutory control over the establishments or their methods of operating. The NGS cannot become
involved in legal or contractual matters and cannot get involved in seeking financial recompense.

ngs The Yellow Book 2006

gardens open
for charity

£7.99 including UK p&p

Available through **www.ngs.org.uk** or by enquiry to the NGS.
T +44 (0)1483 211535 F +44 (0)1483 211537 Email ngs@ngs.org.uk
Cheques should be in £ sterling, made payable to The National Gardens Scheme and sent to:

**The National Gardens Scheme, Hatchlands Park,
East Clandon, Guildford, Surrey GU4 7RT**

The book will be posted on publication (Feb/Mar 2006)

Royal and National Trust gardens
open in aid of The National Gardens Scheme Charitable Trust

Sandringham House Museum and Grounds, Norfolk

By gracious permission of Her Majesty The Queen, the House and Grounds at Sandringham will be open from 26 March to 30 October but the House and Grounds will be closed from 24 July to 30 July inclusive. Coach drivers and visitors are advised to confirm these closing and opening dates nearer the time. Picnics and dogs are not permitted inside the grounds.

Hours: Sandringham House: 11.00am - 4.45pm (3.00pm in October); Museum: 11.00am - 5.00pm. Grounds: 10.30am - 5.00pm (4.00pm in October)

Admission charges: House, Grounds and Museum: adults £7.50, OAPs £6.00, children (5-15 years) £4.50. Family ticket (2 adults & 3 children) £19.50 Grounds and Museum only: adults £5.00, OAPs £4.00, children £3.00. Advance party bookings will be accepted. There are reductions in admission fees for pre-paid parties. Free car and coach parking.

Sandringham Church: Open afternoons when the grounds are open - subject to weddings, funerals and special services.

Sandringham Flower Show: Wednesday 27 July 2005.

Enquiries: The Public Enterprise Manager, Estate Office, Sandringham or by telephoning 01553 612908 during office hours.

Frogmore House Garden, Berkshire

By gracious permission of Her Majesty The Queen, Frogmore House Garden, Windsor, will be open on Tuesday 17 May 2005.

Hours: 10.00am – 5.30pm (last admission 4.00pm). Entrance to Gardens and Mausoleum through Long Walk gate.

Coaches: By appointment only: apply to The National Gardens Scheme, Hatchlands Park, East Clandon, Guildford, Surrey GU4 7RT (Tel 01483 211535) stating whether you are interested in a morning or afternoon visit.

Admission Charges: £3.50, accompanied children between 8-16 free of charge. Dogs, other than assistance dogs, not allowed. Visitors are requested kindly to refrain from entering the grounds of the Home Park. Light refreshments will be available.

Royal Mausoleum: Also open and included in admission charge for Gardens.

Frogmore House: Open in aid of the Royal Collection Trust via Frogmore House Garden.

Admission charges: Adults £4.00, over 60s £3.00, 8-16 year olds £2.00. House not suitable for wheelchairs or children under 8.

National Trust gardens

Over 100 National Trust gardens are open in aid of The National Gardens Scheme on the dates shown in the book. National Trust Members are requested to note that where the National Trust property has allocated an opening day to The National Gardens Scheme which is one of their normal opening days, members can still gain entry on production of their National Trust Membership Card. On such days donations to The National Gardens Scheme will be welcome. However where the day allocated is one on which the property would normally be closed, then payment of The National Gardens Scheme admission fee will be required.

Garden visiting around the world

AUSTRALIA   Australia's Open Garden Scheme, a non-profit organisation founded in 1987, promotes the knowledge and pleasure of gardens and gardening across Australia by opening inspiring private gardens to the public. 35% of the proceeds from entry fees are returned to the garden owner or the charity of their choice. 65% covers AOGS operating costs, with any surplus being returned to the community as grants for garden and horticulture-related projects. Publication: Australia's Open Garden Scheme Guidebook, published annually in August, available from major booksellers or from the Scheme's head office, lists around 700 gardens open in every state of Australia. Contact: Neil Robertson, Chief Executive Officer, National Office, PO Box 187, New Gisborne, Australia 3438. Tel: +61 3 5428 4557 Fax: +61 3 5428 4558 Email: national@opengarden.org.au Website: www.opengarden.org.au

BELGIUM   Jardins Ouverts de Belgique - Open Tuinen van België is a non-profit organisation founded in 1994. Most of the proceeds from entry fees support charities chosen by garden owners. Publication: Catalogue of Belgian Open Gardens, published annually in March, may be obtained for a one-year membership (valid for two people) at 15€ or £10 sent to: Post Account 000-1390451-53, 'Jardins Ouverts de Belgique', Chaussée de Vleurgat 108, 1000 Brussels, Belgium. Please ensure your name and address is clearly printed. Around 225 private gardens are listed. Contact: Christine de Groote. Email: info@jardinsouverts.be Website: www.jardinsouverts.be

NETHERLANDS   The Nederlandse Tuinenstichting (Dutch Gardens Society, NTs) was founded in 1980 to protect and restore gardens, public parks and cemeteries. Publication: The NTs Open Tuinengids is published annually in March. This guide (in Dutch) has details of 220 private gardens belonging to members of the NTs, which give free access to NTs members. The guide is sent free to members of the NTs. Annual membership 2005: 1 year: €35; 5-year: €140. Contact: Tel: +31 (0) 20 6235058 Fax: +31 (0) 20 6385851 Email: nederl.tuinenst@hetnet.nl Website: www.tuinenstichting.nl

SCOTLAND   Scotland's Gardens Scheme is a registered charity founded in1931. Garden owners donate entry fees and revenue from teas and plant sales to support the Scheme's beneficiaries, and charities of the owners' choice. Publication: Gardens of Scotland, an annual guide published every February, is available through major booksellers in the UK for £4.50 or from the Scheme's head office for £5.50 to include p&p. Over 350 gardens open for the Scheme. Contact: Robin St Clair-Ford, Director, Scotland's Gardens Scheme, 22 Rutland Square, Edinburgh, Scotland EH1 2BB. Tel: +44 (0)131 229 1870 Fax: +44 (0)131 229 0443 Email: office@sgsgardens.fsnet.co.uk Website: www.gardensofscotland.org

UNITED STATES OF AMERICA   The Garden Conservancy, founded in 1989, is a national non-profit organisation dedicated to preserving America's gardening heritage. Their Open Days Program began in 1995 and opens private gardens nationwide to the public. Entry fees support both the Garden Conservancy's preservation work and local non-profits chosen by Garden Hosts. Publication: Open Days Directory published annually, both as a national edition (US $15.95 plus shipping) and as regional editions (US $5 plus shipping). Nearly 400 gardens in 22 states are open in 2004. Contact: Laura Palmer, Director, The Garden Conservancy's Open Days Program, PO Box 219, Cold Spring, New York 10516. Tel: +1 (845) 265-5384. Fax: +1 (845) 265-5392. Email: info@gardenconservancy.org Website www.gardenconservancy.org

JAPAN   The N.G.S. Japan was launched and founded in June 2001. Most of the proceeds from entry fees support the charities recognised by garden owners for children and welfare. The promotion of the gardening tradition by the events etc. makes a contribution to garden conservation, gardeners' training and garden cultural interchange between UK and Japan. Contact: Tamie Taniguchi, Representative, The N.G.S. Japan 4-19-21 Yutaka-cho Shinagawa-ku, Tokyo, 142-0042 Japan. Tel: 0081-3- 3782-8977 Fax: 0081-3-5749-2322 Email: tamieta@syd.odn.ne.jp Website: www.ngs-jp.org

Patron, Vice-Presidents and Trustees of
The National Gardens Scheme Charitable Trust

The Yellow Book 2005

Index to Gardens

Advertisers Index

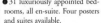